	Symbol	Atomic Number	
NEODYMIUM	Nd	60	144.27
NEON	Ne	10	20.183
NICKEL	Ni	28	58.71
NIOBIUM	Nb	41	92.91
NITROGEN	N	7	14.008
OSMIUM	Os	76	190.2
OXYGEN	O	8	16.0000
PALLADIUM	Pd	46	106.4
PHOSPHORUS	P	15	30.975
PLATINUM	Pt	78	195.09
POTASSIUM	K	19	39.100
PRASEODYMIUM	Pr	59	140.92
PROTACTINIUM	Pa	91	231
RADIUM	Ra	88	226.05
RADON	Rn	86	222
RHENIUM	Re	75	186.22
RHODIUM	Rh	45	102.91
RUBIDIUM	Rb	37	85.48
RUTHENIUM	Ru	44	101.1
SAMARIUM	Sm	62	150.35
SCANDIUM	Sc	21	44.96
SELENIUM	Se	34	78.96
SILICON	Si	14	28.09
SILVER	Ag	47	107.880
SODIUM	Na	11	22.991
STRONTIUM	Sr	38	87.63
SULFUR	S	16	32.066
TANTALUM	Ta	73	180.95
TELLURIUM	Te	52	127.61
TERBIUM	Tb	65	158.93
THALLIUM	Tl	81	204.39
THORIUM	Th	90	232.05
THULIUM	Tm	69	168.94
TIN	Sn	50	118.70
TITANIUM	Ti	22	47.90
TUNGSTEN (WOLFRAM)	W	74	183.86
URANIUM	U	92	238.07
VANADIUM	V	23	50.95
XENON	Xe	54	131.30
YTTERBIUM	Yb	70	173.04
YTTRIUM	Y	39	88.92
ZINC	Zn	30	65.38
ZIRCONIUM	Zr	40	91.22

GENERAL CHEMISTRY
A Systematic Approach

Photograph of the launching of an experimental three-stage rocket designed to place a small earth satellite in orbit. (*U.S. Navy*)

GENERAL CHEMISTRY

CHEMISTRY

SECOND EDITION

A Systematic
Approach

HARRY H. SISLER
The University of Florida

CALVIN A. VANDERWERF
AND
ARTHUR W. DAVIDSON
The University of Kansas

THE MACMILLAN COMPANY • New York

Library of Congress catalog card number: 59–5132

The Macmillan Company, New York
Brett-Macmillan Ltd., Galt, Ontario
Previous edition copyright 1949 by The Macmillan Company

Printed in the United States of America

Preface

In this second edition of *General Chemistry—A Systematic Approach,* as in the first, our goal has been to offer a sound, balanced foundation in general chemistry on a logical, inductive basis. We have attempted to present first a clear, interesting, and thoroughly teachable treatment of the fundamental principles of chemistry, with lucid explanations and ample illustrative material. This is followed by a systematic study of the nonmetals and the metals, correlated on the basis of these fundamental principles. The entire treatment has as its guiding and unifying principle the structural basis of the properties of matter. Specific properties of individual elements and compounds then become for the student simply predictable consequences of the atomic, molecular, and ionic structure.

The whole-hearted and steadily increasing acceptance of the first edition by teachers and students alike has encouraged us to retain the same logical development which was the hallmark of the earlier edition. We have tried throughout to present not only a logical, but also a psychologically sound approach. The theoretical matter is arranged with a view to meeting the students' questions at the time they first arise. Theoretical concepts are not presented in dogmatic fashion to be accepted on faith. Step by step, in logical fashion, the student is led to see why we believe what we believe, always in such a way that his background will enable him to make an adequate analysis of the evidence. Thus he is invited to assume an active role in a compelling intellectual adventure.

In any course in general chemistry, it is certainly the teacher who holds the key to successful learning. Our aim in the present edition has been then, simply to assist the teacher more effectively in conveying to the student a thorough understanding, based upon a clear conceptual picture, of the fundamental principles of chemistry. Every change that has been made has had as its purpose a more complete realization of that aim. We have not hesitated to retain unchanged those sections which upon careful consideration we felt we could not improve.

Wherever greater clarity, simplicity, or teachability would result, discussions and explanations have been condensed and tightened. This has resulted in an actual reduction in the over-all length of the book, despite the addition of many new illustrations, carefully conceived to aid the student in grasping important concepts.

Both the theoretical and the descriptive sections are brought up-to-the-minute by inclusion of the most recent advances. Latest developments in the chemistry of the newer elements, in rocketry and satellites, in medicine, and in applied organic chemistry have been included. The section on nuclear changes, including nuclear fission and nuclear fusion as sources of energy, and the general chapter on metals have been completely rewritten to conform with modern advances in these fields. We have attempted throughout to give the reader an awareness of the unfinished business of chemistry, which is presented as a series of challenges and problems, some solved, many still in the process of solution. The scientific method is taught largely through examples; by thinking through repeated significant examples, the student is led to an awareness of the way in which problems are solved by science.

In this, as in the earlier edition, the first chapters are devoted to a concise and logical development, beginning with familiar phenomena, of the particle concept of matter and of the structure of atoms, molecules, and ions. This is followed by a treatment of chemical equilibrium, of the nature of solutions, and of the behavior of various types of substances in solution. The basic principles developed in the early chapters are then continuously exploited in a systematic study of the nonmetals and metals. The descriptive material is organized on the basis of families of elements as found in modern forms of the periodic table.

The inert gases are discussed first, then the halogens and the other nonmetallic elements, family by family, in the reverse order of the periodic system, to carbon and silicon, an order which we have found most successful from a teaching standpoint. The metals are then discussed in the order of the periodic system, from the alkali and alkaline earth families, through the transition metals, to the aluminum family, germanium, tin and lead.

Properties of families of elements are clearly related to the position of the elements in the periodic system, and to the electronic structures of their atoms. The chemistry of compounds is discussed consistently in terms of molecular and ionic structure, with emphasis on types of chemical bonds.

We have chosen to include only basic, essential principles. Every principle and topic introduced, however, is covered thoroughly, with clear explanations and ample illustrative material. Intended for the use of all college students taking a full year of general chemistry, the text should be altogether intelligible to the student who has had no previous contact with the subject, yet equally stimulating to one who has studied chemistry in high school.

Organic chemistry is given more thorough treatment than in the earlier edition, not only because of its vital and interesting relation to everyday life, but especially because it provides such excellent illustrations of the relationship between structure and properties. The unusually comprehensive treatment of acids and bases will be of great value to the student in later courses in qualitative or quantitative analysis and in organic chemistry. The thorough coverage of the metals and their compounds makes the book especially suitable as a text for engineering students.

The working of numerical problems is thoroughly taught and amply illustrated. Simple methods based on understanding rather than on rote memorization of formulas are stressed. A larger selection of thought-provoking problems of graduated difficulty is provided.

Certainly the unfolding of the chemist's present concept of the structure of matter is one of the great triumphs of the human intellect. To the student, the acquiring of an understanding appreciation of that concept should present a stimulating intellectual challenge and afford a deep intellectual satisfaction. We sincerely hope that this text may serve as a worthy guide to those unsung leaders—the teachers who each year know anew the thrill of starting eager minds in the eternal quest.

Harry H. Sisler
Calvin A. Vander Werf
Arthur W. Davidson

Table of Contents

GENERAL CHEMISTRY
A Systematic Approach

Introduction

1. Chemistry in the Modern World. "Chemistry," some unknown wit has recently observed, "cannot promise man complete and lasting happiness; it can only guarantee him the privilege of enjoying unhappiness in comfort." Without subscribing to so cynical a doctrine, we, who are living in the midst of an era frequently described as "the chemical revolution," must nevertheless be aware of the great contribution of chemical science to our well-being.

Under the watchful eye of the trained research chemist, the test tube is constantly providing man with better things for more abundant living and, at the same time, a longer, healthier life with increased leisure in which to enjoy them. Death-cheating chemicals such as the antibiotics and sulfa drugs, synthetic vitamins and hormones, and new anesthetics and disinfectants are serving miraculously to save and prolong life and to banish disease. Synthetic fertilizers; insecticides which deal sudden death to ravaging pests; chemical agents which not only increase the quality, size, and vitamin content of fruits and vegetables, but may even give rise to new and delicious species; soilless gardens where nutritious vegetables grow in trays of water and chemicals—all these are assuring a more abundant supply of wholesome food. Man's versatile new servants, the plastics, are replacing wood, ivory, amber, bone, tortoise shell, gems, porcelains, and many metals in hundreds of thousands of uses.

Radical improvements in automobile and aircraft design have been made possible by the production of high octane super-fuels and synthetic rubber, and by startling developments in the manufacture and fabrication of light metal alloys, plastics, and plywood. New types of glass are replacing cork, steel, and silk in thermal and electrical insulation, in life preservers and lifeboats, in surgical sutures, and in fireproof textiles. New and improved synthetic fibers have already put the silkworm "on relief," as they are threatening to do to the sheep, and are even challenging the reign of King Cotton. Almost daily some new chemical triumph is announced—the harnessing of nuclear energy,

Fig. 1.1.   Molten steel being cast into ingots. (*Courtesy United States Steel Corporation.*) Of all commercial chemical processes, the one which is carried out on the largest scale is the metallurgy of iron; upon this metal, our modern industrial civilization is largely dependent. Here we see a step in the production of steel, the most widely used form of iron (p. 749).

synthetic quinine from coal tar, a plastic from petroleum that is as tough as steel but only one-third as heavy, or a new super-fuel for the launching of satellites. Constantly, man is gaining greater control over his environment, as well as increasing independence of it.

But all these developments constitute only a beginning. Perhaps the most significant feature of present chemical progress lies in the fabulous future it portends. Many of the the most intriguing and promising secrets of nature remain as yet unfathomed. How, for example, does the green leaf utilize sunlight to convert carbon dioxide and water into food and fuel? What are the chemical forces that distinguish living from nonliving material? By what mechanism are minute traces of vitamins and hormones enabled to produce their far-reaching effects in the human body? The practical implications of answers to questions such as these cannot even be imagined.

2. Development of the Science of Chemistry. Students conditioned to think in terms of our scientific age are often less amazed by the rapid advance of chemical technology during the past one hundred and fifty years than they are perplexed over the slow progress during the preceding history of mankind. Over two-thirds of all the products of our present factories were unknown two centuries ago. Colonial Jamestown's chemical industry made only pitch, tar, soap ashes, and glass beads for the Indian trade; American patriots on the threshold of the Revolution had never seen a match, nor did they understand the phenomenon of burning.

The fact that lack of mastery and lack of understanding of the material universe went hand in hand was no mere coincidence. Chemical conquest of nature is the consequence of a true understanding of natural phenomena. Historically, applied chemistry began a steady development only after the turn of the nineteenth century because it was then that chemists first began to apply and utilize a systematic, efficient method for the acquisition of knowledge concerning the material universe, and for testing the validity of their conclusions. It was the development of this, the *scientific method*, which marked the beginning of chemistry as a science, and which is responsible for the phenomenal rate at which man is expanding knowledge of his universe and is translating that knowledge into power. A short historical sketch of the development of the scientific method will show how slow, how halting, and how haphazard was the progress which preceded its advent and its application.

3. Ancient Arts (Prehistoric–600 B.C.). Although the science of chemistry is a mere youngster of a century and a half, primitive men practiced some of the so-called chemical arts before the dawn of connected history, especially in Egypt, India, China, and Chaldea. Among the most important crafts, the origins of which are lost in the dim mists of prehistoric times, are those of the extraction and working of metals. The Egyptians of predynastic times used gold, which was regarded as a magic medicine; they extracted copper and lead from their ores, and worked with silver, brass, and bronze at least as early as five thousand years ago.

Dwellers along the Nile four or five thousand years ago used leather as a covering for stools, and manufactured glass and enamel. They were skilled in the art of dyeing and in the use of mordants. Mummy cloths dating back to 3000 B.C. were dyed with indigo, and the red dye alizarin came into use a short time later. Various processes for producing alcoholic beverages were known to the ancient world.

Medicine in ancient Egypt was closely associated with religion, and the priest-physicians of that day attempted cures which were based mainly on incantation, and only incidentally on the drugs they compounded. Nevertheless, they extracted many useful vegetable oils and alkaloids, and were skilled in the use of a variety of narcotics.

The technical achievements of the early Egyptian artisans and craftsmen, though frequently overrated, were considerable; but real progress was thwarted because they made no attempt to classify or to correlate their observations of natural phenomena. Their knowledge was entirely empirical or rule of thumb. They had almost no curiosity concerning the nature of the processes they developed, and failed completely to establish any sound predictions of future behavior on the basis of their observations.

4. Greek Philosophy (600–200 B.C.). Cast from a different mold were the classical Greek philosophers who flourished from the sixth to the second century, B.C. These armchair scientists, skilled in philosophic inquiry, speculated freely on the baffling problems of the origin of the universe, the ultimate constitution of matter, and the causes of the constant changes observed in the material world. It was the Greek philosophers who first recognized and stated lucidly many of the fundamental problems of science. They were men of acute intellect and vigorous imagination, and in some cases their attempts at the solution of these problems clearly foreshadowed universally accepted modern concepts. The ideas of Democritus (about 460–370 B.C.) concerning the ultimate constitution of matter, for example, find their counterpart in the present atomic theory.

It is astonishing, however, that such men should have valued experimental evidence so lightly that many of their abstract deductions led to grotesque theories, quite out of harmony with experimental fact. Pure thought alone was considered the proper realm of the philosopher; but no amount of subtlety and skill in deductive reasoning could bring a continuous advance in the knowledge of the material universe, or lead to great practical progress, when that reasoning was based upon false premises, or when the validity of its conclusions was never tested on the touchstone of fact.

5. Alchemy (400–1650). In retrospect, it is clear that the slow progress of science among the ancients was a result of the almost complete divorce of theory and practice. Curiously enough, this state of affairs was remedied to some extent in the Dark and Middle Ages by the rise and spread of alchemy, the pretended art of changing baser metals into gold. The idea of the transmutation of metals, which dominated the alchemy of the Middle Ages, came from the Greek philosopher Aristotle by way of the Egyptians and the Arabs.

Fig. 1.2. The Alchemist, by Wyeth. (*Courtesy Hercules Powder Company.*)

Aristotle's doctrine that all substances are composed of one primordial species of matter which serves as a carrier of various essential qualities, seemed to hold peculiar fascination, and suggested the notion that transmutation of baser metals into gold might be effected by proper control over the proportions of these essential qualities.

The quest of the alchemists was for the miraculous "philosopher's stone," which by mere contact would convert the baser metals into gold. Such a goal suggests chicanery and quackery, and there can be no doubt that many wily alchemists prospered by their deception of credulous kings and princes. Others, however, seem to have been motivated by loftier aims, for through much of the literature of alchemy there runs the idea that the philosopher's stone would heal all diseases and enrich the mind and regenerate the character of the discoverer. Under the intellectual domination of their erroneous theory, the alchemists devoted themselves to the search with an intense and feverish activity.

Such diligence did not go completely unrewarded; the alchemists prepared a large number of new and important substances, perfected many useful types of apparatus, and developed techniques which formed the basis for later chemical experimentation. They achieved little fundamental scientific progress, however, largely because they started from a false premise on a quest for which they were inadequately equipped in apparatus, experimental skill, and knowledge. Whatever truth they discovered was smothered in secrecy, for their writings, if not pure jargon, were obscure and incoherent.

6. Iatrochemistry and the Scientific Renaissance (1400–1750). Although belief in the transmutation of metals persisted until the nineteenth century, the efforts of many alchemists were directed toward a nobler goal as early as the sixteenth century by Paracelsus (1493–1541). This tempestuous Swiss medical practitioner induced alchemists to devote their chemical skill to the preparation of remedies and drugs, proclaiming that the true aim of alchemy was the healing of disease. Through his influence there was inaugurated a new era in the development of chemistry known as the period of iatrochemistry, or medical chemistry.

Meanwhile the death knell of alchemy was being sounded, even by men who were themselves alchemists. Roger Bacon (1214–1294), a profound believer in alchemy, had helped to pave the way for its demise by emphasizing in his writings that there is no certain way of arriving at any competent knowledge except by experimentation. The great thinker and scholar Francis Bacon (1561–1626) exposed the fallibility of the doctrines of Aristotle, and further argued the necessity of seeking truth by careful experimentation and observation.

Almost at once, this new spirit of scientific inquiry gripped many of the best minds of the day. Startling discoveries followed in all branches of science. The broad-minded Irish chemist Robert Boyle (1627–1691) broke completely from the alchemical tradition, and in his famous treatise, *The Sceptical Chymist*, breathed a new life and spirit into the science. He deplored the absence of chemical theory founded on experiment, challenged the foggy thinking and ambiguous writings of the alchemists, and for the first time drew a clear distinction between mixtures, compounds, and elements. On the experimental side, this humble-minded nobleman improved the air pump, established the relationship between the pressure and the volume of a fixed weight of air, discovered the effect of pressure upon the boiling point of a liquid, and isolated and prepared many new and important compounds.

7. The Phlogiston Theory (1700–1777). Forceful and lucid as were the writings of Boyle, they did not serve at once to free the chemists from the shackles of medieval thought. A product of that type of thinking, the so-called phlogiston theory, still dominated their minds and delayed the development of chemistry as an exact science for three-quarters of a century. According to this theory, which was first advanced in 1702 by the German, Stahl, all combustible substances contained a "fiery principle," phlogiston, which escaped as flame when they were heated, leaving behind an ash or "calx." All substances which would burn, as well as many of the metals, were considered to be compound substances made up of the calx plus the elusive phlogiston. Lead, for example, when heated in air, forms a yellow powder, litharge. Therefore, according to the phlogistonists, lead was a compound, litharge plus phlogiston. Carbon burns, leaving no ash, and therefore must be practically pure phlogiston. When litharge is heated with carbon the requisite amount of phlogiston is restored to the litharge to form metallic lead. The discovery that in many cases the ash or calx weighed more than the original metal caused phlogistonists to squirm until some adroit imaginative genius saved the day with the principle of negative density, or levity, which was promptly assigned to phlogiston. Because it served as a solvent for phlogiston, air was necessary for combustion, which ceased when the surrounding atmosphere had become saturated with phlogiston.

This entire theory is interesting today chiefly because it demonstrates how a false, almost ludicrous, hypothesis may explain a large body of facts, and how widely, if it is not subjected to the most rigorous experimental scrutiny, it may be accepted.

So erroneous an interpretation of the phenomenon of burning could not long survive the development and application of more exact methods of qualitative and quantitative analysis, which were greatly extended and improved by the English chemist Joseph Black (1728–1799) and by the Swedish chemist and mineralogist Olaf Bergman (1735–1784). It remained for Lavoisier (1743–1794), however, in 1777, to overthrow completely the phlogiston theory and to provide the true explanation of combustion. To this brilliant French chemist and public servant we owe, also, the origin of the chemical equation and the enunciation and verification of the fundamental law of conservation of mass. So significant was the work of Lavoisier that the birth of modern chemistry as an exact science, based on the law of conservation of mass and on the quantitative study of chemical processes, is dated from the time of this "author of a chemical revolution."

8. The Scientific Method. Thus the scientific method was gradually developed and adapted to chemistry, and the road cleared for chemical progress. Starting from sound theories firmly based upon experimental fact, man could strike out toward his goal with freedom of thought, inquiry, and expression. At his disposal were the tools and techniques necessary for his advance, as well as the type of thinking whereby natural laws are discovered, correlated, and explained, and trustworthy predictions concerning natural phenomena made possible—in short, the scientific method.

9. Goal. What is the goal and what are the mental attitudes of the adventuring chemist who pursues his quest in the spirit of the scientific method? He is driven by curiosity—an impelling desire to reveal nature's secrets, to push back the frontiers of the unknown, and to enlarge the horizon of truth. Although he knows that a broader understanding of the natural universe inevitably leads to a more complete mastery of nature for the welfare of man, he is inspired primarily by a desire to seek truth for truth's sake. The technological developments which distinguish the present era constitute convincing proof that progress follows closely on the heels of knowledge.

10. Experimentation. There is no place in the scientific method for any *a priori* doctrines. The inquiring scientist approaches each problem with an open mind, and carefully and patiently pushes on toward his goal, following the well defined steps of the scientific method. The first of these is the collection of facts, the data supplied by observation of natural phenomena. In chemistry, such observation is usually conducted in the laboratory under carefully planned and controlled conditions, and is called *experimentation.*

All possible data pertinent to a problem must be ascertained completely, clearly, and precisely. The trained investigator must be skilled in devising pertinent experiments, and possessed of the highest intellectual integrity. He employs delicate instruments of all types to increase the accuracy and expand the range of his measurements, and to provide more precise control of experimental conditions.

11. Natural Law. An assorted collection of unrelated facts, however, does not constitute a science. Someone has said that "science consists of the tying of facts into bundles." In the second step of the scientific method, the data are examined, classified, and correlated, so that a generalized statement, or *natural law*, concerning the observed phenomena may be formulated. A natural law is thus a description of the uniform behavior of nature. A law of nature differs from a man-made law, or statute, in that it neither ordains behavior nor prescribes penalties; it merely summarizes a general, constant, and uniform mode of behavior. Thus it may not be said that a man who deliberately walks off the edge of a cliff *disobeys* the law of gravitation, but rather that he proceeds to *illustrate* it.

12. Hypothesis and Theory. The collection of data, and their formulation into chemical laws, cannot in themselves explain the remarkable progress of the science of chemistry. Following these first two steps, the true chemical adventurer next strikes out into the realm of the imagination. Not content with the mere statement of a law, he seeks next to coordinate and to explain a group of interrelated laws by setting up a mental picture of an actual mechanism which would account for the behavior of nature described by the laws. Such a set of assumptions concerning the structure and nature of some portion of the universe is called a *hypothesis*. The various laws describing the behavior of gases led to a set of assumptions as to the discontinuous nature of gases, called the Kinetic-Molecular Hypothesis. Each hypothesis proposed immediately sets into motion a new series of investigations. By its very nature a hypothesis is usually beyond the scope of sensory perception, and therefore not subject to direct experimental test. Scientists reasoning deductively, however, may conclude that if a given hypothetical explanation is correct, then certain other facts which can be observed with the senses must inevitably follow. During the course of experiments devised to test these deductions, new data are collected and additional laws may be discovered.

Once the validity of a hypothesis has been tested by all possible experiments and is found to be in harmony with all the facts, it assumes the status of a *theory*. In the hands of the scientist, a theory is a mighty tool in the further search for truth. A theory not only explains and correlates, it also predicts.

Often facts are discovered which necessitate the modification or rejection of a long-accepted theory. Many theories, such as the present Kinetic-Molecular Theory, having proved infallible in the prediction of new facts, are universally accepted as truths.

Throughout this text special emphasis will be placed upon the presentation of subject matter in the order of the logical steps of the scientific method by which that knowledge was acquired. Whenever the limitations of space and student background permit, the process of inductive reasoning which has led to the development of a theory will be traced. A clear understanding of the exact processes, both experimental and mental, by which knowledge has been gained, is often as important as the knowledge·itself.

From the foregoing account of the place of chemistry in modern life, and its development as a science, the inference should not be drawn that chemistry, or physical and biological science in general, holds the key to the solution of all the ills of the world. Certainly, many of man's most critical and complex problems lie in different realms, such as economics and the other social sciences, and in the moral and spiritual aspects of life. But to a student in any field, a thorough understanding and keen appreciation of the scientific method will prove invaluable. A wider adaptation of the scientific spirit to the most urgent of man's problems would undoubtedly facilitate their solution. With a broader appreciation and application of the scientific method, ours would be a better world, freed of much of its fear, superstition, prejudice, and intolerance.

2

Matter, Change, and Energy

1. What is Chemistry? To one about to begin what should prove to be a thrilling intellectual adventure—the study of chemistry—no question could be more appropriate than "What is chemistry?" The answer to that query cannot be condensed into a short definition or even into a single chapter, for the field of chemistry is too broad and complex to be described adequately in so brief a space. Every thoughtful student will, it is to be hoped, develop a continually expanding appreciation of the scope of chemistry as his study of it progresses. At the outset we shall attempt to present only a general outline of those parts of nature with which chemistry is concerned.

2. Science and the Scientific Method. Chemistry is, first of all, a science. You have probably heard science defined as a collection of established, verifiable, and organized knowledge. But an element of even greater importance than the body of established data and laws itself is the method by which these data and laws are obtained and the attitude of the people whose effort has secured them. In other words, the essential element in science is the *scientific method.*

3. Subdivisions of Science. Any field of study may be classed as a science to the extent that the people who cultivate that field adhere to the rigid application of the scientific method. The scientific method has been applied with notable success to the study of the stars and other heavenly bodies; that branch of science is called *astronomy.* The science of *geology* deals with the structure of the earth, the successive physical changes it has undergone, and the causes which have produced those changes. The science of *physics* is concerned with the production, nature, transformations, and effects of various types of energy such as heat, light, electricity, and mechanical energy. The science of *biology* deals with the origin, structure, functions, and history of vegetable and animal organisms. Astronomy, geology, physics, and chemistry are commonly classified as physical sciences; the various subdivisions of biology, such as botany, zoology, and physiology, are called the biological sciences.

Despite the arbitrary classifications used in the preceding paragraphs, all science is, in reality, one; subdivisions of science arise only for purposes of practical convenience. Chemistry, together with physics, is often described as the basic science, because the principles of chemistry underlie all the physical and biological sciences, and the findings of chemistry are daily proving to be of incalculable value in all the branches of science.

4. The Scope of Chemistry. No branch of science is broader in its scope than chemistry. It deals with all matter, or with the entire material universe which is revealed to us by our senses. One of the first tasks of chemistry, then, is to study how materials may be identified or distinguished. Chemistry is not primarily concerned with *bodies* or *objects*, as represented by such words as bottle, table, wire, and tire; but rather with the *substances* of which the objects are composed, as represented by such words as glass, wood, copper, and rubber. To a chemist, therefore, it is not the *accidental properties* or *attributes,* such as shape and size, of a particular specimen of matter, or object, that are important. He is interested, rather, in the *specific properties* of the kind of matter or substance which may be recognized in any specimen of that substance. A copper vase, a piece of conducting wire, and an electrotype are likely to differ widely in size, weight, shape, and esthetic appeal, as well as in the uses to which they are put; yet, from the chemist's point of view, they are essentially the same because they are all composed of the same substance, copper.

No discerning student can contemplate the material universe without being impressed by the fact of its never-ceasing change. Continuously, various kinds of matter or substances are changed into other substances of different composition and with new properties. Such changes or transformations are called chemical reactions.

Chemistry is concerned with the conditions necessary not only to bring about chemical reactions, but also to prevent them, or at least to control the rate at which they proceed. In the production of iron from its ore, or of synthetic rubber from acetylene and chlorine, for example, exact conditions favorable for the required chemical reactions must be met; having obtained these essential materials, the chemist is interested in the conditions necessary to retard or prevent the reactions which are responsible for the corrosion of the iron and the deterioration of the rubber.

Many specific reactions are important, not because of the products which result from them, but rather by reason of the energy which they use or supply. The harassed head of a household, struggling with the weekly deposit of ashes in his coal furnace, requires no chemist to explain to him that he does not burn coal for the purpose of producing ashes, any more than for producing the carbon dioxide that goes up the chimney. The important aspect of such reactions is the amount of energy produced as power, heat, or light. Chemistry is concerned with the energy relationships involved in chemical reactions.

Regardless of whether a given reaction is important chiefly because of the product it yields, or because of the energy it supplies, the chemist is always interested in the *relative amounts* of materials entering into and resulting from the reactions. We are perhaps aware of the fact that, whenever we adjust the draft of a furnace or the carburetor of an automobile, we are attempting in a rough way to insure a proper supply of materials for a desired reaction. Even our breathing is unconsciously controlled so that oxygen may reach the tissues in amounts required for metabolism. Chemistry as a science is concerned with a determination of the relative proportions of materials involved in reactions.

In all of the changes cited above, the original materials (*reactants*) completely lose their identity. New substances (*products*) with distinctly different properties are produced. Synthetic rubber produced from acetylene and chlorine is obviously totally different from either of these two gases. When coal is burned in a furnace it combines with oxygen to give carbon dioxide, a new substance differing in both composition and properties from coal or oxygen. Such changes that result in the formation of new kinds of matter with new properties and of different composition are called, as has already been indicated, *chemical changes* or *reactions*.

The chemist is also concerned with *physical changes,* in which one or more of the properties of a substance are altered with no change in its composition or identity. Iron tapped from a blast furnace may be drawn into thin wire, hammered into sheets, or cast into steam radiators, but it is still iron. Even though it be magnetized or charged with electricity, it nevertheless retains the characteristics by which we recognize it as iron. When cooled sufficiently, gaseous carbon dioxide may be converted into the familiar white solid, dry ice. Many of the properties of the gas are changed in the process, and it might appear that a new substance had been produced. But the composition of dry ice is exactly the same as that of the gas; under ordinary conditions, a given weight of dry ice evaporates to give the same weight of pure gaseous carbon dioxide. Of the many possible kinds of physical changes, the chemist is concerned especially with changes in state (melting, freezing, evaporation, condensation, etc.), and with the corresponding changes in energy.

Summarizing the foregoing discussion, we see that *chemistry is that branch of science which deals with the composition and properties of matter, with the changes in composition and properties which various kinds of matter undergo, with the conditions which are necessary to effect or prevent these changes, or to alter the rates at which they proceed, and with the relative amounts of materials and energy involved.*

5. Matter, Mass, and Weight. Matter and energy are the two fundamental entities in terms of which the chemist seeks to interpret the universe about him and the changes which it undergoes. Matter is so fundamental that the word defies definition. There are no simpler concepts which can be used to describe it; the best that we can do is to list those qualities which all forms of matter possess.

Very early in his evolutionary career, man discovered that such bodies as rocks, logs, and coconuts offer resistance to any change in their state of motion (possess inertia). Today we recognize this property as inherent in all matter, and we may say that *matter is anything which possesses inertia.*

The quantity of matter in any body is measured by its *mass*. It is the mass of a body that is responsible for its inertia and weight, and both of these are proportional to the mass. Because we have no way of ascertaining mass by direct sense perception, we can compare the masses of bodies only by comparing their inertias or their weights. The inertia of bodies may be compared by measurement of the forces required to overcome their resistance to any change in their state of motion; this method, however, is not practicable. It is reasonably simple, on the other hand, to compare the force of gravity on objects; in short, to *weigh* them. This practice is so familiar that mass and weight, which are by no means identical, are often confused. *Mass* is that property of matter which gives it inertia, whereas *weight* is a force.

The distinction between the two can best be understood if we recall that the weight of a body is the gravitational force of attraction between the body and the earth. It is dependent upon three things: (1) the mass of the body, (2) the mass of the earth, and (3) the distance of the body from the center of the earth. The second, of course, remains constant; at any given point on the earth's surface the last is constant also, and the weights of various bodies are then exactly proportional to their masses. Now the mass of an object, as may be demonstrated by measurement of its inertia, is not altered merely by a change in its position. Obviously, however, the distance from the center of the earth to various points on its surface varies. Consequently, the weight of an object as measured by its pull on a spring balance is appreciably more at either pole, for example, than it is at the equator. This book would weigh substantially zero if taken to the far reaches of astronomical space, yet its mass and inertia would remain unchanged.

6. Measurement of Mass. How, then, is it possible to measure the mass of an object, which is not affected by a change in location, by means of the

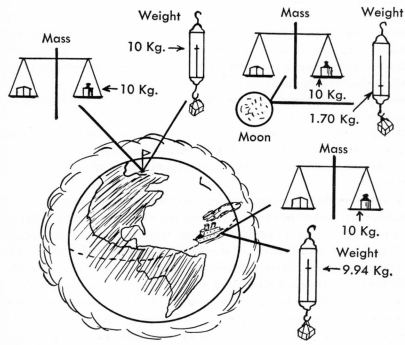

Fig. 2.1. Mass is constant at the North Pole, the Equator, and on the Moon. An object which weighs 10 kg., as measured by its pull on a spring balance, at the North Pole does not, however, weigh as much at the Equator or on the Moon.

force of gravity which varies from one place to another? That problem is solved by the use of the chemical or analytical balance, in which a given sample of matter on the left-hand pan is balanced against a standard mass on the right-hand pan. As the weights of the two bodies, i.e., the forces with which they are attracted to the earth, are necessarily compared at the same place, the mass of any sample of matter is equal to that of the standard which exactly balances it; this means that at a given place the weights of equal masses are equal. The numerical value expressing the mass of a given object thus becomes independent of locality. In common practice, this value is called *weight*.

7. Physical and Chemical Properties. *Density*, or mass per unit volume, is one of the properties that are commonly employed to distinguish among various kinds of matter. Similarly, many other marked characteristics enable us to recognize and distinguish among substances. A housewife, who has been less conscientious than are chemists in labeling her reagents, may at times distinguish her sugar from salt by *taste*. A single introduction to ether usually enables one to recognize it thereafter by its *odor*, and the *color* of ferric oxide (jeweler's rouge) is an obvious clue, though not in itself sufficient, as to its identity. Mercury may be recognized by its *physical state*, because of all the metals it alone is a liquid at room temperature.

Other properties of matter commonly determined include solubility, luster, melting point, boiling point, hardness, elasticity, malleability, ductility, tensile strength, refractivity, conductivity for heat and electricity, and specific heat. All of these properties can be observed without changing the substance into some new kind of matter, and are therefore called *physical properties* of a substance.

Equally important are the *chemical properties*; i.e., those properties of a substance that can be observed only when that substance undergoes a change in composition. Early prospectors in the West frequently mistook pyrite (fool's gold) for gold because of the physical similarity of the two. Chemically they are readily distinguishable by virtue of the fact that gold is completely unreactive toward nitric acid, whereas pyrite reacts with the acid to give a soluble product, ferric nitrate, and a residue of insoluble sulfur. Such properties as the capacity of carbon to combine with oxygen at elevated temperatures to form carbon dioxide, and of iron oxide to react with coke to produce metallic iron and carbon dioxide, are classified as chemical in nature.

8. Units of Measurement—The Metric System. Almost invariably, the usefulness of a given substance is determined by a combination of its physical and chemical characteristics. For this reason, as well as for purposes of identification, it is highly important that these properties be measured accurately and be described in precise mathematical terms. Chemists constantly employ instruments such as meter-sticks, balances, and graduated cylinders in their observations. Even so, the measurements of one investigator could not be communicated intelligibly to other workers throughout the world if he could not record them in terms of universally accepted units. For this reason, scientists of all nations have adopted the so-called metric or c.g.s. (centimeter, gram, second) system. The standard units of the metric system are defined in the Appendix (p. 825), where tables comparing various metric and English units are also listed.

9. Heterogeneous and Homogeneous Samples of Matter. From everyday observation, we are familiar with the fact that all of the various forms of matter can be divided into two broad classes. Such types of matter as iron, sulfur, salt, and brine are uniform in properties and composition throughout and are, therefore, said to be *homogeneous*. Many other samples of matter, on the other hand, are not uniform but consist of two or more physically distinct portions, differing in properties and composition and separated from each other by definite bounding surfaces. Such nonuniform forms of matter are *heterogeneous* mixtures. Each physically distinct, homogeneous portion of a heterogeneous mixture is called a *phase*. We can clearly distinguish in a particular specimen of granite, for example, three phases; one consisting of tiny, shimmering, black specks (mica), the second of small, hard, transparent crystals (quartz), and the third of grayish or pinkish oblong crystals (feldspar). Each of the three phases is characterized by its own specific properties. We can precisely determine the color, hardness, solubility, and density of the mica, quartz, or feldspar, separately. It is quite another matter, however, to specify the properties of granite itself, for each property will depend upon the particular phase for which it is determined. We cannot even ascertain average or mean values for the various properties of the three phases taken together as they occur in granite, because the relative proportions of mica, quartz, and feldspar are found to vary widely in different specimens of granite. The composition of all heterogeneous mixtures can be varied continuously without limit, and the possible number of different mixtures is therefore infinite.

By far the greater part of matter as it occurs in nature is heterogeneous; to a chemist, therefore, the separation of the different phases of a heterogeneous mixture is frequently a practical necessity. Because each phase of a heterogeneous mixture exhibits its own characteristic properties, the various phases are always separable by mechanical means such as filtration, sedimentation, or even hand-picking of crystals. One can easily separate salt from pure sand in a finely ground mixture of the two by adding water to dissolve the salt and then filtering or decanting the liquid phase from the sand. We can distinguish two phases in an intimate mixture of powdered sulfur and iron only with the aid of a microscope; yet we can easily separate one from the other by means of a magnet.

10. Solutions. Close inspection of homogeneous matter may reveal that it is not a pure substance but rather a mixture of two or more substances known as a *solution*. A solution is defined as a homogeneous mixture of two or more substances, the composition of which can be varied continuously, although usually only within certain limits. For example, at ordinary room temperature, 100 g. of water will dissolve a maximum of 36 g. of table salt. An infinite variety of different salt solutions can be prepared in which the concentration of salt varies continuously from a minute trace to 36 g. per 100 g. of water.

All the specific properties of a solution, such as density, freezing point, boiling point, and refractivity, vary with its concentration.

11. Compounds. Any substance which the chemist characterizes as pure is homogeneous; it is characterized by definite and constant composition, and its properties are constant under given external conditions such as temperature and pressure. Water and salt are both pure substances; each has an invariable composition and its properties depend only upon temperature and pressure. Even so, however, water and salt are not truly elementary substances; each, by means of a chemical reaction, can be broken down into two simpler substances. If we pass an electric current through water (containing a small amount of sulfuric acid to increase the conductivity), the amount of water is steadily decreased and bubbles of gas are liberated at both electrodes. We can collect the gas at the positive electrode and prove that it is slightly heavier than air, that such substances as wood, sulfur, and iron burn in it with great brilliance, and that it sustains life. This gas is oxygen, the most reactive constituent of the atmosphere. Quite different is the gas which can be collected at the negative electrode; it is much lighter than air, so that balloons filled with it rise rapidly. The flame of a burning splint thrust into it is immediately extinguished, and instead the gas itself burns. This very light, combustible gas is hydrogen. By accurate quantitative analyses, we know that water always contains 88.81% oxygen by weight, and 11.19% hydrogen.

Likewise, common table salt in the molten state can be broken down by means of an electric current to yield at the positive electrode a greenish-yellow poisonous gas, chlorine, and at the negative electrode, an easily corroded solid, sodium. Salt is composed of 39.34% sodium, by weight, and 60.66% chlorine.

Many other pure substances are readily decomposed merely upon being heated. The red solid called mercuric oxide is broken down by heat into a shining liquid, mercury, and the gas oxygen. This process of resolving a pure substance into two or more simpler constituent substances is called *analysis,* or, more commonly, *decomposition*; the reverse step, *synthesis,* or *combina-tion*, is another common form of chemical change. When hydrogen burns in air, the product is water; i.e., hydrogen combines with the oxygen of the air to form the more complex substance water.

A pure substance which can be broken down into two or more different simpler substances by appropriate means is called a *compound*. Conversely, any pure substance which is the sole product resulting from the combination of two or more other substances is a compound. Probably over a half million different compounds are known at the present time. Since new compounds are being discovered and synthesized daily, it appears that the number which may eventually be described is practically limitless. For convenience, com-pounds are often subdivided into two classes: (1) *organic*, or carbon-con-taining compounds, and (2) *inorganic* compounds, those which do not con-tain carbon.

12. Elements. Both mixtures and compounds can be resolved ultimately into pure substances which have never been decomposed into simpler substances by chemical reactions. Hydrogen, oxygen, sodium, chlorine, mercury, and iron, for example, cannot be resolved into simpler substances, nor can any one of them be formed as the sole product of the reaction of two or more other substances. Such simple substances, which are never decomposed in any chemical reaction, are called *elements*. All the myriad forms of matter, including both mixtures and compounds, are, as far as is now known, com-posed of about a hundred ultimate constituents, the elements. Most of these elements have been discovered during the last century and a half. Among the most familiar elements are such common metals as iron, aluminum, zinc, lead, copper, tin, and mercury. Familiar nonmetallic elements are the solids carbon, sulfur, phosphorus, and iodine, as well as such gases as oxygen and nitrogen.

For brevity, convenience, and international uniformity in referring to ele-ments, each element is represented by means of a symbol. In the case of most elements, the symbol consists of the first letter (capitalized) in the name of the element, or the first letter (capitalized) followed by a second appropriate letter. Thus, carbon is represented by C, chlorine by Cl, calcium by Ca, oxy-gen by O, and hydrogen by H. At the time (1819) that the celebrated Swedish chemist Jöns Jakob Berzelius (1779–1848) first proposed the adoption of such a system, the Latin names for several metals were in com-mon use. This fact is reflected in such symbols as Fe (from the Latin ferrum) for iron, Cu (cuprum) for copper, Au (aurum) for gold, and Ag (argen-tum) for silver. The symbol W (wolfram) for tungsten is derived from the

German name. At the present point in our study, these symbols may be regarded as nothing more than mere abbreviations or shorthand methods of representing the elements. We shall find later, however, that to the chemist several important additional meanings are implicit in the symbol for each element.

The foregoing discussion of the classification of matter on the basis of composition is summarized in Table 2.1.

Table 2.1

Chemical Classification of Matter

Matter			
	Homogeneous Matter		
Mixtures		Pure substances: Materials of definite composition and properties	
Heterogeneous matter: Nonuniform mixtures separable by mechanical means into homogeneous matter.	Solutions: Mixtures of variable composition and indefinite properties. Separable by changes of state into pure substances.	Compounds: Resolvable by chemical means into two or more simple substances (elements).	Elements: Not decomposable by ordinary chemical means.

13. Relative Abundance of the Elements. Extended studies on the composition of the earth by physicists, geologists, and astronomers, as well as chemists, have revealed striking inequalities in the distribution and abundance of the various elements. It has been calculated that just twelve elements account for a total of over 99.5% of the weight of the outer ten-mile layer of the earth's crust. The most abundant element, oxygen, makes up almost one-half of the weight of this layer, and silicon (the impure oxide of which we know as sand) more than one-quarter of the total. Aluminum, iron, calcium, sodium, potassium, and magnesium follow in that order. Although carbon is present in approximately nine-tenths of all the different known compounds, it makes up less than 0.1% of this outer layer of the earth's crust.

Table 2.2 shows the approximate average composition of the earth's crust, including the terrestrial waters and the atmosphere.

Table 2.2

Element	O	Si	Al	Fe	Ca	Na	K	Mg	H	Ti	Cl	P	Mn	All others
% in Earth's Crust	49.2	25.7	7.4	4.7	3.4	2.6	2.4	1.9	0.9	0.6	0.2	0.1	0.1	0.8

There is convincing evidence that the composition of the earth varies markedly from its crust to its center. For example, although the density of the earth's crust is only 2.79 g. per cc., the average density of the entire planet, as calculated from its total volume and mass, is 5.52 g. per cc. Evidence from magnetic, seismological, and other data has led investigators to the conclusion that beneath the earth's crust there is a transition zone increasingly rich in iron, and finally a central core about 3400 km. (2100 miles) in radius with a density of 9.6 g. per cc., and consisting almost entirely of iron with about 0.8% nickel. Calculation of the total composition of the earth on this basis places iron as the most abundant element, with oxygen second. Table 2.3 is that of the Geophysical Laboratory, Washington, D. C.

Table 2.3

Total Composition of the Earth

Element	Per Cent	Element	Per Cent
Iron	39.76	Sodium	0.39
Oxygen	27.71	Cobalt	0.23
Silicon	14.53	Chromium	0.20
Magnesium	8.69	Potassium	0.14
Nickel	3.16	Phosphorus	0.11
Calcium	2.52	Manganese	0.07
Aluminum	1.79	Carbon	0.04
Sulfur	0.64	Others	0.02

Examination of the light from the sun and stars by means of the spectroscope (p. 156) has revealed a remarkable correspondence between their composition and that of the earth. Hydrogen, calcium, magnesium, iron, and many other elements have been identified. Only in one instance (p. 374) has spectroscopic evidence indicated the presence on any star of an element not previously known, and in that case the element in question, helium, was discovered on the earth 27 years later.

14. Energy. All changes and transformations in nature are accompanied by changes in energy. Such diversified phenomena as the flight of a golf ball, the lifting of a book, the fall of a stone, the flashing of a light, the charging of a battery, as well as all life processes, involve the emission, absorption, and redistribution of energy. The concept of energy is as fundamental as that of matter, and therefore equally difficult to define. Energy manifests itself in such obvious forms as mechanical energy, heat energy, electrical energy, and light or radiant energy. Apparently distinct as these forms may appear, each possesses in common with every other form the feature that under certain conditions it may be made to do work. The mechanical energy of moving pistons propels an automobile; heat applied to a boiler produces steam which drives an engine; an electric current can turn a motor; light striking a propeller, the blades of which are blackened on one side, causes the propeller to revolve. A stationary body can possess energy by virtue of its position; i.e., potential energy. When the sluice gates are opened, the potential energy of water from a reservoir at the top of a hill may be utilized to drive a turbine. The potential energy of a stretched spring is commonly applied to close screen doors.

15. Law of Conservation of Energy. Repeated studies have demonstrated that in all ordinary transformations energy can neither be created nor destroyed. For any quantity of one form of energy that disappears, an equivalent amount of other forms is produced. This important generalization is known as the Law of Conservation of Energy. Different forms of energy are often measured in different units; it follows from the Law of Conservation of Energy, however, that a definite and invariable relationship exists among the various energy units.

16. Chemical Energy. The chemist's interest in energy centers about another form more complex than any yet mentioned. We have already observed that when carbon (in the form of coal) burns it combines with oxygen to produce carbon dioxide; much energy in the form of heat and light is released in this process. According to the Law of Conservation of Energy, the heat and light must have been produced at the expense of some other form of energy. The original carbon and oxygen, together, possessed more energy, by an amount equivalent to that of the heat and light released, than did the carbon dioxide which was formed from them. This excess of energy, stored in the carbon and oxygen, which is transformed into heat and light when the two unite chemically, represents part of their *chemical energy*. In general, chemical energy is defined as the energy that all substances possess by virtue of their composition. The absolute value of the chemical energy of any given substance depends on many complicated factors which cannot be accurately determined. We can measure only the *changes* in chemical energy which result whenever substances undergo changes in composition (react chemically).

Not all chemical reactions are accompanied by a release of energy. Many reactions take place with the absorption of energy, indicating that the chemical energy content of the products is greater than that of the reactants. The direct union of two or more elements to form a compound, as well as the reverse reaction in which the compound is decomposed into its elements, is, like all chemical changes, almost invariably accompanied by a change in chemical energy. This means that the chemical energy of a compound almost always differs from the sum of the chemical energies of the elements of which it is constituted.

The energy of a reaction is commonly liberated or absorbed in the form of heat. We are, nevertheless, familiar with many reactions in which chemical energy is released, wholly or partially, in some other form. All the various forms of energy required for such diverse and complex functions of the animal body as motion and locomotion, temperature control, illumination (the firefly), and electrical discharge (the electric eel), are derived from the chemical energy originally present in the animal's supply of food and oxygen. When dynamite explodes, a large amount of its chemical energy is spectacularly converted into mechanical energy. In a lantern, chemical energy is transformed, though rather inefficiently, into light. The common dry cell is a device by which the chemical energy released in a certain reaction is converted into electrical energy. On the other hand, when water is decomposed by an electric current, the electrical energy supplied is stored as chemical energy in the products—oxygen and hydrogen.

Light and mechanical energy may also bring about certain chemical changes and thus undergo transformation into chemical energy. No process is more important than that by which green plants utilize sunlight to convert carbon dioxide and water into starch, a product of higher energy content. Silver bromide, the light-sensitive agent in most photographic films, can be decomposed into free silver and bromine by means of the mechanical energy produced upon vigorous rubbing, as well as by light.

17. Unit of Heat; The Calorie. Energy changes involved in chemical reactions are usually measured and expressed in terms of heat units. The unit of heat in the metric system is the *calorie* (cal.), which is defined as the amount of heat required to raise the temperature of one gram of water from 14.5° to 15.5° centigrade (C.). For anything but the most precise work, the heat required to raise one gram of water through one degree centigrade at any temperature between the freezing and boiling point of water may be taken as a calorie. The kilocalorie (Cal.) is equal to 1000 cal. In technical work in Britain and the United States the standard unit of heat is the British thermal unit (Btu), which is the amount of heat required to raise the temperature of one pound of water at its maximum density through one degree Fahrenheit. One British thermal unit is equal to 252 cal.

18. Temperature Scales. *Temperature* is the quality which determines the direction of heat transfer. Heat can flow only from a body at a higher temperature to one at a lower temperature. During the course of the evolution of scales of temperature, various fixed points were proposed as standards. The centigrade scale, now universally used in scientific work, was introduced by Anders Celsius, professor of astronomy at Upsala, in 1742. Its fixed points, the freezing and boiling points of pure water at atmospheric pressure, are easily reproducible in the laboratory. The temperature of freezing water is arbitrarily set as the zero point of the centigrade thermometer and that of boiling water at standard atmospheric pressure as 100° C. The range between these two points is marked off into 100 equal divisions, each division thus representing 1° C.

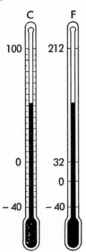

Fig. 2.2. Comparison of the centigrade and Fahrenheit temperature scales.

The Fahrenheit thermometer, introduced in 1724 by the German instrument worker Daniel Gabriel Fahrenheit, is in everyday use in English speaking countries. On his scale the melting point of ice is arbitrarily called 32°, and the boiling point of water is 212°. Thus, there are 100 equal divisions between the freezing and melting points of water on the centigrade scale, and 212 − 32 = 180 divisions on the Fahrenheit scale. Each centigrade degree, therefore, equals 9/5 Fahrenheit degrees. Chemists frequently desire to convert temperature readings from one scale to the other. In view of the fact that 0° C. = 32° F., and that 100° C. = 212° F., as shown in Figure 2.2, the reasoning involved in solving such problems is apparent.

Let us suppose, for example, that a centigrade temperature of 20° is to be converted to the corresponding Fahrenheit temperature. We know that 20° C. is 20 centigrade degrees, or 9/5 × 20 = 36 Fahrenheit degrees, above centigrade zero. But 0° C. = 32° F.; therefore, 20° C. = (9/5 × 20) + 32, or 68° F. For converting centigrade to Fahrenheit readings, then, we employ the equation:

Fahrenheit temperature = 9/5 centigrade temperature + 32.

By similar reasoning, one may calculate the centigrade temperature which corresponds to, say, 98.6° F., the temperature of the human body. We know that 98.6° F. is 98.6° − 32 = 66.6 Fahrenheit degrees above centigrade zero. But each Fahrenheit degree is only 5/9 of a centigrade degree, or 98.6° F. is 5/9 × (98.6 − 32) = 37° C. This method may be generalized in the following equation:

Centigrade temperature = 5/9(Fahrenheit temperature − 32).

In conformity with the usual practice in scientific work, all temperatures hereafter cited in this book will refer to the centigrade scale.

STUDY QUESTIONS AND PROBLEMS

1. Would an ordinary pound of butter appear to have a weight of one pound if weighed on the moon on a pan-balance with a standard set of weights? on a spring balance? Would the moon be a particularly good place on which to establish a new high-jump record? a new broad-jump record? Would an automobile be easier to lift on the moon than on the earth? Would it be easier to push on the level? Would it be easier to brake?

2. (See Appendix for conversion factors.) (a) How many grams are there in an ounce? Calculate your weight in kilograms. If a man weighs 75 kg., what is his weight in pounds?

(b) How many milliliters are there in a half pint (the volume of an ordinary drinking glass)? A gallon is 231 cu. in.; how many liters are there in a cubic foot?

3. A kilogram of osmium, the most dense substance known, occupies a volume of only 44.4 cc. What is the density of osmium in grams per cubic centimeter?

4. (a) A thermostat is set to maintain a temperature of 69.8° F. What is the corresponding centigrade temperature?

(b) If a clinical thermometer were graduated in centigrade degrees, what temperature would it show for a patient with a fever of 102.2° F.?

5. At what temperature are the centigrade and Fahrenheit readings identical? At what temperature are they equal numerically, but opposite in sign?

6. What experimental evidence might reveal whether the following are pure substances or mixtures: air, gasoline, bronze, dry ice, water, brine, acetylene?

7. Classify each of the following substances according to Table 2.1: soil, salt, paint, mercury, mayonnaise, tincture of iodine, copper, honey, hydrogen, wood.

8. Cite specific instances in which chemical energy is transformed directly into mechanical energy, heat, light, or electricity for commercial use.

9. (a) How many calories are required to warm 500 g. of water from 10° to 20° C.? From 40° to 50° F.?

(b) If 50 ml. of water at 85° C. is added to 600 ml. of water at 20° C. in an insulated system, what is the final temperature?

3

The Gaseous State—Kinetic-Molecular Theory

1. Introduction. In the preceding chapter, we reviewed certain important facts concerning the nature and behavior of matter, most of which were already familiar to us from everyday observation. If we wish, however, to gain a more penetrating insight into our physical environment, we are led inevitably to the problem of the ultimate constitution of matter. Is matter continuous or discontinuous? Can any sample of matter be divided and subdivided again and again without limit? Or would such a process lead ultimately to the isolation of minute unit particles which would resist further subdivision? The mental pictures or theories which scientists have constructed in answer to these queries are among the chemist's most powerful tools enabling him to understand, to correlate, and to predict the behavior of various forms of matter. These theories have brought order out of a chaos of apparently unrelated phenomena and have made possible in the last 150 years more chemical progress than man had achieved in all the previous millenniums of his existence.

2. Evidence for the Discontinuity of Matter. Unfortunately, we cannot prove by direct sense perception whether matter is continuous or discontinuous, since neither our sense of sight, even though aided by the finest precision instruments, nor our sense of touch is sufficiently sensitive to explore the realm of almost infinitesimally small particles. Nevertheless, convincing support for the concept of the discontinuity of matter comes from two distinct lines of evidence: (1) the properties of gases, and (2) the laws of chemical combination. In the present chapter, we shall explore the evidence offered by the laws describing the behavior of gases and shall attempt to construct the theory to which these laws gave rise. This theory will serve immediately as the basis for our study, in the next chapter, of the liquid and solid states. A discussion of the fundamental laws of chemical combination and of the theory correlating these laws will follow in Chapter 5.

THE GASEOUS STATE

3. General Characteristics of Gases. All matter, as we know it, exists in one of three states of aggregation, solid, liquid, or gaseous. Substances in the liquid and gaseous states are sometimes classed together as fluids. The particular physical state of a given substance is determined by the conditions of temperature and pressure under which it is observed. Most substances may be obtained in any one of the three states of aggregation. Water, for example, occurs as a solid (ice), as a liquid (water), and as a gas (water vapor). It is usually thought of as a liquid because it exists as such at ordinary temperatures and pressures.

The study of the gaseous state has proved particularly fruitful in leading to a theory regarding the structure of matter. All of us are familiar with the unlimited expansibility of gases. We know that all gases expand indefinitely, so as to fill uniformly the entire space in which they are contained. A given sample of gas, therefore, has neither a definite shape nor a definite volume. The gaseous state is further characterized by a high degree of compressibility. Whereas tremendous pressures are required to produce any appreciable decrease in the volume of a given amount of liquid or solid, gaseous volumes may readily be compressed to a small fraction of their original values. It is in the gaseous state that matter exists in its most attenuated form. In general, the density of a substance as a gas at ordinary pressures is roughly only 1/1000 to 1/2000 of that which it would possess in the liquid or solid state. Furthermore, two or more gases, when placed in contact, mix completely and uniformly in all proportions; there is practically no tendency for the heavier gases to settle. Any mixture of gases, therefore, is homogeneous; i.e., it is a solution.

Why do all gases exhibit these properties of expansibility, compressibility, and diffusibility? We might pause at this point to attempt the construction of some mental picture of the possible structure of all gases which would account for their observed behavior. We shall be able to approach this problem from a sounder experimental basis, however, after we have reviewed the quantitative generalizations, known as the gas laws, which concern the behavior of gases under different conditions. These laws are not only relatively simple, but are almost entirely independent of the nature of the individual gas under observation.

4. Measurement of Atmospheric Pressure—The Barometer. Before we consider the first of these laws, that dealing with the relationship between volume and pressure of gases, it is important that we understand clearly what is

meant by atmospheric pressure, the standard by which the pressure of a gas
is usually measured. The pressure of the atmosphere is measured by means of
an instrument known as a barometer, devised in 1644 by Evangelista Torri-
celli, who had been a pupil of Galileo. One may construct the simplest type
of Torricellian barometer (Figure 3.1) by first filling completely with pure
mercury a tube slightly over 80 cm. long, closed at one end, and then care-

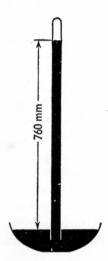

Fig. 3.1. A simple
barometer.

fully inverting the tube, thrusting the lower or open
end below the surface of a well of mercury so that no
air is admitted in the tube. The mercury falls for a short
distance within the tube, giving rise to a vacuum (except
for a negligible amount of mercury vapor) at the top of
the tube. The mercury column is held by the pressure of
the atmosphere at such a height that its pressure, or
weight per unit area, at the bottom of the tube, is
exactly equal to that exerted by the atmosphere upon
the free surface of the mercury in the well. The pressure
of the atmosphere is measured by the height of this
column of mercury, and is commonly expressed in millimeters of mercury. Thus, when we observe that the vertical distance (shown by arrows) between the surface of
the mercury at the top of the column and in the well of a
barometer is 760 mm., we say that the atmospheric pressure is equal to that exerted by a column of mercury
760 mm. in height, and it is therefore expressed as
760 mm. of mercury.

   The pressure of the atmosphere is not constant, but fluctuates daily or even
hourly, and decreases at increasingly higher altitudes. At sea level, the atmospheric pressure may vary from approximately 740 to 780 mm. The mean
value, which is equal to that of a column of mercury 760 mm. in height at
0° C., is called 1 atmosphere. In chemical calculations, pressures are often
expressed in terms of atmospheres. A pressure of 1 atm. is equivalent to 14.7
lb. per sq. in.

5. Boyle's Experiment; Change in Volume of Gases with Pressure. Every-
one who has inflated a tire with a bicycle pump is well aware of the fact that
an increase of pressure upon a given specimen of air reduces its volume. The
exact relation between the volume and pressure of a fixed weight of air was
first stated by Robert Boyle in 1660. In a series of carefully conducted experiments, he measured, at room temperature, the volume of a sample of air
under various pressures. Part of Boyle's data is included in Table 3.1

Table 3.1

Robert Boyle's "Table of the Condensation of the Air"

VOLUME, V (expressed in terms of the relative lengths of the air spaces in the tube used)	PRESSURE, P (atmospheres)	PV
48.0	1.00	48.0
38.0	1.27	48.3
23.0	2.10	48.3
13.0	3.70	48.1

6. Boyle's Law. Upon inspecting Boyle's data, one is struck by the fact that, however the pressure on a sample of air is varied, the product of the pressure multiplied by the corresponding volume is a fixed value (a constant).

We may express this relationship, which was later found to hold true for gases in general, as follows:

$$\underset{\text{(pressure)}}{P} \times \underset{\text{(volume)}}{V} = \underset{\text{(a constant)}}{k} \quad \text{(at constant temperature)} \tag{1}$$

Transposing, we obtain

$$V = k \times \frac{1}{P}, \text{ or } V = \frac{k}{P} \text{ (at constant temperature)} \tag{2}$$

This equation expresses *Boyle's law: at constant temperature, the volume of a fixed weight of a given gas is inversely proportional to the pressure*

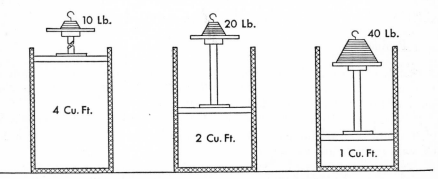

Fig. 3.2. The relation between the volume of a gas and the pressure under which it is measured (Boyle's law).

under which it is measured. If the pressure is *doubled,* the volume is *halved;* if the pressure is *halved,* the volume is *doubled;* if the pressure is increased by a factor of $771/760$, then the volume is decreased by a factor of $760/771$.

Boyle's law may be expressed mathematically in several other ways. Since for a fixed weight of a given gas $PV = k$, we may write

$$P_1V_1 = P_2V_2 \text{ (at constant temperature)} \tag{3}$$

where V_1 is the volume of a given weight of a certain gas at pressure P_1, and V_2 is the volume at pressure P_2. Dividing throughout by P_1V_2, we obtain

$$\frac{V_1}{V_2} = \frac{P_2}{P_1} \text{ (at constant temperature)} \tag{4}$$

It is sometimes convenient to use still another equation, which is readily obtainable from (4).

$$V_2 = V_1 \times \frac{P_1}{P_2} \text{ (at constant temperature)} \tag{5}$$

7. Standard Pressure. In measuring quantities of gases, we usually find it much more convenient to determine their volumes than their weights. Boyle's law indicates that a value for the volume of a given sample of a gas has almost no meaning unless the pressure is specified. For uniformity, 760 mm. of mercury, or 1 atmosphere, has been adopted arbitrarily as the standard pressure. Unless otherwise stated, values given for gaseous volumes—as well as for specific properties of gases, such as densities—are always those at standard pressure. It is rarely convenient to measure gas volumes at exactly 1 atm., but Boyle's law provides a simple method of "correcting" the volume of a sample of gas determined at any other pressure to the corresponding volume which that gas would occupy at the standard pressure.

Problem 1

A sample of gas occupies a volume of 86.8 ml. at a pressure of 730 mm. of mercury and a temperature of 27° C. What will be its volume at the standard pressure (760 mm.) and 27° C.?

In solving problems such as this, we shall find that an orderly arrangement of the data is invariably an aid to clear thinking. For this example, assuming constant temperature, we may write

$V_1 = 86.8$ ml.	$P_1 = 730$ mm.
↓ decreased	↓ increased
$V_2 = $?	$P_2 = 760$ mm.

We might solve this problem by applying equation (5) directly; equations which are merely memorized, however, are easily misapplied and soon forgotten. In this case, if we understand Boyle's law, we shall undoubtedly find it quicker and simpler, as well as more instructive, to work the problem with the aid of simple logic.

From equation (5), which we derived from Boyle's law, we know that the new volume will be equal to the old volume multiplied by the ratio of the two pressures. If the pressure is *increased,* the volume will be *decreased,* and this ratio must be less than 1; that is, the smaller pressure must then be the numerator. Conversely, if the pressure is *decreased,* the volume will be *increased,* and the ratio must be greater than 1; the greater pressure must then be the numerator.

In the problem stated, the pressure is *increased* from 730 to 760 mm. The volume is therefore *decreased,* and the original volume must be multiplied by a fraction less than 1, 730/760.

$$V_2 = 86.8 \times \frac{730}{760} = 83.4 \text{ ml.}$$

Problem 2

Calculate the volume which 22.4 liters of a gas measured at the standard pressure would occupy at a pressure of 732 mm. of mercury. (Assume constant temperature.)

$$V_1 = 22.4 \text{ l.} \qquad\qquad P_1 = 760 \text{ mm.}$$
$$\downarrow \text{ increased} \qquad\qquad \downarrow \text{ decreased}$$
$$V_2 = \quad ? \qquad\qquad\quad P_2 = 732 \text{ mm.}$$

Since the pressure is *decreased* to 732/760 of its original value, the volume is *increased* by the factor 760/732.

$$V_2 = 22.4 \times \frac{760}{732} = 23.3 \text{ l.}$$

8. Charles' Experiment—Change in Volume of Gases with Temperature.

From everyday experience most of us have become aware of the fact that gases expand when heated and contract when cooled. The first reliable measurements of the exact relationship between the volume and the temperature of a gas were made by Jacques A. C. Charles, a French physicist, about 1787, but his data were never published. Fifteen years later, his countryman, Joseph L. Gay-Lussac, repeated Charles' experiment with better technique and obtained more accurate results.

Both investigators found that the volume of a given specimen of gas is increased by 1/273 of its value at 0° C. for every degree rise in temperature.

Thus, if a gas at $0°$ C. is warmed to $1°$ C. at constant pressure, the volume is increased by $1/273$ of its original value; if the temperature is raised to $10°$ C., the volume is increased by $10/273$ of its value at $0°$ C.; at $273°$ C. the volume is double that at $0°$ C. On the other hand, if the gas is cooled, its volume is decreased by $1/273$ of its value at $0°$ C. for every degree through which the temperature is lowered. These relationships are readily apparent if we arbitrarily select 273 ml. as the volume at $0°$ C., as shown in Table 3.2.

Table 3.2

t (in degrees centigrade)	V (in ml.)	T (in degrees absolute)
273	546	546
100	373	373
1	274	274
0	**273**	**273**
−1	272	272
−100	173	173
−273	0 (theoretically)	0

9. Absolute Zero; Absolute Temperature Scales. Two facts of great interest emerge from a study of the relationship between volume and temperature. First of all, we deduce that if a sample of gas could be cooled to a temperature of $-273°$ C., its volume would presumably shrink by $273/273$ of its volume at $0°$ C. In other words, at $-273°$ C. the gas would occupy no volume at all! Actually, all real gases first liquefy and then solidify before reaching this temperature. Nevertheless, the data suggest that $-273°$ C. may be a fundamental fixed point in nature. Many additional lines of evidence, which need not be cited here, prove that it is in reality the lowest possible limit of temperature.

We observe, in the second place, that although the volume of gas changes uniformly with changes in temperature, the volume is, nevertheless, not directly proportional to the centigrade temperature. For example, 274 ml. of a gas measured at $1°$ C. would occupy 275 ml. at $2°$ C. The centigrade temperature is doubled, but the volume is not. We may, however, employ a simple arithmetical device to bring about a direct proportionality between the two. We need only add algebraically to the centigrade temperature the constant 273. The temperatures $1°$ C. and $2°$ C., for example, then become $274°$ and $275°$, respectively, and the corresponding volumes, 274 ml. and 275 ml., are directly proportional to the new temperatures.

These facts show us the advantage of a new temperature scale the zero point of which is —273° C. (or more exactly, —273.16° C.). This point is called the *absolute zero* and temperatures measured from it are called abso-lute temperatures (abbreviated °A.) or temperatures Kelvin (abbreviated °K.), after Lord Kelvin, the originator of this temperature scale. The abso-lute temperature scale is actually the centigrade scale with the base moved down 273 degrees. Any centigrade temperature may be converted into the corresponding absolute temperature by the addition of 273 degrees. Thus 0° C., the freezing point of water, be-comes 273° A., and 100° C., the boil-ing point of water, is 373° A. In order to convert any temperature on the ab-solute scale to the corresponding centi-grade temperature, we must subtract 273.

Engineers frequently use still another scale in which absolute zero is again the starting or zero point, but in which Fahrenheit degrees are employed. This so-called Rankine scale is the "abso-lute" Fahrenheit scale, just as the Kel-vin is the "absolute" centigrade scale. Inasmuch as centigrade degrees are 9/5 as large as Fahrenheit degrees, any Kelvin temperature multiplied by 9/5 gives the corresponding Rankine (here abbreviated as R.) temperature. Thus 273.16° K. (0° C. or 32° F.) is 9/5 × 273.16 = 491.7° R. As 32° F. is

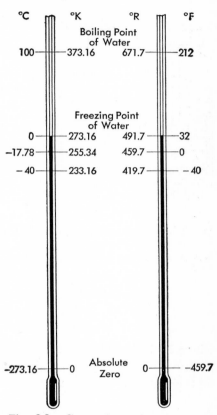

Fig. 3.3. Comparison of various tem-perature scales.

491.7° R., 0° F. = 491.7 — 32, or 459.7° R.; it follows that 459.7 degrees must be added to any Fahrenheit temperature to give the corresponding Rankine reading. Hence 0° R. = —459.7° F. The four temperature scales are compared in Figure 3.3.

10. Charles' Law. Study of the volume–absolute temperature relation-ships in Table 3.2 makes obvious the advantage of the absolute scale. The values for any volume and the corresponding temperature are identical. This exact agreement occurs, it is true, only because we began with a volume of 273 ml. at 0° C. (273° A.); for any sample of gas, however, we should find that the ratio between the volume and the corresponding absolute temperature is a fixed number (a constant). This general relationship, which is known as Charles' law, may be expressed mathematically as follows:

$$\frac{V}{T} = k \text{ (at constant pressure)} \quad (6)$$

Transposing, we obtain

$$V = kT \text{ (at constant pressure)} \quad (7)$$

In words, *Charles' law states that at constant pressure, the volume of a fixed weight of gas is directly proportional to the absolute temperature.* If the absolute temperature is *doubled,* the volume is *doubled;* if the absolute temperature is halved, so is the volume. If the absolute temperature is *increased* by the factor 293/273, the volume is *increased* by this same factor.

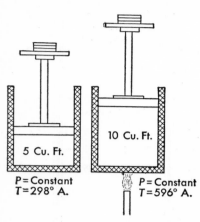

5 Cu. Ft.

10 Cu. Ft.

P = Constant
T = 298° A.

P = Constant
T = 596° A.

Fig. 3.4. The relation between the volume and the absolute temperature of a gas at constant pressure (Charles' law).

Charles' law may also be represented mathematically by the equation

$$\frac{V_1}{V_2} = \frac{T_1}{T_2} \text{ (at constant pressure)} \qquad (8)$$

where V_1 is the volume of a given weight of a certain gas at absolute temperature T_1, and V_2 is the new volume at temperature T_2. By multiplying throughout by $V_2 T_2$, we find that

$$V_1 T_2 = V_2 T_1 \text{ (at constant pressure)} \qquad (9)$$

or, solving this equation for V_2, we have

$$V_2 = V_1 \times \frac{T_2}{T_1} \qquad (10)$$

11. The Combined Gas Law Equation. We know from experience that the pressure of a sample of gas at fixed volume increases as the gas is heated. In fact, *at constant volume, the pressure of a fixed weight of a given gas is directly proportional to the absolute temperature.*

$$P = kT, \text{ or } \frac{P_1}{P_2} = \frac{T_1}{T_2} \text{ (at constant volume)} \qquad (11)$$

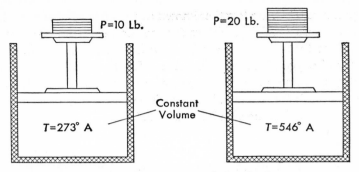

Fig. 3.5. The relation between the pressure and the absolute temperature of a gas.

This relationship can be derived by combining Boyle's and Charles' laws. Assume that a gas in an initial state in which its volume is V_1, its pressure P_1, and its absolute temperature T_1, is changed to a final state in which its volume is V_2, its pressure P_2, and its temperature T_2. We may consider the changes as being carried out in two separate steps. First, let us keep the temperature constant at T_1, and change the pressure to its final value, P_2. We can represent the new volume at pressure P_2 and temperature T_1 as V_x. Then, according to equation (5)

$$V_x = V_1 \times \frac{P_1}{P_2} \tag{12}$$

Now, let us keep the pressure constant and change the temperature of this new volume, V_x, to T_2. Then, by equation (10), the final volume, V_2, is

$$V_2 = V_x \times \frac{T_2}{T_1} \tag{13}$$

Substituting for V_x its value in equation (12), we have

$$V_2 = V_1 \times \frac{P_1}{P_2} \times \frac{T_2}{T_1} \tag{14}$$

For many purposes, equation (14) is useful as it stands. It may, however, be rearranged to read

$$\frac{P_1 V_1}{T_1} = \frac{P_2 V_2}{T_2} = k \tag{15}$$

This very important equation is known as the Combined Gas Law Equation. If the volume remains constant, i.e., if $V_1 = V_2$, then it follows that

$$\frac{P_1}{T_1} = \frac{P_2}{T_2}, \text{ or } \frac{P_1}{P_2} = \frac{T_1}{T_2} \text{ (at constant volume)} \tag{11}$$

12. Standard Temperature. In order to provide a uniform basis for comparing properties of different gases, 0° C. (273° A.) has been selected as the standard temperature. The pressure 760 mm. of mercury (1 atm.) and

the temperature $0°$ C. are together known as *standard conditions* of temperature and pressure (S.T.P.). Values for specific properties of gases are customarily those that obtain at standard conditions. Thus, the statement that
the density of oxygen is 1.429 g. per liter refers to standard conditions. It is
true that gas volumes are almost never measured at $0°$ C., but Charles' law
provides the basis for a method by which values at any other temperature
may be "corrected" to the standard temperature.

Problem 1

A gas measures 83.4 ml. at 1 atm. pressure and a temperature of $27°$ C.
Calculate its volume at standard conditions.

$$V_1 = 83.4 \text{ ml.} \qquad T_1 = 300° \text{ A.}$$
$$\downarrow \text{ decreased} \qquad \downarrow \text{ decreased} \qquad \text{(at constant}$$
$$\qquad\qquad\qquad\qquad\qquad\qquad\qquad\qquad \text{pressure)}$$
$$V_2 = \quad ? \qquad\qquad T_2 = 273° \text{ A.}$$

We know from Charles' law and equation (10) that the final volume is equal
to the original volume multiplied by the ratio of the absolute temperatures.
Since the temperature is *decreased*, the volume will also be *decreased*. The
original volume must therefore be multiplied by a fraction less than 1,
273/300.

$$V_2 = 83.4 \times \frac{273}{300} = 75.9 \text{ ml.}$$

Problem 2 (Combined gas laws.)

A sample of gas occupies a volume of 86.8 ml. at a pressure of 730 mm. and
a temperature of $27°$ C. What will be its volume at standard conditions?
    First let us organize the data:

$$V_1 = 86.8 \text{ ml.} \qquad P_1 = 730 \text{ mm.} \qquad T_1 = 300° \text{ A.}$$
$$\downarrow \text{ decreased} \qquad \downarrow \text{ increased} \qquad \downarrow \text{ decreased}$$
$$V_2 = \quad ? \qquad\quad P_2 = 760 \text{ mm.} \qquad T_2 = 273° \text{ A.}$$

The answer may be obtained by substitution of the proper values in the combined gas laws equation, but the simple method based on logical reasoning
is preferable. The student will recognize that this problem actually combines
the previous one with *Problem 1* under Boyle's law. Since, in this case, both
pressure and temperature are changed, the final volume will be equal to the
original volume multiplied by two independent correction factors, one due
to the change in pressure and the second to the change in temperature:
$V_2 = V_1 \times$ (ratio of pressures) $\times$ (ratio of temperatures). The reasoning

involved in determining whether each of the two independent factors should be greater or less than 1 is exactly similar to that previously outlined and may be summarized as follows:

Pressure factor

Pressure increase → volume decrease → pressure factor < 1

Pressure decrease → volume increase → pressure factor > 1

Temperature factor

Temperature increase → volume increase → temperature factor > 1

Temperature decrease → volume decrease → temperature factor < 1

Here the *pressure* is *increased* from 730 to 760 mm.; since the effect of this change in pressure is to *decrease* the volume, we therefore multiply the original volume by the pressure fraction 730/760. The temperature decrease from 300° to 273° A. likewise *decreases* the volume, and hence we multiply by the temperature fraction 273/300.

Therefore,

$$V_2 = 86.8 \times \frac{730}{760} \times \frac{273}{300} = 75.9 \text{ ml.}$$

Both changes operate in the same direction, toward a reduction in volume, so that it is immediately apparent that the answer must be less than 86.8. By comparing this problem with the two others of which it is a combination, we see that the total effect of changes in both pressure and temperature is exactly the same as if the process were accomplished in two distinct steps. The calculations are simplified, however, if these are combined into one step as shown.

Problem 3

A certain gas measures 546 ml. at a pressure of 1 atm. and a temperature of −80° C. Calculate the volume it would occupy at a pressure of 1.5 atm. and a temperature of 30° C.

First, we change the centigrade temperatures to absolute:

$$-80° \text{ C.} = -80° + 273° = 193° \text{ A.}$$

$$30° \text{ C.} = 30° + 273° \text{ A.} = 303° \text{ A.}$$

$V_1 = 546$	$P_1 = 1$ atm.	$T_1 = 193°$ A.
↓	↓ increased	↓ increased
$V_2 = $?	$P_2 = 1.5$ atm.	$T_2 = 303°$ A.

The *increase* in pressure from 1 to 1.5 atm. brings about a *decrease* in the volume, hence we multiply by the fraction 1/1.5. The effect of the *increase* in temperature from 193° to 303° A. is to *increase* the volume by the fraction 303/193. Because the pressure and temperature changes in this case act in opposition to each other, the actual numerical calculations are required before we can be certain whether the final volume will be greater or less than 546 ml.

$$V_2 = 546 \times \frac{1}{1.5} \times \frac{303}{193} = 571 \text{ ml.}$$

13. Dalton's Law of Partial Pressures. The pressure exerted independently by any single gas in a mixture of gases is called its *partial pressure*. It has already been pointed out that different gases introduced into the same container mix, or interdiffuse, but we have not considered what each gas contributes to the total pressure. In general, the behavior of gaseous mixtures is expressed in the important generalization first stated by John Dalton, an English schoolmaster, in 1807, and known as Dalton's law of partial pressures: *Each gas in a gaseous mixture exerts a partial pressure equal to the pressure which it would exert if it were the only gas present in the same volume, and the total pressure of the mixture is the sum of the partial pressures of all the component gases.*

We may express this law in symbols by representing the total pressure by P_{total} and the pressures which the individual gases would exert if contained alone in the same volume and at the same temperature as the mixture, i.e., the partial pressures, as $p_1, p_2, p_3, \ldots$ Then

$$P_{\text{total}} = p_1 + p_2 + p_3 \ldots \text{ (at constant temperature)}$$

Likewise, if the volumes which the individual gases would occupy if present alone at the given temperature and at the *total pressure* of the mixture are represented by $v_1, v_2, v_3 \ldots$, the total volume, V_{total}, is given by the equation

$$V_{\text{total}} = v_1 + v_2 + v_3 \ldots \text{ (at constant temperature)}$$

Thus it may be stated that when two or more gases are mixed at constant *volume* and temperature, their *pressures* are additive; when they are mixed at constant *pressure* and temperature, their *volumes* are additive.

Air is approximately 1/5 oxygen and 4/5 nitrogen by volume. This means that we might consider a sample of 500 ml. of air measured at 1 atm. as having been obtained by the mixing of 100 ml. of oxygen and and 400 ml. of nitrogen, each at 1 atm. pressure. In the total volume of 500 ml., however, this quantity of oxygen would exert a pressure of only $\frac{1}{5}$ of 1 atm., and the nitrogen, $\frac{4}{5}$ of 1 atm. Hence we might also think of the mixture as consisting of 500 ml. of oxygen at a partial pressure of $\frac{1}{5}$ atm., and 500 ml. of nitrogen at a partial pressure of $\frac{4}{5}$ atm. Thus the partial pressures of the gases in the mixture are proportional to their volumes when both are measured at the same pressure.

14. Rates of Diffusion; Graham's Law. All gases that do not react chemically diffuse into each other completely when placed in contact for some time, regardless of their relative densities. It has long been known, however, that the rates at which different gases diffuse throughout a container, or escape from a vessel through a small opening, depend on the densities of the gases. The lower the density of a gas, the more rapidly it diffuses. Hydrogen is the least dense of all gases and therefore exhibits the highest rate of diffusion. Air, for example, diffuses much more slowly than hydrogen, as may be easily demonstrated in a rather striking fashion. A bell jar (A) filled with hydrogen is lowered around a porous cup (B) of an apparatus such as is pictured in Figure 3.6. The hydrogen diffuses through the pores into the cup much more rapidly than the air diffuses outward. As a result, the pressure inside the apparatus is increased sufficiently to force water out of the bottle through the jet in the form of a miniature fountain.

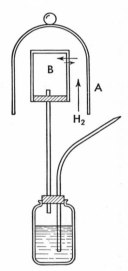

Fig. 3.6. Demonstration of the rapid diffusion of hydrogen.

In 1829, the English chemist Thomas Graham determined *quantitatively* the relationship between the rates of diffusion and the densities of gases. His results are summarized in Graham's law of diffusion:
The rates of diffusion of various gases are inversely proportional to the square roots of their respective densities. This law may be stated mathematically in the form

$$\frac{r_1}{r_2} = \sqrt{\frac{d_2}{d_1}} \quad \text{(at the same temperature and pressure)} \qquad (16)$$

where r_1 and d_1 represent the rate of diffusion (volume diffusing per unit of time) and density of one gas, and r_2 and d_2 the corresponding values for a second gas.

Using Graham's law, we can calculate exactly the relative diffusion rates of hydrogen and oxygen. We know that

$$\frac{r_{\text{hydrogen}}}{r_{\text{oxygen}}} = \sqrt{\frac{d_{\text{oxygen}}}{d_{\text{hydrogen}}}}$$

The density of oxygen is 1.42904 and that of hydrogen 0.08987 g. per liter at standard temperature and pressure. Therefore

$$\frac{r_{\text{hydrogen}}}{r_{\text{oxygen}}} = \sqrt{\frac{1.42904}{0.08987}} = 3.988$$

This means that hydrogen diffuses almost 4 times as rapidly as the more dense oxygen.

THE KINETIC-MOLECULAR THEORY

15. A Theory of Gas Structure. We have now completed a review of many of the experimental *facts* regarding the behavior of gases under various conditions, and of the *laws* summarizing these facts. The properties of all gases, we have found, are strikingly similar. This fact suggests that the ultimate structure or nature of all gaseous matter is much the same, and challenges us to construct a thought model of that structure. Our goal is a theory by means of which we can explain and correlate the behavior of gases, which will enable us to predict new facts, and which no amount of rigorous testing will prove invalid.

16. The Particles of Gases; Molecules. We can best account for the perfect expansibility of gases by assuming that matter in the gaseous state is discontinuous. Certainly, no continuous elastic material in our experience, such as a sheet of rubber, for example, can be stretched indefinitely. The additional fact that any gas will diffuse into a space already occupied by another gas suggests that gases are composed of particles too small to be visible, and that there are spaces between the particles. From the fact that gases may be compressed into minute fractions of their original volumes, we are led to the conclusion that the intervening spaces must be large compared to the dimensions of the particles themselves. Even stronger evidence for this supposition is provided by Boyle's law, which tells us that all gases respond in the same manner to changes in pressure. We can best interpret this fact by assuming that at pressures under which gases are ordinarily observed, the volume of the particles is very small as compared with the entire volume occupied by the gas. We might accept as an appropriate name of these particles the word "molecules," which is derived from the Latin and means "tiny masses."

Our first postulate, then, is this: *Gases are made up of minute particles called molecules, the total volume of which is a small fraction of the entire space occupied by the gas.* In other words, *the dimensions of the molecules are small as compared with the average distance between them.*

17. Gaseous Pressure and Molecular Motion. Our assumption that gases are made up of molecules answers one question posed by diffusion phenomena, but leaves a second problem unsolved. We can account for the fact that there is adequate free space between the molecules of gases to permit the interpenetration or diffusion of other gases. But what causes gas molecules to take advantage of this empty space, i.e., why do all gases diffuse rapidly when placed in contact? The obvious answer is that the molecules of gases are in constant motion at high average speeds.

We have evidence that such motion of the molecules is rapid, indeed. Many motorists have learned that there is nothing deliberate about the diffusion of air as it escapes from a tire after a blowout. The fact that any sudden diminution of the external pressure upon an enclosed sample of gas results in its instantaneous expansion likewise suggests that the molecules are moving constantly, and very rapidly.

The most convincing evidence on this point, however, is afforded by a consideration of the *manner* in which gases exert pressure. The pressure of a gas is the force per unit area exerted by the gas. But the striking fact concerning this force is that it is exerted uniformly in all directions. Consequently we cannot account for the nature of gas pressures in terms of such unidirectional forces as the pull of a stretched spring, or the weight of an object. Can we explain gaseous pressures in terms of molecules? We know that moving bodies exert a force upon any object which they strike. Let us, therefore, expand our previous assumption and imagine that the molecules of a gas are in a state of ceaseless, rapid, chaotic motion, colliding with each other and the walls of the container in a perfectly random fashion. Each impact of a molecule with a wall of the container will produce a force, and the combined forces resulting from all of the bombardments against a wall will have the effect of one continuous force or steady pressure on that wall. If the molecular motion is perfectly chaotic, the total number of molecules moving in any one direction will, on the average, be equal to the number moving in any other direction; i.e., the pressure will be uniform in all directions.

Still another fact concerning gas pressures demands our attention. Compared with the forces exerted by other much larger moving bodies which we can observe, the combined force produced by any aggregation of molecules is, in proportion to their total mass, enormous. We are struck with this fact when we observe the tremendous pressure which even a tiny mass of a gaseous material exerts when confined in a sufficiently small volume. To account for the production of such great forces by relatively small weights of gases, we must assume both that the molecular impacts are frequent and that the change of momentum at each impact is comparatively large. Each of these assumptions requires that the molecules must be moving at extremely high average velocity.

From our consideration of gaseous pressures, then, we have arrived at our second postulate: *The molecules of gases are not stationary, but are in constant, rapid, chaotic motion, colliding with each other and with the walls of their container in a perfectly random fashion.*

18. Boyle's Law Explained in Terms of Molecular Motion. We have assumed that the impacts of the molecules of a gas on the walls of the containing vessel give rise to the pressure of the gas. This must be proportional to the number of impacts per second on unit area, and hence to the number of molecules per unit space, or the molecular concentration, as it is called. If the external pressure on a gas is doubled, at constant temperature, the molecular concentration of the gas must also be doubled so that the pressure exerted by the gas can balance that from without. This means that the molecules must be crowded into half of the volume that they first occupied. In other words, when the pressure is doubled at constant temperature, the volume must be halved. This is in complete agreement with Boyle's law.

19. Elasticity of Molecules. In order to explain the facts that gases show no tendency to settle toward the bottom of a container, and that the pressure of a gas within a container does not vary with time at a given temperature, we must assume that molecular collisions involve no energy loss due to friction. We may then state as our third postulate: *All molecular collisions are perfectly elastic.*[1] This hypothesis, it is true, is somewhat difficult to accept, for perfectly elastic bodies are beyond the realm of our experience. The kinetic energy of a freely bouncing tennis ball, for example, decreases rapidly with each bounce, being converted into heat because of friction. The temperature of the ball, as well as that of the surface which it strikes, is increased slightly by the heat released.

The kinetic energy of gas molecules, on the other hand, cannot be transformed into heat to increase the temperature of the gas itself or of any other body at the same temperature. Perhaps we shall be able to explain this

[1] This statement assumes that the molecules do not react chemically.

curious fact if we investigate the effect of changes in temperature upon the kinetic energy of gas molecules.

20. Temperature and Kinetic Energy. According to our second postulate, the pressure of a gas upon the walls of a container is due to the steady bombardment of the walls by the perfectly elastic molecules. We may logically reason that the pressure, or force per unit area, exerted by the molecules of a given sample of gas is directly proportional to each of two factors: (1) the number of bombardments on unit area per unit time, and (2) the change of momentum at each bombardment. The first of these, the frequency of bombardments, must in turn be directly proportional to the number n of molecules per unit volume (concentration) and the average velocity u of these molecules. The average change of momentum, in addition, is directly proportional to the mass m of each molecule and to the average velocity u of all the molecules. We conclude, then, that the pressure exerted by a gas is directly proportional to each of several independent variables: the concentration n, the average velocity u of the molecules, the mass m per molecule, and again their average velocity u. Therefore, the pressure is proportional to the product of all these variables;[2] or using the proportionality symbol α, we may write

$$P \ \alpha \ numu$$

or

$$P \ \alpha \ nmu^2 \qquad\qquad (17)$$

This is a most revealing equation. Since the kinetic energy ($K.E.$) of any body is equal to one-half the product of its mass and its velocity squared, or

$$K.E. = \tfrac{1}{2}mu^2 \qquad\qquad (18)$$

and since either side of a proportionality may be multiplied by a constant without changing its validity, we may write

$$P \ \alpha \ nmu^2 \ \alpha \ n\tfrac{1}{2}mu^2 \ \alpha \ nK.E. \qquad\qquad (19)$$

In words, the pressure exerted by a gas is dependent only upon the *number* of molecules per unit volume and their average *kinetic energy*. We have already proved (p. 34) that at constant volume the pressure of a given sample of gas is proportional to the absolute temperature. This means that the average kinetic energy of the molecules must be directly proportional to the absolute temperature.

In symbols,

$$mu^2 \ \alpha \ K.E. \ \alpha \ T \qquad\qquad (20)$$

---

[2] It may be shown mathematically that if a quantity is proportional to each of several independent variables, then it is proportional also to their product.

Expressed in words, this proportionality constitutes our fourth major postulate: *The absolute temperature is a measure of the kinetic energy of the molecules of a gas.* For a given gas m is constant and may be dropped from the
proportionality. Therefore

$$u^2 \, \alpha \, T \; \text{(for any given gas)} \tag{21}$$

This conclusion explains the fact that the rates of diffusion of all gases increase as the temperature is raised.

   If the average kinetic energy of gas molecules is measured by the absolute
temperature alone, we understand at once why molecules, in constrast to
larger bodies, are perfectly elastic. The ordered kinetic energy of a bouncing
tennis ball is converted, by inelastic collisions, into the random chaotic kinetic energies of its molecules (if we assume that a tennis ball, like gases, is
made up of molecules), which is classified as *heat energy.* As a result, the
temperature of the ball, as well as that of the surface with which it collides,
is increased slightly. Molecules, on the other hand, cannot increase the
temperature of the gas which they comprise at the expense of their own
kinetic energy, *because this very temperature is actually nothing but a
measure of their kinetic energy.*

   How, then, do molecules undergo a decrease in kinetic energy? Our observation of familiar moving bodies suggests an answer. We know that when
any two bodies meet—as a baseball and a bat, for example—there is a
tendency toward redistribution of kinetic energies; the body possessing the
higher kinetic energy, if conditions permit, imparts all or a portion of it to
the body with which it collides. Now if perfectly elastic bodies in rapid
motion were permitted to collide with each other repeatedly, we should
expect that they would undergo interchanges of kinetic energy in such a way
as to equalize, over a period of time, the average kinetic energies of all the
bodies. Whenever two samples of the same or of different gases at different temperatures are mixed without reaction, there is an immediate equalization of temperatures. The temperature of the cooler gas is increased at the
expense of that of the warmer gas, until the components of the mixture are
at the same temperature. In terms of kinetic energies, we assume the following to happen: when two gases, the molecules of which possess different
average kinetic energies, are mixed, there is a rapid equalization of kinetic
energies. The average kinetic energy of the molecules of the cooler gas is
increased at the expense of the energy of the molecules of the warmer gas
until the average kinetic energies of the molecules of the two gases are equal.
In short, we assume that *at the same temperature the molecules of all gases
possess the same average kinetic energy.* The average kinetic energy of gas

molecules depends only upon the temperature. Hence light molecules, such as those of hydrogen, must move much faster at a given temperature than heavier ones, such as oxygen.

21. Absolute Zero—Charles' Law. If the molecules of all gases are moving with kinetic energies directly proportional to the absolute temperature, it follows that at *absolute zero* the kinetic energy of all gas molecules is zero. At this temperature, 0° A. (−273.16° C.), all molecular motion theoretically ceases. A gas at this temperature, therefore, could exert no pressure, and if any external pressure were exerted upon it, its volume would be reduced to zero. Absolute zero, in terms of our theory, is the lowest conceivable temperature, a remarkable conclusion confirmed by the fact that many properties of substances approach either zero or infinity as the temperature approaches −273.16° C. Physicists and chemists have actually succeeded in reaching within 0.005 degree of that point.

When the absolute temperature of a gas is doubled, the total kinetic energy of the molecules of the gas will likewise be doubled, and hence only one-half of the original concentration of molecules is required to exert the original pressure. In other words, if the pressure is to remain constant, the volume must double. These conclusions are in perfect accord with Charles' law.

22. Dalton's Law of Partial Pressures. Mixing of two or more gases at the same temperature consists merely of adding one species of molecules to one or more other species of molecules, all of which possess the same average kinetic energy. Unless the gases react chemically, we should expect the mixing to produce no change in the average kinetic energy of the molecules of any one of the gases. Each gas, then, should exert the same pressure which it would if confined alone in the same volume. The total kinetic energy of the mixture would be equal to the sum of the kinetic energies of all the individual gases, so the total pressure would equal the sum of the partial pressures. All these predictions are in complete agreement with Dalton's law.

23. Relative Numbers of Molecules. The assumption that the average kinetic energies of the molecules, regardless of weight or size, of all the gases are the same at the same temperature leads to an almost startling conclusion. Let us imagine that we have samples of any pair of gases at the same pressure and temperature. Then both gases have the same average kinetic energy per molecule. But the pressure of a gas depends only upon the concentration and average kinetic energy of its molecules. If the pressures are equal, and the average kinetic energies are equal, then the only other variable, the number of molecules per unit volume, must also be equal. This most significant con-

clusion, stated in somewhat more general terms, constitutes our fifth postulate: *Equal volumes of all gases, under the same conditions of pressure and
temperature, contain the same number of molecules.*

Surprising as this assumption may seem, it gains support from the fact
that as early as 1811, an Italian physicist, Amadeo Avogadro, following
quite a different line of reasoning, advanced the identical hypothesis. In
order to understand how Avogadro reached his conclusion we must first
consider the evidence upon which it is based, namely *Gay-Lussac's law of
combining volumes.*

24. Gay-Lussac's Law of Combining Volumes. Whenever water vapor is
formed from its elements, it is found that two volumes of hydrogen are required to combine with one volume of oxygen, and two volumes of gaseous
water are formed. These relative volumes—which, of course, are to be measured at the same pressure and temperature above the boiling point of water
—may be pictured as follows:

hydrogen	+	oxygen	→	water vapor
1 vol. 1 vol.		1 vol.		1 vol. 1 vol.

This is not a mere coincidence, for experiment shows that in other reactions
involving gases the ratios of the volumes of the reacting gases and the gaseous
products may also be expressed in small whole numbers. In the synthesis of
hydrogen chloride, for example, an equally simple relationship exists; one
volume of hydrogen combines with one volume of chlorine to produce two
volumes of hydrogen chloride:

hydrogen	+	chlorine	→	hydrogen chloride
1 vol.		1 vol.		1 vol. 1 vol.

When carbon burns in oxygen to give carbon dioxide, one volume of oxygen
is required for every volume of carbon dioxide formed, but the volume of the
solid carbon bears no simple relationship to those of the two gases. We may
represent this recation by

carbon	+	oxygen	→	carbon dioxide
solid		1 vol.		1 vol.

These facts are summarized in the generalization known as Gay-Lussac's
law: *In any chemical reaction, the volumes of all gaseous products and
reactants, measured at the same conditions, may be expressed in ratios of
small whole numbers.*

25. Avogadro's Hypothesis. The simple volume ratios which exist in gaseous reactions stand in marked contrast to the weight relationships in chemical reactions. The latter, almost invariably, *cannot* be expressed in terms of small whole numbers. Thus, although exactly two volumes of hydrogen combine with one volume of oxygen to form exactly two volumes of water vapor, the weight relationship is found experimentally to be that 1 part by weight of hydrogen combines with 7.9365 parts by weight of oxygen to give 8.9365 parts by weight of water.

According to Gay-Lussac's law, gases react in small whole number ratios by volume. Avogadro reasoned that since molecules are the unit particles of gases, they must undergo reaction in ratios of small whole numbers. Thus, two molecules of one gas might combine with one molecule of another gas to give, perhaps, two molecules of a third gas. Now, is it not logical to assume that the volume ratios and the corresponding molecule ratios are the same? But this can be the case only if equal volumes of the gases entering into and resulting from the reaction contain the same number of molecules, the volumes being measured under the same conditions of pressure and temperature. Using the example of the synthesis of water, for example, Avogadro assumed that as two *volumes* of hydrogen combine with one *volume* of oxygen to form two *volumes* of water vapor, so also two *molecules* of hydrogen combine with one *molecule* of oxygen to form two *molecules* of water:

(1 vol. + 1 vol.)   +   (1 vol.)   →   (1 vol. + 1 vol.)

| hydrogen | oxygen | water vapor |
| 2 molecules | 1 molecule | 2 molecules |

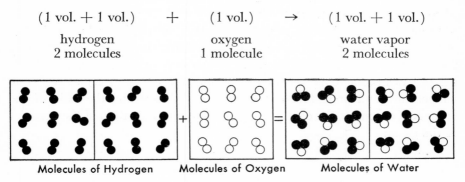

| Molecules of Hydrogen | Molecules of Oxygen | Molecules of Water |

Fig. 3.7. Two molecules of hydrogen combine with one molecule of oxygen to produce two molecules of water.

On the basis of such reasoning, Avogadro supposed that "equal volumes of all gases at the same pressure and temperature contain the same number of molecules." Although Avogadro's hypothesis was little more than a thoughtful guess when first proposed in 1811, it has since been verified so completely by experimental data that it is often called Avogadro's law, and it is now recognized as one of the cornerstones of chemical science.

26. Relative Densities of Gases. The reason that Avogadro's hypothesis is of such fundamental importance is that it provides the basis for the standard method of determining the relative weights of molecules of different gases. We cannot weigh individual molecules on a balance, any more than we can weigh individual dimes, nickels, or quarters on scales accurate only to the nearest pound. We could, however, accurately determine on such scales the relative weights of 1 dime, 1 nickel and 1 quarter by weighing large *equal* numbers of each. Similarly, to determine the *relative* masses of the molecules of two different gases, we need only to compare the weights of *equal* numbers of them; this means, in terms of Avogadro's hypothesis, *equal* volumes under the same conditions of temperature and pressure.

Let us assume, for example, that a certain volume of gas$_1$ weighs exactly twice as much as the same volume of gas$_2$. Even if we do not know the actual numbers of molecules in the two volumes, we know that these numbers are the same. If we represent the number of molecules of gas$_1$ by n, the number of molecules of gas$_2$ is likewise n. Then

$$\frac{n \times (\text{weight of 1 molecule of gas}_1)}{n \times (\text{weight of 1 molecule of gas}_2)} = \frac{2}{1}$$

Canceling n we obtain

$$\frac{\text{weight of 1 molecule of gas}_1}{\text{weight of 1 molecule of gas}_2} = \frac{2}{1}$$

In words, the ratio of the weights (or masses) of the individual molecules of two gases is the same as the ratio of the weights (or masses) of any equal volumes of the two gases at the same temperature and pressure. The densities of gases are actually the weights of equal volumes (1 l.) at the same temperature and pressure (usually standard). Therefore, the ratio of the weights of the molecules of any two gases is equal to the ratio of the densities of the gases:

$$\frac{m_1}{m_2} = \frac{d_1}{d_2}$$

where d_1 represents the density of gas$_1$, and m_1 the mass of a single molecule; d_2 and m_2 are the corresponding values for gas$_2$. From the ratio of the densities of oxygen and hydrogen, $1.42904/0.08987$, we calculate that the mass of an oxygen molecule is almost 16 times that of a hydrogen molecule.

The relative weights of molecules, as thus calculated from gaseous densities, are not exact, because, as we shall see presently, the behavior of all gases deviates somewhat from that described by the gas laws. Fairly accurate values are obtained, however, if the densities are measured at extremely low pressures.

27. Derivation of Graham's Law of Diffusion. At the same temperature, the kinetic energies of gas$_1$ and gas$_2$ are equal:

$$\tfrac{1}{2}m_1u_1{}^2 = \tfrac{1}{2}m_2u_2{}^2 \tag{23}$$

Transposing, we obtain

$$\frac{u_1{}^2}{u_2{}^2} = \frac{m_2}{m_1} \tag{24}$$

Extracting square roots

$$\frac{u_1}{u_2} = \sqrt{\frac{m_2}{m_1}} \tag{25}$$

In words, equation (25) states that the average velocities of the molecules of two different gases are inversely proportional to the square roots of their masses. As the masses of these molecules are directly proportional to the densities of the gases, we may write

$$\frac{u_1}{u_2} = \sqrt{\frac{d_2}{d_1}} \tag{26}$$

Now, if we make the altogether logical assumption that the rates of diffusion of gases are directly proportional to the average velocities of their molecules, we may say that

$$\frac{r_1}{r_2} = \frac{u_1}{u_2} \tag{27}$$

Then, combining (26) and (27), we obtain

$$\frac{r_1}{r_2} = \sqrt{\frac{d_2}{d_1}} \;\text{(at the same temperature and pressure)} \tag{28}$$

This is Graham's law of diffusion (p. 39).

28. Summary of the Kinetic-Molecular Theory. Reasoning from experimental facts, in logical step-by-step fashion, we have constructed a thought model of the possible structure of gases. We must remember always to distinguish sharply between our theory, which is an imaginary picture, and the actual facts, such as those summarized in the gas laws, which are elucidated and correlated and may even be predicted by means of the theory. The five major postulates, developed in the preceding pages and listed below for convenience, are:

1. Gases are made up of minute particles called molecules, the total volume of which is but a small fraction of the entire space occupied by them. The dimensions of molecules are small as compared with the average distance between them. Molecules of any one gas are the same in mass and size.

2. The molecules of gases are not stationary, but are in constant rapid, chaotic motion, colliding with each other and with the walls of their containers in a perfectly random fashion.

3. All molecular collisions are perfectly elastic, resulting in no decrease in the total kinetic energy.

4. The average kinetic energy of the molecules of a gas is proportional to the absolute temperature, and at the same temperature, the average kinetic energy of the molecules of all gases is the same.

5. Equal volumes of all gases at the same pressure and temperature contain the same number of molecules.

These postulates are actually those of the kinetic-molecular theory that gradually emerged during the period 1738 to 1860 as the result of the contributions of many brilliant chemists and physicists, and which has undergone further development up to the present. This fundamental theory has proved to be of such immense service in explaining and predicting the behavior, not of gases alone, but of liquids and solids as well, that today its validity is hardly questioned by anyone. Recent investigations, which can be described more adequately later in the book, not only have furnished unmistakable evidence of the existence of molecules, but have also revealed how almost unimaginably minute molecules are, and what inconceivably large numbers are contained even in minute amounts of matter.

It has been calculated that in 2.016 g. of hydrogen there are 6.024×10^{23} molecules.[3] Each hydrogen molecule, therefore, weighs 3.347×10^{-24} g. At standard temperature, the average velocity of a molecule of hydrogen, the lightest of all gases, is 1840 meters, or 1.14 miles, per second. This is about five times the velocity of sound in air, and almost twice that of a high-velocity rifle bullet. For the molecules of all other gases, the speeds are lower in accord with Graham's law. At the end of one second, a hydrogen molecule may have traveled a distance of over one mile and still be near its starting point, because during that time it will have undergone over 5×10^{10} collisions, which, of course, cause it to travel a zigzag path.

29. Deviations from the Gas Laws. Thus far, in order to simplify the discussion, we have assumed that Boyle's and Charles' laws are exact; actually they are only an approximation to the truth. As experimental measurements were improved, and especially as they were extended to high pressures, it became apparent that the volumes actually observed deviated from the calculated volumes by more than any error due to methods of measurement.

---

[3] This equals 602,400,000,000,000,000,000,000, or six hundred and two sextillion, four hundred quintillion.

The gas laws hold well for most gases at ordinary pressures; at high pressures, however, all gases show marked deviations from the pressure-volume-temperature relationships as expressed by these laws.

From experimental data concerning the behavior of various gases under different conditions, these generalization may be drawn: With increasing pressure, if the temperature is sufficiently low, all gases are slightly more

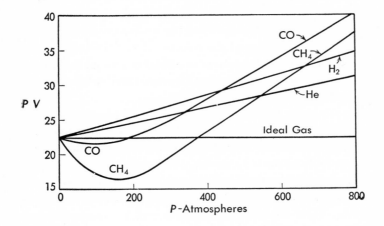

Fig. 3.8. Deviation of the behavior of actual gases from Boyle's law. CO, carbon monoxide; CH_4, methane; H_2, hydrogen; He, helium.

compressible than predicted by the gas laws. At very high pressures, however, all gases become *less* compressible than would be expected in terms of the gas laws. The pressure at which this reversal takes place varies from one gas to another and decreases with increasing temperature. At sufficiently high temperatures, gases are less compressible than expected, at any pressure.

In Figure 3.8, the value of the product PV (at 0° C.) for a number of gases is plotted against the pressure (P). If Boyle's law predicted the behavior of gases exactly, PV should be a constant $(PV = k)$ at all pressures, as indicated by the horizontal line. Actually, at low pressures and 0° C., carbon monoxide (CO) and methane (CH_4) are *more* compressible than Boyle's law requires (PV *decreases* with increasing pressure). The deviation in each case reaches a maximum (PV passes through a minimum) as the pressure is increased. From that point on the compressibility is *less* than expected (PV *increases* with increasing pressure, eventually exceeding its original value, k). At much lower temperatures, hydrogen (H_2) and helium (He) would behave similarly. Hydrogen and helium at 0°, however, are less compressible than required by Boyle's law throughout the entire pressure range. Carbon monoxide and methane exhibit this latter behavior only at higher temperatures.

These abnormalities by no means invalidate but, on the contrary, actually support the kinetic-molecular theory; for they are readily explainable in terms of that theory if we take into account certain factors which we have hitherto neglected. We made the assumption in the development of the postulates that the volume of the molecules is insignificant as compared with the free space between them. At low pressures, this is true; at higher pressures, however, the incompressible volume of the molecules themselves becomes an appreciable fraction of the total gas volume. Hence the fraction remaining as free space for compression becomes considerably less, with the result that the compressibility of the gas is decreased as compared with that predicted by the simple theory.

In the second place, we have tacitly assumed that in the gaseous state there are no attractive forces between molecules. The very fact that all gases may be liquefied indicates, however, that such cohesive forces do exist. These forces of attraction between molecules, often called van der Waals forces, are mainly electrical in nature. They become more significant as the average kinetic energy of the molecules becomes less; i.e., as the temperature of the gas decreases. Their effect, of course, is to pull the molecules together and thus to decrease the volume; i.e., to increase the compressibility.

The two factors which are responsible for deviation from the gas laws thus tend to act in opposition to each other. The combined effect of the two, that which is observed experimentally, may be either a decrease or an increase in compressibility, depending upon whether the effect of the volume of the molecules or that of the van der Waals forces predominates. Comparison of the direction and extent of the deviation from the gas laws in different gases affords valuable information concerning the relative magnitudes of the forces of attraction between different molecules.

No actual gas obeys Boyle's and Charles' laws exactly, although at ordinary conditions the deviations are no greater than the errors due to the method of measurement. In reality, the gas laws describe the behavior of an imaginary gas the molecules of which are dimensionless points with no attraction for each other. Such a hypothetical gas is referred to as an *ideal gas*, and the gas laws therefore describe *ideal behavior*. At constant temperature, all gases become more nearly ideal as the pressure is lowered, approaching ideal behavior as the pressure approaches zero.

30. The Joule-Thomson Effect. Further evidence that attractive forces exist between gas molecules is offered by the fact that gases are cooled upon sudden expansion from high to low pressures, even if they do no external work. This phenomenon is called the Joule-Thomson effect, from the original investigators, the English physicists James Joule and William Thomson (Lord Kelvin). It may be observed, for example, when air is permitted to escape from a highly inflated tire. As the gas expands the molecules pull apart from each other, and work must be done to overcome the cohesive forces which tend to hold the molecules together. Since this work is done at the expense of the kinetic energy of the molecules of the gas, the temperature is lowered on expansion. The Joule-Thomson effect is of great practical importance in the liquefaction of gases.

31. Liquefaction of Gases; Critical Temperature and Pressure. Under proper conditions of temperature and pressure all gases may be liquefied; that is, they may be changed to a second fluid phase of greater density, called a liquid. Liquefaction occurs only when the cohesive forces which tend to bind the molecules together counteract their kinetic energy to a sufficient extent to keep the molecules confined to a relatively small volume. Obviously, then, two conditions favor liquefaction: (1) low temperatures, so that the kinetic energy of the molecules is low; and (2) high pressures, so that the molecules are brought sufficiently close together to permit the cohesive forces to be significant. In general, the higher the temperature of a gas, the greater the pressure required in order to liquefy it. According to the kinetic-molecular picture, however, it appears logical that for every gas there should exist a certain temperature above which the kinetic energy becomes so high that it cannot be overcome by the attractive forces, no matter how close together the molecules are brought. In other words, for each gas there should be a definite maximum temperature at which the gas can be liquefied, and above which it cannot be liquefied no matter how great is the pressure applied. Actually, there is such a temperature for every gas; it is called the *critical temperature,* and the pressure just necessary to liquefy a gas at its critical temperature is called its *critical pressure.* For carbon dioxide, the critical temperature is 31.35° C. and the critical pressure 73 atm. Thus, although carbon dioxide is a gas under ordinary conditions, it may be liquefied at a temperature as high as 31° C., solely by the application of a pressure of 73 atm. or greater. At room temperature (about 20° C.) only 56.5 atm. of pressure are required.

Neither oxygen nor hydrogen can be liquefied at room temperature, regardless of the pressure. For oxygen, the critical temperature is —118.8° C. and the critical pressure 49.7 atm.; for hydrogen, the corresponding constants are —240° C. and 12.8 atm. Thus, hydrogen cannot exist in the liquid state unless its temperature is lowered at least to $-240°$ C., and even then a pressure not less than 12.8 atm. must be applied.

If the temperature of a gas is progressively decreased below its critical temperature, the pressure required for liquefaction decreases steadily, until finally a point is reached at which the gas liquefies at 1 atm. pressure. This temperature is called the *boiling point* of the liquid, a term which will be defined from another standpoint in the next chapter. Ordinary air liquefies under 1 atm. pressure at about $-190°$ C. In practice, gases to be liquefied are often cooled either by repeated sudden expansion from high to low pressures, utilizing the Joule-Thomson effect, or by expansions against external pressure exerted on a movable piston, in which case additional heat is absorbed equivalent to the work done in moving the piston. The Linde process for the liquefaction of air employs the first method; the Claude process, the second. The latter is complicated by the difficulties of lubrication at low temperatures, but has an advantage in that part of the work done by the air in its expansion against the piston is recovered and may be utilized in the compression of additional air. In either process, the heat released when the air is compressed is removed by passing the air through coils surrounded by water or ammonia.

STUDY QUESTIONS AND PROBLEMS

1. A sample of gas at atmospheric pressure, while the barometer reading was 756 mm., measured 540 ml. A few hours later the barometer had fallen to 729 mm., although the temperature remained unchanged. What was the new volume of the gas?

2. A certain quantity of gas occupies 100 ml. at 4 atm. and 0° C. How could its volume be reduced to 80 ml. at constant temperature? at constant pressure?

3. If a sample of gas occupies 84.0 l. at standard conditions of temperature and pressure, what will be its volume at 26° C. and 736 mm. pressure?

4. Assume that a perfectly expansible toy balloon occupies a volume of 1 l. at 31° C. and 760 mm. pressure. What will be its volume at 25° C. and 745 mm. pressure?

5. (a) As a perfectly expansible meteorological balloon was released from the ground at a pressure of 740 mm. and a temperature of 23° C. its volume was 100 cubic meters. Now as the balloon ascended to the stratosphere, it passed through a region where the pressure was 42 mm. What would the volume of the balloon have been at this point if there had been no temperature drop?

(b) Actually, however, the temperature had dropped to $-63°$ C. What, then, was the actual volume of the balloon?

(c) Which factor, pressure or temperature, had the greater effect in changing the volume of the balloon?

6. An automobile tire is inflated to 29.4 lb. per sq. in. gauge pressure at 40° F. Assuming a constant volume of 10 l. for the tire, what will be the pressure if the tire is heated to 95° F. by rapid driving? What volume of air, measured at 95° F. and 1 atm., must be allowed to escape to restore the pressure to its original value?

7. If the density of a certain gas at standard conditions is 2.00 g. per liter, what is the weight of 1 l. of the gas at 570 mm. pressure and 182° C.?

8. Which contains more molecules, 500 ml. of a gas at 600 mm. pressure and 21° C., or 525 ml. of a gas at 640 mm. pressure and 30° C.?

9. If 1 l. of a certain gas diffuses through a porous plug in exactly twice the time required for 1 l. of oxygen under the same conditions, what is the density of this gas? (The density of oxygen at standard conditions is 1.429 g. per liter.)

10. Assume that ammonia and hydrogen chloride gases are released simultaneously in two ends, respectively, of a 100-cm. long glass tube. The two gases, ammonia and hydrogen chloride, will diffuse through the tube until they meet; the point at which this occurs will be indicated by the formation of a ring of white, solid ammonium chloride. At what position in the tube will this happen? The density of ammonia at standard conditions is 0.760 g. per l., and of hydrogen chloride 1.63 g. per l.

11. A sample of a certain gas is heated from 0° C. to 273° C. By what fraction is the average kinetic energy of the molecules increased?

12. A pressure cooker is provided with a safety valve set at 25 lb. per sq. in. pressure (above atmospheric pressure). If dry air at 0° C. was sealed in the cooker, at what temperature would the safety valve open?

13. Assume that a cylinder fitted with a movable piston contains enough oxygen molecules to exert a pressure of 0.5 atm. when the volume is 1 l. If 3 times as many hydrogen molecules and 4 times as many nitrogen molecules are introduced, what must be the total pressure if the volume is to be maintained at 1 l.? What will be the total volume, if the external pressure is kept at 0.5 atm.?

14. When 1 l. of carbon dioxide at 40° C. and 1 atm. pressure is put under a pressure of 10 atm., the volume is reduced to 96 ml. At 1000 atm., the volume is 1.6 ml. What should be the values for the two new volumes according to Boyle's law? How do you account for the discrepancies in terms of the kinetic-molecular theory?

15. Why is air cooled as it escapes from a tire under pressure? Why does a bicycle pump get hot while being used to pump air into a tire?

16. State in quantitative terms the effect upon (1) the number of molecular impacts per unit time upon a unit area of containing wall, and (2) the change of momentum at each impact, of each of the following changes:

    (a) A sample of gas is heated from 0° to 273° C. at constant volume.

    (b) A sample of gas is allowed to expand from a volume of 3 l. to a volume of 4 l. at constant temperature.

4

The Liquid and Solid States

1. The Kinetic-Molecular Theory Applies to Liquids and Solids. As we have seen in the preceding chapter, the kinetic-molecular theory was formulated originally to explain the behavior of gases. Its usefulness is enhanced by the fact that it may be extended to account for the nature and the behavior of liquids and many solids, as well.

THE LIQUID STATE

2. General Characteristics of Liquids. Unlike gases, liquids do not have the property of infinite expansibility; as a result, a given sample of a liquid has clearly defined bounding surfaces. Compared with gases, liquids are only slightly compressible and expansible, their volumes changing relatively little with changes in temperature and pressure. The densities of many common substances in the liquid state are more than a thousand times as great as their densities as gases, measured at ordinary pressures. One gram of water vapor, for example, undergoes a reduction in volume from about 1680 to 1.04 ml. wnen it is liquefied at 100° C. and 1 atm. pressure; this represents more than a 1600-fold increase in density.

In terms of the kinetic-molecular theory, all of these facts point to the assumption that the average distances between molecules are much less in liquids than in gases. Furthermore, in liquids the kinetic energy of the molecules is apparently largely overcome by the cohesive forces between them. We may consider the liquid state, then, simply as an extension of the gaseous state into the region of short intermolecular distances and high intermolecular attractions.

3. Viscosity of Liquids. Despite the strong forces of attraction, the molecules in a liquid cannot be considered as rigidly fixed. All liquids flow, a fact which is best explained by the assumption that there is a continuous movement or diffusion of the molecules throughout the body of a liquid. As a result of the attractive forces between molecules, however, all liquids are characterized by a certain internal friction which tends to resist the movement of one portion of the liquid in relation to another. This internal resistance to flow is called *viscosity*.

The viscosity of a liquid depends upon the nature of the molecules in question, and particularly upon the magnitude of the forces of attraction between the molecules. Some liquids—such as ether and chloroform—in which these forces are relatively small, flow easily, and are said to have low viscosities, or to be highly mobile. Molasses and honey, on the other hand, are highly viscous because of the large forces of attraction between their molecules.

As a liquid is heated, the average kinetic energy of the molecules is increased; as a result, the viscosity of the liquid is decreased. The lowering has been found to be roughly 2% for each degree rise in temperature.

Viscosity is an important property from a practical as well as from a theoretical standpoint. For example, the value of an oil for lubricating purposes is determined to a large extent by its viscosity and by the exact manner in which its viscosity varies with temperature. A "heavy" oil is one that is highly viscous, whereas a "light" oil has a lower viscosity. Various devices for determining the relative viscosities of liquids are in common use; most of them depend either upon the rates of flow of liquids through capillary tubes or standard orifices, or upon the resistance which the liquids offer to the rotation of discs or paddles, or the dropping of balls through the liquids.

4. Surface Tension. The intermolecular forces of attraction account not only for the viscosities but also for the surface behavior of liquids. Any molecule in the center of a liquid is attracted equally in all directions by the surrounding molecules. At the surface, however, a molecule is surrounded by other molecules of the liquid only in those directions which lie within the 180° arc below the plane of the surface. As a consequence, a surface molecule experiences intermolecular attractions only in those directions which lie within that imaginary arc (Figure 4.1). The resultant of these attractions is an

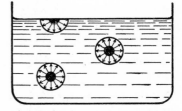

Fig. 4.1. Unequal distribution of intermolecular forces at the surface of a liquid.

unbalanced force downward, tending to draw the surface molecules into the body of the liquid and therefore to reduce the surface to a minimum. The liquid, therefore, behaves as if it were under a strain or tension. It is this contracting force, called *surface tension*, which accounts for the tendency of a small mass of liquid to assume a spherical shape, since in a sphere the ratio of surface to volume is at a minimum. It is surface tension, likewise, which accounts for the rise of certain liquids in capillary tubes, as well as for the movement of water in blotting paper or in the soil.

As the temperature of a liquid is increased, the kinetic energy of its molecules tends more and more to overcome the intermolecular forces of attraction. The surface tension of a liquid, therefore, decreases as the temperature rises. At the critical temperature, the forces of attraction are just overcome by the kinetic energy of the molecules, and the surface tension becomes zero; i.e., the bounding surface between liquid and gas disappears and only one phase is present.

5. Evaporation. The fact that the kinetic energies of the molecules in a liquid are acting continually in opposition to the intermolecular forces is even more strikingly demonstrated by the familiar phenomenon of evaporation. As in gases, not all of the molecules of a liquid have the same kinetic energy. At a given instant, some possess kinetic energies much greater, and others much less, than the average. Those with the highest kinetic energy (the greatest velocity) can actually escape into the free space above before being pulled back down by the attractive forces of the material left behind. If the space is sufficiently great, this process of evaporation may continue gradually until all of the liquid changes to a vapor, or *evaporates*.

Since evaporation involves the escape of molecules with energies greater than the average, the average kinetic energy of the molecules which remain within the liquid must decrease; hence, the temperature of the liquid drops unless heat is supplied from the outside. The cooling produced by evaporation is familiar to all, as it constitutes the basis of the mechanism for the regulation of body temperature through perspiration in man and in all other mammals which possess sweat glands.

Evaporation of a given body of liquid proceeds more readily the larger the surface area, and any factor which tends to facilitate the escape of molecules from the surface of a liquid likewise increases the rate of evaporation. Thus, the process is accelerated by rise in temperature, which increases the average kinetic energy of the molecules, as well as by decrease of the gaseous pressure above the liquid, which reduces the concentration of molecules that tend to block the escape of other molecules from the liquid.

6. Vapor Pressure. Evaporation of a liquid in a closed vessel does not appear to proceed indefinitely, for after a time the volume of the liquid remains constant. This fact is readily explainable in terms of the kinetic-molecular theory. As the concentration of free molecules above the liquid increases, more and more molecules of the vapor, in the course of their motion, collide with the surface and are recaptured by the liquid. Eventually a condition is attained in which the rate of *condensation* of the vapor is equal to the rate of evaporation of the liquid. Such a condition, in which two changes—each the exact opposite of the other—are proceeding at equal rates, is called a state of *dynamic equilibrium*. Once the equilibrium has been established, the relative amounts of liquid and vapor remain constant at a given temperature, since for every molecule that evaporates another condenses. The concentration of the molecules in the vapor likewise remains constant, and the vapor exerts a definite constant pressure at a fixed temperature. The pressure of the vapor in equilibrium with a liquid at a given temperature is called the *vapor pressure* of the liquid at that temperature. Thus the vapor pressure of water at 0° C. is 4.6 mm. of mercury. In an open vessel, the vapor gradually diffuses away from the surface of the liquid, with the result that equilibrium is not attained and continuous evaporation takes place.

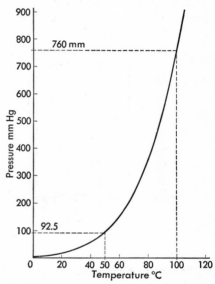

Fig. 4.2. Vapor pressure curve for water.

As the temperature of any liquid is increased, a greater proportion of the molecules acquire sufficient energy to escape from the surface of the liquid. As a result, a higher concentration of molecules in the vapor is necessary to establish equilibrium between liquid and vapor. Because a rise in temperature increases the equilibrium concentration as well as the average speed of vapor molecules, the vapor pressure of a liquid increases continuously with increase in temperature. If the vapor pressures of a liquid at a number of different temperatures are determined experimentally, a plot of vapor pressure against temperature (called the vapor pressure curve of the liquid) can be made. The vapor pressure of water,[1] for example, in mm. of mercury, is 17.5 at 20° C., 41.8 at 35° C., 233.3 at 70° C., and 760.0 at 100° C. These data are

---

[1] See Appendix, p. 825, for a complete table of experimentally determined vapor pressures of water at different temperatures.

represented graphically in the vapor pressure curve of water (Figure 4.2), the general form of which is common to all liquids. From this curve, one may read that at 50° C., for example, the vapor pressure of water is 92.5 mm. of mercury, or, in other words, that at 50° C. the vapor which exists in equilibrium with liquid water exerts a pressure of 92.5 mm. of mercury. Thus the vapor pressure curve for any liquid represents graphically the various conditions of pressure and temperature at which liquid and vapor phases can exist in equilibrium.

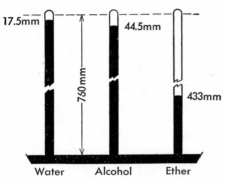

Fig. 4.3. Comparison of the vapor pressures of three liquids.

Above the critical temperature, only a single phase can exist; consequently, the vapor pressure curve extends only up to the critical temperature. The vapor pressure of a liquid at its critical temperature is the critical pressure.

The vapor pressures of different liquids at the same temperature vary widely. Liquids in which the intermolecular forces are weak have higher vapor pressures and evaporate more rapidly than those with strong intermolecular attractions. Thus, at 20° C., ether has a vapor pressure of 433 mm. of mercury; alcohol, of 44.5 mm.; water, of 17.5 mm.; and mercury, of 0.0012 mm. The simplest method of measuring the vapor pressure of a liquid is as follows: A small quantity of the liquid is introduced above the mercury surface of a barometer by means of a medicine dropper held below the barometer tube; as the liquid evaporates, the pressure of its vapor forces the mercury column down to some extent. When equilibrium between the liquid and its vapor is established, the depression in the barometer reading measures the vapor pressure of the liquid above the mercury at the given temperature. Figure 4.3 illustrates how this method may be applied in the comparison of the vapor pressures of water, alcohol, and ether at 20° C.

7. Boiling Point. Ordinary evaporation is a surface phenomenon only. As a liquid is heated, however, a temperature is reached at which bubbles of vapor form rapidly throughout the whole volume of liquid. These bubbles rise to the surface and burst as the vapor escapes. The liquid is then said to *boil*, and the phenomenon is called *boiling* or *ebullition*. The pressure within the bubbles is equal to the vapor pressure of the liquid at that temperature, and the bubbles obviously cannot form and increase in size until that value equals the external pressure upon the liquid. In other words, the *boiling point* of a liquid is that temperature at which the vapor pressure of the liquid is equal to the external pressure acting upon the surface of the liquid.

This temperature, of course, decreases with a decrease of external pressure, and increases with an increase of external pressure. In fact, a liquid can be made to boil at any temperature between its melting point and its critical temperature if the external pressure is properly controlled. It is apparent, then, that the vapor pressure curve of a liquid may also be called the boiling point curve. Thus Figure 4.2 may be interpreted as indicating the temperatures at which water boils under the various corresponding external pressures. On top of Mount Everest, for example, where the average atmospheric pressure is about 235 mm. of mercury, water boils at approximately 71° C. The *normal boiling point* of a liquid is the temperature at which the liquid boils under an external pressure of 1 atm., or 760 mm. of mercury. Any liquid has a vapor pressure of 1 atm. at its normal boiling point. Thus, water vapor in equilibrium with the liquid at 100° C. exerts a pressure of 760 mm. of mercury; the temperature 100° C. is therefore the normal boiling point of water.

All the heat energy absorbed by a liquid at its boiling point is used to vaporize the liquid; i.e., to free the molecules from the attractive forces of surrounding molecules and to do work in pushing back the atmosphere. For this reason, no matter how rapidly heat is supplied, the temperature of a pure boiling liquid remains constant, as long as the pressure is unchanged.

8. Heat of Vaporization. As indicated (p. 58), both evaporation and boiling (which is merely a type of evaporation occurring throughout the whole body of a liquid) involve a loss of energy by the liquid. Because the faster molecules escape, leaving the slower ones behind, the liquid remaining is cooled. Hence, heat must be supplied if the temperature is to be held constant, whether the process is accomplished at the boiling point or below it. So long as evaporation continues at a faster rate than condensation, the continual escape of the more rapidly moving molecules must be compensated for by the continuous addition of energy, if the average speed of the molecules left behind (the temperature of the liquid) is to remain constant. The quantity of heat which thus is required to evaporate a unit mass of a given liquid at constant temperature is called the *heat of vaporization* of the liquid. This value, in general, decreases with increase in temperature, reaching zero at the critical temperature. Heats of vaporization are usually measured at the boiling point of the liquid and are frequently expressed in calories per gram.

Condensation of a unit mass of any gas to the liquid state at constant temperature is accompanied by the evolution of an amount of heat numerically
equal to the heat of vaporization of that substance. This quantity is then
called the *heat of condensation*. The heat of vaporization of water at 100° C.
is 539 calories per gram.

9. Measurement of Gases over Water. Gases which are insoluble in water
are most conveniently collected over water. The volumes of such gases are
easily measured over water, but in converting the value so obtained to the
volume at standard conditions, one must always apply
a correction for the water vapor present in the measured volume.

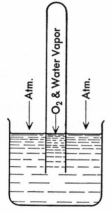

Suppose, for example, that a sample of oxygen has
been collected over water in the tube pictured in
Figure 4.4, and it is necessary to find the volume which
the oxygen would occupy if measured *dry* at standard
conditions. The actual conditions of temperature and
pressure under which the volume is measured experimentally over water must first be determined. If sufficient time is allowed to permit equilibrium conditions
to be established, the gas and the water will be at the
same temperature, so the temperature of the water may
be taken as that at which the gaseous volume is measured. The total pressure of the gas (a mixture of oxygen and water vapor) within the tube is most easily
determined if it is made equal to the atmospheric
pressure. This can be accomplished by the simple expedient of lowering or
raising the tube until the level of the water within the tube is the same as
that without (Figure 4.4). The total gaseous pressure within the tube is
then given by the barometric reading.

Fig. 4.4. Collection
of a gas over water at
atmospheric pressure.

This total gaseous pressure, however, is not all due to oxygen; part of it is
due to water vapor. Water molecules which have escaped from the surface
of the liquid are in the vapor phase along with the oxygen molecules. Both
types of molecules strike the surface of the water and the walls of the tube, and
the total pressure is the result of this combined bombardment. Thus, according to Dalton's law of partial pressures (p. 38), the total pressure P is the
sum of the partial pressure of the oxygen, p_{oxygen}, and the partial pressure of
the water vapor, p_{water}:

$$P = p_{oxygen} + p_{water}$$

The actual pressure exerted by the oxygen is therefore equal to the total pressure minus the vapor pressure of water at the given temperature:

$$p_{\text{oxygen}} = P - p_{\text{water}}$$

It is this pressure, the difference between the barometric pressure and the vapor pressure of water at the measured temperature, which must be taken as the true pressure of any gas the volume of which is measured over water, as described in the preceding paragraph. For work of ordinary accuracy, a similar correction is not required when gaseous volumes are measured over mercury, for the vapor pressure of mercury is negligible at room temperatures.

Problem

A gas, measured *over water* at a pressure of 750 mm. of mercury, and a temperature of 24° C., occupies a volume of 85.5 ml. What will be the volume of the *dry* gas at standard conditions?

The pressure actually exerted by the gas itself is 750 mm. — the vapor pressure of water at 24° C., or, $750 - 22$ mm. (see Appendix, p. 825) = 728 mm.

Organizing the data, we have:

$V_1 = 85.5$ ml. $P_1 = 728$ mm. $T_1 = 297°$ A.

$V_2 = \quad ?$ ml. $P_2 = 760$ mm. $T_2 = 273°$ A.

Both the pressure and temperature change in a direction such as to decrease the final volume. Therefore,

$$V_2 = 85.5 \times \frac{728}{760} \times \frac{273}{297} = 75.3 \text{ ml.}$$

THE SOLID STATE

10. General Characteristics of Solids. Solids differ from liquids and gases in that a given sample of a solid has both a definite volume and a definite shape. In addition, solids have considerable mechanical strength and rigidity. These properties cannot be attributed to any great difference in compactness between the solid and liquid states, for, in general, the density of a substance in the solid state is only slightly greater than that in the liquid state. In some few cases, such as that of water, the solid is actually less dense than the corresponding liquid.

The rigidity of solids results, rather, from the fact that the structural units [2]

---

[2] These structural units may be molecules, atoms, or ions (p. 186), but the term "molecule" will be used in a general sense to refer to them.

in a solid, unlike the molecules of a liquid or a gas, are not free to move at random with respect to each other but maintain fixed relative positions in the crystal of the solid. (A crystal is defined as a solid body, bounded by symmetrically arranged plane surfaces, or faces.) This does not imply that these units are absolutely stationary; it suggests, rather, that each unit vibrates about a fixed point in the crystal.

The fact that the unit particles of a crystalline solid are arranged in an orderly, systematic pattern, characteristic of that substance, is clearly indicated by the regularity of crystal form. Not only does each of the crystals of a given substance exhibit the same general geometric form, but also, even the angles between corresponding faces are exactly the same in all the crystals. In fact, many substances, particularly minerals, may be most easily identified through a study of their crystal forms.

Some substances, such as glass, glue, tar, and asphalt, although they possess a certain degree of hardness and rigidity, are not characterized by any definite crystalline form. For this reason, they are properly classified as pseudosolids, and are called *amorphous substances* or *glasses*. When heated, such substances do not melt at fixed temperatures, as do crystalline solids, but gradually soften and become less viscous. Conversely, the resulting liquids, upon being cooled, do not solidify at any constant temperature, but only gradually harden and become more viscous. Amorphous substances may therefore be regarded as greatly *undercooled liquids* of high viscosity. This undercooled state is actually not a stable one, for even such rigid amorphous substances as glass tend to crystallize after a number of years.

11. Crystallization and Fusion. As a pure liquid is slowly cooled, the kinetic energy of its molecules is gradually lowered, and the temperature drops continuously until the freezing point is reached. At this temperature, the molecules begin to become oriented in the definite geometric pattern characteristic of the substance; i.e., crystals of the solid begin to separate. Only the slower molecules near the crystal will attach themselves to it. The faster molecules are left in the liquid, and crystallization can continue only if the supply of slower molecules is maintained by constant external cooling. The temperature of the liquid–solid mixture therefore remains constant, in spite of further external cooling, until the entire mass has solidified.

If the solid is heated to this temperature, the process is reversed; the vibrational energy of some of the molecules becomes sufficient to overcome the binding forces in the crystal, and the solid begins to melt. As further heat is supplied, additional molecules acquire sufficient energy to break away from the crystal, and all of the solid eventually passes into the liquid state at constant temperature. If, however, heat is neither supplied nor withdrawn at this temperature, the solid and liquid phases remain in equilibrium indefinitely, because the rates of freezing and melting are exactly equal. The temperature at which the liquid and solid phases of a given substance exist in equilibrium is called the *freezing point* of the liquid, or the *melting point* of the solid substance. Because the melting point is characteristic of the substance, it is frequently employed in the identification of unknown compounds.

12. Heat of Fusion. The number of calories of heat required to convert a unit mass of a solid substance to the liquid at the melting point is called the *heat of fusion* of the substance. It represents the difference between the energy content of the liquid, in which the molecules are in random motion, and that of the solid, in which the particles vibrate about fixed positions in the crystal. Exactly the same quantity of heat, the *heat of crystallization*, is *evolved* when a unit mass of a liquid crystallizes at its freezing point. The heat of fusion of water is 80 calories per gram.

13. Undercooled Liquids. It is possible, especially if the cooling is carried out with no agitation, to lower the temperature of many liquids far below their freezing points before crystallization sets in. A liquid which has been cooled below its freezing point is said to be *undercooled*, or *supercooled*. An undercooled liquid is in a *metastable* condition; i.e., it may be kept in that state for a long time, but it cannot exist in equilibrium with the solid. The introduction of a "seed" crystal of the substance, by providing an ordered structure to which the slower-moving molecules can attach themselves, often induces immediate crystallization. Sometimes vigorous stirring accomplishes the same result, presumably because it may accidentally re-orient the molecules in a manner favorable to crystal formation. When crystallization begins, the heat evolved warms the mixture to the freezing point, and the temperature then remains constant, in spite of further external cooling, until solidification is complete.

Amorphous solids or glasses result most frequently from the cooling of extremely viscous liquids. High viscosity indicates a lack of mobility of the molecules, and if the viscosity is extremely high, i.e., if the motion of the molecules is greatly restricted, the orientation of the molecules required for crystal formation and growth may be rendered impossible. Under such conditions, no crystals form, and the viscous liquid sets to a glass upon being cooled.

14. Vapor Pressure of Solids. The familiar facts that many solids—such as snow and ice, for example—evaporate at temperatures below their melting points, and that certain solid substances give off characteristic odors, indicate that the molecules of such solids, like those of liquids, may pass directly into the vapor state. The pressure exerted by the vapor in equilibrium with a solid is called the vapor pressure of the solid at that temperature. Many solids, especially those in which the forces binding the molecules in the crystal are feeble, exhibit measurable vapor pressures at room temperature. As the temperature of the solid is increased, the fraction of its molecules having sufficient energy to break away from the crystal into the vapor phase is increased; accordingly, the vapor pressure of a solid increases with rise in temperature.

At the melting point, as we have seen, the solid and liquid phases exist in equilibrium. It is apparent that such an equilibrium can exist only if the vapor pressures of the solid and liquid phases are equal, for, if they were not equal, the form having the higher vapor pressure would gradually pass, by way of the vapor phase, to the form with the lower vapor pressure. For this reason, the melting or freezing point of a substance may be defined as the temperature at which the solid and liquid forms of that substance have the same vapor pressure.

In the case of some substances, such as dry ice, the vapor pressure of the solid form reaches a value equal to that of the atmospheric pressure at a temperature below the melting point, i.e., before it becomes equal to the vapor pressure of the liquid. When this occurs, all of the energy supplied to the solid by further heating is absorbed by the molecules as they break away from the surface of the crystal and pass into the vapor state, at the same time pushing back the atmosphere from the surface of the crystal. As a result, further heating does not increase the temperature, but rather causes all of the solid to pass directly into the vapor state, or to *sublime*, at a constant temperature without melting. Such a substance can be obtained as a liquid only if the external pressure is increased to some value greater than the vapor pressure of either the solid or the liquid phase at the melting point. On the other hand, a solid which melts under ordinary pressures may be caused to sublime when heated, if the external pressure is decreased below the value for the vapor pressure at the melting point.

The vapor pressure of solid carbon dioxide (dry ice) reaches a value of 1 atm. at $-78.51°$ C., but does not become equal to that of the liquid until a temperature of $-56.4°$ C. is reached, when both solid and liquid are in equilibrium with vapor at a pressure of 5.11 atm. Consequently carbon dioxide under a pressure of 1 atm. sublimes at $-78.51°$ C., but it can be melted at −56.4° C. if the external pressure is greater than 5.11 atm. The vapor pressure of ice and water in equilibrium at the melting point, on the other hand, is only 4.6 mm. of mercury; hence, ice can be made to sublime only at pressures below 4.6 mm. Many substances, particularly organic compounds, are purified by sublimation under vacuum.

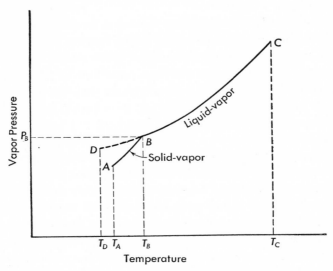

Fig. 4.5. Solid–vapor and liquid–vapor equilibria.

15. Equilibrium Diagrams. Many of the general facts presented in the preceding section may be conveniently and concisely shown by means of a pressure–temperature diagram (Figure 4.5). The portion of the curve from A to B gives the experimentally determined vapor pressures of the solid at temperatures from T_A to T_B. In other words, line AB indicates the values for the pressure of the vapor in equilibrium with the solid at temperatures from T_A to T_B, just as line BC gives the vapor pressure values for the liquid at temperatures from T_B to T_C. At the melting point T_B the vapor pressures of the solid and liquid are both equal to P_B, and here all three phases—gas, liquid, and solid—are in equilibrium.

The extension BD of the liquid–vapor equilibrium curve gives the vapor pressure of the undercooled liquid from the melting point T_B to temperature T_D. This curve is dotted to indicate that the undercooled liquid exists in a metastable condition. Since the vapor pressure of the undercooled liquid is greater than that of the solid at the same temperature, the two phases cannot exist in equilibrium at these temperatures; the addition of a crystal of the solid to the undercooled liquid induces immediate crystallization. When both solid and liquid phases are present, the system must come to equilibrium conditions. This means, of course, that the temperature must rise to its value, T_B, at the melting point. It is the crystallization of part of the under-cooled liquid (the slower molecules are removed) that supplies the heat required to bring about this increase in temperature (the faster molecules are left in the liquid).

The solid will melt at temperature T_B when heated under atmospheric pressure unless the vapor pressure (P_B) at the melting point is greater than 760 mm. In that case, the solid will sublime at the temperature below T_B at which its vapor pressure equals 760 mm., and can be melted only if the external pressure is increased to a value greater than P_B. If P_B is less than 760 mm., on the other hand, the solid can be sublimed only if the external pressure is reduced below the value P_B.

16. The External Form of Crystals. In general, under the same conditions, a given substance will crystallize in the same definite geometric form. The study of the various forms of crystals, together with their classification, is termed *crystallography*. It has been found that all the numerous types of crystals may be classified as belonging to one of six fundamental crystal systems. These six systems are described in terms of the arrangement of three or four imaginary axes, drawn through the crystal, to which the crystal faces may be referred.

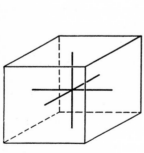 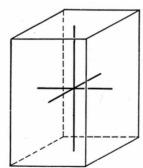 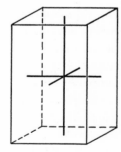

Fig. 4.6. Regular   Fig. 4.7. Tetragonal   Fig. 4.8. Orthorhombic
system.   system.   system.

The names and axial characteristics of the six fundamental crystal systems are as follows.

1. *Regular, Cubic,* or *Isometric System* (Figure 4.6). Three axes, all of equal length, intersecting at right angles.

2. *Tetragonal System* (Figure 4.7). Two axes of equal length, and a third of different length, all intersecting at right angles.

3. *Orthorhombic System* (Figure 4.8). Three axes of unequal length, all intersecting at right angles.

4. *Hexagonal System* (Figure 4.9). Three equal axes in one plane, all at equal angles, and a fourth axis of different length perpendicular to the plane of the other three.

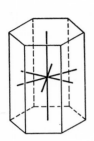 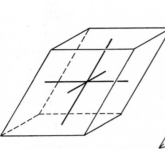 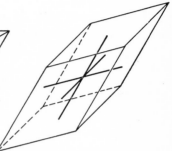

Fig. 4.9.   Hexagonal system.   **Fig. 4.10.**   Monoclinic system.   **Fig. 4.11.**   Triclinic system.

5. *Monoclinic System* (Figure 4.10). Three axes of unequal length, two intersecting at right angles, and the third perpendicular to one of these but not to the other.

6. *Triclinic System* (Figure 4.11). Three axes of unequal length, no two intersecting at right angles.

Many substances may, under different conditions, crystallize in two or more different forms. This phenomenon is called *polymorphism*, or, when it occurs in elements, one type of *allotropism*. The various *polymorphic* forms of the same substance have different physical properties and different energy contents. Diamond and graphite, two allotropic forms of carbon, for example, differ widely in their physical properties.

On the other hand, two or more different substances may exist in the same geometric pattern, with interfacial angles and axial ratios that do not differ appreciably from each other. Such substances are said to be *isomorphous*.

17. The Internal Structure of Crystals. Refinements in experimental techniques and advances in the chemist's ability to interpret data have made possible the actual determination of the exact arrangement of the unit particles within crystals. The methods customarily employed for this purpose make use of the diffraction or reflection, by crystals, of x-rays, which are similar in nature to ordinary light waves, but possess much shorter wave lengths. More recently, the diffraction of rapidly moving electrons (p. 119) by crystals has also been made the basis of a method of crystal analysis. Experiments of this nature clearly indicate that any crystal may be considered to be built up according to a fundamental geometric pattern known as the crystal lattice. It has been shown that fourteen different types of lattice are possible, each of which consists of a simple arrangement of unit particles, which may be either molecules, atoms, or ions (p. 186).

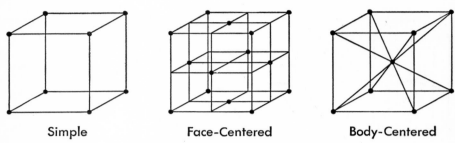

| Simple | Face-Centered | Body-Centered |

Fig. 4.12.   Three types of cubic lattice.

The lattice must, in every case, conform to the same geometric system as the crystal itself. In a crystal which belongs to the cubic system, for example, the lattice may be either simple cubic, face-centered cubic, or body-centered cubic (Figure 4.12).

The particular crystal structure which a given substance exhibits depends in part upon the size or relative sizes of the molecules, atoms, or ions from which the crystal is formed. In recent years, chemists and physicists have succeeded in interpreting many of the physical and chemical properties of substances in terms of their crystal structures.

STUDY QUESTIONS AND PROBLEMS

1. What properties serve to distinguish solids, liquids, and gases? Account for these distinctions in terms of the kinetic-molecular theory.

2. Why does a fan have a cooling effect on a hot day, even though it does not lower the temperature of the surrounding atmosphere?

3. A sample of nitrogen, collected over water at a pressure of 744 mm. and a temperature of 24° C., occupies 100 ml. What would be the volume of the nitrogen at standard conditions?

4. A sample of oxygen, collected over mercury at a pressure of 746 mm. and a temperature of 22° C., measures 363 ml. What volume would it occupy if collected over water at the same temperature and the same total pressure? To what is this increase in volume due?

5. Refer to Figure 4.2 in answering the following questions.

(a) Approximately under what external pressure does water boil at 75° C.? at 50° C.? at 25° C.?

(b) At what external pressure and temperature might water be expected to freeze if any heat was removed from it, but also to boil if any heat was supplied to it?

(c) What is the approximate external pressure at which water boils at 105° C.?

(d) Can liquid water be obtained at an external pressure of 0.05 mm.? Explain.

6. How can you explain the fact that the snow sometimes disappears from the ground after a light snowfall, even at temperatures far below freezing? On what sort of day would this be most likely to occur?

7. Iodine melts at 114.15° C.; at this temperature its vapor pressure is 90.1 mm. How might an impure sample of iodine be purified by sublimation?

8. Explain why condensation and freezing are heat-evolving processes. Which produces more severe scalding, water at 100° C. or steam at the same temperature?

9. Why are liquids of high viscosity particularly susceptible to undercooling?

10. Give at least two reasons for believing that glass is an undercooled liquid.

11. Explain why a pressure cooker would be particularly useful on top of a 15,000-foot mountain.

12. What total quantity of heat is required to convert 10 g. of ice at 0° C. to steam at 100° C.?

13. Suppose that you had 10 g. of ice and 10 g. of water in contact at 0° C. in an insulated system. What can be said about the relative rates of the freezing of the water and the melting of the ice under those conditions? If you should suddenly supply 400 cal. of heat to this system by means of a burner, what momentary change in these relative rates would result? When and how would equilibrium again be restored?

14. If a small crystal of ice and an open beaker containing 500 g. of undercooled water at −5° C. were suddenly placed (out of contact with each other) in a completely insulated vessel at 0° C., how would equilibrium be established in the system?

15. A farmer who stores fruit and vegetables in his basement during the winter calculated that on the coldest days 2000 kilocalories of heat would be required to keep the produce from being frozen. He decided to place an open container of water in his basement as a safety measure. What would be the minimum permissible size for the container, assuming that all of the water in it would freeze? Is this assumption a safe one?

16. The heat of vaporization of water at its boiling point is 539 calories per gram, whereas the corresponding value for benzene is 94, for ether 84, for alcohol 204, and for hexane 89. Considering the fact that all the heat absorbed by a liquid as it boils is used to free the molecules from the attractive forces of surrounding molecules and to push back the atmosphere, what general statement can you make about the attractive forces between water molecules?

5

Chemical Evidence for the Discontinuity of Matter —The Atomic Theory

1. Laws of Chemical Combination. We have seen from a study of the two preceding chapters that the physical behavior of gases points to the assumption that matter is discontinuous. The physical properties of liquids and solids have likewise been explained on the basis of that theory. It is not surprising, therefore, that the chemical behavior of matter also affords convincing evidence of the discontinuity of matter. This evidence is summarized in four general principles of chemistry—the four fundamental laws of chemical combination—all of which support the theory of a discontinuous structure of matter and may be explained readily in terms of that theory.

These four laws, defining in a general way the quantitative relationships in chemistry, were gradually elucidated following the development, chiefly by Black (1728–1799), Bergman (1735–1784), and Lavoisier (1743–1794), of exact methods of analysis which made possible the precise determination of the relative quantities of the elements present in a given compound. Interpretation of a vast amount of quantitative data of this type, which soon became available through the combined efforts of many chemists, led to the discovery of these four fundamental laws of chemical combination.

2. The Law of Conservation of Mass. In 1785, Lavoisier completed a series of careful quantitative experiments on the combination of various substances with oxygen. By measuring accurately the weights of the gases, as well as of the liquids and solids, entering into and resulting from each reaction, Lavoisier was enabled to state on the basis of sound experimental evidence that the total mass of the products of a chemical reaction is identical with that of the reactants. This principle, which has been confirmed repeatedly by a vast amount of scientific experimentation, is known as the *Law of Con-*

*servation of Mass: In all chemical and physical changes, the total mass of
the substances involved remains unchanged.* In even more general terms,
the law states that *matter cannot be created nor destroyed,* and it is therefore
often called the *Law of Indestructibility of Matter.*[1]

3. The Law of Constant Composition. It has been pointed out (p. 18),
that *a given pure compound always contains the same elements in exactly
the same proportions by weight.* This fundamental generalization is called
the *Law of Constant Composition* or the *Law of Definite Proportions.* Testing by the most refined experimental techniques has served only to confirm
this law and it is now accepted without question.[2]

4. The Law of Multiple Proportions. *When two elements combine to form
more than one compound, the several weights of one element that combine
with a fixed weight of the second are in the ratio of small whole numbers.*
Carbon and oxygen, for example, combine to form two familiar compounds,
carbon monoxide, the deadly gas in the exhaust fumes of automobiles, and
carbon dioxide, the common gas in carbonated beverages. In carbon
monoxide, exactly 8 g. of oxygen is combined with 6.006 g. of carbon,

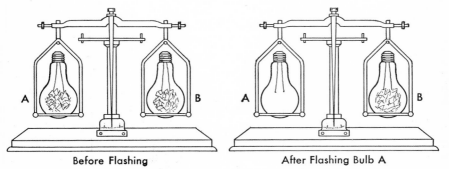

Before Flashing   **After Flashing Bulb A**

Fig. 5.1. When a photoflash bulb is flashed, the magnesium and oxygen combine in the
weight ratio 24.32 parts of magnesium to 16.00 parts of oxygen to form 40.32 parts of
magnesium oxide. Hence the total weight of the bulb is the same before and after the
flash (law of conservation of mass), and the magnesium oxide formed always contains
magnesium and oxygen in the weight ratio 24.32 to 16.00.

[1] Recent theoretical and practical advances, particularly the harnessing of atomic
energy, have proved conclusively that under certain conditions mass and energy are interconvertible. Strictly speaking, therefore, the Law of Conservation of Mass and the Law of
Conservation of Energy (p. 22) do not constitute separate laws, but should be incorporated into a single Law of Conservation of Mass-Energy (p. 139). Except for those special
processes which involve nuclear changes (p. 143), however, the laws as stated separately
are entirely practicable.
[2] Small apparent departures from the law, observed in the case of certain compounds,
may be attributed to the existence of two or more forms of some of the elements (p. 127).

whereas in carbon dioxide, 16 g. (exactly twice 8 g.) of oxygen is combined with 6.006 g. of carbon.

Similarly, we know of a second compound, in addition to water, composed of hydrogen and oxygen—hydrogen peroxide, a widely used bleaching agent and antiseptic. The weight of hydrogen which is combined with 8 g. of oxygen is 0.5040 g. in hydrogen peroxide and 1.0080 g. (2×0.5040 g.) in water.

5. The Atomic Theory. The only logical explanation of the first three laws of chemical combination is that matter must be made up of minute unit particles. Chemists today speak with the utmost assurance of these unit particles, called *atoms;* in fact, the atomic theory is the basis of all chemical thought. Although the concept of the atom was suggested as early as 400 B.C. by the Greek philosopher Democritus, it was not until 1805 that the English schoolteacher-chemist, John Dalton, first enunciated the atomic theory as derived from experimental data. His work is recognized today as one of the most brilliant triumphs of speculation in the whole field of science. Dalton's atomic theory, the basic theory upon which all of chemistry rests, includes four major postulates or assumptions.

1. *The elements are made up of minute, discrete, indivisible, and indestructible particles called atoms. These atoms maintain their identity through all physical and chemical changes.*

2. *Atoms of the same element are identical in physical and chemical properties and have the same mass.*[3] *Atoms of different elements differ in physical and chemical properties and have different masses.*

3. *Chemical combination between two or more elements consists in the union of the atoms of these elements in simple numerical ratios to form the smallest possible unit particles (molecules) of a compound.*

4. *Atoms of the same elements can unite in more than one ratio to form more than one compound.*

6. Explanation of the Laws of Chemical Combination. The atomic concept of matter provides a simple explanation for the three laws of chemical combination thus far discussed. If atoms maintain their identity through all physical and chemical changes, then we should expect the total mass to remain unchanged (Law of Conservation of Mass). If the molecules of a given compound always contain atoms of the same elements combined in

---

[3] We know today that individual atoms of the same element may differ somewhat in mass (see isotopes, p. 127); the average mass of all the atoms in a weighable sample is nevertheless constant for any given element.

the same ratio, then the relative weights of the elements in the compound should be constant (Law of Constant Composition). For example, if hydrogen and oxygen atoms are present in a 1:1 ratio in a molecule of hydrogen peroxide, then the ratio of the weights of hydrogen to oxygen in hydrogen peroxide should always be exactly the same as that of a hydrogen to an oxygen atom. This conclusion would mean, then, that the ratio of the weight of hydrogen atoms to oxygen atoms is 0.5040 to 8.0000.

Now if we assume that hydrogen and oxygen atoms combine in some simple ratio other than 1:1 to form a different compound, the weight of hydrogen combined with 8 parts of oxygen in this compound should be a simple multiple or fraction of 0.5040 (Law of Multiple Proportions). Thus, if 2 atoms of hydrogen combined with 1 atom of oxygen, the weight ratio in the new compound would be 1.0080 to 8.0000, as is the case in water. These facts are summarized in Table 5.1.

Table 5.1

Compound	Ratio of number of H atoms to number of O atoms	Ratio of weight of hydrogen to weight of oxygen
Hydrogen peroxide	1:1	0.5040 : 8.0000
Water	2:1	1.0080 (2 × 0.5040) : 8.0000

7. The Law of Equivalent Proportions. From the atomic theory it may be deduced that the weights of two different elements which combine with the same weight of a third element are often equivalent in the sense that they are the weights that will exactly combine with each other. For example, consider three elements A, B, and C, the weights of whose atoms are in the ratio $a:b:c$. If elements A and C combine in the ratio of one atom of A to one atom of C, then in the resulting compound AC, c grams of C would be combined with a grams of A. Likewise, in the compound AB, b grams of B would be combined with a grams of A. Now in the compound BC, b grams of B would be combined with c grams of C. In other words, the weight (b grams) of element B and the weight (c grams) of element C which combine with the same weight (a grams) of element A, are in exactly the right ratio to combine with each other.

On the other hand, in the compound BC_2, not c grams of C but exactly $2c$ grams of C would be combined with b grams of B. Similarly, in the compound B_3C, not b grams of B, but exactly $3b$ grams of B, would be combined with c grams of C.

These simple combining relationships between elements, which are predicted by the atomic theory, have been shown to hold experimentally for thousands of compounds. This fact is summarized in the fourth law of chemical combination, the *Law of Equivalent Proportions: The weights of two or more different elements which combine with the same weight of a third element are (1) either the relative weights which react with each other, or (2) simple multiples or fractions of these weights.*

In order that the combining or equivalent weights of a majority of the elements might be determined by direct, simple experimental methods, it was found convenient to set oxygen as the standard. The weight of any element which will combine with 8.0000 parts by weight of oxygen or with 1.0080 parts of hydrogen is called the *equivalent weight* of that element.

Many elements form more than one compound with oxygen or with hydrogen and therefore have more than one equivalent weight. In all such cases, however, the different weights are simple multiples of each other. Thus the weights of carbon (6.006 g. and 3.003 g.) combined with 8.0000 g. of oxygen in carbon monoxide and in carbon dioxide, are in the ratio 2:1. In terms of Dalton's atomic theory, this must be the ratio of the numbers of carbon atoms combined with one atom of oxygen in the two compounds.

8. Unanswered Questions. In the two preceding chapters, evidence has been presented which points to the theory that gases, as well as many liquids and solids, are composed of unit particles called *molecules*. In the present chapter, we have considered generalizations summarizing experimental data known as laws of chemical combination, which can be explained only on the basis of the assumptions that elements are composed of unit particles (*atoms*), and that compounds are formed by simple combinations of different kinds of atoms. Still unanswered, however, are many intriguing questions of both practical and theoretical importance: are molecules of gaseous elements identical with atoms of those elements, or, if not, what is the relationship between the two? How are the relative weights of different *atoms* and *molecules* determined? Can the ratios in which the atoms of different elements combine to form the various compounds be ascertained, and, if so, by what methods? An attempt to reason logically from experimental facts toward the solution of these problems is the challenging project to be undertaken in the next chapter.

STUDY QUESTIONS AND PROBLEMS

1. The atomic theory of the ancient Greek philosopher Democritus had no basis other than that of speculation, whereas Dalton based his theory on a considerable body of experimental evidence. Outline the nature of this evidence.

2. Following are data obtained in the analysis of carbon dioxide and of carbon monoxide from various sources:

Sample	Gas	Weight of Carbon	Weight of Oxygen
A	Carbon dioxide	0.2002 g.	0.5333 g.
B	Carbon dioxide	0.1682 g.	0.4480 g.
C	Carbon monoxide	0.1543 g.	0.2056 g.
D	Carbon monoxide	0.5147 g.	0.6856 g.

Demonstrate how these data illustrate the Law of Constant Proportions; the Law of Multiple Proportions. What is the most specific conclusion that can be drawn, on the basis of these data alone, comparing the relative numbers of carbon and oxygen atoms in the molecules of the two oxides?

3. Show by appropriate calculations which laws of chemical combination are illustrated by the following data:

(a) The oxide which constitutes the most important source of manganese contains 63.19% of manganese.

(b) On analysis, a sample of a rather uncommon oxide of manganese was found to contain 0.3873 g. of manganese and 0.1128 g. of oxygen.

(c) In an oxide of manganese which is formed in many reactions of potassium permanganate, manganese and oxygen are combined in the ratio by weight of 1.717 to 1.000.

(d) For every 54.94 g. of manganese in potassium permanganate, there is 64.00 g. of oxygen.

4. Prove that the following data illustrate the Law of Equivalent Proportions.

(a) 74.91 g. of arsenic is combined with 3.024 g. of hydrogen in arsine.

(b) 24.00 g. of oxygen is combined with 3.024 g. of hydrogen in water.

(c) 74.91 g. of arsenic is combined with 24.00 g. of oxygen in the oxide known as white arsenic.

(d) 74.91 g. of arsenic is combined with 40.00 g. of oxygen in the oxide known as arsenic anhydride.

5. Calculate the equivalent weight of arsenic in each of the arsenic compounds mentioned in problem 4.

6. Devise an experiment by means of which the equivalent weight of zinc might be determined.

7. (a) What is the equivalent weight of silicon in the oxide known as silica, which contains 53.25% of oxygen?

(b) What is the equivalent weight of calcium in quicklime, which contains 71.47% of calcium?

8. (a) There are two common oxides of sulfur, one of which contains exactly 50% of oxygen by weight, the other almost exactly 60%. Show how these data illustrate the Law of Multiple Proportions.

(b) There are two oxides of copper, one black, the other red. In the former, very nearly four-fifths of the weight of the compound is copper; in the latter, almost eight-ninths is copper. Show that these data provide an illustration of the Law of Multiple Proportions.

9. (a) Phosphorus forms two common oxides. An early investigator was surprised to find upon analysis that whereas one of these contained 56.35% of phosphorus by weight, the other one contained 56.35% of oxygen. Show how these data illustrate the Law of Multiple Proportions.

(b) There are also two common oxides of antimony. In one of these 40.59 g. of antimony is combined with 8.000 g. of oxygen. The second contains 75.27% of antimony by weight. Show how these data illustrate the Law of Multiple Proportions.

10. There are two compounds of mercury and chlorine. One of these, called corrosive sublimate, contains 73.88% of mercury; the other, called calomel, contains 84.98% of mercury. Compare the weights of mercury per gram of chlorine in the two compounds; also the weights of chlorine per gram of mercury.

11. (a) From the weight ratios given in Table 5.1, calculate the percentage of oxygen in water, and in hydrogen peroxide.

(b) If the equivalent weight of hydrogen is taken to be 1.008 in *all* hydrogen compounds, what is the equivalent weight of oxygen in hydrogen peroxide?

12. There are no less than five different oxides of nitrogen, which contain, respectively, 1.7510, 0.8755, 0.5837, 0.4378, and 0.3502 parts by weight of nitrogen to one part by weight of oxygen. Calculate for each compound the number of parts by weight of oxygen to one of nitrogen, and show that these values are in accord with the Law of Multiple Proportions.

13. Assume that matter is continuous rather than atomistic in nature. On that basis, how could you account for the Laws of Chemical Combination?

14. Demonstrate how the Law of Equivalent Proportions may actually be derived from the Law of Constant Composition and the Law of Multiple Proportions.

15. One volume of nitrogen combines with 3 volumes of hydrogen to form 2 volumes of ammonia. Can you show how this constitutes evidence that a nitrogen molecule contains at least 2 atoms?

Determination of the Weights of Molecules and Atoms

1. Importance of Atomic and Molecular Weights. Our quest for a more complete understanding of the structure and behavior of matter leads us next to the question: "How can the weights of the unit particles, molecules and atoms, be determined?" This question is a particularly significant one, for its answer will enable us more completely to understand and to interpret such quantitative relationships in chemical reactions as were presented in the preceding chapter. It would, for example, provide us at once with a simple method for determining the ratios in which the atoms of various elements combine to form compounds.

We know from analysis that in water exactly 1.0080 g. of hydrogen is combined with 8.0000 g. of oxygen. Now if we were to assume that the weights of hydrogen and oxygen atoms are in the ratio 1.0080:8.0000, then it would be obvious that *one* atom of hydrogen combines with *one* atom of oxygen to form water. We have no basis for supposing this to be the case, however. Perhaps the atomic weights of hydrogen and oxygen are actually in the ratio 1.0080:4.0000; then we should be certain from the combining weight ratio, 1.0080:2 × 4.0000, that *one* atom of hydrogen is combined with *two* atoms of oxygen in water. If, however, we knew the atomic weight ratio to be 1.0080:16.0000, we could conclude from the combining weight ratio, 2 × 1.0080:16, that *two* atoms of hydrogen are combined with every *one* atom of oxygen in water. Knowledge of the relative weights of the hydrogen and oxygen atoms would thus enable us to decide which of the many conceivable ratios in which these atoms might combine is the true one for the water molecule. In fact, a real understanding of all the quantitative relations which govern the production of compounds depends upon a knowledge of the weights of the atoms of different elements and the ratios in which the atoms combine.

The problem of determining the relative weights of molecules and atoms is, of course, greatly complicated by the fact that these unit particles are almost infinitesimally small. Just as a peanut or a coconut cannot be weighed on scales sensitive only to the nearest ton, so atoms and molecules cannot be weighed *singly* even on the most sensitive balance which could be constructed; as has already been indicated (p. 48), however, we could determine the *relative* weights of a peanut and a coconut on even so rough a scale by weighing large *equal* numbers of each, because we can be sure that the ratio of the weight of, say, 1,000,000 peanuts to 1,000,000 coconuts is exactly the same as the ratio of the weight of 1 peanut to 1 coconut (p. 48). But the case of atoms and molecules is not so simple as that of peanuts and coconuts because these unit particles are far too small to be handled individually, and therefore we have no direct general method for counting them. The starting point, then, for the determination of the relative weights of molecules and atoms must be the establishment of some criterion which will enable us to judge, on some experimental basis, when we are dealing with *equal* numbers of molecules or of atoms of different substances.

2. Relative Molecular Weights by Vapor Density. In the case of molecules the necessary criterion is provided by Avogadro's hypothesis (p. 48), which states that *equal volumes of all gases at the same pressure and temperature contain the same number of molecules*. By application of Avogadro's principle, the determination of the relative weights of the molecules of different gases becomes, at least in theory, a simple process. It consists merely of comparing the densities of the different gases, or the weights of equal volumes measured under the same conditions of pressure and temperature. Because of the relatively low densities of gases or vapors as compared with liquids and solids, it is customary in such comparisons to express the density in terms of the weight of a liter rather than of a cubic centimeter. The *vapor density of a substance* is defined as the weight of a liter of that substance in the gaseous state under standard conditions.

If the relative molecular weights which are assigned to a series of different substances are to be useful, it is necessary that they all be expressed in terms of the weight of the molecule of some one substance which is selected as the *standard*. The oxygen molecule has been chosen as the standard for molecular weights, and has arbitrarily been assigned the molecular weight value of 32. Thus, the *molecular weight* of any substance is a *number* expressing the relative weight of a molecule of that substance compared to the weight of the oxygen molecule with an assigned value of 32. If the molecules of another substance are exactly twice as heavy as oxygen molecules, the molecular weight of the substance is 64; if the molecules are one-half as heavy as an oxygen molecule, the molecular weight is 16. We know today that sulfur dioxide has a molecular weight of 64.066. This number tells us that a sulfur dioxide molecule is 64.066/32.000 times, or approximately twice, as heavy as an oxygen molecule. This relationship may also be regarded from a slightly different point of view. For the purpose of expressing weights of atoms and molecules, we may establish a minute weight unit which, since the molecular weight of oxygen is set at 32, would conveniently be 1/32 of the actual weight of an oxygen molecule. This unit is commonly referred to as an "atomic weight unit," which we shall abbreviate "a.w.u." The statement that the molecular weight of oxygen is 32 may then be interpreted as meaning that the weight of an oxygen molecule is 32 a.w.u. Similarly, the weight of a sulfur dioxide molecule is 64.066 a.w.u. The molecular weight of hydrogen has been found to be 2.0160; i.e., the weight of a hydrogen molecule is 2.0160 a.w.u., or 2.0160/32.000 that of the oxygen molecule.

It should be mentioned that Avogadro's hypothesis, like the gas laws, is not exact, but applies rigidly only to the hypothetical ideal gas; and since all actual gases deviate more or less from the ideal behavior, molecular weights determined by application of Avogadro's hypothesis are only approximate. For most gases, however, these deviations are small, and in all cases they approach zero as the pressure is reduced at constant temperature. If the densities are measured at very low pressures, therefore, fairly exact molecular weights can be obtained.

3. Gram-Molecular Weight. We frequently find it desirable, both for chemical calculations and in laboratory and industrial practice, to deal with actual weighable quantities of various substances which we know to contain *equal* numbers of molecules. We have seen (p. 48) that any weights of different substances which are in the same ratio as their molecular weights must contain the same number of molecules. Thus, if the molecular weight of hydrogen is 2.0160, and of oxygen, 32.0000, then 2.0160 g. of hydrogen contains exactly the same number of molecules as 32.0000 g. of oxygen. These actual weights are called *gram-molecular weights* or *moles*. We may define a *gram-molecular weight* or a *mole* of any substance as *the quantity of that substance whose weight in grams is numerically equal to its molecular weight.*

4. The Gram-Molecular Volume. Since moles of all substances, including gases, contain the same number of molecules, it follows from Avogadro's hypothesis that a mole of any gas, under identical conditions of pressure and temperature, occupies the same volume as a mole of any other gas. At S.T.P., 32.0 g. of oxygen occupies a volume of 22.4 l. Hence, at standard conditions, the volume occupied by a *mole* or *gram-molecular weight* of any gas is 22.4 l.; this volume is called the *gram-molecular volume,* abbreviated G.M.V. (see Figure 6.1).

The concept of the gram-molecular volume enables us to calculate the density of any gas or vapor from its molecular weight. The molecular weight

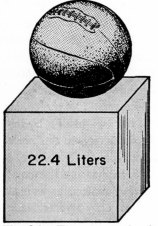

of hydrogen is 2.0160; i.e., at standard conditions 22.4 l. of hydrogen weighs approximately 2.016 g. To determine its density, let us first organize the data.

22.4 l. of hydrogen weighs 2.016 g.

1 l. of hydrogen weighs   ?   g.

We know that 1 l. weighs 1/22.4 as much as 22.4 l., or

$$\frac{1}{22.4} \times 2.016 = 0.0900 \text{ g.}$$

Fig. 6.1. The gram-molecular volume, 22.4 l., compared to a basketball.

The approximate density of hydrogen at standard conditions is therefore 0.0900 g. per liter. Similarly, we could determine the approximate weight of any other volume of hydrogen, at standard or any other conditions. Conversely, from the molecular weight, one can calculate the volume occupied by a given weight of gas under any conditions.

Problem

Calculate the volume which 1.50 g. of oxygen would occupy, measured over water at 740 mm. pressure and at a temperature of 20° C.

At standard conditions,

32.0 g. of oxygen occupies 22.4 l.

1.50 g. of oxygen occupies   ?   l.

It is obvious that 1 g. would occupy a volume 1/32.0 as great as 32.0 g., or 1/32.0 × 22.4 l. But 1.50 g. would occupy a volume 1.50 times as great as that of 1 g., or

$$\frac{1}{32.0} \times 22.4 \times 1.50 = 1.05 \text{ l. (at standard conditions)}$$

Collected over water at 740 mm. pressure and a temperature of 20° C., the gas would occupy the volume

$$1.05 \times \frac{760}{740 - 17.5} \times \frac{293}{273} \quad \text{or} \quad 105 \times \frac{760}{723} \times \frac{293}{273} = 1.18 \text{ l.}$$

5. Experimental Determination of Approximate Molecular Weights. Application of the gram-molecular volume concept likewise provides a convenient method for the experimental determination of the approximate molecular weight of a gaseous substance; we need only find the weight of 22.4 l. of the substance at standard conditions. It is not necessary actually to weigh so unwieldy a volume as 22.4 l., nor does the measurement have to be made at

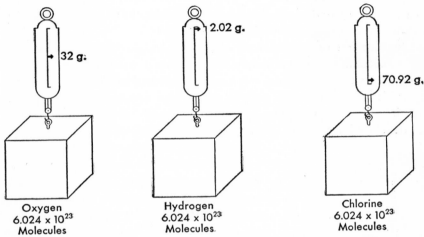

Fig. 6.2. The weights (in grams) of 22.4 l. at standard conditions (6.024×10^{23} molecules) of some common gases are: oxygen, 32.00 g.; hydrogen, 2.02 g.; chlorine, 70.92 g. The weights of the individual molecules are, therefore, in the same ratio, 32.00:2.02:70.92.

standard conditions. The weight of 22.4 l. at standard conditions can readily be calculated from the weight of any convenient volume of the gas at any given conditions of pressure and temperature. In the method first employed in 1837 by the French chemist Jean Baptiste André Dumas, a small bulb of known capacity is evacuated and weighed, then filled with the gas whose weight is to be determined, and weighed again. The difference between the two weighings is, of course, the weight of the known volume of gas under the prevailing conditions of pressure and temperature.

Problem

Calculate the approximate molecular weight of carbon dioxide, if 594 ml. of the gas, at a pressure of 765 mm. and a temperature of 24° C., weighs 1.08 g. The volume at standard conditions would be

$$594 \times \frac{765}{760} \times \frac{273}{297} = 550 \text{ ml. or } 0.550 \text{ l.}$$

Thus, at standard conditions,

0.550 l. weighs 1.08 g.

22.4   l. weighs   ? g.

Obviously 22.4 l. weighs 22.4/0.550 as much as 0.550 l. Hence a gram-molecular weight is

$$\frac{22.4}{0.550} \times 1.08 = 44.0 \text{ g. (approximately)}$$

Since a mole of carbon dioxide is approximately 44.0 g., the approximate molecular weight of carbon dioxide is 44.0.

Determination of approximate molecular weighs by application of the gram-molecular volume principle is not limited to substances which are gaseous at room temperature, but may be employed as well for many liquids and solids which are fairly *volatile,* i.e., which are vaporized at comparatively low temperatures. The method most widely used for this purpose is that developed by Victor Meyer, a former professor of chemistry at the University of Heidelberg. In this method, a weighed quantity of liquid in a small glass bulb is evaporated in a tube maintained at a constant high temperature. A volume of air equivalent to that of the vapor formed is driven out of the tube and measured at known pressure and temperature (Figure 6.3). From these data the density of the vapor, and therefore its approximate molecular weight, can be calculated.

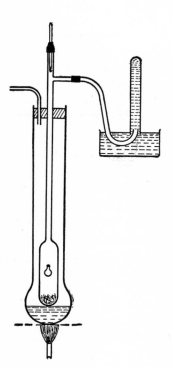

Fig. 6.3.   Victor Meyer apparatus.

6. Avogadro's Number. The actual number of *molecules* in a mole of any substance, or in 22.4 l. of an ideal gas at standard conditions, has been calculated by a variety of independent methods from several types of experimental data (see, for instance, p. 304). The value accepted at present as the most reliable is 602,400,000,000,000,000,000,000 or 6.024 $\times 10^{23}$ molecules per mole. This very important constant is called *Avogadro's number.* It is actually known to be correct within less than 0.1 per cent, a greater degree of accuracy than that with which the population of any city of over 10,000 is known.

From the above discussion, it is apparent that the molecular weight of a substance is numerically equal to the weight in grams of 6.024×10^{23} molecules of that substance. The gram-molecular volume, 22.4 l., may likewise be thought of as the volume occupied under standard conditions by 6.024×10^{23} molecules of any gas. It is especially important that we distinguish clearly between a *mole* and a *molecule* of a substance. A mole is 6.024×10^{23} molecules. One mole (6.024×10^{23} molecules) of oxygen weighs 32 g., whereas one molecule of oxygen weighs 32 a.w.u. Hence, in 32 g. there are $32 \times 6.024 \times 10^{23}$ a.w.u. In other words, 1 g. $= 6.024 \times 10^{23}$ a.w.u., and 1 a.w.u. $= 1/6.024 \times 10^{23}$ or 1.660×10^{-24} g. The *actual* weight of an oxygen molecule (32 a.w.u.) is, therefore, $32 \times 1.660 \times 10^{-24}$ or 5.312×10^{-23} g. It is obvious that the relative molecular weight values are more convenient to use than the actual weights of molecules.

7. The Ounce-Molecular Volume. In engineering calculations, the English units of weights and measures are frequently used in preference to the metric units. Thus, engineers often deal with a *pound-molecular weight*, which is defined as that quantity of substance whose weight in pounds is numerically equal to its molecular weight. A pound-molecular weight of oxygen is 32 lb. of oxygen; similarly an ounce-molecular weight of oxygen is 32 ounces. A pound-molecular weight of one substance contains just as many molecules as a pound-molecular weight of any other substance, because these weights are in the same ratio as the weights of the individual molecules. The same, of course, is true of ounce-molecular weights of various substances.

Engineers likewise make calculations in which they employ the *ounce-molecular volume* of a gas, i.e., the volume occupied at standard conditions by an ounce-molecular weight of a gas. The ounce-molecular volume of any gas happens to be 22.4 cu. ft.; i.e., an ounce-molecular weight of any gas, under standard conditions, occupies 22.4 cu. ft. The curious fact that the ounce-molecular volume expressed in cubic feet has the same numerical value as the gram-molecular volume expressed in liters, arises from the coincidence that the factors for converting grams to ounces, and liters to cubic feet, respectively, are almost identical. There are approximately 28.35 g. in an avoirdupois ounce, and 28.32 l. in a cubic foot. The *pound-molecular volume* is 16 times as large as the ounce-molecular volume; the value ordinarily used is 359 cu. ft.

8. Approximate Atomic Weights. One of the knotty problems in the development of chemical science was the determination of the relative weights of the atoms of the various elements; i.e., the *atomic weights*. Early in the nineteenth century, techniques were developed by which the combining or equivalent weights of the known elements could be determined with a high degree of precision. Unfortunately, however, neither the atomic weights nor the ratio in which atoms combine to form any given compound can be deduced from equivalent weight data alone.

Historically, the determination of the atomic weights was a long and difficult process of trial and error. Gradually, however, a number of fundamental principles emerged which served as the basis for the selection of the approximate atomic weights of elements. Three of these principles are (1) the combining volume principle, (2) Cannizzaro's principle, and (3) the law of Dulong and Petit.

9. The Combining Volume Principle.
We have already reasoned (p. 47), from the fact that *1* volume of oxygen combines with *2* volumes of hydrogen to form *2* volumes of water vapor, that *1* molecule of oxygen supplies the oxygen atoms for *2* molecules of water. Since atoms combine as indivisible units, each molecule of water must have in it at least 1 atom of oxygen. Then *1* molecule of oxygen must have supplied at least 2 atoms of oxygen.

Repeated studies of many reactions of oxygen to form gaseous products have revealed numerous other cases in which *1* oxygen molecule forms *2* molecules of an oxygen-containing compound, and must therefore be supplying at least *2* oxygen atoms. *Never, however, has it been shown that 1 oxygen molecule can furnish more than 2 oxygen atoms.* Hence, we may logically conclude that an oxygen molecule is composed of *2* oxygen atoms. We therefore represent the oxygen molecule by the *molecular formula* O_2. One oxygen atom, then, weighs one-half as much as an oxygen molecule, or 16 a.w.u., and oxygen has an atomic weight of 16. An atomic weight unit may alternatively be defined as $1/16$ the weight of an oxygen atom.

Similar studies have shown that the molecules of most of the other common elementary gases, such as hydrogen, chlorine, fluorine, and nitrogen, also contain *2* atoms. Such molecules are called *diatomic,* and their formulas are written H_2, Cl_2, F_2, and N_2. The atomic weight of each of these elements is one-half of its molecular weight.

The relationship between *molecules* and *atoms* of the common elementary gases is now clearly revealed. *Atoms* are the simplest units which can enter into chemical combination; *molecules* are the simplest particles in which these gases ordinarily exist in the free state. When such a gaseous element reacts chemically, each molecule supplies two atoms for chemical reaction, and hence, one volume affords two volumes of any gaseous product whose molecules contain only one atom of the element in question.

10. Cannizzaro's Principle. Molecules are always made up of *integral numbers* (1, 2, 3, etc.) of atoms, never of fractional atoms. Hence the *lowest weight of an element which can exist in a molecule of any compound containing the element must be the weight of one atom of that element.*

Stanislao Cannizzaro, an Italian chemist, pointed out in 1863 that this principle could be used to determine the approximate atomic weights of elements which form gaseous compounds. Cannizzaro reasoned as follows: the weight of a molecule of a gas in a.w.u. is numerically equal to the weight in grams of 22.4 l. of the gas at S.T.P. Further, the weight of any element in the molecule may be obtained simply by multiplying the weight of the molecule by the percentage of that element in the compound. This weight of the element in the molecule must represent the weight of 1, 2, 3, or more atoms of the element. If a considerable number of gaseous compounds of the element are studied, it is a reasonable assumption that one or more will be compounds whose molecules contain only one atom of the element. The weight of the element in one molecule of such compounds will be the lowest found in the entire series because it is the weight of one atom of the element. The weights of the element per molecule of all the other compounds of the series will be simple multiples of this weight, depending upon the number of atoms of the element per molecule.

Table 6.1 summarizes the experimental data which might actually be used in the determination of the approximate atomic weight of chlorine.

Table 6.1

The Approximate Atomic Weight of Chlorine

	1	2	3	4 $\left(\frac{2\times 3}{100}\right)$	5
Compound of chlorine	Weight of 22.4 l. of gas or vapor at standard conditions ($\pm 1\%$) (g.)	Weight of one molecule of compound ($\pm 1\%$) (a.w.u.)	Per cent of chlorine ($\pm 0.01\%$)	Weight of chlorine per molecule of compound ($\pm 1\%$) (a.w.u.)	Number of atoms of chlorine in one molecule of compound
Chlorine	71.0	71.0	100	71.0	2
Chloroform	119	119	89.10	106	3
Carbon tetrachloride	154	154	92.19	142	4
Hydrogen chloride	36.5	36.5	97.24	35.5	1
Sulfur monochloride	135	135	52.51	70.9	2
Ethyl chloride	64.5	64.5	54.96	35.4	1

The conclusion that the molecule of free chlorine contains two atoms, i.e., that chlorine gas is diatomic, confirms that reached by application of the combining volume principle. The approximate atomic weight, 35.5, of chlorine is one-half of its approximate molecular weight, 71.0.

11. The Law of Dulong and Petit. As early as 1819, two French scientists, Pierre Louis Dulong and Alexis Thérèse Petit, discovered the following approximate relationship to be valid for solid elements of higher atomic weight:

$$\text{atomic weight} = \frac{6.3}{\text{specific heat}}$$

The specific heat of a substance is the number of calories required to raise the temperature of 1 gram of the substance through one degree centigrade. The law of Dulong and Petit states, in effect, that the quantity of heat required to raise the temperature of 1 gram-atom (Avagadro's number of atoms) of any heavy element in the solid state by 1° C. is 6.3 calories.

This law expressed by the equation above provided a simple method for determining the approximate atomic weights of the heavier metals—for just those elements whose approximate atomic weights cannot conveniently be determined by Cannizzaro's method because they do not form many volatile compounds. Iron, for example, has a specific heat of 0.113 cal. per gram. The atomic weight of iron, therefore, is approximately

$$\frac{6.3}{0.113} = 56$$

12. Exact Atomic Weights. Once the approximate atomic weight of an element is known, its exact atomic weight can be calculated from its combining or equivalent weight. The combining weight—the weight of the element which combines with 8.0000 parts by weight of oxygen—can be determined with great accuracy. Now, if, as is the case for hydrogen, *2* atoms of the element combine with *1* atom of oxygen, we know that the atom and weight relationships will be as follows:

$$2 \text{ atoms of the element} \quad : \quad 1 \text{ atom of oxygen}$$
$$2 \times (\text{weight of 1 atom}) : 16 \text{ a.w.u. of oxygen}$$
$$1 \times (\text{weight of 1 atom}) : \quad 8 \text{ a.w.u. of oxygen}$$

Hence in this case the exact atomic weight of the element is the same as its combining or equivalent weight. Such an element, e.g., hydrogen or one which can replace or combine with hydrogen atom for atom, is said to have a *combining capacity or valence of 1.*

On the other hand, if the element combines with oxygen atom for atom, its exact atomic weight is twice its exact equivalent weight. Elements of this type, such as magnesium and zinc, have a *combining capacity or valence* of 2.

In general, we may say that for any element

exact atomic weight = exact combining or equivalent weight × valence.

If the approximate atomic weight and an accurate value for the equivalent weight of an element are known, its valence, and hence an accurate value for its atomic weight, can always be determined. For example, the approximate atomic weight of iron has already been shown (p. 88) by means of the law of Dulong and Petit to be 56. Now there is a compound of iron called ferric oxide in which 2.3271 g. of iron is found experimentally to be combined with 1.0000 g. of oxygen. The weight of iron combined with 8.0000 g. of oxygen in this compound is

$$8 \times 2.3271 = 18.617$$

This value, 18.617, is, of course, the equivalent weight of iron in the compound. The valence of iron in this instance is

$$\frac{56 \text{ (approx.)}}{18.617} = 3.01 \text{ (approximately)}$$

and therefore 3, exactly, since the valence must be a whole number. The exact atomic weight of iron is therefore

$$18.617 \times 3 = 55.85$$

The combining capacities or valences of many elements vary in different compounds, and the equivalent weights then vary accordingly. The exact atomic weight, however, is always equal to the equivalent weight in any given compound multiplied by the valence of the element in that compound.

13. Gram-Atomic Weights. *A gram-atom, or gram-atomic weight, is the quantity of an element having a weight in grams equal to its atomic weight, or the weight of one of its atoms in a.w.u.* A gram-atom of oxygen is 16.000 g.; a gram-atom of hydrogen is 1.0080 g.; a gram-atom of chlorine is 35.457 g.; and a gram-atom of iron is 55.85 g.

Just as a mole of any substance contains 6.024×10^{23} molecules, so a gram-atom of any element contains 6.024×10^{23} atoms. In fact, a gram-atom of an element may be defined as 6.024×10^{23} atoms of that element. Exactly 16.0000 g. of oxygen, 1.0080 g. of hydrogen, 35.457 g. of chlorine, and 55.85 g. of iron each contain 6.024×10^{23} atoms.

The major significance of gram-atomic weights lies in the fact that *weights of different elements which are in the same ratio as their atomic weights contain the same number of atoms.* We know, for example, that 4 pounds of oxygen contains the same number of atoms as 0.2520 pound of hydrogen or 8.8644 pounds of chlorine.

A *gram-equivalent,* or *gram-equivalent weight,* of an element is the quantity of that element whose weight in grams is numerically equal to the equivalent weight. Thus a gram-equivalent of oxygen is 8.0000 g., and of hydrogen, 1.0080 g. The number of atoms in a gram-equivalent of an element is equal to Avogadro's number only when the valence of the element is 1; in general it is equal to Avogadro's number divided by the valence.

14. Molecular Formulas—Exact Molecular Weights. From the combining ratio of hydrogen to oxygen in water (1.0080 to 8.0000) and from the atomic weights of hydrogen and oxygen (1.0080 and 16.0000), we know that the ratio of the number of hydrogen to the number of oxygen atoms in the water molecule must be $2:1$. By means of the vapor density method, it is found that the *approximate molecular weight* of water is 18. We can be certain then, that the water molecule actually contains 2 atoms of hydrogen and 1 atom of oxygen. Water vapor may therefore be represented by the *molecular formula* H_2O.

Such a chemical formula serves not merely as an abbreviation for a particular compound, but also as a shorthand device for designating the exact composition and weight of its molecules. Thus, the molecular formula H_2O not only represents the compound water, but also tells us that a molecule of water in the vapor state contains 2 atoms of hydrogen and 1 atom of oxygen, and that hydrogen and oxygen are present in the weight ratio $2.0160:16.0000$. The exact molecular weight is obtained by adding the atomic weights of all of the atoms of which the molecule is composed:

$$\begin{array}{ll} \text{2 atomic weights of hydrogen } (2 \times 1.0080) = & 2.0160 \\ \text{1 atomic weight of oxygen} \qquad (16.0000) = & 16.0000 \\ \hline \text{exact molecular weight of water} = & \overline{18.0160} \end{array}$$

15. Percentage Composition. The percentage composition by weight of water may be readily calculated from the formula. Out of every 18.0160 parts of weight of water, 2.06160 parts are hydrogen; hence the fraction of hydrogen in water is

$$\frac{2.0160}{18.016} = 0.11190$$

This means that out of every 1 part of water, 0.11190 part is hydrogen. But percentage is defined as parts per hundred; out of every 100 parts of water, then, the number of parts (percentage) of hydrogen is

$$0.1119 \times 100 = 11.19 \text{ parts, or } 11.19\%$$

Similarly, the fraction by weight of oxygen in water is 16.000/18.016, or 0.88810; and the percentage of oxygen in water is

$$\frac{16.000}{18.016} \times 100 = 88.81\%$$

The same result is, of course, obtained by subtracting the percentage of hydrogen (11.19%) from 100%.

The weights of hydrogen and of oxygen in any given weight of water may obviously be found in an entirely similar way. Thus, for example, in 32.00 g. of water there are

$$\frac{2.0160}{18.016} \times 32.00 = 3.581 \text{ g. of hydrogen}$$

and

$$\frac{16.000}{18.016} \times 32.00 = 28.419 \text{ g. of oxygen}$$

It is apparent that the percentage composition of any compound of known formula may be calculated by use of the following equation:

$$\% \text{ of each element} = \frac{\text{weight of element in molecular weight}}{\text{total molecular weight}} \times 100$$

In general, the molecular formula and the exact molecular weight of any compound may be determined if the following values are known: (1) the approximate molecular weight of the compound, (2) accurate atomic weights of the constituent elements, and (3) the relative weights of the various elements in the compound. For example, it can be shown by analysis that carbon dioxide consists of 27.29% carbon and 72.71% oxygen by weight; vapor density measurements indicate an approximate molecular weight of 44 for the compound, and the exact atomic weights of carbon and oxygen are 12.011 and 16.0000, respectively. These facts enable us to determine both the molecular formula and the exact molecular weight of carbon dioxide. We know that the molecular weight must be equal to the sum of a certain number of atomic weights of carbon and a certain number of atomic weights of oxygen. Of the total molecular weight (approximately 44), only 27.29% by weight is carbon. It follows then, that

$$44 \times 0.2729 = 12 \text{ (approximately) units}$$

of the total molecular weight of carbon dioxide are carbon. Since the atomic weight of carbon is 12.011, this must represent 1 atom of carbon. Likewise of the total molecular weight,

$$44 \times 0.7271 = 32 \text{ (approximately) units}$$

are oxygen. But this value represents 32/16.0000, or 2 atoms, of oxygen. The molecular formula for carbon dioxide is, therefore, CO_2, and the molecular weight is accurately obtained as follows:

$$
\begin{aligned}
1 \text{ atomic weight of carbon} \quad (1 \times 12.011) &= 12.011 \\
2 \text{ atomic weights of oxygen} \quad (2 \times 16.0000) &= 32.000 \\
\hline
\text{molecular weight of carbon dioxide} &= 44.011
\end{aligned}
$$

16. Empirical Formulas—Formula Weights. When the approximate molecular weight of a compound cannot be determined, it is impossible to determine its molecular formula. It is now known that many compounds, including especially the salts (p. 205), do not ordinarily exist in the form of molecules (p. 186). Such compounds, like all others, are formed by the combination of atoms in definite ratios, but the combination does not result in the formation of simple unit particles, or molecules, of the compound. In such cases, it is still possible from analytical data to determine the ratio in which the atoms of the elements combine to form the compound. The formula that represents the simplest integral ratio of the number of atoms of each element in a compound is called the *empirical formula* of the compound.

To illustrate how the empirical formula of a compound may be calculated from analytical data on the relative weights of the elements present in the compound, let us consider the case of trisodium phosphate. Analysis shows that this compound, which is commonly used as a water softener, has the following composition by weight:

$$
\begin{aligned}
\text{Sodium,} \quad &\text{Na} = 42.07\% \\
\text{Phosphorus,} \quad &\text{P} \;\; = 18.89\% \\
\text{Oxygen,} \quad &\text{O} \;\; = 39.04\%
\end{aligned}
$$

These figures mean, of course, that out of every 100 g. of trisodium phosphate, 42.07 g. is sodium, 18.89 g. phosphorus, and 39.04 g. oxygen. Now our problem in deducing the empirical formula is to find the simplest ratio of the numbers of atoms (or gram-atoms) of sodium, phosphorus, and oxygen which will account for this composition. One gram-atomic weight of sodium is 22.991 g. (inside cover). In 100 g. of trisodium phosphate there is 42.07 g. of sodium, and therefore

$$\frac{42.07}{22.991} = 1.830 \text{ gram-atoms of sodium}$$

Likewise, in 100 g. of trisodium phosphate, there are

$$\frac{18.89}{30.975} = 0.610 \text{ gram-atom of phosphorus and}$$

$$\frac{39.04}{16.00} = 2.440 \text{ gram-atoms of oxygen}$$

The atoms of the various elements are therefore present in the ratio 1.830 of Na to 0.610 of P to 2.440 of O; hence, we might write the formula, provisionally, $Na_{1.830} P_{0.610} O_{2.440}$. Inasmuch as atoms combine as units, however, we should prefer the relative numbers of the several kinds of atoms to be represented by whole numbers. Such a ratio of integers is readily obtained if we assume that the smallest ratio number (0.610 for P in this case) represents one atom of the element concerned. If there is but one atom of phosphorus in the empirical formula, there must be

$$\frac{1.830}{0.610} = 3 \text{ atoms of sodium and}$$

$$\frac{2.440}{0.610} = 4 \text{ atoms of oxygen}$$

The empirical formula is therefore Na_3PO_4.

The empirical formula of a gaseous compound might be determined by this method, but whenever the molecular weight is known, it is preferable to determine the molecular formula directly, as illustrated on page 92.

The sum of the relative weights of all the atoms in the formula of a compound as it is usually written is called the *formula weight*. For trisodium phosphate, the formula weight is obtained as follows:

3 atomic weights of sodium	$(3 \times 22.991) =$	68.97
1 atomic weight of phosphorus	$(1 \times 30.975) =$	30.98
4 atomic weights of oxygen	$(4 \times 16.0000) =$	64.00
formula weight of trisodium phosphate	$=$	$\overline{163.95}$

Empirical formulas, as we shall see in the next chapter, may be just as useful in some types of chemical calculations as molecular formulas. Gram-formula weights, like gram-molecular weights, are called *moles*. Thus we speak of 163.95 g. of trisodium phosphate as being one mole of that compound.

As a somewhat more complicated example of a compound whose approximate molecular weight cannot be determined, let us consider ferric oxide, often called jewelers' rouge. Analysis of a 1.3472 g. sample of ferric oxide gives: iron (Fe) 0.9423 g.; oxygen (O) 0.4049 g. But 0.9423 g. represents

$$\frac{0.9423}{55.85} = 0.01687 \text{ gram-atom of Fe, and } 0.4049 \text{ g. is}$$

$$\frac{0.4049}{16.00} = 0.02531 \text{ gram-atom of O}$$

Since for every 0.01687 gram-atom (or atom) of iron there is 0.02531 gram-atom (or atom) of oxygen, we might write the provisional formula $Fe_{0.01687}O_{0.02531}$. If we assume that there is one atom of iron in the conventional empirical formula we find that there are

$$\frac{0.02531}{0.01687} = 1.5 \text{ atoms of oxygen}$$

and we obtain the formula $Fe_1O_{1.5}$. The smallest ratio of whole numbers may be obtained by doubling this formula; i.e., the empirical formula is Fe_2O_3.

STUDY QUESTIONS AND PROBLEMS

1. The weight of a liter of oxygen at standard conditions is 1.43 g., that of a liter of sulfur dioxide is 2.93 g.

(a) How many molecules of each gas are there in this volume? (b) What is the weight in grams of a single molecule of each gas? (c) What are the relative weights of the molecules? (d) What is the approximate molecular weight of sulfur dioxide; the approximate weight of a sulfur dioxide molecule in a.w.u.? (e) If the weight of a sulfur atom is approximately 32 a.w.u., what is the formula for sulfur dioxide? What are the relative numbers of oxygen atoms in equal volumes of the two gases at the same conditions?

2. (a) If 168 ml. of a gas, at standard conditions of temperature and pressure, weighs 0.255 g., what is the approximate molecular weight of the gas?

(b) Calculate the approximate molecular weight of a gas 1140 ml. of which at 78° C. and 780 mm. weighs 5.20 g. If the gas contains iodine, what is it?

3. Why cannot accurate values for atomic weights be determined from combining proportions alone? From vapor density or heat capacity data alone?

4. The approximate molecular weights and compositions by weight of several volatile compounds of carbon are shown in the following table:

Compound	Molecular weight	Composition (%)		
		C	H	O
Methane	16	75	25	
Heptane	100	84	16	
Formaldehyde	30	40	6.7	53.3
Propylene	42	85.7	14.3	
Acetic acid	60	40	6.7	53.3
Ether	74	64.9	13.5	21.6

(a) From these data, calculate the approximate atomic weight of carbon.

(b) Given that the atomic weight of hydrogen is approximately 1, determine the molecular formula of each compound.

(c) Exact analysis of carbon dioxide shows that it contains 0.3753 g. of carbon per gram of oxygen. Calculate the equivalent weight of carbon in this compound. From these data and those of (a), calculate the exact atomic weight of carbon. What is the valence of carbon in carbon dioxide? What is the formula of carbon dioxide?

(d) Suppose that the compounds methane and formaldehyde had been omitted from the table. Could you then prove that none of the compounds listed contained only one atom of carbon per molecule?

5. (a) The specific heat of thallium is 0.0315 cal. per gram. What is the approximate atomic weight of thallium? (b) Thallium forms an oxide in which exactly 68.130 g. of thallium is combined with 8.0000 g. of oxygen. What is the valence of thallium; the exact atomic weight; the formula of the oxide?

6. A certain sample of a heavy metal releases 250 cal. when cooled from 155 to 20° C. What is the approximate number of atoms present in the sample? How much heat would be required to raise the temperature of 1×10^{25} atoms of a heavy metal through 10° C.?

7. (a) What fraction of a mole of any gas is there in 1 liter of the gas at standard conditions? How many molecules? (b) What is the vapor density of each of the following gases: nitrogen, carbon dioxide, ammonia (NH_3), methane (CH_4)? (c) What volume at standard conditions is occupied by 1 g. of chlorine, acetylene (C_2H_2), hydrogen chloride, hydrogen?

8. What is the volume occupied at 19° C. and 730 mm. pressure by 8.40 g. of carbon monoxide (CO)? How many molecules are present?

9. (a) Calculate the percentage composition of the following compounds: alcohol, C_2H_6O; sulfuric acid, H_2SO_4; soda ash, Na_2CO_3; uranium hexafluoride, UF_6; limestone, $CaCO_3$. (b) What weight of silicon is there in a rock crystal weighing 9 lb., if the crystal is pure quartz (SiO_2)? Calculate the weight of manganese in 2.55 tons of an ore containing 85% of manganese dioxide, MnO_2.

10. (a) An oxide of nitrogen whose approximate vapor density is 1.98 g. per liter contains 63.7% of nitrogen. What is its molecular formula? (b) A compound (cyanogen) of carbon and nitrogen is 46.2% carbon and 53.8% nitrogen. Its vapor density is 2.32 g. per liter. What is its molecular formula?

11. Calculate the empirical formula of each of the compounds whose percentage compositions are as follows:

(a) P = 7.19%; Br = 92.81%; (b) Na = 25.35%; As = 27.52%; S = 47.13%; (c) K = 31.90%; Cl = 28.93%; O = 39.17%; (d) K = 26.58%; Cr = 35.35%; O = 38.07%.

12. Determine the molecular formula of each compound listed in Table 6.1.

7

Quantitative Relations in Chemical Reactions

1. Use of Symbols and Formulas. To represent the myriad chemical changes which occur in nature and in the laboratory, the chemist employs a concise, simple method based on the use of symbols for the elements and formulas for the compounds. To use this method, we must know the formulas for all compounds involved. The final test of any formula is an experimental one; every formula depends for its validity upon analytical, and in the case of molecular formulas, molecular weight data. But study of the experimentally determined formulas of thousands of compounds has revealed that many elements exhibit a fairly constant combining capacity, or valence. Knowledge of the valences of elements makes it possible for one to write the correct formulas for many compounds.

2. Valence from Formulas. Hydrogen and chlorine combine to form the compound hydrogen chloride, HCl. One atom of chlorine is combined in that compound with one atom of hydrogen. Since hydrogen has been assigned (p. 88) a standard valence of 1, the valence of chlorine in HCl is therefore 1, also. The formulas and names of several other common compounds of chlorine are as follows:

NaCl	$CaCl_2$	$AlCl_3$[1]	CCl_4
Sodium chloride	Calcium chloride	Aluminum chloride	Carbon tetrachloride

Based on a valence of 1 for chlorine in each of these compounds, the valences of sodium, calcium, aluminum, and carbon are 1, 2, 3, and 4, respectively. Stated in another way, sodium is univalent, calcium bivalent, aluminum trivalent, and carbon quadrivalent. Hydrogen combines with bromine to form the compound HBr, hydrogen bromide, and with iodine to form HI,

[1] For simplicity, the empirical formula for aluminum chloride is used here, instead of the molecular formula, Al_2Cl_6 (p. 807).

hydrogen iodide. The valence of bromine and of iodine here is 1. In their bromides and iodides, again sodium, calcium, aluminum, and carbon have valences of 1, 2, 3, and 4, respectively.

NaBr	CaBr$_2$	AlBr$_3$	CBr$_4$
Sodium bromide	Calcium bromide	Aluminum bromide	Carbon tetrabromide

NaI	CaI$_2$	AlI$_3$	CI$_4$
Sodium iodide	Calcium iodide	Aluminum iodide	Carbon tetraiodide

This same regularity is apparent among the following oxygen compounds of these elements:

Na$_2$O	CaO	Al$_2$O$_3$	CO$_2$
Sodium oxide	Calcium oxide	Aluminum oxide	Carbon dioxide

Two atoms of sodium are required to unite with one atom of oxygen (valance $= 2$) in Na$_2$O; the valence of sodium in this oxide is therefore 1. Calcium, which unites with oxygen atom for atom, exhibits a valence of 2. In Al$_2$O$_3$, two aluminum atoms have a total combining capacity equal to that of three oxygen atoms; inasmuch as the total combining capacity of three oxygen atoms is 3×2, or 6, the total combining capacity of two aluminum atoms is also 6, and the valence of aluminum is $6 \div 2$, or 3. The carbon atom in carbon dioxide has twice the combining capacity of the oxygen atom; hence the valence of carbon, once again, is 4.

3. Valences of Common Metals. The valences of a number of important metals listed in Table 7.1 are apparent from the formulas of their chlorides. The symbol of the metal is written first, and the metal is indicated first in the name of the compound. All compounds, such as those listed in Table 7.1, that contain only two elements are called *binary compounds*. The chemical names of binary compounds usually end in the suffix *-ide;* e.g., sodium chloride, calcium oxide.

Table 7.1

Valence $= 1$		Valence $= 2$		Valence $= 3$	
Metal	*Chloride*	*Metal*	*Chloride*	*Metal*	*Chloride*
Lithium	LiCl	Magnesium	MgCl$_2$	Aluminum	AlCl$_3$
Sodium	NaCl	Calcium	CaCl$_2$	Lanthanum	LaCl$_3$
Potassium	KCl	Zinc	ZnCl$_2$		
Rubidium	RbCl	Strontium	SrCl$_2$		
Silver	AgCl	Cadmium	CdCl$_2$		
Cesium	CsCl	Barium	BaCl$_2$		

4. Variable Valence Among the Metals. A number of metals commonly exhibit two different valences. Copper, for example, forms two series of compounds in which its valences are 1 and 2, respectively. Thus, we have the compounds Cu_2O (cuprous oxide) and $CuCl$ (cuprous chloride), as well as CuO (cupric oxide) and $CuCl_2$ (cupric chloride). Iron forms ferrous compounds, such as FeO (ferrous oxide) and $FeCl_2$ (ferrous chloride), in which its valence is 2, and ferric compounds, such as Fe_2O_3 (ferric oxide) and $FeCl_3$ (ferric chloride), in which its valence is 3. Tin commonly exhibits valences of 2 and 4, as in SnO, stannous oxide; $SnCl_2$, stannous chloride; SnO_2, stannic oxide; and $SnCl_4$, stannic chloride. The suffix -*ous* is employed for the metal in its lower valence state, and the suffix -*ic*, in its higher valence state.

Another large group of metals exhibit more than two different valences in their various compounds. Vanadium, for example, forms compounds in which it has valences of 2, 3, 4, and 5. The names of the various valence states are commonly derived by the use of Latin numeral prefixes (uni-, bi-, etc.). In the naming of the compounds themselves, however, the number of atoms of one or both of the elements shown in the formula is commonly indicated by means of a Greek prefix (*mono-, di-*, etc.), as in titanium tetrachloride, $TiCl_4$, divanadium pentoxide, V_2O_5, and osmium octafluoride, OsF_8. This practice is illustrated in Table 7.2.

Table 7.2

Element	Valence	Name of Valence State	Formula of Compound	Name of Compound
In	3	Trivalent	$InCl_3$	Indium trichloride
Ti	4	Quadrivalent	$TiCl_4$	Titanium tetrachloride
V	5	Quinquivalent	V_2O_5	Divanadium pentoxide
W	6	Sexavalent	WCl_6	Tungsten hexachloride
Mn	7	Septavalent	Mn_2O_7	Dimanganese heptoxide
Os	8	Octavalent	OsF_8	Osmium octafluoride

5. Valences of Nonmetals. Most of the typical nonmetals exhibit characteristic constant valences toward hydrogen and the metals. These values for various nonmetallic elements are shown in Table 7.3. The valence of sodium of each compound is 1. Corresponding compounds in which hydrogen takes the place of the sodium as a univalent element are known also, in every case.

Carbon does not form a compound with sodium, but in many of the metal

Table 7.3

Elements	Valence	Compounds with sodium
F, Cl, Br, I	1	NaF, NaCl, NaBr, NaI (sodium fluoride, chloride, bromide, and iodide)
O, S	2	Na_2O (sodium oxide), Na_2S (sodium sulfide)
N, P	3	Na_3N (sodium nitride), Na_3P (sodium phosphide)

carbides, such as Al_4C_3 (aluminum carbide), as well as in CH_4 (methane), it exhibits a valence of 4.

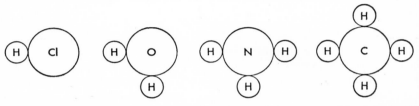

Fig. 7.1. Toward hydrogen, chlorine has a valence of 1; oxygen, of 2; nitrogen, of 3; and carbon, of 4.

Most of the nonmetals show more than one combining capacity in their compounds with one another. Sulfur has a valence of 4 in sulfur dioxide, SO_2, and of 6 in sulfur trioxide, SO_3. Phosphorus forms such compounds as P_4O_6 (phosphorous anhydride) and PCl_3 (phosphorus trichloride) in which its valence is 3, as well as P_4O_{10} (phosphoric anhydride) and PCl_5 (phosphorus pentachloride) in which its valence is 5. Toward oxygen, carbon exhibits a valence of 4 in CO_2 (carbon dioxide) and of 2 in CO (carbon monoxide).

6. Radicals and Their Valences. Much more numerous than the binary compounds are the *ternary compounds*, which contain three different elements. In many ternary compounds, the nonmetallic portion of the formula consists of a group of atoms which, as a unit, behaves in many ways like a single atom. For example, in the compounds H_2SO_4 (sulfuric acid), Na_2SO_4 (sodium sulfate), $CaSO_4$ (calcium sulfate), and $Al_2(SO_4)_3$ (aluminum sulfate), the sulfate (SO_4) group recurs repeatedly. Such a group of atoms which remains intact throughout many chemical reactions, and which exhibits a constant valence in all compounds in which it is present, is called a radical. The valence of the sulfate radical is 2.

Many of the compounds in which the various radicals are combined with hydrogen belong to a class of substances called acids (p. 204). The valence of a radical can be determined from the number of hydrogen atoms combined with the radical, as illustrated for some of the common radicals in Table 7.4.

All of the ternary acids listed contain both hydrogen and oxygen, and the name for each acid is derived from that of the third element present. If this element forms only one ternary acid with hydrogen and oxygen, the name of the acid ends in -*ic,* e.g., carbon*ic* acid, H_2CO_3. If the element forms two familiar ternary acids with hydrogen and oxygen, the name of the acid containing the smaller number of oxygen atoms is commonly changed to -*ous.* For example, H_2SO_4 is called sulfur*ic* acid, but H_2SO_3 is sulfur*ous* acid.

Table 7.4

Valence = 1	
COMPOUND	RADICAL
HOH, Water	OH, Hydroxyl
HNO_2, Nitrous acid	NO_2, Nitrite
HNO_3, Nitric acid	NO_3, Nitrate
$HClO_3$, Chloric acid	ClO_3, Chlorate
$HMnO_4$, Permanganic acid	MnO_4, Permanganate
Valence = 2	
COMPOUND	RADICAL
H_2SO_3, Sulfurous acid	SO_3, Sulfiite
H_2SO_4, Sulfuric acid	SO_4, Sulfate
H_2CO_3, Carbonic acid	CO_3, Carbonate
H_2CrO_4, Chromic acid	CrO_4, Chromate
Valance = 3	
COMPOUND	RADICAL
H_3PO_3, Phosphorous acid	PO_3, Phosphite
H_3PO_4, Phosphoric acid	PO_4, Phosphate
H_3AsO_3, Arsenious acid	AsO_3, Arsenite
H_3AsO_4, Arsenic acid	AsO_4, Arsenate

Many of the binary compounds in which metals are combined with non-metals, and ternary compounds in which metals are combined with non-metallic radicals, are commonly called salts (p. 205). The name of a given radical, together with the names of the salts in which it is contained, may be regarded as derived from the name of the acid in which the radical occurs. If the name of the acid ends in -*ic,* the name of the corresponding radical ends in -*ate.* Thus, the salts Na_2SO_4, $CaSO_4$, and $Al_2(SO_4)_3$, which contain the same radical as sulfuric acid, are named sodium sulf*ate,* calcium sulf*ate,* and aluminium sulf*ate,* respectively. On the other hand, Na_2SO_3, $CaSO_3$, and $Al_2(SO_3)_3$, which contain the same radical as sulfurous acid, are named, respectively, sodium sulf*ite,* calcium sulf*ite,* and aluminum sulf*ite.* These facts may be summarized by the statement that an *-ite* salt corresponds to an *-ous* acid, and an *-ate* salt to an *-ic* acid.

In addition to the radicals listed, which form compounds only with hydrogen or metals, there is at least one important radical which behaves like a metal in that it is found in combination with nonmetallic elements or radicals. This group, the ammonium (NH_4) radical, like sodium and potassium, has a valence of 1. It forms such typical compounds as NH_4Cl (ammonium chloride), $(NH_4)_2S$ (ammonium sulfide), $(NH_4)_2SO_4$ (ammonium sulfate), and $(NH_4)_3PO_4$ (ammonium phosphate).

Radicals may be regarded as having their own characteristic equivalent weights just as do elements. The equivalent weight of a radical is equal to

$$\frac{\text{sum of atomic weights of all atoms in radical}}{\text{valence of radical}}$$

For the sulfate radical, the equivalent weight is

$$\frac{1 \times \text{atomic weight of S} + 4 \times \text{atomic weight of O}}{2} = \frac{96.066}{2} = 48.033$$

A gram-equivalent of sulfate is therefore 48.033 g. The equivalent weights of elements and radicals are frequently used in chemical calculations.

7. Writing Formulas from Known Valences.

With a knowledge of the valences of common elements and radicals, we can write the correct empirical formulas for a large number of important compounds. For example, potassium has a valence of 1—as is conveniently indicated thus: K^I. Bromine in binary compounds with metals likewise has a valence of 1 (Br^I). Potassium and bromine therefore combine atom for atom to form the compound with the empirical formula KBr (potassium bromide). Similarly the compound formed between barium and oxygen is $Ba^{II}O^{II}$ (barium oxide), and between aluminum and the phosphate radical, $Al^{III}PO_4{}^{III}$ (aluminum phosphate). In general, atoms (or radicals) which have the same valence unite in a 1:1 ratio.

When elements (or radicals) of different valence are combined, the empirical formula of the resulting compound shows the lowest possible subscripts required to make the total combining capacities of the two constituent elements or radicals of the compound equal to each other. Thus, magnesium and chlorine together form $Mg^{II}Cl_2{}^I$ (magnesium chloride); the ammonium and sulfate radicals form $(NH_4)_2^{I}SO_4^{II}$ (ammonium sulfate); aluminum and the nitrate radical form $Al^{III}(NO_3)_3^{I}$ (alumium nitrate); and calcium and the phosphate radical form $Ca_3^{II}(PO_4)_2^{III}$ (calcium phosphate). In the last case, which is perhaps the most difficult of those listed, it is apparent that 3 calcium atoms are required to give the same total combining capacity as 2 phosphate radicals; i.e., $3 \times 2 = 2 \times 3$. Using the method illustrated, we may write other formulas such as $H_2^{I}S^{II}$, hydrogen sulfide; $Mg_3^{II}N_2^{III}$, magnesium nitride; $K^{I}ClO_3^{I}$, potassium chlorate; $Na_2^{I}SO_3^{II}$, sodium sulfite; $Fe_2^{III}O_3^{II}$, ferric oxide; $Fe^{II}Br_2^{I}$, ferrous bromide; $Sn^{IV}O_2^{II}$, stannic oxide; and $Sn^{II}(OH)_2^{I}$, stannous hydroxide.

8. Equations.

Just as it is convenient to represent chemical compounds by means of their formulas, so also chemical reactions may conveniently be summarized in what are called chemical equations. An equation is a condensed shorthand statement which expresses a chemical reaction in terms of the symbols and formulas, rather than the names, of the elements and compounds involved. As in the case of a formula, the ultimate test for the validity of any equation is, of course, experimental. We cannot write an equation for any reaction unless we know the reactants and the products of that reaction. If we do know what substances enter into and result from any given reaction, and if we know the formulas of these substances, then we can always write the correct equation for the reaction.

For example, it is a fairly simple matter to establish experimentally the fact that zinc reacts with hydrochloric acid (an aqueous solution of hydrogen chloride) to form zinc chloride and hydrogen gas. Experiment also reveals that the formula for hydrogen chloride is HCl, and for zinc chloride, $ZnCl_2$. These are, of course, the formulas we should have predicted on the basis of the generalizations concerning the valences of hydrogen, chlorine, and zinc (p. 97). We know also (p. 86) that hydrogen gas in the free state exists as diatomic molecules represented as H_2. We might, then, by means of symbols and formulas, indicate the reactants on the left-hand side of an equation and the products on the right-hand side, using an arrow as an abbreviation for the word "yields."

$$Zn + HCl \rightarrow ZnCl_2 + H_2 \ (not \ balanced)$$

Qualitatively, we read this skeleton equation as follows: Zinc reacts with hydrochloric acid to form zinc chloride and hydrogen. A correct equation must also, however, represent precisely the quantitative relationships involved in the reaction. Inspection of the equation above reveals that it is not quantitatively accurate. In the light of the Law of Conservation of Mass and of the atomic theory, we know that in any ordinary chemical change there will be the same number of atoms of each element in the products of the reaction as there were in the reactants. Yet the above equation shows *two* atoms of chlorine and *two* atoms of hydrogen on the right-hand side of the equation and only *one* atom of each of these elements on the left; this means that the equation is not balanced. In order to make the equation quantitatively accurate, or to "balance" it, as this process is called, we might be tempted to change the formulas for zinc chloride and hydrogen gas to ZnCl and H, respectively. This is not permissible, however, for it would contradict the experimental facts which prove that zinc chloride should be represented by the formula $ZnCl_2$, and free hydrogen by H_2. We can, however, balance the equation very simply by doubling the number of molecules of hydrochloric acid used, thus doubling the number of atoms of hydrogen and chlorine on the left-hand side of the equation:

$$Zn + 2HCl \rightarrow ZnCl_2 + H_2$$

We now have a true quantitative statement of the reaction: 1 atomic weight of zinc combines with 2 molecular weights of hydrochloric acid to yield 1 formula weight of zinc chloride and 1 molecular weight of hydrogen. Because of the fact that in a correctly balanced equation not only the total masses, but also the masses of each element involved, are the same on both sides of the equation, an "equals" sign ($=$) instead of an arrow is often used to separate the reactants from the products. Thus the above equation is often written

$$Zn + 2HCl = ZnCl_2 + H_2$$

In the same way, we can readily balance the equation for the reaction which occurs when potassium chlorate is heated. It may be shown experimentally, in a rather simple manner, that the products of this decomposition are potassium chloride and free oxygen. Therefore we may write the skeleton equation

$$KClO_3 \rightarrow KCl + O_2 \text{ (not balanced)}$$

It is clear that the total number of atoms of oxygen shown in the equation must be divisible by both 2 and 3; i.e., at least 6 oxygen atoms are required. If we keep the correct formulas throughout, the only means by which we can arrive at a total of 6 atoms of oxygen on the left-hand side of the equation is by doubling the number of $KClO_3$ units—the coefficient of $KClO_3$, as it is called—in the equation. Temporarily, then, we might write

$$2KClO_3 \rightarrow KCl + O_2 \text{ (not balanced)}$$

It then appears that the coefficients of KCl and O_2 on the right-hand side of the equation must be 2 and 3, respectively.

$$2KClO_3 = 2KCl + 3O_2$$

9. The Complete Meaning of Equations. The importance and usefulness of equations become all the more apparent when we consider how many experimental facts are summarized in a single equation. For example, let us examine the equation for the combustion of the gas methane (p. 560), a reaction in which the products are carbon dioxide and water.

$$CH_4 + 2O_2 = CO_2 + 2H_2O$$

There are several distinct ways in which we may interpret this equation. In a purely qualitative way, the equation may be read: (1) methane reacts with oxygen to yield carbon dioxide and water. Extending our interpretation to include the quantitative point of view, we read: (2) 1 molecule of methane reacts with 2 molecules of oxygen to yield 1 molecule of carbon dioxide and 2 molecules of water. If we wish to express this quantitative relationship in terms of weighable amounts of materials, we might say: (3) 1 mole of methane reacts with 2 moles of oxygen to yield 1 mole of carbon dioxide and 2 moles of water. We may give the actual values of the gram-molecular weights: (4) 16.043 g. of methane reacts with 64.000 g. of oxygen

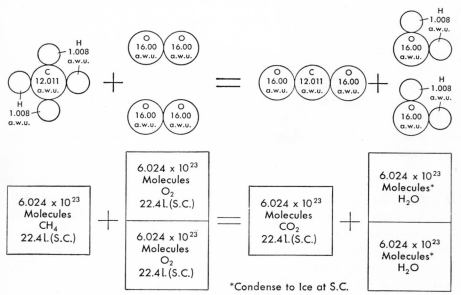

Fig. 7.2.   The weight and volume relationships in the combustion of methane.

to yield 44.011 g. of carbon dioxide and 36.032 g. of water. (We can, of course, state this same relationship in terms of ounces, pounds, kilograms, or tons, provided the same unit is employed throughout in any given statement.) The fact that gaseous substances are involved in this reaction makes possible several additional interpretations of the equation. We know that at standard conditions 1 mole (16.043 g.) of methane occupies 22.4 l.; 2 moles (64.000 g.) of oxygen, 44.8 l.; and 1 mole (44.011 g.) of carbon dioxide, 22.4 l. Therefore we may expand statement (4) to read: 16.043 g. or 22.4 l. of methane reacts with 64.000 g. or 44.8 l. of oxygen to yield 44.011 g. or 22.4 l. of carbon dioxide and 36.032 g. of water (all the volumes being those occupied at standard conditions). From Avogadro's hypothesis we may conclude that the volumes of methane, oxygen, and carbon dioxide participating in the reaction are always in the ratio $1:2:1$, provided that the volumes are all measured under the same conditions. Finally, if the volumes are all measured at some fixed temperature above $100°$ C., so that the water is likewise in the gaseous state, we may write: (5) 1 volume of methane reacts with 2 volumes of oxygen to yield 1 volume of carbon dioxide and 2 volumes of water vapor.

For convenience, these facts are summarized:

	CH_4	+	$2O_2$	=	CO_2	+	$2H_2O$
(1)	Methane	+	Oxygen	=	Carbon dioxide	+	Water
(2)	1 molecule of methane	+	2 molecules of oxygen	=	1 molecule of carbon dioxide	+	2 molecules of water
(3)	1 mole	+	2 moles	=	1 mole	+	2 moles
(4)	16.043 g. or 22.4 l.	+	64.000 g. or 44.8 l.	=	44.011 g. or 22.4 l. (S.T.P.)	+	36.032 g.
(5)	1 volume	+	2 volumes	=	1 volume	+	2 volumes (above 100° C.)

10. Weight Relations in Chemical Reactions.

As suggested by the data given, a balanced equation for any chemical reaction provides the most convenient basis for the calculation of the weight relations in that reaction. Assume, for example, that we wish to determine the weight of oxygen required to burn 50.00 g. of methane to carbon dioxide and water. The first step is to write the balanced equation. Next we read from the equation the data which are pertinent to the solution of the particular problem, and indicate in the proper place what is given and what is sought in the problem as stated. The adoption of a uniform method for organizing these data, although arbitrary, is time-saving. We shall find it helpful, in solving problems of this type, to summarize what is sought above the equation and to state the pertinent relationship, as read from the equation, directly below the equation. Thus, in the problem given, we write

$$
\begin{array}{cc}
(50.00 \text{ g.}) & (\ ?\ \text{g.}) \\
CH_4 & + 2O_2 \\
(16.043 \text{ g.}) & (64.00 \text{ g.})
\end{array} = CO_2 + 2H_2O
$$

We know that 16.043 of methane requires 64.000 g. of oxygen for complete combustion. Then 50.00 g. of methane would require 50.00/16.043 times as much, or

$$
\frac{50.00}{16.04} \times 64.00 = 199.5 \text{ g. of oxygen}
$$

Or, we might wish to know what weight of methane would be required to produce 10.00 g. of carbon dioxide. Organizing the data, we have

$$
\begin{array}{cc}
(\ ?\ \text{g.}) & (10.00 \text{ g.}) \\
CH_4 & + 2O_2 = CO_2 \\
(16.043 \text{ g}) & (44.011 \text{ g.})
\end{array} + 2H_2O
$$

We see that 44.011 g. of carbon dioxide is formed from 16.043 g. of methane. Then 10.00 g. of carbon dioxide is formed from only 10.00/44.011 as much, or

$$
\frac{10.00}{44.01} \times 16.04 = 3.645 \text{ g. of methane}
$$

11. Weight–Volume Relations from Equations. Suppose that we wish to calculate the volume of methane, measured at standard conditions, which would have to be burned to give 150 g. of carbon dioxide. Inasmuch as we wish to express the answer in terms of liters of methane, and the amount of carbon dioxide desired is given in terms of grams, we shall find it simplest to interpret the balanced equation in terms of the corresponding units.

$$
\begin{array}{cc}
(\ ?\ \text{l.}) & (150 \text{ g.}) \\
CH_4 & + 2O_2 = CO_2 \\
(22.4 \text{ l.}) & (44.01 \text{ g.})
\end{array} + 2H_2O
$$

We know that 44.01 g. of carbon dioxide is formed from 22.4 l. of methane (measured at standard conditions). Then 150 g. of carbon dioxide would be formed from 150/44.0 times as much, or

$$
\frac{150}{44.0} \times 22.4 = 76.4 \text{ l. of methane (S.T.P.)}
$$

12. Volume Relations from Equations. As we have seen, the volumes of the different gases entering into or resulting from a chemical reaction are in the same ratio as the numbers of molecules of these gases which are involved in the reaction. To calculate the volumes of oxygen required, and of carbon dioxide and water vapor formed, from the complete combustion of 1.5 l. of methane, all the volumes being measured at 300° C., we should write

$$\begin{array}{cccc}
(1.5\ \text{l.}) & (?\ \text{liters}) & (?\ \text{liters}) & (?\ \text{liters}) \\
\text{CH}_4 & +\ 2\text{O}_2 & =\ \text{CO}_2 & +\ 2\text{H}_2\text{O} \\
(1\ \text{l.}) & (2\ \text{l.}) & (1\ \text{l.}) & (2\ \text{l.})
\end{array}$$

The volume of carbon dioxide would be the same as that of methane, or 1.5 l., the volumes of oxygen and water vapor twice as much, or 3.0 l.

ENERGY RELATIONS IN CHEMICAL REACTIONS

13. Heat of Reaction. The energy relations involved in a chemical change often constitute a highly important characteristic of the reaction. If the total energy content of the products of a reaction is less than that of the reactants, energy will be evolved, usually (although not always) in the form of heat, during the course of the reaction, which is then said to be *exothermic*. If the energy content of the products is greater than that of the reactants, the additional energy must be supplied, usually in the form of heat, from the surroundings, if the reaction—which is then called *endothermic*—is to proceed at constant temperature. The number of calories evolved or absorbed in a reaction, when it takes place without doing any work other than against the constant pressure of the atmosphere, is called the *heat of reaction*. In so-called *thermochemical equations,* this value is conventionally indicated on the right-hand side of the equation, as a positive quantity if heat is evolved, or as a negative quantity if heat is absorbed. Inasmuch as the heat of reaction depends somewhat upon the physical states both of the reactants and the products, the state of each substance taking part in the reaction should be clearly indicated by a subscript in such an equation.

The thermochemical equation for the combustion of carbon is written

$$C_{(graphite)} + O_{2(g)} = CO_{2(g)} + 94{,}030 \text{ cal.}$$

This equation indicates that when 1 gram-atom (12.011 g.) of carbon in the form of graphite reacts with 1 mole (32.000 g.) of gaseous oxygen to form 1 mole (44.011 g.) of gaseous carbon dioxide, 94,030 calories of heat is evolved. Similarly, the equation

$$2H_{2(g)} + O_{2(g)} = 2H_2O_{(1)} + 136{,}800 \text{ cal.}$$

is read: 2 moles (4.032 g.) of gaseous hydrogen reacts with 1 mole (32.000 g.) of gaseous oxygen to form 2 moles (36.032 g.) of liquid water, and 136,800 cal. of heat is evolved. It follows from the Law of Conservation of Energy (p. 22), that, for the reverse reaction, the same number of calories is absorbed; hence, we may write

$$2H_2O_{(l)} = 2H_{2(g)} + O_{2(g)} - 136,800 \text{ cal.}$$

14. Heat of Formation. A very important constant for any compound is its *heat of formation* ; this term is defined as the heat of reaction in the formation of *one mole* of a compound from its elements in the states in which they commonly exist at room temperature and atmospheric pressure (commonly called their *standard states*). Thus, the heat of formation of carbon dioxide, i.e., the heat of the reaction which consists of the formation of one mole of gaseous carbon dioxide from one gram-atom of carbon in the form of graphite and one mole of gaseous oxygen, as shown in the preceding section, is 94,030 cal. The heat of reaction in the formation of two moles of liquid water from its gaseous elements is 136,800 cal.; the heat of formation of water is therefore $\frac{1}{2} \times 136,800$, or 68,400 cal. per mole. A comparatively small number of compounds have negative heats of formation; i.e., they have an energy content greater than the sum of the energy contents of their constituent elements, and hence are formed from their elements by an endothermic change. Thus, for carbon disulfide, we have

$$C_{(graphite)} + 2S_{(rhombic)} = CS_{2(l)} - 22,000 \text{ cal.}$$

It is apparent that compounds which possess negative heats of formation evolve energy when decomposed into their constituent elements. The heats of formation of a number of compounds are listed in Table 7.5.

15. The Law of Hess—Additivity of Thermochemical Equations. Most calculations involving heat changes in thermochemical equations are based on the fundamental law enunciated by the Russian chemist G. H. Hess in 1840: *The heat evolved or absorbed in a given chemical process is always the same, whether the process takes place in one or in several steps.* This generalization, often called Hess' *Law of Constant Heat Summation,* actually follows from the Law of Conservation of Energy, of which it is merely a special application.

The law of Hess states, in effect, that if a given chemical process takes place in several steps, the overall heat change in the total process is equal to the algebraic sum of the heats of reaction of the several steps, and that this sum in turn is identical with the heat which would be evolved or absorbed in the process if it were to take place in a single step. This means that thermochemical equations may be added to or subtracted from one another, or multiplied or divided by constant factors, exactly as may be done with ordinary algebraic equations. Consequently, this law makes possible the calculation, from related equations, of the heats of many reactions which do not lend

Table 7.5

Compound	Heat of formation (cal. per mole)	Compound	Heat of formation (cal. per mole)
Water, $H_2O_{(l)}$	$+ 68,400$	Sodium chloride, $NaCl_{(s)}$	$+ 98,300$
Water, $H_2O_{(g)}$	$+ 57,800$	Sodium bromide, $NaBr_{(s)}$	$+ 86,700$
Carbon monoxide, $CO_{(g)}$	$+ 26,400$	Sodium iodide, $NaI_{(s)}$	$+ 69,300$
Carbon dioxide, $CO_{2(g)}$	$+ 94,030$	Sodium nitrate, $NaNO_{3(s)}$	$+111,700$
Nitric oxide, $NO_{(g)}$	$- 21,500$	Silver nitrate, $AgNO_{3(s)}$	$+ 29,400$
Sulfur dioxide, $SO_{2(g)}$	$+ 70,900$	Sulfuric acid, $H_2SO_{4(l)}$	$+189,800$
Sulfur trioxide, $SO_{3(g)}$	$+ 93,900$	Sodium sulfate, $Na_2SO_{4(s)}$	$+332,200$
Aluminum oxide, $Al_2O_{3(s)}$	$+380,000$	Calcium carbonate, $CaCO_{3(s)}$	$+283,500$
Ferric oxide, $Fe_2O_{3(s)}$	$+198,500$	Sodium carbonate, $Na_2CO_{3(s)}$	$+271,000$
Calcium oxide, $CaO_{(s)}$	$+151,800$	Hydrogen sulfide, $H_2S_{(g)}$	$+ 4,800$
Ferrous oxide, $FeO_{(s)}$	$+ 64,300$	Copper sulfide, $CuS_{(s)}$	$+ 11,600$
Silver oxide, $Ag_2O_{(s)}$	$+ 6,900$	Ammonia, $NH_{3(g)}$	$+ 11,050$
Sodium oxide, $Na_2O_{(s)}$	$+ 99,500$	Methane, $CH_{4(g)}$	$+ 17,900$
Sodium hydroxide, $NaOH_{(s)}$	$+102,000$	Ethane, $C_2H_{6(g)}$	$+ 20,400$
Hydrogen fluoride, $HF_{(g)}$	$+ 64,000$	Benzene, $C_6H_{6(l)}$	$- 12,300$
Hydrogen chloride, $HCl_{(g)}$	$+ 22,000$	Ethylene, $C_2H_{4(g)}$	$- 12,500$
Hydrogen bromide, $HBr_{(g)}$	$+ 8,650$	Acetylene, $C_2H_{2(g)}$	$- 53,700$
Hydrogen iodide, $HI_{(g)}$	$- 6,240$	Ethyl alcohol, $C_2H_5OH_{(l)}$	$+ 66,300$
Silver chloride, $AgCl_{(s)}$	$+ 30,300$	Acetic acid, $CH_3COOH_{(l)}$	$+116,700$

themselves to direct experimental determination, or which are inconvenient to measure. For example, it is extremely difficult to measure the heat evolved when carbon burns to form carbon monoxide. From the law of Hess, we know, however, that the heat of that reaction must be equal to the sum of the heats of reactions of the following two steps for which the heats of reaction can be accurately measured, and by which carbon monoxide might theoretically be prepared: (1) the burning of carbon to carbon dioxide, and (2) the reaction of carbon dioxide to form carbon monoxide and oxygen. (The heat effect of this second reaction is equal in magnitude but opposite in sign to that of the reverse reaction, viz., the burning of carbon monoxide to carbon dioxide.) The equations are as follows:

$$C_{(graphite)} + O_{2(g)} = CO_{2(g)} + 94{,}030 \text{ cal.} \tag{1}$$

$$CO_{2(g)} = CO_{(g)} + \tfrac{1}{2}O_{2(g)} - 67{,}630 \text{ cal.} \tag{2}$$

Adding (1) and (2), and cancelling all terms which appear on both sides of the equation, we obtain

$$C_{(graphite)} + \tfrac{1}{2}O_{2(g)} = CO_{(g)} + 26{,}400 \text{ cal.}$$

It is apparent from these values that only a small part of the total chemical energy of coal is utilized when coal is burned incompletely to carbon monoxide.

In a similar manner, we can calculate the heat of formation of Fe_2O_3 (ferric oxide) from the following data:

$$3C_{(graphite)} + 2Fe_2O_{3(s)} = 4Fe_{(s)} + 3CO_{2(g)} - 114{,}900 \text{ cal.} \tag{3}$$

$$C_{(graphite)} + O_{2(g)} = CO_{2(g)} + 94{,}030 \text{ cal.} \tag{4}$$

Now we know that the heat of formation of Fe_2O_3 is one-half of the heat of reaction indicated for the equation

$$4Fe_{(s)} + 3O_{2(g)} = 2Fe_2O_{3(s)} \tag{5}$$

Therefore, we shall proceed, just as we would in algebra, to manipulate the equations in such a way as to eliminate from (3) and (4) those factors which do not appear in the desired equation (5). This can be accomplished by transposing equation (3), multiplying equation (4) by the value 3, and adding the resulting equations (6) and (7):

$$4Fe_{(s)} + 3CO_{2(g)} = 3C_{(graphite)} + 2Fe_2O_{3(s)} + 114{,}900 \text{ cal.} \tag{6}$$

$$3C_{(graphite)} + 3O_{2(g)} = 3CO_{2(g)} \qquad\qquad + 282{,}100 \text{ cal.} \tag{7}$$

_____

$$4Fe_{(s)} + 3O_{2(g)} = 2Fe_2O_{3(s)} \qquad\qquad + 397{,}000 \text{ cal.} \tag{5}$$

which, on being divided by 2, gives

$$2Fe_{(s)} + \tfrac{3}{2}O_{2(g)} = Fe_2O_{3(s)} \qquad\qquad + 198{,}500 \text{ cal.}$$

The heat of formation of solid ferric oxide is therefore 198,500 cal. per mole.

An interesting energy relationship which can be determined by means of calculations based on the law of Hess is that involving the allotropic forms of carbon, graphite and diamond. When these two forms of carbon are burned, the heats evolved differ slightly, as shown by the equations

$$C_{(diamond)} + O_{2(g)} = CO_{2(g)} + 94,480 \text{ cal.} \tag{8}$$

$$C_{(graphite)} + O_{2(g)} = CO_{2(g)} + 94,030 \text{ cal.} \tag{4}$$

By subtracting (4) from (8) and transposing, we obtain

$$C_{(diamond)} = C_{(graphite)} + 450 \text{ cal.} \tag{9}$$

It is apparent from these calculations that diamond has a greater heat content than graphite, for 450 cal. of heat would be evolved in the conversion of one gram-atomic weight of diamond into graphite.

Heat of formation data, such as those listed in Table 7.5, when available, may conveniently be used in the calculation of heats of reaction. For example, let us calculate the heat evolved in the important, highly exothermic thermite reaction (p. 825), in which ferric oxide and aluminum react to give iron and aluminum oxide.

$$Fe_2O_{3(s)} + 2Al_{(s)} = 2Fe_{(s)} + Al_2O_{3(s)} \tag{10}$$

From the heats of formation of aluminum oxide and ferric oxide, as given in Table 7.5:

$$2Al_{(s)} + \tfrac{3}{2}O_{2(g)} = Al_2O_{3(s)} + 380,000 \text{ cal.} \tag{11}$$

$$Fe_2O_{3(s)} = 2Fe_{(s)} + \tfrac{3}{2}O_{2(g)} - 198,500 \text{ cal.} \tag{12}$$

Adding (11) and (12) we obtain

$$Fe_2O_{3(s)} + 2Al_{(s)} = 2Fe_{(s)} + Al_2O_{3(s)} + 181,500 \text{ cal.} \tag{10}$$

A study of this problem reveals that the heat of reaction is actually obtained by subtraction of the sum of the heats of formation of the reactants from the sum of the heats of formation of the products. This fact may be generalized as follows:

Heat of reaction = sum of heats of formation of all compound products (i.e., heat of formation per mole of each product $\times$ number of moles of that compound indicated in equation) — sum of heats of formation of all compound reactants.

Thus, for the heat of combustion of methane, we have:

$$CH_{4(g)} + 2O_{2(g)} = CO_{2(g)} + 2H_2O_{(l)}$$

Heat of the reaction = (heat of formation of $CO_2 + 2 \times$ heat of formation of H_2O) — (heat of formation of CH_4) = $94,030 + 2(68,400) - 17,900 = 212,930$ cal.

Exactly the same result will be obtained if the problem is solved stepwise, as was done in the previous example.

16. The "Driving Force" of a Chemical Reaction. Since, as was stated in the preceding section, the heat effect of a reaction is a measure of the difference in what might be called the levels of chemical energy of the reactants and the products, it might be supposed that this heat effect would provide a reliable measure of the tendency for the reaction to take place. Such, indeed, was the hope of the early workers in the field of thermochemistry—a hope which, however, has proved illusory. Although it is often true that the heat evolved in a reaction provides a measure of the "driving force" of a reaction, this is by no means always the case. There are, for example, many instances of *endothermic* reactions which proceed spontaneously. The melting of ice at temperatures above 0° C., although it is usually classified as a physical rather than as a chemical change, is a familiar case; a chemical example is provided by the decomposition of ammonium carbonate ("smelling salts") into ammonium bicarbonate and ammonia at ordinary temperatures.

$$(NH_4)_2CO_3 = NH_4HCO_3 + NH_3$$

The true measure, then, of the driving force of a chemical change is not the heat of reaction, nor the decrease in the total energy; it is rather to be found in the decrease, per gram-equivalent of any of the reactants used or any of the products formed, in what is called *free energy*. In other words, the driving force of a reaction is measured by the total free energy of the reactants minus the total free energy of the products, divided by the number of gram-equivalents of any substance involved in the reaction. An extended discussion of free energy would be far beyond the scope of this text. It may be stated here, however, that the decrease in free energy in a reaction (sometimes loosely called the free energy of a reaction) is measured not by the amount of heat evolved when the reaction takes place, but rather by the maximum amount of actual work (mechanical or electrical) that can be obtained from the reaction, under the most favorable conditions conceivable. This quantity is often *approximately* the same as the heat of reaction, but it is almost never identical with it.

If the heat of reaction is greater than the free energy decrease, a certain amount of heat which cannot by any means be transformed into work is always given up to the surroundings during the progress of the reaction. If, on the other hand, the free energy decrease is greater than the heat of reaction, then the reacting system is able to absorb some heat from the surroundings and convert it into work. It is evident, then, that chemical elements and compounds act not merely as containers or reservoirs of energy, but, in some cases at least, as machines by means of whose action the energy of the surroundings may be converted into a more useful form.

STUDY QUESTIONS AND PROBLEMS

1. (a) Making use of information derived from Tables 7.1 and 7.4, write the name and the formula for a salt representing each of the possible combinations (16 in all) of one of the metals in the first line, below, with one of the radicals in the second.

potassium	zinc	aluminum	silver
phosphate	nitrate	sulfate	carbonate

(b) Write formulas for ferrous oxide, ferric sulfate, stannous phosphate, stannic sulfate, ammonium carbonate, cupric arsenate, uranium hexafluoride.

2. Write a balanced equation for each of the following reactions:
   (a) phosphorus + oxygen = phosphorus pentoxide
   (b) arsenic trioxide + water = arsenious acid
   (c) barium nitrate + silver sulfate = barium sulfate + silver nitrate
   (d) ferric oxide + sulfuric acid = ferric sulfate + water
   (e) stannic oxide + carbon = tin + carbon dioxide

3. What is the equivalent weight of the ammonium radical? of hydroxyl? of phosphate? of carbonate?

4. State in words all the information that is comprised in the equation

$$N_{2(g)} + 3H_{2(g)} = 2NH_{3(g)}$$

5. (a) What volume of nitrogen, measured at 400 atm. pressure and 500° C., is needed to react completely with 78 cu. ft. of hydrogen measured under the same conditions? What is the volume, still under the same conditions, of the ammonia (NH_3) formed in this reaction? (b) Hydrogen and oxygen combine, under suitable conditions, to give liquid water, according to the equation

$$2H_2 + O_2 = 2H_2O$$

If 63 ml. of hydrogen and 28 ml. of oxygen, measured under the same conditions of temperature and pressure, are mixed in a closed tube and caused to react, what gas remains, and what is its volume under the initial conditions of temperature and pressure?

6. How many pounds of oxygen may be obtained by the decomposition of 40.852 lb. of potassium chlorate?

7. (a) What weight of chlorine is obtained by the action of 260.8 g. of manganese dioxide upon concentrated hydrochloric acid, according to the equation

$$MnO_2 + 4HCl = MnCl_2 + 2H_2O + Cl_2$$

(b) What weight of manganese chloride is produced at the same time?
(c) What is the volume, at 39° C. and 700 mm. pressure, of the chlorine produced in the same reaction?

8. (a) What weight of antimony sulfide (Sb_2S_3) is required for the production of 4.20 l. of hydrogen sulfide at S.T.P., according to the equation

$$Sb_2S_3 + 6HCl = 2SbCl_3 + 3H_2S$$

(b) What weight of hydrochloric acid, containing 35% HCl by weight, would be required in the above reaction?

(c) What volume of gaseous hydrogen chloride, at S.T.P., would have to be dissolved in water to give sufficient hydrochloric acid to liberate 3×10^{20} molecules of hydrogen sulfide?

9. Current market prices for aluminum, zinc, and iron, per pound, are 24, 13, and 3 cents, respectively. If hydrogen is to be prepared by the reaction of one of these metals with sulfuric acid, which would be the cheapest metal to use? Which would be the most expensive?

10. How many metric tons (1 metric ton = 1000 kg.) of coke (99% carbon) would be required for the production of 1000 cu. m. of a mixture of carbon monoxide and hydrogen (water gas), at S.T.P., according to the reaction

$$C + H_2O = CO + H_2$$

11. Calculate the heat of reaction for the process by means of which iron is produced in the blast furnace:

$$Fe_2O_3 + 3CO = 2Fe + 3CO_2$$

This quantity of heat is associated with the production of how many grams of iron?

12. How many calories would be evolved or absorbed during the production of the amount of water gas specified in question 10?

13. What volume of nitrous oxide (N_2O), at S.T.P., would be formed by the decomposition of a barrel (275 kg.) of ammonium nitrate (NH_4NO_3) according to the reaction

$$NH_4NO_{3(s)} = N_2O_{(g)} + 2H_2O_{(l)}$$

The heat of formation of ammonium nitrate is 87,130 cal., and of nitrous oxide, −19,650 cal. What heat effect would accompany the above decomposition?

14. The heat of reaction for the production of acetylene from calcium carbide and water according to the equation

$$CaC_{2(s)} + 2H_2O_{(l)} = Ca(OH)_{2(s)} + C_2H_{2(g)}$$

is 31,000 cal. The heat of reaction for the slaking of lime according to the equation

$$CaO_{(s)} + H_2O_{(l)} = Ca(OH)_{2(s)}$$

is 15,900 cal. What is the heat of formation of calcium carbide?

8

Atomic Structure I

1. Introduction. Up to this point no attempt has been made to explain why atoms differ in their combining capacities (valences) or their combining tendencies (reactivities), or indeed, why they should combine at all. In fact, no such explanation would have been possible in terms of the experimental data thus far presented. It was not until many years after the publication of the atomic theory that the first of the developments took place in the fields of physics and chemistry which have led to at least a partial answer to this question. In the pages that follow we shall consider the more important of these advances and try to follow the arguments which have led to the modern picture of the nature of the atom.

The earliest of the developments which contributed greatly to the understanding of atomic structure, although its usefulness in this respect was not at first appreciated even by its author, was the discovery of the periodic law.

THE PERIODIC LAW

2. Mendeleeff's Arrangement of the Elements. It was in the early years of the nineteenth century, when Dalton's atomic theory was winning general acceptance, that the first attempts were made toward classification of the elements into groups or families on the basis of similarities of physical and chemical properties. For example, certain resemblances in the chemical behavior of oxygen and sulfur had long been obvious; and when tellurium and then selenium were discovered, it was found that they too had many properties in common with sulfur. The very active metals lithium, sodium, and potassium were evidently closely related to each other, as were the active nonmetals chlorine, bromine, and iodine. During the years which followed, various regularities and relationships between properties of the elements and their atomic weights were observed. It was not until 1869, however, that the first reasonably satisfactory arrangement of the elements in terms of their properties was made. In that year the famous Russian chemist Dmitri Mendeleeff (1834–1907), reasoning from his knowledge of the chemical properties of the elements, stated the following principle: *The physical and chemical properties of the elements are periodic functions of their atomic weights.* In other words, if the elements are arranged in order of increasing atomic weights, the properties go through a repeated cycle of changes, similar elements recurring at intervals. This principle has come to be known as the *periodic law.*

Group →	0	I-A	I-B	II-A	II-B	III-A	III-B	IV-A	IV-B	V-A	V-B	VI-A	VI-B	VII-A	VII-B	VIII		
Period ↓																		
I		H 1.0																
II	He 4.0	Li 6.9		Be 9.0			B 10.8		C 12.0		N 14.0		O 16.0		F 19.0			
III	Ne 20.2	Na 23.0		Mg 24.3			Al 27.0		Si 28.1		P 31.0		S 32.1		Cl 35.5			
IV	Ar 39.9	K 39.1		Ca 40.1		Sc 45.0		Ti 47.9		V 51.0		Cr 52.0		Mn 54.9		Fe 55.9	Co 58.9	Ni 58.7
			Cu 63.5		Zn 65.4		Ga 69.7		Ge 72.6		As 74.9		Se 79.0		Br 79.9			
V	Kr 83.8	Rb 85.5		Sr 87.6		Y 88.9		Zr 91.2		Nb 92.9		Mo 96.0		Tc		Ru 101.1	Rh 102.9	Pd 106.7
			Ag 107.9		Cd 112.4		In 114.8		Sn 118.7		Sb 121.8		Te 127.6		I 126.9			
VI	Xe 131.3	Cs 132.9		Ba 137.4		La * 138.9		Hf 178.5		Ta 181.0		W 183.9		Re 186.2		Os 190.2	Ir 192.2	Pt 195.1
			Au 197.0		Hg 200.6		Tl 204.4		Pb 207.2		Bi 209.0		Po 210		At			
VII	Rn 222	Fr		Ra 226.1		Ac **												

*	Ce 140.1	Pr 140.9	Nd 144.3	Pm	Sm 150.4	Eu 152.0	Gd 157.3	Tb 158.9	Dy 162.5	Ho 164.9	Er 167.3	Tm 168.9	Yb 173.0	Lu 175.0
**	Th 232.1	Pa 231	U 238.1	Np	Pu	Am	Cm	Bk	Cf	Es	Fm	Md	No	

Fig. 8.1. A revised form of the Mendeleeff periodic chart.

The table in Figure 8.1 is a modification of one of Mendeleeff's, extended to include elements more recently discovered. The most important of these, so far as the periodic arrangement is concerned, are the inert gases (Chapter 21), which are placed in a column called Group 0 at the left of the table. If these elements and others discovered since 1869 are included, the first complete cycle (Period II) contains eight elements, the second cycle (Period III) also contains eight, the third and fourth cycles (Periods IV and V) contain eighteen elements each, and the fifth cycle (Period VI) contains thirty-two. The sixth cycle (Period VII) is incomplete and contains only seventeen elements. The place of hydrogen (Period I) in the table was not clearly understood and was the subject of much discussion.

Mendeleeff fitted the elements into his periodic table by splitting the long periods and running them across the table twice as is shown above.

In the case of Period VI, fourteen elements are very similar in properties, and, in more recent versions of Mendeleeff's chart, have been placed in a separate row across the bottom of the table. For reasons which will appear in the next chapter this has also recently been done with some of the elements in the incomplete Period VII. It will be noted that the last column on the right of the table (Group VIII) is made up of three sets of three elements each, one set from each of the three long periods (IV, V, and VI).

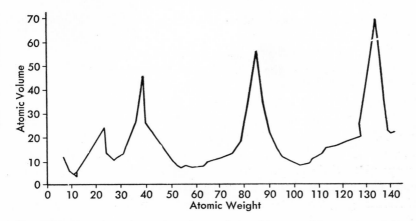

Fig. 8.2. Variation of atomic volume of the elements with atomic weight.

In 1870, the German chemist Lothar Meyer, reasoning from the physical properties of the elements, arrived at a classification of the elements practically identical with that of Mendeleeff. The periodicity of physical properties of the elements is illustrated by Figure 8.2, in which the gram-atomic volumes of the elements (the volume occupied by 6.024×10^{23} atoms of the element—calculated by dividing the gram-atomic weight of the element by its density in the solid state) are plotted against their atomic weights.

3. Characteristics of Mendeleeff's Table. Space does not permit a detailed consideration of the periodic table constructed by Mendeleeff, for a more usable form of the table has been developed as a result of our knowledge of atomic structure. It is this latter form which we shall use, and it will be discussed in detail in the next chapter.

The work of Mendeleeff on the periodic table was of great significance, however, and some of the more important aspects of the table which he developed, as modified by the addition of recently discovered elements, should be summarized.

1. Elements which resemble each other sufficiently to be regarded as a

single family are found, in most cases, in the same column, or group, in the table, e.g. the six alkali metals (lithium, sodium, potassium, rubidium, cesium, and francium).

2. Except for Groups 0 and VIII, however, each group contains two families, which are designated in Figure 8.1 as A and B subgroups. The elements of a single family resemble each other very much more closely than they resemble those of the other family which shares the column with them. Thus, copper, silver, and gold resemble each other closely but show only minor resemblances to the alkali metals which constitute the other family of Group I.

3. There is a more or less uniform gradation of most physical and chemical properties within a given family with increase in atomic weight. For example, consider the following melting points of the alkali metals: Li, 186° C.; Na, 97.9° C.; K, 62.7° C.; Rb, 39.0° C.; Cs, 28.4° C.

4. Elements in the same family exhibit similar combining properties, and, in most cases, the same maximum valence toward oxygen.

5. In order that elements might be placed in positions in the table which correspond to their properties, Mendeleeff found it necessary in two instances (later increased to four) to depart from the order of atomic weights by interchanging two successive elements. The pairs of elements which are thus out of order with respect to atomic weights are argon and potassium, cobalt and nickel, tellurium and iodine, and thorium and protactinium. In general, moreover, the changes of atomic weights from element to element, though in the right order (except as just noted), are exceedingly irregular.

4. Significance of the Discovery of the Periodic Law and the Construction of a Periodic Table. The work of Mendeleeff and of Lothar Meyer constitutes one of the most important milestones in the development of the science of chemistry. The periodic table that Mendeleeff developed provided for the first time a convenient and comprehensive classification of the elements. The chemist could study the elements as families rather than as individuals; this enormously simplified the task of acquiring and maintaining a fund of chemical information. The periodic system rendered, and its more up-to-date form continues to render, outstanding service as a stimulus and guide in research, and as a constant check on the results of experimental work. Any experimental result in apparent contradiction to the implications of the periodic table relationships is sure to be subjected to careful re-examination.

Furthermore, the periodic system made possible the prediction of new elements, and gave clues as to where they should be sought. When Mendeleeff set up his table, he found it necessary to leave certain blank spaces in order that the then known elements might fall into groups in which, from their properties, it was apparent they belonged. He boldly predicted that elements would be discovered to fill the blanks, and made quantitative predictions as to the properties which these new elements would have. In every case his predictions were brilliantly fulfilled.

In addition to all these important contributions, the discovery of the periodic law served as a marked stimulus to the study of the structure of the atoms, and the attempt to explain the properties of the elements in terms of their atomic structures. As we shall see in Chapter 9, the periodic table was of invaluable assistance in the establishment of the electronic configurations of the elements. Increase in our knowledge of the structure of the atom has, in turn, resulted in a modification of the statement of the periodic law, as we shall shortly see, and in changes in the form of the periodic table. A modern version of the periodic table is given on page 170.

THE ELECTRON

5. Early Evidence for the Existence of Electrons. One of the most important steps in the development of the theory of atomic structure was the discovery of the electron and the determination of its characteristics. The first experimental evidence that electrical charge is not a continuous fluid but is made up of discrete particles was obtained in 1833 by Michael Faraday in his studies of the conduction of an electric current by solutions of various substances. These studies will be discussed in a later chapter (p. 302), but it may be said here that it was G. J. Stoney (1874) and H. von Helmholtz (1881) who first clearly understood their theoretical significance, and stated the principle of the atomic nature of electricity. In 1891, Stoney proposed the name *electron* for the elementary unit of electrical charge.

6. Cathode Rays and the Photoelectric Effect. Of all the studies involving the electron, none has been more fruitful than those concerning the rays which emanate from the cathode (the negative electrode) when an electric discharge is passed through a tube containing a gas at low pressure, and hence are known as *cathode rays*. At ordinary pressures, gases are extremely poor conductors of electricity, and a very high voltage is therefore required to produce a discharge through a gas between two electrodes under these conditions. If the pressure of the gas in the tube is decreased, however, the conductivity rises rapidly. When the pressure has been reduced to the range of 0.01 to 0.001 mm. of mercury, the tube is filled with an invisible radiation, the presence of which is indicated by the fluorescence produced where it strikes the walls of the tube or a fluorescent screen placed in the tube.

That these rays proceed in straight lines from the negative electrode (i.e. the cathode) is indicated by the fact that an opaque object in the tube casts a sharply defined shadow in the fluorescence at the end of the tube opposite the cathode (Figure 8.3). If a small paddle wheel is properly suspended in

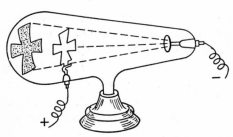

the path of a thin beam of the rays, their impact on the wheel causes it to rotate (Figure 8.4). These cathode rays, also, are deflected by an electric or a magnetic field in the manner indicated by Figures 8.5 and 8.6. All of these properties, as well as many others, indicate that cathode rays are composed of negatively charged particles of appreciable mass. When it

Fig. 8.3. Cathode rays proceed in straight lines.

became apparent that these particles are identical with the elementary particles of electricity postulated by Stoney, they were called electrons. It is important to note that the nature of these cathode-ray particles is independent both of the nature of the metal used for the cathode and of the nature of the residual gas in the tube.

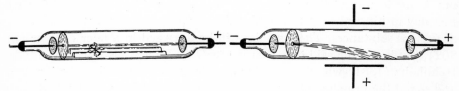

Fig. 8.4. Cathode rays have mass.   **Fig. 8.5.** Cathode rays are negatively charged.

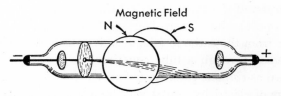

Fig. 8.6. Cathode rays are deflected by a magnetic field (magnetic field perpendicular to the paper).

Metals have a tendency to emit electrons under the influence of electromagnetic radiation; this phenomenon is known as the photoelectric effect. Only a few of the metals show this effect under the action of visible light, but many more exhibit it when irradiated with electromagnetic radiation of shorter wave length, and hence higher energy (see p. 157), such as ultra-violet light. Regardless, however, of these differences in the ease with which electrons are emitted, the electrons themselves, from the various metals, are identical.

7. The Charge and Mass of an Electron. The ratio of the charge on an electron to its mass was determined in 1897 by the English physicist Sir J. J. Thomson by investigation of the behavior of beams of electrons in electric and magnetic fields. Such a calculation is possible because the extent to which a beam of electrons is deflected under these conditions depends upon the charge on the electron, its mass, and the velocity with which the electron is moving. The student is referred to more advanced texts for the exact method by which the determination and calculations are made. The most recent work indicates that the ratio of the charge to mass of the electron is 1.759×10^8 coulombs per gram, irrespective of the source of the electrons. The famous American physicist R. A. Millikan showed by a series of brilliant experiments (1913) that the charge on a single electron is 1.602×10^{-19} coulomb. The mass of the electron is therefore equal to $1.602 \times 10^{-19}/1.759 \times 10^8$, or 9.107×10^{-28} gram. This weight is about 1/1837 of that of the hydrogen atom, and, therefore, corresponds to 0.0005486 atomic weight unit. Since the electron may be regarded as one atom of electricity, any particle bearing the same charge as the electron is said to have a unit negative charge, and one bearing a charge of the same magnitude but opposite in sign is said to have a unit positive charge.

We may conclude from the various experiments described in this section that one component common to all varieties of atoms is a negatively charged particle having the mass and charge indicated in the preceding paragraph, and known as the electron.

RADIOACTIVITY

8. Discovery of Radioactivity. No other single event offered such a stimulus to the study of the structure of the atom as did the discovery of the phenomenon of radioactivity, together with the series of brilliant researches which followed thereupon. In 1896, the French physicist Becquerel found that a photographic plate, which had been accidentally placed in a drawer with some uranium minerals, had become fogged. Since the plate had been wrapped in black paper to protect it from ordinary light, he concluded that uranium compounds give off a new form of radiation that is capable of penetrating paper and thin layers of other substances. Furthermore, he soon found that this radiation has the remarkable property of rendering the surrounding air a conductor of electricity. This was shown by means of a device known as an electroscope, a simple form of which is pictured in Figure 8.7. When the electroscope is charged, the gold leaf D and the rod C acquire like charges, which repel each other, and hence the leaf stands away from the rod as is shown in the figure. When a uranium compound is brought near the knob A, the leaf immediately falls back to its normal posi-

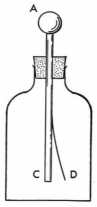

Fig. 8.7. An elec-
troscope.

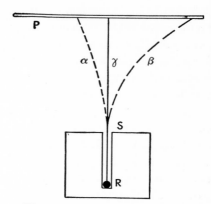

Fig. 8.8. Types of radiations from radioactive substances.

tion against the rod. This collapse indicates that the electroscope has been discharged; the charge has escaped to the ground through the air, which has been "ionized," i.e., atoms of which have been broken into positive and negative particles, by the radiations from the uranium compound. Uranium compounds, and other substances showing similar properties, are said to be *radioactive*. The electroscope has proved an especially valuable instrument for the study of the phenomenon of radioactivity, since it is possible to determine the intensity of the radioactivity of a given body from the rate at which it brings about the discharge of such a device.

In addition to the effects described above, radiations from radioactive substances have been found to be capable of causing certain minerals such as zinc sulfide or calcium fluoride to glow, or fluoresce; they also bring about certain chemical reactions (such as the change of molecular oxygen to ozone, page 206) which would not occur without excitation, and they have a destructive effect on plant and animal tissue.

9. Discovery of Radium. Shortly after the discovery of radioactivity, Marie Sklodowska Curie (1867–1934) and her husband, Pierre, took up the study of this new phenomenon and began a search for other radioactive substances.

They were soon able to prove that the radioactivity of any pure uranium compound, regardless of its type, is exactly proportional to the amount of uranium present. Yet it was found that certain uranium minerals, such as pitchblende, an impure uranium oxide, show a radioactivity several times that attributable to their uranium content. In fact, even after all the uranium has been extracted, pitchblende residues still exhibit strong radioactivity.

The Curies carefully separated large quantities of pitchblende into its constituents, and examined the radioactivity of each fraction. In the course of these experiments, a highly radioactive substance was found in the fraction which contained the bismuth. Marie Curie showed that this was a new element, which she named polonium in honor of her native country, Poland. Continuation of these experiments revealed that another fraction, containing the barium salts, was still more highly radioactive than the polonium fraction. Starting with a ton of pitchblende residues, the Curies, after a long and tedious process of extraction and fractional crystallization, obtained toward the end of 1898 a few hundredths of a gram of the bromide of an element which is at least a million times as radioactive as uranium. This new element they named *radium*; its chemical properties indicate that it is an alkaline earth metal (p. 657), its properties being very similar to those of barium. The element is considered in detail from this point of view in Chapter 35; it is the only element in its family, however, which exhibits radioactivity.

10. Radiations from Radioactive Substances. It soon became apparent that the radiations from a radioactive substance such as a uranium mineral are not homogeneous, but consist of three different types. This was first shown by the eminent British physicist Ernest Rutherford (1871–1937), who named the three types of radiation *alpha rays, beta rays,* and *gamma rays.* Rutherford placed a small amount of a radioactive substance R at the bottom of a small hole in a block of lead S (Figure 8.8). The radiations were absorbed by the lead, so that only the rays headed directly upward were able to emerge from the hole. These radiations were allowed to pass between the poles of a powerful magnet. A photographic plate P was placed above the magnet so that a record might be obtained of the points at which the rays impinged upon it. In Figure 8.8 the magnetic field is perpendicular to the plane of the paper. On development of the plate, it was found that one group of rays (the gamma rays) had not been deflected at all. Two other groups had been deflected from their original course in opposite directions and to different degrees. Such deflections could be accounted for only on the assumption that the two groups of rays bore electrical charges of opposite sign; those whose direction of deflection indicated positive charge were called alpha rays, those of negative charge, beta rays. The beta rays, as shown in the diagram, were found to be deflected to the greater extent. From data collected from experiments of this type it was possible to show that both alpha and beta rays consist of streams of material particles, and to calculate the masses and the charges of the individual alpha and beta particles which respectively compose these two types of radiations.

Alpha rays are emitted with varying initial velocities, depending upon the particular radioactive element from which the rays originate, but averaging somewhat less than one-tenth the velocity of light. The penetrating power of these rays is rather slight, however, for they are stopped by a few centimeters of air, or even by a sheet of paper. The mass of an alpha particle has been found to be four atomic weight units, and each particle has been found to carry a positive charge of twice the magnitude of the negative charge on the electron. Since helium has an atomic weight of four, it is logical to conclude that alpha particles are identical with helium atoms which have acquired double positive charges by the loss of two electrons per atom. It has been shown experimentally that these helium ions, as they are called, eventually pick up electrons to form ordinary helium atoms.

Though an individual alpha particle is, of course, far too small to be seen, it is nevertheless possible by direct visual means not only to demonstrate that alpha rays consist of streams of particles, but even to count these particles. A small sample of a radioactive substance is placed close to a screen coated with a fluorescent substance such as zinc sulfide. When the screen is viewed with a microscope, after the eyes of the observer have been rested for some minutes in a dark room, weak but distinct flashes of light may be detected as the individual alpha particles strike the screen.

Alpha particles have the greatest effect of any of the three types of radiation in rendering air a conductor of electricity. This ionizing effect is due to the fact that alpha particles, in passing through the air, occasionally knock electrons out of the molecules they encounter, producing ions which move under the influence of an electric field, and which therefore carry a current. The tracks of alpha particles (as well as those of other radiations capable of producing ionization) may be detected and photographed by means of the "cloud chamber" apparatus designed by C. T. R. Wilson. The apparatus is arranged so that the particles are given off in a chamber which contains air saturated with moisture, and which is fitted with a movable piston. If the volume of the chamber is suddenly increased by motion of the piston, the temperature drops slightly (p. 53), the air becomes supersaturated with moisture, and droplets condense on the ions formed along the path of the particle. Such trails of water droplets may be observed visually or photographed; Figures 8.17 and 8.18 (pp. 141–2) are examples of photographs of fog tracks obtained in this manner.

Beta rays are emitted with very great velocities, in some cases as high as 180,000 miles per second, which approaches the speed of light. They have greater penetrating power than do alpha rays, though they are stopped by a sheet of aluminum 1 cm. in thickness. Because of their small masses, however, they are not so effective in bringing about the ionization of gases through which they pass, and hence the tracks which they leave in the cloud chamber are much less distinct. Measurements of the charge and mass of the particles composing beta rays indicate that these particles are identical with those composing cathode rays, and are therefore electrons. Thus, they have a mass 1/1838 of that of the hydrogen atom, and a unit negative charge.

The fact that gamma rays are not deflected in either an electrical or a magnetic field indicates that they are not composed of charged particles as are alpha and beta rays. Rather, it appears that gamma rays consist of electromagnetic radiations analogous to light waves, except that they are of much shorter wave length, and hence of much greater energy and penetrating power. Careful experiments have shown that, with a few exceptions, a single radioactive element does not emit both alpha and beta particles, but only one or the other of these types. When both alpha and beta particles are emitted, more than one radioactive element must be present. Gamma rays, however, are emitted along with either alpha or beta radiation. It appears that gamma radiation arises as a result of internal readjustments in the atom, with consequent loss in energy, which follow the loss of an alpha or of a beta particle.

11. Atomic Disintegration. A gram of radium has been found to give off billions of alpha particles in a second, and to evolve heat at the rate of nearly 140 cal. per hr. Rutherford and Soddy, in 1902, made the suggestion that the emission of alpha and beta particles is a result of the spontaneous disintegration of atoms of radioactive substances. Rutherford was the first to show that radium and its compounds slowly evolve a gas which he called radium emanation (now known as radon), and that this gas is the residue left when radium atoms emit one alpha particle per atom. This emanation does not combine with other elements; but it was found to be highly radioactive and to deposit a solid radioactive residue on bodies with which it comes in contact. Furthermore, every known uranium ore has been found to contain radium in amounts proportional to the uranium content (about 1 part of radium to 3,000,000 parts of uranium), and also to contain appreciable amounts of the nonradioactive element lead. Rutherford and Soddy concluded from these facts that uranium is the starting point in a series of radio active transformations. Their studies revealed that the distintegration proceeds in steps producing a number of elements in succession; each of these is formed by the loss of an alpha particle or a beta particle, as the case may be, by the preceding element, and in turn loses one of these types of particles to produce the next element in the series. That these disintegrations are entirely different from the ordinary chemical changes which matter undergoes, is evident from the fact that the former are entirely unaffected by external conditions. Nothing we can do alters the rate of a radioactive distintegration; it proceeds no more rapidly at white heat than at the temperature of liquid air. Furthermore, the disintegration goes on at the same rate regardless of whether the radioactive element is in the free or in the combined state; i.e., a bit of radium metal has the same radioactivity as does an amount of radium bromide containing the same quantity of radium.

The rates at which the various steps in the disintegration of uranium take place differ widely. Some of the products remain practically unchanged over millions of years, while others disappear almost completely in a few seconds. There is a simple law, however, also discovered by Rutherford, which describes these rates, namely: a certain constant fraction of any sample of a radioactive element undergoes change in a unit of time. In other words, the number of atoms that disintegrate per unit of time is a constant fraction of the total number of atoms present. Thus, as the total amount diminishes because of the change, the amount changing during each unit of time, being a constant fraction of the residue, must be less than for the preceding unit. Hence, the time required for the complete disintegration of any one sample would be infinitely long. It is convenient, therefore, to designate the rate at which an element disintegrates in terms of its *half-life period*, i.e., the time required for the disintegration of half the atoms of that element in any sample. This value is always constant for a given radioactive element.

In Table 8.1 are listed the elements which are formed in the radioactive disintegration series which begins with uranium. Listed also are the approximate atomic weights and the half-life periods of each element along with the kind of particle it emits in its disintegration. Two other somewhat similar series are known; these begin with thorium and protactinium, respectively, and likewise end with lead.

An examination of this table reveals some very interesting facts. In the first place one may note that the element uranium appears twice in the series, the element thorium also twice, polonium three times, lead three times, and bismuth twice. Each time one of these elements appears in the series it has an atomic weight different from those of its other appearances. Furthermore, in general, the atomic weights listed in Table 8.1 do not agree with the atomic weights determined for the elements as they occur in the earth's crust and listed in the periodic system (Figure 8.1). It is apparent, therefore, that the identity of an element (as determined by its chemical and physical properties) is not primarily a function of its atomic weight. Furthermore, it is clear that all the atoms of a given element are not necessarily alike, but that a given element may be made up of several different kinds of atoms *differing in their atomic weights*. Varieties of atoms having different atomic weights but closely similar chemical and physical properties, i.e., belonging to the same element, are called *isotopes*. If we wish to distinguish among the various isotopes of an element, we write the approximate atomic weight (commonly called the mass number) of the isotope we wish to denote as a superscript at the right of the symbol of the element, thus: U^{235} (see p. 142).

The lack of primary dependence of physical and chemical properties of elements on their atomic weights is further emphasized by the presence in Table 8.1 of atoms of closely similar atomic weights but having distinctly different properties, i.e., characteristic of different elements. Such varieties of atoms are called *isobars*.

Finally, we note that the loss of an alpha particle by an element results in a new element two places to the left in the Mendeleeff table, whereas the loss of a beta particle produces an element one place to the right. The modern theory of atomic structure provides an explanation for these rather striking facts.

Table 8.1

Name of Element	Approximate Atomic Weight	Symbol	Half-life Period	Particle Emitted
Uranium	238	U^{238}	4.51×10^9 years	α
Thorium	234	Th^{234}	24.10 days	β
Protactinium	234	Pa^{234}	1.175 minutes	β
Uranium	234	U^{234}	2.48×10^5 years	α
Thorium	230	Th^{230}	8.0×10^4 years	α
Radium	226	Ra^{226}	1622 years	α
Radon	222	Rn^{222}	3.825 days	α
Polonium	218	Po^{218}	3.05 minutes	α
Lead	214	Pb^{214}	26.8 minutes	β
Bismuth	214	Bi^{214}	19.7 minutes	β
Polonium	214	Po^{214}	1.64×10^{-4} second	α
Lead	210	Pb^{210}	19.4 years	β
Bismuth	210	Bi^{210}	5.0 days	β
Polonium	210	Po^{210}	138.40 days	α
Lead	206	Pb^{206}	. . . .	None

12. Significance of Radioactivity. The fact that certain elements undergo spontaneous disintegration constitutes the most convincing evidence of the complex nature of the atom, and, as we shall see, the facts accumulated in the study of this phenomenon have been of great value in the development of the present theory of atomic structure. Above all, however, the discovery of radioactivity so fired the imagination of many scientists throughout the world that a new and successful assault on the hitherto impregnable citadel of the atom was begun. Speaking literally, radioactive substances provided the artillery for one of the important phases of this assault.

THE NUCLEAR ATOM

13. Rutherford's Experiments. Although knowledge of the properties of the electron and of the phenomenon of radioactive disintegration made it evident that atoms could not be homogeneous and indivisible, but must have a complex structure, before 1910 no acceptable picture of the structure of the atom had been proposed.

In 1911, Lord Rutherford published the results of a series of experiments from which he was able to draw far-reaching conclusions. He had been studying the effects of interposing a very thin metal foil between a source of alpha particles such as Po^{210}, and a fluorescent screen upon which the impact of the alpha particles could be observed. He found that the placing of such a barrier in the path of a beam of these alpha particles had surprisingly little effect, for almost all of them passed through the foil with no, or almost no, deflection. A very few particles, however, were deflected through wide angles. For example, using a gold foil 0.00004 cm. thick, he found that one alpha particle in 20,000 was deflected through an angle greater than 90°. On the basis of a series of such experiments Rutherford reached the following conclusions:

1. Since most of the alpha particles pass through the foil undeflected, the volume occupied by an atom must consist largely of empty space (Figure 8.9).

2. Since some alpha particles, which are positively charged and relatively high in mass, are strongly deflected, there must be present within each atom a heavy, positively charged body. (An electron, with its mass of only 0.0005486 atomic weight unit, would not appreciably affect the course of the heavier alpha particle.) Since so few of the alpha particles are deflected, it must be assumed, however, that the volume occupied by this heavy body is only a minute fraction of the total volume of the atom.

In terms of these conclusions, Rutherford outlined what has been called the nuclear theory of the atom, in which he assumed that most of the mass of the atom is concentrated in a minute positively charged body at its center called the *nucleus*. Distributed about this nucleus at relatively large distances are electrons sufficient in number to balance the positive charge on the nucleus. Rutherford assumed these electrons to be revolving about the nucleus at high velocities, the centrifugal force resulting from this motion balancing the electrostatic attraction of the positive nucleus for the negative electrons. These rapidly moving electrons have the effect of a spherical cloud of negative charge about the nucleus.

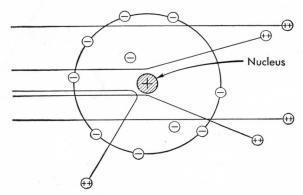

Fig. 8.9. Bombardment of an atom with alpha particles.

Calculations based upon such bombardment experiments as have been described showed that whereas atomic radii are usually of the order of 10^{-8} cm., the nuclei of the atoms are of the order of only 10^{-12} to 10^{-13} cm. in radius. From other considerations it is estimated that the radius of an electron is also of the order of 10^{-13} cm. Based on this value, calculations can be made which indicate that less than 10^{-12}, or one-trillionth, of the volume of the atom is actually occupied by material particles.

From calculations based upon additional data from this same series of experiments, Rutherford showed that the number of positive charges on the nucleus of an atom is, at least in many cases, somewhere near one-half the atomic weight of the element. The number representing the position of an element in the periodic system, allowances having been made for vacant spaces, had previously been given the name *atomic number*. Since in many cases this number is about one-half the atomic weight, A. van den Broek made the suggestion, in 1913, that the atomic number of an element is equal to the number of positive charges on the nucleus of its atom. This hypothesis was soon confirmed by the brilliant work of the young British physicist H. G. J. Moseley (p. 130).

14. X-Rays. In 1895, the German physicist **W. K. Roentgen** discovered that when a beam of electrons of high velocity (cathode rays) is allowed to strike a target as is shown in Figure 8.10, a previously unknown type of radiation is produced. This radiation consists of electromagnetic waves; i.e., waves of the same nature as visible light. Since it is of much shorter wave length than light, however, it is capable of penetrating many objects opaque to ordinary light. These waves are called *x-rays*.

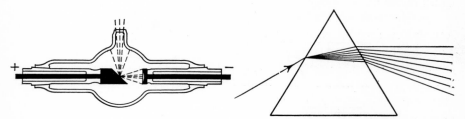

Fig. 8.10.   An x-ray tube. (From Hopkins, *General Chemistry for Colleges,* D. C. Heath and Co.)

Fig. 8.11.   Refraction of a beam of light by a prism.

It is a familiar fact that a beam of visible light can be separated into its various component wave lengths, i.e., its spectrum can be obtained, by the use of a glass prism or a ruled diffraction grating. By the use of methods analogous to, but different from those used for visible light, x-ray spectra are obtained; these spectra cannot, of course, be seen directly, as can spectra of visible light, but can be recorded photographically.

Study of the spectra of the x-rays given off when a number of different substances are used as targets in x-ray tubes reveals that in each case there are really two spectra: (1) a continuous band, the lower limit of wave length of which is dependent upon the speed of the electrons striking the target, and (2) a spectrum composed of a few lines which are characteristic of the element or elements composing the target. It is the second type, only, which is of significance to this discussion.

15. Moseley's Experiments. Henry G. J. Moseley (1887–1915), in 1913 and 1914, studied the characteristic x-ray spectra of the then known elements of atomic number between 13 (aluminum) and 79 (gold). These spectra are all relatively simple and show approximately the same pattern of lines for all elements. On comparing the wave lengths of corresponding lines in the various spectra, however, Moseley found that they vary progressively with increasing atomic number, i.e., with the order of the elements as arranged in the periodic system. This is illustrated in Figure 8.12. He found, moreover, that there is an inverse linear relationship between the atomic numbers of the element and the square roots of the wave lengths of corresponding lines in their x-ray spectra. Since the frequency of any electromagnetic wave is equal to the velocity of light divided by the wave length, the square roots of the frequencies of corresponding lines in the x-ray spectra of the elements are in direct linear relationship to their atomic numbers. This is shown in Figure 8.13, in which it is evident that if the square roots of the frequencies are plotted against the atomic numbers a straight line is obtained. It is therefore apparent that there is in the atom a quantity of fundamental importance which increases by uniform steps as one passes from one element to the next

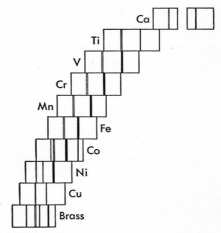

Fig. 8.12. Diagram of characteristic x-ray spectra.

in the periodic system. Moseley reached the conclusion that the suggestion of van den Broek (p. 129) had been correct, for in the paper in which he published these results in 1914 he wrote, "the atomic number of the element

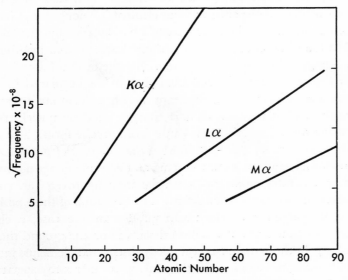

Fig. 8.13. Variation of frequency of x-rays with atomic number.

is identified with the number of positive units of electricity contained in the atomic nucleus"; and further, "the order of atomic numbers (as established by these x-ray studies) is the same as that of atomic weights except where the latter disagrees with the order of the chemical properties" (p. 118). Thus we see that the fundamental property of an atom which determines its chemical and most of its physical properties is the number of positive charges on its nucleus, or the number of electrons surrounding the nucleus in the neutral atom, since these two numbers are equal.

16. Atomic Numbers and the Periodic System. Since it is the atomic number which determines the chemical and most of the physical properties of an element, it is apparent that all atoms having the same atomic number, even though they may differ somewhat in atomic weight, should be considered as atoms of the same element. We have previously defined isotopes as varieties of an element having the same chemical properties but different atomic weights. We may now define this term more precisely as applying to varieties of atoms having the same number of charges on their nuclei (i.e., the same atomic numbers), but different atomic weights. Thus Pb^{214}, Pb^{210}, and Pb^{206} all have the atomic number 82, and hence are isotopes of lead, indistinguishable from one another by chemical means. We now know that almost all the elements, even the non-radioactive ones, consist of mixtures of isotopes. We shall return to this point when we discuss the structure of the nucleus, but it is important that we recognize now that the characteristic of an atom which determines to what element it belongs is not its atomic weight but its atomic number. This fact is emphasized by the finding of Moseley that the discrepancies of the periodic law as stated by Mendeleeff (namely the unexplained necessity for reversing the order of atomic weights of certain pairs of elements in order that they might be placed in accordance with their chemical properties) disappear when the atoms are arranged in order of increasing number of unit charges on their nuclei. We may therefore now restate the periodic law in a more precise form: *The properties of the elements are periodic functions of the numbers of positive charges on their nuclei.* Since all atoms of the same atomic number are atoms of the same element, the total number of elements from hydrogen (at. no. $= 1$) through nobelium (at. no. $= 102$) is limited to 102; each of these positions is now occupied by a known element. In more than one case, a claim of the discovery of a new element has been disproved on the ground that there is no place for it in the system. Several newly discovered elements, including hafnium and rhenium, were identified by means of their x-ray spectra.

17. Atomic Numbers and the Radioactive Disintegration Series. We have already seen (p. 127) that when an atom of a radioactive element loses an alpha particle, it is transformed into an atom of an element two places to the left in the periodic system; whereas the loss of a beta particle yields an atom of an element one place to the right in the periodic system. Since we have learned that the positions of the elements in the periodic system are determined by their atomic numbers and not by their atomic weights, this phenomenon is not difficult to understand. The loss by the nucleus of an atom of a doubly charged apha particle must reduce the mass by four atomic weight units and the total positive charge on the nucleus by two units, yielding an atom of an element two places to the left in the periodic system. Likewise, the loss of a negatively charged beta particle by the nucleus must increase the positive charge on the nucleus by one unit, thus yielding an atom of an element one place to the right in the periodic system, and of approximately the same atomic weight.

It is now easy to understand, also, why several radioactive isotopes of the same element, e.g., Po^{218}, Po^{214}, and Po^{210}, can have the same chemical properties and yet differ in their radioactive behavior. As long as they have the same total number of positive charges on their nuclei they are varieties of the same element, chemically speaking; their radioactive behavior, however, is a function of the internal structure of their nuclei. It is possible, and, in fact quite common, for two atoms of the same total charge to have different nuclear structures, and therefore to exhibit quite different radioactive properties.

THE NUCLEUS

18. Positive Rays. Let us now return briefly to our discussion of the phenomena observed when an electric discharge takes place through a tube containing a gas at low pressure. In 1886, E. Goldstein found that in a tube having a perforated disc as cathode, if the pressure is not too low, colored rays may be seen to emerge from the side of the cathode opposite to the anode. This is illustrated in Figure 8.14.

It thus appears that these luminous rays move toward the cathode, rather than in the opposite direction, and that they must therefore consist of positively rather than negatively charged particles. Moreover, studies of these particles by methods to be described below indicate that they are not all identical in nature; unlike the electrons which make up cathode rays, these positive particles have charges and masses which vary with the identity of the residual gas in the tube. It would thus appear that, whereas the cathode rays

actually start from the cathode, these positive rays originate in the space between the two electrodes. These facts support the now well established view
that these positive rays consist of the positive residues or ions which are left
when one or more of the electrons are knocked out of an atom or molecule
of a gas in the tube by the stream of electrons from the cathode. The study
of such positive rays has been of profound importance in the development of
the theory of the structure of the atom.

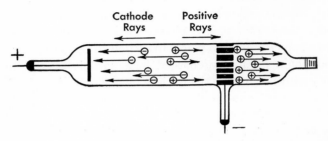

Fig. 8.14.   Positive rays.

By the use of methods similar to those previously employed in the study
of cathode ray particles (p. 121), the ratio of charge to mass ($e:m$) was
determined for the particles constituting the positive rays obtained with
various residual gases in the discharge tube. The largest value of $e:m$ for
any positive ray particle was that found when hydrogen was used in the
tube. This means, of course, that if we assume the charge (e) to have the
same value in each case, the mass (m) of the positive ray particle obtained
in the hydrogen tube is less than that for any other gas. Careful study has
shown that such is indeed the case, and that this positive particle is one of
the fundamental particles of matter. Its charge is equal in magnitude, but
opposite in sign, to that of the electron, and its mass is 1836 times that of
the electron, or 1.0073 atomic weight units; this special type of particle
has been given the name *proton*. The simplest of all atoms, the hydrogen
atom, consists of a proton and an electron.

19. The Mass Spectrograph. The study of positive ray particles has yielded
a great deal of information with regard to atomic structure during the past
quarter century. The technique of measuring the ratio $e:m$ for positive ray
particles has been highly refined by F. W. Aston and others, and very
accurate data of this type have been obtained for a large number of substances. If we assume that the charge on a positive ray particle is always
either equal in magnitude to that on the electron, or some small integral

multiple of it, the values of the masses of such particles may be determined from these data.

The apparatus which Aston used in these studies is known as the mass spectrograph; it is illustrated in Figure 8.15. A thin beam of positive rays is obtained when the rays from a discharge tube are allowed to pass through slits A_1 and A_2. This beam next passes between the oppositely charged plates B^+ and B^-. All the particles are, of course, deflected toward the negatively charged plate; but because of differences in charge, mass, and velocity, the angle of deflection varies and the beam is spread out into a wide band. A portion of this band emerges through the small opening in C and then passes between the poles of a powerful electromagnet D. The field of this magnet is perpendicular to the paper, and the polarity such that the beam of positive particles is bent in the opposite direction to, but in the same plane as, the bending caused by the electric field. When the relative positions of the various parts of the apparatus and the strengths of the electric and magnetic fields have been properly adjusted, all the particles having the same $e:m$ ratio are brought to a focus in a single sharp line on the photographic plate E. From the location of each line on the photographic plate, the mass of the particular variety of particles to which it corresponds may be accurately calculated. The portion of the beam focused on the plate can be altered by variation of the strengths of the deflecting fields, so that the whole beam may eventually be studied.

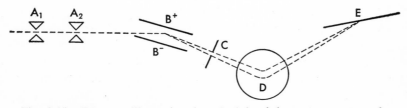

Fig. 8.15.   Diagram illustrating the principle of the mass spectrograph.

The masses of the positive ions produced by practically all the elements have been determined by means of the mass spectrograph, and it has been found that in most cases the element is made up not of a single type of atom, but of two or more types, of the same atomic number but different atomic weights: i.e., the element is made up of two or more isotopes. Thus, when chlorine is examined by this method two separate lines are obtained, corresponding to particles having masses of approximately 35 and 37, respectively. Not only does the mass spectrograph reveal the number of the isotopes composing an element and the mass of each, but also, by an examination of

Table 8.2

Naturally Occurring Isotopes* of the Elements

At. No.	Symbol	Approx. At. Wts. (Mass Numbers)	At. No.	Symbol	Approx. At. Wts. (Mass Numbers)
1	H	1, 2	51	Sb	121, 123
2	He	3, 4	52	Te	120, 122, 123, 124, 125, 126,
3	Li	6, 7			128, 130
4	Be	9	53	I	127
5	B	10, 11	54	Xe	124, 126, 128, 129, 130, 131,
6	C	12, 13			132, 134, 136
7	N	14, 15	55	Cs	133
8	O	16, 17, 18	56	Ba	130, 132, 134, 135, 136, 137,
9	F	19			138
10	Ne	20, 21, 22	57	La	138, 139
11	Na	23	58	Ce	136, 138, 140, 142
12	Mg	24, 25, 26	59	Pr	141
13	Al	27	60	Nd	142, 143, 144, 145, 146, 148,
14	Si	28, 29, 30			150
15	P	31	62	Sm	144, 147, 148, 149, 150, 152,
16	S	32, 33, 34, 36			154
17	Cl	35, 37	63	Eu	151, 153
18	Ar	36, 38, 40	64	Gd	152, 154, 155, 156, 157, 158,
19	K	39, 40, 41			160
20	Ca	40, 42, 43, 44, 46	65	Tb	159
21	Sc	45	66	Dy	156, 158, 160, 161, 162, 163,
22	Ti	46, 47, 48, 49, 50			164
23	V	50, 51	67	Ho	165
24	Cr	50, 52, 53, 54	68	Er	162, 164, 166, 167, 168, 170
25	Mn	55	69	Tm	169
26	Fe	54, 56, 57, 58	70	Yb	168, 170, 171, 172, 173, 174,
27	Co	59			176
28	Ni	58, 60, 61, 62, 64	71	Lu	175, 176
29	Cu	63, 65	72	Hf	174, 176, 177, 178, 179, 180
30	Zn	64, 66, 67, 68, 70	73	Ta	181
31	Ga	69, 71	74	W	180, 182, 183, 184, 186
32	Ge	70, 72, 73, 74, 76	75	Re	185, 187
33	As	75	76	Os	184, 186, 187, 188, 189, 190,
34	Se	74, 76, 77, 78, 80, 82			192
35	Br	79, 81	77	Ir	191, 193
36	Kr	78, 80, 82, 83, 84, 86	78	Pt	192, 194, 195, 196, 198
37	Rb	85, 87	79	Au	197
38	Sr	84, 86, 87, 88	80	Hg	196, 198, 199, 200, 201, 202,
39	Y	89			204
40	Zr	90, 91, 92, 94, 96	81	Tl	203, 205
41	Nb	93	82	Pb	204, 206, 207, 208
42	Mo	92, 94, 95, 96, 97, 98, 100	83	Bi	209, 210, 211, 212, 214, 215
44	Ru	96, 98, 99, 100, 101, 102,	84	Po	214, 215, 216, 218
		104	85	At	218, 219
45	Rh	103	86	Rn	219, 220, 222
46	Pd	102, 104, 105, 106, 108, 110	87	Fr	223
47	Ag	107, 109	88	Ra	223, 224, 226, 228
48	Cd	106, 108, 110, 111, 112, 113,	89	Ac	227, 228
		114, 116	90	Th	227, 228, 230, 231, 232, 234
49	In	113, 115	91	Pa	231, 234
50	Sn	112, 114, 115, 116, 117, 118,	92	U	234, 235, 238
		119, 120, 122, 124			

* Either stable or having long half-lives, or derived from radioactive isotopes that have geologically long half-lives.

the relative intensities of the lines corresponding to the several isotopes, the relative abundance of each isotope may be determined.

We shall soon see that the massive part of the atom, i.e., the nucleus, is made up of particles having masses of approximately 1 a.w.u., and the weights of individual atoms, therefore, are approximately integers. The main reason, though not the only one, for the fact that the atomic weights of many of the elements are not whole numbers is that these atomic weights represent weighted averages of the masses of several different isotopes. Thus, the atomic weight of chlorine, 35.457, represents the average weight of a mixture of about 3 parts of the isotope of mass about 35 to 1 part of the isotope of mass about 37. Since the average atomic weight of an element, except in a few cases, is the same regardless of the source of the element, it is apparent that the proportion of the isotopes composing the element is constant, unless special measures are taken to bring about separation of the isotopes. A notable exception to this statement is found in lead from radioactive and non-radioactive sources (p. 127). The reason for this divergence is that the lead occurring as end-product of a radioactive disintegration series consists of a single isotope only, whereas ordinary lead is a mixture of several isotopes, which, however, are always present in the same proportions. A list of the naturally occurring isotopes so far discovered is given in Table 8.2.

Since refinements in the mass spectrograph have made it possible to determine not only the masses of the isotopes of an element but also the proportions of each isotope present, it is possible to obtain average atomic weights from mass spectrographic data. Such determinations have yielded results which agree well with purely chemical determinations (p. 88) and which, in some cases, are even more accurate. The physical scale of atomic weights thus derived is commonly based upon the assignment of the value 16.0000 to the mass of the most abundant isotope of oxygen, whereas the chemical scale is based on the assignment of the value 16.0000 a.w.u. to the *average* atomic weight of oxygen. Thus, in the comparison of atomic weights on the two scales, a slight adjustment must be made; to convert atomic weights on the physical scale to the usual chemical atomic weights, it is necessary to divide by 1.00027.

Very recently, the principle of the mass spectrograph has been applied to the actual separation of isotopes on a large scale. This application will be referred to later in the chapter (p. 151).

20. The Neutron and Nuclear Structure. With the single exception of the isotope of hydrogen having a mass of 1, all the atoms have more units of mass than of positive charge in their nuclei. It is therefore evident that the nuclei of these atoms must contain fundamental particles other than protons, and in 1932 the English physicist J. Chadwick discovered a third type of fundamental sub-atomic particle. He was able to show that the highly penetrating radiation emitted by metallic beryllium under bombardment by alpha particles, consists of streams of particles having a mass of approximately 1 atomic weight unit (1.0087 a.w.u.), and carrying no charge whatever. This type of particle was given the name *neutron*. Although the internal structure of the atomic nucleus still remains a good deal of a mystery, the hypothesis that it is composed of protons and neutrons is now fairly generally accepted. It is accordingly assumed that an atom of approximate atomic weight (mass number) A and atomic number Z has a nucleus composed of Z protons and $A - Z$ neutrons. According to this view, the nucleus of the isotope of lithium of mass number 7 consists of 3 protons and 4 neutrons, while the isotope of lithium of mass number 6 contains 3 protons also, but only 3 neutrons. The isotope of hydrogen of mass number 1 has a nucleus consisting of 1 proton only, whereas the isotope of hydrogen having a mass number 2 has 1 proton and 1 neutron in its nucleus. The oxygen isotope having a mass number 16 has a nucleus containing 8 protons and

Table 8.3

Symbol	Atomic Number	Mass Number (a.w.u.)	Nucleus protons	neutrons	Electrons
H	1	1	1		1
He	2	4	2	2	2
Li	3	7	3	4	3
Be	4	9	4	5	4
B	5	11	5	6	5
C	6	12	6	6	6
N	7	14	7	7	7
O	8	16	8	8	8
F	9	19	9	10	9
Ne	10	20	10	10	10
Na	11	23	11	12	11
Mg	12	24	12	12	12
Al	13	27	13	14	13
Si	14	28	14	14	14
P	15	31	15	16	15
S	16	32	16	16	16
Cl	17	35	17	18	17
Ar	18	40	18	22	18

8 neutrons, while that of mass 17 has 8 protons and 9 neutrons. Thus we see that the nuclei of different isotopes of a given element differ only in the number of neutrons they contain; the nuclei of all isotopes of a given element have the same number of protons (the same positive charge), and the atoms therefore have the same chemical properties. The number of protons and of neutrons in the nucleus, and the number of electrons in the atom, for the most abundant isotope of each of the first eighteen elements in the periodic system, are given in Table 8.3.

The student may wonder how, if the nuclei of all atoms are made up of protons and neutrons alone, it is possible for beta particles (electrons) to be emitted by radioactive atoms. The answer to this question is that a neutron may, under certain conditions, spontaneously decompose into a proton and an electron which is emitted as a beta particle. Such a change would, of course, increase the nuclear charge by one unit, without appreciably changing the mass.

21. The Interconvertibility of Mass and Energy. Since all atomic nuclei are made up of protons and neutrons, it might be expected that the atomic weight of any atomic species would be exactly equal to the sum of the masses of the protons and neutrons in the nucleus of that variety of atom. The accurate determination of the atomic weights of isotopes by the mass spectrograph reveals, however, that this is not the case; instead, it is found that the mass of any nucleus (except, of course, that of a hydrogen atom) is a little less than the sum of the masses of its ultimate components. Let us consider, for example, the helium nucleus, which, as may be seen from Table 8.3, consists of 2 protons and 2 neutrons. The sum of the masses of these particles is $(2 \times 1.0073$ a.w.u.$) + (2 \times 1.0087$ a.w.u$) = 4.0320$ a.w.u. The mass of the helium nucleus, however, is actually only 4.0017 a.w.u., which fact indicates that in the assembling of such a nucleus from two protons and two neutrons, 0.0303 a.w.u. is lost.

The clue to the explanation of this somewhat startling conclusion, which is completely at variance with the law of conservation of mass, had already been provided in 1905 by Albert Einstein, who had stated, in his theory of relativity, that mass and energy are interconvertible, and had derived the equation $E = mc^2$, where E is energy in ergs, m is mass in grams, and c is the velocity of light $(3 \times 10^{10}$ cm. per second$)$. Recent developments in chemistry and physics have abundantly confirmed this relationship.

Now, therefore, we have no choice but to recognize that the laws of conservation of mass and of conservation of energy are not strictly true; in their place we must substitute the more general principle of the conservation of mass energy. Since the value of c is so large, it follows that changes involving an appreciable loss in mass must be accompanied by the release of tremendous quantities of energy. The formation of a single gram-atom of helium from protons and neutrons, for example, would liberate almost 650,000,000,000 cal. of heat, or enough to raise the temperature of 6,500,000 l. of water from 0° C. to the boiling point. It is now generally believed that a series of nuclear changes leading eventually to the formation of helium from hydrogen is the means by which the energy of the sun is maintained. Furthermore, it is obvious that if the conversion of mass into energy could be brought about at will by means of man-made devices, it would provide an almost limitless source of energy in unimaginable quantities. The realization of this apparently fantastic possibility will be discussed later in this chapter.

22. The Packing Effect. The loss of mass which always results from the union of protons and neutrons to form a stable atomic nucleus, and which is known as the *packing effect,* is equivalent, as has just been indicated, to the energy which would be released during the combination of these constituent particles. Since this is the quantity of energy that would have to be supplied in order to disrupt the nucleus completely, it is known as the binding energy of the nucleus (Fig. 8.16). The binding energy, commonly expressed in millions of electron-volts per nucleon (proton or neutron) is greatest for the nuclei of elements of atomic weights between 40 and 100, and gradually falls off toward both ends of the periodic system.

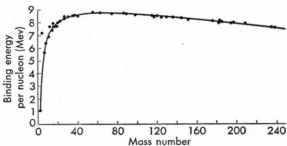

Fig. 8.16. Binding energies of the elements (energy per nuclear particle).

It may be noted that the atomic weights listed in Table 8.3 and in the accompanying discussion are not exact, but are given as whole numbers. Each of these integers, which are used in the calculation of the number of neutrons in the nucleus, is that nearest to the actual atomic weight of the isotope in question. Such integers are called *mass numbers.*

23. The Positron. In connection with the question of the interconvertibility of mass and energy, it is interesting to note that the American physicist C. D. Anderson discovered, in 1932, that when cosmic rays, a form of electromagnetic radiation apparently originating in interstellar space and having very great penetrating power, were allowed to pass through a sheet of lead, two types of particles were obtained. From the photographs of the tracks they produced in a cloud chamber under the influence of a strong magnetic field (Figure 8.17), it was shown that one of these types was the negative electron with which we are familiar. The other type was soon shown to have the same mass as the electron and the same amount of charge; the charge in this case is positive, however, and these particles were named *positrons*. Other

highly penetrating electromagnetic waves, such as gamma rays, likewise produce positrons and electrons when absorbed by metals. However, positrons have a very short existence (probably of the order of 10^{-8} second), since they quickly unite with electrons to produce electromagnetic radiation. We have here an outstanding example of the conversion of energy into mass followed by the reconversion of mass into energy. In 1955 the formation of a particle having the mass of a proton, but carrying a negative charge, was announced. This particle, called an *antiproton*, has, like the positron, a very short existence, for it unites with a proton to give electromagnetic radiation.

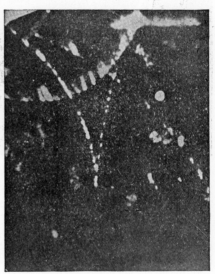

Fig. 8.17. Formation of electron-positron pairs by gamma radiation (cloud chamber photograph). [From Curie and Joliot, *Le Journal de Physique et Le Radium*, Series 7, vol. 4, p. 494 (1933).]

24. Artificial Disintegration of Atoms.
About twenty years after the discovery of radioactivity, the first of a series of experiments was begun which have much further broadened man's knowledge of the atom, for it was in the year 1919 that Rutherford, who had already contributed so greatly toward the understanding of natural radioactive disintegrations, carried out the first artificial transmutation of one element into another. In that year he found that when high energy alpha particles from Po^{210} are projected into a space containing nitrogen gas, an occasional alpha particle collides with a nitrogen nucleus in such a

manner as to produce a proton and an isotope of oxygen of mass number 17
(Figure 8.18). It has become customary to represent such a change by the
following type of equation:

$$_7N^{14} + {}_2He^4 \rightarrow {}_8O^{17} + {}_1H^1$$

Fig. 8.18. Formation of O^{17} by bombardment of N^{14} with alpha particles (cloud
chamber photograph). The heavy branched line is the path of the O^{17} nucleus; the
light line is the path of the proton.

$$_7N^{14} + {}_2He^4 \rightarrow {}_8O^{17} + {}_1H^1$$

(From Rutherford, Chadwick, and Ellis, *Radiations from Radioactive Substances*,
Cambridge University Press, England. By permission of The Macmillan Company,
New York.)

The subscripts preceding the symbols are atomic numbers, while the super-
scripts following the symbols are mass numbers. It should be noted that the
sums of the atomic numbers and of the mass numbers, respectively, are the
same on both sides of the equation. It should furthermore be thoroughly
understood that this equation does not represent an ordinary chemical reaction. We are dealing here with the interaction and disintegration of the
nuclei of the atoms involved, whereas, as we shall see, ordinary chemical
reactions involve only the outermost electrons. The particles represented in
the preceding equation, therefore, are atomic nuclei, not atoms. Rutherford
was able to prove that this transmutation had taken place by a comparison
of the tracks produced, in a Wilson cloud chamber apparatus such as that
described on p. 124, by the incident alpha particle and by the resulting

oxygen nucleus and proton. The observation of such tracks in the cloud chamber has been one of the most important experimental procedures in the study of nuclear transmutations, for, until recently, the quantities of products have always been insufficient to be detected chemically.

After Rutherford's initial experiment, the effects of bombardment with alpha rays from radioactive atoms upon many of the elements of lower atomic number were tried, and it was found that the atoms of Be, N, F, Na, Al, P, Ne, Mg, Si, S, Cl, Ar, and K all undergo transmutation into other types of atoms. However, because of the higher positive charges on their nuclei, the atoms of the heavier elements resisted the attack of the positively charged alpha particles. There are, therefore, two methods of approach to the solution of the problem of the artificial disintegration of the heavier elements: (1) the use of uncharged particles in the bombardment of the atoms; (2) the use of alpha particles, or other positively charged particles, of higher kinetic energies than those available from naturally radioactive materials. Both of these methods have been used.

It has already been stated that neutrons, particles having a mass number of 1 and an electrical charge of zero, are obtained when beryllium is bombarded with alpha particles from radioactive materials (p. 138). This nuclear reaction may be represented by the equation

$$_4Be^9 + {_2He^4} \rightarrow {_6C^{12}} + {_0n^1}$$

Since these neutrons are emitted with high velocity, a tube containing a beryllium salt and a little radon yields a powerful beam of neutrons which, because they are not repelled by the positively charged nuclei, are capable of interacting with a great many varieties of atoms. In fact, nearly all of the known elements, in one or another of their isotopic forms, interact with neutrons. More types of distintegration have been produced by neutron bombardment than in any other manner. The following equations are representative of the main types of nuclear change which result from such bombardment.

$$_7N^{14} + {_0n^1} \rightarrow {_6C^{14}} + {_1H^1}$$

$$_8O^{16} + {_0n^1} \rightarrow {_6C^{13}} + {_2He^4}$$

$$_1H^1 + {_0n^1} \rightarrow {_1H^2} + \gamma \text{ radiation}$$

$$_{19}K^{39} + {_0n^1} \rightarrow {_{19}K^{38}} + 2{_0n^1}$$

Carbon, boron, and lithium, which resist disintegration by alpha particles from radioactive materials, are readily attacked by neutrons. One of the isotopes of each of the last two yields an isotope of hydrogen of mass 3 (tritium).

$$_5B^{10} + _0n^1 \rightarrow _1H^3 + 2_2He^4$$

$$_3Li^6 + _0n^1 \rightarrow _1H^3 + _2He^4$$

A second method of approach to the problem of the disintegration of heavy nuclei is the use of positively charged particles which have been speeded up by artificial means. Several methods have been developed by means of which extremely high kinetic energies may be imparted to alpha particles, deuterons (nuclei of hydrogen atoms of mass number 2), protons, or electrons. Two types of apparatus which are widely used for the acceleration of positive particles in "atom smashing" are the electrostatic generator developed by R. J. Van de Graaff at the Massachusetts Institute of Technology, and the cyclotron developed by E. O. Lawrence at the University of California. Betatron is the name given to an instrument used for the acceleration of electrons. For a discussion of these instruments, the student is referred to textbooks in physics. A large number of transmutations have been carried out by the use of these devices. The following equations represent typical reactions.

$$_4Be^9 + _1H^1 \rightarrow _3Li^6 + _2He^4$$

$$_{20}Ca^{44} + _1H^1 \rightarrow _{21}Sc^{44} + _0n^1$$

$$_{83}Bi^{209} + _1H^2 \rightarrow _{83}Bi^{210} + _1H^1$$

$$_1H^2 + _1H^2 \rightarrow _1H^3 + _1H^1$$

$$_{18}Ar^{40} + _2He^4 \rightarrow _{20}Ca^{43} + _0n^1$$

$$_{21}Sc^{45} + _2He^4 \rightarrow _{22}Ti^{48} + _1H^1$$

Instances are also known in which disintegration of nuclei has been brought about by gamma radiation; e.g.,

$$_4Be^9 + \gamma \text{ radiation} \rightarrow _4Be^8 + _0n^1$$

25. Induced Radioactivity. Not only have almost all of the naturally occurring isotopes been produced by the various types of transmutation methods outlined above, but many new types of nuclei, which do not occur in nature, have been created also. Such nuclei are, in general, unstable isotopes of known elements, which in time undergo further disintegration to yield stable nuclei. This phenomenon, which is known as artificial or induced radioactivity, was first observed in 1934 by Irene Curie (daughter of Marie) and F. Joliot, who found that when boron, magnesium, or aluminum is bombarded with alpha particles, neutrons and positrons are emitted. When the source of alpha particles is removed, the emission of neutrons ceases, but positrons continue to be given off for some time. This can plausibly be explained, e.g., in the case of magnesium, by the supposition that the bombardment yields an isotope of silicon and a neutron,

$$_{12}Mg^{24} + {}_2He^4 \rightarrow {}_{14}Si^{27} + {}_0n^1$$

and that the silicon nucleus thus produced is unstable and undergoes radioactive disintegration according to the equation

$$_{14}Si^{27} \rightarrow {}_{13}Al^{27} + {}_1e^0$$

($_1e^0$ represents a positron)

It is this second step that continues for a period of time after the alpha particle bombardment has ceased. Many other examples of artificial radioactivity are known; in fact, artificially produced radioactive nuclei have been obtained by all the common transmutation methods. In Table 8.4 are listed only a few of the many radioactive isotopes which have been made, the equations for the nuclear reactions by which they are produced, the equations for their disintegration, and their half-life periods.

Table 8.4

Isotope	Production	Disintegration	Half-life	
$_9F^{17}$	$_7N^{14} + {}_2He^4 \rightarrow {}_9F^{17} + {}_0n^1$	$_9F^{17} \rightarrow {}_8O^{17} + {}_1e^0$	70	sec.
$_{47}Ag^{111}$	$_{46}Pd^{108} + {}_2He^4 \rightarrow {}_{47}Ag^{111} + {}_1H^1$	$_{47}Ag^{111} \rightarrow {}_{48}Cd^{111} + {}_{-1}e^0$	7.5	days
		($_{-1}e^0$ represents an		
		electron)		
$_{29}Cu^{66}$	$_{29}Cu^{65} + {}_0n^1 \rightarrow {}_{29}Cu^{66} + \gamma$ radiation	$_{29}Cu^{66} \rightarrow {}_{30}Zn^{66} + {}_{-1}e^0$	5	min.
$_{11}Na^{24}$	$_{12}Mg^{24} + {}_0n^1 \rightarrow {}_{11}Na^{24} + {}_1H^1$	$_{11}Na^{24} \rightarrow {}_{12}Mg^{24} + {}_{-1}e^0$	14.8	hr.
$_7N^{13}$	$_6C^{12} + {}_1H^2 \rightarrow {}_7N^{13} + {}_0n^1$	$_7N^{13} \rightarrow {}_6C^{13} + {}_1e^0$	9.93	min.
$_{78}Pt^{197}$	$_{78}Pt^{196} + {}_1H^2 \rightarrow {}_{78}Pt^{197} + {}_1H^1$	$_{78}Pt^{197} \rightarrow {}_{79}Au^{197} + {}_{-1}e^0$	18	hr.

It is interesting to note that in every artificial atomic disintegration which takes place instantaneously the light particle emitted is a proton, a neutron, or some other particle which may be considered to consist of protons and neutrons, such as an alpha particle or a deuteron. Positrons or electrons are obtained only as secondary products from the spontaneous disintegration of artificially produced nuclei resulting from the primary step in the disintegration. This is in accordance with the hypothesis that the nuclei of atoms contain only protons and neutrons, or aggregates composed of these. Positrons and electrons, on the other hand, do not exist as free particles in the nucleus. When an electron is emitted, a neutron in the nucleus changes into a proton; when a positron is emitted, a proton changes into a neutron.

26. New Elements Formed by Induced Radioactivity. An especially interesting and significant instance of transmutation by nuclear bombardment was discovered by Dr. G. T. Seaborg and his co-workers at the Radiation Laboratory of the University of California in 1940. It was found that the bombardment of uranium with neutrons whose velocities fall within a certain critical range, results in the occasional capture of a neutron by a uranium atom, according to the equation

$$_{92}U^{238} + {}_0n^1 \rightarrow {}_{92}U^{239} + \gamma \text{ radiation}$$

This new isotope of uranium is enormously more radioactive than natural uranium, its half-life period being only 23 min. In its spontaneous disintegration, it emits a beta particle and forms an entirely new element of atomic number 93, which does not occur in nature. This element was named neptunium, for the planet Neptune, and the symbol Np was assigned to it. The equation for this radioactive change is

$$_{92}U^{239} \rightarrow {}_{93}Np^{239} + {}_{-1}e^0$$

Neptunium itself, however, has a half-life period of only 2.3 days; its atoms spontaneously disintegrate with the emission of another beta particle. In this distintegration, still another new element is produced, which was aptly named plutonium, for Pluto, the outermost known planet; its symbol

$$_{93}Np^{239} \rightarrow {}_{94}Pu^{239} + {}_{-1}e^0 + \gamma \text{ radiation}$$

is Pu. Unlike its two immediate predecessors in this disintegration series, plutonium is a comparatively stable element. Like ordinary uranium, it has a very long half-life period, slowly emitting alpha particles.

Elements of atomic numbers 95 through 102 have likewise been prepared by artificial means. These new elements have been named americium (Am), curium (Cm), berkelium (Bk), californium (Cf), einsteinium (Es), fermium (Fm), mendelevium (Md), and nobelium (No) (p. 166).

The discovery of elements 43, 61, 85, and 87 in nature had been reported. Later work showed, however, that the existence of stable isotopes of these elements is extremely doubtful, if not impossible. Radioactive isotopes of these elements have been obtained by nuclear reactions, however, and, in 1947, three of the elements were given new names: element 43, technetium (Tc), element 85, astatine (At), and element 87, franeium (Fr). For element 61, the name promethium (Pm) was adopted in 1950.

27. Significance of Artificial Disintegration. Twenty years after Rutherford's first successful experiment in transmutation, it appeared that the ancient dream of the alchemists had at last been not merely realized, but actually surpassed. The baser elements had not, indeed, been changed to gold, although such a transformation seemed no longer impossible but merely impractical. Large expenditures of energy were required to bring about nuclear disintegrations, and the amounts of matter which underwent transmutation in any of the processes described were extremely small—far too small, in fact, to be detected by chemical means, or even by means of their spectra. The knowledge gained from these reactions, however, had been of inestimable value in throwing light upon the internal structure of the atomic nucleus. Furthermore, new isotopes of known elements, and even several entirely new elements, had been created, and it seems not unlikely that some of these may be of practical value. To cite a single example, the chloride of radioactive sodium, Na^{24}, which, unlike radium, is nonpoisonous and has a rather short half-life period, may eventually be useful in the treatment of cancer.

However, great as may be the potential significance of the types of disintegration which have so far been discussed, they have all been overshadowed by the tremendous events which have followed upon the discovery, in 1939, of a new and essentially different variety of nuclear disintegration, in which huge amounts of energy are liberated.

28. Nuclear Fission. Early in 1939, Hahn and Strassman, in Germany, discovered that an isotope of barium was produced in the bombardment of uranium by neutrons. Later in the same year, Lise Meitner, a refugee from Germany, suggested that the only reasonable explanation for this fact lay in the hypothesis that the impact of a neutron upon a uranium nucleus sometimes causes that nucleus to break up into two approximately equal parts. Further experiments showed that, under neutron bombardment, at least two of the naturally occurring isotopes of uranium, viz., those of mass numbers 235 and 238,[1] do indeed occasionally split into two fragments, one of mass number in the neighborhood of 140, the other in the neighborhood of 95. This type of distintegration, so unlike those previously known in which mere chips are split off the nucleus, soon came to be known as *nuclear fission*. It was found that fission of U^{238} (and a few other elements) can be brought about only by neutrons having very high velocities, relatively few of whose impacts are effective; but that U^{233}, U^{235}, and Pu^{239} readily undergo fission when bombarded by relatively slow neutrons.

The enormous significance of the fission process arises from two causes. First, in this variety of distintegration there occurs a loss of mass which cor-

---

[1] More recently it has been found that a third isotope of uranium, U^{233}, which does not occur in nature but can be prepared by the bombardment of thorium with neutrons, is also subject to fission.

responds to the release of a vast quantity of energy. Second, the fission products of a heavy nucleus include not only the two large fragments already mentioned, but in addition one, two, or more neutrons of sufficient kinetic energy to bring about the fission of neighboring atoms. This suggests the possibility of a continuous self-sustaining series of nuclear disintegrations, known as a chain reaction, as shown in Figure 8.19, which might be the source of tremendous amounts of energy.

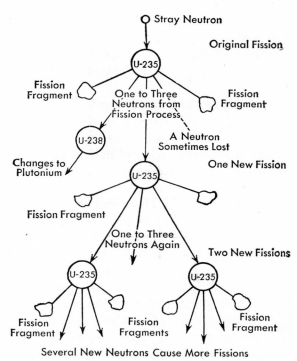

Fig. 8.19. Schematic diagram of chain reaction from fission, neglecting effect of neutron speed. In an explosive reaction the number of neutrons multiplies indefinitely. In a controlled reaction the number of neutrons builds up to a certain level and then remains constant. (From H. D. Smyth, *Atomic Energy,* Princeton University Press.)

29. The Nuclear Reactor. By 1940, it had been firmly established, on a theoretical basis, that a chain reaction could be made to take place in pure uranium[235]. This discovery suggested the possibility that energy might be released by this means either explosively, for military use, or gradually, for peaceful industrial application. This uranium isotope, however, is present in natural uranium only to the extent of 0.7%, and cannot be separated from the much more abundant uranium[238] (with practically identical chemical properties) by any chemical means. On the other hand, it was evident that no self-sustaining chain reaction could occur in a large mass of natural uranium, because in this substance most of the neutrons originating in nuclear fission, if they do not escape from the mass altogether, either lose energy by collision with U^{238} nuclei without bringing about any nuclear change at all, or else are captured by such nuclei to form U^{239}.

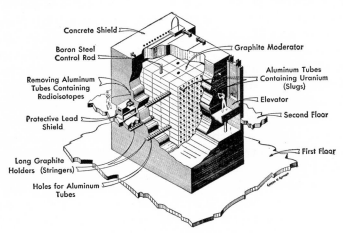

Fig. 8.20. A nuclear reactor.

The problem presented by these facts was solved in 1941 by the Italian physicist Enrico Fermi. He suggested that a nonexplosive chain reaction in ordinary uranium might be brought about if the fast neutrons resulting from the fission of U^{235} atoms in a piece of uranium were made to pass through a substance such as graphite, called a *moderator,* before encountering a second mass of uranium. The function of the moderator would be to slow down the neutrons to velocities of the same order as those of gas molecules; such thermal neutrons, as they are called, are especially effective in causing fission of U^{235} atoms.

This principle was applied in a device which was originally called an *atomic pile,* but which is now generally known as a *nuclear reactor.* The first atomic pile, which was constructed under the stadium at the University of Chicago, consisted of a series of layers of graphite bricks, among which lumps of uranium metal were distributed at regular intervals in a lattice-like arrangement. A number of cadmium rods were placed in slots passing through the pile. Since cadmium very effectively absorbs neutrons, the rate of the fission process could readily be regulated by varying the depth to which these control rods were inserted. This reactor was first put into successful operation on December 2, 1942, an important date in the history of science.

A significant feature of the operation of a nuclear reactor is that it results not only in the liberation of energy in the form of heat, but also in the conversion of U^{238} by neutron capture to U^{239}, which then spontaneously disintegrates with beta ray emission (p. 146) to plutonium^{239}, an element which is itself susceptible to fission in the same manner as uranium^{235}.

Plutonium was first produced on a large scale at a huge plant on the Columbia River near Hanford, Washington. The first step in this process takes place in a large nuclear reactor in which rods of ordinary uranium, encased in aluminum cans to protect them from corrosion by the cooling water constantly circulating through the pile, are distributed at regular intervals in a block of graphite. Once the chain reaction has been started by stray neutrons resulting from spontaneous fission, or, perhaps, from cosmic rays, it proceeds of its own accord. After a time the rods of uranium–plutonium mixture are removed and dissolved in acid, and pure plutonium is separated from the uranium and its radioactive fission products by chemical means. The chemistry of this relatively new element has of course by this time been thoroughly studied. The element is known, for instance, to be somewhat similar to uranium and to exhibit oxidation states of $+3$, $+4$, $+5$, and $+6$ in various series of compounds. Its soluble salts are highly poisonous.

Since 1942, many different types of nuclear reactors have been built, some primarily for power generation, some for the production of plutonium, and many merely for experimental purposes. In various reactors, enriched uranium (i.e., uranium of high U^{235} content, obtained as described in the next section) or a uranium compound, instead of natural uranium, has been used as fuel; air or molten sodium, instead of water, has been used for absorbing the heat produced, and heavy water, instead of graphite, has been used as a moderator.

30. Separation of Uranium Isotopes. As was suggested at the beginning of the preceding section, a chain reaction which proceeds at tremendous speed and with explosive violence can be brought about in nearly pure uranium^{235} or in plutonium^{239}. The U^{235} isotope occurs in natural uranium to the extent of only 1 part to 139 parts of U^{238}, whereas Pu^{239} does not occur in nature in appreciable quantities. The production of plutonium was accomplished by the method described in the preceding section. The separation of U^{235} on a large scale from its much more abundant isotope presented an even more difficult problem, which, however, was eventually solved in 1945 by the combined efforts of many physicists and chemists of various nationalities in what was undoubtedly the greatest cooperative scientific project in history.

The preparation of the first supply of U^{235} was carried out at a plant at Oak Ridge, Tennessee, where four physical methods of separation were successfully applied. One process involves the use of an apparatus known as the "calutron," a device in which the principle of the mass spectrograph (p. 134) is applied on a large scale. A beam of positively charged uranium ions is made to pass through an electric and a magnetic field, and the atoms of different masses are collected at different points. The other three processes all depend upon the slight difference in density between corresponding compounds of the two isotopes. In the centrifugal process, a liquid or gaseous mixture is spun rapidly in a cylindrical container, and the lighter U^{235} compound is concentrated near the axis of the cylinder. The third process is based upon a little understood physical phenomenon known as thermal diffusion; when a liquid mixture is circulated in a double-walled vessel in which the outer tube is cold and the inner one hot, the less dense component tends to concentrate at the top. The fourth method, the one which eventually proved to be the most practicable, depends upon the variation with density of the rate of gaseous diffusion (p. 39). When, for instance, the vapor of uranium hexafluoride (a compound which sublimes at 56° C.) is allowed to diffuse through a porous barrier, the $U^{235}F_6$, having a lower molecular weight and therefore a smaller density than the $U^{238}F_6$, passes through somewhat more rapidly. Hence, for a short time at least, the proportion of the lighter isotope in the gas beyond the barrier is slightly greater than it was in the original mixture. By repetition of the diffusion in many stages, a substantial concentration of U^{235} is obtained.

31. The Atomic Bomb. Extensive calculations, as well as experiments on a small scale, had shown that once pure U^{235} or Pu^{239} was available in appreciable quantities the construction of an explosive device would involve merely the rapid assembling of a mass of at least a certain critical size. The explanation of this curious fact is that in an object of any given shape— a sphere, for instance—the ratio of surface to volume decreases with increasing diameter. In a small sphere of a substance which is subject to fission, the fraction of all emitted neutrons which escapes through the surface is relatively large, so that a chain reaction cannot take place. As the size of the sphere is increased, the fraction of escaping neutrons decreases; and when the critical size is exceeded, not only does a very rapid self-sustaining release of energy become possible, but it is impossible to prevent the initiation of a chain reaction by stray neutrons from cosmic rays, spontaneous fission, or other sources. Hence, before detonation, the bomb must consist of at least two separate pieces, each too small to be explosive, which can be brought together rapidly.

The work on the first atomic bomb was carried on at Los Alamos, New Mexico. Details of its construction have not yet been made public—the exact critical size, for instance, is not generally known, nor the mechanism used for bringing the parts together. It is difficult to imagine, however, how anyone could be ignorant of the momentous experiment that took place at Alamogordo in the New Mexican desert, where the first atomic bomb was detonated on July 16, 1945, or of the far-reaching consequences of the fact that the experiment was successful.

32. Nuclear Fusion; the Hydrogen Bomb. The source of energy in the nuclear reactor and in the atomic bomb—or A-bomb, as it sometimes designated—is the fission of U^{235} or Pu^{239} nuclei. Even larger amounts of energy per unit mass of nuclear fuel are liberated by the union of nuclei of light elements to form heavier ones, a type of reaction which has come to be known as nuclear *fusion*. It is by such reactions that the energy emitted by the sun and the stars is produced (p. 140).

Substances which might be used as fuels for fusion reactions include some of the isotopes of hydrogen, lithium, and boron. A reaction which is particularly efficient, in terms of energy released per gram of fuel, is that in which tritium and deuterium react to give helium, as shown by the equation

$$_1H^3 + {}_1H^2 \rightarrow {}_2He^4 + {}_0n^1$$

The chief problem to be overcome in the application of nuclear fusion, either for military or for industrial purposes, lies in the fact that such reactions take place only at temperatures higher than 1,000,000° C., such as prevail on the sun but are very difficult to attain on earth. The problem has been solved in the construction of the hydrogen bomb—or H-bomb, as it has come to be called—by using an atomic bomb of the fission type as detonator.

Since the explosion of a hydrogen bomb depends upon the attainment of a very high temperature rather than a critical size, there is no apparent upper limit to the possible size of such a weapon, nor to its destructive power.

33. Peacetime Applications of Nuclear Reactions. Fission in the nuclear reactor results in the production of a large variety of radioactive isotopes of elements of medium atomic weight. Other radioisotopes are readily produced in the reactor by neutron bombardment of common elements. Up to the present, this has been the chief practical nonmilitary application of nuclear energy. The United States government annually supplies thousands of samples of radioisotopes to laboratories in universities, research institutes, and industries, and to hospitals, for a great variety of uses in research and therapy.

The heat given out in the fission process can be used for the generation of electricity at a cost only slightly greater than that involved in the use of coal, oil, or gas as fuel. A number of experimental nuclear power plants are already in operation in the United States, England, and Russia, and several other nations are now constructing nuclear reactors to be used for this purpose. It has been estimated that the efficient use as fuel of heavy elements subject to fission will increase twentyfold the known fuel reserves of the world.

Intensive research is at present being directed toward a controlled fusion process, in which the source of energy would be hydrogen, obtainable from water in unlimited quantities. Since the fusion of hydrogen nuclei will take place efficiently only at temperatures of many millions of degrees, the devising of a reactor for such a thermonuclear process, as it has come to be called, presents a very difficult problem, which as yet is far from being solved. Nevertheless, well-informed scientists have predicted that within twenty-five years all new power plants will utilize nuclear energy.

Thus, in the development of atomic energy, mankind is confronted with the possibility of tremendous destruction or tremendous progress. This is not the place for an extended discussion of the economic, social, political, and moral implications of this situation. We can only hope that humanity will find in itself the intellectual insight and spiritual resources to choose the second alternative, that the two nuclear bombs that fell on Hiroshima and Nagasaki will have been the last ever to be used for military purposes, and that this dreadful weapon may even eventually prove to be the instrument that will forever banish warfare from the earth.

STUDY QUESTIONS AND PROBLEMS

1. Make a table listing the chief uses and defects of the Mendeleeff periodic chart. What part did the discovery of the periodic law play in the development of our modern theory of atomic structure?

2. What is the mass and the charge of an electron? How were these quantities determined? What is the experimental evidence for the statement that all atoms contain electrons?

3. What three types of radiation are emitted by naturally radioactive substances? What are the characteristics of each of these three types of radiation and what evidence do you have for the validity of the characteristics which you have just stated?

4. What is the significance of the discovery and study of natural radioactivity in the development of our present theory of atomic structure?

5. What did the discovery of radioactive isotopes imply with reference to Mendeleeff's statement of the periodic law?

6. List the chief points in the nuclear theory of the atom as proposed by Rutherford. Outline the experimental evidence upon which this theory is based.

7. What are x-rays? What contribution did Moseley's study of the x-ray spectra of the elements make toward our modern theory of the structure of the atom?

8. If you should read in the daily press of the discovery of an element of atomic weight intermediate between that of nitrogen and of oxygen but different in chemical properties from either, would you be inclined to believe the report? Explain your answer.

9. How did the results of Moseley's work affect the statement of the periodic law?

10. Define the term "isotope." List the known isotopes of ten nonradioactive elements.

11. Outline briefly the principle upon which the mass spectrograph operates.

12. List the number of protons and of neutrons in the most abundant isotope of each of the elements between potassium and krypton in the periodic system.

13. From the study of the material in this chapter and from any outside reading you may have done, list as many bits of evidence as you can for the interconvertibility of matter and energy. Calculate the amount of energy which would be obtained if the matter in one pound of coal were completely destroyed, that is, if its mass were completely converted to energy. Roughly, how does this compare with the amount of energy actually obtained when this pound of coal is burned in an ordinary furnace? In the latter case, is there any appreciable loss in mass?

14. What is meant by the binding energy of an atomic nucleus? How may this binding energy be calculated?

15. Using reference works in your library, list ten artificial nuclear disintegrations not discussed or listed in this chapter, writing the correct nuclear equations. List ten radioactive isotopes which are not found in nature and give the nuclear equation for the disintegration of each.

16. Make a list of the elements which are not found in nature but which have been prepared artificially by nuclear reactions, and give nuclear equations for their methods of preparation. (This will require some library work.)

17. If a U^{235} nucleus, upon being struck by a neutron, undergoes fission with the formation of a Ba^{145} nucleus and three neutrons, what must the other fission product be?

18. From your outside reading of material concerning atomic energy, make a list of the difficulties attendant upon the application of atomic energy to practical peacetime purposes. For what peacetime purposes is atomic energy likely to be used first?

Atomic Structure II

1. Importance of Electronic Arrangements in Atoms. In the discussion of the structure of the atom in the preceding chapter, little was said concerning the electronic structure of the atoms. However, as we approach the two important and interrelated problems of correlating the properties of the elements with the structures of their atoms and of explaining why atoms combine with each other, it is necessary that we consider in detail the arrangement of the electrons about the atomic nucleus.

ELECTRONIC STRUCTURE AND THE PERIODIC SYSTEM

2. Sources of Data. Information concerning the configurations of the electrons in the atoms of the various elements has come from a variety of sources, the most important of which have been (1) the study of the chemical properties of the elements, particularly in relation to the periodic law, and (2) the observation of atomic spectra. The former has already been discussed in the preceding chapter.

3. Atomic Spectra. It is a well known fact that when a beam of light (and by the term "light" we mean here not visible light alone, but light of any wave length, including gamma rays, x-rays, ultraviolet rays, infrared rays, etc.) is passed through a transparent prism (usually glass), it is bent out of its course and emerges at an angle with its original direction. Light of different wave lengths is bent to different degrees. Thus, a beam containing light of a variety of wave lengths is spread out into a spectrum (see Figure 8.11, p. 130). For example, a beam of white light from the sun contains all wave lengths of visible light, and hence gives the familiar continuous visible spectrum containing "all the colors of the rainbow." There are, of course, additional wave lengths in the invisible ultraviolet and infrared regions of the solar spectrum, which may be detected photographically.

When matter, regardless of its form, is sufficiently excited by the addition of energy from some outside source, it emits light, and a great deal can be learned from the spectrum obtained from this light. Monatomic gases yield spectra that consist of series of distinct lines which are characteristic of the elements composing the gas. Such spectra are, therefore, attributed to the atoms and are called atomic spectra. Other more complex types of spectra yielded by excited gaseous molecules, or by excited solids or liquids, need not concern us here.

Atomic spectra of the type mentioned, which consist of the bright lines observed in the light emitted from the excited substance, are called *emission* spectra. Substances may be excited to produce emission spectra by the following general methods: (1) heating of a sample of the substance in a Bunsen flame; (2) passage of an electric discharge through the substance in the gaseous state, and (3) striking of an arc between electrodes impregnated with the substance.

A second type of atomic spectrum is obtained when radiation that gives a continuous spectrum, such as white light, is passed through the vapor of an element before being analyzed. The spectrum is then found to contain dark lines, the positions of which correspond exactly with those of the bright lines in the emission spectrum of the same element. Since it is apparent that these dark lines are the result of the absorption—by the vapor—of light of the same wave lengths which it emitted when excited, such spectra are called *absorption* spectra.

Since a rigorous discussion of the details of the various atomic spectra would be beyond the scope of this text, we shall limit ourselves to a consideration of the general principles involved, and a statement of the conclusions which have been reached.

In the first place, it must be understood that light consists of beams of radiant energy, and that the magnitude of this energy is directly related to the *wave length* of the light as well as to its intensity. Light is commonly considered to be a wave phenomenon; we are able to determine its wave length and frequency, and many of the other properties of light are also in accord with this point of view. However, modern physics has proved beyond question that light is also corpuscular in nature, behaving as if it consists of discrete "particles" of energy called *photons* or *quanta*. Difficult as it may be to reconcile these two ideas in terms of any mechanical picture or model that may be visualized, there can no longer be the least doubt that both are valid. Considering the wave aspects of light, we may write the equation

$$\lambda v = c$$

where λ is the wave length, ν the frequency (i.e., the number of waves passing a given point per unit time), and c is the velocity of light. A study of the corpuscular properties of light has revealed that the energy of an individual photon or quantum is directly proportional to the frequency, and therefore inversely proportional to the wave length of the light. This fact is expressed by the equation

$$E = h\nu = h\frac{c}{\lambda}$$

where h is a quantity known as Planck's constant, one of the most important constants in nature.

In consideration of the above statements, and of the fact that atomic spectra are discontinuous, i.e., are composed of lines characteristic of the individual element yielding the spectrum, the following conclusions may be drawn:

1. Each line in the spectrum corresponds to a definite wave length, and hence to quanta of energy of a single magnitude.

2. The atoms of a given element in the vapor state can absorb or emit light of certain definite wave lengths only; i.e., only quanta of certain definite magnitudes can be absorbed or emitted by the atoms of a given element.

Most atomic spectra are very complex; i.e., they consist of a very large number of lines. It is significant to note, therefore, that a careful study of such spectra has revealed that the energy corresponding to the wave length represented by each of the various lines in the spectrum of an element can be expressed as the difference between two of a relatively small number of quantities characteristic of that element. In other words, there exist for atoms of each element certain characteristic energy states such that the energy corresponding to each line in the spectrum of that element is equal to the difference between two of these energy states. It is apparent that the existence of a relatively few such energy states accounts for a great many possible spectral lines, since the number of combinations of n things taken two at a time is equal to $n(n-1)/2$.[1] These facts can be simply interpreted if we assume that an atom can emit or absorb light only one quantum at a time. In other words, an atom absorbs energy not continuously but only in quanta of definite magnitude, which just suffice to raise it from one to another of the definite energy states in which alone the atom can remain for an appreciable period of time. All of these ideas are implied in the statement that the atom is quantized. When an atom is in one of its higher energy

---

[1] The number of possible spectral lines is considerably reduced by a number of "selection rules" but is still quite large.

states it may lose energy, but only in the form of quanta which correspond to the difference between the higher energy state and one of the lower energy states in which it can exist. This situation is illustrated by Figure 9.1. Most of the important developments in the determination of the electronic configurations of the atoms have resulted from the effort to account for the existence of these atomic energy states.

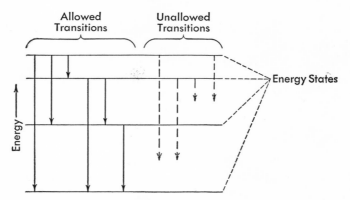

Fig. 9.1.   Diagram illustrating quantization of an atom.

4. Atomic Energy States. The first theoretical explanation of atomic energy states to attain any considerable degree of success was that proposed in 1913 by the Danish physicist Niels Bohr. The essential assumption of the Bohr theory was that the energy states of an atom correspond to the states of motion of its electrons. In an "unexcited" atom, each electron was supposed to revolve in a particular orbit, which might be called its normal orbit. When an atom absorbed energy, an electron was supposed to be displaced to one or another of a relatively small number of definite orbits at a greater distance from the nucleus than the normal orbit. Thus Bohr considered each line in the emission spectrum of an element to result from the falling back of an electron from an orbit in which its energy is, for example, E_2, to one in which the energy had as lower value, E_1; the difference in energy is emitted as a photon of such wave length that $E_2-E_1 = h\nu$, or $\nu = \dfrac{1}{h}(E_2-E_1)$.

It had long been known that among the frequencies corresponding to the lines of the visible region of the spectrum of hydrogen (Balmer series) there is a simple numerical relationship. Each of these frequencies may be expressed as $1/h$ times the difference between two energy terms, one variable

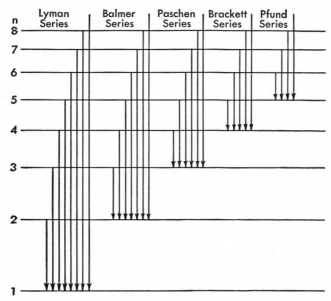

Fig. 9.2. Diagram of the transitions in energy which yield the various series of lines in the hydrogen spectrum.

and one constant, each containing an integer n; in the constant term n has the value 2, in the variable term the series of values 3, 4, . . . For a second series of lines in the ultraviolet region (Lyman series) the frequencies may similarly be expressed as $1/h$ times the excesses, over an energy term in which n has the value of 1, of a series of terms in which it has the successive integral values 2, 3, . . . By supposing n to be 1 for the orbit of lowest energy, i.e., the one nearest the nucleus, and to be 2, 3, . . . for orbits successively farther from the nucleus, Bohr was able to account not only for these two series, but for another (Paschen series) in the infrared region, and to predict two other infrared series which were discovered later. The relationships among these series of lines in the hydrogen spectrum are shown diagrammatically in Figure 9.2.

As a result of recent developments in physics, Bohr's original assumptions have been considerably modified. As a matter of fact, it has been shown that the paths (orbits) of the electrons in an atom cannot be precisely defined. Indeed, it has been shown that electrons, in fact all matter, are not only corpuscular in nature, but like light possess wave properties. This has led to the development of an entirely new system of mechanics known as *wave*

Table 9.1

Shells	Subshells	Electron capacity	
1	s	2	2
2	s	2	
	p	6	8
3	s	2	
	p	6	18
	d	10	
4	s	2	
	p	6	
	d	10	32
	f	14	
5	s	2	
	p	6	
	d	10	32
	f	14	
6	s	2	
	p	6	18
	d	10	
7	s	2	
	p	6	8

mechanics, by means of which physicists have met with outstanding success in dealing with atomic spectra and other atomic and subatomic phenomena.

The results of the wave mechanical treatment indicate that the electrons in an atom may be grouped into shells and subshells having certain definite energies and certain definite capacities for electrons. Each shell, in order of increasing energy, is usually denoted by a number n ($n = 1, 2, 3, 4, 5, \ldots$), known as the *principal quantum number,* or by a letter (K, L, M, N, O, . . .). The maximum number of subshells possible in each shell is n. These subshells are designated by the letters s, p, d, f, g, . . . The K shell, then, contains only an s subshell, the L shell an s and a p subshell, the M shell an s, a p, and a d subshell, and the N shell an s, a p, a d, and an f subshell. The maximum number of electrons in the last possible subshell in a shell of principal quantum number n is $4n - 2$ [or twice the nth term in the series of odd numbers, $1, 3, 5, \ldots, (2n - 1)$]. Thus the maximum number of electrons in an s subshell is 2, in a p subshell 6, in a d subshell 10, and in an f subshell 14. It follows that the maximum *total* number of electrons in the nth shell is twice the sum of the first n odd numbers, or $2 \times [1 + 3 + 5 + \ldots + (2n–1)]$. This total may also be expressed, more simply, as $2n^2$.

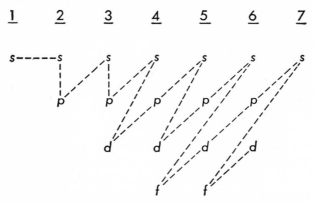

Fig. 9.3.   Order of building up of electron subshells.

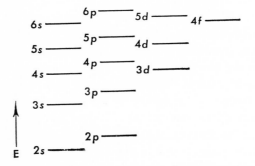

Fig. 9.4.   Approximate relative energy levels corresponding to various electron subshells.

So far we have considered only the maximum *capacity* of each shell for electrons. Actually, no elements are known in which, when the atom is in its normal or unexcited state, any shell beyond the fourth contains its maximum number of electrons. The several shells and subshells, and the largest number of electrons found in each in any unexcited atom, are shown in Table 9.1. In any given shell the energies corresponding to the various subshells increase in the order $s < p < d < f$, so that in some cases higher subshells from a lower shell overlap with lower subshells of a higher shell. This overlapping is illustrated by Figure 9.3, in which the *order* of increasing energy, and hence the order in which the subshells fill up with electrons, is shown schematically, and by Figure 9.4, in which the energy *levels* corresponding to the several subshells are approximately represented. As represented in this diagram the order of increasing energy is $1s < 2s < 2p < 3s < 3p < 4s < 3d < 4p < 5s < 4d < 5p < 6s \; (< 4f < 5d) < 6p < 7s \; (< 5f < 6d)$. Subshells $4f$ and $5d$ lie very close together and in certain atoms their order is reversed. The same is true of subshells $5f$ and $6d$.

This discussion of electron shells and subshells has been presented with no attempt to give in detail either the experimental or the theoretical basis upon which it rests. It is to be hoped, however, that the student will not conclude that such a foundation is lacking, but will accept our assurance that the reason for not discussing it lies in the mathematical and physical difficulties involved in this material, which preclude its presentation in an elementary text. It is hoped that the student will become increasingly aware of the validity of the general conclusions, as he sees, in the pages which follow in this chapter and throughout the book, how successfully they may be used.

5. Electronic Configurations of the Elements. We are now ready to consider the electronic configurations of the various elements in their normal, i.e., unexcited, states. In general, it may be assumed that, of all the possible orbits available to it, each electron will occupy that particular one in which it has the least energy. As a corollary to this principle, it follows that all but one of the electrons of an atom of any element will occupy the same orbits as the electrons of the element of atomic number one less, and the last electron will occupy the orbit of next higher energy. Starting with the hydrogen atom, which, with an atomic number of 1, has but a single electron, we should expect to find that electron in the subshell of lowest energy, viz., the $1s$ subshell. Helium, with an atomic number of 2, has two electrons in its $1s$ subshell. In the lithium atom there are again 2 electrons in the $1s$ subshell, but since the total capacity of that subshell is only two, the third electron must go into the $2s$ subshell. In the beryllium atom, two of the four electrons are in the $1s$ level and two in the $2s$ level. In the boron atom, since the $2s$ level can contain only two electrons, the fifth electron must enter the next or $2p$ subshell. Carbon with its six electrons has two electrons in the $2p$ subshell; nitrogen, three; oxygen, four; fluorine, five; and neon, six. The electronic structures of these first ten of the elements, then, are as shown in Table 9.2.

Since both the K shell and the L shell have now been filled to capacity, the last, or eleventh, electron in the sodium atom, which is the next element in the series, must find a place in the s subshell of the M or third shell; and in the next seven elements the $3s$ and $3p$ subshells are filled as is indicated in Table 9.3.

Table 9.2

Atomic number	Element	K shell ($n = 1$)	L shell ($n = 2$)	
		s	s	p
1	H	1		
2	He	2		
3	Li	2	1	
4	Be	2	2	
5	B	2	2	1
6	C	2	2	2
7	N	2	2	3
8	O	2	2	4
9	F	2	2	5
10	Ne	2	2	6

Table 9.3

Atomic number	Element	K shell ($n = 1$)	L shell ($n = 2$)		M shell ($n = 3$)	
		s	s	p	s	p
11	Na	2	2	6	1	
12	Mg	2	2	6	2	
13	Al	2	2	6	2	1
14	Si	2	2	6	2	2
15	P	2	2	6	2	3
16	S	2	2	6	2	4
17	Cl	2	2	6	2	5
18	Ar	2	2	6	2	6

It might be expected by this time that in the next element, potassium, the nineteenth electron would go into the $3d$ subshell, which is as yet unoccupied. However, as was stated on p. 165, the energies of the various subshells within a given shell increase in the order $s < p < d < f$; it happens that these differences among subshells are sufficiently large so that an electron in any s subshell has a lower energy than it would have in the d subshell of the preceding shell. Thus, the $4s$ subshell has a lower energy than the $3d$ subshell; hence the nineteenth electron in the potassium atom goes into the $4s$ subshell. The twentieth electron in the calcium atom does likewise, thereby filling this subshell. In the scandium atom, the twenty-first electron goes back into the $3d$ subshell, which, though higher in energy than the $4s$, is nevertheless lower than the $4p$ subshell. Beginning with scandium there is a series of nine elements in the atoms of which successive electrons are added to the

$3d$ subshell, i.e., to the third shell rather than to the fourth. Elements included in such a series are known as *transition elements* (see Chapter 36). After the $3d$ subshell has attained its full complement of ten electrons, the $4p$ subshell fills up. The electronic configurations of the elements from potassium to krypton are given in Table 9.4. There are minor irregularities in this series of configurations, it is true, in the cases of chromium and copper, but we need not at present concern ourselves as to the reasons for this.

Table 9.4

Atomic number	Element	K shell ($n = 1$)	L shell ($n = 2$)		M shell ($n = 3$)			N shell ($n = 4$)	
		s	s	p	s	p	d	s	p
19	K	2	2	6	2	6		1	
20	Ca	2	2	6	2	6		2	
21	Sc	2	2	6	2	6	1	2	
22	Ti	2	2	6	2	6	2	2	
23	V	2	2	6	2	6	3	2	
24	Cr	2	2	6	2	6	5	1	*Transi-*
25	Mn	2	2	6	2	6	5	2	*tion*
26	Fe	2	2	6	2	6	6	2	*elements*
27	Co	2	2	6	2	6	7	2	
28	Ni	2	2	6	2	6	8	2	
29	Cu	2	2	6	2	6	10	1	
30	Zn	2	2	6	2	6	10	2	
31	Ga	2	2	6	2	6	10	2	1
32	Ge	2	2	6	2	6	10	2	2
33	As	2	2	6	2	6	10	2	3
34	Se	2	2	6	2	6	10	2	4
35	Br	2	2	6	2	6	10	2	5
36	Kr	2	2	6	2	6	10	2	6

For the same reason that the nineteenth electron in the potassium atom enters the fourth shell rather than the third, the thirty-seventh electron in the rubidium atom enters the $5s$ subshell instead of the $4d$. In fact, with a few minor variations, the elements of atomic numbers 37 to 54 all have electronic structures analogous to those of atomic numbers 19 to 36. The electronic structures of these additional elements are given in Table 9.5. In the elements number 39 to 47, it will be noted, we have a *second series of transition elements*.

The electron structures of elements number 55, 56, and 57 are analogous both to those of elements number 19, 20, and 21, respectively, and to those of elements number 37, 38, and 39. Thus the last electron in the cesium atom enters the $6s$ subshell, the last electron in the barium atom completes this sub-shell, and in the lanthanum atom the last electron goes into the $5d$ subshell. After lanthanum, however, there follows a series of fourteen elements in which the chief change in electronic configuration which occurs is that the $4f$ sub-shell fills up with 14 electrons. With the element ytterbium, atomic number 70, the fourth shell is complete. The electronic structures of elements number 72 to 86 are analogous to those of elements number 40 to 54 and 22 to

Table 9.5

Atomic number	Element	K shell ($n=1$) s	L shell ($n=2$) s	L shell ($n=2$) p	M shell ($n=3$) s	M shell ($n=3$) p	M shell ($n=3$) d	N shell ($n=4$) s	N shell ($n=4$) p	N shell ($n=4$) d	O shell ($n=5$) s	O shell ($n=5$) p	
37	Rb	2	2	6	2	6	10	2	6		1		
38	Sr	2	2	6	2	6	10	2	6		2		
39	Y	2	2	6	2	6	10	2	6	1	2		
40	Zr	2	2	6	2	6	10	2	6	2	2		
41	Nb	2	2	6	2	6	10	2	6	4	1		*Transi-*
42	Mo	2	2	6	2	6	10	2	6	5	1		*tion*
43	Tc	(2)	(2)	(6)	(2)	(6)	(10)	(2)	(6)	(6)	(1)		*ele-*
44	Ru	2	2	6	2	6	10	2	6	7	1		*ments*
45	Rh	2	2	6	2	6	10	2	6	8	1		
46	Pd	2	2	6	2	6	10	2	6	10			
47	Ag	2	2	6	2	6	10	2	6	10	1		
48	Cd	2	2	6	2	6	10	2	6	10	2		
49	In	2	2	6	2	6	10	2	6	10	2	1	
50	Sn	2	2	6	2	6	10	2	6	10	2	2	
51	Sb	2	2	6	2	6	10	2	6	10	2	3	
52	Te	2	2	6	2	6	10	2	6	10	2	4	
53	I	2	2	6	2	6	10	2	6	10	2	5	
54	Xe	2	2	6	2	6	10	2	6	10	2	6	

36. The electronic configurations of elements number 55 to 86 are given in Table 9.6. It will be observed that elements number 57 to 79 constitute a *third transition series,* whereas in elements number 58 to 71 we have a *transition series within a transition series.* As has already been pointed out in the preceding chapter, elements number 57 to 71, which are known collectively as the rare earth elements, are very closely similar in properties.

In the elements 89 to 102 (Table 9.7), we have an almost complete new "rare earth" series; in this case it is the $5f$ subshell which is being filled. It is interesting to note that element 95, whose position in this series corresponds to that of europium (named for the continent of Europe) in the first series, was named americium, for America. Element 96, corresponding to gadolinium (named for Gadolin, who made important contributions to

Table 9.6

At. no.	Element	K shell (n=2)	L shell (n=2)		M shell (n=3)			N shell (n=4)				O shell (n=5)			P shell (n=6)	
		s	s	p	s	p	d	s	p	d	f	s	p	d	s	p
55	Cs	2	2	6	2	6	10	2	6	10		2	6		1	
56	Ba	2	2	6	2	6	10	2	6	10		2	6		2	
57	La	2	2	6	2	6	10	2	6	10		2	6	1	2	
58	Ce	2	2	6	2	6	10	2	6	10	2	2	6		2	
59	Pr	2	2	6	2	6	10	2	6	10	3	2	6		2	
60	Nd	2	2	6	2	6	10	2	6	10	4	2	6		2	
61	Pm	(2)	(2)	(6)	(2)	(6)	(10)	(2)	(6)	(10)	(5)	(2)	(6)		(2)	
62	Sm	2	2	6	2	6	10	2	6	10	6	2	6		2	
63	Eu	2	2	6	2	6	10	2	6	10	7	2	6		2	
64	Gd	2	2	6	2	6	10	2	6	10	7	2	6	1	2	
65	Tb	2	2	6	2	6	10	2	6	10	9	2	6		2	
66	Dy	2	2	6	2	6	10	2	6	10	10	2	6		2	
67	Ho	2	2	6	2	6	10	2	6	10	11	2	6		2	
68	Er	2	2	6	2	6	10	2	6	10	12	2	6		2	
69	Tm	2	2	6	2	6	10	2	6	10	13	2	6		2	
70	Yb	2	2	6	2	6	10	2	6	10	14	2	6		2	
71	Lu	2	2	6	2	6	10	2	6	10	14	2	6	1	2	
72	Hf	2	2	6	2	6	10	2	6	10	10	2	6	2	2	
73	Ta	2	2	6	2	6	10	2	6	10	14	2	6	3	2	
74	W	2	2	6	2	6	10	2	6	10	14	2	6	4	2	
75	Re	2	2	6	2	6	10	2	6	10	14	2	6	5	2	
76	Os	2	2	6	2	6	10	2	6	10	14	2	6	6	2	
77	Ir	2	2	6	2	6	10	2	6	10	14	2	6	9		
78	Pt	2	2	6	2	6	10	2	6	10	14	2	6	9	1	
79	Au	2	2	6	2	6	10	2	6	10	14	2	6	10	1	
80	Hg	2	2	6	2	6	10	2	6	10	14	2	6	10	2	
81	Tl	2	2	6	2	6	10	2	6	10	14	2	6	10	2	1
82	Pb	2	2	6	2	6	10	2	6	10	14	2	6	10	2	2
83	Bi	2	2	6	2	6	10	2	6	10	14	2	6	10	2	3
84	Po	2	2	6	2	6	10	2	6	10	14	2	6	10	2	4
85	At	(2)	(2)	(6)	(2)	(6)	(10)	(2)	(6)	(10)	(14)	(2)	(6)	(10)	(2)	(5)
86	Rn	2	2	6	2	6	10	2	6	10	14	2	6	10	2	6

(Bracket annotations at right: elements 57–70 — *Rare earth elements (Lanthanides)*; elements 57–78 — *Transition elements*)

our knowledge of the rare earths), was named curium, for the Curies. Element 97 was named berkelium, for Berkeley, the city where its discovery took place, and element 98, californium, for the state of California. Element 99, einsteinium, was named for Albert Einstein; element 100, fermium, for Enrico Fermi, the well known nuclear physicist, element 101, mendelevium, for Mendeleeff, and element 102, nobelium, after the Nobel

Table 9.7

At. no.	Element	K shell (n=1)	L shell (n=2)		M shell (n=3)			N shell (n=4)				O shell (n=5)				P shell (n=6)			Q shell (n=7)
		s	s	p	s	p	d	s	p	d	f	s	p	d	f	s	p	d	s
87	Fr	(2)	(2)	(6)	(2)	(6)	(10)	(2)	(6)	(10)	(14)	(2)	(6)	(10)		(2)	(6)		(1)
88	Ra	2	2	6	2	6	10	2	6	10	14	2	6	10		2	6		2
89	Ac	2	2	6	2	6	10	2	6	10	14	2	6	10		2	6	1	2
90	Th	2	2	6	2	6	10	2	6	10	14	2	6	10		2	6	2	2
91	Pa	2	2	6	2	6	10	2	6	10	14	2	6	10	2	2	6	1	2
92	U	2	2	6	2	6	10	2	6	10	14	2	6	10	3	2	6	1	2
93	Np	2	2	6	2	6	10	2	6	10	14	2	6	10	4	2	6	1	2
94	Pu	2	2	6	2	6	10	2	6	10	14	2	6	10	5	2	6	1	2
95	Am	2	2	6	2	6	10	2	6	10	14	2	6	10	6	2	6	1	2
96	Cm	2	2	6	2	6	10	2	6	10	14	2	6	10	7	2	6	1	2
97	Bk	2	2	6	2	6	10	2	6	10	14	2	6	10	8	2	6	1	2
98	Cf	2	2	6	2	6	10	2	6	10	14	2	6	10	9	2	6	1	2
99	Es	2	2	6	2	6	10	2	6	10	14	2	6	10	10	2	6	1	2
100	Fm	2	2	6	2	6	10	2	6	10	14	2	6	10	11	2	6	1	2
101	Md	2	2	6	2	6	10	2	6	10	14	2	6	10	12	2	6	1	2
102	No	2	2	6	2	6	10	2	6	10	14	2	6	10	13	2	6	1	2

Institute in Sweden where the element was discovered.

In the elements of atomic number greater than 90 there is considerable uncertainty as to distribution of electrons between subshells $5d$ and $6f$.

Current theory concerning the electron configurations of the atoms in their normal states may be summarized as follows:

1. The maximum capacities of each of the shells and subshells in the atoms are in accordance with the figures given in Table 9.1.

2. No d subshell ever receives any electrons until the s subshell of the next higher shell has been filled. Hence, there are never more than eight electrons in the outermost shell of an atom.

3. The d subshell always begins to fill up immediately after the s subshell of the next higher shell has been filled.

4. The $4f$ subshell does not, in general, begin to receive electrons until after the $5s$, $5p$, and $6s$ subshells have been filled and one electron has gone into the $5d$ subshell, nor does the $5f$ begin to fill until the $6s$, $6p$, and $7s$ subshells have been filled and one electron has entered the $6d$ subshell. Hence, there are never more than eighteen electrons in the next to the outermost shell of an atom.

6. Electron Configurations and the Periodic Law. The crucial test of the theory of electronic configurations is that of explaining the periodic law. For, although the atomic numbers give the correct *order* of the elements in the system, yet the continuous and regular increase in nuclear charge, by one unit at a time, does not explain the *periodicity* of properties.

If we examine the electron configurations of the elements of a given family in the periodic chart, we find that configurations are very similar to each other, indeed identical so far as the outermost shells are concerned. This point may be illustrated by a tabulation of the electronic configurations for one of these families (Table 9.8).

Table 9.8

Atomic number	Element			Configuration			
3	Li	2	1				
11	Na	2	2, 6	1			
19	K	2	2, 6	2, 6	1		
37	Rb	2	2, 6	2, 6, 10	2, 6	1	
55	Cs	2	2, 6	2, 6, 10	2, 6, 10	2, 6	1

Since it is but logical to suppose that properties of the elements must be determined in very large measure by their electron configurations, and especially by the nature of the outermost shells, we can readily see why the elements lithium, sodium, potassium, rubidium, and cesium show a strong family relationship. Likewise, the marked similarity of fluorine, chlorine, bromine, and iodine is easily interpreted in terms of the structures of their atoms. A similar explanation applies to the close resemblances observed within other families in the periodic system. It may now be stated, therefore, that the recurrence, at regular though not uniform intervals in the periodic system, of elements with similar properties, is the direct result of the recurrence, at the same intervals, of similar electronic configurations. Furthermore, the regular variation in properties which is observed as we pass from left to right in any period may reasonably be attributed to the regular change in configuration in the outer electron shells of the atoms of the elements. Thus, for the first time, we have an adequate explanation of the periodic law.

It may further be observed that, after the first two elements in the periodic system, each period begins with an element which has one electron in the s subshell of the outermost shell, and ends with an element (an inert gas) in which the s and p subshells of that shell have been completely filled, so that there is a total of eight electrons in the outermost shell. That the first period, consisting of hydrogen and helium, constitutes an exception to this rule, is due, of course, to the fact that the first electron shell contains an *s* subshell only, and hence has a maximum capacity of two electrons. The second period, beginning with lithium and ending with neon, and the third, beginning with sodium and ending with argon, contain eight elements each. In the case of these first eighteen elements, the continuous variation of properties with atomic number is exhibited in its simplest form, for here the difference in electron configuration between successive elements in a period is confined to the outermost shell alone.

Table 9.9

Atomic number	Element	Configuration					
				VA			
23	V	2	2, 6	2, 6, 3	2		
41	Nb	2	2, 6	2, 6, 10	2, 6, 4	1	
73	Ta	2	2, 6	2, 6, 10	2, 6, 10, 14	2, 6, 3	2
				VB			
33	As	2	2, 6	2, 6, 10	2, 3		
51	Sb	2	2, 6	2, 6, 10	2, 6, 10	2, 3	
83	Bi	2	2, 6	2, 6, 10	2, 6, 10, 14	2, 6, 10	2, 3

With potassium and calcium, the fourth period begins, indeed, as if it were to be a repetition of the second and third. From this point on, however, the relationships are no longer so simple. The fourth period, because of the building up of the 3*d* subshell, and the fifth period, because of the filling up of the 4*d* subshell, contain eighteen elements each. The sixth period contains thirty-two elements, for both the 5*d* and 4*f* subshells must be filled, in the long transition series beginning with lanthanum and ending with gold. As has already been pointed out, Mendeleeff managed to crowd these long periods into the eight columns of his chart by dividing each period into two parts, consisting respectively of members of A and B subgroups. Mendeleeff also tried to fit the rare earth elements into these eight columns, but in later versions of his table, these elements are relegated to the bottom of the table. The Mendeleeff chart has never been completely satisfactory, however, for, as was pointed out (p. 118), the A and B subgroups of a given group bear, in general, only a superficial resemblance to each other. It is now apparent that the reason for this lack of similarity lies in the distinctly different electron configurations of the two subgroups. This difference is illustrated in Table 9.9, in which the electronic configurations of corresponding elements of subgroups VA and VB are given.

As a result of recent efforts to overcome these difficulties and to demonstrate more thoroughly the intimate relationship between the periodic law and the electronic structures of the elements, the periodic table as presented by Mendeleeff has been subjected to a number of modifications. Many new forms of the periodic chart have been published; one of the most useful of these, and the one which we shall use throughout the remainder of this book, is illustrated in Figure 9.5. In this table each of the periods (except for the

Ia	2a	3b	4b	5b	6b	7b		8b		1b	2b	3a	4a	5a	6a	7a	0
1 H 1.0080						*Transition Elements*										1 H 1.0080	2 He 4.003
3 Li 6.940	4 Be 9.013											5 B 10.82	6 C 12.011	7 N 14.008	8 O 16.0000	9 F 19.00	10 Ne 20.183
11 Na 22.991	12 Mg 24.32											13 Al 26.98	14 Si 28.09	15 P 30.975	16 S 32.066	17 Cl 35.457	18 Ar 39.944
19 K 39.100	20 Ca 40.08	21 Sc 44.96	22 Ti 47.90	23 V 50.95	24 Cr 52.01	25 Mn 54.94	26 Fe 55.85	27 Co 58.94	28 Ni 58.71	29 Cu 63.54	30 Zn 65.38	31 Ga 69.72	32 Ge 72.60	33 As 74.91	34 Se 78.96	35 Br 79.916	36 Kr 83.80
37 Rb 85.48	38 Sr 87.63	39 Y 88.92	40 Zr 91.22	41 Nb 92.91	42 Mo 95.95	43 Tc	44 Ru 101.1	45 Rh 102.0	46 Pd 106.04	47 Ag 107.880	48 Cd 112.41	49 In 114.82	50 Sn 118.70	51 Sb 121.76	52 Te 127.61	53 I 126.91	54 Xe 131.30
55 Cs 132.91	56 Ba 137.36	57-71 see La Series	72 Hf 178.50	73 Ta 180.95	74 W 183.86	75 Re 186.22	76 Os 190.2	77 Ir 192.2	78 Pt 195.09	79 Au 197.0	80 Hg 200.61	81 Tl 204.39	82 Pb 207.21	83 Bi 209.00	84 Po 210	85 At	86 Rn 222
87 Fr	88 Ra 226.05	89-102 see Ac Series															

Lanthanide Series	57 La 138.92	58 Ce 140.13	59 Pr 140.92	60 Nd 144.27	61 Pm	62 Sm 150.43	63 Eu 152.0	64 Gd 157.26	65 Tb 158.93	66 Dy 162.51	67 Ho 164.94	68 Er 167.27	69 Tm 168.94	70 Yb 173.04	71 Lu 174.99
Actinide Series	89 Ac 227	90 Th 232.05	91 Pa 231	92 U 238.07	93 Np	94 Pu	95 Am	96 Cm	97 Bk	98 Cf	99 Es	100 Fm	101 Md	102 No	

Fig. 9.5. A modern periodic chart.

rare earth elements which are still left at the bottom of the table) is spread out in a single row. Hydrogen is similar in some respects both to the alkali metals and to the halogens; with helium, it constitutes the first period. The next two periods remain exactly as they were in the Mendeleeff chart except for the gap between the second and third members of each series. Below this gap are the elements of the fourth, fifth, and sixth periods in which the $3d$, $4d$, and $5d$ subshells, respectively, are being built up. Since neither the electron configurations nor the properties of these elements closely resemble those of any of the elements in the second or third series, it is appropriate that they should be so arranged. All the elements (except zinc, cadmium, and mercury) in this portion of the table are, as indicated in Figure 9.5, transition elements. As we shall see later, each of these transition elements bears a very close resemblance not only to the other elements in the same column, but also to the other transition elements to its immediate right or left (Chapter 36). We shall drop the Mendeleeff notation of A and B subgroups, but, in view of the fact that each of the families in the central part of the table (except the elements of Group 8) has some at least superficial resemblance to one of the nontransitional families, we shall retain the system of numbering the groups of elements from 0 to 8, and shall denote the transitional groups (along with the zinc family) by a small letter "*b*" and the nontransitional groups by a small letter "*a*". Thus the alkali metals constitute Group 1*a*, while the copper metals are Group 1*b*; oxygen, sulfur, selenium, and tellurium constitute Group 6*a*, while chromium, molybdenum, and tungsten form Group 6*b*.

THE ELECTRONIC THEORY OF CHEMICAL BINDING

7. Early Investigations. Numerous attempts had been made, prior to the publication in 1913 of Bohr's theory of the arrangement of the electrons in the atom, to develop an explanation of chemical combination in atomic terms; but these attempts had met with little success. Within three years of the publication of Bohr's work, however, two papers, one by W. Kossel and the other by G. N. Lewis, which laid the groundwork for the modern electronic theory of chemical binding, were published.

When chemists surveyed the electronic configurations of the elements, they were impressed by the fact that, of all the elements in the periodic system, the only ones which show practically no tendency to combine with other elements are the inert gases, each of which comes at the end of one of the periods in the periodic system.

In view of their special significance in this connection, it will be well for us to recapitulate here (Table 9.10) the electronic structures of these six inert elements.

Table 9.10

At. no.	Element	K shell ($n=1$)	L shell ($n=2$)		M shell ($n=3$)			N shell ($n=4$)				O shell ($n=5$)			P shell ($n=6$)	
		s	s	p	s	p	d	s	p	d	f	s	p	d	s	p
2	He	2														
10	Ne	2	2	6												
18	Ar	2	2	6	2	6										
36	Kr	2	2	6	2	6	10	2	6							
54	Xe	2	2	6	2	6	10	2	6	10		2	6			
86	Rn	2	2	6	2	6	10	2	6	10	14	2	6	10	2	6

Each of these elements, it will be noticed, has eight electrons in its outer-most electron shell (except helium, in which case the outermost, and only, electron shell has a maximum capacity of two electrons). It was therefore concluded that a group of eight electrons in the outer electron shell consti-tutes a configuration of exceptional stability, which has been called an octet, and that the driving force in the combination of atoms is a tendency for them to attain these or other especially stable configurations. It is scarcely more than a matter of definition to say that all systems tend to change from less stable to more stable states, and that all chemical and physical changes which take place spontaneously result in an overall increase in the stability of the system concerned. There are two general ways in which atoms can attain stable configurations through chemical combination.

8. Electrovalent Bonds. Kossel was impressed by the fact that the ele-ments in the column immediately preceding the inert gas family very com-monly show a valence of 1 and, furthermore, that many of the compounds in which these elements show this valence are electrolytes, i.e., their aqueous solutions conduct electricity (p. 301); when a current is passed through solutions of such compounds, the elements of this family migrate toward the positive electrode. The elements immediately following the inert gas family are likewise univalent, but when their compounds are electrolyzed these ele-ments travel to the negative electrode. Similar statements may be made of the second family preceding the inert gases and of the second family fol-lowing the inert gases, except that the elements of both these families are commonly bivalent in their simpler compounds. In consideration of these facts, Kossel, in 1916, proposed the theory that an atom can attain one of the especially stable configurations characteristic of the inert gases by the loss or gain of electrons. Thus, when metallic sodium and free chlorine are brought together, each sodium atom, which differs from neon in having one $3s$ electron, loses that electron to a chlorine atom, which differs from argon in having one less $3p$ electron. The result of this transfer is that the sodium atom has attained the stable neon configuration; because it has lost a nega-tive electron, however, it now bears a *positive* charge. This charged particle is called a sodium *ion*; although it has the same electron configuration as a neon atom, its nucleus, of course, is still that of sodium. This change, then, is in no sense a transmutation. The chlorine atom, on the other hand, now has attained the stable argon configuration, but, by virtue of the added electron, bears a *negative* charge; or, in other words, it has become a chloride *ion*. These two kinds of ions are held together by the electrostatic attraction of their opposite charges, in the sodium chloride crystal lattice.

$$\text{Na} \quad + \quad \text{Cl} \quad \rightarrow \quad \text{Na}^+ \quad + \quad \text{Cl}^-$$

configuration (2 2, 6 1)   (2 2, 6 2, 5)   (2 2, 6)   (2 2, 6 2, 6)

Another example of this type of combination occurs in the reaction of magnesium with sulfur.

$$\text{Mg} \quad + \quad \text{S} \quad \rightarrow \quad \text{Mg}^{++} \quad + \quad \text{S}^{--}$$

configuration (2 2, 6 2)   (2 2, 6 2, 4)   (2 2, 6)   (2 2, 6 2, 6)

In this reaction each magnesium atom attains the stable neon configuration by losing two electrons to a sulfur atom, which thereby attains the stable argon configuration; in other words, a doubly positively charged magnesium ion and a doubly negatively charged sulfide ion are formed. The reaction of calcium with fluorine is another example of electron transfer. Each calcium atom loses one electron to each of two fluorine atoms, producing a doubly positively charged calcium ion and two singly negatively charged fluoride ions; the calcium ion has the argon configuration and the fluoride ion the neon configuration.

$$\text{Ca} \quad + \quad 2\text{F} \quad \rightarrow \quad \text{Ca}^{++} \quad + \quad 2\text{F}^-$$

configuration (2 2, 6 2, 6 2) (2 2, 5)   (2 2, 6 2, 6)   (2 2, 6)

It is evident that in reactions of this type the valence of an atom is equal to the number of electrons it must gain or lose, as the case may be, in order to have the total number requisite for a stable configuration. If the atoms of an element lose electrons to form a positive ion, the element is said to have a positive electrovalence. Thus, for example, the electrovalence of sodium is $+1$, that of magnesium $+2$, and that of calcium $+2$. Likewise, elements whose atoms gain electrons are said to have negative electrovalences. Thus fluorine has an electrovalence of -1; chlorine, -1; sulfur, -2; and oxygen, -2. Since the bonding force which results from such combinations consists of the electrostatic attraction between oppositely charged ions, compounds formed in this way are said to be *electrovalent* or *ionic,* and to be held together by electrovalent or ionic bonds.

Kossel's theory of electrovalent bonds has met with outstanding success in the interpretation of the simple compounds between the elements in the two families preceding the inert gases, on the one hand, and the elements of the two groups immediately succeeding the inert gases, on the other, and in certain other cases as well. The properties of such compounds, as will be shown later, are in remarkable accord with their postulated electrovalent nature.

9. Covalent Bonds. There is, however, an even larger group of substances, including compounds of closely related elements, as well as most compounds of elements in the middle groups of the periodic system, whose physical and chemical properties are such as to preclude the possibility of their being electrovalent. A different theory, therefore, was required to account for the formation of these compounds. As we shall see when we study their properties, there are many substances such as chlorine, sulfur dioxide, carbon dioxide, hydrogen chloride, water, and ammonia which are clearly non-ionic in nature. The vast majority of the multitude of carbon compounds are likewise of nonionic character. The theory that provided a solution to this problem was formulated in 1916 by the great American chemist G. N. Lewis and was later expanded by Heitler and London. In this theory, it is assumed that electrons may be *shared* between two atoms and thus contribute toward the provision of a stable configuration for each. Let us first consider, as a simple example, the formation of a chlorine molecule, Cl_2. Each chlorine atom has seven electrons in its third shell (two $3s$ and five $3p$ electrons) ; thus, each needs one more electron in order to attain the stable argon configuration. This goal is attained if each chlorine atom shares one of its electrons with the other atom ; i.e., if two electrons are held in common by the two atoms. Thus the combination of two chlorine atoms may be represented by the following equation, in which we follow the practice, initiated by Lewis, of allowing the symbol of the element to represent the "kernel" of the atom, i.e., the nucleus together with all the electrons except those in the outermost shell, and of using dots to represent the outer electrons, or valence electrons, as they are sometimes called:

$$: \overset{..}{\underset{..}{Cl}} \cdot \; + \; \cdot \overset{..}{\underset{..}{Cl}} : \; \rightarrow \; : \overset{..}{\underset{..}{Cl}} : \overset{..}{\underset{..}{Cl}} :$$

Another simple example of this type of bonding is provided by the compound methane, CH_4. The carbon atom, with four electrons in its outer shell, requires four more to attain the stable neon structure. Each of the hydrogen atoms, with one electron, needs one more to attain the stable helium configuration. These requirements are met when the carbon atom shares one of its electrons with each of four hydrogen atoms, and in turn receives a share in each of the electrons furnished by the four hydrogen atoms.

$$\overset{\cdot}{\underset{\cdot}{C}} \cdot \; + \; 4H \cdot \; \rightarrow \; H : \overset{..}{\underset{..}{\underset{\textstyle H}{C}}} : H \quad (\text{with } H \text{ above})$$

The type of bond which is thus formed by the sharing of a pair of electrons between two atoms is called a *covalent* or *electron-pair* bond. Electronic formulas for other covalent molecules include

$$\cdot\ \overset{\cdot\cdot}{\underset{\cdot\cdot}{N}}\ \cdot\ +\ 3H\ \cdot\ \rightarrow\ H : \overset{H}{\underset{\cdot\cdot}{\overset{\cdot\cdot}{N}}} : H$$

ammonia

$$: \overset{\cdot\cdot}{\underset{\cdot}{O}}\ \cdot\ +\ 2H\ \cdot\ \rightarrow\quad : \overset{\cdot\cdot}{\underset{\cdot\cdot}{O}} \cdot H$$

$$\overset{}{\underset{H}{}}$$

water

The reader should not be tempted to consider these conventional electronic formulas as actual pictures of the molecules, or to regard the electrons as particles occupying static positions. The formulas indicate merely that the shared pairs of electrons, in some manner, fill vacancies in the incomplete electron groups of both atoms.

In some cases, two or even three pairs of electrons are shared between two atoms. Thus:

$$\overset{\cdot\ \ \cdot}{\underset{\cdot\ \ \cdot}{C}}\ +\ 2 : \overset{\cdot\cdot}{\underset{}{O}}\ \cdot\ \rightarrow\ \overset{\cdot}{\underset{\cdot}{:}}\ O :: C :: O\ \overset{\cdot}{\underset{\cdot}{:}}$$

carbon dioxide

$$2\ \overset{\cdot}{\underset{\cdot}{C}}\ +\ 2H\ \cdot\ \rightarrow\ H : C : : : C : H$$

acetylene

When two atoms share two pairs of electrons between them, they are said to be connected by a double covalent bond; the sharing of three such pairs constitutes a triple covalent bond.

In simple covalent compounds the valence of an element is numerically equal to the number of electron pairs it shares with other atoms. Since there is no transfer of electrons in such cases, however, it is apparent that covalence cannot properly be classified as positive or negative (see Chapter 12).

10. Coordinate Covalent Bonds. Lewis, in his original paper, made the further suggestion, which has since been accepted and expanded, that covalent bonds can be formed in a manner somewhat different from that already illustrated: namely, that one of the bonded atoms may furnish *both* of the shared electrons. For example, an ammonia molecule, which contains in the outer shell of its nitrogen atom a pair of electrons not yet shared with any other atom, may contribute this pair of electrons toward a covalent bond with a proton or hydrogen ion (H^+); thus an ammonium ion is formed:

$$H : \overset{H}{\underset{H}{\overset{\cdot\cdot}{N}}} : +\ H^+ \rightarrow H : \overset{H}{\underset{H}{\overset{\cdot\cdot}{N}}} : H\quad ^+$$

Similarly a boron trifluoride molecule may share a pair of electrons furnished by a fluoride ion, to form a fluoborate ion:

$$
\begin{array}{ccc}
\;\;:\ddot{F}:\; & & \;:\ddot{F}:\;\quad^{-}\\[2pt]
:\ddot{F}:B\; +\; :\ddot{F}:^{-} \rightarrow & :\ddot{F}:B:\ddot{F}: \\[2pt]
\;\;:\ddot{F}:\; & & \;:\ddot{F}:\;
\end{array}
$$

Electron-pair bonds in which one atom furnishes both of the shared electrons are called coordinate covalent bonds. Likewise, compounds which result from the combination of molecules, atoms, or ions by means of such bonds are called coordination compounds. The molecule, atom, or ion which furnishes the pair of electrons is called the donor, and the molecule, atom, or ion with which the pair of electrons is shared, the acceptor.

As we shall see, electron-pair bonds of the coordinate covalent type account for the formation of many complex compounds, including many of the complex ions which we shall encounter in the study of the heavier metals. Thus, a zinc ion can share four pairs of electrons furnished by four ammonia molecules to form the zinc-ammonia complex ion, $Zn(NH_3)_4^{++}$:

$$
\begin{array}{c}
H\\
H:\ddot{N}:H \qquad ^{++}\\
\\
Zn^{++} + 4H:\ddot{N}:H \rightarrow \quad
\begin{array}{ccc}
H & & H\\
H:\ddot{N}: & Zn & :\ddot{N}:H\\
H & & H
\end{array}\\
\\
H:\ddot{N}:H\\
H
\end{array}
$$

In general we may say that all chemical combination results from the fact that atoms can by their union attain a more stable state than that in which they existed as separate elements. In many cases this increase in stability is attained by the sharing or transfer of electrons in such a manner as to yield electronic configurations which are the same as those of one of the inert gases. This is not always true, however, for there are configurations other than those of the inert gases which in various instances offer some increase in stability over those of the uncombined elements. Specific examples of this will be considered as they arise. A consideration of the factors which determine whether a bond between two given atoms will be electrovalent or covalent, and of the relationship between the properties of chemical compounds and the types of bonds they contain, will be undertaken in the next chapter.

STUDY QUESTIONS AND PROBLEMS

1. What is meant by a spectrum? What is the significance of the fact that atomic spectra are discontinuous?

2. Express by means of an equation the relation between the energy of a photon and its wave length. Which have the more energy, photons of red light or photons of ultraviolet light?

3. What information can be derived concerning atomic structure by the study of atomic spectra? What is meant by an "energy state of an atom"?

4. Upon what basis do we account for the existence of light of definite wave lengths in the spectra of atoms?

5. Make a chart showing the various electron shells and subshells as derived by the new wave mechanics and list the maximum number of electrons which each subshell and shell can contain.

6. From your outside reading or from reference works in your library collect some experimental evidence that electrons do have wave properties.

7. Why is the outer electron in the potassium atom in the $4s$ subshell rather than in the $4p$? the $3d$?

8. Account for the marked similarity of the rare earth elements in terms of their electronic configurations.

9. Why do the halogens differ so greatly in properties from the elements of the manganese family, which is in the same group in the Mendeleeff periodic chart?

10. Describe the mechanism by which elements are united by electrovalent bonds. Give several examples. What determines the number of electrovalent bonds that can be formed by a given atom?

11. What is meant by a covalent bond? Give electronic formulas for several covalent compounds.

12. Give several examples of coordinate covalent bonds. How do these bonds differ from ordinary covalent bonds?

10

Relation of Chemical and Physical Properties to Atomic and Molecular Structure

1. Introduction. In the preceding chapter it was shown that there are several different ways in which atoms can combine with each other. There is no other single factor that is of such prime significance in determining the properties of a compound as the nature of the bonds by which its atoms are united. Hence it is logical that, having discussed the types of chemical bonds, we should now turn our attention to the factors which determine what sort of bond will be formed between given atoms; and further to the question of what sort of chemical and physical properties each type of bond confers upon the compound in which it exists.

2. Electron Attraction and Bond Formation: Metals and Nonmetals. Let us consider the general case of the two atoms A and B which have at least one valence electron each. If these two atoms differ widely in their attraction for electrons, i.e., if, let us say, B has a much stronger attraction for electrons than A, the valence electron from A will be *transferred* completely from A to B and an electrovalent or ionic compound will be formed. This may be represented by the equation

$$A\cdot \ + \ \cdot B \rightarrow A^+ \ + \ :B^-$$

On the other hand, the electron affinities of A and B may be equal, in which case reaction between A and B will involve the *sharing* of the pair of electrons to form a covalent bond, as is represented by the equation

$$A\cdot \ + \ \cdot B \rightarrow A:B$$

It should be noted that in this case the pair of electrons is shared equally between the two atoms and that the electrical charges in the molecule are symmetrically distributed; i.e., the "centers of gravity" of positive and negative charge coincide. Such a covalent bond is said to be nonpolar.

It is, however, only in the case where A and B are atoms of the same element that we expect to find *exactly* the same electron attractive forces for the two combining atoms. Therefore, we must next consider the common case where A and B differ in their attraction for electrons, yet insufficiently so as to bring about complete electron transfer. In such a case the atoms still combine by sharing electrons to form a covalent bond, but the electrons are shared unequally; i.e., the pair of electrons is shifted toward the atom with the greater attraction for electrons. Such a bond is known as a *polar* covalent bond, since the pair of electrons is more closely associated with one of the atoms than with the other; the first atom is negatively charged, whereas the other is positively charged. This situation can be represented by the equation

$$A\cdot + \cdot B \rightarrow A^{\delta+} : B^{\delta-}$$

where $\delta+$ and $\delta-$ represent the small equal increments of positive and negative charge on the respective atoms which result from the unequal sharing of the electron pair. The magnitude of the polarity of the bond will, of course, depend upon the difference in the attraction which the two atoms have for electrons. In any case, however, $\delta+$ and $\delta-$ will be less than the unit electrical charge on the proton and the electron; for, should $\delta+$ and $\delta-$ become in any case equal to 1, we should then have that complete electron transfer which constitutes the formation of an electrovalent compound, as in the first instance described above.

On the basis of the foregoing discussion, we may now conveniently divide the elements in two groups. Those elements whose atoms have a small attraction for their valence electrons are know as *metals,* whereas elements whose atoms have a high attraction for their valence electrons are called *nonmetals.* Metals react by losing electrons to form positive ions, or if they form covalent bonds with nonmetals they constitute the positive ends of such bonds. Nonmetals, on the other hand, tend to take up electrons to form negative ions, or if they form covalent bonds with metals, they constitute the negative ends of such bonds. Of course when two nonmetals form a covalent bond, the less nonmetallic forms the positive end of the bond. Physical characteristics of metals and nonmetals will be discussed in detail in a later chapter (p. 622). As we shall see in the study of the individual elements, these definitions, although neither precise nor entirely accurate, are nevertheless extremely useful. Familiar elements belonging to the class of metals include sodium, calcium, magnesium, iron, zinc, copper, aluminum, mercury, lead, and many others; in fact, more than three-fourths of all the elements are classified as metals. Familiar nonmetals include oxygen, nitrogen, carbon, chlorine, iodine, phosphorus, sulfur, and others.

3. Measures of Electron Attraction. It is apparent from the preceding section that the major factor which determines bond type is the relative attraction which the two combining atoms have for electrons. The attractive force which an atom of an element exerts on its valence electrons is conveniently stated in terms of the gaseous *ionization potential*, which is a direct measure of the energy required to bring about the removal of an electron from an atom of the element. The first ionization potential is a measure of the energy required to remove the least tightly bound electron from the unexcited atom, and hence corresponds to the process $A \rightarrow A^+ + e^-$, where A is unexcited and in the gaseous state. The second ionization potential is a measure of the energy required to bring about the process $A^+ \rightarrow A^{++} + e^-$; the third ionization potential refers to the change $A^{++} \rightarrow A^{+++} + e^-$; and so on for the fourth, fifth, sixth, ... and nth ionization potentials. For the methods by which ionization potentials are determined the student is referred to textbooks of physics or physical chemistry.

4. Ionization Potentials and Atomic Structure. In order that we may fully appreciate the significance of the variation in the ionization potentials of the elements with their positions in the periodic system, we must first consider those atomic characteristics which determine the ionization potentials. A rigorous discussion of this question would be beyond the scope of this text, but a fairly simple, though admittedly approximate, approach to the question may be made through a consideration of the following factors: (1) the charge on the atomic nucleus, (2) the shielding effect of inner electron shells, (3) the atomic radius, and (4) the nature of the subshell in which the electron is located, i.e., whether it is an s, a p, a d, or an f subshell.

The relationship of the first of these factors to the ionization potential is immediately evident; as the positive charge on the nucleus of the atom is increased, the attractive force acting upon the negatively charged electrons, and hence the ionization potential, will be augmented. It is likewise apparent that the existence of inner shells of electrons between the least tightly bound electron and the nucleus will to a certain extent "shield" the electron from the nucleus, for the attractive force of the nucleus on the outer electron will be partially counterbalanced by the repulsion from the inner shells of electrons, as is indicated in Figure 10.1. Thus, an increase in the number of electrons in the inner shells tends to decrease the ionization potential. Similarly, since the force between two electrical charges varies inversely with the square of the distance between them, it is easy to see that the farther the outer electron is from the nucleus—that is, the greater the atomic radius—

the smaller will be the force of attraction between them, and therefore the lower will be the ionization potential.

With respect to the fourth factor, it has already been pointed out (p. 161) that within a given election shell the subshells increase in energy in the order $s < p < d < f$. This means that the ease with which electrons may be removed will increase, or that the ionization potential will decrease, in the

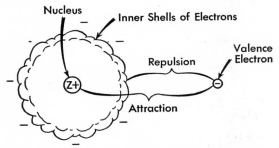

Fig. 10.1.   Effect of inner electron shells on a valence electron.

same order. Hence the ionization potential of an atom whose least tightly bound electron is in an s subshell is greater than if that electron were in a p subshell; similarly, other factors being constant, a p electron is more difficult to remove than a d or an f electron.

With an understanding of these basic principles, we may now undertake a discussion of existing data on the ionization potentials of the elements, and attempt to correlate these data with the structures of the atoms. Ionization potential data for the elements of the first three series of the periodic system are given in Table 10.1.

APPLICATION AND INTERPRETATION OF IONIZATION POTENTIALS

5. Variation Within a Single Period. An examination of the data in Table 10.1 reveals a number of interesting relationships. In the first place, it may be observed that there is a general increase in ionization potential as one proceeds from left to right in a given period in the periodic system. Thus, in the third period, sodium—the first element on the left—has the lowest ionization potential, and argon—the last element in the period—the highest. This general increase is easily explainable as the result of the fact that, whereas within a given period the electrons that are being added as we go from element to element are in the same electron shell, the charge on the nucleus is steadily increasing. The energy required to remove these outer electrons increases, therefore, with increasing nuclear charge. This is indicated graphically in Figure 10.2.

Furthermore, it can be seen from this figure that after each inert gas, i.e., at the beginning of each new period in the periodic system, there is a marked drop in ionization potential. This is to be expected, for the outer electron is going into a higher shell and is relatively well shielded by all the previously added electrons.

Table 10.1

	Electron Configuration			Period	Ionization Potentials (in volts)							
	1 s	2 s p	3 s p		1st	2nd	3rd	4th	5th	6th	7th	8th
H	1			Period I	13.6	....	.....	.....	.....	.....	.....	.....
He	2			Period I	24.6	54.4	.....	.....	.....	.....	.....	.....
Li	2	1			5.4	75.6	122.4	.....	.....	.....	.....	.....
Be	2	2			9.3	18.2	153.9	217.7	.....	.....	.....	.....
B	2	2, 1		Period II	8.3	25.1	37.9	259.3	340.1	.....	.....	.....
C	2	2, 2		Period II	11.3	24.4	47.9	64.5	392.0	489.8	.....	.....
N	2	2, 3		Period II	14.5	29.6	47.4	77.5	97.9	551.9	666.8	.....
O	2	2, 4			13.6	35.1	54.9	77.4	113.9	138.1	739.1	871.1
F	2	2, 5			17.4	35.0	62.6	87.2	114.2	157.1	185.1	935.6
Ne	2	2, 6			21.6	41.1	64.0	97.2	126.4	157.9	.....	.....
Na	2	2, 6	1		5.1	47.3	71.7	98.9	138.6	172.4	208.4	264.2
Mg	2	2, 6	2		7.6	15.0	80.1	109.3	141.2	186.9	225.3	266.0
Al	2	2, 6	2, 1	Period III	6.0	18.8	28.4	120.0	153.8	190.4	241.9	285.1
Si	2	2, 6	2, 2	Period III	8.1	16.3	33.4	45.1	166.7	205.1	246.4	303.9
P	2	2, 6	2, 3	Period III	11.0	19.7	30.2	51.4	65.0	220.4	263.3	309.3
S	2	2, 6	2, 4		10.4	23.4	35.0	47.3	72.5	88.0	281.0	328.8
Cl	2	2, 6	2, 5		13.0	23.8	39.9	53.5	67.8	96.7	114.3	348.3
Ar	2	2, 6	2, 6		15.8	27.6	40.9	59.8	75.0	91.3	124.0	143.5

The increase in ionization potential which takes place as one passes from left to right through a given period, may be used as a basis for at least a partial explanation of the marked change in the chemical properties of the elements in this same order. At the left of a period we have elements of low ionization potential which react by losing electrons. These elements, therefore, form ionic compounds in which they exist as positive ions; in other words they are typical metals (p. 179). As one proceeds to the right, the increase in ionization potential is accompanied by a decrease in tendency to form *positive* ions, and an increase in the tendency for the bonds formed to be covalent rather than electrovalent. Near the end of the period, however, elements of very high ionization potential, which tend to form *negative* ions by taking up electrons, are encountered; these elements are typical non-metals (p. 179). It must be noted, of course, that ionization potential is not an inverse measure of tendency to take up electrons. Atoms of every high ionization potential, however, which have unfilled places in their valence shells, have, in general, strong tendencies to take up electrons. The trend from metallic to nonmetallic behavior is thus easily correlated with ionization potential data.

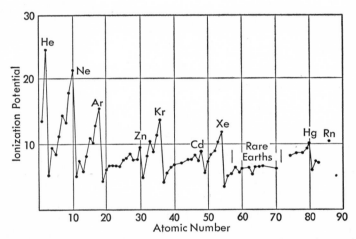

Fig. 10.2. Variation of the first ionization potential with atomic number.

This trend is emphasized even more decisively when it is pointed out that in order that stable inert gas configurations may be attained by the loss of electrons, not one but *all* the valence electrons must be lost. Thus, the sodium atom must lose only one electron; the magnesium atom, two; aluminum, three; silicon, four; phosphorus, five; sulfur, six; and chlorine, seven. The data in Table 10.1 indicate that the energy required to remove each successive electron from an atom is higher than for the previous electron. Thus, the energy required to remove all the valence electrons increases even more rapidly from left to right in a given period than does the potential for the first electron. This is clear from the data of Table 10.2. In view of these data, it is not surprising that there is little tendency for elements other than those in the alkali and alkaline earth metal groups to form simple positive ions.

It is interesting to note from the data in Table 10.1 and from Figure 10.2

that whereas the general trend of first ionization potentials is an increase from left to right in a given period in the periodic system, there are minor retrogressions between beryllium and boron in the second period, between magnesium and aluminum in the third period, and between the corresponding elements in the succeeding periods. These retrogressions are the result of the fact that p electrons are held less tightly than s electrons. Likewise, less important retrogressions occur between nitrogen and oxygen, phosphorus and sulfur, and arsenic and selenium, and there is an unexplained irregularity in the curve between antimony and tellurium.

Table 10.2

Ionization Potentials for Removal of the Last Valence Electron (in volts)

H							He
13.6							54.4
Li	Be	B	C	N	O	F	Ne
5.4	18.2	37.9	64.5	97.9	138.1	185.1	....
Na	Mg	Al	Si	P	S	Cl	Ar
5.1	15.0	28.4	45.1	65.0	88.0	114.3	143.5

6. Ionization Potential Data and the Number of Valence Electrons. Table 10.1 provides excellent experimental evidence as to the number of valence electrons in an atom. In the case of lithium, the first ionization potential is low (5.4 v.) but the second is much higher (75.6 v.), indicating that one electron is much more easily removed than the rest; in other words a lithium atom has one valence electron. There is a marked increase between the second and third ionization potentials of beryllium, indicating two valence electrons. Similarly, sharp increases occur between the third and fourth ionization potentials of boron, the fourth and fifth of carbon, the fifth and sixth of nitrogen, the sixth and seventh of oxygen, and the seventh and eighth of fluorine, indicating three, four, five, six, and seven valence electrons, respectively. Analogous conclusions hold for the elements from sodium to chlorine and for the heavier elements for which data are available.

7. Variation within a Given Group. As seen in Table 10.3, the ionization potentials of the elements in a given family decrease, with minor exceptions discussed later (p. 759), from the top of the group to the bottom. This fact may be explained as follows. In a given group in the periodic system, the effect of higher nuclear charge, alone, would be to cause the elements of higher atomic number in the group to have higher ionization potentials than the members of lower atomic number. This effect is more than counterbalanced, however, by the fact that in the atoms of higher atomic number the valence electrons are farther from the nucleus, and are shielded by more intervening shells of electrons. The result is that the ionization potentials decrease with increasing atomic number within any family.

Table 10.3

Ionization Potentials for Removal of the Last Valence Electron

Group 1a		Group 2a		Group 6a	
Li	5.4	Be	18.2	O	138.1
Na	5.1	Mg	15.0	S	88.0
K	4.3	Ca	11.9	Se	81.4
Rb	4.2	Sr	11.0	Te	72.0
Cs	3.9	Ba	10.0		

This explains the rule that, in general, metallic properties become more prominent and nonmetallic characteristics less prominent within any family as the atomic number is increased. Combined with the observed trends from left to right in the periodic system, this rule explains the fact that the most active metal and nonmetal are found at the lower left and upper right, respectively, of the periodic chart, and the fact that the nonmetals may be roughly separated from the metals by means of a zigzag line (Figure 10.3).

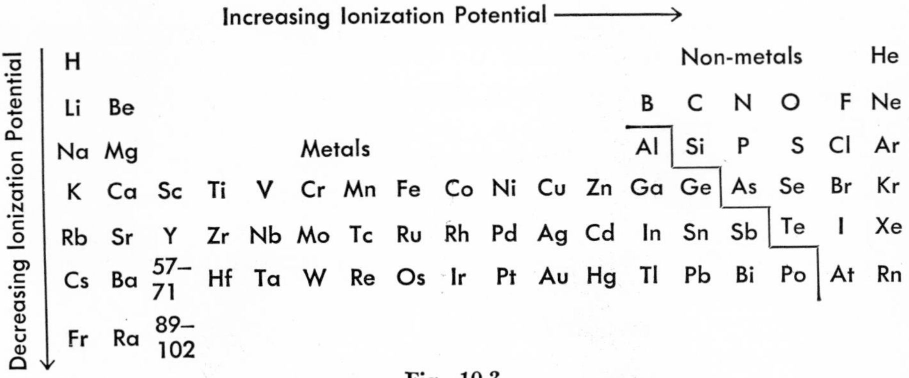

Fig. 10.3.

RELATION OF CHEMICAL AND PHYSICAL PROPERTIES
TO BOND TYPE

8. Scope of Discussion. We are now ready to undertake the discussion of the second question posed in the introduction to this chapter, viz., what sort of chemical and physical properties are conferred upon a substance by the presence in its molecules of a certain type of chemical bond. Much of the information relevant to the discussion of this question must, for various reasons, either be postponed to later sections of the book, or, in certain cases, omitted entirely; but certain basic principles will be discussed here.

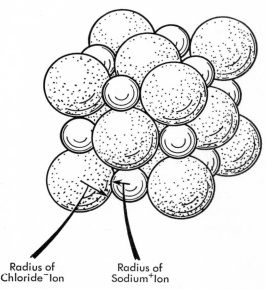

Radius of
Chloride⁻Ion

Radius of
Sodium⁺Ion

Fig. 10.4   Diagram of a sodium chloride crystal; the concept of ionic radius.

9. Ionic or Electrovalent Substances. Compounds which contain electrovalent or ionic bonds are composed of positive and negative ions, and such substances in the solid state consist of crystals made up of regular geometrical arrangements of these ions. The force which holds together the ions in such crystals is the electrostatic attraction which the oppositely charged ions exert on each other. Any given ion in a crystal exerts a similar force on all the oppositely charged ions in its immediate vicinity, and it is therefore impossible for us to select any group of atoms which might properly be called a molecule; indeed, in the case of ionic substances the whole crystal must be considered to be a single huge molecule (Figure 10.4). It is incorrect, therefore, to speak of a molecule of an ionic compound or of the molecular weight of such a substance. Examples of ionic substances include sodium chloride, potassium nitrate, and calcium fluoride. Because the electrostatic forces which hold ionic crystal lattices together are rather large, such crystals are hard and nonvolatile; ionic substances, therefore, have high melting points, and their boiling points in most cases are above 900° C.

The magnitude of the electrostatic force f between charged bodies is given by the formula $f = q_1q_2/Dr^2$, where q_1 and q_2 represent the charges on the two bodies, and r the distance between them, while D is a constant, known as the dielectric constant, which is 1 in a vacuum and otherwise has a larger value characteristic of the medium in which the charged bodies are placed.[1] It is apparent from this formula that the attractive forces between oppositely charged ions have their highest possible value in a crystal of the ionic compound. In order for an ionic substance to go into solution, the crystal must be broken down. This can occur only if these forces, which according to the formula are inversely proportional to the dielectric constant of the medium, are reduced to a fraction of their original value. It is not surprising, therefore, to find that ionic substances are more soluble in liquids of high dielectric constant than in those of low; for example, water (p. 233) and liquid ammonia (p. 482) are excellent solvents for ionic substances. Either in solution or in the molten state, ionic substances conduct an electric current, since under these conditions the ions are free to move in response to an external electrical force.

10. Covalent Substances. Before we proceed to consider the typical properties of covalent substances, we must first distinguish between two types of molecules, nonpolar and polar. Consider the case of a diatomic molecule AB. If the pair (or pairs) of electrons connecting the two atoms is shared equally between them—in other words, if the bond is nonpolar—the molecule as a whole is symmetrical with respect to the distribution of electrical charge and is therefore nonpolar. On the other hand, if the two atoms are connected by a polar covalent bond, the charges are not symmetrically distributed (p. 179) and the molecule is polar. The degree of polarity of the molecule depends, of course, on the degree of polarity of the bond, which, in turn, as has already been pointed out (p. 179), is dependent upon the extent to which the two atoms differ in their attraction for electrons. In molecules containing more than two atoms, and hence more than one bond, however, the polarity is the resultant of the individual polarities of all the polar covalent bonds in the

---

[1] Thus, the statement that H_2O has a dielectric constant of 79 indicates that the force between a given pair of charged particles in water is only $\frac{1}{79}$ of what it would be in a vacuum.

molecule. Thus, a molecule which is completely symmetrical with respect to its polar covalent bonds is nonpolar, even though it contains polar bonds. An example of such symmetry is provided by carbon tetrachloride, a molecule of which contains four polar carbon to chlorine bonds. However, these bonds are symmetrically distributed, as shown in Figure 10.5, and hence their polarities cancel each other; i.e., they have a resultant of zero. The molecule

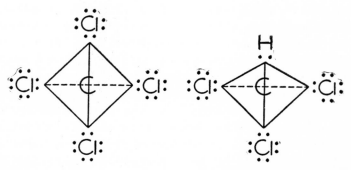

Fig. 10.5.   The CCl_4 molecule.   Fig. 10.6.   The $CHCl_3$ molecule.

of chloroform, $CHCl_3$, on the other hand, lacks this complete symmetry and is, therefore, polar. (See Figure 10.6.) In general, any molecule which contains polar covalent bonds is polar unless it is symmetrical with respect to those bonds.

Since neither polar nor nonpolar covalent substances contain ions in ap-

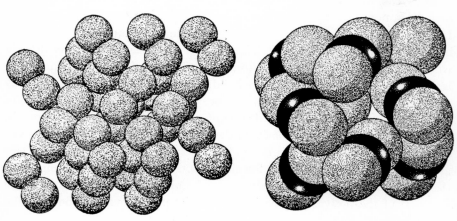

Fig. 10.7 (a). Section of an iodine crystal—a typical nonpolar molecular substance.   Fig. 10.7 (b). Section of a carbon dioxide crystal—a typical nonpolar molecular substance.

preciable quantities, neither of these types of substance are good conductors
of electricity in the liquid state.

Covalent substances of both the polar and the nonpolar type form crystal
lattices in which their molecules retain their identity. Thus, a crystal of solid
methane consists of a lattice of CH_4 molecules, the forces which unite these
molecules into the crystal lattice being very small as compared to the forces
which bind the carbon and the four hydrogen atoms in each molecule. The
intermolecular forces which come into play in crystals of nonpolar covalent
substances in general, being of the same type as those which cause deviation
from the ideal gas laws (p. 52), are relatively weak. Hence, nonpolar
covalent substances are highly volatile and have extremely low melting and
boiling points. Examples of substances of this type include the nonmetallic
elements, and such compounds as carbon dioxide, methane (CH_4), and
many other compounds of carbon.

In crystals of polar substances, besides the forces just mentioned, there is
an additional intermolecular attractive force, viz., the electrostatic attraction which occurs between polar molecules which are suitably oriented with
respect to each other. Because of the mutual attraction of opposite charges,
polar molecules tend to be oriented so that the positive end of one is adjacent to the negative end of the next, and so on, as illustrated in Figure 10.7.
Because of the increased intermolecular forces which result from the electrostatic attraction between polar molecules, polar covalent substances are considerably less volatile than the nonpolar ones. Consequently, polar covalent

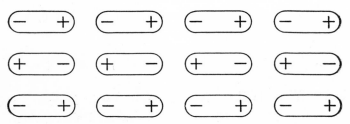

Fig. 10.8.   Orientation of polar molecules in crystals.

substances are intermediate between ionic and nonpolar covalent with
respect to volatility, melting point, and boiling point. Examples of polar
covalent substances include water, hydrogen fluoride (HF, p. 394), nitrous
acid (HNO_2, p. 488), ethyl alcohol (C_2H_5OH, p. 579), and many others.
In some of these substances still another type of intermolecular force,
resulting from the formation of hydrogen bonds, must be considered; this
bonding force will be discussed later in the text (pp. 579, 395, 471).

Since not only the melting points but also the boiling points of polar substances are higher than those of nonpolar substances, it is apparent that the electrostatic forces between polar molecules persist even in the liquid state; indeed, it has been shown that these forces are sufficient to cause association (or weak chemical combination) of the molecules of these substances. Because of such association, the behavior of polar liquids deviates considerably from many of the laws which describe the behavior of unassociated liquids; on this account polar liquids, i.e., liquids composed of polar molecules, are sometimes termed abnormal.

The polarity of a liquid is of primary significance in determining its solvent properties. Since the molecules of a polar liquid are drawn together by electrostatic forces as described in the preceding paragraph, any attempt to mix a nonpolar substance with a highly polar liquid is usually unsuccessful, because nonpolar molecules cannot take part in the association of the molecules of the polar liquid and are "squeezed out." Similarly, molecules of a highly polar substance will not distribute themselves throughout a nonpolar liquid. Nonpolar liquids and highly polar liquids are, therefore, generally immiscible with each other.

Polar substances (especially liquids) tend to be most soluble in polar solvents, while nonpolar substances (especially liquids) exhibit their highest solubilities in nonpolar solvents. Thus gasoline, a mixture of substances of low polarity, is immiscible with the highly polar liquid water, but is completely miscible with the nonpolar carbon tetrachloride.

The dielectric constant of a liquid is directly related to the polarity of its molecules. Hence, highly polar liquids, with high dielectric constants, tend, in accordance with the discussion on p. 187, to be good solvents for ionic substances. Ionic substances, on the other hand, show little tendency to dissolve in nonpolar liquids.

11. Atomic and Metallic Crystals.

In addition to the ionic and polar and nonpolar molecular types of crystal lattices discussed above, there are two other types which must be mentioned. The first of these is the atomic crystal lattice. Such a lattice consists throughout of atoms which are connected to their nearest neighbors by covalent bonds, so that the whole crystal must be considered to be a single gigantic molecule. Usually, such crystals are formed either by elements in periodic Group 4a or by binary compounds in which the two elements are in periodic groups the average of whose numbers is 4. Examples include carbon—in the form of diamond (p. 531)—silicon, silicon carbide, aluminum nitride, beryllium oxide, and scandium nitride. Since all the atoms in such crystals are connected by strong covalent bonds, the

Table 10.4

Diagrammatic Illustration	Particles in Crystal	Attractive Forces Between Particles	Melting Points and Boiling Points	Electrical Conductivity of Liquid	Other Physical Characteristics of Crystal	Conditions for Formation	Examples
Ionic Crystals	+ and − ions	Electrostatic attraction between ions (strong)	High	High	Hard, brittle. Usually dissolve in polar liquids.	Formed between atoms of widely differing attractions for electrons (or widely differing ionization potentials).	$NaCl$, CaF_2, Cs_2S
Polar Molecular Crystals	Polar molecules	Electrostatic attraction between dipoles plus van der Waals forces (intermediate)	Intermediate	Very low	Much weaker than ionic crystals. Usually dissolve in polar liquids.	Formed from unsymmetrical molecules containing polar covalent bonds. Such bonds are formed between atoms having a moderate difference in attraction for their valence electrons.	H_2O, PCl_3, S_2Cl_2, HCl
Nonpolar Molecular Crystals	Nonpolar molecules	van der Waals forces (weak)	Low	Extremely low	Soft. Usually dissolve in nonpolar liquids.	Formed from symmetrical molecules or molecules containing only nonpolar covalent bonds. Such bonds are formed between like atoms or atoms having no appreciable difference in attraction for electrons.	Cl_2, H_2, He, CO_2, CCl_4
Atomic Crystals	Atoms	Covalent bonds (very strong) (the whole crystal is a gigantic molecule)	Very high		Very hard. Insoluble in most ordinary liquids.	Usually formed by elements of Group 4a or by binary compounds in which the two elements are in periodic groups the average of whose numbers is 4.	C (diamond) SiC, AlN, BeO

crystals are very hard, have extremely high melting points, and are nonvolatile.

The fifth type of crystals includes most of the free metals. The bonding forces and properties of such crystals, which are distinctly different from those of any of the other types, are discussed in detail in Chapter 33. The various types of crystalline solids are summarized in Table 10.4.

It must be stated that the types of crystals discussed here represent ideal extremes and that there are numerous instances in which a compound is intermediate in properties between two types. Thus silver iodide crystals are intermediate between the atomic and ionic types; the same may be said of silicon dioxide. Bismuth crystals have characteristics of the atomic type along with the predominant metallic character. The cadmium iodide crystal furnishes an excellent example of a crystal having characteristics of three of the above types: viz., molecular, ionic, and atomic.

Table 10.5

Electronic Configurations					Ionic Radii in Angstrom Units. $(1\ \text{Å} = 10^{-8}\ \text{cm.})$						

2 ....
Li^+ Be^{++} B^{3+} C^{4+} N^{5+} O^{6+} F^{7+}
0.60 0.31 0.20 0.15 0.11 0.09 0.07

2 2,6 .... C^{4-} N^{3-} O^{--} F^- : 2.60 1.71 1.40 1.36
Na^+ Mg^{++} Al^{3+} Si^{4+} P^{5+} S^{6+} Cl^{7+}
0.95 0.65 0.50 0.41 0.34 0.29 0.26

2 2,6 2,6 .... Si^{4-} P^{3-} S^{--} Cl^- : 2.71 2.12 1.84 1.81
K^+ Ca^{++} Sc^{3+} Ti^{4+} V^{5+} Cr^{6+} Mn^{7+}
1.33 0.99 0.81 0.68 0.59 0.52 0.46

2 2,6 2,6,10 ....
Cu^+ Zn^{++} Ga^{3+} Ge^{4+} As^{5+} Se^{6+} Br^{7+}
0.96 0.74 0.62 0.53 0.47 0.42 0.39

2 2,6 2,6,10 2,6 .... Ge^{4-} As^{3-} Se^{--} Br^- : 2.72 2.22 1.98 1.95
Rb^+ Sr^{++} Y^{3+} Zr^{4+} Nb^{5+} Mo^{6+}
1.48 1.13 0.93 0.80 0.70 0.62

2 2,6 2,6,10 2,6,10 ....
Ag^+ Cd^{++} In^{3+} Sn^{4+} Sb^{5+} Te^{6+} I^{7+}
1.26 0.97 0.81 0.71 0.62 0.56 0.50

2 2,6 2,6,10 2,6,10 2,6 Sn^{4-} Sb^{3-} Te^{--} I^- : 2.94 2.45 2.21 2.16
Cs^+ Ba^{++} La^{3+} Ce^{4+}
1.69 1.35 1.15 1.01

2 2,6 2,6,10,14 2,6,10 2,6,10 ....
Au^+ Hg^{++} Tl^{3+} Pb^{4+} Bi^{5+}
1.37 1.10 0.95 0.84 0.74

12. The Concept of Ionic Radius. Let us visualize an ionic crystal lattice as consisting of spherical ions in contact with each other. The radius of an ion may then be defined as the radius of this spherical space occupied by the given ion, as illustrated in Figure 10.4. We shall not undertake to discuss the manner in which the radii of various ions are measured, except to point out that these data are based upon x-ray diffraction experiments on crystals of various compounds containing the ion. For ions such as Sn^{4+}, P^{5+}, and Cl^{7+}, which do not actually exist in any crystal, hypothetical ionic radii may be calculated; i.e., the radii which these ions might be expected to have if they did exist. Although such calculation may seem to be far-fetched, it is justi-

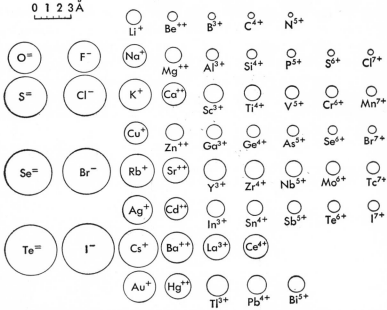

Fig. 10.9. Relative sizes of some ions. (Redrawn from Pauling, *The Nature of the Chemical Bond*, Cornell Univ. Press, 1940, Fig. 44–2.)

fied by the fact that these hypothetical ionic radii, like the radii of actual ions, have proved to be of great utility in the explanation of the properties of compounds of these elements.

The magnitudes of the radii of various ions are listed in Table 10.5, and some of these data are represented graphically in Figure 10.9. In Figure 10.10 the relative sizes of the various atoms and some of their ions are shown as related to the positions of the elements in the periodic system. It will be noted that positive ions are always smaller than the corresponding neutral atoms. Likewise the negative ions are larger than the atoms from which they are formed.

All the ions listed in a single horizontal row of Table 10.5 have the same electronic configuration, but the nuclear charge increases from left to right. It is to be noted that, as would be expected, the ionic radius decreases in the

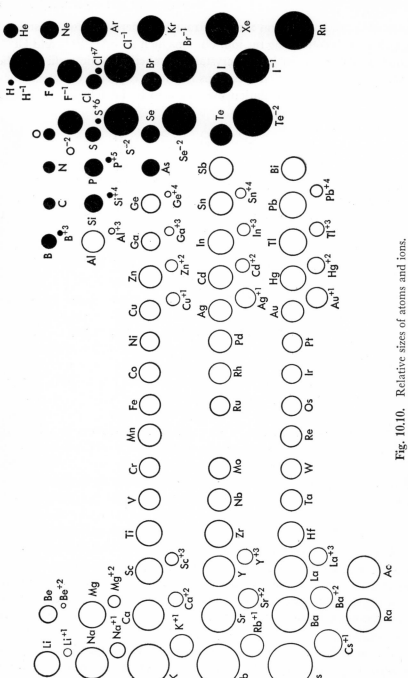

Fig. 10.10. Relative sizes of atoms and ions.

(Reproduced by permission of Dr. J. A. Campbell, Oberlin College.)

same direction. Thus, for ions of a given electronic configuration, the negatively charged ions are always larger than the positively charged ones, and
the radius decreases with decreasing negative charge or increasing positive
charge.

Applications of ionic radius data to the explanation of chemical and
physical properties are too numerous and varied to be considered in detail at
this point; many such applications will be discussed later in the text. At
present, we shall concern ourselves only with the general implications of ionic
size in relation to chemical properties. The intensity of the electrical field
which surrounds an ion depends upon two factors: the ionic charge, and the
size of the ion. Small ions with high positive charge concentrated upon them
are surrounded by very intense positive electrical fields, and hence their
attraction for electrons is very strong. On the other hand, large ions bearing
small positive charges are surrounded by much less intense fields, and hence
have much smaller attraction for electrons. One may use these ideas to
explain the fact that compounds containing such ions as P^{5+} or S^{6+} do not
exist. If such ions did exist, their attraction for electrons would be so great
that they would share pairs of electrons with any neighboring molecules or
negative ions to form either covalent molecules or complex ions.

Ionic radius and charge data are particularly useful in the explanation of
the acidic or basic properties of various compounds and in the explanation
of the variation in the relative tendencies of positive ions to form complex
ions.

13. The Concept of Resonance. There are many instances in which the
properties of a substance do not correspond with any single electronic structure of the usual type which may be written for its molecules. When this is
so, however, it is usually possible adequately to explain the properties of
the substance in terms of a combination or hybrid of two or more electronic structures of the ordinary type. In such instances, we say that the
molecule is a *resonance hybrid of two (or more) electronic structures*. This
does not mean that the molecule has two (or more) different structures or
that there is a mixture of two (or more) different kinds of molecules present.
It means rather that the one kind of molecule has an electronic structure
which is intermediate between, or is a hybrid of, two (or more) ordinary
valence bond structures. These are said to be contributing structures to the
resonance hybrid.

As an example of the resonance phenomenon, consider the structure of
sulfur dioxide. From the known electronic configurations of the oxygen
and sulfur atoms we might write the formula

which contains one double bond and one single bond. We know, however, from the properties of sulfur dioxide that both of the bonds are the same. Furthermore, we see that there is another exactly equivalent structure.

Actually, the sulfur dioxide molecule is a resonance hybrid of the two, each sulfur to oxygen bond being intermediate between a double and a single bond. This is sometimes represented thus:

STUDY QUESTIONS AND PROBLEMS

1. Under what conditions will electrovalent bonds be formed? nonpolar covalent bonds? polar covalent bonds?

2. How does a polar covalent bond differ from a nonpolar covalent bond?

3. What is the ionization potential of an element? What factors determine the magnitude of the ionization potential of an element? Explain. On the basis of this discussion distinguish between metals and nonmetals.

4. Strontium has a much larger nuclear charge than magnesium. How do you account for the considerably higher ionization potential of the latter?

5. Explain the fact that activity within Group 7a increases in the order $I < Br < Cl < F$, but within Group 1a increases in the order $Li < Na < K < Rb < Cs$.

6. Why are crystals of ionic substances harder than those of molecular substances?

7. Why does the melting of ionic crystals produce a liquid which conducts electricity?

8. Explain the extremely low volatility of atomic crystals such as diamond.

9. What evidence do we have that quartz (SiO_2) does not form molecular crystals such as those formed by carbon dioxide? (Hint: Look up the properties of SiO_2.)

10. Using the general principles discussed in this chapter, predict the general sort of properties which the following compounds would have: RbF, ICl, $GeBr_4$, $SrBr_2$. Using reference books from your library, look up the properties of these compounds and compare with your predictions.

11

Oxygen

1. Importance of Oxygen; Characteristics of the Oxygen Atom. Discussion as to which of the elements is the most important is futile, for there are many elements without which the existence of life, as we know it, would be impossible. However, if it were worth while to engage in such a discussion, a strong case could certainly be made for the element oxygen. Not only is oxygen the most abundant element in the earth's crust, but it is the reaction of this element with other substances which provides the energy to support animal life. The source of energy in animal organisms is the reaction of oxygen with food materials which the animal consumes. The reaction of oxygen with various fuels such as coal, gas, or petroleum products furnishes much of the energy required for the operation of industrial plants, as well as for heating our homes, for moving our automobiles, airplanes, ships, and trains, and for numberless other tasks which are important parts of our everyday lives. Oxygen is important also because of the fact that water (Chapter 14), one of its compounds with hydrogen, is an altogether essential substance, both biologically and industrially.

Oxygen is the first element of Group 6a; it has the following electronic configuration:

$$
\begin{array}{cc}
1 & 2 \\
s & s\ p \\
2 & 2\ 4
\end{array}
$$

The oxygen atom thus lacks two electrons in its outer shell of having the stable neon configuration, and in its chemical reactions it attains this stable configuration by taking up two electrons to form the oxide ion, O^{--}, or by forming two covalent bonds. The first of these processes occurs in reactions with the active metals, the second in reactions with hydrogen and with other nonmetals. The oxygen atom can also attain the neon configuration in still another way, namely by forming a single coordinate covalent bond with another atom which furnishes a pair of electrons. In general, the valence of oxygen in its compounds is 2; this point is discussed more thoroughly in Chapter 12. Because of the large amount of energy required to remove electrons from an oxygen atom (p. 182), this element does not form positive oxygen ions in any of its reactions.

2. History and Occurrence. Credit for the discovery of oxygen is shared by two men, Joseph Priestley, an English clergyman and amateur scientist, who later moved to the United States to escape religious persecution, and Carl Wilhelm Scheele, a Swedish pharmacist. Working independently, these two men both obtained the gas which we know as oxygen by heating various compounds of the element, particularly mercuric oxide (p. 199). They also found evidence that this gas is a component of the atmosphere. Priestley's work was published in 1774, but although Scheele's experiments had probably been performed even earlier, their publication was delayed and no account of them appeared until 1777. Though Priestley recognized that the gas he had discovered plays an important role in combustion, he remained, along with Scheele, an ardent adherent of the phlogiston theory of combustion (p. 7); in fact he called the gas "dephlogisticated air."

It was the brilliant French chemist Lavoisier (p. 8) who, in 1777, on the basis of the experimental results of Priestley, Scheele, and others, as well as some very fine experimental work of his own, established the modern concept that the combustion of a substance consists in its combination with the new gas which Priestley and Scheele had described, and which Lavoisier conclusively proved to be an important constituent of the atmosphere. Since the combustion of many substances (now known as nonmetals) such as phosphorus and sulfur yields products which react with water to give acidic solutions, Lavoisier named this gas *oxygen,* derived from Greek words meaning "acid former." We may now question the appropriateness of this name, for we know that many oxides yield basic solutions (p. 203), while there are many acids which do not contain oxygen. The epoch-making character of Lavoisier's introduction of quantitative experimentation into chemical research has already been mentioned (p. 8). Unfortunately, Lavoisier was guillotined by French revolutionary extremists at the height of his scientific career.

Oxygen occurs in the free state as the second most abundant component of the atmosphere; about one-fifth of the air by volume is oxygen. In the combined state it makes up 88.81% by weight of pure water, and, on the average, 85.79% of sea water. It occurs in the earth's crust, in the form of a multitude of compounds, to the estimated extent of 46.43%. In fact, in our study of inorganic chemistry, we shall encounter this element, either free or combined, more often than any other.

3. Preparation. Oxygen may be produced in the laboratory by the thermal decomposition of a number of its less stable binary and ternary compounds (i.e., compounds containing two and three elements, respectively). The following equations represent typical examples:

$$2HgO = 2Hg + O_2$$
mercuric   mercury   oxygen
oxide

$$2BaO_2 = 2BaO + O_2$$
barium   barium   oxygen
peroxide   oxide

$$2KNO_3 = 2KNO_2 + O_2$$
potassium   potassium   oxygen
nitrate   nitrite

The most widely used laboratory method involves the thermal decomposition of potassium chlorate, $KClO_3$. The apparatus in which this reaction is carried out is illustrated in Figure 11.1. The oxygen is collected by dis-

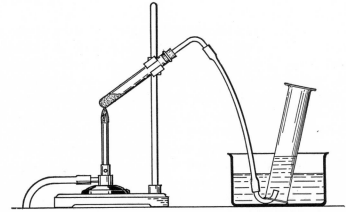

Fig. 11.1. Laboratory preparation of oxygen from potassium chlorate.

placement of water from a bottle inverted in a tank of water. Pure potassium chlorate must be heated considerably above its melting point (357° C.) before evolution of oxygen begins to take place. The products of the reaction are oxygen and potassium chloride, as is indicated by the following equation:

$$2KClO_3 = 2KCl + 3O_2$$

This reaction takes place much more rapidly, and at a lower temperature, if a little manganese dioxide, MnO_2, is added to the potassium chlorate.

Surprisingly, the manganese dioxide is not used up, but may be recovered unchanged at the end of the reaction. This is an example of a rather common phenomenon known as *catalysis* (p. 252). Any substance which affects the rate of a chemical reaction, but which itself may be recovered unchanged at the end of the reaction, is known as a *catalyst* for that reaction. Individual catalysts may either increase or decrease the rate of a reaction, and hence may be classed as positive or negative, respectively.

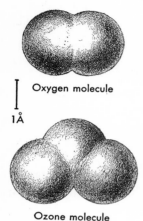

Oxygen molecule

1Å

Ozone molecule

Fig. 11.2. Scale models of oxygen and ozone molecules.

Other methods of preparation adaptable to laboratory use include the addition of sodium peroxide ("oxone") to water (p. 647), and the electrolysis of water. The latter process is carried out by passing an electric current through water to which has been added a little sulfuric acid or sodium hydroxide. Hydrogen gas is liberated at one electrode and oxygen at the other.

$$2H_2O = 2H_2 + O_2$$

Commercially, oxygen is almost always obtained from air, the main components of which are nitrogen and oxygen (p. 371). Liquid nitrogen boils at a lower temperature than does liquid oxygen, and, in a mixture of the two, the former tends to boil off more rapidly than the latter; thus both of these substances may be obtained by the distillation (p. 238) of liquid air. Oxygen of a purity as high as 99.5 per cent can be obtained by the application of proper distillation techniques. For commercial use, the gas is stored and transported under high pressures in steel cylinders.

4. Physical and Chemical Properties. Oxygen exists in two molecular forms, one corresponding to the formula O_2 and the other to the formula O_3 (Figure 11.2). The former is the common and more stable form. The latter is known as ozone, and will be discussed later in this chapter.

Ordinary oxygen, O_2, is a colorless, odorless, and tasteless gas which cannot be liquefied under any pressure, no matter how large, until it has been cooled to $-118.84°$ C., its critical temperature, at which temperature a pressure of 49.71 atm. (its critical pressure) is sufficient to bring about liquefaction. Under a pressure of 1 atm., oxygen liquefies at a temperature of $-182.97°$ C. Since the type of bonding involved in the O_2 molecule is unusual and rather complex, it will not be discussed in this text.

Oxygen gas under standard conditions has a density of 1.4290 g. per liter. It is only very slightly soluble in water. Fish and many other aquatic organisms, however, satisfy their respiratory needs with dissolved oxygen.

Stable binary compounds of oxygen with all the elements except the inert gases are known; most of these oxides may be obtained by direct combination of oxygen with the element concerned, although the oxides of the halogens (p. 401) and of the less active metals such as gold, silver, and platinum are exceptions. In spite of this fact, however, oxygen is only moderately reactive at room temperature. Most of its reactions take place at appreciable rates only at elevated temperatures. The great majority of these reactions are exothermic, however, and, once initiated, produce enough heat to keep the temperature at such a level that the reaction proceeds rapidly without further application of heat. Examples of typical reactions of oxygen with metals and nonmetals are represented by the following equations:

Metals:

$$2Ca + O_2 = 2CaO$$
calcium   calcium
oxide

$$4Al + 3O_2 = 2Al_2O_3$$
aluminum   aluminum
oxide

$$4Li + O_2 = 2Li_2O$$
lithium   lithium
oxide

Nonmetals:

$$S_8 + 8O_2 = 8SO_2$$
sulfur   sulfur
dioxide

$$P_4 + 5O_2 = P_4O_{10}$$
phosphorus   phosphoric
anhydride

$$C + O_2 = CO_2$$
carbon   carbon
dioxide

Oxygen reacts also with many compounds, the result of such reactions usually being the formation of oxides of one or more of the elements in the compound. Thus, natural gas, which consists largely of methane (CH_4), burns in air or oxygen to yield carbon dioxide and water.

$$CH_4 + 2O_2 = CO_2 + 2H_2O$$

Similarly, gasoline, which contains compounds such as heptane (C_7H_{16}), burns in air to give the same products.

$$C_7H_{16} + 11O_2 = 7CO_2 + 8H_2O$$

Paper and wood consist largely of cellulose, whose empirical formula may be written $C_6H_{10}O_5$. Cellulose burns to form carbon dioxide and water.

$$C_6H_{10}O_5 + 6O_2 = 6CO_2 + 5H_2O$$

The rates at which the reactions of oxygen with elements and compounds proceed vary widely. The rusting of iron at ordinary temperatures takes place very slowly, whereas the burning of hydrogen at temperatures above $600°$ C. takes place so rapidly as to be explosive. In general, such reactions, which take place with the emission of energy in the form of both heat and light, are known as *combustions*. The rates of all reactions with oxygen are higher in pure oxygen than in air. For example, when iron is heated in a stream of oxygen it burns with great brilliance, whereas when heated in air it reacts relatively slowly.

The reactions of elements and compounds with oxygen are known as *oxidation* reactions, and the element that combines with oxygen is said to be *oxidized*. The term oxidation is also used in a much broader sense, which will be discussed in the next chapter.

5. Acids and Bases. Many oxides have the property of combining directly with water to form ternary compounds, the formulas of which include one or more univalent groups each consisting of one oxygen and one hydrogen atom. This OH group, one of the simplest and probably the most frequently encountered of all radicals, has the electron structure $\cdot \overset{..}{\underset{..}{O}} : H$, and is called the hydroxyl radical; the compounds just referred to may thus be called *hydroxyl compounds.*

A considerable number of these compounds are readily soluble in water, and may be obtained simply by dissolving the corresponding oxide in water. The following cases will serve as examples:

$$Na_2O + H_2O = 2NaOH$$

$$CO_2 + H_2O = CO(OH)_2$$

$$BaO + H_2O = Ba(OH)_2$$

A few of the slightly soluble hydroxyl compounds, such as $Ca(OH)_2$, may also be prepared by the combination of the oxide with water, but most of the difficultly soluble compounds, such as $Cd(OH)_2$ and $WO_2(OH)_2$, are obtainable only by indirect means, to be considered presently. Mention should also be made at this point of a large class of related substances which consist also of oxides and water, but which are of indefinite or variable composition; these substances are called *hydrous oxides*, and will be referred to frequently in subsequent chapters.

Hydroxyl compounds which are soluble in water may, in general, be classified into two main groups, according to the properties of the solutions which they form.

1. Aqueous solutions of the compounds obtained by the combination of oxides of the nonmetals (and some of the higher oxides of certain metals) with water have a sour taste, react with active metals such as magnesium or zinc to yield free hydrogen, react with carbonates such as sodium carbonate to produce carbon dioxide, change the color of blue litmus paper to red, and undergo many other characteristic reactions. Substances whose solutions exhibit such properties are commonly known as *acids*. An oxide which combines with water to form an acid is called an *acidic oxide*, or the *anhydride* of the particular acid. The following examples may be cited:

$$SO_2 + H_2O = SO(OH)_2$$

sulfur   sulfurous
dioxide   acid

$$SO_3 + H_2O = SO_2(OH)_2$$

sulfur   sulfuric
trioxide   acid

$$P_4O_{10} + 6H_2O = 4PO(OH)_3$$

phosphorus   phosphoric
pentoxide   acid

2. Aqueous solutions of the compounds obtained by the combination with water of such of the lower oxides of the metals as will dissolve, have a bitter taste, change the color of red litmus to blue, and undergo many other characteristic reactions. These substances, which may properly be called *hydroxides*, are known also as *alkalis* or *bases*; an oxide which combines with water to form a base is called a *basic oxide*. Examples are

$$Na_2O + H_2O = 2NaOH$$

sodium   sodium
oxide   hydroxide

$$CaO + H_2O = Ca(OH)_2$$

calcium   calcium
oxide   hydroxide

Solutions of bases react with and are said to *neutralize* solutions of acids; i.e., if the solutions are mixed in equivalent proportions, the resulting solution is practically devoid of either acidic or basic properties. In fact, most of the oxides, hydrous oxides, and hydroxyl compounds which are not appreciably soluble in water also show either acidic or basic properties, by reacting with solutions of bases or solutions of acids, respectively. Thus, ferric oxide, Fe_2O_3, is insoluble in water, but we know it to be basic because it dissolves in and neutralizes aqueous solutions of acids. On the other hand, insoluble silicon dioxide, SiO_2, shows its acidic nature by dissolving in strongly basic solutions. There is also a group of oxides and hydroxyl compounds, difficultly soluble in water, which dissolve readily either in strongly acid or in strongly basic solutions, thereby showing themselves to be *both* bases and acids. Such compounds are said to be *amphoteric*.

It must be emphasized at this point that, although hydroxyl compounds of the nonmetals are acids, and hydroxides of metals are bases, yet not all acids and bases contain hydroxyl groups. Some of the most important and commonest acids, in fact, are binary compounds which do not even contain oxygen; e.g., hydrogen chloride, HCl. We shall not attempt at this stage to formulate exact definitions of the terms acid and base. Definitions which are both more precise and more general than those which we have given here will be stated in Chapter 17.

Table 11.1

Neutralization Reactions

Acid	+	Base	=	Salt	+	Water
HCl hydrochloric acid	+	NaOH sodium hydroxide	=	NaCl sodium chloride	+	H_2O
H_2SO_3 sulfurous acid	+	2KOH potassium hydroxide	=	K_2SO_3 potassium sulfite	+	$2H_2O$
$2H_3PO_4$ phosphoric acid	+	$3Ca(OH)_2$ calcium hydroxide	=	$Ca_3(PO_4)_2$ calcium phosphate	+	$6H_2O$

For the present we may point out that the most important and most familiar of the acids, both of the hydroxyl type and of the binary type, have this in common: they all contain hydrogen in combination either with a nonmetal or with a radical which behaves as a nonmetal. It is, therefore, customary to write the formulas of the acidic compounds in such a way as to emphasize this fact. Thus, the formula for sulfurous acid is commonly written H_2SO_3 rather than $SO(OH)_2$, sulfuric acid is commonly written H_2SO_4 rather than $SO_2(OH)_2$, phosphoric acid is commonly written H_3PO_4 rather than $PO(OH)_3$, etc. Likewise, it is to be noted that many of the most frequently encountered bases contain a metal in combination with hydroxyl radical.

The neutralization reaction between such acids and bases consists simply in the combination of the hydrogen from the acid and the hydroxyl radical from the base to form water, leaving the metal from the base and the non-metal or radical from the acid to form a *salt*. Equations for typical neutralization reactions are listed in Table 11.1.

Examples of other types of reactions which we have mentioned as being typical of acids or bases are listed in Table 11.2. These types of reactions are very often encountered and deserve careful study.

Table 11.2
Typical Reactions of Acids and Bases

(a)	*Active metal* +	*Acid*	=	*Salt*	+ *Hydrogen*		
	Mg + magnesium	H_2SO_4 sulfuric acid	=	$MgSO_4$ magnesium sulfate	+ H_2 hydrogen		
(b)	*Carbonate* +	*Acid*	=	*Salt*	+ *Water*	+	*Carbon dioxide*
	$CaCO_3$ + calcium carbonate	2HCl hydrochloric acid	=	$CaCl_2$ calcium chloride	+ H_2O water	+	CO_2 carbon dioxide
(c)	*Basic oxide* +	*Acid*	=	*Salt*	+ *Water*		
	ZnO + zinc oxide	$2HNO_3$ nitric acid	=	$Zn(NO_3)_2$ zinc nitrate	+ H_2O water		
(d)	*Base* +	*Acidic oxide*	=	*Salt*	+ *Water*		
	2NaOH + sodium hydroxide	SO_2 sulfur dioxide	=	Na_2SO_3 sodium sulfite	+ H_2O water		
(e)	*Basic oxide* +	*Acidic oxide*	=	*Salt*			
	BaO + barium oxide	SO_3 sulfur trioxide	=	$BaSO_4$ barium sulfate			

It has been pointed out that certain insoluble acidic and basic oxides do not react with water, and that the corresponding hydroxyl compounds or hydrous oxides must therefore be prepared by other means. In general, if the insoluble hydroxide or hydrous oxide is basic in nature it may be obtained by the treatment of a solution of a salt of the corresponding metal with a soluble base. Thus, magnesium hydroxide is obtained when magnesium nitrate solution is mixed with sodium hydroxide solution:

$$Mg(NO_3)_2 + 2NaOH = Mg(OH)_{2(s)} + 2NaNO_3$$

On the other hand, an acidic hydroxyl compound or hydrous oxide may be obtained by treatment of a salt which contains the corresponding nonmetal radical with a soluble acid. For example, tungstic acid may be obtained from sodium tungstate solution and sulfuric acid:

$$Na_2WO_4 + H_2SO_4 = Na_2SO_4 + H_2WO_{4(s)} \text{ (or } WO_2(OH)_2)$$

6. Industrial Applications of Oxygen. The importance of atmospheric oxygen in combustion, as well as in respiration and other biological processes, has already been mentioned. Pure oxygen, too, has numerous uses, and between two and three billion cubic feet of the gas is produced annually in this country. The most important industrial applications of oxygen include its use in the oxy-acetylene welding torch and the oxy-hydrogen torch for the cutting of metals, especially steel, and its use to replenish the oxygen of the air in submarines, or to furnish a breathable atmosphere in airplanes during high altitude flights. Medicinally, oxygen is used in the treatment of pneumonia and other diseases which result in impaired respiration, and as a component of gaseous anesthetic mixtures. A mixture of liquid oxygen and finely divided carbon is a powerful explosive which has found a limited application in mining operations.

OZONE

7. Allotropic Modifications of Elements. The fact that oxygen exists in two molecular forms has already been mentioned, and the properties of the ordinary form, consisting of O_2 molecules, have been discussed. We are now ready to consider the properties of the less common variety, the molecular formula of which is O_3. Different forms of the same element existing in the same physical state are known as *allotropic modifications*, or simply as *allotropes*. The phenomenon of *allotropy* results from the possibility that the atoms or molecules of an element can sometimes be arranged so as to attain reasonably stable configurations in more than one way; it is exhibited by a considerable proportion of the elements, especially by a number of nonmetals. Some nonmetals, such as sulfur and phosphorus, exist in several allotropic forms.

8. Structure and Properties of Ozone. Whereas the vapor density of ordinary oxygen corresponds to the formula O_2, the vapor density of ozone is 50% higher, thus indicating the formula O_3.

Ozone is a faintly bluish gas which, unlike oxygen, has a very characteristic pungent odor; this, in fact, is the source of its name, which comes from a Greek word meaning "to smell." The fact that this odor may be detected in a room just after a high voltage electrical discharge has taken place indicates that ozone is formed from oxygen during such a discharge. The gas condenses to a dark blue liquid at a temperature of $-111.5°$ C. under a pressure of 1 atm., and the liquid solidifies at $-249.6°$ C. to a dark violet, crystalline mass. Ozone is only slightly soluble in water, but is readily soluble in carbon tetrachloride.

That ozone is less stable than ordinary oxygen is indicated by the fact that the change from ozone to oxygen takes place spontaneously, with the liberation of 34,220 cal. of heat per mole of ozone; hence we may write

$$2O_3 = 3O_2 + 68,440 \text{ cal.}$$

The decomposition of ozone is hastened by rise in temperature and is catalyzed by a variety of substances.

The outstanding chemical property of ozone is its very great oxidizing power, which may be attributed to its greater energy content, just referred to, as compared to ordinary oxygen. For example, some of the less active metals such as silver and mercury, which are unaffected by ordinary oxygen, are readily oxidized by ozone; many organic compounds, also, are oxidized by this substance. In some instances, only one-third of the oxygen atoms in ozone are consumed in the formation of oxide, the other two-thirds appearing as ordinary gaseous oxygen.

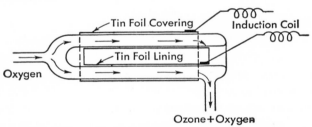

Fig. 11.3.   Apparatus for the preparation of ozone.

9. Preparation and Applications of Ozone. Since energy is liberated in the change of ozone to ordinary oxygen, the reverse process, in which oxygen gas is converted to ozone, requires that this energy be supplied. Since the rate of decomposition of ozone is greatly increased by rise in temperature, it is not practicable to provide this energy in the form of heat. It is usually supplied by means of an electric discharge in a device such as that illustrated in Figure 11.3. The oxygen is passed between the walls of a double-walled glass tube; the outside of the outer tube is wrapped in metal foil, and a cylinder of metal foil is likewise placed inside the inner tube. The two pieces of metal foil are connected to the terminals of 20,000–30,000 v. transformer. Only a few per cent of the oxygen is converted to ozone by this method, but the yield is somewhat increased if the emerging gas is rapidly cooled, and the oxygen gas is thoroughly dried before it enters the ozonizer. In some ozone generators the inner metal cylinder is replaced by a solution of an electrolyte such as copper sulfate.

Traces of ozone in the air result from lightning flashes and from the action of ultraviolet light from the sun on the oxygen in the upper atmosphere.

The practical application of ozone is limited by the difficulty and high cost of producing it. It does find limited application, however, as a bleaching agent, disinfectant, and deodorant, and in water purification. All these uses depend upon its oxidizing power.

STUDY QUESTIONS AND PROBLEMS

1. Discuss in terms of its structure the ways in which the oxygen atom enters into chemical combination.

2. Write balanced chemical equations for six different reactions by which oxygen may be produced. How is oxygen produced industrially?

3. Define the term *catalysis*. From reference books in the library and from your own text tabulate a number of examples of catalysis. Can you classify these examples into two or three general types?

4. Complete and balance the following equations:

$$Mg + O_2 =$$
$$P_4 + O_2 =$$
$$C_6H_{14} + O_2 =$$

5. Discuss the meaning of the terms *acid, base, acidic oxide,* and *basic oxide,* and give examples of each.

6. Complete and balance the following equations:

$$SO_2 + H_2O \quad =$$
$$H_2SO_4 + CaO \quad =$$
$$HNO_3 + CaCO_3 \quad =$$
$$NaOH + SO_3 \quad =$$
$$MgO + N_2O_5 \quad =$$
$$H_3PO_4 + Ba(OH)_2 =$$
$$Al + HCl \quad =$$

7. Outline the chief industrial applications of oxygen.

8. What is meant by the term allotropic modification? Give several examples.

9. Outline the physical and chemical properties of ozone.

10. If 20 l. of oxygen (measured at standard conditions) is passed through an ozonizer and 6% of the oxygen converted to ozone, what is the volume of the resulting gaseous mixture (at standard conditions)?

Types of Reactions. Oxidation State. Oxidation-Reduction Reactions.

1. Classification of Chemical Reactions. Many of the chemical changes which we have thus far considered, as well as others to be described subsequently, may be assigned to one or another of four classes of simple reactions: namely, combination, decomposition, displacement, and metathesis.

2. Combination. *Combination* consists in the formation of a single substance from two or more substances. Thus, for example, ferrous sulfide is formed when iron and sulfur are heated together; the equation for the reaction may be written

$$Fe + S = FeS$$

Magnesium burns in oxygen to give magnesium oxide.

$$2Mg + O_2 = 2MgO$$

Compounds, as well as elements, may take part in combination reactions; thus the slaking of quicklime consists in the combination of calcium oxide and water to form calcium hydroxide.

$$CaO + H_2O = Ca(OH)_2$$

3. Decomposition. *Decomposition,* the reverse of combination, consists in the formation of two or more substances from one. For example, mercuric oxide, on being heated, yields mercury and oxygen.

$$2HgO = 2Hg + O_2$$

The products of decomposition, however, need not be elements. Thus when potassium chlorate is heated, potassium chloride and oxygen are obtained.

209

Calcium carbonate may readily be decomposed into *two* compounds, calcium oxide and carbon dioxide.

$$CaCO_3 = CaO + CO_2$$

4. Displacement. In *displacement* reactions, an element reacts with a compound, entering into combination with one of the constituents and freeing the other. As an example, we have the familiar method for the production of hydrogen by the action of zinc on an acid (p. 222).

$$Zn + 2HCl = ZnCl_2 + H_2$$

A reaction of similar type occurs when a piece of iron immersed in a solution of cupric sulfate becomes coated with a layer of metallic copper.

$$Fe + CuSO_4 = FeSO_4 + Cu$$

The direction in which a reaction of this type will proceed can often be predicted, for it has been possible to arrange the metals and hydrogen in a *displacement series* such that each element in the series will displace any of those following it *from an aqueous solution of any of its salts*.[1] Such a series, including a few of the more important metals only, is given below:

$$Ca, Mg, Al, Zn, Fe, H, Cu, Hg, Ag, Au$$

(A more extensive discussion of the displacement series is given in Chapter 24.) Thus metallic calcium will displace any of the other metals in the list, whereas gold will not displace but will be displaced by any one of the others. Only those metals which precede hydrogen in the list can liberate hydrogen from aqueous solutions of acids.

Reactions in which a nonmetal is displaced from one of its compounds by another nonmetal are also well known. An industrially important method for the preparation of bromine, for example, is based upon the liberation of this element from its salts by the action of free chlorine.

$$Cl_2 + 2NaBr = 2NaCl + Br_2$$

It is possible to arrange the nonmetallic elements, also, in a displacement series:

$$F, Cl, Br, I, S, Se$$

Each element in this series will displace any of those following it from water solutions of any of their binary compounds. Fluorine, indeed, is so active an element that its preparation in the free state is very difficult.

---

[1] It seems advisable to add a word of caution against the drawing of too general conclusions from this displacement series. It cannot safely be used, for instance, to predict the direction of a displacement reaction between pure substances, in the absence of water.

5. Metathesis. A fourth common class of chemical changes, known as *metathesis,* comprises those reactions in which there is an exchange of elements (or of radicals) between two compounds. A simple illustration is the reaction between silver fluoride and sodium chloride, in aqueous solution, which results in the formation of solid silver chloride, sodium fluoride remaining in solution.

$$AgF + NaCl = AgCl_{(s)} + NaF$$

A slightly soluble solid which separates out when two solutions are mixed is called a *precipitate,* or is said to be *precipitated.*

Another important group of metathetic reactions consists of neutralization reactions (p. 204), in which an acid and a base react to form a salt and water; e.g.,

$$HCl + NaOH = NaCl + HOH$$

6. Valence, Oxidation State, and Oxidation Number. All but the last of the four types of reactions which have just been discussed, together with many others, are included in a large and important class of chemical changes which is known as oxidation-reduction. Before we proceed to the discussion of this class of reactions it will be necessary for us to subject our ideas of valence to review and extension.

The word "valence" has already been used in two distinct senses. First (p. 88), the valence of an element was defined as a *number* indicating its combining capacity. Second (p. 173), the term was used also to denote the *means* by which one atom is able to combine with another, and a distinction was drawn between electrovalence and covalence, depending on the nature of the bond by which the atoms are united. Now it is necessary to introduce a new concept, which, rather than to assign still another shade of meaning to the overworked word "valence," we shall designate as *oxidation state.*

In ionic compounds, the oxidation state of an element (or of a radical) is the same as the charge on the ion formed from an atom of the element (or on the ion formed from the radical), and hence is identical with the electrovalence as previously defined (p. 173). Thus in sodium chloride, sodium is said to be in the $+1$ and chlorine in the -1 oxidation state, or sodium and chlorine are said to have oxidation numbers of $+1$ and -1, respectively. In aluminum oxide, Al_2O_3, the oxidation state of aluminum is $+3$ and of oxygen -2; the total oxidation number of the two aluminum atoms is $+6$, and that of the three oxygen atoms is -6. Thus the oxidation state of an element in a compound is the same as its oxidation number *per atom*. Since any compound as a whole is electrically neutral, it follows as a general rule that *the sum of the oxidation numbers of all the atoms in the formula for any electrovalent compound is always zero.* This constitutes the first oxidation number rule. This same principle is then extended to covalent compounds by means of the simple device of assigning to *each of certain key elements a constant oxidation number,* usually based upon the charge of its ion in electrovalent compounds, and allowing the oxidation numbers of all other elements to be determined by application of a quite similar rule. The only justification for this somewhat arbitrary procedure is the entirely sufficient one of its practical utility.

7. Rules for the Determination of Oxidation Numbers. The rules and conventions for the determination of oxidation numbers, then, may be stated as follows:

Fundamental Rules

1. The sum of the oxidation numbers of all the atoms in the formula for a neutral compound is zero.

2. The oxidation number of any element in the free or uncombined state is zero.

3. The oxidation number of an ion is the same as its charge.

Special Conventions

1. In all hydrogen compounds (except hydrides of very active metals such as lithium, sodium, and calcium) the oxidation number of hydrogen, per atom, is taken to be $+1$.

2. In all oxygen compounds (except hydrogen peroxide and related substances, which will be considered separately in Chapter 14) the oxidation number of oxygen is taken to be -2.

3. In all halides (fluorides, chlorides, bromides, and iodides) the oxidation number of the halogen is taken to be -1.

4. In all sulfides the oxidation number of sulfur is taken to be -2.

The difference between the concept of valence as combining capacity and that of oxidation number as set forth in these rules is clearly brought out by consideration of the following compounds of carbon:

Methane	Methyl Chloride	Methylene Dichloride
CH_4	CH_3Cl	CH_2Cl_2

Chloroform	Carbon Tetrachloride
$CHCl_3$	CCl_4

In each of these compounds, the carbon evidently exhibits the same combining capacity; one atom of carbon, in every case, shares a total of four pairs of electrons with other atoms, and hence carbon is said to be quadrivalent. By the application of our conventional rules, however, we arrive at a different oxidation number for carbon in each of the five compounds, as follows:

$$\begin{array}{ccccc}
\text{C}\ \ \text{H}_4 & \text{C}\ \ \text{H}_3\ \ \text{Cl} & \text{C}\ \ \text{H}_2\ \ \text{Cl}_2 & \text{C}\ \ \text{H}\ \ \text{Cl}_3 & \text{C}\ \ \text{Cl}_4 \\
-4\ +4 & -2\ +3\ -1 & 0\ +2\ -2 & +2\ +1\ -3 & +4\ -4
\end{array}$$

Thus, while the valence of carbon remains constant at 4, its oxidation state varies all the way from -4 in methane to $+4$ in carbon tetrachloride.

In order to determine the oxidation state of any one element in a compound, those of the other elements present being known, we need only apply the first oxidation number rule. In the case of a ternary compound (one containing three elements) it is usually the case that two of the elements will be among those whose oxidation numbers are fixed by convention. For example, let us consider the oxidation number of manganese in potassium permanganate, $KMnO_4$. Since potassium forms an ion with a charge of $+1$, and the oxidation number of oxygen is always -2 per atom, we may write, if x is the oxidation number of manganese in this compound,

$$\text{K}\quad \text{Mn}\quad \text{O}_4$$

$$+1\ +x\ -8 = 0$$

whence $x = 7$.

It should be noted that it is necessary to distinguish between the characteristic oxidation state, or oxidation number per atom, of an element, and the total oxidation number of all the atoms of a given kind in the formula of a compound. We shall follow the practice of placing the former number *above* the symbol of the element, the latter number *below*. Thus, in sodium dichromate, we have, if x is the oxidation number of chromium (per atom),

$$+1\quad\ \ x\quad\ \ -2$$

$$\text{Na}_2\quad \text{Cr}_2\quad \text{O}_7$$

$$+2\ +2x\ -14 = 0$$

whence $2x = 12$, or $x = 6$. Note also that the sum of the oxidation numbers of all the atoms in an ion is not zero, but is equal to the charge carried by the ion. Thus, in sulfate ion, if x is the oxidation number of sulfur, we have

$$x\quad\ \ -2$$

$$\text{S}\quad \text{O}_4{}^{--}$$

$$x - 8 = -2$$

whence $x = +6$.

The inert gases, which form no compounds, never have an oxidation number other than zero. All the other elements, however, exhibit at least two oxidation states—zero in the free condition and some positive or negative value in compounds—while a considerable number of the elements display several oxidation states in different compounds. Sulfur, for example, has an oxidation number of -2 in hydrogen sulfide, H_2S; 0 in free sulfur; $+4$ in sulfur dioxide, SO_2; and $+6$ in sulfur trioxide, SO_3. In this connection it is useful to remember that the highest positive oxidation number exhibited by an element in any of its compounds is usually equal to the number of the group in which it occurs in the periodic system. (The most important exceptions to this rule are to be found in compounds in which copper has an oxidation number of $+2$, and in those in which gold has an oxidation number of $+3$.) Similarly, if an element shows a negative oxidation number, the magnitude of this number is usually equal to and never exceeds the difference between eight and the number of the group in which the element falls. It follows, therefore, for any element in Group 4a, 5a, 6a, or 7a, that the sum of its maximum positive oxidation number and its maximum negative oxidation number (disregarding the sign of the latter) is usually equal to eight.

8. Oxidation and Reduction. Equipped with the oxidation state concept, we are prepared for a more general definition of the terms oxidation and reduction than has been available up to this point. *Oxidation* may be simply defined as a chemical change in which the oxidation state of an element is increased. *Reduction*, which is the opposite of oxidation, is a chemical change in which the oxidation state of an element is decreased. In order that there may be no doubt as to the sense in which the words "increased" and "decreased" have been used in the above definitions, let us suppose all possible oxidation states to be represented on a vertical scale, thus:

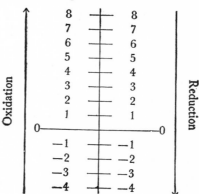

Any change in an upward direction on this scale is to be classed as oxidation; any change in a downward direction, as reduction. In general, metathetic reactions are not of the oxidation-reduction type.

It will readily be seen that several of the types of reaction enumerated earlier in this chapter involve oxidation and reduction. Thus, when magnesium combines with oxygen, according to the equation $2Mg + O_2 = 2MgO$, the oxidation state of magnesium increases from 0 to $+2$, while that of oxygen decreases from 0 to -2, so that the magnesium has been oxidized, and the oxygen reduced. In the decomposition of potassium chlorate, according to the equation $2KClO_3 = 2KCl + 3O_2$, the oxidation state of chlorine decreases from $+5$ to -1, while that of oxygen increases from -2 to 0; hence the chlorine has been reduced, and the oxygen oxidized. (Obviously, however, not *all* combination or decomposition reactions constitute oxidation and reduction. In the formation of an acid from an oxide and water, for example, there is no change in oxidation state.) In the displacement reaction $Zn + 2HCl = ZnCl_2 + H_2$, the zinc is oxidized from an oxidation state of 0 to one of $+2$, while the hydrogen is reduced from $+1$ to 0. Evidently, also, the formation of a positive ion from an elementary substance is oxidation and the formation of a negative ion from an elementary substance is reduction; while the formation of the free element from a positive or from a negative ion is reduction or oxidation, respectively.

9. Oxidizing and Reducing Agents. It is inherent in the nature of oxidation and reduction that neither of these types of change can occur without the other; further, these processes occur not only simultaneously but also to the same extent in a given chemical reaction. These conclusions inevitably follow from the oxidation number conventions which were stated on p. 212. For, by these conventions, the sum of the oxidation numbers of all the atoms of the reactants in a molecular equation must be 0, and the sum of the oxidation numbers of all the atoms of the products must be 0 likewise. Hence, any increase in oxidation number of one or more atoms must be balanced by an equal decrease in oxidation number of one or more other atoms.

Because an element can undergo oxidation only by the reduction of another, the element that is oxidized is called a *reducing agent*. Conversely, because an element which is reduced must inevitably oxidize something else, it is called an *oxidizing agent*. In practice, the terms oxidizing and reducing agent are commonly applied also to the compounds containing the elements which undergo change in oxidation state.

10. Equations for Oxidation-Reduction Reactions. In some instances, the equation for an oxidation-reduction reaction is very simple. Let us consider first, for example, the displacement of one metal by another. It has been stated previously that when a piece of iron is placed in a solution of copper sulfate, metallic copper is deposited on the surface of the iron, while iron goes into solution as ferrous sulfate. The equation for this reaction is immediately obvious.

$$Fe + CuSO_4 = FeSO_4 + Cu$$

We are confident that this equation is correctly balanced, because we can see at once that oxidation and reduction have taken place to the same extent; the oxidation number of the iron has been increased by 2, while that of the copper has been decreased by 2. Iron is oxidized and copper is reduced; iron is the reducing agent, copper the oxidizing agent.

Suppose, however, that aluminum is used as reducing agent, instead of iron. Evidently the equation

$$Al + CuSO_4 = Al_2(SO_4)_3 + Cu$$

is not correctly balanced with respect to oxidation and reduction, because the oxidation number of the aluminum is increased by 3, while that of the copper is decreased by only 2. A single cupric ion, therefore, is insufficient to oxidize an aluminum atom. Obviously, however, *two* aluminum atoms would undergo an increase in oxidation number equal to the decrease in oxidation number of *three* atoms of copper, since $2 \times 3 = 3 \times 2$. The equation, then, should be written

$$2Al + 3CuSO_4 = Al_2(SO_4)_3 + 3Cu$$

In the above instances, the balancing of the equations might have been accomplished readily enough by inspection. However, in many instances the balancing of oxidation-reduction equations is a matter of considerable difficulty, unless some systematic plan is used for arriving at the coefficients of the oxidizing and reducing agents. The general nature of such a plan has already been indicated; two specific methods, however, will be discussed in detail. In the remainder of this chapter, we shall make use of the *oxidation number method*, which is, in fact, universally applicable; consideration of the *ion-electron method*, which has certain advantages in the case of reactions among substances in the ionic state, will be postponed to Chapter 24.

11. Oxidation Number Method. In brief, the method consists in the selection of such coefficients for the oxidizing and the reducing agent, respectively, as will serve to make the total decrease in oxidation number for the former equal to the total increase in oxidation number for the latter.

As our first illustration, let us consider the reaction between cupric oxide and ammonia to give copper, nitrogen, and water, according to the skeleton equation

$$CuO + NH_3 = Cu + N_2 + H_2O$$

It is evident that it is the oxidation states of copper and of nitrogen that have undergone change, which we may indicate as follows:

$$\overset{+2}{}\ \overset{-3}{}\ \ \overset{0}{}\ \ \overset{0}{}$$

Skeleton: $CuO + NH_3 = Cu + N_2 + H_2O$

decrease of 2

increase of 3

In order that the total increase in oxidation number may be equal to the total decrease, there must be three atoms of copper for two of nitrogen. When these coefficients have been supplied, and we have provided for the same numbers of atoms of copper and nitrogen, respectively, on the right side of the equation as on the left, the equation reads

Incomplete: $3CuO + 2NH_3 = 3Cu + N_2 + H_2O$

The coefficients of the oxidizing and the reducing agent are now determined and may not be altered. We find, however, that there are now six H atoms on the left side of the equation; hence, the coefficient of the H_2O, not as yet fixed, must obviously be 3. This coefficient also provides the same number of oxygen atoms on each side; our completed equation, therefore, is

Balanced: $3CuO + 2NH_3 = 3Cu + N_2 + 3H_2O$

As a second example, let us take the oxidation of iodine by nitric acid, as a result of which iodic acid and nitrogen dioxide are formed:

$$\overset{+5}{}\ \ \ \overset{0}{}\ \ \overset{+5}{}\ \ \ \overset{+4}{}$$

Skeleton: $HNO_3 + I_2 = HIO_3 + NO_2 + H_2O$

decrease of 1

increase of 5

Here the oxidation number of each nitrogen atom decreases by 1, while the oxidation number of each iodine atom increases by 5. Hence, there will have to be five nitrogen atoms for each atom of iodine. However, since each iodine molecule contains two atoms, we shall need ten nitrogen atoms for one molecule of iodine. With these coefficients supplied, as well as those necessary to provide the same number of iodine and of nitrogen atoms on the right side of the equation as on the left, we have

$$\text{Incomplete:} \quad 10HNO_3 + I_2 = 2HIO_3 + 10NO_2 + H_2O$$

Now, of the ten H atoms on the left, two are used in the two molecules of HIO_3, leaving eight which must appear in H_2O; hence the coefficient of the latter substance must be 4. This gives us, as the completed equation,

$$\text{Balanced:} \quad 10HNO_3 + I_2 = 2HIO_3 + 10NO_2 + 4H_2O$$

The fact that the number of oxygen atoms is the same (30) on each side of the equation provides a further check on its correctness.

As a final example, let us consider the formation of chlorine by the action of manganese dioxide upon hydrochloric acid:

$$\overset{+4}{MnO_2} + \overset{-1}{HCl} = \overset{+2}{MnCl_2} + \overset{0}{Cl_2} + H_2O$$

Skeleton:

decrease of 2

increase of 1

Only those chlorine atoms which form free chlorine are oxidized; of these, two atoms are oxidized by one of manganese. Thus we get the equation

$$\text{Incomplete:} \quad MnO_2 + 2HCl = MnCl_2 + Cl_2 + H_2O$$

But it now becomes apparent that, in addition to those chlorine atoms which appear in the free chlorine, two additional chlorine atoms (not oxidized) are required for the manganous chloride. Supplying these, and adjusting the coefficient of the H_2O so as to provide the same number of H atoms on each side of the equation, we have, as the completed equation,

$$\text{Balanced:} \quad MnO_2 + 4HCl = MnCl_2 + Cl_2 + 2H_2O$$

12. Equivalent Weights of Oxidizing and Reducing Agents. The equivalent weight of an element, or of a radical, has been previously defined (p. 76) as that weight which combines with 1.0080 parts by weight of hydrogen or eight parts of oxygen. Now, by a slight extension of this concept, we may arrive at the definition of the equivalent weight of an oxidizing agent as that weight which will oxidize 1.0080 parts of hydrogen (or an equivalent amount of another element), and the equivalent weight of a reducing agent as that weight which will reduce eight parts of oxygen (or an equivalent amount of another element). It will be evident that these definitions may also be worded as follows: The equivalent weight of an *element* acting as an oxidizing agent or as a reducing agent is its atomic weight divided by the decrease or increase, respectively, in oxidation number per atom in the reaction. Further, the equivalent weight of a *compound* that is regarded as an oxidizing agent or as a reducing agent is its formula weight divided by the total decrease or increase in oxidation number (per unit of compound) of the atoms reduced or oxidized in the reaction.

Thus, for example, in the reaction

$$\overset{+6}{K_2Cr_2O_7} + \overset{-2}{3H_2S} + 4H_2SO_4 = \overset{+3}{Cr_2(SO_4)_3} + K_2SO_4 + \overset{0}{3S} + 7H_2O$$

there is an increase in oxidation number of 2 per atom of sulfur, or 2 per molecule of hydrogen sulfide; and a decrease of 3 per atom of chromium, or 6 per unit of potassium dichromate. Hence, the equivalent weight of sulfur is $32.066/2 = 16.033$, and that of hydrogen sulfide, $34.082/2 = 17.041$. Similarly, the equivalent weight of chromium is $52.01/3 = 17.34$, and that of potassium dichromate, $294.22/6 = 49.037$. It is clear that in the equation there are six equivalent weights each of potassium dichromate and hydrogen sulfide, and hence that one equivalent weight of potassium dichromate would react with exactly one equivalent weight of hydrogen sulfide. Similarly, in any oxidation-reduction reaction, one equivalent weight of oxidizing agent and one equivalent weight of reducing reagent will just react with each other. In accordance with our previous definition (p. 90), a gram-equivalent of an oxidizing or reducing agent is a number of grams equal to the equivalent weight.

STUDY QUESTIONS AND PROBLEMS

1. Characterize each of the following reactions as combination, decomposition, displacement, or metathesis:

(a) $NH_4Cl = NH_3 + HCl$
(b) $Pb(NO_3)_2 + 2KI = PbI_2 + 2KNO_3$
(c) $2Al + 3H_2SO_4 = Al_2(SO_4)_3 + 3H_2$
(d) $P_4O_{10} + 2H_2O = 4HPO_3$
(e) $4HI + O_2 = 2H_2O + 2I_2$
(f) $4HNO_3 + P_4O_{10} = 2N_2O_5 + 4HPO_3$
(g) $As_2S_5 + 3(NH_4)_2S = 2(NH_4)_3AsS_4$
(h) $2Al + Cr_2O_3 = Al_2O_3 + 2Cr$
(i) $2SbCl_3 + 3H_2S = Sb_2S_3 + 6HCl$
(j) $(NH_4)_2Cr_2O_7 = N_2 + Cr_2O_3 + 4H_2O$

2. Which of the reactions of question 1 involve oxidation and reduction?

3. Determine the oxidation state of the underlined elements in the following compounds or ions. CH_2O; $\underline{Ru}O_4$; $K_2\underline{Ta}F_7$; $(NH_4)_2\underline{Mo}O_4$; $\underline{S}_2O_3{}^{--}$; $\underline{Sb}_2S_5$; $\underline{Fe}(CN)_6{}^{----}$ (the oxidation number of the CN radical is -1); $K_2\underline{Pt}Cl_6$.

4. Balance the following oxidation-reduction reactions:

(a) $H_2S + HNO_3 = S + NO + H_2O$

(b) $AsH_3 + KClO_3 = H_3AsO_4 + KCl$

(c) $KMnO_4 + FeSO_4 + H_2SO_4 = K_2SO_4 + MnSO_4 + Fe_2(SO_4)_3 + H_2O$

(d) $P + HNO_3 + H_2O = H_3PO_4 + NO$

(e) $NaBiO_3 + MnO_2 + H_2SO_4 = Bi_2(SO_4)_3 + NaMnO_4 + Na_2SO_4 + H_2O$

5. Find the equivalent weight of potassium permanganate, $KMnO_4$, and of ferrous sulfate, in question 4(c); of nitric acid in 4(d); of sodium bismuthate, $NaBiO_3$, in 4(e).

6. After you have balanced equation 4(c), show that the weights of potassium permanganate ($KMnO_4$) and ferrous sulfate ($FeSO_4$) which react with each other are in the ratio of their equivalent weights.

7. What weight of concentrated nitric acid containing 68% by weight of HNO_3 is required to oxidize 100 g. of phosphorus to phosphoric acid?

8. Write the formula for a compound formed by each of the following pairs of elements, assigning a positive oxidation number to the first of each pair and a negative oxidation number to the second, and making use of the maximum values corresponding to the position of the element in the periodic system:

S and O	I and F	P and Br	Al and C
W and Cl	Mn and O	Mg and N	Os and F
Cs and O	Ca and P	Bi and Se	Zr and I

Hydrogen

1. Characteristics of the Hydrogen Atom. Because of the many interesting aspects of its chemistry, including its presence in the most familiar of all chemical compounds, and because of the industrial importance of some of its reactions, we now turn our attention to the discussion of the element hydrogen.

Of all the elements, hydrogen has the simplest atomic structure. The nucleus of its most abundant isotope, that of mass 1, consists of a single proton, while the nuclei of the rarer isotopes of mass 2 and 3 have, respectively, 1 and 2 neutrons in addition. Thus, the hydrogen atom has but a single electron. The physical properties of hydrogen are those of a nonmetal; certain of its chemical properties are like those of the metals, and others like those of the nonmetals. It has an oxidation number of $+1$ in most of its compounds; yet, as we shall see, the simple, positively charged hydrogen ion, H^+, does not exist in appreciable quantities in compounds or in solution. In certain circumstances, however, the negatively charged hydride ion, H^-, having the electron configuration of the inert gas helium, is formed. Thus in some ways, hydrogen appears to belong in Group 1a, while in other respects it resembles the elements of Group 7a. Hydrogen must, therefore, be regarded as a special case among the elements of the periodic system.

2. History and Occurrence. Hydrogen had undoubtedly been prepared centuries before it came to be recognized as an individual substance. The latter accomplishment is generally credited to the English scientist Sir Henry Cavendish, who in 1766, prepared "inflammable air," as he called it, by the action of certain acids upon active metals, and by the action of steam upon iron. Although Cavendish studied and described its properties, it was Lavoisier, again, who showed that this "inflammable air" was a new element; and since he was able to prove that this element is a constituent of water, he suggested for it the name *hydrogen*, which means "water former."

It is estimated that 16% of all the atoms in the atmosphere, hydrosphere, and earth's crust combined are hydrogen atoms; only atoms of oxygen and silicon are more abundant. Hydrogen atoms are so very light, however, that the element is estimated to constitute less than 1% of the combined weight of the atmosphere, the hydrosphere, and the earth's crust; in this respect hydrogen ranks ninth among the elements. Hydrogen occurs in nature in the free state in minute quantities only; it occurs most commonly in combination with oxygen in the form of water, and to a lesser extent in combination with carbon, sulfur, nitrogen, and the halogens. Combined usually with carbon, oxygen, and nitrogen, hydrogen is a universal constituent of organic matter. Traces of free hydrogen are found in our atmosphere, appreciable concentrations are found in natural gas and in volcanic gases, and it is believed that much higher percentages (though not larger absolute quantities) of this light gas are present in the upper reaches of the atmosphere. Solar spectra indicate that hydrogen is a major constituent of the sun's atmosphere; streams of incandescent hydrogen are shot out from the sun's surface for distances of thousands of miles.

3. Preparation. The common laboratory methods for the preparation of hydrogen involve its displacement from acids, water, or bases. It was pointed out in the preceding chapter that the metals, along with hydrogen, can be arranged in a series, known as the displacement series, such that each element will displace any of the elements following it in the series from aqueous solutions of its compounds. (A more complete tabulation of the series will be given in Chapter 24, p. 426.) Thus any of the metals preceding hydrogen in the displacement series will displace hydrogen from solutions of acids (except for acids which contain another easily reducible element, in which case other products may be obtained; see, for instance, the reactions of nitric acid with metals (p. 493)).

Examples of such displacement reactions are the following:

$$Zn + H_2SO_4 = ZnSO_4 + H_2$$

$$Mg + 2HCl = MgCl_2 + H_2$$

The very active metals at the head of the series, including lithium, sodium, potassium, barium, calcium, and several others, readily displace hydrogen from water, even at ordinary temperatures, to yield basic hydroxides. The reactions of sodium and of calcium with water are typical.

$$2Na + 2HOH = 2NaOH + H_2$$

$$Ca + 2HOH = Ca(OH)_2 + H_2$$

In the absence of an excess of water, these active metals may displace all the hydrogen in the water molecules to yield the metal oxide rather than the hydroxide; e.g.,

$$2Na + H_2O = Na_2O + H_2$$

At higher temperatures, a number of other metals above hydrogen in the series displace all the hydrogen from water; in these cases the metal oxide is obtained. Thus hot magnesium or iron displaces hydrogen from steam.

$$Mg + H_2O = MgO + H_2$$

$$3Fe + 4H_2O = Fe_3O_4 + 4H_2$$

Certain nonmetals, such as silicon, will displace hydrogen from aqueous solutions of strong bases such as sodium hydroxide.

$$Si + H_2O + 2NaOH = Na_2SiO_3 + 2H_2$$

A few metals whose hydroxides have the capacity to act either as acids or as bases (p. 208) likewise undergo, under certain circumstances, the same sort of reaction. Examples include the reactions of zinc and aluminum with solutions of sodium hydroxide.

$$Zn + 2NaOH + 2H_2O = Na_2Zn(OH)_4 + H_2$$
sodium zincate

$$2Al + 2NaOH + 6H_2O = 2NaAl(OH)_4 + 3H_2$$
sodium aluminate

Industrial methods for the production of hydrogen include the following:

1. The electrolysis of water. We have already seen (p. 200) that oxygen and hydrogen are produced when water containing a little sulfuric acid or sodium hydroxide is electrolyzed. Hydrogen gas is obtained, likewise, along with chlorine gas and sodium hydroxide, in the electrolysis of aqueous solutions of sodium chloride (p. 386).

2. Decomposition of hydrocarbons. Some hydrogen is obtained by the catalytic decomposition at high temperatures of compounds of carbon and hydrogen such as those found in natural gas.

$$CH_4 = C + 2H_2$$

3. Reaction of steam with coke. When steam is passed over hot coke (1000° C.) it reacts in accordance with the equation

$$C + H_2O = CO + H_2$$
carbon   hydrogen
monoxide

The mixture of gases thus obtained is known as "water gas." Since both carbon monoxide and hydrogen react with oxygen, water gas is widely used as a fuel.

$$2CO + O_2 = 2CO_2$$

$$2H_2 + O_2 = 2H_2O$$

In the manufacture of pure hydrogen, the water gas, along with steam, is passed over a catalyst consisting of various metal oxides at a temperature of about 500° C. The reaction which takes place can be represented by the following equation:

$$\underset{\text{(water gas)}}{(CO + H_2)} + H_2O = 2H_2 + CO_2$$

The carbon dioxide is removed from the gaseous mixture by being dissolved in cold water under pressure. Since hydrogen is only slightly soluble in water, this is an effective method of separation.

4. Reaction of hydrocarbons with steam. In the presence of suitable catalysts, the reaction of various compounds of carbon and hydrogen with steam yields carbon monoxide and hydrogen.

$$CH_4 + H_2O = 3H_2 + CO$$

5. The iron–steam reaction mentioned (p. 221) is used frequently. Steam is passed over hot iron until the iron becomes coated with oxide; the iron is then regenerated by passing water gas over it.

$$Fe_3O_4 + 4CO = 3Fe + 4CO_2$$

4. Physical and Chemical Properties of Hydrogen. Hydrogen is a colorless, odorless, and tasteless gas, the lightest of all known substances. That the hydrogen molecule consists of at least two atoms is indicated by the fact that one volume of hydrogen gas yields on reaction with chlorine two volumes of hydrogen chloride. Hence, according to Avogadro's principle, one molecule of hydrogen yields two molecules of hydrogen chloride and must contain, therefore, at least two atoms of hydrogen (p. 86). This is confirmed by measurement of the density of hydrogen gas; the value obtained (0.08988 g. per liter, at standard conditions) corresponds to the formula H_2. Because of the fact that it is less than one-fourteenth as heavy as air, it can readily be transferred from one vessel to another by being poured upwards as is indicated in Figure 13.1. Because of its low molecular weight, hydrogen diffuses more rapidly than any other gas (p. 39).

Hydrogen gas may be liquefied by the application of sufficient pressure at temperatures below −240° C., its critical temperature. It liquefies at −252.7° C. under 1 atm. pressure. The colorless, water-like liquid which is thus obtained solidifies to an ice-like solid when cooled to −259.14° C. Such cooling is usually accomplished by allowing some of the liquid to evaporate under reduced pressure. Hydrogen is even less soluble in water than is oxygen.

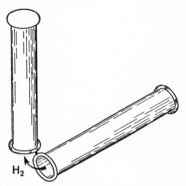

Fig. 13.1. Upward pouring of hydrogen gas.

In its chemical reactions the hydrogen atom tends to attain the stable helium configuration by taking up an electron to form a negative hydride ion, $H:^-$, or by sharing a pair of electrons with another atom to form a single covalent bond; the latter type of combination is by far the more common. Notwithstanding frequent statements to the contrary, hydrogen atoms do not release electrons to form simple hydrogen ions, H^+, i.e., free protons. As we shall see presently, hydrogen does form positive ions, but these are invariably complex in nature.

The sharing of a pair of electrons by a hydrogen atom with another atom is exemplified, in the simplest case, by the hydrogen molecule itself. Such a molecule consists of two hydrogen atoms which share a pair of electrons between them, thus: H : H. This bond is very stable, and the union of two hydrogen atoms to form a molecule results in the evolution of a large amount of energy. Advantage is taken of this fact in the atomic hydrogen torch, which will be discussed later in the chapter.

Covalent compounds are formed by the reaction of hydrogen with most of the nonmetals. At room temperature such combination usually takes place only slowly, if at all, but the rate increases rapidly as the temperature is raised. Examples of such reactions are represented by the following equations:

$$2H_2 + O_2 = 2H : \overset{\cdot\cdot}{O} : \quad \text{water}$$
$$H$$

$$3H_2 + N_2 = 2H : \overset{\cdot\cdot}{N} : H \quad \text{ammonia}$$
$$H$$

In mixtures of oxygen and hydrogen, the rate of the reaction is exceedingly slow in the absence of a catalyst at room temperature, or indeed at any temperature up to 400° C. At about 525° C. the reaction takes place somewhat more rapidly, forming appreciable quantities of water after several hours. At 700° C. the reaction is explosive. If accidents are to be avoided, therefore, mixtures of hydrogen and oxygen should be protected from contact with a flame.

An important characteristic of many such reactions with hydrogen is the fact that they are catalyzed by various metals such as finely divided platinum, palladium, or nickel. Hydrogen is readily absorbed by these metals; in fact, 1 ml. of finely divided palladium takes up as much as 900 ml. of hydrogen gas without appreciable increase in the volume of the metal. The fact that this hydrogen is so much more reactive than hydrogen in the gaseous state is frequently explained by the assumption that, in the absorption on the catalyst, the hydrogen molecules are dissociated into atoms.

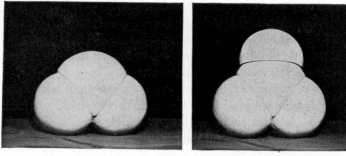

Fig. 13.2.   Models of the H_2O molecule and of the H_3O^+ ion. (*Courtesy of Dr. J. A. Campbell, Oberlin College.*)

It should be emphasized that the compounds of hydrogen with nonmetals, such as water, ammonia, hydrogen sulfide, and hydrogen chloride, should not, strictly speaking, be called hydrides, since they do not contain negative hydride ions. It should be further noted that, although the molecules of these compounds are held together by polar covalent bonds in which the hydrogen atoms are at the positive ends, yet they contain no simple hydrogen ions. Some of these substances, such as hydrogen chloride, hydrogen iodide, and hydrogen sulfide, give aqueous solutions containing positive ions which were formerly considered to be free protons. We know now, however, that these are complex ions of which the simplest is H_3O^+, with the electronic structure

$$\begin{array}{c} H \\ \ddot{} \\ H : O : H^+ \\ \ddot{} \end{array}$$

For convenience, however, such ions are commonly represented by the symbol H^+; this point will be discussed further in Chapter 17. The fact that hydrogen does not form a simple positive ion is not surprising in view of the exceedingly small radius of the H^+ ion, and the very intense positive electrical field which therefore would surround such an ion. Molecular models of the water molecule and the H_3O^+ ion are illustrated in Figure 13.2.

Hydrogen does not react with the less active metals, but when it is brought at elevated temperatures in contact with the more active metals, particularly the members of Group 1a and the heavier members of Group 2a, it combines with these elements to form hydrides. These are ionic compounds whose crystal lattices are made up of positive metal ions and negative hydride ions.

$$Ca : + H : H = Ca^{++}, 2H : ^-$$

$$2Li \cdot + H : H = 2Li^+, 2H : ^-$$

These hydrides are very strong reducing agents. They react vigorously with water, with the liberation of hydrogen and formation of the corresponding metal hydroxides. In this reaction, expressed in its simplest terms, the hydride ion takes a proton from a water molecule to form a hydrogen molecule and a hydroxide ion.

$$H :^- + H : \overset{..}{\underset{..}{O}} : H = H : H + : \overset{..}{\underset{..}{O}} : H^-$$

It has been indicated that in all hydrogen compounds except the ionic metal hydrides each hydrogen atom shares a pair of electrons with another atom. It has been noted, however, that most of these bonds are polar, the hydrogen atom forming the positive end of the bond. In accordance with the convention discussed in the preceding chapter, hydrogen is assigned the oxidation state of $+1$ in all of its compounds except the metal hydrides. Since, in most of its reactions, free hydrogen is oxidized from an oxidation state of 0 to an oxidation state of $+1$, it behaves as a reducing agent. It is particularly useful for the reduction of oxides. Many metal oxides, on being heated with hydrogen, are reduced to the free metal; the following equations represent typical reactions of this kind:

$$CuO + H_2 = Cu + H_2O$$

$$WO_3 + 3H_2 = W + 3H_2O$$

5. Industrial Applications. Hydrogen is an important industrial material. It is usually stored and transported in steel cylinders under high pressure. A few of the more important uses are listed here.

Fig. 13.3. The Hindenburg disaster. (*Acme News Pictures.*)

1. The oxy-hydrogen torch and its use in welding have already been mentioned in Chapter 11.

2. Hydrogen is used as a reducing agent for the production of certain metals from their oxides, e.g., in the metallurgy of tungsten (p. 698). It is likewise used in other processes where a reducing atmosphere must be provided.

3. The hydrogenation of liquid fats to form solid fats (p. 601). Coconut and cottonseed oils are commonly used; these are treated with hydrogen gas under pressure at about 175° C. in the presence of metal catalysts such as finely divided nickel. The solid fats so obtained are used in the manufacture of oleomargarines, vegetable shortenings, soap, and candles.

4. Several processes have been developed whereby coal, which consists largely of carbon, can be converted to the various compounds of carbon and hydrogen which constitute such petroleum products as gasoline, kerosine, and lubricating oils. These are particularly important in countries where petroleum supplies are limited. In the Bergius process, which has been carried out on a large scale since 1925, powdered coal is treated with hydrogen at moderately high temperatures and extremely high pressures.

5. Because of the fact that a given volume of hydrogen weighs so much less than the same volume of air under a given set of conditions, hydrogen has been used to fill balloons, dirigibles, and blimps. Because of its great inflammability, however, its use for this purpose is exceedingly dangerous; hence, it has largely been displaced for this purpose (in the United States) by the slightly less buoyant but noninflammable helium (p. 377).

6. Hydrogen is used in the manufacture of a large number of industrially useful compounds, among the more important of which are ammonia, NH_3 (p. 478), methanol or methyl alcohol, CH_3OH (p. 578), and formaldehyde, HCHO (p. 600).

7. The atomic hydrogen torch is used for the production of a flame of extremely high temperature. In this torch, hydrogen gas is passed through an electric arc before being burned in oxygen or air. In this arc, the hydrogen molecules are dissociated into atoms, and, when the atomic hydrogen thus formed burns, the heat obtained includes not only the ordinary heat of combustion of hydrogen but also the heat of recombination of atomic hydrogen into the molecular form. Temperatures exceeding 4000 °C. can be obtained in this way.

STUDY QUESTIONS AND PROBLEMS

1. Outline and give examples of the various methods for producing hydrogen.

2. How many grams of calcium hydroxide are obtained by the reaction of 60 g. of calcium with water?

3. How many liters of hydrogen (measured at standard conditions) are required to reduce completely 159.08 g. of cupric oxide, CuO?

4. Outline the various ways in which hydrogen atoms enter into chemical reactions.

5. Outline briefly the reasons for considering the formation of free H^+ ions unlikely in ordinary chemical reactions.

6. Complete and balance the following equations:

$$NiO + H_2 \ =$$

$$H_2O + H^- =$$

$$Cd + H_2SO_4 =$$

$$Ca + H_2 \ =$$

7. Make an outline of the chief commercial applications of hydrogen.

14

Water and Hydrogen Peroxide

1. Importance of Water. No other chemical compound is so familiar to us as is water, nor, though we sometimes tend to overlook the fact because of the relative abundance of this compound, does any other substance play a more important part in our lives. Water is a major constituent of all living organisms. It is estimated that the human body contains 65% by weight of this compound, and the water content of some green vegetables is as high as 90%. In fact, water is present to some extent in almost all natural objects, even in those which are ordinarily considered "dry." Variable quantities of water vapor are present in the air (p. 371). The largest amounts of naturally occurring water, of course, are in the rivers, lakes, and oceans which cover about three-quarters of the surface of the earth. In addition, vast quantities of water in the solid state occur in the huge polar ice-caps.

Living organisms are dependent upon water in a multitude of ways. Food and oxygen are transferred from one part of the body to another in the form of aqueous suspensions or solutions; similarly, the transfer and elimination of much of the waste material of the metabolic process take place in aqueous solution. Since relatively large quantities of heat must be absorbed or evolved to bring about small changes in the temperature of water, the large water content of the animal body makes the body less susceptible to drastic changes in temperature. Furthermore, the evaporation of water from the skin provides a means of cooling the body in hot weather, or whenever its temperature tends to rise excessively. In the case of plants, all the nutrient material which the plant receives from the soil is absorbed through the roots in aqueous solution, and the food which is manufactured in the leaves is transported in aqueous solution to other parts of the plant. The raw materials used by green plants in the manufacture of starches and sugars are carbon dioxide and water (pp. 538, 596).

In industry, water is of prime importance in both hydroelectric and steam power plants, as a cooling agent in many processes, as a heating agent in hot water or steam heating systems, as a medium in which chemical reactions are carried out, and as an actual chemical raw material. A primary consideration in determining the location of a new manufacturing plant is the availability of a convenient and adequate water supply.

In addition to all these uses, we may note also the tremendous effect which large bodies of water, because of their resistance to rapid temperature change, exert upon climate, as well as the importance of the work of running water and ice in shaping the earth's surface.

2. Physical Properties of Water. Water is a colorless, odorless, and tasteless liquid. Its chief physical properties are listed in Table 14.1.

Table 14.1

Physical Properties of Water

Melting point	0.000° C.
Boiling point	100.0° C.
Heat of vaporization (cal./mole)	9710
Heat of fusion (cal./mole)	1436
Density of liquid (g./cc. at 4° C.)	1.0000
Density of ice (g./cc. at 0° C.)	0.917

The zero point on the centigrade temperature scale is defined as the freezing point of water under very carefully specified conditions, and the size of the centigrade degree is fixed by assignment of the value 100° C. to the boiling point of water under 1 atm. pressure.

The physical properties of water are abnormal in the sense that its melting point, boiling point, heat of vaporization, and heat of fusion are all much higher than would be predicted from the corresponding properties of the hydrogen compounds of the other members of the oxygen family. This abnormality is illustrated by Figure 14.1, in which are plotted the values of the melting points and boiling points of water, hydrogen sulfide, hydrogen selenide, and hydrogen telluride, along with similar data for the hydrogen compounds of Groups 4a, 5a, and 7a. In every case, a continuation of the general trend indicated by the values for H_2Te, H_2Se, and H_2S leads to values for H_2O which are much lower than the actual experimental values.

The manner in which the density of this substance changes with temperature is likewise abnormal. As the temperature of water is lowered its density gradually increases, i.e., the sample of water contracts, until a temperature of 3.98° C. is reached. Further cooling, however, brings about a decrease in density, i.e., the sample expands. Furthermore, in contrast to the behavior of most liquids, water undergoes a marked expansion (about 9%) on freezing, the density of ice at 0° C. being only 0.917 g. per cc. This peculiar behavior accounts for the fact that large bodies of water do not usually freeze throughout, but only from the surface downward. As long as

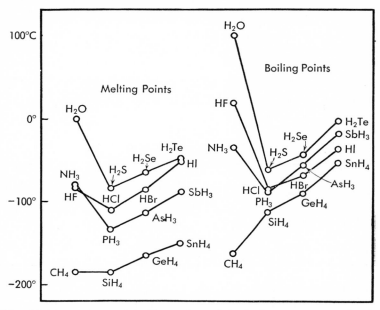

Fig. 14.1. Melting points and boiling points of the hydrogen compounds of the elements of groups 4a, 5a, 6a, and 7a. (Redrawn from Pauling, *The Nature of the Chemical Bond*, Cornell Univ. Press, 1940, Fig. 39–1.)

the temperature of the water is above 3.98° C., cooling of the surface brings about an increase in density which causes the surface water to sink toward the bottom, setting up convection currents which tend to equalize the temperature throughout the body of liquid. As soon as the water reaches this temperature, however, further cooling of the surface water decreases its density and prevents its settling, so that freezing takes place at the surface only. Freezing in the interior of the body of water can take place only as heat is conducted (without convection) through the water and ice to the surface, and this is a very slow process.

3. Molecular Structure. The fact that liquid water is an extremely poor conductor of electricity indicates that the water molecule is essentially nonionic; i.e., that its atoms are held together by covalent bonds. Covalent bonds between hydrogen and oxygen, however, because of the difference in the electron affinities of the two atoms (p. 179), exhibit a considerable degree of polarity. If the water molecule is linear, that is, if the three atoms are in a straight line,

$$H \overset{\delta+ \ \delta-}{\underset{}{\text{——}}} \overset{\cdot \, \cdot}{\underset{\cdot \, \cdot}{O}} \overset{\delta- \ \delta+}{\underset{}{\text{——}}} H$$

the polarities of the two bonds will cancel each other, causing the molecule to be nonpolar. If, however, the water molecule, instead of being linear, has an angular configuration, the polarities of the two bonds will not cancel each other and the molecule as a whole will have a definitely polar nature,

$$H \overset{\delta+ \ \delta-}{\underset{}{\text{——}}} \overset{\cdot \, \cdot}{\underset{\delta-\cdot \mid \cdot}{O}} \, \cdot$$
$$\underset{H}{\overset{\delta+}{\mid}}$$

That the latter hypothesis is correct is indicated by the fact that water is a highly polar liquid, and has a very high dielectric constant (p. 187). As was pointed out in Chapter 10, such liquids are good solvents for many other polar substances, as well as for ionic compounds. Water is, in fact, one of the best solvents for substances belonging to either of these classes.

The fact that water molecules are strongly polar, and hence tend to associate (p. 190), partially accounts for the exceptionally high melting point, boiling point, heat of vaporization, heat of fusion, and specific heat of water. A considerably more important factor, however, is the phenomenon to be discussed in the following section.

4. Hydrogen Bonds. The Structure of Ice. There is abundant evidence to indicate that molecules containing an O—H, N—H, or F—H linkage have a tendency to unite with other molecules containing an oxygen, a nitrogen, or a fluorine atom, and that such combination takes place through the hydrogen atom. In other words, it has been found that a hydrogen atom may serve as a bridge between two strongly electronegative atoms, especially atoms of oxygen, nitrogen, or fluorine. Such bonds are, therefore, appropriately known as hydrogen bonds; and even though they are much weaker than covalent bonds, they are strong enough to exert a major influence upon the physical and chemical properties of molecules capable of forming them. Water molecules are capable of forming such bonds not

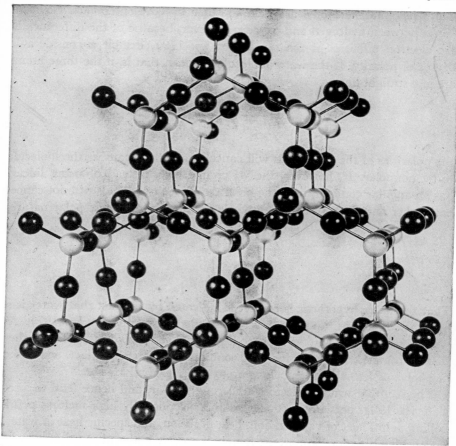

Fig. 14.2.   The crystal structure of ice. (From Hildebrand, *Principles of Chemistry*, by permission of The Macmillan Company, publishers.)

only with other molecules containing oxygen, nitrogen, or fluorine atoms, but also with each other, and this constitutes the most important factor tending to bring about association of water molecules.

Investigation of the crystal structure of ice has shown that the water molecules in this substance are so arranged that the oxygen atoms form a lattice in which each oxygen atom is connected to four other oxygen atoms by hydrogen bonds, as is illustrated in Figure 14.2. This somewhat open type of structure accounts for the relatively low density of ice. When ice melts, some of these hydrogen bonds are broken, and the structure collapses to a more closely packed arrangement; thus, the liquid water occupies a smaller volume than the ice from which it was formed. Furthermore, as the temperature of the water is raised the breaking of hydrogen bonds continues and the volume continues to decrease, until at 3.98° C. the normal tendency toward expansion due to increased thermal vibration of the molecules finally outweighs the contractive effect of the breaking of hydrogen bonds, and the liquid begins to expand.

The existence of hydrogen bonds between water molecules is mainly responsible for the abnormally high melting point, boiling point, heat of fusion, heat of vaporization, and specific heat of water. The melting of ice necessarily involves the breaking of some of the hydrogen bonds; since this requires the expenditure of energy, ice melts only at a much higher temperature and with the absorption of a considerably greater amount of heat than would otherwise be expected. The continued breaking of hydrogen bonds as liquid water is heated accounts for the high specific heat of this substance. Furthermore, when water is changed from the liquid to the vapor state, all of the remaining hydrogen bonds are broken; hence, the boiling point and heat of vaporization are high also. Finally, because of the tendency of water to combine with substances with which it can form hydrogen bonds, such substances are usually quite soluble in water (p. 281).

5. Chemical Properties of Water: (1) Hydrate Formation. Both because of its ability to associate with other molecules or ions through hydrogen bond formation, and because of its tendency to form coordinate covalent bonds through the sharing of one of the pairs of electrons on the oxygen atom, the water molecule is capable of forming many addition compounds; these are usually called *hydrates*. For example, a great many salts, in the form obtained by crystallization from aqueous solution, contain definite quantities of water. Thus, magnesium chloride crystallizes with six moles of water per mole of salt to give the hexahydrate $MgCl_2 \cdot 6H_2O$. Similarly, barium chloride forms the dihydrate $BaCl_2 \cdot 2H_2O$, and cadmium nitrate crystallizes as the tetrahydrate $Cd(NO_3)_2 \cdot 4H_2O$. In many of these salt hydrates the water molecules are coordinated to the positive ion of the salt. Thus, the formulas for the salt hydrates named here may properly be written $[Mg(H_2O)_6]Cl_2$, $[Ba(H_2O)_2]Cl_2$, and $[Cd(H_2O)_4](NO_3)_2$, respectively, and the electronic structures of the resulting positive ions may be represented as shown on the next page.

As was indicated, hydration sometimes takes place also through the mechanism of hydrogen bond formation. For example, it is significant that in a number of cases the hydrate of a metal sulfate contains one more mole of water per mole of salt than does the corresponding chloride. Thus we have, for example, $MgCl_2 \cdot 6H_2O$ and $MgSO_4 \cdot 7H_2O$, $ZnCl_2 \cdot 6H_2O$ and

$ZnSO_4 \cdot 7H_2O$, $CoCl_2 \cdot 6H_2O$ and $CoSO_4 \cdot 7H_2O$. In these cases the seventh molecule of water is attached to the sulfate ion by means of hydrogen bonds.

$$\left[\begin{array}{c} H \\ H : \ddot{O} : \\[1ex] \begin{array}{cc} H & H \quad H \\ \ddot{O} : & : \ddot{O} : \\ H & \end{array} \\ Mg \\ \begin{array}{cc} : \ddot{O} : & \quad H \\ H \quad H & : \ddot{O} : \\ & H \end{array} \\ : \overset{..}{O} : H \\ \ddot{H} \end{array} \right]^{++}$$

$$\left[\begin{array}{c} H \\ \overset{..}{O} \\ H : \ddot{O} : Ba : \ddot{O} : H \\ H \end{array} \right]^{++}$$

$$\left[\begin{array}{c} H \\ : \overset{..}{O} : H \\ \begin{array}{ccc} H & & \\ H : \ddot{O} : & Cd & : \ddot{O} : H \\ & & H \end{array} \\ H : \ddot{O} : \\ H \end{array} \right]^{++}$$

It should be noted that a given salt may form more than one hydrate. Thus, in the case of copper sulfate, the hydrates $CuSO_4 \cdot 5H_2O$, $CuSO_4 \cdot 3H_2O$, and $CuSO_4 \cdot H_2O$ are known. Which hydrate is actually obtained in such a case as this depends on the conditions under which the hydrate is formed. The relationship between the stability of hydrates and such environmental factors as temperature and the partial pressure of water vapor in the air will be discussed in Chapter 15, p. 263.

An important instance of hydrate formation with a nonionic substance through hydrogen bonding is the formation of the hydrate of ammonia (p. 474).

$$\begin{array}{ccc} \text{H} & & \text{H} \\ \ddot{} & & \ddot{} \\ \text{H}:\text{N}: + \text{H}:\text{O}:\text{H} = \text{H}:\text{N}:\text{H}:\text{O}:\text{H} \\ \ddot{} & & \ddot{} \\ \text{H} & & \text{H} \end{array}$$

This hydrate, NH_4OH, is commonly called ammonium hydroxide. Hydrates of various other compounds will be referred to throughout the text.

6. Chemical Properties of Water: (2) Hydrolysis. A second group of reactions in which water participates may be represented by the general equation

$$AB + HOH = AOH + HB$$

where A and B represent either single atoms or groups of atoms. Metathetic reactions of the type indicated by this general equation are known as *hydrolytic* reactions; the compound AB is said to be hydrolyzed, or to undergo *hydrolysis*. In such reactions, one of the products is a compound in which the hydroxyl group from the water molecule is associated with the positive ion of the hydrolyzed substance, or, in the case of a polar covalent molecule, with the atom or group which had formed the positive end of the molecule; in the other product, the hydrogen is associated with the negative ion, or, in the case of a polar covalent molecule, with the atom or group which formed the negative end of the molecule. It is obvious that if AB is a salt the hydrolytic reaction is the reverse of the neutralization reaction between the base AOH and the acid HB. This type of hydrolysis will be discussed at greater length in Chapter 17. Other hydrolytic reactions will be encountered throughout the text. The following equations represent some typical examples of hydrolysis:

$$SO_2Cl_2 \quad + \quad 2H_2O \quad = \quad SO_2(OH)_2 \quad + \quad 2HCl$$

sulfuryl chloride   sulfuric acid   hydrogen chloride

$$PBr_3 \quad + \quad 3H_2O \quad = \quad P(OH)_3 \quad + \quad 3HBr$$

phosphorus tribromide   phosphorous acid   hydrogen bromide

$$NH_4CN \quad + \quad H_2O \quad = \quad NH_4OH \quad + \quad HCN$$

ammonium cyanide   ammonium hydroxide   hydrogen cyanide

7. Chemical Properties of Water: (3) Oxidation-Reduction Reactions. In addition to its participation in hydration and hydrolysis, water is also capable of undergoing chemical reactions which, in terms of the discussion in Chapter 12, are to be classified as oxidation-reduction reactions. Such reactions may be divided into two groups (1) those in which water acts as oxidizing agent, and (2) those in which it acts as reducing agent. The first group is represented by the reaction of liquid water with active metals, and of steam at high temperatures with less active metals and other substances, as already discussed in Chapter 13. Examples of this group of reactions are

$$2Na + 2H_2O = 2NaOH + H_2$$

$$CO + H_2O = CO_2 + H_2$$

In these cases the hydrogen is reduced. The second group is illustrated by the displacement of oxygen from water by very active nonmetals, such as fluorine.

$$2F_2 + 2H_2O = 4HF + O_2$$

In this reaction the fluorine is reduced and the oxygen of the water is oxidized.

8. Water Supplies. As found in nature in springs, streams, lakes, and oceans, water is almost never in a state of high purity. The amount and composition of the impurities present depend upon the nature of the material with which the water has been in contact. Water dissolves appreciable quantities of mineral matter from the soil through which it seeps, and from the rocks over which it runs. In contact with organic materials such as decaying leaves, it dissolves appreciable quantities of organic compounds. Water that has come in contact with refuse and sewage from inhabited areas is likely to contain bacteria and other microorganisms of the types that cause many of the diseases which afflict human beings. Finally, through its contact with the air, water always contains appreciable quantities of dissolved gases, unless special precautions are taken to insure their absence. Then, in addition to dissolved substances, water commonly contains suspended matter, such as mud or silt. The problem of the treatment of natural waters so as to enhance their suitability for various purposes is, therefore, an important and a difficult one.

For use in scientific laboratories, and for certain other technical purposes, water of a high degree of purity is required. The necessary purification is accomplished by the process of *distillation*, as is illustrated in Figure 14.3. Most of the impurities in water are much less volatile than water itself; when the water is boiled, therefore, these impurities remain behind in the flask. The steam from the flask is passed through a water-cooled condenser, in which it is condensed to the liquid state. The product thus obtained is called *distilled water*. Some components of ordinary glass are very slightly soluble in water; hence, when water of an extremely high degree of purity is required, the distillation is carried out in an apparatus constructed of fused quartz (p. 549). Volatile impurities such as ammonia or carbon dioxide are not readily removed by distillation.

The maintenance of an adequate supply of water suitable for consumption by human beings is an important consideration for any community; and since natural waters of such character are, in many cases, not obtainable, initially unsuitable contaminated waters from rivers and streams must be treated so as to make them safe for drinking. Purification of water for such

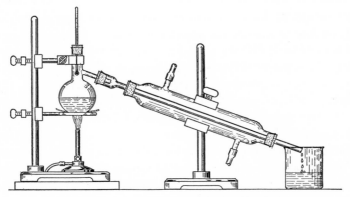

Fig. 14.3   A simple apparatus for distillation.

purposes usually involves filtration through layers of sand and gravel, followed by treatment with small quantities of chlorine (less than one part per million parts of water), or in some cases with ozone or with ultraviolet light, in order to kill harmful microorganisms. Sometimes a clarifying agent is added before filtration; usually sodium aluminum sulfate (sodium alum, p. 806) is used for this purpose. When water so treated is made alkaline by the addition of soda ash (p. 653), a heavy, flocculent precipitate of hydrous aluminum oxide is formed (p. 369); on settling out, this precipitate carries with it suspended foreign matter including many microorganisms.

Mineral matter in the amounts usually present in natural waters is not objectionable so far as the use of the water for drinking is concerned; indeed in certain cases, at least, it actually improves the taste. However, the presence of considerable concentrations of calcium, magnesium, or iron salts is undesirable in water which is to be used for laundry or for various industrial purposes. Water containing appreciable quantities of such salts is said to be *hard*; the nature and methods of treatment of hard waters are described in a later chapter (p. 674).

9. Deuterium and Heavy Water. In Chapter 8 it was pointed out that the quantity which determines the chemical properties of an atom—which, indeed, determines the very identity of the element—is the atomic number;

i.e., the charge on the atomic nucleus. It was stated in that discussion that all of the isotopes of a given element have the same chemical properties; in other words, the variations in atomic mass among the isotopes of a given element have only very small effects upon the chemical properties of the atoms, and isotopes therefore cannot readily be separated by chemical means. Although this statement is generally true, the case of hydrogen constitutes an exception, for in comparing hydrogen of mass 2 with hydrogen of mass 1, we find that while the absolute increase in mass is only one a.w.u., the relative increase is 100 per cent. Such a large relative difference in mass does bring about some difference in chemical properties. It has become customary to take cognizance of this chemical difference by giving the heavier isotope of hydrogen a special name, deuterium, and a corresponding symbol, D. The properties of compounds of heavy hydrogen also differ slightly from those of corresponding compounds of ordinary hydrogen.

Mass spectrograph studies indicate that the D:H ratio in ordinary hydrogen and its compounds, as they occur in nature, is 1:5000. Natural water contains three types of molecules, HOH, HOD, and DOD.[1] Because of its higher density, water containing a high concentration of deuterium oxide, D_2O, is known as "heavy" water. The possible presence of a hydrogen isotope of mass 3, tritium, as it is called, has been suggested; if this isotope exists, however, its concentration in ordinary hydrogen must be exceedingly small, for neither tritium nor tritium oxide has ever been isolated from naturally occurring substances. Tritium has been prepared by nuclear reactions, however.

Pure deuterium oxide may be isolated by the prolonged electrolysis of aqueous solutions of alkalies, for H_2 is discharged at the cathode at a faster rate than is D_2. Whereas various methods for the separation of the H_2 and the D_2 in ordinary hydrogen have been tried with only moderate success, pure D_2 is readily obtainable by the decomposition of pure D_2O. In Tables 14.2 and 14.3 are listed some of the properties of pure D_2 and D_2O, as compared with those of ordinary hydrogen and ordinary water.

Deuterium oxide, when taken internally, has no noticeable effect on animal organisms. Since the replacement of an ordinary hydrogen atom by one of the heavier deuterium atoms can be detected by an increase in the density of the compound, deuterium is useful as a "tracer" element in the study of the mechanism of various chemical reactions, especially those which take place in the metabolism of living organisms.

[1] If we take into consideration also that ordinary oxygen contains the three isotopes O^{16}, O^{17}, and O^{18}, the number of types of water molecules is increased to nine; viz., $HO^{16}H$, $HO^{17}H$, $HO^{18}H$, $HO^{16}D$, $HO^{17}D$, $HO^{18}D$, $DO^{16}D$, $DO^{17}D$, and $DO^{18}D$.

Table 14.2

	Ordinary Hydrogen	Deuterium
Boiling point	−252.8° C.	−249.5° C.
Melting point	−259.2° C.	−254.5° C.
Molecular volume at m.p.	26.15 cc.	23.15 cc.
Heat of fusion (cal./mole)	28	47

Table 14.3

	Ordinary Water	Deuterium Oxide
Density (g./cc. at 20° C.)	0.99820	1.10515
Boiling point	100.00° C	101.42° C.
Melting point	0.00° C.	3.82° C.
Temp. of maximum density	3.98° C.	11.6 ° C.
Heat of vaporization (cal./mole)	9710	9969
Heat of fusion (cal./mole)	1436	1520
Solubilities (g./g. liquid at 25° C.)		
NaCl	0.359	0.297
BaCl$_2$	0.357	0.289

HYDROGEN PEROXIDE AND ITS DERIVATIVES

10. Bond Structure of Hydrogen Peroxide. In addition to water, the elements hydrogen and oxygen form a compound, known as hydrogen peroxide, whose composition and molecular weight correspond to the formula H_2O_2. In accordance with the conventions discussed in Chapter 12 the oxidation state to be assigned to oxygen in this compound and its derivatives is −1, rather than −2 as in all other oxygen compounds. However, as is indicated by the following electronic formula for hydrogen peroxide,

$$H : \overset{..}{\underset{..}{O}} :$$
$$: \overset{..}{\underset{..}{O}} : H$$

each oxygen atom is linked by two covalent bonds, just as is the oxygen atom in the water molecule. One of these two linkages, however, is to another oxygen atom; and it is this single bond between two oxygen atoms that is characteristic of hydrogen peroxide and its derivatives.

11. Preparation. Dilute solutions of hydrogen peroxide may be prepared by the treatment of barium peroxide or sodium peroxide with sulfuric acid (other acids may also be used).

$$BaO_2 + H_2SO_4 = H_2O_2 + BaSO_{4(s)}$$

$$Na_2O_2 + H_2SO_4 = H_2O_2 + Na_2SO_4 \text{ (at } 0° \text{ C.)}$$

The dilute solutions obtained by such means may be concentrated to 30% H_2O_2 by careful distillation at atmospheric pressure. Further concentration at this pressure is impossible, however, because of the thermal decomposition of the hydrogen peroxide. Under reduced pressure, at temperatures of about 60° C., distillation may be continued until a solution of a concentration as great as 98% H_2O_2 is obtained. In such distillations, it is absolutely essential that impurities be absent and that the glassware be scrupulously clean, for many substances catalyze the decomposition of hydrogen peroxide into water and oxygen. Pure hydrogen peroxide may be obtained from the 90% solution, which is now available commercially, by a process of continuous fractional crystallization.

12. Physical and Chemical Properties. Peroxides. The fact that the reaction

$$2H_2O_{2(l)} = 2H_2O_{(l)} + O_{2(g)}$$

takes place with the liberation of 46,900 cal. of heat (at 20° C.) indicates that hydrogen peroxide is not very stable. Although, with extreme precautions, the pure compound may be prepared as described in the preceding section, even a moderately concentrated solution explodes violently upon being heated, or on contact with any of the numerous catalysts for the reaction given. Hydrogen peroxide, therefore, is usually handled in dilute aqueous solution. The physical properties of the pure material are listed in the following table.

Table 14.4

Physical Properties of Hydrogen Peroxide

Melting point	−0.89° C.
Boiling point	151° C.
Density (g./cc. at 20° C.)	1.442
Heat of vaporization (cal./mole)	12,400
Heat of fusion (cal./mole)	3,000

Hydrogen peroxide is a very weak (p. 315) acid; in reaction with strong bases, one or both of the hydrogen atoms in the molecule may be replaced by a metal atom or atoms; e.g.,

$$H_2O_2 + NaOH = NaHO_2 + H_2O$$

$$NaHO_2 + NaOH = Na_2O_2 + H_2O$$

Compounds of the general formulas M_2O_2, where M represents a singly charged metal ion, and MO_2, where M represents a doubly charged metal ion, are known as peroxides. They contain in their crystal lattices the peroxide ion, which, with the structure

$$: \overset{..}{O} : \overset{..}{O} :^{--}$$

exhibits the oxygen-to-oxygen linkage characteristic of all peroxides. Such compounds are not to be confused with the dioxides such as MnO_2 which contain the metal in the $+4$ oxidation state along with simple oxide ions $(: \overset{..}{\underset{..}{O}} :^{--})$. The peroxides differ in two important ways from ordinary oxides: (1) the former are invariably strong oxidizing agents; (2) they react with acids to yield salts and hydrogen peroxide (or water and oxygen) rather than salts and water. Thus, for example,

$$MO_2 + H_2SO_4 = MSO_4 + H_2O_2$$
peroxide

$$MO_2 + 2H_2SO_4 = M(SO_4)_2 + 2H_2O$$
dioxide

The properties and uses of various individual peroxides will be discussed in later chapters.

Hydrogen peroxide itself, in many of its reactions, acts as a strong oxidizing agent, although in a few instances its function is that of a reducing agent. In the former case the peroxide group is reduced to ordinary combined oxygen atoms; in the latter, it is oxidized to a molecule of oxygen. Examples of the oxidizing action of hydrogen peroxide are

$$2HI + H_2O_2 = I_2 + 2H_2O$$

$$PbS + 4H_2O_2 = PbSO_4 + 4H_2O$$

Examples of the reducing action of hydrogen peroxide include its reduction of manganese dioxide, and of potassium permanganate, in solutions containing sulfuric acid. The equation for the first of these reactions is simple enough to be balanced by inspection.

$$MnO_2 + H_2O_2 + H_2SO_4 = MnSO_4 + O_2 + 2H_2O$$

For the second, however, we shall do well to make use of the oxidation number method discussed in Chapter 12. The products of the reaction are manganous sulfate, potassium sulfate, oxygen, and water; hence, we have

$$\overset{+7}{}\quad\overset{-1}{}\quad\overset{+2}{}\quad\overset{0}{}$$

Skeleton: $KMnO_4 + H_2O_2 + H_2SO_4 = MnSO_4 + K_2SO_4 + O_2 + H_2O$

decrease of 5

increase of 1

It is evident that there will have to be five oxygen atoms for each manganese atom. Since each molecule of hydrogen peroxide contains two atoms, however, an even number of oxygen atoms are required; hence we find it more convenient to express the ratio as ten oxygen atoms to two manganese atoms. Supplying the necessary coefficients for the $KMnO_4$ and the H_2O_2, and providing for two manganese atoms and ten free oxygen atoms on the right side of the equation, we have

Incomplete:

$$2KMnO_4 + 5H_2O_2 + H_2SO_4 = 2MnSO_4 + K_2SO_4 + 5O_2 + H_2O$$

The two potassium atoms on the left side of the equation suffice for only one K_2SO_4 unit, so that the coefficient of the K_2SO_4 is fixed also. We now find that there are three sulfate groups on the right side of the equation; hence, the coefficient of H_2SO_4 on the left must be 3. This gives a total of 16 hydrogen atoms on the left, which must appear in 8 molecules of H_2O on the right. Thus we obtain the complete equation

Balanced:

$$2KMnO_4 + 5H_2O_2 + 3H_2SO_4 = 2MnSO_4 + K_2SO_4 + 5O_2 + 8H_2O$$

The fact that the eight H_2O molecules contain the eight oxygen atoms not previously accounted for serves as a final check of the correctness of the equation.

13. Peroxyacids. We have already seen that many of the common acids are hydroxyl compounds obtainable by the reaction of water with acidic oxides (p. 203). Thus, for example, sulfuric acid and phosphoric acid have the following electronic structures:

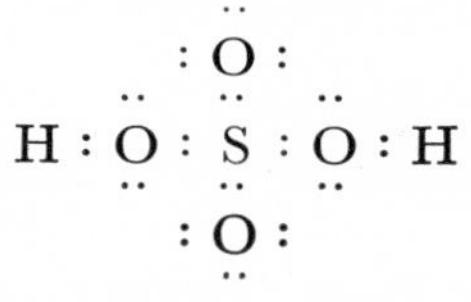

$$
\begin{array}{cc}
\ddot{:}\ddot{O}\ddot{:} & \ddot{:}\ddot{O}\ddot{:} \\
H:\ddot{O}:S:\ddot{O}:H & H:\ddot{O}:P:\ddot{O}:H \\
\ddot{:}\ddot{O}\ddot{:} & \ddot{:}\ddot{O}\ddot{:} \\
 & H \\
H_2SO_4 & H_3PO_4
\end{array}
$$

Such acids are commonly called oxyacids. It may now be pointed out that by the reaction of acidic oxides, or of oxyacids or their salts, with solutions of hydrogen peroxide, acids are obtained in which one or more oxygen atoms are replaced by peroxide ($\cdot \overset{..}{O} : \overset{..}{O} \cdot$) groups. Simple examples of this type of compound, analogous to the above oxyacids, are

$$
\begin{array}{cc}
\overset{\displaystyle :\overset{..}{O}:}{\underset{\displaystyle :\overset{..}{O}:}{H:\overset{..}{O}:\overset{..}{O}:S:\overset{..}{O}:H}}
&
\overset{\displaystyle :\overset{..}{O}:}{\underset{\displaystyle \underset{\displaystyle H}{:\overset{..}{O}:}}{H:\overset{..}{O}:\overset{..}{O}:P:\overset{..}{O}:H}}
\\[2em]
H_2SO_5 & H_3PO_5
\end{array}
$$

Such substances are known as peroxyacids. Their existence led in the past to the questionable postulation of abnormally high oxidation states for the central atom in these substances. Thus in peroxysulfuric acid, H_2SO_5, an oxidation state of $+8$ would have to be attributed to the sulfur, unless it were taken into consideration that two of the five oxygen atoms are peroxy oxygen atoms, and hence are to be assigned an oxidation state of -1 rather than the usual value of -2. A similar disregard of the special state of the oxygen atoms in peroxyphosphoric acid, H_3PO_5, would lead to the questionable assignment of the oxidation state of $+7$ to the phosphorus in this compound.

The formation of a blue peroxychromic acid when a solution of hydrogen peroxide, acidified with sulfuric acid, is treated with a solution of potassium dichromate, is used as an analytical test for hydrogen peroxide. In the carrying out of this test, ether—a liquid which is immiscible with water—is added to the reaction mixture in order to extract the peroxychromic acid from the aqueous solution, in which it very quickly decomposes; in the ether layer it is possible to observe the blue color for several minutes.

14. Uses of Hydrogen Peroxide. Because of its oxidizing properties, hydrogen peroxide is used as a bleaching agent for delicate fibers and textiles, such as hair, silk, and wool. For these purposes it is usually marketed as a 3% solution. Such a solution has also been used as a germicidal agent, although its efficacy in this respect has been questioned. Concentrated hydrogen peroxide (90% H_2O_2 or higher) is used as an oxidizing agent in rocket propulsion. During World War II the German Armed Forces used the catalytic decomposition of hydrogen peroxide in the propulsion of robot (V-2) bombs, the forerunners of the intercontinental ballistic missile.

STUDY QUESTIONS AND PROBLEMS

1. Make a brief outline of the physical properties of water, indicating in which cases and in what sense these properties may be considered to be abnormal.

2. Why do not bodies of water freeze solid during the winter?

3. What is the experimental evidence for the following statements?

   (a) Water is a non-ionic substance, i.e., is covalent.

   (b) Water molecules are polar.

   (c) Water molecules are associated in the liquid state.

   (d) Water molecules are angular rather than linear.

4. How do you account for the fact that water expands when it freezes? for its high heat of fusion? its high heat of vaporization? What is meant by a "hydrogen bond"?

5. How many grams of water would be required to form the hydrate $BaCl_2 \cdot 2H_2O$ from 100 g. of anhydrous barium chloride? What is the probable electronic formula for the $Cu(H_2O)_4^{++}$ ion?

6. Write a general definition for the term hydrolysis and give equations for four examples.

7. Write equations for four reactions in which water acts as oxidizing or reducing agent.

8. Discuss briefly the molecular structure of hydrogen peroxide and the oxidation number of oxygen in that compound.

9. How many liters of oxygen at standard conditions would be produced by the decomposition to water and oxygen of 34 g. of H_2O_2? of 18 g. of D_2O_2?

10. Give equations for three methods for producing hydrogen peroxide.

11. Write the electronic formulas for three peroxyacids. Why are peroxyacids strong oxidizing agents?

12. How would you go about determining whether an oxide of the formula MO_2 is a dioxide or a peroxide?

13. Calculate the percentage of water in gypsum, $CaSO_4 \cdot 2H_2O$; in washing soda, $Na_2CO_3 \cdot 10H_2O$.

14. When the hydrated compound known as borax is heated it loses 47.23% of its weight as water vapor, and the anhydrous salt, $Na_2B_4O_7$, remains. What is the formula of the hydrate?

Chemical Equilibrium

1. Introduction. To know that a given substance or group of substances will, under certain unspecified conditions, react more or less completely to give certain other substances, is only the first step toward the practical application of a chemical change. If the reaction is to be successfully carried out in the laboratory, and especially if it is to be utilized industrially, it is essential that we should understand the factors that determine both the speed of the reaction and the extent to which it goes on. Thus, for example, although the fact that nitrogen and hydrogen react to form ammonia (p. 229) had been known for many decades, it was only comparatively recently, through a newly won understanding of these factors, that the industrial manufacture of ammonia by means of this reaction was achieved. It is with the problems of direction, speed, and extent of chemical reactions that we shall be concerned in the present chapter.

2. Reversibility. We have already had occasion to discuss changes of various kinds, both physical and chemical, which can proceed in either of two opposite directions. Thus, for example, when the temperature of a liquid is raised, or when the external pressure upon it is reduced, some of the liquid evaporates; when the temperature is lowered, or the pressure of the vapor is increased, some of the vapor condenses to liquid (p. 53). In the case of water these changes may be conveniently represented by the equation

$$H_2O_{(l)} \rightleftharpoons H_2O_{(v)}$$

in which reversibility is indicated by the double arrow ($\rightleftharpoons$). As another example of reversible change we may cite the melting of ice and the freezing of water:

$$H_2O_{(s)} \rightleftharpoons H_2O_{(l)}$$

or the dissolving of a solid, such as salt, and its deposition from a solution:

$$NaCl_{(s)} \rightleftharpoons NaCl_{(dissolved)}$$

In each of these cases, there is a certain set of conditions under which no further change appears to take place. Thus, in the evaporation of water, when the pressure of water vapor in the atmosphere reaches the vapor pressure of water at the prevailing temperature (p. 59), evaporation apparently ceases, and the system is said to have reached *equilibrium*. Such equilibria, in contrast to the static equilibria with which we are sometimes concerned in mechanical problems, are dynamic and consist of a state of balance between opposing changes proceeding at equal rates, rather than one of actual rest. Thus, as has been previously stated, when a liquid apparently ceases to evaporate, it is only because the process of condensation is taking place at exactly the same rate as that of evaporation; or, in other words, because just as many molecules are returning to the surface of the liquid per unit of time as are leaving it to enter the vapor phase.

3. Reversible Chemical Changes. Not only such physical changes as have just been discussed, but also most chemical reactions, are reversible. For example, we may bring about both the formation of mercuric oxide by the heating of mercury in air to a relatively low temperature (p. 787), and also the decomposition of the same oxide at a higher temperature.

$$2Hg + O_2 \rightleftharpoons 2HgO$$

Similarly, although ammonia can be made from its elements, it readily decomposes at high temperatures.

$$N_2 + 3H_2 \rightleftharpoons 2NH_3$$

As still another example, we may consider the reaction between water vapor and red-hot iron, say at a temperature of 600° C., which was cited as a method for the preparation of hydrogen (p. 223). When hydrogen at atmospheric pressure is passed over iron oxide, at the same temperature, free iron and water vapor are produced. Hence we may write

$$4H_2O + 3Fe \rightleftharpoons Fe_3O_4 + 4H_2$$

Many other illustrations might be given; in fact, the quality of reversibility is so nearly universal that even in the infrequent instances of reactions which appear to be capable of proceeding in one direction only, such, for example, as the decomposition of potassium chlorate (p. 199):

$$2KClO_3 = 2KCl + 3O_2$$

we are disposed to say that potassium chloride does not combine with oxygen to form potassium chlorate under any experimentally attainable conditions, rather than to state flatly that the reaction is irreversible.

4. Chemical Equilibrium. In order to consider the consequences of reversibility, without for the present limiting ourselves to specific compounds, let us consider a reaction between two substances A and B to form two other substances C and D (which together are made up of the same elements as A and B); and let us suppose that C and D are also capable of reacting, under the same conditions, to form A and B. This state of affairs may be concisely represented by the equation

$$A + B \rightleftharpoons C + D$$

(According to convention, the substances on the left side of the equation, A and B in this instance, are called the reacting substances, or reactants, and those on the right side, C and D, are called the resulting substances, or products.)

A little reflection will show that the reaction cannot possibly proceed to completion in either direction. It would obviously be absurd to suppose that if we started with equivalent quantities of A and B, they would change completely to C and D before the latter substances would begin to react to form A and B; or that if we started with equivalent quantities of C and D, they would have an opportunity to go over completely into A and B before the reverse reaction would begin. Rather, whether we start with A and B or with equivalent quantities of C and D under the same conditions, we should expect the change to stop at some intermediate point—the same in both cases—at which all four substances are still present. When this state has been attained the system may be said to be in equilibrium.

The foregoing conclusion is, in fact, borne out by experiment. Suppose the reaction between water vapor and iron is allowed to proceed until equilibrium has been reached, not in a tube through which a constant stream of water vapor is passing—carrying the hydrogen along with it and away from the oxide as fast as it is formed—but in a closed vessel from which none of the participating substances can escape. When the vessel is opened, it is found that the solid consists of iron and iron oxide, while the gaseous phase is a mixture of water vapor and hydrogen. If, in an exactly similar vessel, equivalent quantities of iron oxide and hydrogen are brought together at the same temperature and the mixture is allowed to stand until equilibrium is reached, the resulting product, both gaseous and solid, is found to be identical with that obtained in the preceding case. This state of affairs is illustrated in Figure 15.1.

It must be emphasized, however, that the equilibrium is dynamic, and when equilibrium has been reached in a chemical reaction we do not have a state of rest, but rather one of balanced changes. As long as there is *any* iron present, and *any* water vapor, these substances will not cease to react with each other—nor will the hydrogen and iron oxide, as long as these substances are in contact. When change appears to have ceased, it is because the two opposing reactions are both going on at the same rate. It is easy to show that such a balance must inevitably come about eventually. Suppose we start with iron and water vapor alone. Since no iron oxide or hydogen is present, the initial rate of reaction between these substances must be zero.

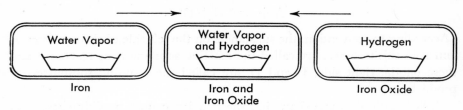

Fig. 15.1.   Equilibrium in the reaction $4H_2O + 3Fe \rightleftharpoons Fe_3O_4 + 4H_2$.

As the reaction between iron and water vapor proceeds, however, iron oxide and hydrogen accumulate, and the reaction between the latter pair of substances gradually picks up speed. Meanwhile, as more and more of the surface of the iron becomes coated with iron oxide, and as the concentration of the water vapor decreases, the reaction between iron and water gradually slows down. Eventually, then, a state must be reached in which hydrogen and iron oxide are being formed exactly as rapidly as they are reacting to form water and iron.

SPEED OF CHEMICAL REACTIONS

5. Factors Determining Speed of Reactions. Since, as has just been shown, chemical equilibrium results from the equality of the speed of two opposing reactions, it is evident that in order to be in a position to make any useful generalizations concerning equilibrium, we shall have to consider in some detail the factors upon which reaction speed depends.

The speed of a chemical reaction, known also as reaction rate or reaction velocity, is defined as the number of moles of one of the reacting substances, per unit of space occupied by the reacting mixture, that are used up in a unit of time; or an alternative definition would be the number of moles of one of the resulting substances, likewise per unit volume, that are formed in unit time. The rate of a particular reaction depends chiefly, of course, upon the nature of the substances reacting; in addition to this, however, there are several factors which affect reaction rates in general. The most important of these are the temperature, the presence of catalysts, and the concentrations of the reacting substances.

6. The Nature of the Reactants. That there is a wide variation in the speeds with which different chemical reactions take place, even under the same conditions, is so well known as to require little discussion. Charcoal and powdered red phosphorus can both be ignited in air; the latter, however, burns very much more rapidly. Calcium and potassium both react with water at ordinary temperature, the former at a moderate rate, the latter so rapidly that the reaction is of almost explosive violence.

In the reaction between two different phases such as a solid and a gas, the speed of the reaction is greatly influenced by the magnitude of the surface of contact between the phases. Finely divided solids, because of their more extensive surfaces, react more rapidly than do coarser specimens of the same substances.

7. The Effect of Temperature. It is a familiar fact that practically all chemical changes are accelerated by increases in temperature. Thus, it can readily be shown by experiment that iron, even in the form of powder, filings, or steel wool, is only very slowly oxidized in dry air at ordinary temperatures, whereas these forms of iron burn vigorously when heated to redness in air. In the laboratory, the student learns that with the aid of a Bunsen burner he is able to bring about numerous reactions which do not take place at a perceptible rate at ordinary temperatures, and likewise that reactions which even at room temperature have a tendency to get out of hand may often be kept under control by the occasional application of a pan of cold water to the outside of the reaction vessel. In many cases, the speed of a reaction in a homogeneous system is increased two- to threefold by an increase in temperature of only $10°$ C.

In terms of the kinetic-molecular theory, it is easy to understand why the speed of a reaction, at least in the gaseous state, must increase with increasing temperature, although at first sight the magnitude of this temperature effect appears surprisingly great. Whatever may be our picture of the mechanism of a chemical reaction—and this is a problem as yet but very incompletely understood—we can scarcely escape the hypothesis that two molecules, in order to react with each other, must be in contact; and this, in turn, means that they must have collided with each other. Since the average speed of the molecules increases with increasing temperature, molecular collisions, and therefore opportunities for reaction, become more numerous as the temperature increases. It may readily be shown, however, that the increased frequency of collision, alone, is far from sufficient to account for the observed increase in reaction rate. Between $20°$ and $30°$ C., for example, the average speed of the molecules of a gas is increased by only about 2 per cent; yet the rate of a reaction in which the gas participates may be more than doubled. Evidently some factor other than the slightly increased number of collisions must be involved.

The most plausible supposition is that not every molecular collision results in a reaction, but that only the more energetic collisions have such an outcome. From this it follows that if molecules are to react they must be in an "activated" state, as it is called, in which they have energies above a certain minimum value (usually far in excess of the average). There is good evidence, which cannot be discussed here, for the supposition that in a given mass of gas the fraction of all the molecules having energies above the average increases very rapidly with increasing temperature—much more rapidly, in fact, than does the average energy. Thus the number of "activated" molecules may well be doubled, or even tripled, for a 10° C. rise in temperature. It is important to note, however, that not all reaction rates are equally affected by temperature.

8. The Effect of Catalysts. As has been pointed out previously, the rate of a reaction may be greatly affected by the presence of a small amount of a substance which itself undergoes no permanent change during the reaction; such a substance is known as a catalyst, and the process as catalysis. Although, strictly speaking, catalysis may be either positive or negative, i.e., a reaction may be either accelerated or retarded by the presence of a non-reacting substance, the term is more commonly used to designate acceleration; negative catalysts are now frequently referred to as retarders or inhibitors.

Catalysis plays an essential part in many reactions of primary industrial importance. Thus, for example, the industrial synthesis, from nitrogen and hydrogen, of ammonia, the key compound of the nitrogen fertilizer industry, is dependent upon the use of a catalyst; and it will be shown later (p. 457) that both of the common methods for sulfuric acid manufacture, which is one of the largest of chemical industries, involve catalysis also. Hence, an immense amount of effort has been devoted to the study of such phenomena, the mechanisms of which are still imperfectly understood. It has become clear, however, that there are two fairly distinct types of catalysis, which have been called homogeneous and heterogeneous, respectively.

In homogeneous catalysis, the catalytic agent is present in the same gaseous or liquid phase as the reacting substances. As an example of homogeneous catalysis in the gaseous state, we may cite the very marked effect of nitric oxide in speeding up the combination of carbon monoxide, CO, or of moist sulfur dioxide, SO_2, with oxygen. The most familiar instance of homogeneous catalysis in the liquid state consists in the accelerating effect of acids or of bases upon many reactions in solution. A specific example is the so-called inversion of ordinary cane sugar, which consists in the reaction

$$C_{12}H_{22}O_{11} + H_2O = C_6H_{12}O_6 + C_6H_{12}O_6$$

$$\underset{\substack{\text{(ordinary} \\ \text{sugar)}}}{\text{sucrose}} \qquad \underset{\text{invert sugar}}{\overline{\underset{}{\text{glucose} \qquad \text{fructose}}}}$$

The simplest explanation that has been offered for homogeneous catalysis is that the catalyst combines readily with one or more of the reactants to form an intermediate compound. This combination is then immediately followed by a second rapid reaction in which the catalyst is again liberated; the whole process, it must be supposed, takes place much more rapidly than would the direct or uncatalyzed reaction. Thus, for example, we might suppose that in the catalysis of the oxidation of carbon monoxide by oxygen the two successive reactions

$$2NO + O_2 = 2NO_2$$

$$2NO_2 + 2CO = 2NO + 2CO_2$$

take place much more rapidly than does the simpler reaction which leads to the same net result in a single step:

$$2CO + O_2 = 2CO_2$$

Although this explanation is probably oversimplified, it undoubtedly represents at least a close approach to the true mechanism.

In heterogeneous catalysis, the reaction between liquid or gaseous reactants takes place at the surface of contact between a liquid or gas phase and the solid catalyst; hence, this variety is often designated as contact catalysis. As instances of this type of catalysis may be cited the effect of platinum on the reaction between hydrogen and oxygen (p. 226), and the use of nickel in the hydrogenation of oils (p. 228). A catalyst of this type always has the property of bringing about at its surface an increase in concentration of one or more of the reacting substances. The molecules of a substance so held are often in a strained or distorted condition, so that they are more susceptible to reaction. Finely divided platinum, for instance, is able to take up (and thereby to activate) appreciable quantities of various gases. This phenomenon has sometimes been called absorption; since, however, the quantity of gas thus condensed on a solid is determined not by the volume of the solid but rather by the magnitude of its surface, the term *adsorption* (suggesting that it is a surface phenomenon) is now regarded as preferable.[1] Adsorption of a liquid, or of one or more components of a solution, at the surface of a solid is also of frequent occurrence.

Many reactions of organic compounds are catalyzed by complex substances known as *enzymes*, which are produced by living organisms. Thus, for example, in the alcoholic fermentation of sugars, the enzyme zymase produced by living yeast cells serves as catalyst. Even minute traces of the substances known as hormones, produced in the ductless glands of the animal body, have profound effects upon growth and other biological processes; possibly these effects, also, should be regarded as catalytic.

9. The Effect of Concentration. At a fixed temperature and in the absence of a catalyst (or in the presence of a fixed quantity of a given catalyst), the rate of a given reaction depends mainly upon the concentrations of the reacting substances. The *concentration* of a substance in a given phase is best defined as the quantity of that substance per unit volume of the phase. Concentrations may be expressed in any convenient mass and volume units, such as, for instance, grams per cubic centimeter or per liter, or as in the English system of units, pounds per cubic foot. The chemist, however, often prefers to express concentrations in moles, rather than in grams, per unit volume— most commonly, in moles per liter. Since a mole of any substance always consists of the same number of molecules (Avogadro's number, p. 84), it is evident that the concentration of a substance, when expressed in moles per liter, provides a direct measure of the number of molecules per unit of space.

As has already been pointed out (p. 251), the speed of a reaction must depend upon the frequency of molecular collisions that are sufficiently energetic to be effective. The total number of collisions that occur in any given period of time, and hence also the number of effective collisions during the same interval, would certainly be expected to increase as the molecules are more closely crowded together; that is, with increasing concentration of the reactants. Many familiar facts might be cited which are in qualitative agreement with this conclusion. For example, iron burns very much more rapidly in pure oxygen (p. 202) than it does in air, in which only about 20% of the molecules are oxygen.

10. The Law of Mass Action. The quantitative relationship between reaction rate and concentration was established on an experimental basis in 1867

---

[1] There are, however, a few instances, notably the taking up of hydrogen by platinum and palladium, in which the gas appears to be uniformly distributed throughout the entire volume of the metal; in these cases the phenomenon may properly be called absorption.

by the Norwegian scientists C. Guldberg and P. Waage. They first stated what came to be known as the law of mass action, as follows: *At constant temperature, the rate of a chemical reaction is directly proportional to the concentration of each of the reacting substances.* Thus, for example, in the reaction between hydrogen and iodine vapor represented by the equation

$$H_2 + I_2 = 2HI$$

if the number of moles of hydrogen or of iodine per liter that combine per second to form hydrogen iodide is represented by r, we may write

$$r = k[H_2][I_2]$$

where $[H_2]$ and $[I_2]$ are the concentrations of hydrogen and iodine, respectively,[2] and k is a proportionality constant the value of which is greater the higher the temperature. This quantity, k, is often referred to as the rate constant of the reaction.

The case just cited is an especially simple one, in that only one molecule each of hydrogen and iodine, as shown in the equation, is involved in the combination. It has been found that if more than one molecule of the same substance takes part in a reaction, the concentration of that substance must appear in the equation for the reaction rate as a factor, as many times as there are molecules of the substance in the balanced equation. Thus, for example, let us consider the *reverse* of the reaction we have just discussed; i.e., the decomposition of gaseous hydrogen iodide according to the equation

$$2HI = H_2 + I_2$$

If the concentration of hydrogen iodide in a given vessel is represented by $[HI]$, and the number of moles per liter of this compound decomposing per second by r', then it is found experimentally that

$$r' = k'[HI]^2$$

where k' is another proportionality constant whose value depends upon the temperature. The fact that the rate of decomposition is proportional not to the first power but to the *square* of the concentration of hydrogen iodide may perhaps seem less surprising if the equation is written as if hydrogen iodide reacts with itself:

$$HI + HI = H_2 + I_2$$

We may suppose that this reaction can occur only if a molecule of hydrogen iodide collides with a second molecule of the same compound; hence, we have

[2] For convenience in the formulation of this and other relationships involving concentrations, we shall follow a common convention and represent the concentration of a substance by its formula enclosed in brackets.

$$r' = k'[\text{HI}][\text{HI}] = k'[\text{HI}]^2$$

as before.

In the general case represented by the chemical equation

$$m\text{A} + n\text{B} + \ldots = p\text{C} + q\text{D} + \ldots$$

where m, n, p, and q are the coefficients of A, B, C, D, respectively, in the equation for the reaction, let us represent by r_1 the rate at which A, B, etc., react to form C, D, etc., and by r_2 the rate of the reverse reaction. According to the law of mass action, we have, then,

$$r_1 = k_1[\text{A}]^m[\text{B}]^n \ldots$$

and

$$r_2 = k_2[\text{C}]^p[\text{D}]^q \ldots$$

Although the law of mass action has proved to be extremely useful, yet the statement made in the preceding paragraph is, from one point of view, a drastic oversimplification. Actually, the rate of a reaction involving three or more molecules can usually not be predicted by means of the law of mass action alone. Very few reactions, in fact, take place as a result of the simultaneous collision of more than two molecules; more complex reactions usually proceed by a mechanism involving two or more steps. The rate of the over-all reaction is then determined by the rate of the slowest step. Hence, in all but the simplest cases, the quantitative relationship between reaction rate and the concentrations of the reactants must be determined experimentally.

THE LAW OF CHEMICAL EQUILIBRIUM

11. Determining Factors. We are now ready to consider the factors that determine the state of equilibrium which is reached in a particular reaction under given conditions, and through these to seek an answer to the all-important question, "What determines which way a reversible reaction will go, or how far it will go, before equilibrium is reached?"

12. The Equilibrium Constant. Our most useful clue is to be found in the fact (p. 248) that the equilibrium state is that in which two opposing reactions are both proceeding at the same rate. From this fact, together with the law of mass action, it immediately follows that whenever a particular system is in equilibrium, a definite relationship among the concentrations of all of the reacting substances must prevail. Let us suppose, for example, that equilibrium has been reached at some fixed temperature in the reaction represented by the general equation

$$m\text{A} + n\text{B} \rightleftharpoons p\text{C} + q\text{D}$$

For the rate (r_1) at which A and B are reacting to form C and D we may write

$$r_1 = k_1[A]^m[B]^n$$

and similarly, for the rate (r_2) at which C and D are reacting to form A and B,

$$r_2 = k_2[C]^p[D]^q$$

The condition for equilibrium is that

$$r_1 = r_2$$

Hence, at equilibrium, we have

$$k_1[A]^m[B]^n = k_2[C]^p[D]^q$$

Dividing both sides of this equation by $k_2A^mB^n$, we obtain

$$\frac{k_1}{k_2} = \frac{[C]^p[D]^q}{[A]^m[B]^n}$$

Or, if we represent k_1/k_2 by K, we may put the equation in the form

$$\frac{[C]^p[D]^q}{[A]^m[B]^n} = K$$

Since the rate constants k_1 and k_2 have constant values for a particular reaction at a fixed temperature, K is also a constant at a given temperature; it is known as the *equilibrium constant* of the reaction.

This last equation may be regarded as a mathematical formulation of the *law of chemical equilibrium*, and, indeed, it constitutes the most concise and satisfactory expression of this law. Any verbal statement of the same relationship is unavoidably cumbersome, like the following: *When equilibrium has been attained in a reversible reaction at a given temperature, the product of the concentrations of the resulting substances divided by the product of the concentrations of the reacting substances—each concentration taken as a factor as many times as there are molecules of that substance in the equation for the reaction—is a constant.*

The significance of the law lies in the fact that, however the individual concentrations may be varied, the composition of the mixture will always adjust itself so that, when equilibrium is attained, the quotient $[C]^p[D]^q/[A]^m[B]^n$ has the value K. The equilibrium constant, K, is to be thought of as a number whose value may be found by analysis of the equilibrium mixture. Once the value of K for a given reaction is known, the behavior of any mixture of the substances in question can be predicted. There are, of course, an infinite number of combinations of individual concentrations at which equilibrium can exist, but in every such case the value of the quotient $[C]^p[D]^q/[A]^m[B]^n$ must be the same. If, on the other hand, a mixture is prepared of A, B, C, and D in proportions such that the ratio of $[C]^p[D]^q$ to $[A]^m[B]^n$ is not equal to K, then the system cannot be in equilibrium, and its composition will change in one direction or the other until equilibrium is attained. Specifically, if the ratio is less than K, just enough of the A and B in the mixture will be converted to C and D to increase the value of the quotient to K; if the ratio is greater than K, the opposite change will occur to the necessary extent.

It may be seen readily that a large value of K indicates that equilibrium is attained only when the reactants A and B have been converted almost completely into the products C and D. In other words, a high value of K corresponds to a strong tendency for the composition of the mixture to change in the direction indicated by the chemical equation, as read from left to right. A very small value of K—much less than unity—corresponds to a great tendency for the opposite change to take place.

It must not be supposed that the law of chemical equilibrium is applicable only to cases in which the reaction rates vary with concentration in accordance with the law of mass action. The concept of equilibrium constant can be arrived at more rigorously by methods which are beyond the scope of this text. However, even though the derivation given here is oversimplified, the conclusion is nevertheless valid.

13. An Application of the Law of Chemical Equilibrium. As an example of the application of this law to an equilibrium in the gaseous state, let us consider the industrially important reaction

$$N_2 + 3H_2 \rightleftharpoons 2NH_3$$

for which, at equilibrium

$$\frac{[NH_3]^2}{[N_2][H_2]^3} = K$$

At ordinary temperatures, however, nitrogen and hydrogen react at such an exceedingly slow rate that no appreciable amount of ammonia is formed —to say nothing of equilibrium being attained—even in a period of many months. At temperatures above 350° C., and in the presence of finely divided iron as a catalyst, equilibrium is reached in a matter of minutes. As a result of careful experimentation by many different workers, the following facts have been conclusively established.

1. At a fixed temperature and a fixed total pressure, the mixture always has the same composition when reaction ceases, regardless of whether the starting substances are free nitrogen and hydrogen in the proportions in

which they react (one volume of nitrogen to three of hydrogen), or whether an equivalent quantity of ammonia is allowed to undergo decomposition.

2. When the total pressure is changed, or when the original mixture contains nitrogen and hydrogen in other than equivalent proportions, the composition of the equilibrium mixture is altered, but the magnitude of the quotient $[NH_3]^2/[N_2][H_2]^3$ remains constant as long as the temperature is unchanged.

3. The proportion of ammonia in the equilibrium mixture, and hence the magnitude of the equilibrium constant, decrease with increasing temperature.

At a temperature of 400° C., when a mixture of nitrogen and hydrogen in equivalent proportions is maintained at a total pressure of 50 atm., experiment has shown that 26.3% of the mixture reacts to form ammonia; if ammonia is maintained at this same temperature and pressure, 73.7% of it decomposes into nitrogen and hydrogen. From these data it may be shown (we need not concern ourselves here with the details of the calculation) that the value of the equilibrium constant K at this temperature is 0.509. Other experiments carried out at the same temperature, but at different pressures and with mixtures of varying initial composition, lead to the same result.

14. Equilibrium Constant in Terms of Partial Pressures. Since the pressure exerted by a gas is due to the impact of its molecules against the walls of the container, it follows that the greater the number of moles of a gas in a given volume, the greater will be the pressure. Hence, the partial pressure of a gas at a constant temperature may be regarded as a measure of its concentration. For reactions involving gases only, it is often convenient to formulate the equilibrium constant in terms of partial pressures instead of concentrations. Thus, for the reaction that we have been considering, we may define a constant K_p (the equilibrium constant in terms of pressures) by means of the following equation:

$$K_p = \frac{p_{NH_3}^2}{p_{N_2}p_{H_2}^3}$$

The value of K_p for this reaction at 400° C. is 0.000167.

15. Another Application: Equilibrium in the Liquid State. One of the simplest instances of chemical equilibrium in a homogeneous liquid system, and one that has been thoroughly studied, is found in the reversible reaction between ethyl alcohol and acetic acid to form ethyl acetate and water.

$$C_2H_5OH + HC_2H_3O_2 \rightleftharpoons C_2H_5C_2H_3O_2 + H_2O$$

ethyl alcohol   acetic acid   ethyl acetate

According to the law of chemical equilibrium, the same equilibrium state should be reached whether we start with ethyl alcohol and acetic acid, or with equivalent quantities of ethyl acetate and water; and when this state has been attained

$$\frac{[C_2H_5C_2H_3O_2][H_2O]}{[C_2H_5OH][HC_2H_3O_2]} = K$$

Experiment shows that when one mole each of the alcohol and the acid are mixed at room temperature, the reaction proceeds until two-thirds of a mole of each of these substances has been used up, with the formation of two-thirds of a mole each of ethyl acetate and water; one-third mole of each of the reactants then remains unchanged. If we denote the volume of the mixture by V, we have for the value of K at room temperature

$$K = \frac{[(\tfrac{2}{3})/V] \times [(\tfrac{2}{3})/V]}{[(\tfrac{1}{3})/V] \times [(\tfrac{1}{3})/V]} = 4$$

The value of this quotient remains constant, at constant temperature, in the presence of an excess of any of the reacting substances, or of another liquid which does not participate in the reaction.

Equilibrium in liquid solutions of ionic substances will be considered in Chapters 18 and 19.

16. Deviations from the Law of Chemical Equilibrium. Before we proceed to the discussion of further applications of the law of chemical equilibrium, it will be well for us to consider some of its limitations. The theoretical explanation of the law is based upon the assumptions that the particles of the reacting substances are of negligible size and do not exert any attractive or repulsive forces upon each other, but are free to move at random and to collide with each other merely by chance. In view of this, we should not be surprised to find that the law of chemical equilibrium does not exactly express the equilibrium behavior of any actual system.

These conditions are not strictly fulfilled even in gases at very low pressures. However, in gaseous mixtures at pressures up to a few atmospheres, and in dilute solutions of non-ionic substances, departures from the ideal conditions are sufficiently small so that the law of chemical equilibrium holds with a fair degree of accuracy. In gases at high pressures, however, and in concentrated solutions, the law is no longer valid, unless the concentration of each substance is multiplied by a correction factor, called an *activity coefficient*, the value of which is not constant but varies with temperature and concentration, and can be determined only by experiment. The corrected concentration is called the *activity* of the substance in question; thus the activity may be regarded as the apparent or effective concentration—a value which, if used in place of the actual concentration in the equation for the law of chemical equilibrium, will make the equation valid. The concept of activity coefficient is especially important in connection with solutions of ionic substances, and we shall have occasion to return to it in Chapter 19. Fortunately, however, in many calculations involving the law of chemical equilibrium, the activity coefficients of all substances concerned may be taken to be unity without serious error; in other words, the law may be applied in the simple form first derived (p. 257).

17. Equilibrium in Heterogeneous Systems. Up to this point in our discussion of the law of chemical equilibrium, we have limited ourselves to homogeneous reactions; i.e., to cases in which the reacting substances are all present in a single phase, either gaseous or liquid. However, the application of the law to heterogeneous reactions, in which two or more phases are involved, introduces no new difficulties; indeed, as will be shown presently, such applications are often simpler than those we have been discussing.

The most important instances of heterogeneous equilibrium are those in which one or more solid substances, as well as liquids or gases, take part in the reaction. Now the concentration of a pure solid or liquid is proportional to the density, and remains constant as long as the temperature is unchanged. It follows that the concentrations of whatever solid substances or pure liquids (not solutions) are involved in an equilibrium, since they are constant, may be included in the value of the equilibrium constant, and need not appear at all in the equation expressing the equilibrium conditions.

As an example, let us consider the decomposition of calcium carbonate into calcium oxide and carbon dioxide according to the equation

$$CaCO_{3(s)} \rightleftharpoons CaO_{(s)} + CO_{2(g)}$$

Here the expression for the equilibrium constant takes the form

$$[CO_2] = K$$

or, for the equilibrium constant in terms of partial pressures

$$p_{CO_2} = K_p$$

The meaning of this equation is that, at any given temperature, there is only one pressure at which carbon dioxide can be in equilibrium with the two solids. In order to clarify this point, let us consider this system from a slightly different point of view. Suppose we had a mixture of calcium carbonate and calcium oxide in a closed container provided with a tight-fitting but movable piston, as shown in Figure 15.2, and suppose the temperature of the whole system to be kept constant at 900° C. The value of K_p at this temperature has been found to be 1.04 atm. This means that, with the piston held stationary, calcium carbonate would decompose until the pressure of carbon dioxide just reached 1.04 atm., and then, equilibrium having been attained, the decomposition would stop. If we should attempt to decrease the pressure

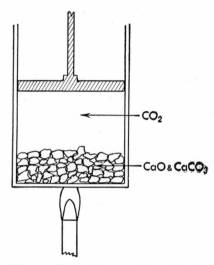

Fig. 15.2. Equilibrium in the decomposition of calcium carbonate.

of carbon dioxide by raising the piston and allowing the gas to expand, just enough more calcium carbonate would decompose to maintain the pressure at its original value of 1.04 atm. If, on the other hand, we should try to increase the pressure by pushing down on the piston, thereby compressing the gas, some of the carbon dioxide would combine with calcium oxide to form the carbonate, and the pressure would still remain at the same level.

Another important example of heterogeneous equilibrium is provided by the decomposition of hydrates (p. 235). For example, at ordinary temperatures the pentahydrate of cupric sulfate, commonly known as blue vitriol, has a slight tendency to decompose according to the equation

$$CuSO_4 \cdot 5H_2O_{(s)} \rightleftharpoons CuSO_4 \cdot 3H_2O_{(s)} + 2H_2O_{(g)}$$

The equilibrium pressure of water vapor in this reaction, at 25° C., is 7.8 mm. If some of the pentahydrate is placed in a closed vessel, evacuated to insure the absence of water vapor and maintained at 25° C., it loses water with the formation of trihydrate until the pressure of water vapor in the vessel has reached 7.8 mm., when the reaction stops. Any attempt to decrease the pressure below this equilibrium value would result in further loss of water by the pentahydrate, whereas an attempt to increase the pressure would bring about combination of water with the trihydrate to form blue vitriol. Hence, any mixture of the two hydrates, regardless of their relative amounts, will maintain a pressure of 7.8 mm. of water vapor in a closed vessel at 25° C. In general, the pressure of water vapor remains constant, at a given temperature, in the presence of a mixture of any hydrate and its immediate decomposition product, whether this be a lower hydrate or the anhydrous compound. Because of the analogy between such an equilibrium and that existing between a liquid and its vapor, it is customary to refer to the equilibrium pressure as the vapor pressure of the hydrate pair or system; thus the vapor pressure of the pair $CuSO_4 \cdot 5H_2O — CuSO_4 \cdot 3H_2O$ at 25° C. is 7.8 mm. It would be incorrect, however, to speak of the vapor pressure of a single hydrate, since such a compound alone would be unable to maintain a constant pressure of water vapor, at a given temperature, under all conditions.

When a hydrate is exposed to the open air, it may or may not lose water, depending upon whether the vapor pressure of the system consisting of the given hydrate and its immediate decomposition product is greater or less than the partial pressure of water vapor in the atmosphere at the particular time and place. The partial pressure of water vapor under normal indoor conditions of temperature and humidity is about 8 to 12 mm. Hence, blue vitriol does not ordinarily lose water vapor when exposed to air in the laboratory; but the trihydrate of cupric sulfate does take up water from the air, since the vapor pressure of the hydrate system is less than 8 mm. On the other hand, the system consisting of washing soda, $Na_2CO_3 \cdot 10H_2O$, and the next lower hydrate of sodium carbonate, $Na_2CO_3 \cdot 7H_2O$, has a vapor pressure of about 18 mm. at 25° C. Hence, washing soda readily loses water on exposure to the atmosphere. It is said to *effloresce*, and the phenomenon is known as *efflorescence*. The vapor pressure of hydrate systems, like that of water, increases with increasing temperature; hence, many hydrated salts may be dehydrated by increase in temperature.

DISPLACEMENT OF EQUILIBRIUM

18. Factors Which Affect Equilibrium. At first thought, it might appear that any of the conditions which affect reaction rates would also have an influence upon the composition of an equilibrium mixture, but careful consideration will show that this supposition is not quite correct. Since the criterion for equilibrium is that the rates of the two opposite reactions shall be equal, it follows that, once equilibrium has been reached, it is disturbed only by such changes as affect the rates of the two reactions *to a different extent*. The state of subdivision or amount of surface presented by solid reactants has no effect upon the point at which equilibrium is reached, nor does the presence of a catalyst, which affects the rates of two opposite reactions equally; it must be remembered, however, that by the use of a catalyst the equilibrium state may be reached in a much shorter time than would otherwise be required.

On the other hand, there is no reason to suppose that changes in *temperature* would have exactly the same effect upon two opposite reactions. Since the equilibrium constant, K, may be regarded as the ratio of the rate constants k_1 and k_2 (p. 257), it is evident that *the value of K will change with temperature* whenever, as is almost always the case, the two rate constants are not both changed in the same ratio by a given change in temperature.

Although the equilibrium constant for a given reaction does not vary with the proportions in which the reacting substances are brought together, it may readily be shown that a change in *concentration* of any of the substances present at equilibrium must cause the reaction to proceed in one direction or another until a new equilibrium is reached. For example, in the reaction

$$A + B \rightleftharpoons C + D$$

an increase in the concentration of either A or B will increase the rate of the reaction toward the right, while it will be without effect upon the opposite reaction. Hence the composition of the equilibrium mixture will change in the direction of larger concentrations of C and D until the rates of the two reactions are again equal. On the other hand, an increase in the concentration of either C or D, or a decrease in the concentration of A or B, will cause the reaction between C and D to be more rapid than that between A and B, and hence will bring about a corresponding change in the composition of the equilibrium mixture.

Inasmuch as concentrations vary with pressure, the *total pressure* to which a system is subjected is also to be considered as a factor which may affect equilibrium. In systems consisting only of liquids or solids, the effect of pressure upon equilibrium is usually slight. However, since the concentration of a gas is directly proportional to its partial pressure, the rate of any reaction in which one or more gases are involved is considerably affected by the total pressure imposed upon the system. If the number of gaseous molecules participating in the forward and the reverse reactions is the same, the rates of both reactions are increased to the same extent by compression, which therefore has no effect on the equilibrium. Whenever there is a difference in the number of molecules on the opposite sides of an equation, however, the rates of the opposing reactions are unequally affected by a change in total pressure on the mixture, which therefore brings about a change in the equilibrium composition.

The factors which influence equilibrium, then, are the concentrations of the reacting substances (which may be affected by the total pressure on the system) and the temperature. Only the latter, however, affects the value of the equilibrium constant.

19. The Principle of Le Chatelier. The effect of a change in any of the factors discussed in the preceding section may be qualitatively predicted by the application of a simple rule known as the Principle of Le Chatelier. This principle may be stated as follows: *When a system is in equilibrium and one of the factors which determine the equilibrium point is altered, the system always reacts in such a way as to tend to counteract the original alteration.*

20. Effect of Concentration. When this principle is applied to changes in concentration alone, it leads immediately to the same qualitative conclusions as were previously reached (p. 264) through the consideration of reaction rates. If the concentration of any of the substances participating in an equilibrium is increased, the reaction proceeds in such a direction as to use up some of that substance, thereby tending to decrease its concentration. On the other hand, if the concentration of any of the participants is decreased, the reaction proceeds in such a way as to produce more of that substance, thereby tending to increase its concentration.

Both of these methods of displacing or shifting an equilibrium, as the process is called, have practical applicability. Thus, if it is desired to obtain the largest possible yield of sulfur trioxide from a given quantity of the dioxide, a large excess of oxygen is used. On the other hand, one of the most familiar methods of causing a reaction to proceed as far as possible in one direction consists in the removal of one or more of the desired products. Thus, for example, in the manufacture of quicklime, CaO, from limestone, $CaCO_3$ (p. 668) by the reaction

$$CaCO_3 \rightleftharpoons CaO + CO_2$$

a good yield is obtained at temperatures far below 900° C. if the carbon dioxide is continuously removed with the aid of an air blast as fast as it can be formed; for by this means the equilibrium, according to the preceding equation, is continually shifted toward the right.

21. Effect of Pressure. The direction in which an equilibrium is displaced by a change in the pressure applied to the system depends solely upon the nature of the change in volume which accompanies the reaction. The strain, as it may be thought of, which is imposed by an increase in applied pressure, may be relieved by a reaction which results in contraction. It follows, then, from the Principle of Le Chatelier, that an increase in pressure causes a system to change in such a direction as to produce more of those substances which occupy a smaller volume. A familiar illustration is provided by the equilibrium at $0°$ C. between water and ice, which may be represented by the equation

$$H_2O_{(l)} \rightleftharpoons H_2O_{(s)}$$

Since the density of ice is appreciably less than that of liquid water, the volume of any given quantity of water is obviously smaller in the liquid than in the solid state. If the pressure on a mixture of ice and water is increased, the equilibrium is displaced in the direction of smaller volume; that is, some of the ice melts. It is largely because of this fact that sliding and skating on ice are possible. If the temperature is not too low, the pressure exerted by a skate runner suffices to melt enough of the ice to provide a thin layer of water on which the runner may slide.

As stated previously (p. 264), the effect of pressure is most pronounced in the case of reactions in which one or more gases take part, since it is in such instances only that the reaction is likely to be accompanied by a large change in volume. Under given conditions, according to Avogadro's hypothesis, the volume of a gas is directly proportional to the total number of moles; it follows, then, that the volume change in a reaction involving gases is indicated directly by the relative numbers of molecules of gases appearing on the two sides of the equation. If the number of molecules of gases on the right side of the equation is smaller than the number on the left, the reaction from left to right is accompanied by a decrease in volume; it is this reaction, then, according to Le Chatelier's principle, which will be favored by an increase in the pressure imposed on the system, while a decrease in applied pressure will, of course, favor the reverse reaction. For example, it is evident from the equation

$$2SO_2 + O_2 \rightleftharpoons 2SO_3$$

in which two molecules of sulfur trioxide are produced from a total of three molecules of sulfur dioxide and oxygen, that a decrease in volume occurs when the reaction proceeds from left to right. Hence, an increase in the pressure upon the system will result in a larger proportion of sulfur trioxide in the equilibrium mixture.

22. Effect of Temperature. The effect of a change in temperature upon a system in equilibrium depends upon the nature of the heat effect which accompanies the reaction. The immediate effect of the absorption of heat in a reaction is to lower the temperature of the reacting mixture; hence, the strain imposed upon a system by an increase in temperature produced from without may be relieved by the progress of the reaction in such a direction as to absorb heat. If, on the other hand, the temperature of a system is lowered by some external means, the system will respond by changing in such a direction as to evolve heat. If we approach the matter from a slightly different point of view, we may arrive at a more concise statement of the same conclusion: In every system in equilibrium, an endothermic and an exothermic reaction are taking place simultaneously; the endothermic reaction is favored by an increase in temperature, the exothermic reaction by a decrease in temperature.

A very simple illustration of the effect of temperature on equilibrium is provided by the vaporization of water. This change is, of course, an endothermic one; for water in equilibrium with its vapor at 25° C. we may write

$$H_2O_{(l)} \rightleftharpoons H_2O_{(v)} - 10,500 \text{ cal.}$$

As the temperature is raised, the equilibrium is displaced toward the right; that is, in the direction of a higher concentration of vapor. Thus, we may arrive at an explanation, in terms of Le Chatelier's principle, of the well known fact that the vapor pressure of water—or, for that matter, of any other liquid—increases with increasing temperature.

In the reaction between sulfur dioxide and oxygen, considerable heat is evolved.

$$2SO_2 + O_2 \rightleftharpoons 2SO_3 + 46,000 \text{ cal.}$$

We may conclude, then, that an increase in temperature will shift the equilibrium toward the left. This conclusion is in accord with the experimental fact that, at constant pressure, the yield of sulfur trioxide in the above reaction decreases with increasing temperature (p. 456). The value of the equilibrium constant in terms of partial pressures

$$K_p = \frac{p_{SO_3}^2}{p_{SO_2}^2 p_{O_2}}$$

decreases from 2800 at 500° C. to only 0.74 at 800° C.

At room temperature, the value of K_p is so large as to correspond to practically complete oxidation of the dioxide. However, it must be remembered that, because of the rapid falling off of reaction rates with decreasing temperature, equilibrium is attained more slowly the lower the temperature. In the commercial production of sulfur trioxide as a step in the manufacture of sulfuric acid (p. 457), it has been found impracticable to use temperatures below 400° C., because at such temperatures, even in the presence of a catalyst, the reaction proceeds too slowly.

23. Practical Applications of Le Chatelier's Principle: The Synthesis of Nitric Oxide and of Ammonia. It will be both interesting and instructive for us to consider two further instances of the application of the principles discussed in the two preceding sections to chemical reactions which are of actual or potential industrial importance.

In the early years of the present century, a great deal of research was devoted to the problem of the economical production of nitrogen compounds from the abundant but inert free nitrogen of the atmosphere. One of the reactions that seemed promising was the direct combination of nitrogen and oxygen to yield nitric oxide.

$$N_2 + O_2 \rightleftharpoons 2NO - 43{,}000 \text{ cal.}$$

It is evident from this equation that no change in volume occurs in this reaction; hence, the pressure imposed on the system will have no effect upon the equilibrium. Since the reaction, as read from left to right, is highly endothermic, the formation of nitric oxide should be favored by increase in temperature. It is only at temperatures approaching 3000° C. that a practically useful yield of nitric oxide can be attained. At these temperatures, however, the reaction proceeds sufficiently rapidly without a catalyst.

For many years nitric oxide was made industrially in Norway by means of the so-called arc process. Air was blown through an arc spread out by means of an electromagnet into a huge disk; the mixture of gases was then cooled as rapidly as possible, in order to prevent immediate decomposition of the nitric oxide. The arc process became obsolete because, even where electricity could be obtained cheaply from abundant water power, this method of producing nitrogen compounds could not compete with the one to be considered in the next paragraph. Very recently, nitric oxide has been produced in a gas furnace heated by the regenerative system (p. 751). Even this much less expensive method, however, has not yet proved to be economically successful.

One of the most important of industrial reactions is the synthesis of ammonia from nitrogen and hydrogen, which has already been briefly considered (p. 258). The thermochemical equation for this reaction is

$$N_2 + 3H_2 \rightleftharpoons 2NH_3 + 22{,}100 \text{ cal.}$$

Since the reaction toward the right evidently takes place with a decrease in volume, the formation of ammonia is favored by increase in pressure. Since the reaction in the same direction is exothermic, however, it is the opposite change which is favored by increase in temperature. We may conclude, therefore, that the best yields of ammonia will be obtained when the process is carried out at high pressure and low temperature. Because of the extreme slowness of the reaction, however (p. 258), it has proved impracticable to carry out the synthesis on an industrial scale at temperatures much below 500° C.; even at that temperature, a catalyst must be used if equilibrium is to be attained sufficiently rapidly to meet practical needs.

The Haber process for the synthesis of ammonia was first used successfully on a commercial scale in Germany in 1913. In this process, a mixture of nitrogen and hydrogen under a pressure of 200 atm. is passed over a catalyst, which usually consists mainly of finely divided iron, at a temperature of about 500° C. A fair yield of ammonia is obtained in this way. In modern synthetic ammonia plants, pressures up to 1000 atm. have been used, and correspondingly higher yields of ammonia have been obtained.

STUDY QUESTIONS AND PROBLEMS

1. Nitric oxide and oxygen react according to the equation

$$2NO + O_2 = 2NO_2$$

Suppose that two moles of nitric oxide and one of oxygen are mixed in a glass vessel and maintained at a constant temperature. How will the rate of combination of the two gases, after half of each has been used up, compare with the rate at the beginning of the reaction?

2. Write a mathematical expression for the equilibrium constant in each of the following reactions:

(a) $4HCl + O_2 \rightleftharpoons 2Cl_2 + 2H_2O_{(g)}$
(b) $CH_4 + Cl_2 \rightleftharpoons CH_3Cl_{(g)} + HCl_{(g)}$
(c) $NH_4Cl_{(s)} \rightleftharpoons NH_3 + HCl$
(d) $4NH_3 + 5O_2 \rightleftharpoons 4NO + 6H_2O_{(g)}$
(e) $2Pb(NO_3)_{2(s)} \rightleftharpoons 2PbO_{(s)} + 4NO_{2(g)} + O_2$
(f) $BaSO_{3(s)} \rightleftharpoons BaO_{(s)} + SO_2$

3. When 1 mole of hydrogen iodide in a sealed 1-liter flask is maintained at a temperature of 500° C., it decomposes until 0.12 mole each of hydrogen and iodine vapor is formed. What is the value of the equilibrium constant for the reaction

$$2HI \rightleftharpoons H_2 + I_2$$

at 500° C.? (Since the volume is 1 l. throughout, the concentration of each substance is numerically equal to the number of moles present.)

4. Carbon monoxide and chlorine react to form a gas called phosgene, according to the equation

$$CO + Cl_2 \rightleftharpoons COCl_2$$

The value of the equilibrium constant at a certain temperature is 5. Suppose that a mixture of 2 moles of carbon monoxide and 1 mole of chlorine is introduced into a liter flask and maintained at this temperature. What will be the concentration of each gas when equilibrium is reached?

5. Suppose that equilibrium has been attained in the reaction

$$CO_2 + H_2 \rightleftharpoons CO + H_2O_{(g)}$$

State in which direction the equilibrium will be shifted by each of the following changes.

(a) Introduction of more carbon dioxide.
(b) Removal of some of the carbon monoxide.
(c) Introduction of more water vapor.
(d) Removal of some of the hydrogen.

6. State in which direction the equilibrium will be shifted by an increase in the total pressure on the system, and by an increase in temperature, in each of the following reactions:

(a) $N_2 + 3H_2 \rightleftharpoons 2NH_3$ (exothermic)
(b) $2SO_2 + O_2 \rightleftharpoons 2SO_{3(g)}$ (exothermic)
(c) $N_2 + O_2 \rightleftharpoons 2NO$ (endothermic)
(d) $3O_2 \rightleftharpoons 2O_3$ (endothermic)
(e) $2H_2 + O_2 \rightleftharpoons 2H_2O_{(g)}$ (exothermic)
(f) $CaCO_3 \rightleftharpoons CaO + CO_2$ (endothermic)

7. Explain the fact that a catalyst is often used to bring about a desired reaction, even though the reverse reaction is also accelerated by the catalyst.

8. In any discussion of reaction rates and chemical equilibrium, why are concentrations always expressed in moles, rather than in grams, per unit volume?

16

Solutions

1. Importance of Solutions. Both from a practical and from a theoretical viewpoint, the fact that two or more substances can, under certain conditions, form a solution with each other, leads to important consequences. We may recall, for example, that one of the most effective means of separating two substances is by taking advantage of the difference in their tendencies to dissolve in a given liquid. In fact, the science of analytical chemistry is based very largely upon the properties of dissolved substances. Also, many reactions that will not take place between the pure reactants at an appreciable rate proceed rapidly in solution. On this account, solutions play an important part in many industrial chemical processes. Furthermore, most of the changes that take place in living matter, such as nutrition, excretion, and growth, are largely dependent upon the properties of solutions.

The importance of solutions from the point of view of chemical theory lies in the fact that a dissolved substance is in an extreme state of subdivision or dispersion. The large aggregates that are sometimes present in pure liquids, and always in crystalline solids, break up in the process of solution into much smaller particles of molecular or atomic dimensions. In consequence, information as to the size and structure of molecules is often more readily obtained by the study of solutions than from the properties of the components in the free state.

2. General Nature of Solutions. A solution has been previously defined (p. 18) as a homogeneous mixture of two or more substances, the proportions of which may vary continuously although usually only within certain limits. The property of variability of composition, as has been pointed out, constitutes the most important criterion of a solution, as distinguished from a chemical compound. Solutions are likewise distinctive in that the properties of a solution partake to a considerable degree of the properties of the components of the solution; compounds, on the other hand, have properties which are distinct from those of the elements from which the compound is formed.

The difference between solutions and ordinary heterogeneous mixtures lies in the fact that the former consist of but a single phase, whereas two or more phases may be distinguished in a heterogeneous mixture. In a mixture of two solids, such as iron and sulfur, for example, even though they may have been finely ground and thoroughly intermixed, the two kinds of particles may readily be distinguished by means of a microscope. In a solution, however, no boundaries between components can be observed; nor is it possible visually to distinguish any particles of either component by means of the most powerful microscope, or even with the aid of the ultramicroscope (p. 363), with which particles only one-millionth of a centimeter in diameter can be detected.

The facts just cited indicate that in a true solution the individual particles of the components are no larger than molecules. Further evidence which points in the same direction is to be found in two related aspects of the behavior of liquid solutions which are markedly analogous to the behavior of gases. First, even though there may be a great difference in density between two components of a solution, no appreciable tendency toward sedimentation is observed; that is, the denser component does not settle to the bottom of the containing vessel.[1] Second, just as a gas uniformly fills any container into which it is introduced (p. 27), so also does a solution tend to become uniform throughout its entire volume. This fact may readily be demonstrated if a solution of a colored substance such as cupric sulfate, $CuSO_4 \cdot 5H_2O$, is placed in the bottom of a glass cylinder and water is carefully introduced above it. Even if the mixture is not stirred—indeed, even if it is carefully protected from agitation—the blue color will be observed to spread gradually until the entire solution is uniform in color. It is evident, then, that the dissolved substance exhibits the phenomenon of diffusion which has already been discussed in connection with gases. This can be accounted for only on the assumption that the particles in a solution of copper sulfate are in constant, rapid, random motion; in other words, that they possess kinetic energy of a nature similar to that which we have attributed to the molecules of a gas. Thus, we are led to the conclusion that the dispersed particles of a dissolved substance are of molecular or atomic magnitude.

It is important to distinguish, at this point, between the simple process of

[1] In a very tall column of solution, a slight increase in concentration of the denser component toward the bottom of the column is observable. This phenomenon, however, which indeed occurs also in gases, is negligible under ordinary conditions, and need not be considered further in an elementary treatment of the subject.

solution, on the one hand, and the formation of a solution as a consequence of a chemical reaction, on the other. Thus, although chemists have fallen into the habit of saying that a metal such as zinc "dissolves" in dilute sulfuric acid, this statement is highly inaccurate. Zinc, as such, does not dissolve in sulfuric acid to any appreciable extent. When the two substances are brought together, a displacement reaction occurs; the products are hydrogen, which escapes into the atmosphere, and zinc sulfate, which is soluble in water. The solution that is formed, therefore, is one of zinc sulfate, not of zinc.

Yet it would not be accurate to assert that the process of solution is never accompanied by chemical change; for direct *combination* of the components of a solution occurs very commonly. It has been pointed out, for example, that many substances separate from water solution in the form of solid hydrates (p. 235), and it is reasonable to suppose in such cases that hydrates must be present in the solution as well. In fact, it will be shown later that the formation of chemical bonds (sometimes only very weak ones, it is true) between the molecules of the components is an important factor in determining solubility. Such combination does not occur in every solution, however. It is evident, then, that the process of solution cannot be definitely classified either as a physical or as a chemical change. This need not cause us any great concern, since the distinction is at best not a sharp one.

3. Types of Solution. The definition of a solution does not imply any particular physical state; solutions may be gaseous, liquid, or solid. Since it is not necessary that both components, in the pure condition, be in the same physical state as the solution, we may distinguish nine classes of solutions altogether, as follows:

		Examples
Solutions in the gaseous state	(a) Gases in gases.	Air, any other mixture of gases.
	(b) Liquids in gases.	Water in air, bromine in chlorine, acetic acid in nitrogen.
	(c) Solids in gases.	Naphthalene in methane, iodine in air.
Solutions in the liquid state	(a) Gases in liquids.	Carbon dioxide in water, hydrogen chloride in benzene.
	(b) Liquids in liquids.	Alcohol in water, bromine in carbon disulfide.
	(c) Solids in liquids.	Sugar in water, iodine in carbon tetrachloride, lead in mercury.
Solutions in the solid state	(a) Gases in solids.	Hydrogen in palladium.
	(b) Liquids in solids.	Mercury in thallium.
	(c) Solids in solids.	Cobalt in nickel, gold in silver, lead chloride in lead bromide.

We shall be especially concerned with solutions in the liquid state, because these are of the greatest practical importance.

4. Terminology. In the discussion of solutions, we shall frequently have occasion to use the term "concentration." In the strictest sense of the word (see p. 254), the *concentration* of a substance in a solution is the quantity of the substance per unit volume of the solution. In a binary solution consisting of two substances A and B, the concentration of A is the quantity of A per unit volume of the solution, and the concentration of B is the quantity of B per unit volume of the solution. In practice, the rigorous definition just given is not always adhered to, and the term concentration is loosely applied to any measure of the relative amounts of the components in a solution. Thus, for example, the concentration of a solution of A in B may be expressed in terms of the percentage by weight of A in the solution, or even by the number of grams of A per gram, or 100 grams, or 1000 grams, of B. Other ways of expressing concentration will be considered in the next section.

It is often convenient to refer to one component of a solution as the solvent, and the other (or the others, if there are more than two components) as the solute (or solutes). This distinction is actually one of convenience only, however, since it does not indicate any real difference in function between the two components. Ordinarily, that component present in the higher concentration is called the solvent, and the one present in the lower concentration, the solute; we customarily think of the solute as being "dissolved in" the solvent, or of a solution of the solute "in" the solvent. Thus we might refer to vinegar as a 5% solution of acetic acid in water, and to the laboratory reagent known as glacial acetic acid, which contains less than 1% of water, as a solution of water in acetic acid. This distinction becomes meaningless, of course, when the two components are present in equal, or nearly equal, concentrations. On the other hand, the distinction between solute and solvent (while still essentially a matter of convention) is of considerably greater significance in the case of two substances which, when pure, are not in the same physical state. Here, that component which retains in the solution its own characteristic physical state is commonly called the solvent; the one which, in dissolving, undergoes a change in state, is commonly called the solute. Thus, in the familiar instance of a solution consisting of water and one or more solid salts, water is universally characterized as the solvent and the salts as solutes. A solution containing but a small concentration of solute is said to be *dilute*; one containing a large concentration of solute is referred to as a *concentrated* solution.

5. Methods of Expressing the Composition of Solutions. Several methods of expressing the composition of solutions are in common use. As will be seen later, each of these methods has its own advantages in particular types of problems. Hence, it is essential for the student to be familiar with all of the various forms of expression, and to be able to convert data from one form to another.

Most of these methods fall into two main classes: (1) those based upon the relative weights of solute (or solutes) and solvent; and (2) those which may be regarded as measures of concentration, in the true sense of the term; those, i.e., which give the *weight* of solute (or solutes) per unit *volume* of solution. In both cases, the weights may be expressed either (a) in physical units (ordinarily in grams), or (b) in chemical units (i.e., in moles or in gram-equivalents). The most widely used methods will be considered in the following paragraphs.

METHODS BASED UPON THE RELATIVE WEIGHTS OF THE COMPONENTS

1. One of the simplest means of expressing the composition is in terms of the *weight fraction*, or more commonly, the *percentage by weight*, of one component. A 28% aqueous solution of sulfuric acid is, exactly as the designation implies, a solution containing 28% by weight of sulfuric acid, H_2SO_4, and 72% by weight of water; it might also be characterized as one that contains 28 g. of sulfuric acid to 100 g. of solution, or to $100 - 28 = 72$ g. of water; or as one that contains 280 g. of sulfuric acid to 1000 g. of solution, or to $1000 - 280 = 720$ g. of water. We may calculate from the percentage composition the weight of solute per 100 g., or per 1000 g. of solvent. Thus, in the solution we have been considering, the number of grams of sulfuric acid in solution in 1000 g. of water is $(28/72) \times 1000 = 388.9$ g.

2. The *molality* of a solution is defined as the number of moles of solute per 1000 g. of solvent. The molality may readily be determined from the composition of the solution in terms of physical weight units; it is necessary only to divide the number of grams of solute by the gram-molecular weight of the solute, in order to find the corresponding number of moles. Thus, the 28% solution of sulfuric acid contains, in 1000 g. of water, $388.9/98.082 = 3.965$ moles of H_2SO_4; it is therefore 3.965 molal. In Table 16.1 we have tabulated the respective molalities of 20% solutions of various solutes; such solutions contain 20 g. of solute to 80 g. of solvent, or $1000/80 \times 20 = 250$ g. of solute per 1000 g. of solvent.

A *molal* solution is one that contains 1 mole of solute per 1000 g. of solvent. Hence, a molal solution of sulfuric acid contains 98.082 g. of H_2SO_4

to 1000 g. of water, or to 1098.082 g. of solution; the percentage of H_2SO_4 in a molal solution is $98.082/1098.1 \times 100 = 8.932\%$.

Table 16.1

Molalities of 20% Solutions of Various Solutes
(250 g. solute per 1000 g. solvent)

Solute	Molecular weight of solute	Molality
Common salt, NaCl	58.448	4.277
Sulfuric acid, H_2SO_4	98.082	2.549
Cane sugar, $C_{12}H_{22}O_{11}$	342.30	0.730
Sodium hydroxide, NaOH	39.999	6.250

3. The *mole fraction* of either component of a solution is the fraction of the total number of moles present that are moles of that particular component; or, in other words, it is the ratio of the number of moles of the component in question to the total number of moles. Thus, in a solution of A and B, if n_A represents the number of moles of A, and n_B the number of moles of B, and the mole fractions of A and B are represented by N_A and N_B respectively, then

$$N_A = \frac{n_A}{n_A + n_B}$$

and

$$N_B = \frac{n_B}{n_A + n_B}$$

The sum of the mole fractions of the components of a solution always must be unity, for

$$N_A + N_B = \frac{n_A + n_B}{n_A + n_B} = 1$$

Now, returning to our 28% solution of H_2SO_4, which contains 28 g. of H_2SO_4 to 72 g. of H_2O, we have

$$n_{H_2SO_4} = \frac{28}{98.082} = 0.2855$$

$$n_{H_2O} = \frac{72}{18.016} = 3.9964$$

$$n_{H_2SO_4} + n_{H_2O} = 4.2819$$

$$N_{H_2SO_4} = \frac{0.2855}{4.2819} = 0.0667$$

$$N_{H_2O} = \frac{3.9964}{4.2819} = 0.9333$$

$$N_{H_2SO_4} + N_{H_2O} = 0.0667 + 0.9333 = 1$$

It may be noted here that this method of expressing composition is frequently used for gaseous mixtures (solutions) because the partial pressures of the components of such a mixture are directly proportional to the mole fractions. Thus, for example, air is a mixture of approximately 4 moles of nitrogen to 1 mole of oxygen. Hence

$$n_{N_2} + n_{O_2} = 5$$

$$N_{N_2} = \tfrac{4}{5} = 0.8$$

and

$$N_{O_2} = \tfrac{1}{5} = 0.2$$

If the total pressure of the air is P, and the partial pressures of nitrogen and oxygen are p_{N_2} and p_{O_2}, respectively, then

$$p_{N_2} = 0.8\,P$$

and

$$p_{O_2} = 0.2\,P$$

$$p_{N_2} + p_{O_2} = 0.8\,P + 0.2\,P = P$$

If the total pressure is 1 atm., the partial pressures of nitrogen and oxygen are 0.8 and 0.2 atm., respectively (p. 39).

The various methods of expressing the composition of a solution that have been discussed thus far are particularly useful, as will be shown presently, in the consideration of such physical properties of liquid solutions as vapor pressure, boiling point, freezing point, etc. It should be noted that since temperature has no effect upon mass, the composition of a solution, as expressed in any of these ways, does not change with temperature.

METHODS BASED UPON THE WEIGHT OF SOLUTE PER UNIT VOLUME OF
    SOLUTION

1. The concentration of a solution is frequently expressed in terms of the weight of solute per 100 ml., or per liter, of solution. The calculation of concentrations on this basis from data based upon the weights of the components obviously requires knowledge of the density of the solution. As an illustration of the calculation of the weight of solute per liter of solution from the percentage by weight, let us once more consider the 28% sulfuric acid solution. The density of this solution, at 20° C., is 1.202 g. per cc. Hence, a liter of the solution weighs 1202 g., and contains $0.28 \times 1202 = 336.6$ g. of

actual H_2SO_4. A 28% solution of sulfuric acid, then, is the same as a solution containing 336.6 g. of sulfuric acid per liter at 20° C.

2. The *molarity* of a solution is defined as the number of moles of solute dissolved in 1 l. of solution, and hence is easily found by division of the number of grams of solute per liter by its gram-molecular weight. Thus, the solution just described contains, in 1 l., $336.6/98.082 = 3.432$ moles of H_2SO_4; it is, therefore, 3.432 molar, or as it is often written, 3.432 *M*. A *molar*, or 1 *M*, solution is one that contains 1 mole of solute per liter. Hence a molar solution of H_2SO_4 contains 98.082 g. of H_2SO_4 in a liter; a molar solution of common salt, 58.448 g. of NaCl in a liter; and a molar solution of cane sugar, 342.31 g. of $C_{12}H_{22}O_{11}$ in a liter. A sodium hydroxide solution containing 0.4000 g. of NaOH in 100 ml. of solution, or 4.000 g. in a liter, is one-tenth molar, also written $M/10$ or 0.1 *M*.

Since a mole of any substance always consists of the same number of molecules (Avogadro's number, p. 86), it is evident that when the concentration of a solute is expressed in terms of molarity it provides a direct measure of the number of solute molecules per unit volume of solution. In solutions of the same molarity, the average distances between solute molecules are equal. This method of expressing the concentration of a solution is particulary useful, therefore, in the consideration of phenomena such as reaction rates and chemical equilibrium (Chapter 15), which depend upon the spatial distribution of the molecules.

When a small amount of solute is dissolved in a solvent, the volume of the solution obtained is practically the same as that of the solvent. Furthermore, the volume of 1000 g. of water, at ordinary temperatures, is practically equal to 1 l. Hence it follows that the molarity of a *dilute* aqueous solution is the same as the molality. This identity does not hold, however, for solutions in solvents other than water, for concentrated aqueous solutions, or even for dilute aqueous solutions at temperatures sufficiently high so that the density of water is appreciably less than 1 g. per cc.

3. The concentration of a solution may also be expressed in terms of its *normality*, which is defined as the number of gram-equivalents of solute dissolved in 1 l. of solution. A *normal*, or 1N, solution is one that contains 1 gram-equivalent of solute per liter. This measure of concentration is particularly applicable to solutions of ionic substances; its further discussion is therefore postponed until Chapter 18, which deals specifically with reactions in such solutions.

6. Saturated Solutions. Two or more substances in the same physical state will often form a homogeneous mixture, or solution, when brought together in any proportions whatever; in such a case, they are said to be *completely miscible*. This is obviously true of all gases; for any gas, as has been previously stated, will distribute itself throughout any container into which it is introduced, regardless of whether or not any other gas is present in the same space. Many liquids, also, are completely miscible with each other; thus, we may have solutions of water and alcohol, of water and glycerol, $C_3H_5(OH)_3$, of alcohol and glycerol, or of all three, which contain anything between 100% of any of the components and none at all. There are even some pairs of solids, such as gold and silver, cobalt and nickel, or sodium nitrate and potassium nitrate, that are completely miscible. In most cases, however, including all those in which substances in two different physical states are involved, there is a definite limit to the amount of one substance that will dissolve in a given quantity of another.

For example, if common salt and water are brought together, at a temperature of 18° C., no more than 35.9 g. of salt will dissolve in 100 ml. of water. If a larger amount of salt is present, the excess over 35.9 g. will simply remain as solid salt; no amount of stirring will bring about its solution. In such a case, the solution is said to be *saturated* with the solute in question. A saturated solution may best be defined as one which can exist in equilibrium with undissolved solute.

No more than in the case of equilibrium between a liquid and its vapor (p. 59), however, is this equilibrium a state of absolute rest in which all change has ceased. Not only would the existence of such a state of rest be impossible to reconcile with the idea of constant molecular motion, but it may be shown experimentally that an interchange of particles actually occurs between the undissolved solute and the solute in solution. For example, an imperfect crystal of a solid solute may be observed to undergo a change in shape—though, of course, not in weight—on long contact with a saturated solution of the same substance. Hence, we must regard a saturated solution as being in a state of dynamic equilibrium (p. 248). Two opposite changes are continually taking place: molecules (or ions) are continually leaving the surface of the solute to go into solution, while other molecules (or ions) of the dissolved solute are being redeposited, at exactly the same rate. This equilibrium may be represented by the equation

$$\text{Solute}_{(s, 1, \text{ or } g)} \rightleftharpoons \text{Solute}_{(\text{dissolved})}$$

Indeed, whenever any solution is in contact with undissolved solute, we may be sure that particles of solute are continually both going into solution and coming out, although not at the same rate unless the solution is saturated. If the concentration of the solution is less than that corresponding to saturation, the rate of solution will be greater than that of deposition, and the net result will be that more of the solute will dissolve; the solution is said to be unsaturated. On the other hand, if the concentration of the the solution is greater than that corresponding to saturation, the rate of deposition will be greater than the rate of solution, and the net result will be that some of the solute will separate out; the solution is supersaturated. The only reliable test for a saturated solution is to bring it in contact with some undissolved solute; if no perceptible change takes place in the amount of undissolved solute, or in the concentration of the solution, the solution is saturated.

When two incompletely miscible liquids are brought into contact, two saturated solutions may be formed instead of one. For example, if a very small amount of ether, $(C_2H_5)_2O$, is shaken with water, it dissolves completely to give an unsaturated solution. If the addition of ether is continued, however, it is observed that two distinct liquid layers are formed. The water solution has become saturated and the excess ether, because of its lower density, floats above it; the upper layer, however, consists not of pure ether but of a saturated solution of water in ether. Still further addition of ether causes the lower layer to decrease in size, until eventually—although only after a very large quantity of ether has been added—there is again but a single layer, consisting of a solution of water in ether.

7. Solubility. The concentration of solute in a saturated solution under any given conditions is called its *solubility,* and is usually expressed in grams of solute per 100 g., or per 100 ml., of solvent. In the case of substances that are completely miscible with each other, as are all gases and some pairs of liquids and of solids, there can be no saturated solution; the solubility of each substance in the other may be said to be infinite. Except in the case of gaseous mixtures, solubility varies widely according to the nature of solute and solvent. Even for a given solute and solvent, the solubility usually varies considerably with the temperature, and, in the case of gaseous solutes, also with the pressure. In the subsequent discussion of solubility, we shall limit ourselves to the most important case, that of solutions in the liquid state.

When both components are liquids, and the molecules of each are nonpolar and similar to each other, the forces between solute and solvent molecules are almost the same as those between molecules of solvent (or between molecules of solute), and the two liquids are completely miscible. This is the case, for example, in such mixtures as benzene and toluene (p. 589), or the various components of petroleum (p. 569). If the nature of the molecules differs appreciably, however, the liquids may be incompletely miscible. This effect of difference in intermolecular forces is especially marked in the case of a highly polar and a nonpolar liquid; such a pair is usually only very slightly miscible. The familiar fact that water and gasoline do not mix is a good illustration.

Differences in type of chemical bonding, however, do not always lead to immiscibility, because another important factor which affects solubility is the formation of compounds between solute and solvent. Many polar liquids, such as water and alcohol, are associated or "abnormal" (p. 190) because of the presence of hydrogen bonds, and such liquids are usually immiscible with nonpolar substances. These two associated liquids, on the other hand, are completely miscible *with each other* because of what is known as co-association, i.e., the formation of aggregates through hydrogen bonding between the two kinds of molecules. Acetone, itself an unassociated or "normal" liquid, is miscible with water or alcohol because of its ability to coassociate with either of these liquids.

The class of solutions with which we are most frequently concerned is that of solids in liquids. Here, in the first place, if the substances are immiscible *in the liquid state,* the solubility of either solid in the other liquid is always very small. Thus the polar compound ice does not dissolve in gasoline or in carbon tetrachloride for the same reason that water does not mix with these liquids; nor are nonpolar solid hydrocarbons like naphthalene or paraffin appreciably soluble in water. Ionic solids such as common salt dissolve to an appreciable extent only in liquids of high dielectric constant (p. 187), which are able to weaken the electrostatic forces which, in the crystalline substance, hold the ions in fixed positions. Atomic crystals of the gigantic molecule type, such as diamond or silicon carbide, are but very slightly soluble in any solvent.

The problem of the solubility of solids, however, is more complicated than that of the mutual solubility of liquids because a solid, on dissolving, undergoes a *change of state* closely analogous to fusion. Thus two new factors enter the situation, namely the melting point and the heat of fusion of the solute. When solid and liquid are both nonpolar, it is these factors which are of primary importance; other things being equal, the higher the melting point and the greater the heat of fusion of the solute, the smaller will be its solubility at a given temperature in *any* liquid solvent. Anthracene (p. 590), for example, whose melting point is 217° C., is not very readily soluble in benzene at ordinary temperatures, even though above its melting point anthracene is completely miscible with benzene. On the other hand, when solute and solvent are polar compounds, the effect of these new factors becomes relatively insignificant in comparison with the tendency toward compound formation. Thus sugar, because of its tendency toward hydration, is extraordinarily soluble in water, even at room temperature, and the enormous solubility of such solids as ferric chloride or aluminum nitrate is attributable mainly to the coordination of water molecules by the small, highly charged cations (p. 195).

8. Effect of Pressure on Solubility. In the case of solid and liquid solutes, pressure has but a slight effect on solubility. However, the effect of pressure on the solubility of gases in liquids is very marked. Except in cases of extremely high solubility (when there is usually extensive combination between the gas and the solvent), the solubility of a gas in a given liquid, at constant temperature, is found to be directly proportional to the partial pressure of the gas above the solution. This generalization is known as Henry's law; like other laws describing the behavior of gases, it is strictly accurate only at relatively low pressures. As an example, the solubility of oxygen in water at 25° C. and 0.50 atm. pressure is 0.02 g. per liter; at 1 atm. pressure, the solubility is just twice as great, or 0.04 g. per liter. In order for the law to be applicable in the form in which it has just been stated, the solubility must be expressed in terms of the *weight* of gas dissolved, rather than the volume. Since the volume of a given amount of gas decreases with increasing pressure just as rapidly as the solubility increases, the volume of a gas which dissolves in a given volume of a liquid is independent of pressure as long as Henry's law is followed.

9. Effect of Temperature on Solubility. The solubility of a gas in a liquid usually decreases with increasing temperature. A familiar illustration of this generalization is observed when cold water from a tap is run into a drinking glass and allowed to come to the temperature of a warm room. Some of the air escapes from the solution in the form of visible bubbles that cling to the inside wall of the vessel. If the water is heated to the boiling point, practically all of the dissolved air is driven off. Since the dissolving of a gas in a liquid, involving as it does a change of state analogous to condensation, is almost always an exothermic process, this relationship is in accord with Le Chatelier's principle.

Since there is usually comparatively little heat evolved or absorbed when two incompletely miscible liquids are brought together, the effect of temperature on the mutual solubility of liquids is ordinarily small. In most cases, however, the solubility of each liquid in the other increases slightly with increasing temperature, until a temperature is reached at which the concentrations of the two saturated solutions have become identical. At or above this temperature, which is called the critical mixing temperature, the liquids are completely miscible.

The dissolving of a solid in a liquid may be considered to consist of two processes: (1) a change in state of the solid, analogous to melting, and (2) possible combination between solute and solvent. In accordance with what we have already learned (p. 65), step (1) is always endothermic. Step (2), on the other hand, is quite likely to be exothermic; indeed, in certain cases, the amount of heat evolved in (2) is sufficient to more than balance that absorbed in (1). Hence the process

$$\text{Solute}_{(\text{solid})} \rightarrow \text{Solute}_{(\text{dissolved})}$$

may be either exothermic or endothermic, depending upon whether the heat effect of (2) or (1) predominates in the given case. Usually the latter is true, for in the great majority of cases a solid dissolves in a liquid (or rather, in its own nearly saturated solution) with the absorption of heat. Accordingly, when the temperature is increased, the equilibrium is shifted in the direction of dissolved solute; in other words, the solubility of a solid in a liquid usually increases with increasing temperature.

The variation of solubility with temperature is most conveniently shown by means of a plot of the solubility (usually expressed as the number of grams of solute per 100 g. of solvent) as ordinate, against the temperature as abscissa; such a plot is called the solubility curve of the substance. The solubility curves of a number of common salts are shown in Figure 16.1. It will be observed that there are wide differences in the effects of temperature on solubility. Most of the curves are continuous; a few, however, including those for calcium chloride and sodium sulfate, show sudden changes of curvature, or "breaks," at one or more points. Such a break in the solubility curve of a substance always corresponds to a change in the crystalline structure, usually (although not always) accompanied by a change in the degree of hydration, of the solute.

10. Supersaturation. In the ordinary case, when the solubility decreases with decreasing temperature, the gradual cooling of a saturated solution usually results in the deposition of crystals of the solute at such a rate that the solution always remains saturated. In some instances, however, if all traces of undissolved solute are carefully removed from the hot saturated solution, if the cooling is allowed to proceed slowly and is not accompanied by agitation of the solution, and if the free surface of the solution is protected from the access of solid particles such as atmospheric dust, the excess solute over that required for a saturated solution at the lower temperature does not immediately crystallize, but remains in solution. It is by this means that a supersaturated solution (p. 280) may be obtained. Three examples of salts which form supersaturated solutions especially readily are the decahydrate of sodium sulfate, $Na_2SO_4 \cdot 10H_2O$, the pentahydrate of sodium thiosulfate, $Na_2S_2O_3 \cdot 5H_2O$, and the trihydrate of sodium acetate,

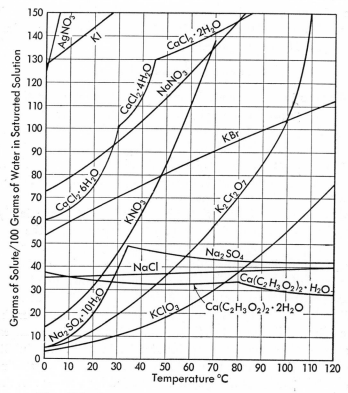

Fig. 16.1. Variation of solubility with temperature.

$NaC_2H_3O_2 \cdot 3H_2O$. A supersaturated solution, like a supercooled liquid, is in what is known as a metastable condition. Left to itself, it may remain unchanged for a indefinite period, but the introduction of even a minute crystal of the solute initiates the process of crystallization, which then continues until all of the excess solute is in the solid state, and a saturated solution remains.

A supersaturated solution of a gas is very commonly obtained when the pressure upon a saturated solution of a gas in a liquid is diminished. A sample of a carbonated beverage which has been allowed to stand in an open vessel is likely to be a supersaturated solution of carbon dioxide. When such a solution is vigorously stirred or shaken, the bubbles given off consist of the carbon dioxide which is present in excess over that required for a saturated solution at atmospheric pressure.

11. "Insoluble" Solids. Water not only is the most widely used of all solvents, but also, of all liquids, it most nearly approaches being the "universal solvent" that was the object of one of the futile quests of the medieval alchemists. Every substance is probably soluble in water to some extent, although in many cases the solubility is so small as to be imperceptible. Thus, a saturated solution of barium sulfate contains less than a quarter of a milligram of solute per liter, and the solubility of silicon dioxide (quartz) is even smaller than this. Yet, water that is allowed to remain for a long time in a quartz vessel must eventually become saturated with quartz; a saturated solution of this substance is so extremely dilute, however, that many liters of it would have to be evaporated to dryness in order to yield a visible residue. Such substances as barium sulfate, silver chloride, quartz, glass, mercury, and cellulose are said to be "insoluble" in water; but this term, it must be remembered, is merely a relative one, and it would be more accurate to say that their solubility is exceedingly small.

12. Distribution of a Solute between Two Immiscible Liquids. When a small sample of a substance is brought into contact with two immiscible liquids at the same time, it dissolves in both of them, although not to the same extent. In such cases, it has been established by experiment that the sample distributes itself so that the ratio of the concentrations of solute in the two liquid layers is the same as the ratio of its solubility in the two solvents. This generalization is known as the law of partition. For example, the solubility of bromine at room temperature, measured in grams per 100 cc. of solvent, is approximately 28 times as great in carbon tetrachloride as in water. In accordance with the law just stated, it is found that whenever a sample of bromine is shaken with these two liquids until equilibrium is attained, the concentration of bromine in the carbon tetrachloride layer, which sinks to the bottom, is 28 times its concentration in the water layer. If equal volumes of the two solvents are used, 28/29 of the total quantity of bromine finds its way into the carbon tetrachloride. If a solution of bromine in water is shaken with pure carbon tetrachloride, the same distribution of the bromine is attained. Thus, most of the bromine in a water solution can be removed even by a single treatment with carbon tetrachloride. This process is known as *extraction*. If two or three successive portions of carbon tetrachloride are used, each being poured off before the next is added, the concentration of bromine remaining in the water solution can be reduced to a negligibly small value.

13. Ideal Solutions; Raoult's Law. Just as our study of gases was greatly facilitated by introduction of the concept of the ideal or perfect gas, which behaves exactly in accordance with the laws of Boyle and Charles, so we may best proceed with the quantitative study of liquid solutions by introducing the concept of the *ideal solution*, in which the relationships between concentration and physical properties are exhibited in their simplest possible form. From the molecular viewpoint, an ideal liquid solution of two components is one in which the molecules of each substance are subjected to forces no different from those which act upon them in the pure component in the liquid state.

From the experimental viewpoint, an ideal solution may be most simply defined in terms of a generalization known as Raoult's law, which may be stated as follows: *At any given temperature, the partial vapor pressure of a component of a solution (i.e., its partial pressure in the mixed vapor in equilibrium with the solution) is equal to the product of the mole fraction of that component and its vapor pressure in the pure liquid state.* Thus, in a solution composed of two volatile liquids A and B, if the vapor pressure of pure A is represented by $p_A°$, and its mole fraction and partial pressure in the solution by N_A and p_A, respectively, we may write

$$p_A = N_A p_A°$$

Likewise, using similar notation for the second component, we have

$$p_B = N_B p_B°$$

An ideal solution is one that behaves in accordance with Raoult's law throughout the entire range of concentrations and at all temperatures and pressures. Few actual solutions are ideal; in many cases, however, when the components do not differ greatly in polarity, or in their chemical nature, the behavior of the mixture approximates closely to that which would be expected of an ideal solution.

As a corollary of Raoult's law, we may readily derive the value of the *total* vapor pressure, p, of an ideal solution; this value is given by the equation

$$p = N_A p_A° + N_B p_B°$$

A little reflection will show that it follows from this equation that the total vapor pressure of an ideal solution, whatever the concentration, must always lie between the vapor pressures of the two pure components. The variation with composition of the partial vapor pressures of the components of an ideal solution, and the variation of the total vapor pressure with composition, are shown in Figure 16.2. Since the boiling point of a solution is the temperature at which its total vapor pressure is equal to the external pressure, it may be further concluded that the boiling point of an ideal solution is always intermediate between those of the pure components.

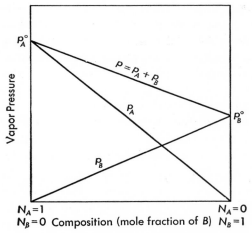

Fig. 16.2.   Vapor pressure of ideal solutions.

The vapor given off when an ideal solution is boiled contains both components, but is always richer in the component having the lower boiling point than is the original mixture. Hence, during the boiling, the composition of the remaining solution changes continuously, containing an ever increasing proportion of the component of higher boiling point. If the vapor is condensed in different fractions, these will differ in composition and in boiling point; and by repeated distillation of the several fractions, each of the components may eventually be obtained in the pure state. The process of separation of components of a solution in this manner is known as *fractional distillation.* It is widely used, for example, in the separation of the various components of crude oil in the refining of petroleum (p. 571).

Although the behavior of actual solutions may deviate from Raoult's law to a considerable extent, the vapor pressure of a mixture is usually intermediate between those of the pure components. Even this is not true, however, in certain cases. The consequences of extreme deviations from Raoult's law will be considered later in this chapter.

14. Vapor Pressure Lowering by a Nonvolatile Solute. In many of the binary solutions with which we shall be concerned, one of the components is nonvolatile; that is, its vapor pressure at ordinary temperatures is so small as to be altogether negligible. The total vapor pressure of the solution, then, is the vapor pressure of the solvent, and this must always be less than the vapor pressure of pure solvent at the same temperature. It is of interest to consider a modification of Raoult's law which is applicable to such a case. Let us consider, for example, a solution of ordinary sugar, $C_{12}H_{22}O_{11}$, in water. Since sugar is nonvolatile, the total vapor pressure of the solution is the same as the vapor pressure of water from it. If the vapor pressure of pure water is denoted by $p°$, the mole fraction of water in the solution by N_w, and the vapor pressure of the solution by p, and the solution is assumed to be ideal, we may write

$$p = N_w p°$$

Since the sum of N_w and N_s (the mole fraction of sugar in the solution) is 1, we have

$$N_w = 1 - N_s$$

and substitution of this value for N_w in the equation for Raoult's law gives

$$p = p°(1 - N_s) = p° - N_s p°$$

Now, on transposing, we obtain

$$p° - p = N_s p°$$

The quantity $p° - p$ (sometimes abbreviated to Δp) may be designated as the vapor pressure lowering produced by the sugar. It is evident that for any other solute besides sugar, the mole fraction being again represented by N_s, we should get exactly the same equation. It follows, then, that the vapor pressure lowering for a given solvent in an ideal solution at a fixed temperature is directly proportional to the mole fraction of the solute, but is quite independent of the specific nature of the latter. Since dilute solutions (except those of ionic substances, which will be considered in the next chapter) usually approach ideal behavior, 1 mole of sugar, glycerol, fructose ($C_6H_{12}O_6$), or urea (CON_2H_4), when dissolved in 99 moles of water, should each bring about a vapor pressure lowering equal to 1/100 of the vapor pressure of pure water at the temperature in question. Experiment shows that this prediction is very nearly accurate.

Since the concentrations of aqueous solutions are rarely expressed in terms of mole fractions, an equation expressing the relationship between the vapor pressure lowering and the molality, in dilute solutions of a nonvolatile solute in a given solvent, is better adapted to our further discussion than the very general equation derived in the preceding paragraphs. For dilute solutions, the mole fraction of solute is practically the same as the number of moles of solute per mole of solvent. Hence, the mole fraction of solute is proportional to the molality of the solution (as long as the solvent remains unchanged); and the vapor pressure lowering, which has just been shown to be proportional to the mole fraction of the solute, must also be proportional to the molality. In algebraic form

$$\Delta p = \text{molality} \times K_v$$

where K_v, the molal vapor pressure lowering, is a constant for a given solvent at a particular temperature. The value of this constant for water at 25° C. is 0.425 mm.

From our present point of view, the main significance of the equation just derived does not lie in the fact that it makes possible the calculation of the vapor pressure lowering which will occur in a solution of given molality. The equation is exceedingly important because, theoretically at least, it provides a means of determining the molality of solutions, and, therefore, of calculating the molecular weights, of nonvolatile solutes; i.e., of just that class of substances for which the determination of molecular weight from the density of the vapor is impossible. In actual practice, however, it is not possible to determine molecular weights accurately by the method of vapor pressure lowering, since both elaborate apparatus and very considerable experimental skill are required to measure the vapor pressure of a solution with sufficient accuracy. There are two other properties, however, namely, the boiling point and the freezing point of a solution, which are closely related to the vapor pressure, but whose variation with concentration is so much more easily measured that they are of much greater utility in the determination of molecular weights.

15. Vapor Pressure, Boiling Point, and Freezing Point of Dilute Solutions. The relationship among these properties can best be explained with the aid of a diagram in which the vapor pressures of both the liquid and the solid forms of a solvent are plotted against the temperature, as in Figure 16.3. (It will be convenient to carry out the discussion for water, the most familiar of liquids, as solvent; it should be recognized, however, that the diagram is not drawn to scale, and that the argument would apply equally well to other solvents.) AO is the vapor pressure curve for ice, and OB that for pure water. By definition (p. 61), the boiling point, which we shall abbreviate as T_b, is the temperature at which the vapor pressure becomes equal to the standard atmospheric pressure, 760 mm.; this is evidently represented by the point P in the diagram. $O'B'$ is the vapor pressure curve for a solution of a nonvolatile solute; since, as was shown in the preceding section, the vapor pressure of such a solution is always less than that of pure water, this curve must lie, as shown, below OB. Now it is evident that at the temperature T_b the vapor pressure of the solution has not yet reached

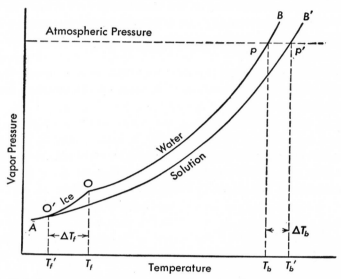

Fig. 16.3.   Relations among vapor pressure lowering, boiling point elevation, and freezing point depression.

760 mm.; the boiling point of the solution is represented by the point P', where $O'B'$ intersects the 760 mm. line, at the higher temperature T'_b. Hence, the boiling point of a solution of a nonvolatile solute is always higher than that of the pure solvent; the difference, $T'_b - T_b$, or ΔT_b, is called the boiling point elevation. Furthermore, since the vapor pressure lowering is the same for dilute solutions of different solutes (except ionic substances) at the same molality, it is evident that the boiling point elevation is also the same for such equimolal solutions; and it may be shown that the boiling point elevation, like the vapor pressure lowering, is proportional to the molality. Hence, if we represent the boiling point elevation in a molal solution by K_b, we may write

$$\Delta T_b = \text{molality} \times K_b$$

where K_b, the molal boiling point elevation, is constant for a particular solvent.

The freezing point of a liquid, which we shall abbreviate as T_f, may be defined (p. 66) as the temperature at which the liquid and the solid form of the same substance have identical vapor pressures. Referring again to Figure 16.3, we see that the freezing point of pure water is represented by the point O. At the temperature T_f, however, the vapor pressure of the solution is less than that of ice, so that ice and solution could not be in equilibrium at this temperature; the freezing point of the solution is the point O', where the curves AO and $O'B'$ intersect, at the lower temperature T'_f. Hence the freezing point of a solution is always lower than that of pure solvent; the difference, $T_f - T'_f$, or ΔT_f, is called the freezing point depression. Since the magnitude of the freezing point depression is determined by that of the vapor pressure lowering, the freezing point depression, too, is proportional to the molality of the solution. Hence we may write

$$\Delta T_f = \text{molality} \times K_f$$

where K_f, the molal freezing point depression, is constant for a given solvent.

The boiling and freezing points, and the values of K_b and K_f, for a few important solvents, are given in Table 16.2.

Table 16.2

Molal Boiling Point Elevations and Freezing Point Depressions

Solvent	T_b	K_b	T_f	K_f
Water	100.00°	0.513°	0.00°	1.86°
Benzene	80.1	2.61	5.50	5.12
Carbon tetrachloride	76.8	5.02	− 22.9	31.8
Ethyl alcohol	78.4	1.19	−115	....
Acetic acid	118.1	....	16.6	3.60
Naphthalene	218	....	80.2	6.9

16. Boiling Point Elevation, Freezing Point Depression, and the Molecular Weight of Dissolved Substances. Although the equations of the preceding section, relating the boiling point elevation and the freezing point depression produced by a solute to the molality of a solution, are not valid for concentrated solutions nor for solutions of ionic substances at any concentration, they do hold very well for dilute solutions of many substances, such as hydrocarbons, alcohol, sugars, glycerol, and urea, in a wide variety of solvents. Hence, if the molecular weight of a substance is known, they may be used for the calculation of the boiling point or the freezing point of a solution of given concentration. Conversely, these equations may be used for the determination of the molecular weight of a solute from the boiling point or the freezing point of its solution. A few examples will serve to make these applications clear.

1. Find the boiling point and the freezing point of a solution of 2.85 g. of cane sugar, $C_{12}H_{22}O_{11}$, in 25.0 g. of water.

First we calculate the weight of sugar that would have to be dissolved in 1000 g. of water to give a solution of the same concentration.

$$\text{weight per 1000 g. water} = \frac{1000}{25.0} \times 2.85 = 114 \text{ g.}$$

Next we find the molecular weight of the solute, and from this the molality of the solution.

$$\text{molality} = \frac{114}{\text{gram-molecular weight}} = \frac{114}{342} = 0.333$$

Now we substitute this value of the molality in the equation for ΔT_b.

$$\Delta T_b = \text{molality} \times K_b = 0.333 \times 0.513$$

$$\Delta T_b = 0.171°$$

$$\text{boiling point of solution} = 100.171° \text{ C.}$$

Similarly

$$\Delta T_f = \text{molality} \times K_f = 0.333 \times 1.86$$

$$\Delta T_f = 0.620°$$

$$\text{freezing point of solution} = -0.620° \text{ C.}$$

2. A solution of 0.3005 g. of urea in 20.0 g. of water has a freezing point of $-0.465°$ C. What is the molecular weight of urea?

The freezing point depression here is 0.465° C. Hence

$$0.465 = \text{molality} \times 1.86$$

$$\text{molality} = \frac{0.465}{1.86} = 0.250$$

The given solution of urea is therefore 0.250 molal. But this solution would contain, per 1000 g. of water,

$$\frac{1000}{20.0} \times 0.3005 = 15.025 \text{ g. urea}$$

Hence, 15.025 g. must be 0.250 mole, and 1 mole is therefore

$$\frac{1.00}{0.250} \times 15.025 = 60.1 \text{ g.}$$

or the molecular weight is 60.1.

17. Vapor Pressure Lowering, Evaporation, and Deliquescence. Although the vapor pressure of an aqueous solution of a nonvolatile solute is always lower than that of pure water at the same temperature, it need not, of course, be lower than the partial pressure of water vapor in the atmosphere. Whether it is or not depends on the concentration of the solution and the humidity of the air with which it is in contact. If the vapor pressure of a solution is greater than the partial pressure of water vapor in the air, water will evaporate from the solution; if it happens to be just equal to the partial pressure of water vapor in the air, neither evaporation nor condensation will take place; while if the vapor pressure of the solution is less than the partial pressure of water vapor in the air, water will condense from the air into the solution. Thus a dilute solution tends to evaporate, especially in a dry atmosphere, whereas a very concentrated solution tends to take up moisture from the air.

There is a tendency for a trace of moisture to condense upon the surface of any solid exposed to the atmosphere; this water dissolves a little of the solid, forming a film of saturated solution. In the case of a very soluble solid, this solution will contain a high concentration of solute, and will therefore have a very low vapor pressure. Such a solution will not be in equilibrium with the air, but will take up additional moisture in the attempt to reach equilibrium. Thus diluted, the solution is unsaturated and dissolves more of the solid; this process continues not only until all of the solid has been dissolved, but further until the solution has become sufficiently dilute so that its vapor pressure is just equal to the partial pressure of water vapor in the air, when equilibrium is reached. A solid which behaves in this way is said to be hygroscopic or *deliquescent*, and the phenomenon is known as *deliquescence*. It is evident that a substance will deliquesce if the vapor pressure of its saturated solution is lower than the partial pressure of water vapor in the atmosphere, and not otherwise. Many familiar substances, such as sodium hydroxide and calcium chloride, are deliquescent under ordinary atmospheric conditions. Liquids such as alcohol, glycerol, and pure sulfuric acid, which are completely miscible with water, also take up water from the atmosphere and are likewise said to be hygroscopic. The fuming in air of hydrogen chloride and certain other very soluble gases is a closely related phenomenon; the gas dissolves in moisture condensed from the air, and the fumes consist of minute droplets of solution.

18. Practical Consequences of Freezing Point Depression. Quite apart from its theoretical significance, the fact that the freezing point of a solution is lower than that of the pure solvent is of interest in several other respects.

For instance, in order to prevent the freezing of the water in an automobile radiator as soon as the temperature drops below 32° F., it is necessary to add a solute, known as an antifreeze. For the protection of radiators at such winter temperatures as are of common occurrence even at moderate latitudes, very high concentrations of solute are required. Because of its low molecular weight and its comparatively low cost, together with the facts that there is no limit to its solubility in water and that its solutions are noncorrosive, ethyl alcohol, C_2H_5OH, is the substance most commonly used as an antifreeze. Because of its volatility, alcohol boils away readily and must be replaced from time to time. Ethylene glycol, $C_2H_4(OH)_2$, although considerably more expensive than alcohol, has the marked advantage of being much less volatile, so that it does not boil away under ordinary operating conditions. This substance is sold under trade names such as "Prestone".

Another application of freezing point lowering occurs in the use of ice–salt mixtures for the production of temperatures below 0° C., both for low-temperature baths in the laboratory and for such practical purposes as the freezing of ice cream. It will be instructive for us to look into this subject of freezing mixtures in some detail. We may start with the fact that a mixture of ice and pure water automatically adjusts itself to a temperature of 0° C., even though the water may be warmer than this, or the ice colder, at the outset. For, if ice at 0° C. is introduced into warm water, some of it promptly melts, absorbing heat from the water until the temperature of the entire mixture has been lowered to 0° C.; if, on the other hand, ice at a temperature below 0° C. is introduced into water at 0° C., some of the water immediately freezes, giving out heat and thereby warming the cold ice to 0° C., when equilibrium is attained. Now, if a solute is added to a mixture of ice and water, it dissolves in the water, and the ice is not in equilibrium with the resulting solution, since the initial temperature of 0° C. is above the freezing point. Hence some ice melts, diluting the solution, and the temperature of the mixture falls until equilibrium between ice and solution has been attained. If solid solute is present in excess, however, the equilibrium temperature finally reached must be the freezing point of a saturated solution. This temperature, at which the solution is in equilibrium with both solid solute and solid solvent, is called the eutectic point. The eutectic point of a solution of sodium chloride, for example, is −21° C.; this is the lowest temperature obtainable by means of a freezing mixture of ice and common salt. Much lower temperatures may be reached, however, by the use of more soluble solutes, such, for example, as calcium chloride. The use of salt for the

melting of ice on sidewalks (when the temperature is not lower than
$-21°$ C.) constitutes another practical application of the same principle.

19. Osmosis and Osmotic Pressure. It was pointed out early in the present
chapter (p. 272) that the concentration of a solution always tends to
become uniform throughout; or, to put it another way, a solute tends to
distribute itself uniformly, by diffusion, throughout the entire volume of the
solution. This process takes place rapidly, it is true, only if the mixture is
stirred, but it occurs slowly even if the solution is left at rest. Thus, if a
layer of concentrated sugar solution were to be placed in the bottom of a
beaker, and water carefully introduced above it, there would at first be a
definite line of demarcation between the solution and the water. Soon,
however, this visible boundary would disappear, and eventually the solution
at the top of the beaker would be just as sweet as that at the bottom.

Now let us consider what will happen if the sugar solution is placed
in a cup, the wall of which is semipermeable. A *semipermeable membrane*
is one that allows one component of a solution, but not the other, to pass
through it. Various membranes, such as parchment paper, collodion, and
animal bladder, exhibit the property of semipermeability to a greater or
less extent with respect to particular solutes. Films of certain gelatinous
precipitates, especially of cupric ferrocyanide, $Cu_2Fe(CN)_6$, are completely
semipermeable so far as water and sugar are concerned; a porous earthenware cup with such a film deposited within its wall allows water to pass
through readily, but is completely impermeable to sugar. If such a cup,
filled with sugar solution, is partially immersed in pure water, diffusion of
molecules of water occurs in both directions. However, the rate of diffusion out of the sugar solution into the pure water is less than in the opposite
direction because of the lower concentration of water molecules inside
the cup. The net result is that water enters the cup. This phenomenon—
the passage of pure solvent into a solution through a semipermeable membrane—is known as *osmosis*.

But now let us suppose the cup to be tightly sealed, as by a rubber stopper
whose lower surface touches the top of the solution, and consider to what
extent osmosis would take place. Under these conditions the entrance of
even a small quantity of water would produce a high pressure in the cup,
and osmosis could not be expected to continue for very long. A state of
equilibrium would soon be attained, in which the tendency for solvent to
enter would be just balanced by the tendency for it to be squeezed out
because of the excess pressure within the cup. The pressure at which this

equilibrium is reached, or, in other words, the excess pressure on a solution which is just sufficient to prevent the entrance of solvent through a semipermeable membrane, is called the *osmotic pressure* of the solution.

The osmotic pressure of a solution might be measured by means of the device shown diagrammatically in cross-section in Figure 16.4. Here, instead of being sealed with a tight-fitting stopper, the cup is closed with a piston, by means of which the solution may be subjected to any desired pressure. For simplicity, let us suppose pressure to be applied by means of weights placed on the piston; the pressure is then the total weight divided by the area of the piston. When the weights have been adjusted so that the piston neither rises nor falls, the corresponding pressure is, by definition, the osmotic pressure of the solution. In practice, the osmotic pressure of solutions is usually determined by a method which differs in detail, though not in principle, from that described.

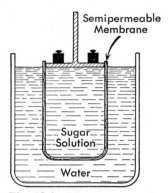

Fig. 16.4. Measurement of osmotic pressure.

Such measurements of osmotic pressure have shown that, for dilute solutions of other than ionic substances, this quantity is directly proportional to the absolute temperature, and also to the molality of the solution. In fact, it has been shown that the osmotic pressure of such a solution is the same as the pressure that the solute would exert if it were a gas occupying the volume of the solvent at the same temperature. Thus, the osmotic pressure of a molal aqueous solution at $0°$ C. is found to be approximately 22.4 atmospheres. The measurement of osmotic pressure, therefore, provides another possible means, though not a convenient one, for the determination of the molecular weight of a dissolved substance. Because of the fact that the osmotic pressure, the vapor pressure lowering, the boiling point elevation, and the freezing point depression are all so closely related to the molality, and therefore to each other, they are sometimes referred to as *colligative* (i.e., joined together) *properties* of solutions.

Many animal and vegetable membranes are more or less completely semipermeable, and osmotic phenomena play an important part in various physiological functions of both animal and plant organisms. The passage of water into and out of living cells, and the action of the kidneys, may be cited as examples. The rise of sap in trees is explainable also, at least in part, in terms of osmosis.

20. Deviations from Raoult's Law. The departure of the behavior of an actual solution from that which we have attributed to an ideal solution may be characterized either as positive or as negative deviation from Raoult's law. If each component of the solution has a partial vapor pressure greater than would be calculated from the law, the deviation is said to be positive, whereas if the partial vapor pressures are lower than the calculated values,

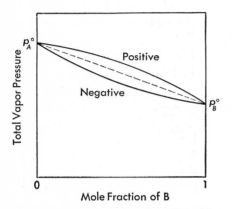

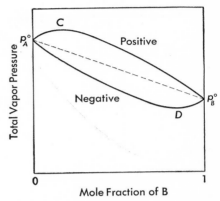

Fig. 16.5. Slight deviations from Raoult's Law.

Fig. 16.6. Large deviations from Raoult's Law.

the deviation is negative. Two liquids which differ considerably in polarity are likely to be incompletely miscible; even if they are miscible in all proportions, however, their solutions will exhibit positive deviations from Raoult's law. Negative deviations, on the other hand, are observed when the components of the solution, usually both polar in this case, tend to combine with each other.

The effects of positive and of negative deviations from Raoult's law upon the total vapor pressure are illustrated in Figures 16.5 and 16.6. If the deviations are comparatively small, as in Figure 16.5, the vapor pressure of any solution of A and B will still be intermediate between the vapor pressures of the pure components. If the deviations are sufficiently large, however (Figure 16.6), there may be a maximum, as at C, or a minimum, as at D, in the vapor pressure-composition curve; in other words, there may be a solution of one particular composition which has a vapor pressure even higher than that of the more volatile component, or even lower than that of the less volatile one. The higher the vapor pressure of a particular solution at a given temperature, the lower will be its boiling point; hence, the variation of the boiling point with composition, for the two hypothetical cases illustrated in Figure 16.6, will be as shown in Figures 16.7 and 16.8.

Thus, when there is a large positive deviation from Raoult's law, we may have a solution of minimum boiling point, as at C, Figure 16.7; with a large negative deviation we may have a solution of maximum boiling point, as at D, Figure 16.8.

The vapor from a solution having either a minimum or a maximum boiling point is of exactly the same composition as the solution itself. Hence,

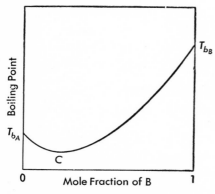
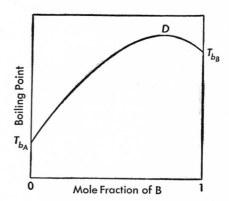

Fig. 16.7. Binary system with a minimum boiling point.

Fig. 16.8. Binary system with a maximum boiling point.

in these special cases, neither the composition nor the boiling point of the solution changes during the process of distillation; on this account, such systems are called constant boiling mixtures. Alcohol and water, for example, form a minimum boiling mixture containing 95.5% of alcohol; nitric acid and water, a maximum boiling mixture containing 68% of nitric acid. Since constant boiling mixtures distill without change in composition, it is impossible, in the case of two substances which form such a mixture, to obtain both pure components from any solution by the process of fractional distillation.

Actual concentrated solutions may deviate greatly from ideal behavior with respect to vapor pressure, freezing point depression, and the other colligative properties discussed in this chapter. Very dilute solutions, however (except those of electrolytes, p. 301) always behave in accordance with the simple laws of the ideal solution, just as gases approach the behavior of the ideal gas at low pressures. But solutions of acids, bases, and salts in polar solvents exhibit an entirely different type of deviation, which, instead of disappearing, becomes more and more marked as their solutions become more dilute. This distinctive behavior, and its significance, will be considered in detail in the next chapter.

21. Solid Solutions. Solid solutions, also known as isomorphous mixtures, or mixed crystals, are sometimes formed when two substances crystallize together from the liquid (or the dissolved) state. In order, however, for a true solution of a solid in a solid to be produced, the substances must very closely resemble each other in crystalline form. If the two are to be miscible in all proportions, it is necessary not only that their crystal lattices be of the same type, but that the lattice dimensions be similar also.

STUDY QUESTIONS AND PROBLEMS

1. The density of the sulfuric acid solution in an almost completely charged storage battery is 1.25 g. per cc., and this solution contains almost exactly 33.3% by weight of sulfuric acid.
  (a) What is the weight of a liter of this storage battery acid?
  (b) What weight of actual H_2SO_4 is there in a liter of this solution?
  (c) What is the molarity of the solution?
  (d) What is the weight of H_2SO_4 per 1000 g. of water in the solution?
  (e) What are the mole fractions of water and of H_2SO_4 in the solution?
  (f) What is the molality of this solution?

2. What is the weight of a liter of a concentrated lye (sodium hydroxide solution), the density of which is 1.43 g. per cc., and which contains 40.0% by weight of sodium hydroxide? Answer the same questions as in (b), (c), (d), (e), and (f) of question 1, substituting the formula NaOH for H_2SO_4 each time it occurs in the preceding question.

3. What is the chemical basis for the common statement "oil and water won't mix"? How can you account for the fact that alcohol and water are completely miscible? Why are many salts, in spite of their relatively high melting points, readily soluble in water?

4. Explain in terms of Henry's law the fact that at ordinary temperatures 1 l. of water dissolves just about 1 l. of carbon dioxide, regardless of the pressure at which the carbon dioxide is measured and brought into contact with water.

5. For each of the following solutes, find the number of grams required to prepare 1 l. of 1 M solution, 300 ml. of 2 M solution, 4 l. of 0.05 M solution:
  (a) Potassium permanganate, $KMnO_4$
  (b) Sucrose, $C_{12}H_{22}O_{11}$
  (c) Aluminum sulfate, $Al_2(SO_4)_3$
  (d) Phosphoric acid, H_3PO_4

6. (a) The vapor pressure of pure water at a certain temperature in the neighborhood of 25° C. is 23.690 mm. A solution made by dissolving 5.40 g. of glucose in 50.0 g. of water is found to have a vapor pressure of 23.435 mm. Assuming Raoult's law to be valid for this solution, find from these data the molecular weight of glucose. (b) The empirical formula for glucose is CH_2O. What is its molecular formula?

7. (a) What is the boiling point of a solution of 2.40 g. of urea, CON_2H_4, in 50.0 g. of water? What is the freezing point of this solution? (b) The freezing point of an aqueous solution of a nonvolatile solute is $-0.651°C$. What is the boiling point of this solution?

8. A solution of 1.50 g. of a substance in 75.0 g. of water has a freezing point of $-0.310°C$. What is the molecular weight of this substance?

9. How many solute particles must be present in 1000 g. of water in order that the freezing point of the solution may be $-0.744°C$.? How many grams of glycol, $C_2H_6O_2$, per 1000 g. of water would be required to give a solution having this freezing point?

10. (a) When 0.491 g. of heptene is dissolved in 10.0 g. of benzene, the freezing point of the solution obtained is $2.94°C$. What is the molar weight of heptene? (b) Heptene is a compound of carbon and hydrogen containing 14.37% of hydrogen. What is its molecular formula?

11. Under what conditions does a solid substance deliquesce? Why is a very soluble substance more likely to be deliquescent than a slightly soluble one?

12. State at least two reasons for believing that the simple process of solution is often accompanied by chemical change.

13. Explain why air containing water vapor at a pressure equal to the vapor pressure of water at the prevailing temperature, may properly be regarded as a saturated solution of water in air.

14. (a) Explain why it would not be practicable to run an engine by means of osmotic work. (b) Explain why it would not be practicable to remove the water from a saturated sugar solution by means of an osmotic piston. (c) Why does salt water fail to quench thirst?

Solutions of Electrolytes

1. Solutions of Acids, Bases, and Salts. In the preceding chapter, it has been mentioned that the simple laws of the ideal solution are inapplicable to dilute solutions of acids, bases, and salts. In the present chapter we shall discuss the properties of such solutions, and explore the theories in terms of which their behavior may be explained.

2. Electrolytes and Nonelectrolytes. All compounds can be divided into two broad classes on the basis of the ability of their water solutions to conduct the electric current. Certain substances, such as hydrochloric acid, sodium hydroxide, and common salt, yield water solutions which readily conduct the electric current (see Figure 17.1). Such substances, which are always either acids, bases, or salts, are called *electrolytes*. On the other hand, substances (especially organic compounds) like sugar and urea whose water solutions are extremely poor conductors of the electric current are classed as *nonelectrolytes*.

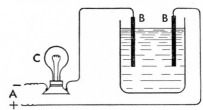

Fig. 17.1. Apparatus for demonstrating conductance of solutions. A source of current, A, is connected with two platinum or graphite electrodes, BB, immersed in the solution, through a lamp, C. The lamp glows only if the solution is a conductor. With pure water, or with a solution of a typical nonelectrolyte such as sugar or urea, the filament remains dark; with a solution of an acid, a base, or a salt between the electrodes, however, the lamp always glows, at least faintly, in most cases very brightly.

3. Electrolysis. Conductance of a direct current by an electrolyte is always accompanied by chemical changes at the electrodes. In many cases, the two changes together constitute decomposition of the electrolyte. When this occurs, hydrogen or a metal is liberated at the negative electrode (*cathode*) and a nonmetal at the positive electrode (*anode*). In solutions of hydrogen chloride, for example, hydrogen gas is liberated at the cathode and chlorine at the anode. Similarly, in a solution of copper chloride, metallic copper is deposited on the cathode, and elementary chlorine is liberated at the anode. The passage of an electric current through a solution, together with the accompanying chemical changes, is called *electrolysis*. Many electrolytic processes are extremely important in science and in industry.

4. Faraday's Laws. The fundamental laws of electrolysis, discovered by the English chemist-physicist Michael Faraday in 1832 and 1833, are among the most exact in chemistry.

1. *The weight of a given element liberated at an electrode in electrolysis is directly proportional to the quantity of electricity passed through the solution.* The unit of electrical quantity is the *coulomb*. One coulomb deposits exactly 0.00111800 g. of silver.[1] Hence, according to Faraday's first law, 10,000 coulombs will deposit 11.1800 g. and 50,000 coulombs, 55.9000 g. of silver.

2. *The weights of different elements liberated by the same quantity of electricity are proportional to the equivalent weights of the elements.*[2] Thus, the quantity of electricity which liberates one gram-equivalent weight of an element is the same for all elements. Since the equivalent weight of silver is 107.880, this quantity must be

$$\frac{107.880}{0.00111800} \text{ or } 96{,}494 \text{ coulombs}$$

From Faraday's second law, we know that 96,494 coulombs (*1 faraday*) will liberate 1.0080 g. of hydrogen and 35.457 g. of chlorine in the electrolysis of hydrochloric acid, and will deposit 58.71/2 g. of nickel from a solution of nickel sulfate, $NiSO_4$, 55.85/2 g. of iron from a solution of ferrous chloride, $FeCl_2$, and 55.85/3 g. of iron from a solution of ferric chloride, $FeCl_3$. For ordinary calculations, 1 faraday may be considered as 96,500 coulombs.

5. Explanation of Electrolysis. In a solution of a typical ionic compound, the ions, freed from their fixed positions in the crystal lattice, move about more or less independently throughout the solution (see p. 187). A water solution of cupric chloride, $CuCl_2$, for example, contains cupric (Cu^{++}) and chloride (Cl^-) ions, both probably hydrated to some extent, darting about in random, zigzag paths as they collide with each other and with molecules of water.

[1] A current of 1 *ampere* deposits 0.00111800 g. of silver (transports 1 coulomb of electricity) per second.
[2] Chemical reactions other than the liberation of elements often take place during electrolysis (see p. 432). In every case, however, the quantities of substances which undergo chemical change are in accord with Faraday's law.

But suppose that two electrodes are placed in the solution and an electric field is applied by means of a battery. The battery acts as an electron pump; it constantly removes electrons from the anode, leaving it positively charged, and drives them through the wire to the cathode, which thus becomes negatively charged. The positive Cu^{++} ions, or *cations*, are attracted by the negatively charged *cathode* and migrate toward it; the negative Cl^- ions, or *anions*, are attracted to and migrate toward

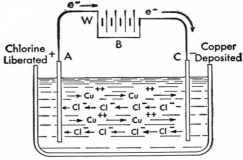

Fig. 17.2.   A typical electrolysis.

the *anode*. It is this motion of cations toward the cathode and of anions toward the anode that constitutes the flow of current through the solution.

Now, when a Cu^{++} ion reaches the cathode, it can be discharged as a neutral atom of copper only by accepting a pair of electrons from the cathode.

$$Cu^{++} + 2e^- \rightarrow Cu$$

Similarly, we can account for the liberation of chlorine gas at the anode, only by postulating that a Cl^- ion, upon reaching the anode, gives up an electron to become a chlorine atom.

$$Cl^- \rightarrow Cl + e^-$$

The atoms so liberated immediately combine in pairs to form molecules of chlorine gas.

$$2Cl \rightarrow Cl_2$$

To liberate 1 gram-equivalent weight of chlorine, or 1 gram-atom (6.024×10^{23} atoms), a total of 6.024×10^{23} electrons must be lost from Cl^- ions. Hence, *a faraday, or 96,494 coulombs, is simply that quantity of electricity which consists of Avogadro's number (6.024×10^{23}) of electrons.* When 1 faraday is passed through a solution, this number of electrons is removed from the cathode by some cation and the same number of electrons is simultaneously lost to the anode by some anion.

In the electrolysis of cupric chloride, each copper ion requires 2 electrons in order to be discharged as a copper atom. Hence, for each faraday, or 6.024×10^{23} electrons, only $\frac{1}{2}$ gram-atom or $\frac{1}{2} \times 63.54$ g. of copper is deposited. Similarly, only $\frac{1}{3} \times 6.024 \times 10^{23}$ atoms, or $\frac{1}{3}$ gram-atom, of a trivalent element is deposited by 1 faraday.

6. Determination of Avogadro's Number. The charge on a single electron is known with extreme accuracy; it is 1.60186×10^{-19} coulomb. To give 96,494 coulombs, therefore, the number of electrons required is

$$\frac{9.6494 \times 10^4}{1.6019 \times 10^{-19}} \text{ or } 6.024 \times 10^{23}$$

This calculation constitutes one of the most accurate of the methods for the determination of Avogadro's number.

7. Characteristic Behavior of Solutions of Electrolytes. All solutions of electrolytes have in common, in addition to their ability to conduct the electric current, two other characteristic types of behavior. Any solution of an electrolyte exhibits a greater freezing point depression (as well as a greater vapor pressure lowering, boiling point elevation, and osmotic pressure) than the standard value for a nonelectrolyte in a solution of the same molal concentration. Furthermore, every electrolyte in solution exhibits *two independent sets* of physical and chemical properties. Once again, these phenomena are simply explained by consideration of the ionic nature of electrolytes in solution.

In the preceding chapter, we have seen that the magnitude of the freezing point depression produced in any given solvent by any nonelectrolyte is determined only by the molality of the solution. The uniform behavior of solutions of equal molality may be attributed to the fact that one mole of *any* nonelectrolyte produces 6.024×10^{23} solute molecules in solution. Thus a 0.01 molal solution of sugar contains $0.01 \times 6.024 \times 10^{23}$ molecules per 1000 g. of water; such a concentration of solute particles in water produces a freezing point depression (ΔT_f) of 0.01 × 1.86 or 0.0186° C.

But now consider the solute particle concentration in a 0.01 molal solution of an electrolyte such as sodium chloride. Each 0.01 mole of sodium chloride supplies $0.01 \times 6.024 \times 10^{23}$ Na^+ ions and the same number of Cl^- ions. The total number of particles per 1000 g. of water is therefore $0.02 \times 6.024 \times 10^{23}$, and it is to be expected that the freezing point depression observed for such a solution should be 0.02 × 1.86, or 0.0372° C. The experimentally observed value is, indeed, very close to this figure.

The ratio of the observed freezing point depression in a solution of an electrolyte to the standard freezing point depression for a nonelectrolyte at the same molal concentration is called the *mole number* of the electrolyte at that concentration, and is designated by the letter i.

$$i \text{ (mole number)} = \frac{\Delta T_f \text{ for the electrolyte}}{\Delta T_f \text{ for a nonelectrolyte of the same molal concentration}}$$

Thus a more concise statement of the fact just mentioned is that the mole number of sodium chloride in 0.01 molal solution is nearly 2. Similarly, for very dilute solutions of electrolytes such as potassium sulfate, K_2SO_4, and cobalt chloride, $CoCl_2$, which contain $3 \times 6.024 \times 10^{23}$ ions per mole, the mole numbers are almost, but not quite, 3. For electrolytes such as potassium ferricyanide, $K_3Fe(CN)_6$, the mole number, in very dilute solution, is nearly 4. One mole of potassium ferricyanide affords $3 \times 6.024 \times 10^{23}$ potassium (K^+) ions and 6.024×10^{23} ferricyanide $(Fe(CN)_6^{---})$ ions.

The two independent sets of physical and chemical properties exhibited by any electrolyte in solution are clearly attributable to the two types of ions present. Cupric chloride in solution, like all soluble cupric salts, forms a black precipitate with sulfide ion, S^{--}, has a characteristic light blue

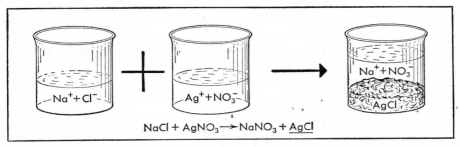

$$NaCl + AgNO_3 \longrightarrow NaNO_3 + \underline{AgCl}$$

Fig. 17.3.   The only ions that take part in this reaction are Ag^+ and Cl^- ions, which unite to form solid silver chloride.

color, and turns intensely violet-blue upon the addition of ammonium hydroxide solution. These are characteristic properties of cupric ion, Cu^{++}, in solution.

Cupric chloride also liberates gaseous hydrogen chloride when treated with concentrated sulfuric acid, and forms an immediate precipitate of silver chloride with silver nitrate. These properties, since they are characteristic of chloride ion, Cl^-, in solution, are common to all soluble chlorides. Reactions of this type, involving only ions, are most concisely represented by *ionic equations*. Thus, for the precipitation for silver chloride, which occurs whenever water solutions of a silver salt and a chloride are mixed, we write the ionic equation

$$Ag^+ + Cl^- = AgCl$$

The properties of a simple ion (containing one element only) are *totally different* from those of the corresponding neutral element as it exists in the free state. Sodium ion, Na^+, and chloride ion, Cl^-, in a solution of common salt, for example, have none of the properties of free sodium, or of free chlorine. Compound ions (containing atoms of two or more elements) are usually unable to exist in the free state at all.

The properties of solutions of electrolytes depend only upon the ions present, and not upon the substances supplying them. For example, a solution obtained by dissolving 1 mole of sodium chloride and 1 mole of potassium nitrate together in 1000 g. of water has exactly the same properties as a solution made similarly with 1 mole of potassium chloride and 1 mole of sodium nitrate, because in each case there are present in solution 1 mole of Na^+ ion, 1 mole of K^+ ion, 1 mole of Cl^- ion, and 1 mole of NO_3^- ion.

8. Variation of Equivalent Conductance and of Mole Number with Concentration. There are two lines of evidence that seem at first sight to contradict the idea that ionic compounds exist entirely as ions in solution. These are (1) the *increase* in equivalent conductance with *dilution* and (2) the *increase* in mole numbers with *decreasing* concentration.

Solutions of different electrolytes, as we might expect, vary in their ability to conduct electricity, i.e., in their conductance.[3] Even for solutions containing a fixed weight of a given solute, however, the conductance varies considerably with the concentration of the solution. The *equivalent conductance*, Λ, of a solution is the total conductance that a solution containing 1 gram-equivalent each of the positive ion and the negative ion of the solute would exhibit if it were placed between two flat electrodes 1 cm. apart. We might expect that in the case of sodium chloride, for example, so long as there are 6.024×10^{23} Na^+ ions and 6.024×10^{23} Cl^- ions to serve as carriers of electricity between the electrodes, the total conductance would remain the same, regardless of concentration. The fact is, however, that, as shown in Table 17.1, the equivalent conductance of solutions of a given electrolyte increases with decreasing concentration, approaching a limiting value, Λ_0, at infinite dilution. It is also noteworthy that for a solution of a given concentration, the deviation from the equivalent conductance at

---

[3] Conductance is actually defined as the reciprocal of the electrical resistance. The unit of resistance is the *ohm,* which is defined as the resistance at 0° C. of a column of mercury 106.300 cm. long and 1 sq. mm. in cross section and weighing 14.4521 g. The unit of conductance, the *reciprocal ohm* or *mho,* is the conductance of such a mercury column.

If the electromotive force applied at the ends of the conductor, in *volts,* is denoted by E, the resistance in ohms by R, and the current in amperes by I, then in accordance with Ohm's law we have the equation

$$I = E/R$$

Now since the conductance, which may be denoted by L, is the reciprocal of the resistance, we may write

$$I = E \times L, \quad or \quad L = I/E$$

Hence the conductance of a solution may be defined as the current which flows through it when an electromotive force of one volt is applied to the electrodes.

infinite dilution increases with the magnitude of the charges on the ions of the electrolyte (cf. barium chloride and sodium chloride in Table 17.1).

Table 17.1

Equivalent Conductances, Λ, of Various Electrolytes at 25° C.
(in reciprocal ohms)

Electrolyte	Concentration in gram equivalents per liter				
	0.1	0.01	0.001	0.0001	0
NaCl	106.7	118.4	123.7	125.6	126.4
KCl	128.9	141.3	146.9	148.9	149.8
KNO_3	120.4	135.8	141.8	144.0	144.9
$BaCl_2$	105.2	123.9	134.3	. . . . .	140.0

Similarly, since each mole of sodium chloride supplies a total of twice Avogadro's number of ions in solution, we might expect that for solutions of sodium chloride, at any concentration, the freezing point depression would be just twice that for a nonelectrolyte at the same molal concentration. In other words, we might expect the mole number, i, for all solutions of sodium chloride to be 2. Likewise, for all solutions of potassium sulfate, K_2SO_4, we might expect a constant mole number of 3, and for potassium ferricyanide, $K_3Fe(CN)_6$, 4. Actually, however, as shown in Table 17.2, the mole numbers of electrolytes approach these expected values only in very dilute solutions. Once again, the deviations from the expected mole number are greater, at a given concentration, for ionic compounds with multiple charged ions (cf. potassium chloride and potassium ferricyanide in Table 17.2).

Table 17.2

Mole Numbers (i) from Freezing Point Lowering

Electrolyte	Concentration in moles per 1000 g. of water							
	0.0005	0.001	0.005	0.010	0.050	0.100	0.200	0.500
KCl	. . . .	. . . .	1.96	1.94	1.88	1.86	1.83	1.80
KOH	. . . .	. . . .	1.99	1.98	1.93	1.87	. . . .	. . . .
$MgSO_4$	. . . .	. . . .	1.69	1.62	1.42	1.32	1.22	1.08
K_2SO_4	. . . .	2.92	2.86	2.80	2.57	2.46	2.33	2.12
$CoCl_2$	. . . .	2.91	2.80	2.75	2.64	2.62	2.66	. . . .
$K_3Fe(CN)_6$	3.92	3.82	3.51	3.31	3.01	2.85	2.69	. . . .

9. **The Contribution of Arrhenius.** The first consistent theory advanced to explain the experimental facts concerning the behavior of electrolytes in

solution was that of the resourceful young Swedish theorist, Svante Arrhenius. In 1887, at a time when the ionic nature of such compounds as sodium chloride and potassium nitrate was completely unknown, Arrhenius, at the age of twenty-eight, much to the scorn of most of his contemporaries, proposed that electrolytes exist in solution in the form of ions.

Considering how far the Arrhenius theory of electrolytic dissociation, as it was called, outstripped the chemical knowledge of its day, this theory will always retain its place as one of the most brilliant landmarks of the science. Arrhenius assumed, however, that the ions were formed as the result of an incomplete reaction which occurred only as the electrolyte dissolved, and that this ionization reaction was favored by dilution. Thus Arrhenius postulated that the equivalent conductivities and mole numbers of electrolytes increase as their solutions are diluted because the total numbers of ions present actually increase with dilution. Today, knowing as we do that ionic compounds exist entirely as ions even in the crystalline state, this view, as applied to ionic compounds, is no longer tenable.

10. The Interionic Attraction Theory. The fact that solutions of ionic compounds do not at all concentrations exhibit the equivalent conductance and mole number values expected on the basis of complete ionization is explained at present by the fact that *the ions, even in solution, are not strictly independent units.* This idea is the core of the *interionic attraction theory,* developed in 1923 by Peter Debye, now of Cornell University, and Erich Hückel. These workers showed that each positive ion in solution must be surrounded on the average by a higher concentration of negative than of positive ions, and conversely, each negative ion by a preponderance of positive ions. Every ion in solution is surrounded by an ion atmosphere of opposite charge, and each central ion is bound by forces of attraction to its ion atmosphere. Thus, each ion is saddled with an entourage of other ions, which hampers its free movement and prevents it from behaving as a completely independent unit. A mole of ions, then, does not have so great an effect on the freezing point of water as does a mole of neutral molecules.

As a solution of an electrolyte is diluted, however, the average distance between the ions is increased and the intensity of the interionic forces is accordingly diminished. At extremely high dilutions, therefore, the ions behave essentially like neutral molecules, and hence the mole numbers of ionic compounds in very dilute solutions approach their limiting values.

The increase in the equivalent conductance of a solution with decreasing concentration may be explained similarly. It is to be expected that the ion atmosphere of each ion would exert a retarding effect upon it, acting as a brake on the motion of a cation toward the cathode and of an anion toward the anode. This so-called drag effect is greater, the smaller the distances between the ions; i.e., the more concentrated the solution. As a solution of an electrolyte is diluted, therefore, this effect becomes less and less significant until at extreme dilution it disappears, and the equivalent conductance reaches a limiting value.

We should expect, also, that the magnitude of the interionic attraction should increase with increasing ionic charges. This explains why the extent to which the equivalent conductances and mole numbers of electrolytes at a given concentration deviate from their limiting values is greater the greater the charges on the ions of the electrolyte.

11. Ionization of Covalent Compounds. There are numerous compounds —including many highly important ones—which, although not ionic, nevertheless behave like typical electrolytes when dissolved in water; obviously, then, they give solutions which contain ions. The properties of the pure compounds themselves, however, clearly indicate that they are covalent in nature. If ions are not present in an electrolyte before it is dissolved, they must be formed from the molecules of the compound as it dissolves. Recent investigations point unmistakably to the conclusion that covalent compounds which form ions in solution can do so only by actual chemical reaction with the solvent. In order to consider more closely the nature of these reactions, we may divide all covalent electrolytes into three general classes: (1) pseudosalts, (2) acids, and (3) nonionic bases.

12. Pseudosalts. Most salts are ionic compounds; in fact, a salt is sometimes defined as an ionic compound. There are, however, a number of compounds that contain a metal in combination with a nonmetallic element or radical, and which are therefore frequently classified as salts (see p. 205), even though they are comparatively low-melting, low-boiling substances that in the liquid state are exceedingly poor conductors of electricity. These so-called salts, or pseudosalts, are therefore not ionic compounds, but are composed of neutral molecules in which the atoms are linked by covalent bonds (p. 174). Anhydrous aluminum chloride, Al_2Cl_6, is a typical pseudosalt. Like most compounds belonging to this class, it contains a metal in an oxidation state higher than $+2$. Its ionization in water results from a reaction such as

$$Al_2Cl_6 + 2xH_2O = 2Al(H_2O)_x{}^{+++} + 6Cl^-$$

No method for determining the exact extent to which the aluminum ion is hydrated has as yet been devised. From the fact that the crystalline hydrate

$AlCl_3 \cdot 6H_2O$ is obtained upon evaporation of the solution, and because there is considerable other evidence indicating that elements following sodium in the periodic system may share as many as six pairs of electrons, it is customary to represent the hydrated aluminum ion in water solution by the formula $Al(H_2O)_6^{+++}$. Other pseudosalts, such as stannic chloride, $SnCl_4$ (a nonconducting liquid at room temperature), ionize by the same general mechanism.

Most cations, indeed, are hydrated to some extent in water solution, but from many standpoints there is no need to distinguish between hydrated and nonhydrated ions. Once the pseudosalt has dissolved, such considerations as Faraday's laws, or the effects of interionic attraction in decreasing mole numbers and equivalent conductance values, apply just as they do to ionic compounds.[4]

13. Acids.

The acids are among the most important of covalent compounds. Many, such as sulfuric and nitric acids, possess the corrosive properties generally associated with the term "acid" in the mind of the layman. Others, like citric and tartaric acids, are common constituents of our food. All acids, when dissolved in water, do, however, have in common the following four functional properties (p. 203): they taste sour, turn blue litmus red, neutralize bases, and react with active metals to give, as one product, free hydrogen. Structurally, the familiar acids all contain the element hydrogen; in the electrolysis of solutions of acids, elementary hydrogen appears as the cathode product.

The most familiar acids, in the pure anhydrous form, are liquids or gases at ordinary temperatures. Hydrogen chloride, hydrogen bromide, and hydrogen sulfide are gases; nitric and sulfuric acids are liquids. A considerable number of acids—particularly organic acids of high molecular weight —are solids at room temperature; even these exist in the form of molecular, rather than ionic, crystals. Pure anhydrous acids in the liquid state are poor conductors of electricity; they are made up of neutral molecules in which all the atoms, including those of hydrogen, are linked by covalent bonds.

Like all other acids, hydrochloric acid in water solution shows all the properties of an electrolyte; its aqueous solutions conduct electricity, have two independent sets of properties, and exhibit mole number values greater than 1. Obviously, hydrogen chloride, like other acids, forms ions as it dis-

---

[4] As a matter of fact, the distinction between ionic and covalent compounds is not entirely clear-cut. There is, in reality, a gradual shift from purely ionic to purely covalent salts; and in many borderline cases, such, for example, as that of beryllium chloride, the mechanism of solution might be considered as intermediate between the two extremes described.

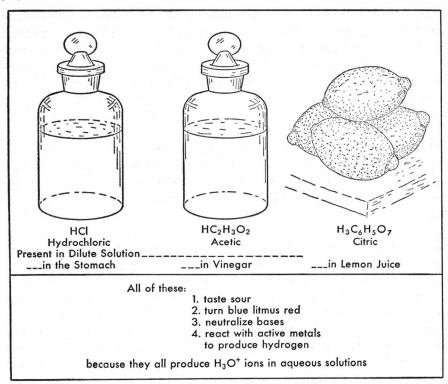

HCl $HC_2H_3O_2$ $H_3C_6H_5O_7$
Hydrochloric   Acetic   Citric
Present in Dilute Solution _____
___in the Stomach   ___in Vinegar   ___in Lemon Juice

All of these:
  1. taste sour
  2. turn blue litmus red
  3. neutralize bases
  4. react with active metals
     to produce hydrogen
because they all produce H_3O^+ ions in aqueous solutions

Fig. 17.4.   Some common acids.

solves in water. Arrhenius assumed that the reaction consisted of a dissociation of some of the hydrogen chloride molecules into positive hydrogen
and negative chloride ions, which he supposed to exist in equilibrium with
undissociated molecules according to the equation

$$HCl \rightleftharpoons H^+ + Cl^- \tag{1}$$

In the light of more recent knowledge, however, we are quite certain
that a hydrogen ion or proton, with its enormously high ratio of charge to
radius, cannot exist unhydrated in water. Hence, we picture the ionization of
hydrogen chloride in water as involving reaction with water molecules.

$$HCl + H_2O \rightleftharpoons H_3O^+ + Cl^-$$

Or, in electronic formulas,

$$H : \overset{..}{\underset{..}{Cl}} : + \quad \overset{H}{\underset{H}{\overset{.}{\underset{.}{O}}}} \overset{.}{\underset{.}{H}} \rightleftharpoons \left[\overset{H}{\underset{H}{\overset{.}{\underset{.}{O}}}} \overset{.}{\underset{.}{H}} \right]^+ + \quad : \overset{..}{\underset{..}{Cl}} : ^-$$

The ion H_3O^+, because of its resemblance to ammonium ion, NH_4^+, is called *hydronium* ion. Inasmuch as water molecules are themselves linked together through hydrogen bonds (p. 233), it appears likely that each proton is associated with more than one molecule of water. Actually, the hydronium ions in solution probably contain a variable number of water molecules, as indicated by such formulas as $(H_5O_2)^+$, $(H_7O_3)^+$, and $(H_9O_4)^+$. The formula H_3O^+, however, is used as the simplest formula which represents a hydrated proton.

So far as the products are concerned, the abbreviated Arrhenius equation (1) and the complete equation (2) for the ionization of hydrogen chloride are essentially the same. Equation (2) stresses the mechanism by which the ions are produced, and emphasizes the fact that the proton in aqueous solution is always hydrated. It is quite customary for chemists to use simple equations of the Arrhenius type to represent the ionization of acids, with the understanding that such an equation is a shortened form of the more complete equation in which water appears as a reactant. Likewise, a hydrated proton is often referred to simply as a "hydrogen ion."

Because hydronium ion is common to aqueous solutions of all acids, we are confident that the characteristic properties of such solutions are in reality the properties of hydronium ion. *An acid may be defined, then, as a substance that in water solution ionizes with the formation of hydronium as one of its ions.* (This will hereafter be referred to as the Arrhenius definition of an acid.) Furthermore, the greater the concentration of hydronium ion, the more strongly will these characteristics be exhibited. Hence, one acid is characterized as being stronger or weaker than another, according to whether a larger or a smaller concentration of hydronium ion is present in a solution of given total concentration of acid.

14. Bases. From the functional standpoint (p. 203), a base may be defined as a compound whose water solution feels soapy, tastes bitter or alkaline, turns red litmus blue, and neutralizes acids. The so-called alkalis, such as potassium hydroxide and sodium hydroxide, whose solutions are excellent conductors of electricity and exhibit mole numbers indicating complete dissociation of the solute into ions, are actually ionic compounds in which the anion is the *hydroxide* ion. It is apparent that the characteristic properties of such bases are actually those of the hydroxide ion. A base may be defined, therefore, as a compound which, in aqueous solution, yields hydroxide ion (Arrhenius definition); and the *strength* of a base is determined by the extent to which it is dissociated in solution to give hydroxide ions. Sodium hydroxide and potassium hydroxide, which, like all ionic com-

pounds, are completely dissociated in water solution, yield high concentrations of hydroxide ion and are, therefore, *strong* bases and are placed with
other ionic compounds in the category of *strong electrolytes*.

In addition to the strong or ionic bases, there are a few covalent compounds, of which ammonia is the most familiar example, which in water
solution exhibit the characteristic properties of bases but conduct electricity
only very poorly, and which (except in extremely dilute solutions) exhibit
mole number values only slightly greater than unity. Such compounds are

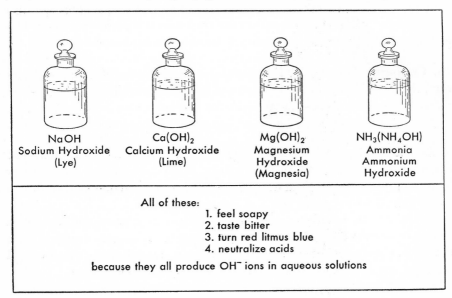

NaOH	Ca(OH)$_2$	Mg(OH)$_2$	NH$_3$(NH$_4$OH)
Sodium Hydroxide	Calcium Hydroxide	Magnesium	Ammonia
(Lye)	(Lime)	Hydroxide	Ammonium
		(Magnesia)	Hydroxide

All of these:
1. feel soapy
2. taste bitter
3. turn red litmus blue
4. neutralize acids

because they all produce OH⁻ ions in aqueous solutions

Fig. 17.5.   Some common bases.

called *weak* bases. Their behavior may be explained by the supposition that
only a small fraction of the molecules react with water to produce hydroxide
ion, together with the characteristic cation of the base. Because they are only
slightly ionized, these compounds are placed in the category of *weak electrolytes*. In the case of ammonia in aqueous solution, for example, the equilibrium attained may be most simply represented as follows (see p. 474):

$$NH_3 + H_2O \rightleftharpoons NH_4^+ + OH^-$$

or, written electronically,

$$\text{H : N : H} + \text{: O :} \rightleftharpoons \left[\text{H : N : H} \right]^+ + \left[\text{: O : H} \right]^-$$

15. The Brønsted Concept of Acids and Bases. It is significant that the function of the base ammonia, in its reaction with water, is the exact opposite of that of an acid, such as hydrogen chloride. Whereas a molecule of the base *accepts a proton from water,* an acid molecule *donates a proton to water.* This general idea has led to a broader definition of acids and bases. Independently in 1923, J. N. Brønsted in Copenhagen, and T. M. Lowry, in Cambridge, proposed that an *acid* be defined as *any substance which can give or donate a proton to any other substance.* A *base,* on the other hand, is defined as *any substance which can receive or accept a proton from any other substance.* An acid is a proton donor, a base is a proton acceptor. This has come to be known as the Brønsted definition of acids and bases.

16. Conjugate Acids and Bases. From the standpoint of the Brønsted concept, the ionization of an acid is a reversible reaction involving two acid-base pairs. In the ionization of acetic acid, for example,

$$HC_2H_3O_2 + H_2O \rightleftharpoons H_3O^+ + C_2H_3O_2^-$$

in the reaction from left to right, acetic acid *donates* a proton to water. The acetic acid, therefore, acts in this reaction as an *acid.* Water, on the other hand, *accepts* a proton from acetic acid, and in this reaction is, therefore, a *base* in the Brønsted sense.

In the reverse reaction (from right to left), hydronium ion *donates* a proton to acetate ion, hence it is an *acid.* Because it *accepts* a proton from the hydronium ion, the acetate ion is a *base.* According to the Brønsted concept, ions, as well as neutral compounds, may be acids or bases.

The acid acetic acid, by losing a proton, forms the base acetate ion, which, in turn, by gaining a proton, can form acetic acid. Such a pair of substances, the members of which can be formed from each other by the gain or loss of a proton, is called a *conjugate* acid-base pair. Thus, acetic acid is the conjugate acid of acetate ion, and acetate ion is the conjugate base of acetic acid. If we designate the acetic acid as, say, Acid$_1$, then its conjugate base, acetate ion, is designated as Base$_1$. Similarly, if we refer to water as Base$_2$, then its conjugate acid, hydronium ion, is Acid$_2$. This convention is illustrated here for the ionization of acetic acid.

$$HC_2H_3O_2 + H_2O \rightleftharpoons H_3O^+ + C_2H_3O_2^-$$

Acid$_1$ Base$_2$ Acid$_2$ Base$_1$
Conjugate Acid-Base Pairs

17. Relative Strengths of Acids and Bases. The *strength* of an *acid,* according to the Brønsted concept, is measured by its tendency to *donate protons;* the strength of a *base,* by its tendency to *accept protons.* The relative acidic and basic strengths of different substances vary between extremely wide limits.

Water solutions of a few acids, such as hydrochloric, nitric, and sulfuric, not only exhibit the characteristic acid properties very strongly, but also are excellent conductors of electricity and have mole numbers comparable to those of ionic compounds at the same concentration. The ionization reactions of these acids, which are called *strong* acids, proceed virtually to completion toward the right.

$$HCl + H_2O = H_3O^+ + Cl^-$$
$$HNO_3 + H_2O = H_3O^+ + NO_3^-$$
$$H_2SO_4 + H_2O = H_3O^+ + HSO_4^-$$

Hence, these acids give a relatively high concentration of hydronium ion in a solution of given total concentration of acid.

The equivalent conductances and mole numbers of dilute solutions of strong acids increase with decreasing concentration of the solution. Just as for ionic compounds, this is explained on the basis of interionic attraction. Strong acids, therefore, are included in the category of strong electrolytes (p. 313).

On the other hand, there are a number of acids, of which hydrogen sulfide, H_2S, hydrogen cyanide, HCN, and acetic acid, $HC_2H_3O_2$, are familiar examples, whose solutions are not nearly so sour as those of strong acids of the same concentration, and which conduct electricity only poorly. These acids, moreover, except in very dilute solutions, exhibit freezing point depressions only slightly greater than the standard values for non-electrolytes. Since water solutions of these *weak* acids contain only relatively low concentrations of hydronium ion (as well as of their characteristic anions), these acids must undergo ionization in water to a small degree only. The reaction with water of acetic acid, as a typical weak acid, is very far from complete; equilibrium is reached when the reaction

$$HC_2H_3O_2 + H_2O \rightleftharpoons H_3O^+ + C_2H_3O_2^-$$

has proceeded to the right only to a slight extent, so that only a small fraction of the total acetic acid present is in the form of ions. Weak acids, along with other slightly ionized substances, are included in the class of weak electrolytes (p. 313).

For solutions of weak electrolytes, freezing point and conductance data provide a fairly accurate measure of the fraction of electrolyte ionized, or its degree of ionization. This point will be dealt with quantitatively in the next chapter.

Considering the ionization of acetic acid from a slightly different point of view, we might compare the acidic strengths of acetic acid and hydronium ion, and the basic strengths of water and acetate ion. The water and the acetate ion may be looked upon as two bases which are competing for the protons. Acetate ion keeps most of the protons and is, therefore, a stronger base than water, which manages to make off with a few protons only. We may also regard the acetic acid and the hydronium ion as competitors in an attempt to donate protons to a base. Obviously, the hydronium ion is more successful in this attempt than is the acetic acid; hence, the former is the stronger acid. In summary, acetate ion is a stronger base than water, and its conjugate acid, acetic acid, is a weaker acid than the conjugate acid of water, hydronium ion.

These facts illustrate the important generalization that *the stronger an acid is, the weaker must be its conjugate base,* and vice versa. If an acid is strong, its conjugate base is weak; if a base is strong, its conjugate acid is weak. Thus, we may say that water is a very weak acid because its conjugate base, hydroxide ion, is a very strong base; or, that hydroxide ion is a strong base because its conjugate acid, water, is weak.

A qualitative comparison of the relative strengths of a number of acids and bases is afforded by the following table. The acids are listed in the

	Conjugate Acid	*Conjugate Base*	
Decreasing Acid Strength	$HClO_4$	ClO_4^-	Increasing Base Strength
	HNO_3	NO_3^-	
	HCl	Cl^-	
	H_2SO_4	HSO_4^-	
	H_3O^+	H_2O	
	HSO_4^-	SO_4^{--}	
	H_3PO_4	$H_2PO_4^-$	
	$HC_2H_3O_2$	$C_2H_3O_2^-$	
	$Al(H_2O)_6^{+++}$	$Al(H_2O)_5OH^{++}$	
	H_2CO_3	HCO_3^-	
	H_2S	HS^-	
	HCN	CN^-	
	NH_4^+	NH_3	
	HCO_3^-	CO_3^{--}	
	H_2O	OH^-	
	NH_3	NH_2^-	

first column in the order of decreasing acid strength; their conjugate bases listed in the second column, then, fall in the order of increasing base strength.

These generalizations serve to emphasize that the Brønsted acid-base concept is an extension of that of Arrhenius. Compounds which qualify as acids according to the Arrhenius definition are also proton donors, but they must be sufficiently strong to donate protons—at least to a measurable extent —to water. Similarly, compounds that are weak bases according to the Arrhenius definition are actually proton acceptors which are sufficiently strong to accept protons to some extent from the weak acid water.

18. Amphiprotic Substances. It is now apparent that the terms "acid" and "base," by definition, are *relative* terms only. Many substances may act as acids in certain reactions and as bases in others; such substances are said to be *amphiprotic*. The most familiar amphiprotic compound is water, which acts as an acid (or proton donor) toward ammonia and as a base (or proton acceptor) toward hydrogen chloride. Certain ions, such as bisulfate ion, HSO_4^-, and bicarbonate ion, HCO_3^-, are also amphiprotic. Sulfuric acid ionizes in water in two steps, as illustrated by the following equations:

$$\text{Acid}_1 \quad \text{Base}_2 \quad \text{Acid}_2 \quad \text{Base}_1$$
$$H_2SO_4 + H_2O \rightleftharpoons H_3O^+ + HSO_4^-$$
$$HSO_4^- + H_2O \rightleftharpoons H_3O^+ + SO_4^{--}$$

In the first step, bisulfate ion, HSO_4^-, acts as a base; in the second, as an acid.

19. The Leveling Effect. All very strong acids, such as hydrogen chloride, hydrogen bromide, hydrogen iodide, nitric acid, and perchloric acid

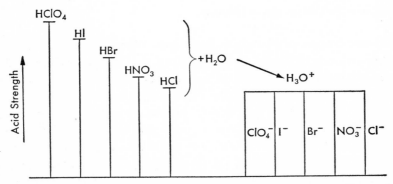

Fig. 17.6. The leveling effect. In aqueous solution, all very strong acids are leveled to the strength of hydronium ion (H_3O^+), for they react completely with water to produce this ion.

($HClO_4$), appear to have exactly equal strengths in water solution. In solvents less basic than water, however, these acids are not of equal strength;

the order of decreasing acidity is $HClO_4 > HI > HBr > HNO_3 > HCl$. In dilute solution all of these acids react almost completely with water to form, in every case, hydronium ion. The apparent acidity in water solution of all very strong acids is therefore reduced to the same level—that of the hydronium ion. This phenomenon is called the *leveling effect*. Since all acids stronger than hydronium ion react practically completely with water, hydronium ion is the strongest acid that can exist in appreciable concentration in aqueous solution.

Let us consider, similarly, what takes place when a base stronger than hydroxide ion is added to water. Since ammonia is a weaker acid than water (p. 316), its conjugate base, amide ion (NH_2^-), must be a stronger base than hydroxide ion, the conjugate base of water. An ionic crystalline compound, sodium amide ($NaNH_2$), may be prepared fairly readily by the reaction of sodium with ammonia, just as sodium hydroxide may be obtained from sodium and water. Now, when sodium amide is added to water, a vigorous reaction ensues, with the liberation of ammonia. The resulting solution has all the characteristic properties of a strong base; in fact, it is found to be a solution of sodium hydroxide. Obviously, the amide ion, being a stronger base than hydroxide ion, reacts practically completely with water to form hydroxide ion, according to the equation [5]

$$\text{Acid}_1 \quad \text{Base}_2 \quad \text{Acid}_2 \quad \text{Base}_1$$
$$H_2O + NH_2^- \rightleftharpoons NH_3 + OH^-$$

In general, hydroxide ion is the strongest base which can exist in any appreciable concentration in water solution.

20. General Nature of Protolytic Reactions.

When a strong acid, such as hydrogen chloride, is added to water, a reaction involving the transfer of a proton occurs; when equilibrium is reached, the reaction is found to have favored the formation of hydronium ion, which is the weaker of the two acids, and chloride ion, the weaker of the two bases participating in the reaction. Similarly, when amide ion comes into contact with water, equilibrium is attained only when proton transfer has occurred in such a way as to favor the formation of the weaker acid, ammonia, and the weaker base, hydroxide ion. The transfer of protons from one substance to another is called *protolysis*; any reaction between an acid and a base which involves proton transfer is a *protolytic* reaction. In *all* protolytic reactions, proton

---

[5] Sodium ion, Na^+, which exists as such both before and after the reaction, may be considered as merely an innocent bystander, or, to borrow a term used by some writers, a "spectator" ion.

transfer tends to occur in such a direction as to favor the weaker of the two possible acids and the weaker of the two possible bases; the point of equilibrium is determined by the ratio of the relative strengths of the two acids or of the two bases. This important generalization applies not only to ionization, but also to such other types of protolytic reactions as neutralization and hydrolysis.

21. Neutralization. By the Brønsted definition, neutralization in aqueous solution is a protolytic reaction in which water is a product. In fact, when strong acids are neutralized by strong bases in dilute solution, water is the *only* product. Ionic bases such as sodium and potassium hydroxide are considered as salts in which the anion happens to be hydroxide ion, the strongest base that can exist in water solution. When a dilute solution of a strong acid (such as hydrogen chloride) is added to a solution of an ionic hydroxide (such as sodium hydroxide), in reality hydronium, chloride, sodium, and hydroxide ions are being mixed. The strong acid hydronium ion and the strong base hydroxide ion react according to the equation

$$\overset{\text{Acid}_1}{H_3O^+} + \overset{\text{Base}_2}{OH^-} = \overset{\text{Acid}_2}{HOH} + \overset{\text{Base}_1}{HOH}$$

The sole product is water, which is both the conjugate base of hydronium ion and the conjugate acid of hydroxide ion. Inasmuch as hydronium ion is a very strong acid and hydroxide ion a very strong base—as compared with water—the reaction proceeds practically to completion toward the right. The sodium and chloride ions obviously do not participate in the reaction and may be classified as "spectator" ions. Thus, the equation shown represents the fundamental reaction that occurs when any strong acid is neutralized by any ionic hydroxide.

When a weak acid such as acetic acid is neutralized by an ionic hydroxide, a slightly different type of protolytic reaction occurs. Since the concentration of hydronium present is very small, the chief reaction is that represented by the equation

$$\overset{\text{Acid}_1}{HC_2H_3O_2} + \overset{\text{Base}_2}{OH^-} \rightleftharpoons \overset{\text{Acid}_2}{HOH} + \overset{\text{Base}_1}{C_2H_3O_2^-}$$

Unlike the reaction between a strong acid and a strong base, this reaction does not proceed quite to completion, because acetic acid, as $Acid_1$, is not so strong an acid as hydronium ion; and acetate ion, as $Base_1$, is not so weak a base as water. Similarly, the neutralization of a weak base such as ammonia by a strong acid, say hydrochloric acid, is best represented by the equation

$$\overset{\text{Acid}_1 \qquad \text{Base}_2 \qquad \text{Acid}_2 \qquad \text{Base}_1}{H_3O^+ + NH_3 \rightleftharpoons NH_4^+ + H_2O}$$

Here, again, the reaction does not proceed quite to completion, and the concentrations of hydronium ion and ammonia remaining in the solution at equilibrium are not insignificant.

22. Protolytic Reactions in Which Weak Acids and Bases Other Than Water Are Formed. When a strong acid is added to a salt of a weak acid, a protolytic reaction occurs in which the weaker acid is formed. Thus, hydrogen sulfide, hydrogen cyanide, carbonic acid, and other weak acids are readily prepared by the addition of a strong acid to solutions of their soluble salts. The preparation of carbonic acid, for example, from sodium bicarbonate and any strong acid, may be represented by the equation

$$\overset{\text{Acid}_1 \qquad \text{Base}_2 \qquad \text{Acid}_2 \qquad \text{Base}_1}{H_3O^+ + HCO_3^- \rightleftharpoons H_2CO_3 + H_2O}$$

Inasmuch as hydronium ion is a considerably stronger acid than carbonic acid, and bicarbonate ion a considerably stronger base than water, the reaction proceeds far toward the right; the carbonic acid so formed then decomposes into carbon dioxide and water. Study of the equation reveals that this reaction is a neutralization; we observe experimentally that sodium bicarbonate does neutralize strong acids in much the same way that sodium hydroxide or ammonia does.

23. Hydrolysis. We have seen that when the ionic salt sodium amide dissolves in water a vigorous reaction occurs, and the solution turns red litmus blue. Obviously, some base must be introduced into the water upon the addition of sodium amide. That base is the amide ion, which accepts a proton from water to form ammonia and hydroxide ion. Such a reaction is an instance of *hydrolysis* (p. 237). The hydrolysis of a salt, therefore, consists simply in a protolytic reaction between an ion and water. The hydrolysis of amide ion is an extreme case in that the ion, being a stronger base than hydroxide ion, reacts completely with water to form hydroxide ion.

There are many salts, however, whose anions are weaker bases than hydroxide ion, but which, nevertheless, give basic water solutions. Thus, lithium bicarbonate, potassium cyanide, sodium acetate, and many other salts dissolve in water without any directly observable reaction; yet the resulting solutions turn red litmus blue. From this experimental fact we conclude that each of these salts must contain an ion that removes protons from water to yield hydroxide ion and which is, therefore, a relatively strong base.

In each case, the basic ion is the anion of the salt. Thus, when sodium acetate is dissolved in water, this salt (or, more strictly speaking, the acetate ion) undergoes hydrolysis as follows:

$$\underset{\text{Acid}_1}{H_2O} + \underset{\text{Base}_2}{C_2H_3O_2{}^-} \rightleftharpoons \underset{\text{Acid}_2}{HC_2H_3O_2} + \underset{\text{Base}_1}{OH^-}$$

This hydrolysis, like that of any salt, is a protolysis in which water is one of the *reactants*, and may be regarded as the reverse of neutralization, in which water is one of the *products*. This hydrolytic reaction was, in fact, already hinted at in the discussion of the neutralization of acetic acid with sodium hydroxide (p. 319), where it was suggested that the neutralization reaction does not proceed quite to completion. Since acetate ion is a considerably weaker base than hydroxide ion—just as water is a weaker acid than acetic acid—the hydrolysis of the acetate ion in sodium acetate proceeds to a very limited extent only. Hydroxide ion is produced in sufficiently high concentration, however, to give the characteristic basic test toward litmus.

A sodium chloride solution does not turn the color of litmus because chloride ion, like other ions which are conjugate bases of strong acids, does not undergo hydrolysis. Only anions which are relatively strong bases are subject to hydrolysis. In fact, the effect of a solution of sodium acetate toward litmus is a direct indication that the acetate ion is a relatively strong base, and constitutes the simplest experimental proof of the fact that acetic acid is a weak acid.

There are a few salts, such as ammonium chloride and ammonium sulfate, whose cations contain hydrogen, which show an acidic reaction in water solution. These salts contain an ion which donates protons to water to form hydronium ion, and which is, therefore, a relatively strong acid. Thus, each of these ammonium salts (or, strictly speaking, the ammonium ion) appears to be slightly hydrolyzed according to the equation

$$\underset{\text{Acid}_1}{NH_4{}^+} + \underset{\text{Base}_2}{H_2O} \rightleftharpoons \underset{\text{Acid}_2}{H_3O^+} + \underset{\text{Base}_1}{NH_3}$$

Here, the ammonia and water are competing for protons; ammonia, as the stronger base, retains the lion's share, but water is sufficiently basic to capture a few, thus forming hydronium ions in high enough concentration to give an acid test toward litmus. This acid reaction constitutes a simple experimental proof that ammonia is, after all, a rather weak base.

Although an aqueous solution of ammonium acetate, $NH_4C_2H_3O_2$, does not show either an acid or an alkaline reaction toward litmus, yet such a solution contains appreciable concentrations of both ammonia and acetic acid. These result from the protolytic reaction

$$\text{Acid}_1 \qquad \text{Base}_2 \qquad \text{Acid}_2 \qquad \text{Base}_1$$
$$NH_4^+ + C_2H_3O_2^- \rightleftharpoons HC_2H_3O_2 + NH_3$$

In this case, since *both* the acidic and the basic product are relatively weak, the reaction proceeds to a greater extent than does either of the hydrolytic reactions just described. The resulting solution, however, shows a neutral reaction toward litmus because the acid strength of ammonium ion and the basic strength of acetate ion are very nearly the same.

In addition to the ammonium salts, there are many salts and pseudosalts, such as cupric sulfate, aluminum chloride, and stannic chloride, containing a multivalent metal, whose solutions in water show an acid reaction toward litmus. In general, the higher the oxidation number of the metal, the greater the extent of the hydrolysis. We have already seen (p. 310) that the cation present in water solutions of aluminum chloride is the hydrated aluminum ion, $Al(H_2O)_6^{+++}$. The slight tendency of water molecules to donate protons is undoubtedly greatly increased when these molecules are attached to a highly charged positive ion, since there is a strong force of repulsion between this ion and the likewise positively charged proton. The hydrated aluminum ion, therefore, undergoes partial hydrolysis according to the equation

$$\text{Acid}_1 \qquad\qquad \text{Base}_2 \qquad \text{Acid}_2 \qquad\qquad \text{Base}_1$$
$$Al(H_2O)_6^{+++} + H_2O \rightleftharpoons H_3O^+ + Al(H_2O)_5(OH)^{++}$$

Similarly, for the hydrated cupric ion, we may write

$$\text{Acid}_1 \qquad\qquad \text{Base}_2 \qquad \text{Acid}_2 \qquad\qquad \text{Base}_1$$
$$Cu(H_2O)_4^{++} + H_2O \rightleftharpoons H_3O^+ + Cu(H_2O)_3(OH)^+$$

24. Relation of Acidity and Basicity to Electronic Structure. Many factors, some rather complex, are involved in determining relative acidities and basicities of substances. In general, molecules which behave as acids are polar, and the hydrogen atom which is "acidic" (or transferable as a proton) is situated at the positive end of the dipole; i.e., electrons are withdrawn from it toward the atom to which it is attached. In cations that contain hydrogen atoms, these hydrogen atoms are, of course, in an electron-poor or *positive* environment because the whole unit in which they are contained is electron-deficient or positively charged. Hence, the hydrogen atoms in such cations tend to be transferred as protons and all hydrogen-containing cations are acids.

Bases in the Brønsted sense, whether molecules or ions, must contain at least one unshared electron pair. This pair must be located on an atom in a *negative* environment, either in an anion or at the negative end of a polar molecule. If the base is to be strong, this unshared electron pair must not be held too tightly by the atom on which it is located, either by virtue of the electron attraction of this atom itself or of other atoms attached to it. Thus the basicity in the series $NH_3 > H_2O > HF$ decreases with increasing electron-attracting power of the central atom.

Some of the most interesting and important generalizations regarding acid-base strengths relate to the compounds containing one or more OH groups in their formulas. Compounds of this type range from such ionic hydroxides as potassium hydroxide, KOH, and sodium hydroxide, NaOH, to such powerful proton donors as sulfuric acid, $SO_2(OH)_2$, and perchloric acid, ClO_3OH. Consider, for example, the hydroxyl compound MOH (in the general case, the central atom M may be surrounded by additional OH groups, as well as by one or more oxygen atoms) where M can represent any element. If MOH is to act as a base it should split in accordance with the electronic formula

$$M^+ \Big| : \overset{..}{\underset{..}{O}} : H^-$$

into M^+ and OH^- ions. This type of behavior would be expected where M^+ is an ion which has only a small attraction for electrons; i.e., an ion formed from a metal of low ionization potential. If the hydroxyl compound is to act as an acid, on the other hand, it must give up a proton as follows:

$$M : \overset{..}{\underset{..}{O}} : \Big| H^+$$

This occurs when M is an atom with a strong attraction for electrons. These facts provide the explanation for the earlier statement (p. 203) that the hydroxides of metals are basic, whereas the hydroxyl compounds of non-metals are acids. Thus the hydroxyl compounds of the elements of the second complete series of the periodic table may be arranged in the following sequence:

Increasing electron-attracting power (and ionization potential) of the central atom

→   →   →   →   →

sodium hydroxide	magnesium hydroxide	aluminum hydroxide	silicic acid	phosphoric acid	sulfuric acid	perchloric acid
NaOH	$Mg(OH)_2$	$Al(OH)_3$	$SiO(OH)_2$	$PO(OH)_3$	$SO_2(OH)_2$	ClO_3OH
strong base	weak base	amphiprotic	weak acid	moderately strong acid	strong acid	very strong acid

Increasing acidity and decreasing basicity

→   →   →   →   →

Consider a series of similar compounds in which all the atoms to which the OH groups are attached belong to the same family and exhibit the same oxidation number. Here the acid strength increases and the basic strength decreases with an increase in the power of the central atom to attract electrons (decrease in metallic nature) or, in general, from bottom to top in the periodic table. This rule is well illustrated by nitric acid together with the corresponding acids of the elements in the phosporus family.

Increasing acidity and electron-attracting power				
bismuthic acid	antimonic acid	arsenic acid	phosphoric acid	nitric acid
$HBiO_3$	$HSb(OH)_6$	H_3AsO_4	H_3PO_4	HNO_3
weak acid				strong acid

For compounds containing the OH group attached to the same atom, the acidity increases and the basicity decreases with an increase in the number of electron-attracting atoms or groups linked to the central atom; i.e., with an increase in the oxidation number of the central atom. This fact is illustrated, for example, by the oxygen acids of chlorine. It is attributed to the increasing electron affinity of the chlorine brought about by the electron-withdrawing effect of the added oxygen atoms.

Increasing Acidity and Oxidation Number			
hypochlorous acid	chlorous acid	chloric acid	perchloric acid
$ClOH$	$OClOH$	O_2ClOH	O_3ClOH

25. The Lewis Concept of Acidity and Basicity.

Despite the fact that the Brønsted concept of acidity and basicity is considerably broader than that of Arrhenius, it has nevertheless been criticized by many chemists on the score of being insufficiently general. These critics point to such experimental facts as that carbon dioxide and sulfur trioxide behave as acids, although they contain no hydrogen. Moreover, basic oxides such as calcium oxide and barium oxide neutralize acidic oxides like sulfur trioxide and carbon dioxide even in the absence of any solvent. Because no hydrogen is transferred, this reaction cannot be interpreted in terms of the Brønsted concept.

From the theoretical viewpoint, the Brønsted definitions have been criticized because they assign a unique position to the proton. A base, in the Brønsted sense, is a substance which shares an electron pair with a proton, and an acid a substance which supplies the proton to accept the electron pair.

It is because the proton is by no means the only type of particle (ion or molecule) which can accept an electron pair, that the Brønsted definition of an acid is a restricted one.

In perfectly general terms, an acid may be defined as any substance that can accept a share in an electron pair from some other substance to form a coordinate bond. A base, then, is any substance that can share one of its electron pairs with an acid. *An acid is an electron pair acceptor, a base an electron pair donor.* These are, in fact, precisely the definitions advanced in 1923 by the versatile American chemist G. N. Lewis (1875–1946). In terms of these new definitions, the union or coordination of calcium oxide with sulfur trioxide to form calcium sulfate is the reaction of a base with an acid, as is evident from the equation

$$
Ca^{++}, : \overset{..}{\underset{..}{O}} : ^{--} + \quad
\begin{matrix}
: \overset{..}{O} : \\
\overset{..}{S} : \overset{..}{O} : \\
: \overset{..}{\underset{..}{O}} :
\end{matrix}
= Ca^{++}, :
\begin{matrix}
: \overset{..}{O} : \\
\overset{..}{O} : S : \overset{..}{O} : \\
: \overset{..}{\underset{..}{O}} :
\end{matrix} ^{--}
$$

According to the broad Lewis concept, a base, as is true in the Brønsted sense, must have an unshared electron pair; the acid which shares that electron pair may be the proton, but may also be any other ion or molecule. The Lewis definition of a base includes all substances which would be classed as bases according to the Brønsted definition, while the new definition of an acid covers not only the proton, and hence all the protonic acids of the Brønsted concept, but also many additional substances such as boron trifluoride, BF_3, stannic chloride, $SnCl_4$, and aluminum chloride. The Lewis concept of acidity and basicity provides a system for the correlation of a vast amount of experimental data.

STUDY QUESTIONS AND PROBLEMS

1. Freezing point depressions of dilute aqueous solutions of several potassium salts at various molalities are as follows.

Molality	0.10	0.05	0.01	0.005	0.001	0.0005
Freezing point depression for						
Potassium nitrate, KNO_3	0.3331	0.1719	0.03587	......	......	......
Potassium sulfate, K_2SO_4	0.4319	0.2280	0.05010	0.02575	0.00528	......
Potassium ferricyanide, $K_3Fe(CN)_6$	0.5370	0.2800	0.0626	0.03265	0.00710	0.00365

Calculate the mole number, i, for each electrolyte at each concentration. Indicate the probable limiting value for i for each electrolyte. What generalizations could you formulate on the basis of these data?

2. (a) One coulomb of electricity will deposit exactly 0.58247 mg. of cadmium from a solution of cadmium sulfate, $CdSO_4$. Calculate the number of coulombs required to deposit one gram-equivalent of cadmium from such a solution. What name is given to this latter quantity of electricity? (b) What total number of electrons must be added to cadmium ions in order that one gram-equivalent of cadmium may be deposited?

3. How many electrons pass, in 0.001 sec., through a given cross section of a wire carrying a current of 0.1 milliampere?

4. A certain quantity of electricity is passed through four separate solutions, (1) zinc sulfate, (2) silver nitrate, (3) cobalt chloride, $CoCl_2$, and (4) chromic iodide, CrI_3, all connected in series. If 0.9807 g. of zinc is liberated in the first solution, what weights of silver and of cobalt are deposited at the cathodes in the second and third, and what weights of chromium and of iodine are simultaneously formed at the two electrodes in the fourth? How many coulombs of electricity are involved? How many faradays? How many electrons?

5. A current of 0.01 amp. is passed through water, containing just enough sodium hydroxide to make it a sufficiently good conductor, for 19 hr. and 18 min. What volumes (at S.T.P.) of hydrogen and oxygen are liberated at the electrodes?

6. How do you account for the fact that the freezing point depression of a 0.1 M solution of potassium chloride is just about the same as that of a solution of nitric acid, twice that of a solution of sugar, and almost twice that of a solution of acetic acid, all at the same molality?

7. The conductance of a 1 cm. cube of a 0.05 M solution of cupric sulfate is 0.00505 reciprocal ohm, and that of a 0.50 M solution is 0.0093. What is the ratio of the total numbers of ions (cupric and sulfate) in the two solutions? How do you account for the fact that this is not also the ratio of the specific conductances (i.e., conductances of 1 cm. cubes) of the two solutions?

8. Solid sodium chloride is made up of sodium and chloride ions, only. Hydrogen chloride is known to be a covalent compound, yet in aqueous solution it is as strong an electrolyte as sodium chloride. How may this fact be explained?

9. Aqueous solutions of sodium hydroxide and of ammonia have one set of properties in common. To what ion are these properties attributed? How does the process which accounts for the presence of this ion differ in the two cases?

10. Write an equation, in terms of the Bronsted concept, for each of the following protolytic reactions; indicate, for each case, conjugate acid-base pairs, and state which of the two acids and which of the two bases is the stronger. In each case except (k), state whether the resulting solution would show an acidic, a neutral, or an alkaline reaction toward litmus.

(a) Ionization of nitric acid in water
(b) Ionization of ammonia in water
(c) Neutralization of a strong acid by a strong base in water solution
(d) Neutralization of acetic acid by sodium hydroxide in water solution
(e) Reaction of a solution of a strong acid with a solution of an acetate to produce acetic acid
(f) Reaction of a solution of a strong base with a solution of an ammonium salt to produce ammonia
(g) Ionization of the weak acid hydrogen cyanide, HCN
(h) Hydrolysis of an ammonium salt
(i) Hydrolysis of an aluminum salt
(j) Hydrolysis of a cyanide
(k) Reaction of an ammonium salt with an amide in liquid ammonia solution.

11. An aqueous solution of ammonium acetate gives a neutral reaction toward litmus, whereas one of ammonium cyanide gives an alkaline reaction. Explain.

12. In each of the following cases, predict which acid of the pair would be the stronger:
(a) Carbonic acid or nitric acid
(b) Sulfuric acid or selenic acid, H_2SeO_4
(c) Sulfurous acid or sulfuric acid
(d) Hydrogen sulfide or hydrogen chloride
(e) Sulfuric acid or bisulfate ion.

13. In each of the following cases, predict which base of the pair would be the stronger:
(a) Silicate ion, SiO_3^{--}, or sulfate ion, SO_4^{--}
(b) Perchlorate ion, ClO_4^-, or chlorate ion, ClO_3^-
(c) Nitrite ion, NO_2^-, or nitrate ion, NO_3^-
$$\qquad\qquad\qquad\qquad H \qquad\qquad\qquad\qquad\qquad H$$
(d) Methide ion, $HC:^-$, or amide ion, $HN:^-$
$$\qquad\qquad\qquad\qquad H \qquad\qquad\qquad\qquad\qquad ..$$
(e) Bicarbonate ion or carbonate ion.

14. How might Faraday, without assuming that electrolytes in water solution always exist in the form of ions, have accounted for the phenomenon of electrolysis?

15. List several properties of each of the following substances: (a) H_2, H_3O^+; (b) Cu, Cu^{++}; (c) Cl_2, Cl^-; (d) Na, Na^+.

16. Many Lewis acids, such as sulfur trioxide and sulfur dioxide, are also acid anhydrides (p. 203). Can you explain on a structural basis why this is often the case?

18

Equilibria Involving Ions in Solution

1. Introduction. In the preceding chapter we learned that solutions of strong electrolytes are essentially completely ionized in dilute aqueous solution, but that in solutions of weak electrolytes there exists an equilibrium between the ions of the electrolyte and un-ionized molecules. In this chapter we shall be concerned with a consideration of some of the quantitative aspects of these equilibria.

2. Weak Electrolytes. In a 0.01 molar solution, the equivalent conductance, Λ, of a strong electrolyte of the type of sodium chloride, whose ions are both singly charged (a so-called 1-1 electrolyte) is usually in the neighborhood of 94% of the limiting value, Λ_0, of the equivalent conductance of the same salt at zero concentration or infinite dilution. In marked contrast to this fact, the equivalent conductance of the common weak acid acetic acid, even in a solution as dilute as 0.01 molar, is only 4.2% of the limiting value to be expected for an infinitely dilute solution of this electrolyte. In a 0.1 molar solution, the equivalent conductance of an electrolyte like sodium chloride is about 85% of the limiting value, while for acetic acid it has fallen to 1.3% of Λ_0. These relationships are shown graphically in Figure 18.1, in which the conductance ratio $\Lambda : \Lambda_0$ is plotted against the square root of the concentration.

We learned in the previous chapter that the small decrease in equivalent conductance with increasing concentration in the case of sodium chloride and other strong electrolytes results from the decrease in mobility of the ions brought about by interionic attraction. However, in the case of weak electrolytes such as acetic acid we cannot but conclude that this factor is too small to account for the very large effect of concentration on equivalent conductance; and that the explanation lies in the increase in degree of ionization with decrease in concentration. Because of the small concentration of ions, in the latter instance, the effects of interionic attraction are very small.

A fairly sharp line may be drawn between strong and weak electrolytes. All ionic or electrovalent compounds are strong electrolytes in aqueous solution, as are a comparatively small number of covalent compounds that undergo practically complete protolysis with water; this second group comprises the strong acids, of which the most important are hydrochloric, hydrobromic, hydriodic, perchloric, nitric, and sulfuric. All the rest of the rather large

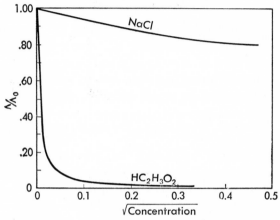

Fig. 18.1.   Variation of equivalent conductance with concentration.

number of electrolytes which contain covalent bonds only belong to the class of weak electrolytes. This class of electrolytes may again be divided into two groups: one (by far the larger) consists of the weak acids, such as phosphoric, sulfurous, nitrous, acetic, carbonic, and silicic; the other consists of the weak bases, of which ammonia (ammonium hydroxide) is the most important, at least to the inorganic chemist.

3. Equilibrium in the Ionization of Weak Electrolytes; the Ionization Constant. According to the theory of Arrhenius, the ionization of a weak electrolyte AB might be regarded as consisting of the reversible reaction

$$AB \rightleftharpoons A^+ + B^-$$

in which equilibrium is reached, as soon as the electrolyte is dissolved in water, between undissociated AB on the one hand and A^+ and B^- ions on the other. According to the principles of chemical equilibrium which were developed in Chapter 16, the following relationship among the concentrations of the several substances present at equilibrium should be valid:

$$\frac{[A^+][B^-]}{[AB]} = K$$

The equilibrium constant in such a reaction has been characterized by the special designation of *dissociation constant*, or *ionization constant*.

Let us now consider the incomplete ionization of a weak acid from this point of view, selecting acetic acid, the familiar acid of vinegar, as a typical example. If we choose to formulate the ionization in terms of the Arrhenius theory, we may write as the equation for this reaction

$$HC_2H_3O_2 \rightleftharpoons H^+ + C_2H_3O_2^- \qquad (1)$$

It must be remembered, however, that the symbol H^+ in such an equation as this is to be regarded as representing not simple hydrogen ion—a substance which is not present in aqueous solutions in appreciable concentration (p. 311)—but rather hydrated hydrogen ion, or hydronium ion. Applying the law of chemical equilibrium to this equation, we have

$$\frac{[H^+][C_2H_3O_2^-]}{[HC_2H_3O_2]} = K \qquad (2)$$

where $[H^+]$ and $[C_2H_3O_2^-]$ represent the concentrations of the ions, and $[HC_2H_3O_2]$ is that of the un-ionized compound; K is the ionization constant of acetic acid, the numerical value of which, if the law is valid, should be independent of concentration, although not of temperature.

As was pointed out in the preceding chapter, we have every reason to believe that the reaction that occurs when an acid is dissolved in water is not so simple as has just been indicated, and that in the case of acetic acid the ionization is more accurately represented by the equation

$$HC_2H_3O_2 + H_2O \rightleftharpoons H_3O^+ + C_2H_3O_2^- \qquad (3)$$

In order to account for the very low equivalent conductance of even rather dilute solutions of acetic acid, we must suppose that, unlike the reaction of a strong acid such as hydrochloric with water, the ionization of acetic acid proceeds to but a small extent before equilibrium is reached.

At first thought, it might seem that the equilibrium constant of the ioniza-tion reaction as formulated in the preceding paragraph would be quite different from that of equation (2). This point requires further scrutiny. For the reaction with water, we may write

$$\frac{[H_3O^+][C_2H_3O_2^-]}{[HC_2H_3O_2][H_2O]} = K' \qquad (4)$$

This equation may be somewhat simplified, however, in view of the fact that except at very high concentrations of solute, the concentration of water in aqueous solutions is so large relative to the concentrations of other substances present, and varies so little, that it may without appreciable error be regarded as remaining constant and equal to its concentration in the pure liquid; in other words, the value of $[H_2O]$ in dilute aqueous solutions is almost constant at about 55.5 moles per liter. Following a general custom, then, we may multiply both sides of equation (4) by the constant factor $[H_2O]$; the equation then becomes

$$\frac{[H_3O^+][C_2H_3O_2^-]}{[HC_2H_3O_2]} = K' \times [H_2O] = K \tag{5}$$

Furthermore, a little consideration will make it clear that the factor $[H_3O]^+$ in equation (5) has the same numerical value as $[H^+]$ in equation (2), since each of them represents the concentration of hydrated hydrogen ion (hydronium ion) in the solution. Hence the K of equation (5) is actually identical with that of equation (2), and may appropriately be designated the ionization constant of acetic acid. In fact, from the modern point of view, equations (1) and (2) are to be regarded merely as conventionally simplified forms of equations (3) and (5), respectively. Since the simpler equations lead to the same quantitative conclusions as the more rigorous ones, we shall not hesitate to use the abbreviated forms whenever it is convenient to do so.

For an example of the incomplete ionization of a weak base, our best choice will be the alkaline solution commonly referred to as ammonium hydroxide, which is obtained when ammonia dissolves in water. Applying the law of chemical equilibrium to the equation represented by the reaction

$$NH_3 + H_2O \rightleftharpoons NH_4^+ + OH^-$$

we have

$$\frac{[NH_4^+][OH^-]}{[NH_3][H_2O]} = K'$$

where $[NH_3]$ represents the concentration of ammonia which has not undergone ionization by reaction with water. Multiplication of both sides of this equation by the constant factor $[H_2O]$ gives, for the ionization constant of ammonia (or of ammonium hydroxide, p. 492),

$$\frac{[NH_4^+][OH^-]}{[NH_3]} = K' \times [H_2O] = K$$

4. Determination of the Degree of Ionization of a Weak Electrolyte. Each weak electrolyte has its own characteristic ionization constant; once this constant is known, the concentrations of the ions, and the degree of ionization of the electrolyte, at any given total concentration, may readily be calculated. Conversely, the determination of the value of the ionization constant of an electrolyte requires a knowledge of its degree of ionization at one concentration at least, and preferably at several, in order that the validity of the law of chemical equilibrium, as applied to the electrolyte in question, may be checked. It will, therefore, be necessary for us to consider how the degree of ionization (often represented by the symbol α, and usually expressed as a percentage) may be determined.

For a dilute solution of a weak electrolyte, the degree of ionization may be determined with a fair degree of accuracy from two entirely different kinds of data; namely, (1) equivalent conductances, and (2) mole numbers as determined from measurements of freezing point or other colligative properties. We shall consider each of these sources of information in some detail.

1. We have already seen (p. 328) that in *dilute* solutions of a *weak* electrolyte the falling off in equivalent conductance (as the concentration increases) from the limiting or maximum value which is characteristic of extremely dilute solutions may be attributed almost solely to a decrease in the number of ions. Thus, if at some particular concentration of electrolyte the equivalent conductance is one-fourth as great as the limiting value, we may conclude that only one-fourth of the electrolyte in the solution is in the form of ions, or that the degree of ionization, α, is 25%. Or, in general, for dilute solutions of weak electrolytes, the degree of ionization may be calculated from the simple formula

$$\alpha = \frac{\Lambda}{\Lambda_0}$$

As an example of the application of this formula, we may consider the calculation of the degree of ionization of the base ammonia in a dilute solution from the following data. The equivalent conductance of ammonium hydroxide in 0.01 molar solution at 25° C. is 11.3 reciprocal ohms; the limiting equivalent conductance of this electrolyte at the same temperature is 271.4 reciprocal ohms. For the degree of ionization we have, then,

$$\alpha = \frac{11.3}{271} = \frac{\Lambda}{\Lambda_0} = 0.0417, \text{ or } 4.17\%$$

2. We have also seen that, in the case of dilute solutions of weak electrolytes, variations in mole number (i) as determined from the colligative properties of the solution result almost entirely from change in the degree of ionization. Hence in such a solution the freezing point depression, for instance, depends not upon the molality alone, but rather upon the total number of moles of all the solutes present, both ions and un-ionized substance, per 1000 g. of water—i.e., upon the product of the original molality of the electrolyte and its mole number. This point will be clarified by a tabulation

of the number of moles of each variety of molecular or ionic substance that results from the incomplete ionization of each mole of acetic acid when the degree of ionization is α; i.e., when the fraction α of each mole of the acid is ionized.

Solute	Number of moles
H^+ (or H_3O^+)	α
$C_2H_3O_2^-$	α
Un-ionized $HC_2H_3O_2$	$1 - \alpha$
Total mole number, i	$1 + \alpha$

Hence the total number of moles of all solutes, per 1000 g. of water, is $(1 + \alpha)$ times the molality.

For the freezing point depression of a dilute solution of acetic acid, then, we may write (p. 291)

$$\Delta T_f = i \times \text{molality} \times 1.86 = (1 + \alpha) \times \text{molality} \times 1.86$$

From this relationship, the following equations may be derived:

$$1 + \alpha = \frac{\Delta T_f}{\text{molality} \times 1.86}$$

$$\alpha = \frac{\Delta T_f}{\text{molality} \times 1.86} - 1$$

As an illustration of the application of this method, let us calculate the degree of ionization of formic acid, $HCHO_2$, from the fact that the freezing point of a solution of 0.690 g. of formic acid in 50.0 g. of water is $-0.569°$ C. Such a solution would contain, per 1000 g. of water, $1000/50.0 \times 0.690 = 13.8$ g. of formic acid, and its molality, therefore, is $13.8/46.0 = 0.300$. Substituting these data in the equation for α, we have

$$\alpha = \frac{0.569}{0.300 \times 1.86} - 1 = 1.02 - 1 = 0.02$$

Hence, formic acid is about 2% ionized at this concentration.

In general, the values calculated for the degree of ionization of a weak electrolyte in a given dilute solution by methods (1) and (2) are substantially the same. This fact tends to confirm our confidence in the validity of the Arrhenius theory for electrolytes of this type.

5. The Ostwald Dilution Law. When the degree of ionization, α, of the electrolyte AB at a given concentration, c, is known, the ionization constant may be calculated as follows. The ionization of each mole of AB yields 1 mole each of A^+ ion and B^- ion; since the number of moles per liter that are ionized is αc, the concentrations of A^+ ion and B^- ion are each αc, while the concentration of un-ionized AB is $(1 - \alpha)c$. Introducing these values into the equation which expresses the law of chemical equilibrium, we have

$$\frac{\alpha c \times \alpha c}{(1 - \alpha)c} = K$$

or

$$\frac{\alpha^2 c}{1 - \alpha} = K$$

This equation, which was first derived by Wilhelm Ostwald, is a mathematical expression of what is known as Ostwald's dilution law. The relationship among the quantities α, c, and K is such that if K is to remain constant, the value of α must increase with decrease in the value of c, approaching a limit of 1 as c approaches 0, i.e., at infinite dilution.

The degrees of ionization at 25° C. of acetic acid at various concentrations (as indicated by the conductance ratios) and the corresponding values of K (as calculated from the dilution law) are shown in Table 18.1.

Table 18.1

Ionization of Acetic Acid

c (moles per liter)	α (as percentage)	K
0.000028	53.85	1.76×10^{-5}
0.000218	24.70	1.77
0.00103	12.32	1.78
0.00591	5.37	1.80
0.0200	2.96	1.81
0.1000	1.33	1.79
0.2308	0.87	1.75

Here the concentration increases nearly 10,000 fold from the top of the table to the bottom, and the degree of ionization in the most concentrated solution is less than one-sixtieth as great as in the most dilute; yet throughout this wide range, none of the values calculated for the ionization constant differs from the mean value of 1.78×10^{-5} by as much as 2%. Results for other weak electrolytes provide similar confirmation of the validity of the dilution law.

It is evident from the form of the Ostwald equation that the smaller the value of K for a particular electrolyte, the smaller will be the degree of ionization at a given concentration. Hence, the magnitude of the ionization constant is a convenient criterion for the strength of an electrolyte; the smaller the value of K, the weaker the electrolyte.

The calculation of the degree of ionization of an electrolyte of known ionization constant may be illustrated for a 0.1 molar solution of acetic acid. For the reaction

$$HC_2H_3O_2 \rightleftharpoons H^+ + C_2H_3O_2^-$$

we have just found the value of K to be 1.78×10^{-5}. Hence, from the dilution law we have

$$\frac{\alpha^2 \times 0.1}{1 - \alpha} = 1.78 \times 10^{-5}$$

This equation may readily be transposed to the form

$$0.1\alpha^2 + 0.0000178\alpha - 0.0000178 = 0$$

or

$$\alpha^2 + 0.000178\alpha - 0.000178 = 0$$

and from the last equation we find that $\alpha = 0.0133$, or 1.33%.

6. Limitations to the Dilution Law. In the preceding chapter, we discussed the deviation from the simple laws of the dilute solution that is brought about in solutions of electrolytes by interionic attraction. Neither is the law of chemical equilibrium strictly applicable, it must now be recalled (p. 260), unless the particles of the reacting substances exert no appreciable attractive or repulsive forces upon each other; otherwise, correction factors (activity coefficients) must be applied to the concentrations. Whenever appreciable concentrations of ions are present in a solution, the activity coefficients of the ionic substances, in particular, will depart from unity to a considerable extent. Hence, it is only in dilute solutions of weak electrolytes, where the concentrations of the ions are very small, that the law of chemical equilibrium in its simple unmodified form may be applied. From the data of Table 18.1, for example, it may be observed that in no instance does the concentration of either of the ions exceed 0.002 mole per liter. Although it is only under such restricted conditions that the dilution law is quantitatively applicable, yet the original Arrhenius theory gives a satisfactory qualitative account of the behavior of weak electrolytes in general.

7. Reaction between the Ions of Weak Electrolytes. In addition to our definition of a weak electrolyte as one which has but a slight tendency to ionize, or one whose degree of ionization at moderate concentrations is small, there is also another viewpoint from which the behavior of weak electrolytes must be considered in order that our picture of the difference between weak electrolytes and strong ones may be completed. We have found (p. 353) that for a 0.1 molar solution of acetic acid, $\alpha = 1.33\%$. This means that when equilibrium is reached in such a solution, regardless of whether we start with undissociated acetic acid or with equivalent quantities of hydrogen and acetate ions, only 1.33% of the total acetic acid present will be in the form of ions, while 98.67% will be in the form of acetic acid molecules.

We may conclude, then, that the ions of a weak electrolyte, whatever may have been their source, have a strong tendency to react with each other. Our definition of a weak electrolyte might, in fact, have been based upon this property of its ions; a weak electrolyte is one whose ions, in dilute aqueous solution, for the most part react with each other to form molecules. This concept of a weak electrolyte leads immediately to an important principle: namely, that *a metathetic reaction between two electrolytes will take place whenever one of the possible products is a weak electrolyte.*

As an example of the type of reaction just mentioned, we may consider the behavior of a mixture of hydrochloric acid and sodium acetate in dilute solution. In such a solution, the presence of acetic acid may be detected by means of its characteristic vinegar-like odor; we know, therefore, that the following reaction has taken place:

$$H_3O^+ + Cl^- + Na^+ + C_2H_3O_2^- = HC_2H_3O_2 + H_2O + Na^+ + Cl^-$$

When the equation is thus written in the ionic form, it becomes evident that although the sodium and chloride ions are present in the solution throughout the reaction, they do not participate in it; the actual reactants are hydronium and acetate ions, which react to form acetic acid and water. Hence the equation may be more accurately as well as more concisely written

$$H_3O^+ + C_2H_3O_2^- = HC_2H_3O_2 + H_2O$$

or, in abbreviated form (p. 331),

$$H^+ + C_2H_3O_2^- = HC_2H_3O_2$$

This reaction, it is true, does not go quite to completion in the direction indicated (i.e., toward the formation of acetic acid); but the value of the equilibrium constant

$$K = \frac{[HC_2H_3O_2]}{[H^+][C_2H_3O_2^-]}$$

(which, it will be recognized, is the reciprocal of the ionization constant of acetic acid) is so high—about 56,000—that only very small concentrations of hydrogen ion and acetate ion remain in the solution when equilibrium has been attained.

A far more important instance of this type of reaction in which a weak electrolyte is formed from its ions is the special case known as neutralization, which has already been described (p. 319), but which will presently be reconsidered from the viewpoint developed in this chapter.

8. The Common Ion Effect. Before we leave the ionization of acetic acid, it will be instructive to inquire into the effect on the ionization of adding another electrolyte which yields one of the same ions as acetic acid itself. Let us return to the consideration of a 0.1 molar solution of acetic acid, in which, as has been shown, the degree of ionization is 1.33% (p. 335). The concentration of hydrogen ion in such a solution is $0.1 \times 0.0133 = 0.00133$ mole per liter. Experimentally, despite the low value of the hydrogen ion concentration, such a solution has a decidedly acid taste and changes the color of blue litmus to a distinct pink. If a sufficient quantity of solid sodium acetate is added, however, the solution loses its sour taste almost entirely, and changes the color of either blue or red litmus to a pinkish violet; in other words, the acidity is so greatly reduced that the solution is almost neutral.

A qualitative explanation of this phenomenon may readily be found by application of Le Chatelier's principle to the equilibrium expressed by the simplified equation

$$HC_2H_3O_2 \rightleftharpoons H^+ + C_2H_3O_2^-$$

In the solution of acetic acid alone, the concentrations of hydrogen and of acetate ions are small and equal; the acidity, which is due to the presence of hydrogen ion, is small but readily detectable. Since sodium acetate is a strong electrolyte, the addition of this substance to the solution enormously increases the concentration of acetate ion. Hence, the equilibrium is displaced toward the left (p. 265), with the formation of a little additional undissociated acetic acid and a marked decrease in the concentration of hydrogen ion and hence in the acidity. It should be emphasized that the *total* amount of acetic acid in the solution remains unchanged. But, in the presence of a huge excess of acetate ions, the competition, so to speak, for the few free hydrogen ions available becomes much keener. Hence, a large fraction of them disappear (by reacting with acetate ions), leaving the solution almost neutral. This effect of sodium acetate (or, of course, of any other readily soluble ionic acetate) upon the acidity of acetic acid might also be treated quantitatively with the aid of the ionization constant previously determined (p. 334).

The concentration of hydrogen ion from any weak acid is thus decreased upon the addition of a salt of that acid to the solution. Indeed, we may draw the even more general conclusion that in a solution of *any* weak electrolyte AB, the concentration of A^+ ion is decreased by the addition of a strong electrolyte which supplies B^- ion, whereas the concentration of B^- ion is decreased by the addition of a strong electrolyte containing A^+ ion. As an example of this latter case, the concentration of hydroxide ion in an ammonium hydroxide solution is greatly diminished upon the addition of solid ammonium chloride, or of a concentrated ammonium chloride solution. The general phenomenon is known as repression of the ionization of the weak electrolyte, or, more concisely, as the *common ion effect*.

9. Polyprotic Acids. Acids which in their ionization yield only one hydrogen ion, or hydrated proton, per molecule of acid, are known as *monoprotic* acids; thus, hydrochloric, hydrobromic, nitric, and acetic acids are all monoprotic. Carbonic acid, H_2CO_3, sulfurous acid, H_2SO_3, and sulfuric acid, H_2SO_4, each of which is able to furnish two protons per molecule, are diprotic acids; phosphoric acid, H_3PO_4, is triprotic. In general, acids which yield more than one proton per molecule are called *polyprotic* acids.

The ionization of polyprotic acids always proceeds in a stepwise manner, and, for a given acid, each step takes place to a lesser extent than the preceding one. Thus, there is no known diprotic acid which is strong with respect to both steps in its ionization. In the case of sulfuric acid, although the first step

$$H_2SO_4 = H^+ + HSO_4^-$$

proceeds practically to completion in moderately dilute solutions, equilibrium is reached in the second step

$$HSO_4^- \rightleftharpoons H^+ + SO_4^{--}$$

when only a relatively small fraction of the HSO_4^- ion, which is known as the hydrogen sulfate or the bisulfate ion, has been further ionized. In other words, bisulfate ion behaves like a weak acid, with an ionization constant of about 1×10^{-2}:

$$\frac{[H^+][SO_4^{--}]}{[HSO_4^-]} = K = 1 \times 10^{-2}$$

In the case of a weak diprotic acid, there is an equilibrium constant corresponding to each step in the ionization; these constants, which are known as the first and second ionization constants, are usually designated by K_1 and K_2, respectively. The value of the second ionization constant is always considerably smaller than that of the first. Thus, in the case of oxalic acid, $H_2C_2O_4$, we have

$$H_2C_2O_4 \rightleftharpoons H^+ + HC_2O_4^-$$

$$\frac{[\mathrm{H^+}][\mathrm{HC_2O_4^-}]}{[\mathrm{H_2C_2O_4}]} = K_1 = 3.8 \times 10^{-2}$$

$$\mathrm{HC_2O_4^-} \rightleftharpoons \mathrm{H^+} + \mathrm{C_2O_4^{--}}$$

$$\frac{[\mathrm{H^+}][\mathrm{C_2O_4^{--}}]}{[\mathrm{HC_2O_4^-}]} = K_2 = 4.9 \times 10^{-5}$$

This marked difference between the values of the two ionization constants is undoubtedly at least partly attributable to the fact that the doubly charged oxalate ion, $C_2O_4^{--}$, exerts a greater attractive force on a proton than does the singly charged hydrogen oxalate ion, $HC_2O_4^-$. Another factor which tends to repress the second step in the ionization of a diprotic acid—although it does not affect the equilibrium constant—is the common ion effect of the hydrogen ion from the first step.

Diprotic acids form two series of salts, corresponding to the two stages in their ionization. When one hydrogen atom per molecule of the acid has been replaced by a metal we have an *acid salt*; when both have been replaced, a *normal salt*. Thus, for example, by the reaction of sodium hydroxide upon sulfuric acid we may obtain either the acid salt $NaHSO_4$, called sodium hydrogen sulfate or sodium bisulfate, or the normal salt Na_2SO_4, sodium sulfate.

10. Water as an Electrolyte. Up to this point we have thought of water as a solvent and an ionizing medium for electrolytes, rather than as an electrolyte itself; and, indeed, the electrical conductance of pure water is exceedingly low. The fact that it does exhibit a measurable conductance, however, is best accounted for by the hypothesis that water is ionized to a very slight extent. Furthermore, as will be shown presently, many chemical reactions in which water takes part are most readily accounted for in terms of a small degree of ionization into hydrogen and hydroxide ions, according to the equation

$$\mathrm{H_2O} \rightleftharpoons \mathrm{H^+} + \mathrm{OH^-} \tag{6}$$

Just as in the case of the ionization of acids (p. 311), this ionization would be more accurately represented by the equation

$$\mathrm{H_2O} + \mathrm{H_2O} \rightleftharpoons \mathrm{H_3O^+} + \mathrm{OH^-} \tag{7}$$

In fact, equation (6) may conveniently be regarded as merely an abbreviated form of equation (7) (cf. p. 331). At 25° C., equilibrium in the ionization of water is reached when only about $1.8 \times 10^{-7}\%$ of the water is ionized; or, to put it another way, when there is only one mole each of hydrogen and hydroxide ion in 10,000,000 l. of water, so that $[H^+] =$ $[OH^-] = 0.0000001$, or 1×10^{-7}, mole per liter. For the ionization constant of water, we may write

$$\frac{[H^+][OH^-]}{[H_2O]} = K \tag{8}$$

Since the value of $[H_2O]$ remains practically constant at 55.5 moles per liter (p. 331), we have for the magnitude of this ionization constant

$$K = \frac{(1 \times 10^{-7}) \times (1 \times 10^{-7})}{55.5} = 1.8 \times 10^{-16} \tag{9}$$

If both sides of equation (8) are multiplied by the constant factor $[H_2O]$, we get

$$[H^+][OH^-] = K \times [H_2O] \tag{10}$$

in which the product, $K \times [H_2O]$, must still be a constant. In fact, this constant of equation (10) is more convenient to use than that of equation (8); it is known as the *ion product of water*, and is usually represented by the symbol K_w, so that equation (8) may be shortened to

$$[H^+][OH^-] = K_w \tag{11}$$

The value of the ion product of water at 25° C. is readily found from equations (9) and (10) to be 1×10^{-14}. With increasing temperature, the value of K_w is somewhat increased.

In any moderately dilute aqueous solution at ordinary temperatures, then, the product of the concentrations of hydrogen and hydroxide ions is 1×10^{-14}. In pure water, the concentrations of these two ions must be equal to each other; in this case

$$[H^+] = [OH^-] = \sqrt{1 \times 10^{-14}} = 1 \times 10^{-7} \text{ mole per liter}$$

However, the concentrations of the two ions do not remain equal when an acid or base is dissolved in water. When an acid is added, the concentration of hydrogen ion increases, and, since the product must remain constant, the concentration of hydroxide ion must decrease; when a base is added to water, the opposite changes take place. An aqueous solution in which the concentration of hydrogen ion is greater than 1×10^{-7}, or greater than that of hydroxide ion, is said to be acidic. An alkaline solution, on the other hand, is one in which the concentration of hydroxide ion is greater than 1×10^{-7}, or greater than that of hydrogen ion. If the concentrations of hydrogen and hydroxide ions are equal, the solution is said to be neutral. Many salt solutions, as well as pure water, are neutral.

11. The pH Scale. The chemist is frequently concerned with nearly neutral solutions in which even minute changes in the concentrations of hydrogen and hydroxide ions may have significant consequences. This situation is of especially common occurrence in the fields of analytical chemistry and of bio-chemistry; the maintenance of a constant concentration of hydrogen ion in the blood, for instance, is absolutely essential to health. The accurate representation of very small concentrations of hydrogen ion in the ordinary decimal notation, or even as multiples of 10 with a negative exponent, is, under some circumstances, inconvenient. On this account, it has become a common practice to express such concentrations by means of a different system of notation, originally devised by biochemists, known as the pH scale. The pH value of a solution, or simply its pH, is defined as the logarithm of the reciprocal of the concentration (in moles per liter) of hydrogen ion which it contains. A mathematically equivalent definition is the negative logarithm of the hydrogen ion concentration; thus

$$pH = \log \frac{1}{[H^+]} = -\log [H^+]$$

From the definition just given, it is evident that the process of finding the pH of a solution of known hydrogen ion concentration consists merely in determining the logarithm of this concentration and changing its sign. Thus, for pure water or a neutral solution, in which the concentration of hydrogen ion is 1×10^{-7} mole per liter, we have

$$\log[H^+] = \log(1 \times 10^{-7}) = -7$$
$$pH = 7$$

If the concentration is originally given in decimal form, it is convenient first to express it as a multiple of an integral power of 10. In 0.0001 molar hydrochloric acid, for example, the concentration of hydrogen ion may be expressed as 1×10^{-4} mole per liter; hence

$$\log[H^+] = \log(1 \times 10^{-4}) = -4$$
$$pH = 4$$

When the hydrogen ion concentration cannot be expressed as 1 multiplied by a positive or negative integral power of 10, it becomes necessary to refer to a table of logarithms in order to determine the pH value; thus for a solution containing 0.04 mole of hydrogen ion per liter we find

$$\log[H^+] = \log(4 \times 10^{-2}) = \log 4 + \log 10^{-2}$$
$$= 0.6 - 2.0 \qquad = -1.4$$
$$pH = 1.4$$

Determination of the concentration of hydrogen ion can rarely be carried out with sufficient precision to warrant the use of more than one, or at most two, decimal places in the pH value.

Table 18.2

	$[H^+]$	$\log [H^+]$	pH	$\log [OH^-]$	$[OH^-]$
Increasingly acid solutions	$10 = 10^1$	1	−1	−15	1×10^{-15}
	$1 = 10^0$	0	0	−14	1×10^{-14}
	$0.1 = 10^{-1}$	− 1	1	−13	1×10^{-13}
	$0.00001 = 10^{-5}$	− 5	5	− 9	1×10^{-9}
Neutral Solutions	$0.0000001 = 10^{-7}$	− 7	7	− 7	$10^{-7} = 0.0000001$
Increasingly alkaline solutions	1×10^{-9}	− 9	9	− 5	$10^{-5} = 0.00001$
	1×10^{-13}	−13	13	− 1	$10^{-1} = 0.1$
	1×10^{-14}	−14	14	0	$10^0 = 1$
	1×10^{-15}	−15	15	1	$10^1 = 10$

Since the product of the concentrations of hydrogen and hydroxide ions in an aqueous solution at room temperature must always be 1×10^{-14}, the pH may also be calculated from the concentration of hydroxide ion, or vice versa. Thus, for example, in 0.1 molar sodium hydroxide solution

$$[H^+](0.1) = 1 \times 10^{-14}$$

$$[H^+] = \frac{1 \times 10^{-14}}{1 \times 10^{-1}} = 1 \times 10^{-13}$$

$$pH = 13$$

In a solution whose pH is 10.7, we have

$$-\log[H^+] = 10.7$$
$$\log[H^+] = -10.7 = 0.3 - 11$$
$$[H^+] = 2 \times 10^{-11}$$

The hydroxide ion concentration in this solution may now readily be found:

$$(2 \times 10^{-11})[OH^-] = 1 \times 10^{-14}$$

$$[OH^-] = \frac{1 \times 10^{-14}}{2 \times 10^{-11}} = \frac{10 \times 10^{-15}}{2 \times 10^{-11}} = 5 \times 10^{-4}$$

$$[OH^-] = 0.0005 \text{ mole per liter}$$

The relation between the hydroxide ion concentration of a solution and its pH may also be expressed in the following simple manner.

Since
$$[H^+][OH^-] = 1 \times 10^{-14}$$
$$\log[H^+] + \log[OH^-] = -14$$

Or
$$-pH + \log[OH^-] = -14$$

Hence
$$\log[OH^-] = pH - 14$$

It is apparent that in an acid solution, the pH is always less than 7; in an alkaline solution, it is greater than 7.

The relationships between pH, the concentrations of hydrogen and of hydroxide ion, and the acidity or alkalinity of the solution are brought out in Table 18.2.

12. Indicators. The accurate determination of the pH value of a solution involves the measurement of the potential of a hydrogen electrode (p. 424) in the solution, and is attended by considerable difficulties, both experimental and theoretical, which cannot be considered here. However, the approximate pH may be determined simply and rapidly by the use of substances known as *indicators*, the colors of which, in solution, change with the hydrogen ion concentration. The particular pH range over which a visible color change occurs may vary considerably from one indicator to another.

Three of the most commonly used indicators are methyl orange, litmus, and phenolphthalein, the characteristics of which are listed in Table 18.3. Extensive tables showing the pH ranges of many other indicators may be found in textbooks of analytical chemistry. The following examples will suffice to suggest that, by means of a series of selected indicators, the pH value of a solution may be determined with a fair degree of accuracy.

Table 18.3

Indicator	Acid Color	pH Range in which Change Occurs	Alkaline Color
Methyl orange	red	3–4.5	yellow
Litmus	red	6–8	blue
Phenolphthalein	colorless	8–10	red

13. Neutralization. We are now ready for a somewhat more detailed and quantitative discussion than was previously possible, of the familiar reaction between an acid and a base. Let us consider first what happens when hydrochloric acid and sodium hydroxide are brought together in the same solution. Since both of these substances are strong electrolytes, we have in the solution, momentarily at least, the four ions Na^+, OH^-, H_3O^+, and Cl^-. Now, there is no reason why the sodium and chloride ions, as the ions of a strong electrolyte, should have any tendency to combine with each other; hence, these ions do not combine, but remain in the solution unchanged. The hydronium and hydroxide ions, however, as the ions of the exceedingly weak electrolyte water, do have a very great tendency to react with each other (p. 336). From a quantitative point of view, the product of the concentrations of these ions cannot permanently exceed 1×10^{-14}; if the ions are brought together at concentrations whose product is larger than this figure, they must react to form water until only very small ionic concentrations remain. Hence, the neutralization reaction which, if we represent the hydronium ion by the simplified formula H^+, may be represented by the equation

$$Na^+ + OH^- + H^+ + Cl^- = HOH + Na^+ + Cl^-$$

must proceed practically to completion toward the right. The same state of affairs prevails, of course, when any other strong acid and strong base are brought together in solution. Thus, for example, for the reaction between barium hydroxide and nitric acid, we may write the equation

$$Ba^{++} + 2OH^- + 2H^+ + 2NO_3^- = 2HOH + Ba^{++} + 2NO_3^-$$

These neutralizations obviously consist merely in the reaction of hydrogen and hydroxide ions to form water. A single simple equation, indeed, suffices to represent the neutralization of any strong acid by any strong base:

$$H^+ + OH^- = H_2O$$

Neutralization, then, consists in the reaction of hydrogen ion and hydroxide ion to form water. It does not, strictly speaking, include the formation of a salt, since the ions of the salt are present throughout the reaction and do not combine with each other unless the solution is evaporated to the point of saturation, when they no longer have any alternative.

Strong evidence for the validity of the simple view of neutralization presented in the preceding paragraph is afforded by the fact that the amount of heat liberated per mole of water formed by the neutralization of any strong acid by any strong base always has the same value, viz., 13,700 cal. It is scarcely possible that this could be the case if all such reactions were not actually identical.

When either the acid or the base involved in neutralization is a weak electrolyte, the course of the reaction is somewhat different. In a dilute solution of acetic acid, for instance, the concentration of hydrogen ion is very small. Yet, such a solution reacts with sodium hydroxide solution to form water practically as rapidly as does hydrochloric acid, and the same quantity of sodium hydroxide is required to neutralize a mole of acetic acid as for a mole of hydrogen chloride. In the case of acetic acid, the neutralization may best be represented by the equation

$$HC_2H_3O_2 + OH^- = H_2O + C_2H_3O_2{}^-$$

Since this reaction does not consist of the simple combination of hydrogen and hydroxide ions, the amount of heat evolved per mole of water formed is not in this case equal to 13,700 cal.

14. Normality; The Equivalent Weight of an Ionic or Ionizable Substance. The normality of a solution has been defined (p. 278) as the number of gram-equivalents of solute in 1 l. of solution, and a normal, or 1 N, solution, as one that contains 1 gram-equivalent of solute per liter. A gram-equivalent of a substance is, of course, a number of grams equal to its equivalent weight; but we must now subject the concept of equivalent weight, especially as it is applied to ionic compounds, to a somewhat closer scrutiny.[1] The equivalent weight of an element or radical may be defined (p. 89) as the atomic weight of the element, or the sum of the atomic weights of the atoms in the radical, divided by the valence of the element or radical. Similarly, the equivalent weight of an ion containing one or more atoms may be defined as the atomic weight of the atom, or the sum of the atomic weights of all the atoms constituting the ion, divided by the charge on the ion (regardless of its sign). In applying the term to ionic or ionizable compounds, we shall consider only those which may be regarded as containing, or as capable of yielding on ionization, two kinds of ions only. The equivalent weight of such a compound is defined as that weight which contains or yields 1 equivalent weight of each of the two ions; or, more simply, it is the sum of the equivalent weights of the two ions of the compound.

A few examples will serve to clarify this apparently complicated definition. One molecular weight, i.e., 36.465 parts by weight, of hydrogen chloride, HCl, obviously yields one equivalent weight each of hydrogen ion and chloride ion; hence, the equivalent weight of this compound is the same as its molecular weight. The same is true for sodium hydroxide, NaOH, for

---

[1] It must be noted that the term "equivalent weight" is used in a special sense when the element or compound in question is a participant in an oxidation-reduction reaction. This special use of the term has already been discussed in detail (p. 219), and will not be further considered here.

sodium chloride, NaCl, or for ammonium nitrate, NH_4NO_3; in each case one formula weight of the compound contains one equivalent weight of each of its ions, so that the equivalent weights are, respectively, 39.999, 58.448, and 80.048. A molar solution of any of these compounds, then, is also a normal solution.

The case of sulfuric acid, however, is somewhat different. A molecular weight of H_2SO_4, 98.082 parts by weight, contains 2.016 parts by weight of hydrogen and 96.066 parts by weight of sulfate. Since the equivalent weight of hydrogen ion is 1.008, and that of sulfate ion 96.066/2 = 48.033, one molecular weight of the compound is evidently capable of yielding *two* equivalent weights of hydrogen ion and *two* of sulfate ion. Hence, the equivalent weight of sulfuric acid is one-half the molecular weight, 98.082/2 = 49.041 (or the sum of the equivalent weights of hydrogen ion and sulfate ion, 1.008 + 48.033 = 49.041); a gram-equivalent is 49.041 g., and a normal solution contains 49.041 g. per liter, or is one-half molar. Similarly, the equivalent weight of calcium hydroxide, $Ca(OH)_2$, of calcium chloride, $CaCl_2$, of sodium sulfate, Na_2SO_4, or of calcium sulfate, $CaSO_4$, is one-half the formula weight, and the normality of a given solution of any of these solutes is twice the molarity. In the case of phosphoric acid, since one molecular weight of the compound can yield three equivalent weights each of hydrogen ion and phosphate ion, the equivalent weight is one-third the molecular weight.

In general, one of the simplest ways of determining the equivalent weight of a compound is by means of the relationship

$$\text{equivalent weight} = \frac{\text{molecular or formula weight}}{\text{total oxidation number of the cations}}$$

$$= \frac{\text{molecular or formula weight}}{-(\text{total oxidation number of the anions})}$$

The data of the two preceding paragraphs are summarized in Table. 18.4.

The equivalent weight has been defined in such a manner that equivalent weights of any two compounds are actually equivalent, in the sense that they are exactly sufficient to react with one another (provided, of course, that the compounds in question do react at all). This simple relationship does not hold, of course, for molar quantities. Thus, for example, 1 mole of hydrochloric acid will react with 1 mole of sodium hydroxide, but with only $\frac{1}{2}$ mole of calcium hydroxide; 1 mole of sulfuric acid, on the other hand, will react with 1 mole of calcium hydroxide, but requires 2 moles of sodium hydroxide for its complete neutralization. But one gram-equivalent of any acid reacts with exactly one gram-equivalent of any base, and exactly one gram-equivalent of salt may be obtained from the resulting solution. It clearly follows that one liter of a normal solution of an acid will exactly react with one liter of a normal solution of a base. We may, however, make this property of equivalent weights the basis of a much more general statement: namely, that equal volumes of two solutions of the same normality contain such quantities of the solutes as are just sufficient for complete interaction. In this relationship, which is widely used in quantitative analysis, lies the particular usefulness of normality as a means of expressing the concentration of solutions.

Table 18.4

Formula of Compound	Molecular or Formula Weight	Total Positive Oxidation Number of Cations, or Total Negative Oxidation Number of Anions	Number of Grams of Solute in 1 liter of Normal Solution	Molarity of a 1 N Solution	Normality of a 1 M Solution
HCl	36.465	1	36.465	1 M	1 N
NaOH	39.999	1	39.999	1 M	1 N
NaCl	58.448	1	58.448	1 M	1 N
H_2SO_4	98.082	2	49.041	$M/2$	2 N
$CaCl_2$	110.99	2	55.50	$M/2$	2 N
Na_2SO_4	142.048	2	71.024	$M/2$	2 N
$MgSO_4$	120.39	2	60.20	$M/2$	2 N
H_3PO_4	97.999	3	32.66	$M/3$	3 N
$Al_2(SO_4)_3$	342.16	6	57.03	$M/6$	6 N

15. Titration. The reaction of neutralization is frequently used in analytical chemistry. The simplest method of determining the amount of a base present in a given solution, for example, consists in measuring the volume of an acid solution of known concentration (called a *standard solution*) which just suffices to neutralize it. This measurement is carried out by means of a process known as *titration*. The basic solution is placed in a beaker, and a few drops of a solution of an indicator, such as litmus, are added to it. The acid solution is introduced into a vessel known as a buret, which is a tube usually of about 50 ml. capacity, graduated in tenths of a milliliter, drawn out to a tip at the lower end, and provided with a stopcock to permit the regulated withdrawal of a slow stream of solution. From the buret, the acid is run into the beaker, with constant stirring, until the color of the litmus just changes from blue to violet. At this point, which is called the *end-point* of the titration, the volume of the acid solution that has been used is read from the buret. The fact that the end-point has been reached may be checked by the addition of an extra drop of acid, which should turn the solution distinctly pink, or by the addition of a drop of alkaline solution, which should change the color back to blue.

This whole process might obviously have been reversed, and a standard solution of a base used for the titration of an unknown amount of acid.

Let us suppose that standard hydrochloric acid has been used for the titration of sodium hydroxide solution. The weight of actual hydrogen chloride in the measured volume of the standard solution might readily be calculated, and with the aid of the equation

$$NaOH + HCl = NaCl + H_2O$$

the weight of sodium hydroxide just sufficient to react with it might be calculated in the usual way (p. 105). However, the calculations involved in *volumetric analysis,* which is the name given to the method that consists in the titration of one solution against another, may be greatly simplified by the use of the concept of normality, as will be explained in the following section.

16. Use of Normality in Volumetric Analysis. In order to make our treatment somewhat more general, let us consider a slightly different application of the method of volumetric analysis, in which the *concentration* of a solution of any acid or base is to be determined by titration with a standard solution of any base or acid. Let us represent the normalities of the acid and base solutions by N_A and N_B, and the volumes (in liters) that exactly neutralize each other in the titration under consideration by v_A and v_B, respectively. Since the normality of a solution is the number of gram-equivalents per liter, the total number of gram-equivalents of acid in v_A liters of solution is $v_A N_A$; and similarly, the total number of gram-equivalents of base in the volume of solution used is $v_B N_B$. Thus for example, the number of gram-equivalents of solute in 3 l. of a 0.4 normal solution is $3 \times 0.4 = 1.2$; the number of gram-equivalents of solute in $\frac{1}{4}$ liter of a 2 normal solution is $\frac{1}{4} \times 2 = \frac{1}{2}$.

Now, since 1 gram-equivalent of an acid will exactly neutralize 1 gram-equivalent of a base (p. 346), it is also true that any number of gram-equivalents of an acid will neutralize the same number of gram-equivalents of a base. Hence, we have the equation

$$v_A N_A = v_B N_B$$

A similar equation will still be valid if the volumes of the solutions are expressed in any units other than liters, as long as the same unit is used for both volumes; for a change in units is equivalent to multiplication of both sides of the equation by the same factor. Hence, if the volumes in milliliters are represented by V_A and V_B, we may write

$$V_A N_A = V_B N_B \qquad (12)$$

It is evident that if any three of these four quantities are known, the fourth may readily be determined.

In order to illustrate the use of the relationship just derived, let us consider the following problem. If 12.0 ml. of a solution of a base requires exactly 38.4 ml. of 0.150 N acid for its neutralization, what is the normality of the base solution?

According to equation (12),

$$38.4 \times 0.150 = 12.0 \times N_B$$

$$N_B = \frac{38.4 \times 0.150}{12.0} = 0.480$$

Hence, the solution of the base is 0.480 N. It will be noted that for this calculation it has not been necessary to identify either the acid or the base. If, however, we are told that the base in solution is sodium hydroxide, and wish to calculate the *weight* of this solute in the 12.0 ml. sample, we then make use of the fact that a liter of a 1 N solution of sodium hydroxide contains $22.991 + 1.008 + 16.000 = 39.999$ g. of this solute. Hence 12.0 ml. of a 0.480 N solution contains

$$\frac{12.0}{1000} \times 0.480 \times 40.0 = 0.230 \text{ g.}$$

17. Selection of a Suitable Indicator. When equivalent quantities of solutions of an acid and a base have been mixed, the pH of the resulting solution is, of course, the same as that of a solution of the salt whose ions remain in the mixture. The pH of the solution of any salt of a strong acid and a strong base is the same as that of pure water, viz., 7; hence, it might be supposed that for the titration of a strong acid against a strong base, an indicator would have to be selected which undergoes a color change at a pH in the immediate neighborhood of 7. This limitation is not actually necessary, however; for, in such a case, the pH changes so rapidly with the addition of acid or base as the end-point is approached that any indicator whose color change falls in the pH range from 4 to 10 gives satisfactory results.

In the titration of a weak acid or a weak base, however, the change in pH as the quantities of acid and base approach equivalence is not so sharp.

Hence, in such a titration, if the results are to be accurate, the indicator must be one whose color changes at a pH very nearly the same as that of a solution of the salt whose ions are accumulating. Furthermore, because of hydrolysis (p. 320), the solution of such a salt may be distinctly acid or alkaline; i.e., its pH may be appreciably different from 7. In the titration of acetic acid with sodium hydroxide, for instance, an indicator whose color changes in a slightly alkaline solution is required; whereas, in the titration of ammonium hydroxide with hydrochloric acid, accurate results are not obtained unless the color change of the indicator occurs in a slightly acid solution. As indicated in Table 18.3, phenolphthalein satisfies the necessary conditions for the first of these titrations, while methyl orange is a satisfactory indicator for the second.

STUDY QUESTIONS AND PROBLEMS

1. The equivalent conductance of acetic acid in 0.1 M solution at 25° C. is 5.19 reciprocal ohms. The limiting equivalent conductance of this electrolyte at the same temperature is 391 reciprocal ohms. What is the degree of ionization of acetic acid in the 0.1 M solution?

2. Oxalic acid, $H_2C_2O_4$, in a solution containing 3.602 g. of this solute per 100 g. of water, is 27.0% ionized into H^+ ion and $HC_2O_4^-$ ion. (The further dissociation of $HC_2O_4^-$ ion may be disregarded.) What is the freezing point of this solution?

3. The degree of ionization of nitrous acid, HNO_2, in 0.01 M solution, is found to be 18.1%. What does this fact indicate as to the approximate value of the ionization constant of nitrous acid?

4. The freezing point of an aqueous solution of sulfurous acid, H_2SO_3, containing 4.1041 g. of this solute per 1000 g. of water, is −0.1339° C. What is the degree of ionization of the acid, at this concentration, into H^+ and HSO_3^- ions?

5. The ionization constant of benzoic acid, $HC_7H_5O_2$, at 25° C. is 6.6×10^{-5}. What is the degree of ionization of this acid in 1 M solution? in 0.1 M solution? in 0.01 M solution?

6. What is the concentration of hydrogen ion in a 0.1 M solution of hydrocyanic acid, HCN, the ionization constant of which is 7.2×10^{-10}? What would be the concentration of hydrogen ion in such a solution after the addition to it of enough sodium cyanide to make it 0.1 M in sodium cyanide also?

7. What is the pH of a 0.01 M solution of each of the following: hydrochloric acid, sodium hydroxide, acetic acid, ammonium hydroxide (ionization constant = 1.8×10^{-5})?

8. What is the equivalent weight (in a reaction not involving oxidation-reduction) of each of the following compounds: KNO_3, Na_2CO_3, $AlBr_3$, $SnCl_4$, $(NH_4)_2SO_4$, $K_4Fe(CN)_6$?

9. Suppose that you have prepared several aqueous solutions using the

amounts of materials and in the concentrations specified in the following table. In each case, supply the additional data suggested by the blank spaces.

Solute	Weight of Solute (in g.)	Number of Moles of Solute	Number of Gram-equiva-lents of Solute	Total Number of Ions per Liter	Volume of Solu-tion (in ml.)	Molar-ity of Solution	Normal-ity of Solution
(a) H_2SO_4	196.164				4000		
(b) KOH			3		500		
(c) $MgSO_4$			0.5			$M/6$	
(d) Na_3PO_4		0.1					$N/100$
(e) $Al_2(SO_4)_3$		0.01		3.01×10^{23}			

10. If 40.0 ml. of 0.150 N sodium hydroxide solution is required to neutralize the solution made by dissolving in water a 0.912 g. sample of a solid acid, what is the equivalent weight of the acid?

11. Very pure sodium hydroxide solution, suitable for analytical use, is sometimes made by dissolving pure metallic sodium in water. If 9.1964 grams of sodium is allowed to react with water and the resulting solution is then diluted to a total volume of exactly 5 liters, what is the normality of the sodium hydroxide solution so formed? What volume of 0.1200 N sulfuric acid will be required to neutralize 30.00 ml. of this sodium hydroxide solution?

12. Is it possible for a given solution to turn methyl orange yellow and litmus blue, and yet give no color with phenolphthalein? If so, what would be the approximate pH of such a solution?

13. A chemist wished to determine the percentage of sodium bisulfate, $NaHSO_4$, present as an impurity in various samples of sodium sulfate. He planned to make his determinations by titration of 1 g. samples of the mixture against standard sodium hydroxide solution, and he wished the number of milliliters of sodium hydroxide solution used, in each case, to be numerically equal to the percentage by weight of sodium bisulfate in the sample. What should be the normality of the standard sodium hydroxide solution?

19

Equilibrium in Saturated Salt Solutions

1. Introduction. In the preceding chapter, we considered the case of homogeneous equilibrium (p. 256) between a weak electrolyte and the ions derived from it in aqueous solution. The present chapter will deal with another important type of equilibrium in which ions are involved, namely heterogeneous equilibrium (p. 260) between a strong electrolyte in the solid state and its ions in solution.

2. Equilibrium Between a Solid Strong Electrolyte and Its Ions in Solution; the Solubility Product Principle. Let us consider first the general case of a solid salt which dissociates in solution according to the equation

$$AB_{(s)} = A^+ + B^-$$
$$\text{(dissolved)}$$

When equilibrium is attained in this reaction, the solution is said to be saturated with the salt; for a saturated solution is by definition (p. 279) one that can exist in equilibrium with the solid solute. *For a saturated solution,* then, we may write

$$AB_{(s)} \rightleftharpoons A^+ + B^-$$
$$\text{(dissolved)}$$

and if we apply the law of chemical equilibrium to this case we have, since the concentration of solid salt is constant,

$$[A^+][B^-] = K \tag{1}$$

where K, at any constant temperature, is a constant. It must be pointed out at once, however, that the activity coefficients of ions, even at moderate concentrations, differ so greatly from unity (p. 335) that this equation is not even approximately valid unless the concentrations of the ions in a saturated solution are very small; i.e., of the order of 0.01 mole per liter or less. Hence, the simple relationship stated in equation (1) is approximately valid for *slightly soluble* strong electrolytes only. Bearing this limitation in mind, then, we may state the relationship in words as follows: *In a saturated solution of a slightly soluble salt which yields two ions whose charges (disregarding signs) are the same, the product of the concentrations of the ions, at constant temperature, is a constant.* The value of this constant is called the *solubility product* of the electrolyte at the given temperature, and is often represented by the symbol K_{SP}.

It is evident that if we wish to express the principle just derived in its most general form, we shall have to consider the case of an ionic substance whose two ions do not necessarily have the same charge. Let us turn, then, to the slightly soluble strong electrolyte A_mB_n, one mole of which dissociates into m moles of $A^+ \cdots$ ion and n moles of $B^- \cdots$ ion. In a saturated solution of this electrolyte we have an equilibrium which may be represented by the equation

$$A_mB_{n(s)} \rightleftharpoons mA^+ \cdots + nB^- \cdots$$

For such a solution, according to the law of chemical equilibrium, we have

$$[A^+ \cdots]^m [B^- \cdots]^n = K_{SP} \qquad (2)$$

where K_{SP} is a constant at constant temperature, and is called the solubility product of A_mB_n. Equation (2) expresses the principle of constancy of solubility product, or, as it is usually called, the *solubility product principle*, which may be stated in words as follows: *In a saturated solution of any slightly soluble strong electrolyte at a given temperature, the product of the concentrations of the ions—each concentration taken as a factor as many times as that ion appears in the equation for the dissociation of the electrolyte—is a constant, which is known as the solubility product of the electrolyte at the given temperature.*

The solubility product principle, then, may readily be derived from the law of chemical equilibrium. Its validity has also been amply confirmed by means of experimental data. As will be shown presently, the wide usefulness of this principle lies in the fact that it is applicable not only to a saturated solution of a slightly soluble electrolyte obtained in the most obvious way— i.e., by agitation of an excess of the solid with water—but also to *any solution in equilibrium with the solid*, regardless of the source of the ions in the solution, and regardless also of whether or not they are present in the proportions in which they would be obtained from the dissolving of the electrolyte in question.

3. Calculation of the Solubility Product.

If the solubility of a slightly soluble strong electrolyte is known, the value of its solubility product may readily be calculated. Let us consider first the case of silver chloride, AgCl; in a saturated solution of this salt we have the equilibrium

$$AgCl_{(s)} \rightleftharpoons Ag^+ + Cl^-$$

The solubility of silver chloride in water at 25° C. is 0.00183 g., or $0.00183/143 = 0.0000128$ mole, per liter. Since each mole, on solution, yields 1 mole each of silver ion and chloride ion, the saturated solution contains 0.0000128 mole of each of the ions; that is, in the saturated solution,

$$[Ag^+] = [Cl^-] = 0.0000128$$

and for the solubility product we have

$$K_{SP} = [Ag^+][Cl^-] = (1.28 \times 10^{-5}) \times (1.28 \times 10^{-5}) = 1.64 \times 10^{-10}$$

The calculation is slightly more complicated for salts whose ions do not bear the same charge. A saturated solution of lead iodide, PbI_2, for example, contains 0.761 g. of solute per liter at 25° C. In this solution we have the equilibrium represented by the equation

$$PbI_{2(s)} \rightleftharpoons Pb^{++} + 2I^-$$

The molar concentration of the saturated solution is $0.761/461 = 0.00165$ mole per liter. In this case, since each mole yields on solution *one* mole of lead ion and *two* moles of iodide ion, the concentration of iodide ion in the saturated solution must be twice that of lead ion:

$$[Pb^{++}] = 0.00165$$

$$[I^-] = 2 \times [Pb^{++}] = 0.00330$$

Furthermore, in this case the solubility product is not simply the product of the concentrations of the ions, but

$$K_{SP} = [Pb^{++}][I^-]^2$$

For the numerical value of the solubility product we have

$$K_{SP} = (1.65 \times 10^{-3}) \times (3.30 \times 10^{-3})^2 = 1.80 \times 10^{-8}$$

4. Significance of the Solubility Product. At first sight, it might appear that the principle of constancy of solubility product is merely an unnecessarily complicated way of stating that the solubility of a given salt remains constant at constant temperature. The additional significance of the solubility product becomes apparent, however, when attention is directed to the fact that although any solution prepared by the addition of water to solid silver chloride must contain silver and chloride ions at the same concentration, yet innumerable solutions can exist in which the concentrations of these two ions are different; and furthermore, that *any* solution containing silver and chloride ions may be regarded as a solution of silver chloride, to which the solubility product principle is applicable, regardless of whether or not the concentrations of silver and chloride ion are the same.

This statement implies that any aqueous solution in which the product of the concentrations of silver and chloride ions is *less than* 1.56×10^{-10} will behave, at room temperature, like an unsaturated solution of silver chloride; when brought in contact with solid silver chloride, it will dissolve the salt until the product of the concentrations of silver ion and chloride ion is 1.56×10^{-10}. Any solution in which the product of the concentrations of silver and chloride ions is *equal to* 1.56×10^{-10}, whatever may be the values of the individual concentrations, will behave like a saturated solution; i.e., it will remain in equilibrium with solid silver chloride. And finally, if in any solution containing silver and chloride ions, from whatever source, the product of their concentrations momentarily *exceeds* 1.56×10^{-10}, the solution will behave like a supersaturated solution, and must eventually yield a *precipitate* of silver chloride.

As a simple example of the application of these rules, let us consider what happens when 5 ml. of 0.01 molar sodium chloride solution (in which the ionic solutes are Na^+ and Cl^-) is mixed with 5 ml. of 0.01 molar silver nitrate solution (which provides the ions Ag^+ and NO_3^-). First of all, it should be noted that since there are now 10 ml. of solution, each solute is distributed through twice as large a volume as it occupied before mixing, so that the concentration of each ion in the mixed solution, momentarily at least, is 0.005 mole per liter. For the product of the concentrations of silver ion and chloride ion, then, we have

$$[Ag^+][Cl^-] = (5 \times 10^{-3}) \times (5 \times 10^{-3}) = 2.5 \times 10^{-5}$$

a value which is far in excess of the solubility product, 1.64×10^{-10}. Hence, silver chloride is precipitated from this solution until the concentrations of silver ion and of chloride have been decreased to 1.28×10^{-5} mole per liter each; and we may write as the equation for the reaction

$$Na^+ + Cl^- + Ag^+ + NO_3^- = AgCl_{(s)} + Na^+ + NO_3^-$$

However, since it is evident that the sodium and nitrate ions play absolutely no part in this reaction, it may be more accurately represented by the simpler equation (p. 305)

$$Ag^+ + Cl^- = AgCl_{(s)}$$

This latter equation is not only correct and concise, but it has the advantage of indicating that it is not sodium chloride and silver nitrate alone which react to form a precipitate of silver chloride, but that *any* soluble ionic chloride will react with *any* silver salt in solution to give the same precipitate. (This conclusion is, of course, completely in accord with experimental facts.) A similar statement may be made concerning many other similar precipitation reactions.

Thus, by way of the solubility product principle, we arrive at another general rule (cf. p. 336) concerning reactions of electrolytes: *A metathetic reaction between two dissolved electrolytes will take place whenever a slightly soluble substance can be formed.* A better statement of this rule, perhaps, would be that whenever the product of the concentrations—each raised to the appropriate power—of two oppositely charged ions in a solution exceeds the solubility product of the corresponding salt, that salt is precipitated.

5. Effect of a Salt with a Common Ion. By the application of the solubility product principle, we are enabled to arrive at a very simple method for removing an ion from a solution as nearly completely as possible; i.e., for decreasing its concentration in a solution to the lowest possible value. In the case of silver chloride, for example, if the product $[Ag^+][Cl^-]$ is to remain constant, it is evident that the higher the concentration of chloride ion remaining in a solution, the smaller must be the remaining concentration of silver ion, and vice versa. Thus, if the silver in a silver nitrate solution has been precipitated as the chloride by the addition of an equivalent quantity of sodium chloride solution, and an excess of sodium chloride is added, the concentration of silver ion may be decreased to a value far below that which is found in a saturated solution made from silver chloride and water alone. The concentration of chloride ion might similarly be decreased by the addition of an excess of silver nitrate. Indeed, we may make the more general statement that in order to reduce the concentration of an ion A^+ to the lowest possible value by precipitation of an insoluble electrolyte AB, it is necessary only to introduce into the solution a considerable excess of a salt which yields the ion B^-, in common with the precipitate. In other words, an electrolyte may be more completely precipitated by increasing the concentration of one of its ions in the solution. This phenomenon may be regarded as a second variety of the *common ion effect* (cf. p. 337).

On the other hand, it is evident from the solubility product principle that a precipitate of an electrolyte may be dissolved by decreasing the concentration of one of its ions. As an example of this process, let us consider the case of magnesium hydroxide, for which we have the equilibrium

$$Mg(OH)_{2(s)} \rightleftharpoons Mg^{++} + 2OH^- \tag{3}$$

For a saturated solution of magnesium hydroxide, we may write

$$[\text{Mg}^{++}][\text{OH}^-]^2 = K_{SP}$$

We know that hydroxide ion has a great tendency to combine with hydrogen ion to form water (p. 344). If, therefore, a strong acid, such as hydrochloric, is added to a solution containing a precipitate of magnesium hydroxide, the concentration of hydroxide ion is greatly reduced by combination with H^+ ion. In order for the value of the appropriate product to remain constant, then, the precipitate must dissolve until the increased concentration of magnesium ion compensates for the decreased concentration of hydroxide ion.

This phenomenon may also be interpreted, without reference to the solubility product, in terms of the universally applicable principle of Le Chatelier. Thus, in the equilibrium between solid magnesium hydroxide and its ions, as expressed in equation (3), if the concentration of hydroxide ion is decreased by any means, the equilibrium will be shifted toward the right; i.e., some of the precipitate will dissolve. Since the anions of weak acids—being, like hydroxide ion, bases in the Brønsted sense (p. 314)—have a strong tendency to combine with hydrogen ion, insoluble salts of weak acids (such as carbonates, sulfides, and phosphates) likewise usually dissolve in solutions of strong acids.

Now, let us return to the case of silver chloride, for which we have the equilibrium

$$\text{AgCl}_{(s)} \rightleftharpoons \text{Ag}^+ + \text{Cl}^- \tag{4}$$

It happens that silver ion has a great tendency to combine with ammonia to form the complex ion $\text{Ag}(\text{NH}_3)_2{}^+$ (p. 472). Hence, if ammonia is added to a solution containing a precipitate of silver chloride, the concentration of silver ion is greatly decreased; and in order for the product $[\text{Ag}^+][\text{Cl}^-]$ to remain constant, solid silver chloride must dissolve until the concentration of chloride ion has increased sufficiently to make up for the decrease in concentration of silver ion. Many other instances in which slightly soluble salts dissolve with the formation of complex ions will be cited subsequently.

6. Deviation from the Solubility Product Principle. Strictly speaking, it is the product of the activities (p. 261) of the ions, each raised the appropriate power, rather than that of the concentrations, which must be constant in a saturated solution. Thus, for the equilibrium represented by equation (4), if we define a quantity K_a by means of the equation

$$K_a = a_{\text{Ag}^+} a_{\text{Cl}^-} \tag{5}$$

then the value of K_a remains rigorously constant. Since each activity may be considered as the product of the concentration, c, and the activity coefficient, f, of the ion in question, equation (5) may be written

$$f_{Ag^+}\, c_{Ag^+}\, f_{Cl^-}\, c_{Cl^-} = K_a$$

From this we readily get

$$K_{SP} = (c_{Ag^+})(c_{Cl^-}) = \frac{K_a}{(f_{Ag^+})(f_{Cl^-})} \tag{6}$$

Since the activity coefficients of ions in dilute solution decrease with increasing ionic concentration, it is apparent from equation (6) that the solubility product of any electrolyte must increase as the total concentration of electrolytes in the solution increases. This conclusion is borne out by extensive data on the solubility of salts in solutions of other salts.

The solubility product principle, then, is actually an approximation, valid only for solutions in which the total concentration of ions is small. The widest application of the principle, however, has been in the study of analytical chemistry; and since the solubilities of most of the precipitates which are used for the detection and for the quantitative determination of ions are exceedingly small, the limitations to the principle, which have just been discussed, have not constituted a serious obstacle to its use.

STUDY QUESTIONS AND PROBLEMS

1. Explain in terms of the solubility product principle why it is that
   (a) Calcium phosphate dissolves in dilute hydrochloric acid
   (b) Zinc hydroxide dissolves in dilute sulfuric acid
   (c) Silver chloride dissolves in ammonium hydroxide (ammonia water)
2. The solubilities of several salts in water at room temperature are given below in grams per 100 ml. of solution. Calculate the solubility product for each salt.

   (a) $CaSO_4$ 0.209   (c) Ag_2CO_3 0.0032

   (b) $BaCrO_4$ 0.0034   (d) MgF_2 0.0087

3. The solubility products of several substances are given below. Calculate the solubility of each in grams per liter.

   (a) $BaSO_4$ 1.1×10^{-10} (c) $Mg(OH)_2$ 1.5×10^{-11}

   (b) $CaCO_3$ 8.7×10^{-9} (d) Ag_2CrO_4 9.0×10^{-12}

4. If a solution contains 0.012 g. of calcium ion per liter, what concentration of carbonate ion, in grams per liter, is just sufficient to give a precipitate of calcium carbonate?

5. A saturated solution of silver sulfate, at 18°C., contains 7.8 g. of Ag_2SO_4 per liter. What concentration of sulfate ion, in grams per liter, is just sufficient to give a precipitate of silver sulfate in a 0.01 molar silver nitrate solution?

6. If a solution contains 0.006 mole of magnesium ion per liter, what is the minimum pH at which a precipitate of magnesium hydroxide will be obtained?

7. (a) The solubility product of cadmium sulfide, CdS, is thought to be only 1×10^{-28}. If this is correct, how many individual cadmium ions and sulfide ions are there in 1 ml. of a saturated solution of cadmium sulfide?

(b) How many cadmium ions are there in 1 ml. of $1 \times 10^{-8}\ M$ cadmium nitrate solution? How many sulfide ions would have to be present in this same milliliter in order for a precipitate of cadmium sulfide to be formed? (c) Under what conditions would the *total* number of Cd^{++} and S^{--} ions per milliliter required for the formation of a precipitate be at a minimum? Can you think of a plausible nonmathematical explanation for this fact?

8. Why is no attempt made to apply the solubility product principle to readily soluble salts?

9. Briefly account for the practice, common in analytical chemistry, of adding a slight excess of the solution containing the precipitating agent, in order to insure complete precipitation of a given ion.

10. What would happen if a very dilute solution of barium chloride were added drop by drop to a very dilute solution of silver sulfate?

CHAPTER

20

The Colloidal State of Matter

1. Definition. When a finely divided insoluble substance, such as sand, is shaken with water, a mixture is obtained which appears cloudy or turbid. On standing, however, the mixture soon becomes clear, as the particles of sand settle to the bottom of the vessel. Such a mixture is called a suspension. On the other hand, if sugar or salt is stirred with water, the particles of solid completely disappear so that they cannot be observed even with the aid of the most powerful microscope. The resulting homogeneous mixture is, of course, a solution.

Now, when powdered starch is treated with boiling water, or when arsenious sulfide is formed by the passage of hydrogen sulfide through an aqueous solution of arsenious oxide, a mixture is obtained which is not homogeneous, yet which shows scarcely any turbidity. The particles of insoluble solid (starch or arsenious sulfide) do not settle out, but remain in suspension indefinitely. Such a system, whose properties are intermediate between those of an ordinary suspension and those of a true solution, is called a *colloidal dispersion*; the finely divided substance is referred to as the *dispersed phase*, and the liquid is called the *dispersion medium*.

2. Colloids. The term "colloid" was first used in 1861 by Thomas Graham, who distinguished between what he believed to be two classes of substances: *crystalloids*, such as sugar, salt, etc., which are easily obtained in crystalline form and which, in solution, diffuse readily; and *colloids* (from a Greek word meaning "glue"), such as starch and gelatin, which in the solid state are usually of an amorphous nature, and which, in solution, show but little tendency to diffuse. These terms, however, are no longer used in this sense; for it has been shown that the properties characterized as colloidal are not peculiar to any special group of substances (although some have a greater tendency than others to assume these properties), but rather that *any* substance may by suitable means be obtained in colloidal form in any liquid in which its solubility is small. At present, then, we do not characterize particular substances as colloids, but rather ascribe certain properties to matter in the *colloidal state*. Furthermore, we recognize that the colloidal state is not limited to systems consisting of solid particles dispersed in liquid media, for we find numerous instances of liquid or solid particles dispersed in gases (fogs or smokes), liquids dispersed in liquids (emulsions, of which milk is probably the most familiar example), and solids dispersed in solids (ruby glass and certain precious stones). Although we shall have occasion to refer briefly to some of these other types of colloidal dispersion, we shall concern ourselves mainly with the most important variety, namely, that comprising dispersions of solid particles in a liquid medium.

There are few industrial chemical processes in which colloidal phenomena do not play a part. As a single example, it may be mentioned that since rubber latex is a colloidal dispersion, all the numerous steps in the production of rubber and in the manufacture of rubber goods are based upon the properties of materials in the colloidal state. Further, since the protoplasm characteristic of living matter is itself a colloidal dispersion, the biochemist, also, is largely concerned with colloidal phenomena.

3. Colloidal Dispersions and Ordinary Suspensions. It is a simple matter to distinguish between a colloidal dispersion and an ordinary suspension. A suspension is opaque or turbid, and the suspended particles settle to the bottom of the vessel on standing and can readily be removed by filtration. A colloidal dispersion, on the other hand, is often quite transparent (although there are some which might be characterized rather as translucent or opalescent in appearance), and the particles show no tendency to settle and cannot be removed by ordinary filtration. All these differences may be accounted for by the supposition that the particles of the colloidally dispersed substance are *smaller* than those of ordinary suspensions.

4. Colloidal Dispersions and True Solutions. The differences between a colloidal dispersion and a true solution are much less obvious. The distinction most readily observed is that noted when the two types of dispersion, while under strong illumination, are viewed in a direction approximately perpendicular to that of the illuminating rays. The path of a beam of light through a true solution, like that through a pure liquid, cannot be seen; that is, none of the light reaches the eye of an observer unless his eye is directly in its path. In the case of a colloidal dispersion, however, especially in a partially darkened room, the path of a light beam is plainly visible as a bright streak. This phenomenon, which is known as the Tyndall effect, is due to the scattering of light by the minute particles of the dispersed substance—exactly as the path of a ray of sunlight in a darkened room is visible because of the scattering of light by the minute dust particles which are never absent from the air. In a true solution, there are no particles of sufficiently large diameter to scatter light; hence, the beam is invisible, as a sunbeam would be in a perfectly dustless room.

Although colloidally dispersed particles pass through ordinary filter paper, they may be retained by means of special filters with very fine pores— usually made by supporting a jelly-like substance such as gelatin or silicic acid upon porous earthenware—through which the dispersion medium may be forced by the application of pressure. This process is known as ultrafiltration. Furthermore, colloidal particles show practically no tendency to diffuse (as particles of a dissolved substance do) through a membrane such as parchment paper, animal bladder, or certain varieties of cellophane.

The effects of colloidally dispersed substances on the vapor pressure, boiling point, and freezing point of the dispersion medium—if indeed they can be detected at all—are exceedingly slight. Since we have learned (p. 304) that the magnitude of these effects depends upon the number of "solute" particles present in a given weight of solvent, we must conclude that the number of particles in a given mass of a colloidal substance is a very small fraction of the number in the same mass of a true solute—and hence that the individual colloidal particles are very much *larger* than those in a true solution.

5. Size of Colloidal Particles. The various lines of evidence cited in the two preceding sections all lead to the conclusion that the particles of a colloidally dispersed substance are *intermediate in size* between those of an ordinary suspension and those of a true solution. Thus, the properties of matter in the colloidal state are essentially those associated with a definite range of particle sizes.

Since the change in properties of a dispersion with particle size is gradual rather than abrupt, it is impossible to draw sharp boundaries between the magnitude of colloidal particles and that of either suspended or dissolved particles. We may, however, somewhat arbitrarily designate approximate limits for the colloidal range. For this purpose, we shall have to make use of very small units of length, the micron (abbreviated μ), which is one-thousandth of a millimeter, and the millimicron ($m\mu$) or one-millionth of a millimeter ($1\ m\mu = 10$ Angstrom units). Colloidal particles are usually defined as those between $1\ m\mu$ and $200\ m\mu$ ($0.2\ \mu$) in diameter. These limits are convenient because particles of diameter greater than 200 mμ may be seen clearly in an ordinary microscope, while those of diameter less than 1 mμ do not scatter light and hence cannot contribute to the Tyndall effect. Molecules of such compounds as water or alcohol are considerably less than 1 mμ in diameter. Colloidal particles, then, are usually clumps or aggregates of hundreds, or even thousands, of molecules.

6. Brownian Movement. In an ordinary microscope, in which the observer looks directly toward the source of light, colloidal particles are quite invisible. A microscope so arranged that the line of vision is directed toward a dark background, and at right angles to the illuminating beam, is known as an ultramicroscope. By means of such an instrument, colloidal particles may be observed—not, it is true, as objects with definite outlines, but as minute luminous specks or points, each of which is in constant motion in an irregular, zigzag path. This phenomenon was first observed as early as 1827 in a suspension of pollen grains in water by the British botanist Robert Brown; it is generally known as the Brownian movement. The motion must undoubtedly be due to the impacts of molecules of the dispersion medium against the colloidal particles. No Brownian movement is observed in ordinary suspensions, because there the mass of a particle is so great that an appreciable velocity could be imparted to it only by the simultaneous impacts, in the same direction, of a large number of molecules—a coincidence which, in view of the fact that the particle is surrounded by solvent molecules moving in all directions, would be extremely improbable. The Brownian movement of colloidal particles is an important factor in causing them to remain suspended indefinitely, instead of settling under the influence of gravitation.

7. Preparation of Colloidal Dispersions. The many diverse methods of preparation of colloidal dispersions may be divided into two classes: dispersion methods and condensation methods. The first group includes all of those methods in which particles of sizes larger than colloidal are reduced to colloidal dimensions; the second, all those methods in which particles of molecular or atomic dimensions are allowed to come together to form finely divided solids or liquids. A few instances of each of these types of preparation will be given.

DISPERSION METHODS

1. The most obvious method of reducing particles to colloidal dimensions is by means of mere mechanical disintegration. It is difficult to attain a sufficiently high degree of dispersion by means of grinding alone, but so-called

colloid mills, in which suspended particles are drawn between rapidly re-volving surfaces placed very close together, are sometimes used for the preparation of paint pigments and other industrial products in which a very high state of subdivision is required.

2. There are a few solid substances which, when brought into contact with water, disperse spontaneously to form colloidal systems. Gelatin, glue, and starch, for example, all behave in this manner, and are said to undergo peptization. Certain other substances are similarly peptized in nonaqueous media; pyroxylin in acetone, for example.

3. In a much larger number of cases, peptization occurs only when a small amount of a dissolved electrolyte is present in the dispersion medium. Thus, for instance, clay is not peptized by water alone, but does form a colloidal dispersion in the presence of a small concentration of sodium hydroxide.

CONDENSATION METHODS

1. When a true solution is mixed with another liquid in which the solute is insoluble, a colloidal dispersion is often formed. Thus, for example, when a solution of sulfur in alcohol is largely diluted with water, the sulfur remains dispersed in the mixed solvent in colloidal form.

2. Colloidal dispersions often result from chemical reactions in solution which yield an insoluble product, especially when only small concentrations of ions remain in the solution. Thus, when a concentrated solution of ferric chloride is diluted with a large volume of hot water, the hydrous ferric oxide formed by hydrolysis remains in colloidal dispersion, dark red in color. When hydrogen sulfide is passed through an aqueous solution of arsenious oxide, As_2O_3, a bright yellow colloidal dispersion of arsenious sulfide is formed. Similarly, a white colloidal dispersion of sulfur (milk of sulfur) may be obtained by the addition of dilute acid to a solution of sodium thiosulfate (see p. 463).

A colloidal dispersion, in the free state, of any metal following hydrogen in the displacement series may usually be obtained by reduction of a dilute solution of a soluble salt of the metal with a soluble reducing agent. For example, if a very dilute solution of auric chloride, $AuCl_3$, is treated with a reducing agent such as ferrous sulfate, the free gold which is formed does not separate out as a precipitate, but remains in colloidal dispersion; such preparations of colloidal gold vary considerably in color, from blue through purple to red, according to the size of the colloidal particles. Even very minute concentrations of colloidal substances often produce intense colora-tions.

3. The Bredig arc process of preparing colloidal dispersions of metals consists in passing an electric arc between the slightly separated ends of two wires of silver, gold, or platinum immersed in water. At first glance, this would appear to be a process of dispersion, but closer consideration shows it to involve condensation; for some of the metal is vaporized at the high temperature of the arc, and the vapor then condenses to the colloidal state.

The success of any of these condensation methods depends upon cessation of the coagulation of the dispersed particles when they have reached colloidal dimensions. Further coagulation would, of course, result in the formation of an ordinary suspension.

8. Dialysis. Purification of a colloidally dispersed substance may often be accomplished by application of the fact (p. 362) that colloidal particles are unable to diffuse through the pores of certain membranes which are readily permeable both to water and to dissolved substances. Separation of substances by this means is known as *dialysis*. A convenient method of carrying out the process is shown in Figure 20.1. The impure colloidal dispersion is placed in a bag made of parchment paper or of cellophane, which is suspended in a vessel filled with water. Pure water is allowed to flow continuously through the outer vessel, so that the concentration of dissolved substances outside of the bag remains very low. In this manner, the soluble impurities in the dispersion may be almost completely removed, without loss of an appreciable quantity of the colloidal constituent.

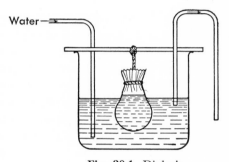

Fig. 20.1. Dialysis.

9. Two Classes of Colloidal Substances. Colloidal systems may conveniently be divided into two large groups, on the basis of the relation between the dispersed phase and the dispersion medium. When the properties of a dispersion are such as to indicate but a small attraction of the colloidal particles for the medium, the colloidal substance is said to be *lyophobic* (from Greek words signifying, approximately, "solvent-hating")—or, in the important special case where water is the dispersion medium, *hydrophobic*. Colloidal aqueous dispersions of free elements, or of oxides, sulfides, or other simple inorganic compounds, are of this character. Such dispersions usually do not differ greatly in viscosity from pure water; the dispersed material may readily be coagulated by the addition of electrolytes, and, once it has been precipitated, does not go back into the dispersed state merely upon the addition of water. When, on the other hand, the properties of the dispersion indicate that the colloidal particles have a great tendency to attract molecules of the medium, the dispersed substance is said to be *lyophilic* ("solvent-loving")— or, in the case of aqueous systems, *hydrophilic*. Examples of hydrophilic colloids are starch, gelatin, and albumen. It is such substances only which may be peptized merely upon being brought into contact with water. Dispersions of hydrophilic colloids are very much more viscous than water and are not readily coagulated, as are dispersions of hydrophobic substances, upon the addition of electrolytes. Most of the solvent may, of course, be removed from such dispersions by evaporation; the residue, however, is usually a gelatinous product which is readily dispersed again upon the addition of water. On this account, lyophilic colloids are said to be *reversible*.

10. Gels. Under certain conditions, a dispersion of a hydrophilic colloid may coagulate in a special manner, such that the whole mass, including the water, sets to a translucent, semi-rigid product known as a *gel*. A hot "solution" of gelatin or agar, for example, sets to a gel on cooling. Again, when hydrochloric acid is added to a dilute solution of sodium silicate, a transparent colloidal dispersion of hydrous silicon dioxide is first formed, which, however, soon sets to a firmly coherent, soft yet brittle, translucent jelly; partially dehydrated, this gives the product known as silica gel (p. 550). Apparently, in such cases, tough fibers and films of the dispersed substance form a complex three-dimensional network, in the cells of which large amounts of water are retained.

The formation of jellies when the juices of certain fruits (notably apples and grapes) are boiled, depends upon the presence in the fruit of a carbohydrate (p. 595) known as pectin, which, when sufficient sugar and acid are present, forms a gel after the solution has been concentrated to the necessary degree.

11. Films and Filaments. Thus far we have regarded as colloidally dispersed substances only such as consist of what might be termed three-dimensionally colloidal particles; i.e., particles all of whose dimensions are in the colloidal range. It would be entirely reasonable to suppose, however, that at least some of the properties of colloidal dispersions would be found also in molecular aggregates with two relatively large dimensions and one in the colloidal range, and in those with one large dimension and two in the colloidal range. Hence colloid chemistry has sometimes been characterized as including the study of the properties not only of small grains and droplets, but also of very thin films (one colloidal dimension) and very fine filaments (two colloidal dimensions). It is of interest to note that some types of very large molecules, such as those of cellulose, rubber, plastics, synthetic fibers, and proteins, are of colloidal size or larger in at least one direction.

12. Adsorption by Colloidal Substances. The phenomenon of adsorption, or the adherence of particles of one substance to the surface of another, has already been mentioned in other connections. The extent to which one given substance is adsorbed by another depends to a large degree upon the *magnitude of the surface* presented by the adsorbent. Now, it is well known that the surface presented by a given volume of material increases rapidly as the body is divided into smaller and smaller units. As a cube is subdivided into smaller cubes, for example, the total surface area increases *in inverse proportion* to the length of an edge of the unit cube. The dimensions of colloidal particles are so small that the total surface presented by a group of such particles, in comparison with their combined mass, is relatively enormous. Hence, colloidal substances show very great adsorptive capacity; in fact, many of the special properties exhibited by colloidal dispersions may be attributed to this peculiarity.

In many instances, the coagulation of a hydrophobic colloidal substance may be greatly retarded, or even prevented, by the presence of a hydrophilic colloid. This is probably due to the adsorption of the second substance upon the particles of the first, with the formation of a protective film or coating which keeps these particles from coming together into larger aggregates. Thus, when a solution of potassium bromide is added to a silver nitrate solution that contains a small concentration of gelatin, the silver bromide formed is not precipitated but remains colloidally dispersed. This protective action is one of the functions of the gelatin used in the preparation of colloidal dispersions of silver salts for photographic films. Similarly, gum arabic is often used as a protective colloid for the coloring materials in inks.

Adsorption on colloidal particles is not limited to other colloids, nor even to neutral molecules. Ions also are subject to such adsorption—a fact which accounts for many otherwise inexplicable aspects of colloid behavior, such as those described in the next paragraph.

13. Electrical Properties of Colloidal Dispersions. Most aqueous colloidal dispersions, including all those of the hydrophobic variety, conduct an electric current, with migration of charged particles toward the electrodes. These particles do not, as in the case of electrolytes, consist of two kinds of ions, oppositely charged, formed by the dissociation of the solute. Rather, in a given dispersion, *all* the colloidal particles migrate in one direction—from which fact we must conclude that they all carry the same type of charge— while one of the ions of water, or of an electrolyte which may be present, migrates in the other direction. Most metal oxides or hydroxides in the colloidal state carry positive charges, and hence migrate toward the cathode; whereas free metals, many of the sulfides, silica, and graphite carry negative charges and migrate toward the anode. On coming in contact with the respective electrode, the colloidal substance loses its charge and is precipitated. The type of migration just described is known as *electrophoresis*. The source of the charges on the colloidal particles is undoubtedly the preferential adsorption of a particular kind of ion on their surfaces. This ion may come from the electrolyte present in the solution in small concentration, or it may be hydronium or hydroxide ion from the water. Particles that have a greater tendency to adsorb positive than negative ions acquire a positive charge, and vice versa. Thus, for example, the positive charge on colloidal ferric oxide is almost certainly due to the presence of adsorbed ferric ions, whereas the negative charge on colloidal arsenious sulfide is due to adsorbed sulfide ions.

As an example of the practical application of the migration of colloidal particles in the electric field and their discharge at an electrode, it may be mentioned that small articles may conveniently be coated with rubber by means of electrophoretic deposition from colloidal dispersions of this substance. The Cottrell process for the elimination of smokes depends upon a similar principle. The smoke-laden air from the chimney of a furnace or of an industrial plant is passed between metal electrodes maintained at a high difference of potential, and the charged solid particles are discharged and deposited as dust at one of the electrodes. This process is useful both for the recovery of valuable substances that would otherwise be wasted, and for the abatement of the smoke nuisance in industrial regions.

14. Coagulation of Colloids. The stability, or permanence, of colloidal dispersions is due to the small size of the particles, which enables them to be kept in motion by collision with the molecules of the dispersion medium. If the small particles, because of their tendency to adhere to each other, were to unite into larger ones, the dispersed material would soon settle out under the influence of gravity as in ordinary suspensions. The fact that all the particles of a given kind carry the same kind of electrical charge causes them to *repel* each other, and so to remain suspended. When the charges are neutralized, however, the fine particles coagulate into larger ones and precipitation soon takes place.

There is a wide variation in the ease with which different colloidal dispersions may be coagulated. In some cases, heating to the boiling point is sufficient. In general, the most effective means of bringing about flocculation or coagulation of a lyophobic colloid is by the addition of an electrolyte in *sufficiently high* concentration. When the dispersed substance is exposed to a *high concentration* of an ion whose charge is opposite to that carried by the colloidal particles, this ion is adsorbed, the charges on the particles are neutralized, and flocculation occurs. A colloidal dispersion of arsenious sulfide, for example, is readily coagulated upon the addition of a strong acid, because hydrogen ions are readily adsorbed, and the negative charges on the colloidal particles are thereby neutralized. Similarly, colloidal ferric oxide is coagulated upon the addition of alkali, because its positive charge is neutralized by the readily adsorbed hydroxide ion. In general, the effectiveness of an ion for this purpose increases with its charge. Thus, calcium ion and especially aluminum ion are more effective than sodium ion in causing the coagulation of negatively charged colloids. Similarly, sulfate ion and especially phosphate ion are good coagulants for positively charged colloids.

The effectiveness of aluminum sulfate in the clarification of water (p. 239) depends in part upon the high charge of the aluminum ion; in part upon the fact that the hydrous aluminum oxide formed by hydrolysis, itself a positively charged colloid, tends to precipitate (and be precipitated by) colloids of opposite charge; and, finally, upon the gelatinous nature of the precipitate, which carries down with it much of the suspended matter.

STUDY QUESTIONS AND PROBLEMS

1. Explain why Graham's classification of substances into colloids and crystalloids is no longer regarded as valid or useful.

2. State three ways in which you could determine by observation or experiment whether a given system in the liquid state was a colloidal dispersion or an ordinary suspension; whether it was a colloidal dispersion or a true solution.

3. A colloidal dispersion of ferric oxide may be obtained by the addition of a small volume of ferric chloride solution to a large volume of hot water. How might this dispersion be purified; i.e., freed from substances in true solution?

4. Which is the more effective for the coagulation of a colloidal dispersion of arsenious sulfide: a solution of sodium phosphate or one of aluminum sulfate? Why? For the coagulation of a colloidal dispersion of chromic oxide? Why?

5. What is the surface presented by 1 cc. of a substance when it is in the form of a 1 cm. cube? What is its total surface after it has been subdivided into 1 mm. cubes? What is the ratio of the second surface to the first?

21

The Atmosphere. The Inert Gases

1. General Characteristics. The envelope of gaseous substances which surrounds the earth is known as the *atmosphere*; limited quantities of this mixture are usually referred to as *air*, although the two words are often used interchangeably. The fact that air is a mixture rather than a pure substance was not recognized by the ancients, who considered it to be one of the four elements, along with earth, water, and fire. The work of Priestley, Lavoisier, Scheele, and others who, near the end of the eighteenth century, showed that air is indeed a mixture of gases, the major components of which are oxygen and nitrogen, has already been discussed in Chapter 11 and will be further considered in Chapter 26. About a hundred years later the inert gases, argon, neon, helium, krypton, and xenon were shown to be minor constituents of the air; the discovery and isolation of these gases will be considered later in this chapter.

Our chief interest in the atmosphere lies, of course, in the fact that it furnishes the oxygen necessary for metabolism in the animal body, for the combustion of fuels, and for many other essential processes (p. 197). An important function of atmospheric nitrogen is that it serves as a diluent for the oxygen and thus slows down the various reactions in which the oxygen of the air takes part. Were it not for this fact many substances, such as iron, for example, which are subject only to slow oxidation in air, would rapidly burn up, especially at elevated temperatures.

Though the atmosphere appears to us to be very light and diffuse, its total weight is estimated to be about 5.7×10^{15} tons, and it serves as an abundant source of chemical raw materials. Because of the decrease in pressure with increase in altitude and because of the high compressibility of air, the density of the atmosphere gradually decreases with increasing distance above sea level, so that at an altitude of 10 miles it is only 2/35 as dense as at sea level, and at 30 miles less than 1/7000 as dense. The average density of air under standard conditions is 1.293 g. per liter.

2. Composition of the Atmosphere. The average composition of clean, dry air from above open country is given in Table 21.1. Since air is a mixture rather than a pure substance, we are not surprised to find that its composition is variable. For example, the percentage of carbon dioxide is considerably higher in large cities than in the open country. Moreover, definite changes in composition occur with increasing altitude. Information concerning the composition of the atmosphere at its extreme upper limits is, of course, difficult to obtain, but it seems certain that the percentage of heavier gases such as oxygen, argon, and carbon dioxide decreases slowly with increasing distance from the surface of the earth. The percentage of nitrogen first increases and then decreases with increasing height. It is believed that the extreme upper levels of the atmosphere may contain only hydrogen gas.

Table 21.1

Composition of the Atmosphere by Volume (Dry)

Nitrogen	78.03%
Oxygen	20.99%
Argon	0.94%
Carbon dioxide	0.031%
Hydrogen	0.01%
Neon	0.0018%
Ozone	0.0006%
Helium	0.0005%
Krypton	0.0001%
Xenon	0.000009%

3. Variable Constituents of the Atmosphere. The percentage of carbon dioxide in the atmosphere varies with the locality in which the sample is collected; and the proportions of the other constituents are also somewhat inconstant. Except for the effects of great differences in altitude, these latter variations are usually insignificant. There are commonly present in the air, however, a number of incidental substances, in addition to carbon dioxide, whose concentrations vary widely with time and place. The most important of these variable constituents is water vapor, the concentration of which in the atmosphere fluctuates over a wide range. Other variable constituents that may or may not be present include dust particles, and traces of hydrogen, hydrogen sulfide, sulfur dioxide, carbon monoxide, and oxides of nitrogen.

4. Water Vapor in the Air. In Chapter 4 it was shown that at a given temperature any liquid (or solid, for that matter) has a definite vapor pressure; hence, if the partial pressure of the vapor exceeds the vapor pressure of the liquid, condensation will take place until the partial pressure of the vapor is reduced to this value. It is clear, therefore, that the partial pressure of water vapor in the air at a given temperature cannot exceed the vapor pressure of water at that temperature. The ratio of the partial pressure of water vapor in the air to the vapor pressure of water at the temperature of the air, usually expressed as a percentage, is called the *relative humidity*. Air in which the partial pressure of water vapor is equal to the vapor pressure of water at the prevailing temperature is said to be *saturated* with vapor, or to have a relative humidity of 100%.

Since the vapor pressure of water decreases with decreasing temperature, the relative humidity of a given sample of air increases as the temperature is lowered. The temperature at which the relative humidity of a sample of air is 100%, i.e., the temperature at which the partial pressure of water vapor in the air becomes equal to the vapor pressure of water, is called the *dew point* of that sample of air. When air is cooled below its dew point, condensation of water vapor takes place. Numerous meteorological phenomena are accounted for by this fact.

5. Carbon Dioxide in the Air. The amount of carbon dioxide in dry country air under normal conditions remains between 0.03 and 0.04%. In highly populated industrial areas, outdoor air may contain as much as 0.07% of carbon dioxide, and in crowded, poorly ventilated rooms the carbon dioxide content sometimes increases to several times this value. Two opposing factors serve to maintain the overall carbon dioxide content of the atmosphere fairly constant. Billions of tons of carbon dioxide are released to the atmosphere each year as a result of the combustion of carbonaceous fuels and of the respiratory processes of animals, which take in oxygen and emit carbon dioxide. This effect is balanced, however, by the fact that green plants take in carbon dioxide and release oxygen (p. 596). The content of carbon dioxide in the air exhaled by human beings is about 5%.

6. Air Conditioning. Our comfort and health are affected by the amounts of such variable constituents as water vapor and carbon dioxide in the air which surrounds us, the relative humidity being particularly important. When the humidity is low, the cooling process of evaporation of perspiration from the skin takes place at a very rapid rate, with the result that we feel cold even at moderate temperatures. On the other hand, the discomfort due to high temperatures is greatly increased if the humidity is high, because the rate of evaporation of perspiration is reduced. At moderate temperatures, a relative humidity of about 50% is most favorable; at higher temperatures, a lower relative humidity increases comfort; and at lower temperatures, a somewhat higher relative humidity is desirable.

It was formerly thought that the drowsiness and discomfort that result from exposure to air in a room which is overcrowded and poorly ventilated are caused by the lowered oxygen content and increased carbon dioxide content of the air. Recent studies indicate, however, that these are relatively minor factors, and that the major cause is the increased humidity.

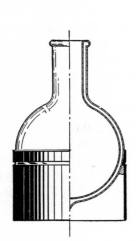

Fig. 21.1. A Dewar flask.

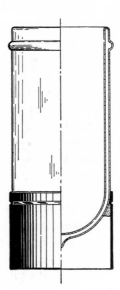

Fig. 21.2. Another type of Dewar flask.

The science of air conditioning deals with the provision of air suitable for the health and comfort of persons, as well as for the carrying out of various industrial processes. A complete air-conditioning unit is designed to accomplish four things: (1) to control temperature, summer and winter; (2) to control humidity; (3) to provide circulation; and (4) to remove harmful impurities from the air. Air conditioning is receiving ever increasing consideration in the planning of homes, as well as in industrial building.

7. Liquid Air. By the use of methods described in Chapter 3, air can be condensed to the liquid state. Since air is a mixture rather than a pure substance, it does not have a sharp boiling point but boils over the range of about $-195°$ to $-185°$ C. at standard atmospheric pressure. Since liquid nitrogen boils at a considerably lower temperature ($-196°$ C.) than liquid oxygen ($-183°$ C.), as liquid air boils away the residue becomes richer in oxygen. By the use of complex techniques involving distillation and adsorption, liquid air may be separated into its components.

Because it boils at such a low temperature, liquid air cannot be kept for any length of time in an ordinary container. Since, however, vaporization of this, as of any, liquid absorbs heat, it may be slowed down by insulation of the liquid from external sources of heat. This is best accomplished by means of a double-walled flask in which the space between the walls has been highly evacuated to minimize the transfer of heat by conduction or convection. If the inner surfaces of the walls are silvered, the transfer of heat by radiation is also minimized. Such containers are called Dewar flasks, after their inventor, James Dewar. The ordinary "thermos" bottle is a type of Dewar flask (see Figures 21.1 and 21.2).

Liquid air is a clear water-like liquid having a slightly bluish tint, and a density of about 0.91 g. per cc. As the liquid boils away, the bluish tint increases because of the increasing percentage of liquid oxygen, and the density increases also. Liquid air is used as a commercial source of oxygen, nitrogen, argon, and the less abundant inert gases, neon, krypton, and xenon. It is also of value as a cooling agent in various types of scientific work in which very low temperatures are required. Since the vapor pressure of water at liquid air temperatures is almost zero, gases may be most effectively freed of moisture by being passed through a tube submerged in liquid air.

THE INERT GASES

8. History. The members of Group 0 of the periodic system are newcomers in the family of elements, for they were unknown at the time that Mendeleeff first published his periodic system. In 1785, Cavendish had shown that a residue "not more than 1/120 part of the whole" remains when the oxygen in a sample of air is caused to combine with nitrogen by means of an electric discharge (p. 268), and the remaining excess of nitrogen is then removed by sparking with additional portions of oxygen. Cavendish, however, had no way of identifying the constituents of this residue. Many years later, in 1868, the English scientist Sir Norman Lockyer discovered a bright yellow line in the solar spectrum which he attributed to an element not then known on earth, to which he gave the name helium, from the Greek word meaning "the sun."

It was not until 1894, however, that Lord Rayleigh and Sir William Ramsay observed that nitrogen produced by chemical means (the decomposition of ammonium nitrite, p. 470) is consistently less dense than nitrogen isolated from the air, and were thus led to the discovery that air contains a relatively heavy element which is chemically very inert, and to which, because of this property, they gave the name argon, from the Greek word meaning "inactive."

Shortly thereafter, Ramsay discovered that a gas which the American chemist W. F. Hillebrand had obtained in 1889, by heating the mineral cleveite, was the same as the element helium which had been discovered by Lockyer in the sun; and in the same year the presence of helium was detected in the atmosphere.

Continuing the study of the inert fraction of the air, Ramsay and Travers discovered, in 1898, three new members of the family of inert gases, to which they gave the names neon, from the Greek word meaning "new," krypton, meaning "hidden," and xenon, meaning "stranger."

In 1905, H. P. Cady and D. F. McFarland of the University of Kansas discovered the presence of appreciable quantities of helium in certain natural gases from wells in Kansas and surrounding areas; these gases shortly became the most important sources of this element.

The sixth of the inert gases was not found in air; but a study of the radio-active disintegration series of thorium, protactinium, and uranium showed that at a certain stage in each of these series an element is produced which has the atomic number 86, and hence is an isotope of the sixth member of the inert gas family. These three isotopes, known respectively as thoron, actinon, and radon, are all radioactive and thus undergo further disintegration. These gases were known at one time as thorium, actinium, and radium "emanations"; but since the half-life periods of thoron and actinon (less than 1 min.) are so much shorter than that of radon (3.82 days), the name of the most stable isotope, radon, with the symbol Rn, has largely replaced the older designations.

9. Occurrence and Preparation. In addition to its occurrence in traces in the atmosphere, and in proportions up to 7% in certain types of natural gas, helium is found also in small quantities in a variety of minerals. We have seen that the alpha particles emitted by various radioactive elements are identical with nuclei of helium atoms (p. 124); it is believed, therefore, that the helium gas enclosed in the pores of these minerals is of radioactive origin. Practically all the helium used in this country for practical and experimental purposes is obtained from natural gas.

Argon, neon, krypton, and xenon are all obtained by complex fractional distillation and adsorption processes from liquid air. As is indicated in Table 21.1, xenon and krypton occur in exceedingly small proportions, and the relative ease and low cost of obtaining them are attributable to the fact that they are obtained as by-products of the large industrial plants which are operated for the production of oxygen and nitrogen.

Radon is obtained only from the radioactive disintegration of the parent elements (Ra^{226}, Ra^{223}, and Ra^{224}), in the radium, protactinium, and thorium disintegration series, respectively.

Table 21.2

Electron Configurations of the Elements of Group 0

Element	1	2		3			4				5			6	
	s	s	p	s	p	d	s	p	d	f	s	p	d	s	p
He	2														
Ne	2	2, 6													
Ar	2	2, 6		2, 6											
Kr	2	2, 6		2, 6, 10			2, 6								
Xe	2	2, 6		2, 6, 10			2, 6, 10				2, 6				
Rn	2	2, 6		2, 6, 10			2, 6, 10, 14				2, 6, 10			**2, 6**	

Table 21.3

Physical Properties of the Elements of Group 0

	He	Ne	Ar	Kr	Xe	Rn
Melting point °C.	−272.2*	−248.67	−189.2	−157.0	−111.50	−110
Boiling point, °C.	−268.9	−245.9	−185.7	−152.9	−107.1	− 61.8
Density (g./1. at S.T.P.)	0.177	0.8990	1.7837	3.708	5.85	9.73
Critical temp., °C.	−267.9	−228.7	−122	− 63	16.6	104
Critical pressure (atm.)	2.26	25.9	48	54	58.2	62

* Under 26 atm. pressure.

10. Electron Configurations and Physical and Chemical Properties. The electron configurations of the elements of Group 0 are listed in Table 21.2. These electron configurations are characterized by great stability (p. 172); the atoms of these elements, therefore, show almost no tendency either to gain, to lose, or to share electrons. Accordingly, although a few very unstable coordination compounds of these elements have been obtained, the elements of Group 0 are, for all practical purposes, nonreactive; hence, the name "inert gases." Since atoms of these elements do not form chemical bonds with each other, their molecules are all monatomic and nonpolar, and have no tendency to associate. The melting points and boiling points of these substances are, therefore, quite low. The more important physical properties of the elements of this family are listed in Table 21.3. The gases are all colorless, odorless, and tasteless.

11. Industrial Applications of the Inert Gases. The chief practical application of helium is in lighter-than-air craft. Although the density of helium is approximately twice that of hydrogen, both these gases have much lower densities than air. Since it is the difference between the density of air and the density of a lighter gas that determines the lifting power in air of the latter, the lifting power of helium gas is more than 11/12 as great as that of hydrogen. This small difference in buoyancy is more than outweighed by the greater safety in the use of helium, resulting from its noninflammability. The terrible Hindenburg disaster of 1937 illustrates the danger accompanying the use of hydrogen gas in balloons, blimps, and dirigibles. The United State is fortunate in being the only nation, so far as is known, to have an ade‐ quate source of helium. All our helium resources are controlled by the Fed eral government.

Helium is used also for the artificial atmosphere that is sometimes supplied to divers and others, such as tunnel workers, who are exposed to high pressures. On leaving the region of high pressure, the workers go into a decompression chamber in which the pressure is slowly reduced to normal. If this is not done, or if the pressure is reduced too rapidly, the excess nitrogen which has dissolved in the blood under the high pressure is suddenly released as small bubbles in the blood stream, causing the very painful and dangerous condition known as caisson disease or "the bends." Because of the very low solubility of helium in the blood, a much faster decompression rate is permissible with helium-oxygen mixtures than with ordinary air.

Neon has the very unusual property of being almost a nonconductor of electricity until a relatively high voltage, usually around 200 volts, depending upon the design of the tube, is applied. Once this "breakdown" potential is reached, however, the neon atoms are rapidly ionized and the resistance drops sharply, so that small amounts of neon will carry exceedingly high currents, much higher than are carried by other gases under similar conditions. Because of this fact, neon is used as the conduction medium in electrical safety devices, known as lightning arresters, for protecting from high voltages such electrical instruments as voltmeters, relays, and rectifiers.

Of greater practical importance, however, is the use of neon at low pressures (10–20 mm.) in gaseous conductor lamps, commonly known as neon tubes, which emit a brilliant red light. Although a relatively high voltage is required, the current which flows through the tube is so small that the energy consumption is not excessive. Neon tubes may readily be made in various shapes and sizes, and hence are ideally suited to electrical display advertising. During the past quarter-century, such lighting has largely displaced the old incandescent bulb type of electrical sign and has become an outstanding feature of the nocturnal aspect of our cities. By the addition of other inert gases, or mercury vapor, and by the use of tubes of colored glass, various colors of light other than red may be obtained. In addition to their versatility as to shape and size, and their high efficiency and low operating cost, neon tubes possess the additional advantage of instantaneous response to the starting and stopping of current flow, so that the flashing of the light does not lag behind the operation of the switch as in the case of incandescent lamps. Neon or other gaseous conductor lamps are therefore ideally suited to that type of ultra-high-speed photography in which the time of exposure is controlled not by opening and closing the shutter of the camera, but by the flashing of a lamp. A krypton and xenon tube that is very useful for this purpose has recently been developed.

The principal application of argon is in metal welding, as an inert gas to shield the electric arc. This is the procedure followed in the arc welding of steel, aluminum, and magnesium. Another important use is in the manufacture of incandescent bulbs. A hot tungsten filament in an evacuated bulb slowly volatilizes, producing a dark deposit on the inner surface of the bulb; eventually, because of this volatilization, the filament will fail. If, however, the tube is filled with an unreactive gas, the rate of volatilization is considerably reduced, and the life and efficiency of the lamp are correspondingly increased. Nitrogen and argon, neither of which reacts with tungsten at the temperature of the filament, have been used to fill incandescent lamp bulbs; of these two argon is superior because (1) its thermal conductivity is lower than that of nitrogen and thus the filament is protected against heat loss to a greater extent than in a nitrogen-filled bulb, and (2) it is even more inert than nitrogen and thus fosters longer filament life and permits a higher temperature of operation. Argon finds some commercial application also in the manufacture of gaseous conductor tubes. The recently developed fluorescent tube lamp usually contains a mixture of mercury vapor and argon at 3 mm. pressure. At the end of 1956, the annual U.S. output of argon was over 500,000,000 cubic feet.

Hospitals with stocks of radium often follow the practice of daily withdrawal of the emitted radon into small tubes, for use in radiotherapy.

STUDY QUESTIONS AND PROBLEMS

1. Calculate the number of grams of water per liter of air if the relative humidity is 55% and the temperature is 25° C.

2. What is the dew point of a sample of air in which the partial pressure of water vapor is 17 mm.?

3. Why does the concentration of oxygen in a sample of liquid air increase as the liquid boils away?

4. Why is the space between the walls of a Dewar flask evacuated? Why are the walls silvered?

5. Which is greater, the lifting power of 1 cu. ft. of hydrogen gas or 1 cu. ft. of helium gas? How much greater?

6. Why are all the inert gases monatomic?

7. Discuss the commercial methods for separating the components of the atmosphere. What important chemical principles are involved?

8. What are the mole fractions of nitrogen, oxygen, and argon in the atmosphere? What are the relative percentages by weight of these gases?

9. Is air saturated with water vapor more or less dense than dry air? Explain.

10. If air at 32° F. with a relative humidity of 50% is warmed to 68° F., what is its relative humidity at the higher temperature?

22

The Halogens and the Hydrogen Halides

1. Introduction. The elements fluorine, chlorine, bromine, and iodine, which constitute Group 7a of the periodic system, are known as the halogens. This name, which is derived from Greek words meaning "salt former," was given to these elements because their binary compounds with the alkali metals are among the most abundant of the soluble salts that occur in nature, and particularly in sea water. The most familiar of all these salts is, of course, sodium chloride, the substance commonly known as table salt or simply as salt.

2. History. Chlorine was the first of the halogens to be prepared. This greenish yellow gas was obtained in 1774 by Scheele, who subjected pyrolusite (naturally occurring manganese dioxide) to the action of muriatic acid (impure hydrochloric acid). He did not, however, know the substance thus obtained to be a free element, but thought it to be a compound containing oxygen. It was not until more than a quarter of a century later that Sir Humphry Davy established its elementary nature. The name chlorine is derived from the Greek word *chloros*, meaning "green."

Iodine was discovered in 1811 by Bernard Courtois, who, upon heating the ashes of certain seaweeds with concentrated sulfuric acid, obtained a violet-colored vapor. The elementary nature of this substance was established in 1814 by Gay-Lussac, who gave it the name of iodine, from the Greek word *iodes*, meaning "violet."

Bromine was probably first prepared in the free state by Justus von Liebig, who subjected salt brines and sea water to the action of chlorine; credit for the discovery of bromine, however, is usually given to Antoine Balard, who first recognized, in 1826, that the substance prepared by Liebig was a new element. The name is derived from *bromos*, a Greek word meaning "stench."

Compounds of fluorine were known, and the existence of the element recognized, long before it was isolated in the free state. The liberation of the element was finally accomplished by Henri Moissan in 1886, when he passed an electric current through a solution of potassium hydrogen fluoride in anhydrous liquid hydrogen fluoride contained in a platinum–iridium cell (Figure 22.1). The name of the element is derived from that of its most important naturally occurring compound, fluorspar (CaF_2).

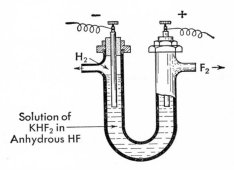

Solution of KHF_2 in Anhydrous HF

Fig. 22.1. Moissan's method for producing fluorine.

The fifth member of the family, element number 85, has not been found in nature. Radioactive isotopes of the element have been prepared by nuclear reactions, and the element has been named *astatine* with the symbol At. It is believed that stable isotopes of the element do not exist (p. 146).

3. General Characteristics of the Elements. The electronic configurations of these elements are listed in Table 22.1. As is indicated by these configurations, each of the halogens differs from the inert gas that follows it in the periodic system by having one less electron in its valence shell. These ele-

Table 22.1

Element	1	2		3			4				5			6	
	s	s	p	s	p	d	s	p	d	f	s	p	d	s	p
F	2	2	5												
Cl	2	2	6	2	5										
Br	2	2	6	2	6	10	2	5							
I	2	2	6	2	6	10	2	6	10		2	5			
At	2	2	6	2	6	10	2	6	10	14	2	6	10	2	5

ments are all nonmetals, since the atoms have a strong tendency to attain the stable inert gas configuration (and an oxidation state of -1), either by taking up an electron from an atom of a metallic element to form a singly charged negative ion, or by sharing electrons with elements whose tendency to release electrons is not sufficiently great to allow complete electron transfer. These two types of reaction are represented by the following equations, where X represents any of the halogens:

$$M \cdot + \cdot \overset{..}{\underset{..}{X}} : \rightarrow M^+ + : \overset{..}{\underset{..}{X}} : ^-$$

$$M \cdot + \cdot \overset{..}{\underset{..}{X}} : \rightarrow M : \overset{..}{\underset{..}{X}} :$$

Under ordinary conditions all the halogens form diatomic molecules. This is a result of the fact that, by sharing a single pair of electrons between them, two halogen atoms attain stable configurations.

$$: \overset{..}{X} \cdot + \cdot \overset{..}{\underset{..}{X}} : \rightarrow : \overset{..}{X} : \overset{..}{\underset{..}{X}} :$$

Models showing the relative sizes of the halogen molecules are given in Figure 22.2.

Fig. 22.2. Models of hydrogen and halogen molecules: H_2, F_2, Cl_2, Br_2, and I_2, respectively. (*Courtesy of Dr. J. A. Campbell, Oberlin College.*)

These elements have very little tendency to lose electrons to form positive ions, although, as will be shown, this tendency becomes appreciable in the case of iodine. This reluctance to form positive ions is understandable in terms of the high ionization potentials of these elements, which are listed in Table 22.2. (The student should review, in this connection, pp. 181 to 185, Chapter 10.)

Table 22.2

	Ionization Potential (volts)	
Element	For 1 Electron	For the 7th Valence Electron
F	17.4	185.1
Cl	13.0	114.3
Br	11.8	. . . . .
I	10.4	. . . . .

It should be noted that, in accordance with the discussion given in Chapter 10 (p. 184), the ionization potentials of these elements decrease in the order of increasing atomic number. Thus, while all are predominantly nonmetallic in their properties, their nonmetallic character decreases in the order $F > Cl > Br > I$. In fact, certain metallic characteristics appear in the physical and chemical properties of iodine; these will be discussed later in the chapter.

Elementary fluorine is the strongest chemical oxidizing agent known. It will displace any of the nonmetallic elements, including the other halogens, from its binary compounds.

$$2F_2 + 2H_2O = O_2 + 4HF$$

$$F_2 + 2Cl^- = Cl_2 + 2F^-$$

$$F_2 + 2Br^- = Br_2 + 2F^-$$

$$F_2 + 2I^- = I_2 + 2F^-$$

Similarly, chlorine displaces bromine from bromides and iodine from iodides, while bromine displaces iodine from iodides.

The halogens form compounds also, although less readily, in which their oxidation states are other than -1. The most important of these compounds are the oxyacids and their salts, which are to be discussed in the next chapter.

4. Occurrence. Because of their strong tendency to take up electrons and thus to form compounds, the halogens are never found in nature in the free state. It is estimated that fluorine occurs in the earth's crust to the extent of 0.1% of the total—mainly in the form of the minerals cryolite, Na_3AlF_6, and fluorspar, CaF_2. Chlorine forms an estimated 0.2% of the earth's crust, mainly in the form of metal chlorides, the most abundant of which is sodium chloride, NaCl (p. 380). This compound constitutes about 2.5% of sea water and is also found in brine wells and as rock salt in large mineral deposits in the earth. Besides the soluble chlorides of sodium, potassium, magnesium, and calcium, the insoluble silver chloride, AgCl, commonly called horn silver, is also found in nature.

Bromine and iodine are far less abundant in the earth's crust than the first two members of this family, the estimated proportion of bromine and iodine being about 0.001% each. Bromine occurs mainly as the sodium, potassium, and magnesium salts, which are obtained from such sources as the famous Stassfurt deposits in Germany (p. 640), brine wells (particularly in Michigan), and sea water. The last of these now constitutes the most important commercial source of the element. The principal sources of iodine are the sodium iodate and periodate which occur as impurities in the huge nitrate deposits of northern Chile. Within the United States, the largest source of iodine is the brine from California oil wells.

Chlorine occurs as chloride ion in various fluids in the bodies of animals. The gastric juices of the stomach contain a small concentration of hydrochloric acid, which plays a part in digestion. Iodine, likewise, is found in various animal tissues, especially, in the case of mammals, in the thyroid gland. Many marine plants selectively adsorb iodide from sea water rather than chloride or bromide, and such seaweed is an important source of iodine.

5. Preparation. Since the principal natural sources of fluorine, chlorine, and bromine are compounds in which these elements exhibit an oxidation state of -1, it is apparent that the processes for obtaining the free halogens from these sources must be oxidation processes; in each case, the following steps are involved:

$$: \ddot{X} :^- = : \ddot{X} \cdot + e^-$$

$$2 : \ddot{X} \cdot = : \ddot{X} : \ddot{X} :$$

Clearly, the greater the tendency of an element to take up electrons to form a negative ion, the more difficult it will be to remove electrons from that ion, or, in other words, to oxidize it to the free element. From this point of view, it is easy to understand why the preparation of fluorine from its compounds is so difficult. Since fluorine is itself the strongest of chemical oxidizing agents, it is evident that there is no chemical oxidizing agent capable of oxidizing fluoride ion to elementary fluorine. In order to obtain this element, therefore, it is necessary to resort to electrolytic oxidation. The electrolysis of an aqueous solution of a fluoride would not serve the purpose, however, since a voltage high enough to liberate fluorine would be more than sufficient to release oxygen from water. Hence, the electrolytic oxidation of fluoride ion to fluorine must be carried out in an anhydrous medium. A further problem is presented by the fact that fluorine is so highly reactive that it vigorously attacks any of the common metals. The electrolysis of a solution of potassium fluoride in anhydrous hydrogen fluoride by Moissan has already been mentioned (p. 381). The method in use at present consists in the electrolysis of fused potassium hydrogen fluoride, KHF_2, between graphite electrodes in a cell of steel, copper, or Monel metal. Elementary fluorine is so difficult to produce, store, and transport that it is only recently that the free element has been made available commercially. Theoretically it should make a superlative oxidizing agent for rocket fuels. All-out attempts are being made to overcome the practical difficulties involved in its use.

Since chlorine has a smaller tendency than fluorine to take up electrons, it follows that chloride ion is considerably easier to oxidize than fluoride ion. Chlorine is commonly prepared in the laboratory by the action of oxidizing agents upon hydrochloric acid, or upon mixtures of sodium chloride and

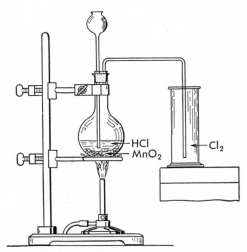

Fig. 22.3. Laboratory preparation of chlorine.

sulfuric acid (which furnish hydrogen ion and chloride ion). Among the oxidizing agents used are manganese dioxide, potassium permanganate, lead dioxide, potassium chlorate, and nitric acid. Of these, manganese dioxide is most commonly employed; the solution of hydrogen chloride is usually added from a dropping funnel or thistle tube to a flask containing the manganese dioxide, and the mixture is warmed. Since chlorine gas is heavier than air, it may be collected by displacement of air from an upright cylinder or bottle, as is shown in Figure 22.3. The oxidation of hydrochloric acid by manganese dioxide may be represented as follows:

$$MnO_2 + 4HCl = MnCl_2 + Cl_2 + 2H_2O$$

This equation shows the formulas for the substances that are actually brought into contact and for those that may actually be isolated as products of the reaction, and hence it may conveniently be designated as a "substantial" equation. Since, however, in aqueous solution the hydrochloric acid and the manganese chloride are practically completely ionized, the reaction may be better represented by the ionic equation

$$MnO_2 + 4H^+ + 4Cl^- = Mn^{++} + 2Cl^- + Cl_2 + 2H_2O$$

It is now evident that two of the chloride ions are mere "spectator" ions and should, therefore, be omitted from the ionic equation, which then takes the form

$$MnO_2 + 4H^+ + 2Cl^- = Mn^{++} + Cl_2 + 2H_2O$$

In formulating such ionic equations it is not necessary that the substantial equations be written first. Ionic oxidation-reduction equations may be balanced directly by means of the oxidation number method, with the additional requirement that the sum of all the charges, positive and negative, must be the same on both sides of the equation. A second method for balancing such equations is given on pp. 430–1. The ionic equations for the action on hydrochloric acid of the other oxidizing agents mentioned are:

$$16H^+ + 10Cl^- + 2MnO_4^- = 2Mn^{++} + 5Cl_2 + 8H_2O$$
$$4H^+ + 2Cl^- + PbO_2 = Pb^{++} + Cl_2 + 2H_2O$$
$$6H^+ + 5Cl^- + ClO_3^- = 3Cl_2 + 3H_2O$$
$$8H^+ + 6Cl^- + 2NO_3^- = 2NO + 3Cl_2 + 4H_2O$$

Almost all industrial chlorine is obtained by the electrolysis of aqueous sodium chloride solution. When such a solution is electrolyzed, chlorine gas is set free at the anode, and hydrogen gas and hydroxide ion are produced at the cathode. Since the solution contains sodium ion, the overall result of this process is the production of gaseous hydrogen, gaseous chlorine, and a solution of sodium hydroxide.

$$2Na^+ + 2Cl^- + 2H_2O = 2Na^+ + 2OH^- + H_2 + Cl_2$$

Chlorine reacts readily either with sodium hydroxide or with hydrogen; it is necessary, therefore, that these three products be kept separate. A cell that makes possible such a separation is the Hooker S cell, which is illustrated in Figure 22.4.

The oxidation of bromide ion to free bromine may be brought about more readily than the corresponding process for chlorine. Bromine, therefore, may be prepared in the laboratory by the use of any oxidizing agent suitable for chlorine, and also by means of other oxidizing agents that will not suffice to liberate chlorine. The commercial production of bromine from salt brines, or from sea water, which has come to be the largest source of the element, is based upon the fact that bromide ion is oxidized to elementary bromine by treatment with free chlorine.

$$Cl_2 + 2Br^- = Br_2 + 2Cl^-$$

Iodide ion is still more easily oxidized to the free element than either chloride or bromide, and any of the laboratory methods used for chlorine or bromine serve equally well for the preparation of free iodine. The chief commercial source of free iodine is the reduction by means of sodium bisulfite of the sodium iodate which occurs in the nitrate deposits of Chile.

$$2IO_3^- + 5HSO_3^- = 5SO_4^{--} + 3H^+ + I_2 + H_2O$$

Some iodine is obtained by the oxidation of iodides from certain seaweeds. by means of chlorine, manganese dioxide, or concentrated sulfuric acid.

Fig. 22.4. Hooker S cells for the electrolysis of aqueous solutions of sodium chloride. (*Courtesy of Hooker Electrochemical Co.*)

6. Physical Properties of the Elements. As is evident from the electronic formulas for the diatomic molecules of these substances, these molecules are completely nonpolar. Moreover, since the configurations of the atoms in these molecules are quite stable, there is little possibility for the formation of chemical bonds between two such molecules. We should expect, therefore, that intermolecular forces in the free halogens would be very weak, and that such substances would be highly volatile. This expectation is borne out by the data in Table 22.3. At room temperature fluorine is a very pale yellow gas, and chlorine a greenish yellow gas; in the liquid and solid states both of

these elements exhibit somewhat deeper colors. Bromine at room temperature is a deep brownish red liquid, which readily volatilizes to a reddish
brown vapor. Bromine, in fact, is one of only two elements which are liquid
at room temperature, the other being mercury. Iodine at room temperature
exists as dark, somewhat lustrous crystals. At pressures below 100 mm.,
crystalline iodine may be sublimed (p. 66). The vapor has a deep violet
color, which is faintly visible even at room temperature in a closed vessel
containing iodine crystals.

Table 22.3

	F_2	Cl_2	Br_2	I_2
Boiling point (°C.)	−187	− 34.05	58.78	183
Freezing point (°C.)	−223	−100.98	− 7.3	114

Chlorine and bromine are appreciably soluble in water, yielding solutions
similar in color to the free gases. Bromine is considerably more soluble in
less polar liquids, such as carbon disulfide, ether, chloroform, and carbon
tetrachloride, than in water. Iodine is not very soluble in water, but dissolves
readily in nonpolar or slightly polar solvents, such as carbon tetrachloride,
carbon disulfide, and chloroform, to give violet-colored solutions. However,
its solutions in more polar solvents such as water or ethyl alcohol are brown.
Both chlorine and bromine form hydrates, of the formulas $Cl_2 \cdot 8H_2O$
and $Br_2 \cdot 10H_2O$, which decompose below 10° C. under 1 atm. pressure of
the halogen.

7. Reactions of the Halogens. The relationship of the combining characteristics of these elements to their atomic structures has already been discussed.
The two most reactive of these elements, viz., fluorine and chlorine, react
directly with all the metals to form metal halides. Bromine and iodine, which,
as we have already pointed out, have less attraction for electrons than the
other two and hence are somewhat less reactive, form halides with all except
the very noble (i.e., unreactive) metals.

The halogens combine also with other nonmetals to form covalent compounds. Fluorine reacts readily with all the nonmetals except nitrogen,
oxygen, chlorine, and the inert gases; fluorine compounds of the first
three of these may be prepared by indirect methods. Chlorine reacts directly
with all the nonmetals except nitrogen, oxygen, fluorine, carbon, and the
inert gases, and chlorine compounds of all of these except the inert gases
have been obtained indirectly. Bromine and iodine, again, do not take part
in as many reactions of this type as do chlorine and fluorine.

The halogens react with water in two ways. The first, which consists of a simple displacement of oxygen, is represented by the equation

$$2X_2 + 2H_2O \rightleftharpoons 4H^+ + 4X^- + O_2$$

As is to be expected, this reaction proceeds less rapidly and completely, the smaller the tendency of the halogen to take on electrons. Thus, in the case of fluorine, the reaction goes to completion almost instantaneously at room temperature, while with chlorine it proceeds slowly—although it is some-what accelerated by sunlight—and incompletely. With bromine, the reaction is very slow and incomplete, and in the case of iodine, it actually proceeds in the reverse direction under ordinary conditions, for oxygen (or air) liberates free iodine from aqueous solutions of hydrogen iodide.

The second type of reaction with water, which may be designated as hydrolysis (cf. p. 237) of the halogen, is represented by the equation

$$X_2 + H_2O \rightleftharpoons H^+ + X^- + HOX$$

This reaction is not observed in the case of fluorine, which, as has been stated, displaces oxygen completely; all the other halogens, however, undergo such hydrolysis to a small extent. The change, in terms of electrons, may be represented thus:

$$: \overset{..}{\underset{..}{X}} : \overset{..}{\underset{..}{X}} : + H : \overset{..}{O} : H = H^+ + : \overset{..}{\underset{..}{X}} :^- + : \overset{..}{\underset{..}{X}} : \overset{..}{O} : H$$

This reaction will be considered in greater detail in the next chapter.

The halogens react with ammonia in a manner analogous to that just described. Thus, for example, in a no more than slightly acidic solution, chlorine displaces nitrogen from ammonia.

$$3Cl_2 + 8NH_3 = 6NH_4^+ + 6Cl^- + N_2$$

Fluorine and bromine react similarly. At higher hydrogen ion concentrations, however, the reaction between chlorine and ammonium ion is one of ammonolysis (corresponding to hydrolysis, p. 237), and yields (in the presence of an excess of chlorine) nitrogen trichloride.

$$3Cl_2 + NH_3 = 3H^+ + 3Cl^- + NCl_3$$

In the case of iodine, the compound $NI_3 \cdot NH_3$ is formed.

The halogens add to compounds containing double or triple covalent bonds (i.e. to "unsaturated" compounds). A few examples of such reactions are:

$$CO + X_2 = COX_2 \quad (X = Cl, Br) \text{ (p. 536)}$$
$$SO_2 + X_2 = SO_2X_2 \quad (X = F, Cl) \text{ (p. 462)}$$
$$C_2H_4 + X_2 = C_2H_4X_2 \quad (X = Cl, Br) \text{ (p. 567)}$$

The reactions of the halogens with hydrogen will be discussed in connection with the hydrogen halides.

All the halogens have an intensely irritating effect on the tissues of the respiratory tract of animals. Chlorine gas, even in concentrations as low as 0.00002 g. per liter, produces inflammation and congestion of the respiratory system; prolonged inhalation of this gas results in death. Bromine and iodine vapor have similar effects, and liquid bromine should be handled with extreme caution, for, on contact with the flesh, it produces serious burns which heal only very slowly.

8. Uses. Chlorine is one of the most important of industrial chemicals. Its major use is as a bleaching agent, especially for wood pulp and paper; it is used also in the bleaching of cotton cloth. Wool, silk, and most other textiles are attacked by chlorine and therefore cannot be bleached with this substance. Large quantities of chlorine are consumed in the manufacture of hypochlorites, such as $NaOCl$ (p. 405) and $CaOCl_2$ (p. 407), which, in turn, are used as bleaching agents. Other applications of chlorine are in the manufacture of many organic compounds, among which are important dyes, drugs, and explosives, and in the manufacture of chlorides of other elements such as sulfur, phosphorus, arsenic, antimony, carbon, silicon, and tin. Chlorine, because of its painful and destructive physiological effects, was the first poison gas used in World War I. A number of compounds of chlorine, however, were found to be more effective and soon completely replaced chlorine in chemical warfare; these compounds include phosgene, $COCl_2$, dichlorodiethyl sulfide or mustard gas, $(ClC_2H_4)_2S$, chloropicrin, CCl_3NO_2, and diphenylchloroarsine, $(C_6H_5)_2AsCl$.

The major portion of the liquid bromine produced goes into the manufacture of ethylene dibromide, which is used as an ingredient in the so-called ethyl gasoline, as well as in the manufacture of lead tetraethyl, the important "anti-knock" agent in this motor fuel. Bromine is used also in the manufacture of various metal bromides (discussed later) and other bromine-containing compounds. Several organic compounds of bromine find important application as dyes and drugs.

The most important use of iodine is as an antiseptic. A solution of iodine in ethyl alcohol, known as "tincture of iodine," is widely marketed for home use. Iodine is used in the preparation of a number of metal iodides, the applications of which are discussed later. It is also used in the synthesis of many organic compounds, including some important dyes and drugs.

Free iodine undergoes an interesting and characteristic reaction with starch; these two substances unite to form a deep blue product of indefinite composition. This reaction is used in analytical chemistry for the detection of iodine. Since moderately strong oxidizing agents change iodide ion into free iodine, the presence of such substances can be detected by virtue of the fact that a strip of paper which has been moistened with solutions of starch and of a soluble iodide will turn blue in their presence. Among the oxidizing agents that can be detected by this method are fluorine, chlorine, bromine, ozone, and hydrogen peroxide.

9. The Interhalogen Compounds. A number of compounds are formed by the union of two of the halogens. These include such substances as IF_7, IF_5, ICl_3, ICl, IBr, BrF_5, BrF, $BrCl$, ClF_3 and ClF. The compounds IF_7, IF_5, and BrF_5 are examples of cases where the valence shell of an atom contains more than four pairs of electrons. Even though the octet is a very common and very stable configuration, the existence of these and other compounds, such as SF_6 and OsF_8, indicates clearly that the valence shell of certain atoms may be expanded to 10, 12, 14, or even 16 electrons.

Iodine monochloride, ICl, a dark red, crystalline solid (m. p. 27° C.), and iodine trichloride, ICl_3, an orange solid, are among the best known of the interhalogens. Both of these substances are in the liquid state conductors of electricity; this indicates that iodine to chlorine bonds have a considerable amount of ionic character, i.e., are highly polar and are partially ionized. The hypothesis that iodine can form I^+ ions is supported by the fact that, in the electrolysis of solutions of ICl in liquid sulfur dioxide, iodine is liberated at the cathode and chlorine at the anode.

THE HYDROGEN HALIDES AND THEIR SALTS

10. Structure of Hydrogen Halide Molecules. The binary compounds of the halogens with hydrogen are one of the most important groups of compounds of these elements. Both from a practical and a theoretical point of view, it is desirable to consider these substances in some detail. The electronic structures of the hydrogen halides may be represented by the general formula $H : \overset{..}{X} :$, which shows the hydrogen atom and the halogen atom to be joined by a single covalent bond. The degree of polarity of this bond depends upon the attraction for electrons of the halogen atom involved; as we shall see, it decreases in the order $HF > HCl > HBr > HI$.

11. Preparation of the Hydrogen Halides. Considerable insight into the nature of these important compounds is to be gained from a study of the methods by which they may be prepared.

Each of the hydrogen halides may be obtained by direct synthesis from hydrogen and the free halogen, in accordance with the equation

$$H_2 + X_2 = 2HX$$

The ease with which this reaction takes place for the various halogens decreases greatly from fluorine to iodine. The former reacts with hydrogen with great violence even in the dark, whereas the reaction of iodine and hydrogen requires a catalyst such as platinum and does not go to completion under ordinary conditions. These facts are in line with the decrease in the heat of formation of the hydrogen halides, as shown in Table 22.4, with increasing atomic number of the halogen.

A second type of reaction which yields hydrogen halides is the reaction of the halogen with hydrogen compounds of less active nonmetals. For example, one method of obtaining a solution of hydrogen iodide consists in the treatment of a solution of hydrogen sulfide with iodine.

$$H_2S + I_2 = S + 2H^+ + 2I^-$$

A third method for obtaining the hydrogen halides is based upon the hydrolysis of other halides, particularly those of nonmetals. This type of reaction is exemplified by the reaction of water with the phosphorus trihalides.

$$PX_3 + 3H_2O = P(OH)_3 + 3HX$$

This reaction is particularly important for the preparation of hydrogen bromide and hydrogen iodide. In the preparation of these substances, it is not necessary to isolate the trihalide before the reaction is allowed to start; hydrogen bromide is formed when liquid bromine is added to a mixture of phosphorus and water, and hydrogen iodide when water is added to a mixture of phosphorus and an excess of iodine.

One of the simplest methods of preparing volatile acids is by the action of a less volatile acid on a salt of the acid desired. The most widely used methods for the industrial preparation of hydrogen fluoride and of hydrogen chloride belong to this class. Thus, hydrogen fluoride is readily prepared by the action of concentrated sulfuric acid on calcium fluoride at slightly elevated temperatures.

$$CaF_{2(s)} + H_2SO_4 = CaSO_4 + 2HF_{(g)}$$

The main industrial source of hydrogen chloride is the reaction of sulfuric acid with sodium chloride. This reaction takes place in two stages; the first step proceeds even at ordinary temperature, while the second requires heating to about 500° C.

$$(1) \ NaCl + H_2SO_4 = NaHSO_4 + HCl_{(g)}$$

$$(2) \ NaCl + NaHSO_4 = Na_2SO_4 + HCl_{(g)}$$

When hydrogen chloride is prepared in glass vessels in the laboratory the reaction is not carried beyond the first stage.

It might be supposed that hydrogen bromide and hydrogen iodide would be obtainable by analogous methods, but this is not the case. As was pointed out earlier in the chapter, as the oxidizing strength of the free elements decreases, the reducing strength of the negative ion increases (p. 384).

$$
\begin{array}{cccc}
F_2 & Cl_2 & Br_2 & I_2
\end{array}
$$

$\longleftarrow$

Increasing Oxidizing Strength

$$
\begin{array}{cccc}
F^- & Cl^- & Br^- & I^-
\end{array}
$$

$\longrightarrow$

Increasing Reducing Strength

The reducing properties of bromides and iodides are such that the reaction of these substances with hot concentrated sulfuric acid does not yield the pure hydrogen halide, for the halide is at least partially oxidized to the free halogen by the sulfuric acid. In the bromide reaction, sulfur dioxide is the reduction product, while with iodide, according to the conditions of the reaction, sulfur dioxide, free sulfur, or even hydrogen sulfide may be obtained.

$$2HBr + H_2SO_4 = SO_2 + Br_2 + 2H_2O$$

$$2HI + H_2SO_4 = SO_2 + I_2 + 2H_2O$$

$$6HI + H_2SO_4 = S + 3I_2 + 4H_2O$$

$$8HI + H_2SO_4 = H_2S + 4I_2 + 4H_2O$$

When a nonvolatile acid of lower oxidizing strength, such as phosphoric acid, is employed, hydrogen bromide and hydrogen iodide may be obtained in the pure state by this method.

12. Properties and Uses of the Hydrogen Halides. The hydrogen halides are colorless gases at room temperature. They may be condensed at low temperatures to colorless liquids that at still lower temperatures freeze to colorless solids. A list of their more important physical constants is given in Table 22.4. The relative sizes of the four HX molecules are illustrated by models in Figure 22.5. All the hydrogen halides possess pungent, disagreeable odors, and are highly irritating to the mucous membranes; hydrogen fluoride is especially poisonous and irritating to the skin. All four hydrogen halides are very soluble in water, yielding solutions that, except in the case of

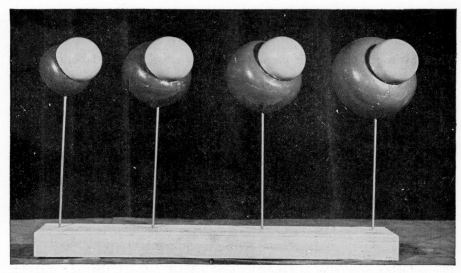

Fig. 22.5. Models of hydrogen halide molecules: HF, HCl, HBr, and HI, respectively.

hydrogen fluoride, are strongly acidic; hydrogen fluoride gives only a weakly acidic solution. Their aqueous solutions are called hydrohalic acids; thus, we have hydrochloric acid, hydrobromic acid, etc.

That the bonds holding the hydrogen and halogen atoms together are not electrovalent is indicated not only by the low melting and boiling points of the hydrogen halides, but also by the fact that the pure liquid hydrogen halides are, without exception, poor conductors of electricity. That the bonds do, however, possess some degree of polarity, and that this degree of polarity decreases in the order HF > HCl > HBr > HI, is indicated by the magnitude of the dielectric constants of the liquid hydrogen halides (Table 22.4).

Table 22.4

	HF	HCl	HBr	HI
Boiling point (°C.)	19.4	− 85	−67	−36
Freezing point (°C.)	−83	−112	−86	−51
Solubility in water at 1 atm. and 20° C. (g./100 g. of solution)	35.3	42	49	57
Heat of formation from the gaseous elements (cal./mole)	64,000	22,000	12,000	1200
Dielectric constant of liquid	66	9	6	3

The aqueous solutions of the hydrogen halides are excellent conductors of electricity; this, as was shown in Chapter 17, results from the reaction of the hydrogen halide with water to form hydronium ion.

$$
\overset{\displaystyle\;\;}{\text{H}} : \overset{..}{\underset{..}{\text{X}}} : + \; \text{H} : \overset{..}{\underset{..}{\text{O}}} : \text{H} = \text{H} : \overset{\displaystyle\text{H}}{\underset{..}{\text{O}}} : \text{H}^+ + : \overset{..}{\underset{..}{\text{X}}} :^-
$$

This reaction goes to completion in dilute solutions of all the hydrogen halides except hydrogen fluoride.

An examination of the data in Table 22.4 reveals that hydrogen fluoride is abnormal with respect to several of its physical properties. Thus, in the series HI, HBr, HCl there is a consistent decrease in melting and boiling points; hydrogen fluoride, however, has a considerably higher melting point and boiling point than hydrogen chloride. Moreover, the difference in the dielectric constants of liquid hydrogen fluoride and hydrogen chloride is much too large to be accounted for solely by the difference in the polarity of the bonds in the two substances. Still further, it has been shown that liquid hydrogen fluoride is highly associated, and that, even in the gaseous state, molecules corresponding to the formula H_6F_6 exist, at least at ordinary temperatures. Similar abnormalities in the properties of water with respect to hydrogen compounds of the other elements of the oxygen subgroup were pointed out in Chapter 14. These abnormalities were explained there (p. 235) in terms of the function of hydrogen bonds in uniting molecules of the water into large aggregates. A similar explanation applies to the abnormal physical properties of hydrogen fluoride.

All the hydrogen halides form mixtures with maximum boiling points (p. 298) with water. The composition of these mixtures with maximum boiling point varies with change in atmospheric pressure. The composition of such mixtures for various barometric pressures has been carefully established for hydrogen chloride solutions, so that "constant boiling hydrochloric acid," containing slightly over 20% of hydrogen chloride and boiling at about 110° C., may be used in the preparation of standard solutions for use in acid-base titrations.

The chemical reactions of the hydrogen halides may be divided into two general groups: those in which the hydrogen halide acts as an acid, and those in which it acts as a reducing agent. In the former group are reactions such as the neutralization of basic hydroxides and oxides, the liberation of carbon dioxide from carbonates, and the liberation of hydrogen upon reaction with active metals, which, as we have learned, are typical of strong acids. As has already been pointed out, the reducing properties of the halide ions, and hence of the hydrogen halides, increase in the order HF < HCl < HBr < HI. Hydrofluoric acid, of course, has no appreciable reducing properties. At the other extreme, however, hydriodic acid is a strong reducing agent, so readily oxidized that even a dilute solution, on exposure to the air, slowly acquires a brown color from the iodine liberated by the action of atmospheric oxygen.

$$4H^+ + 4I^- + O_2 = 2H_2O + 2I_2$$

Hydriodic acid, therefore, is used in a number of reactions involving the reduction of organic compounds.

The most important of the hydrogen halides from the industrial point of view is hydrogen chloride. Concentrated hydrochloric acid (usually about a 12 molar solution, containing about 37% of hydrogen chloride) is used in large quantities for the preparation of chlorides of the metals, for the cleaning of oxide scale from the surfaces of metals before plating, and in the manufacture of many chemical products such as dyes, drugs, and soap. Hydrochloric acid also finds many applications in the chemical laboratory.

Hydrogen fluoride possesses the unusual property of reacting with silicon dioxide and the silicates. The reaction with silicon dioxide is

$$SiO_2 + 4HF = SiF_{4(g)} + 2H_2O$$

Since silicon dioxide and insoluble silicates are the main constituents of glass, this property of hydrogen fluoride makes it impossible to ship or store the acid in glass bottles; usually some sort of plastic container is employed for this purpose. The reaction finds practical application in the etching and frosting of glass. The graduations on chemical glassware such as burets and pipets are made by this means. The glass is coated with paraffin, which is scraped away where the marks are to be etched, and the surface is then treated with hydrofluoric acid. A mixture of hydrofluoric acid and ammonium fluoride is used for such purposes as the frosting of the inner surface of electric light bulbs.

13. The Metal Halides. Since the halogen compounds of the nonmetals are to be discussed in the respective chapters devoted to the other nonmetallic elements, we shall restrict the present discussion to the binary compounds of the halogens with the metals.

The wide range covered by the physical properties of the metal halides is illustrated by the following table of the melting points and boiling points of some of the chlorides. The immense variation in physical properties of the halides depends, among other factors, upon the varying nature of the bonding forces involved. The halides of the elements of low ionization potential are highly electrovalent, and hence form very stable ionic crystals with high melting points. As the ionization potential of the metal increases, however, the bond between the halogen and the metal becomes more and more covalent in nature (see Chapter 10) with the result that the melting and boiling points of the halides are progressively lowered. This explanation is supported by the fact that the low-melting halides are very poor conductors of electricity in the liquid state, whereas the high-melting halides, under similar conditions, are good conductors.

Table 22.5

	M.p. (°C.)	B.p. (°C.)
$NaCl$	801	1413
$CaCl_2$	772	>1600
$MgCl_2$	708	1412
$CuCl_2$	498	Decomposes
$SnCl_4$	-33	114.1
Al_2Cl_6	190 (2.5 atm.)	Sublimes at 177.8
$HgCl_2$	276	302

Chemical differences among the halides are also readily explainable. Since the electron affinities of the halogens decrease in the order $F > Cl > Br > I$, the fluorides have the least tendency, and the iodides have the greatest tendency, to be covalent. Furthermore, since the oxidizing strength of the halogens decreases in the order $F_2 > Cl_2 > Br_2 > I_2$, it is not surprising that the reaction of fluorine with a metal capable of assuming more than one oxidation state usually results in the formation of the fluoride corresponding to one of the higher oxidation states; whereas, in many cases, the iodide in which the metal exhibits a lower oxidation state is the only one which is stable.

The halides, in general, are readily soluble in water. Exceptions to this rule among the fluorides include those of lithium, the alkaline earth metals, and the rare earth metals, which are but slightly soluble. The most important slightly soluble chlorides are silver, mercurous, thallous, cuprous, plumbous, aurous, platinous, and platinic chlorides. The corresponding bromides and iodides are likewise only sparingly soluble—in most cases, less soluble than the chlorides. Bismuth and mercuric iodides, also, are very slightly soluble.

As would be expected, in view of the common ion effect (p. 356), the solubility of any of these slightly soluble halides is decreased by the presence of a slight excess of the corresponding halide ion. On the other hand, the solubility is greatly increased, in most cases, by a large excess of halide. This latter phenomenon is explainable in terms of the fact that practically all of the metal ions, except those of the alkali and alkaline earth metals, form complex anions in the presence of an excess of a halide ion. Silver chloride, for example, though only very slightly soluble in water and even less soluble in dilute chloride solutions, dissolves readily in concentrated solutions of a chloride.

$$AgCl_{(s)} + 2Cl^- = AgCl_3^{--}$$

Other examples of such complexes include FeF_6^{---}, AlF_6^{---}, $AlCl_6^{---}$, $SnCl_6^{--}$, $TlCl_6^{---}$, $CoCl_4^{--}$, $CdBr_4^{--}$, $PtBr_6^{--}$, PtI_6^{--}, HgI_4^{--}, and AuI_4^-.

The halide ions show some tendency also to form a different type of complex anion, consisting of three halogen atoms, by reacting with molecules of free halogen. Thus, iodide ion readily combines with free iodine to form triiodide ion.

$$I^- + I_2 = I_3^-$$

This reaction accounts for the high solubility of iodine in aqueous solutions of iodides. Other polyhalide ions of this type include Br_3^-, ICl_2^-, IBr_2^-, and $IClBr^-$.

The most widely used methods for the preparation of metal halides are the following:

1. Direct synthesis; i.e., the direct combination of the metal and the free halogen. If the metal is at all reactive, such combinations are highly exothermic.

$$Cu + Cl_2 = CuCl_2$$

2. Reaction of the metal with the corresponding hydrohalic acid. This method is, of course, applicable only to metals preceding hydrogen in the displacement series. Example:

$$Zn + 2H^+ + 2Cl^- = Zn^{++} + 2Cl^- + H_{2(g)}$$

3. Reaction of the metal oxide, hydroxide, or carbonate with the hydrohalic acid. Examples:

$$FeO + 2H^+ + 2Cl^- = Fe^{++} + 2Cl^- + H_2O$$

$$NiCO_3 + 2H^+ + 2Br^- = Ni^{++} + 2Br^- + H_2O + CO_{2(g)}$$

$$Co(OH)_2 + 2H^+ + 2F^- = Co^{++} + 2F^- + 2H_2O$$

4. Reaction of the metal oxide with the gaseous halogen at high temperature in the presence of carbon. Anhydrous metal halides are commonly pre-

pared by this means; the free halogen gas is passed over a mixture of the oxide with carbon or some carbonaceous material at red heat. Example:

$$Al_2O_3 + 3C + 3Cl_2 = Al_2Cl_6 + 3CO$$

Among the metal halides are a number of substances which are commercially valuable. Of the fluorides, cryolite (Na_3AlF_6) is one of the most important naturally occurring compounds of aluminum (p. 799). Calcium fluoride occurs in small amounts in animal bones and in somewhat larger proportion in the teeth. A trace of fluoride ion in drinking water appears to be essential to the normal development of the teeth of children, and to play an important part in the prevention of tooth decay in adults. The presence of more than a minute concentration, however, brings about abnormal growth of the teeth and mottling of the dental enamel. Naturally occurring calcium fluoride (fluorspar) is useful as a flux; that is, to lower the melting point of ores or metallurgical products by combining with difficulty fusible substances to form easily fusible mixtures. Sodium fluoride, likewise, is used as a flux, and, since it is highly poisonous, as an insecticide, especially against household insects.

Sodium chloride is by far the most important of the metal halides. Its wide industrial application results from the fact that it is the ultimate source of all metallic sodium and all hydrochloric acid and chlorine, as well as of practically all compounds containing sodium or chlorine (see also p. 645). It is essential to normal digestion and other bodily functions and is used in the preparation and seasoning of many foods. Silver chloride, as well as silver bromide and silver iodide, is used in the production of sensitized paper and film for photographic purposes (p. 772). Potassium and sodium bromides are used medicinally as sedatives and in the treatment of epilepsy and lockjaw.

A small amount of iodine (about 0.005 g. in the adult human body) is essential to human well-being. In the absence of a sufficient quantity of iodine, the thyroid gland does not perform its proper function in the regulation of metabolism, and in cases of extreme deficiency an abnormal swelling of the gland known as goiter may occur. Where the normal food supply does not furnish a sufficient quantity of iodine, the use of "iodized" table salt, which contains a small amount of sodium or potassium iodide, prevents the development of this disease.

14. Tests for the Halides. Chloride, bromide, and iodide ions all yield, with silver nitrate solution, precipitates of silver halides that are insoluble in nitric acid; silver chloride is white, the other two pale yellow. The three ions may be distinguished from each other by treatment of their solutions with chlorine water. With this reagent, chloride, of course, remains unchanged; bromide liberates free bromine, which may be extracted with nonpolar solvents such as carbon tetrachloride or carbon disulfide, in which it gives an orange-colored solution, and iodide is similarly changed to free iodine, which gives a violet-colored solution in nonpolar solvents.

Fluoride ion, which does not give a precipitate with silver nitrate, may be detected by the addition of sulfuric acid; the presence of hydrofluoric acid in the solution is indicated by its ability to etch glass.

STUDY QUESTIONS AND PROBLEMS

1. Make a table of the elements of the halogen family, listing their electronic configurations and their most important physical and chemical properties.

2. List the halogens in order of increasing oxidizing power. Show how this order may be proved by means of a series of displacement reactions.

3. What evidence is there that the halogens form diatomic molecules? Are diatomic molecules explainable in terms of the electronic configurations of these elements? How?

4. Make a list of reactions by which halogens may be obtained from the naturally occurring halides. Which halogen is most difficult to prepare? Why?

5. Which series of metal halides—fluorides, chlorides, bromides, or iodides—is most stable? Why?

6. Complete and balance the following equations, indicating changes in oxidation state:

$$MnO_2 + H^+ + Cl^- =$$

$$PbO_2 + H^+ + Cl^- =$$

$$MnO_4^- + H^+ + Cl^- =$$

$$H^+ + I^- + O_2 =$$

$$Na^+ + Cl^- + H_2O \xrightarrow{\text{electrolysis}} =$$

$$IO_3^- + HSO_3^- =$$

7. Are the Cl_2 and F_2 molecules polar or nonpolar? What evidence can you give for your answer to this question from the physical and chemical properties of elementary chlorine and fluorine? What would you say in this connection of the ICl molecule?

8. In what way is hydrogen fluoride abnormal in its properties when compared with the other hydrogen halides? How may these abnormalities be explained?

9. List as many methods, with equations, as you can find for the preparation of HCl and HF. Which of these methods cannot be used for the preparation of HBr and HI? Why?

The Oxides and Oxygen Acids of the Halogens

1. Oxygen Compounds of the Halogens. In the preceding chapter, it was pointed out that, although the most important halogen compounds are those in which the halogen is in an oxidation state of -1, the elements of this family also enter into compounds corresponding to higher oxidation states. A few of these compounds, the halogen halides, were mentioned in the last chapter. More important, however, are the compounds with oxygen, particularly the oxyhalogen acids and their salts, to be discussed in the present chapter.

In Table 23.1 are listed the formulas of the known oxides and oxyacids, in which the halogens are in oxidation states of from $+1$ to $+7$, inclusive.

Table 23.I

Oxygen Compounds of the Halogens

Oxidation State of the Halogen	Fluorine Oxide	Oxy-acid	Chlorine Oxide	Oxy-acid	Bromine Oxide	Oxy-acid	Iodine Oxide	Oxy-acid
$+1$	OF_2*	....	Cl_2O	$HClO$	(Br_2O)	$HBrO$	**	HIO
$+2$	(O_2F_2)*	....	....	....	....	....	....	....
$+3$	....	....	....	$HClO_2$	....	....	....	....
$+4$	....	....	ClO_2	....	(BrO_2)	....	I_2O_4	....
$+5$	....	....	....	$HClO_3$	....	$HBrO_3$	I_2O_5	HIO_3
$+6$	....	....	Cl_2O_6	....	....	....	....	....
$+7$	....	....	Cl_2O_7	$HClO_4$	....	....	....	HIO_4 and H_5IO_6

* Since fluorine has a greater attraction for electrons than oxygen, these compounds might more appropriately be considered as involving positive oxidation states for oxygen, leaving fluorine with its customary oxidation state of -1.

** Also I_4O_9.

The formulas of oxides the existence of which is subject to some doubt, or which are stable only under unusual conditions, are included in parentheses in the table. The oxyhalogen acids, with their generalized names and those of the corresponding salts, are listed again in Table 23.2.

Table 23.2

Oxyacids of the Halogens

Oxida-tion State	Chlorine	Bromine	Iodine	Name of Acid	Name of Salt
+1	HClO	HBrO	HIO	Hypohalous	Hypohalite
+3	HClO$_2$	.....	....	Halous	Halite
+5	HClO$_3$	HBrO$_3$	HIO$_3$	Halic	Halate
+7	HClO$_4$	.....	HIO$_4$ and H$_5$IO$_6$	Perhalic	Perhalate

The electronic structures for these compounds are readily formulated. Starting with the hypohalous acid, which has the electronic formula

$$H : \overset{..}{\underset{..}{O}} : \overset{..}{\underset{..}{X}} :$$

Hypohalous

the other oxyacids may be considered to be derived by the coordination of one, two, or three additional oxygen atoms, respectively, with the halogen atom, so that the electronic formulas are as follows:

$$H : \overset{..}{\underset{..}{O}} : \overset{..}{\underset{..}{X}} : \overset{..}{\underset{..}{O}} :$$

Halous

$$H : \overset{..}{\underset{..}{O}} : \overset{: \overset{..}{O} :}{\underset{..}{X}} : \overset{..}{\underset{..}{O}} :$$

Halic

$$H : \overset{..}{\underset{..}{O}} : \overset{: \overset{..}{O} :}{\underset{: \overset{..}{O} :}{X}} : \overset{..}{\underset{..}{O}} :$$

Perhalic

Or, if we start with halide ion, $: \overset{..}{\underset{..}{X}} : ^-$, the ions of the four oxyacids may be regarded as being derived by the coordination of one, two, three, or four atoms of oxygen, respectively:

Halide

$$: \overset{..}{\underset{..}{X}} :$$

Hypohalite

$$: \overset{..}{\underset{..}{X}} : \overset{..}{\underset{..}{O}} : ^-$$

Halite

$$: \overset{..}{\underset{..}{O}} : \overset{..}{\underset{..}{X}} : \overset{..}{\underset{..}{O}} : ^-$$

Halate

$$: \overset{..}{\underset{..}{O}} : \overset{..}{\underset{: \overset{..}{O} :}{X}} : \overset{..}{\underset{..}{O}} : ^-$$

Perhalate

$$: \overset{..}{\underset{..}{O}} : \overset{: \overset{..}{O} :}{\underset{: \overset{..}{O} :}{X}} : \overset{..}{\underset{..}{O}} : ^-$$

The oxides that correspond to the oxidation states $+1$, $+5$, and $+7$ may be considered as the anhydrides of the respective oxyacids, and it is not difficult to write electronic formulas for them. Thus, Cl_2O, I_2O_5, and Cl_2O_7 may be formulated as follows:

$$
\begin{array}{ccc}
 & \ddot{O} \quad \ddot{O} & \ddot{O} \quad \ddot{O} \\
:\ddot{Cl}:\ddot{O}:\ddot{Cl}: & :\ddot{O}:I:\ddot{O}:I:\ddot{O}: & :\ddot{O}:Cl:\ddot{O}:Cl:\ddot{O}: \\
 & & \ddot{O} \quad \ddot{O}
\end{array}
$$

The oxides corresponding to the even-numbered oxidation states, however, are more difficult to account for and have been shown to involve unusual types of chemical bonds. The nonexistence of oxyacids of fluorine, or of oxides of this element in higher oxidation states, may be attributed to the firmness with which the electrons of the fluoride ion are held, and the consequent inability of that ion to donate any of these electrons to form the coordinate covalent bonds with oxygen that are characteristic of the oxyacids and the higher oxides.

2. Principal Oxides of the Halogens. Chlorine monoxide, Cl_2O, is the anhydride of hypochlorous acid, and reacts with water to give that substance, or with solutions of hydroxides to yield hypochlorite ion.

$$Cl_2O + H_2O = 2HOCl$$

$$Cl_2O + 2OH^- = 2OCl^- + H_2O$$

The best method for the preparation of chlorine monoxide is by the reaction of chlorine with mercuric oxide.

$$HgO + 2Cl_2 = HgCl_2 + Cl_2O$$

Chlorine monoxide is a brownish-yellow gas which condenses to a brownish-red liquid at $2°$ C. and freezes at $-116°$ C. It is a strong oxidizing agent and is explosive either in the gaseous or the liquid state.

Chlorine dioxide, ClO_2, may be prepared in small quantities by the reaction of concentrated sulfuric acid with a solid chlorate.

$$3ClO_3^- + 3H^+ = 2ClO_2 + H_2O + HClO_4$$

The intensely yellow-colored gas which is obtained usually explodes violently when prepared by this method, so the reaction should be carried out with only small quantities of materials. The gas liquefies at $11°$ C. under atmospheric pressure, forming a liquid the color of bromine, which solidifies to orange crystals at $-59°$ C. The oxide explodes violently, even at ordinary temperatures, in the presence of easily oxidizable substances such as sulfur, phosphorus, or organic matter.

When chlorine dioxide, in which chlorine is in the $+4$ oxidation state, is passed into an alkaline solution, chlorite and chlorate ions are obtained in equivalent quantities.

$$2ClO_2 + 2OH^- = ClO_2^- + ClO_3^- + H_2O$$

Chlorine dioxide is one of the relatively few compounds whose molecules contain an odd number of electrons. Like other substances made up of "odd" molecules, chlorine dioxide is attracted by a magnetic field, i.e., is said to be paramagnetic. Substances which are not attracted, but are slightly repelled, by a magnetic field are said to be diamagnetic.

Recently, chlorine dioxide has been put to practical use in the treatment of water. Although chlorine effectively disinfects water, it often has the disadvantage of producing, through reaction with organic impurities, substances having an unpleasant odor and taste. Chlorine dioxide, a much stronger oxidizing agent than chlorine, completely oxidizes these undesirable products. In the newer process, chlorine is first added to water as a disinfectant, followed by chlorine dioxide to destroy unpleasant tastes, odors, and comparatively inert organic substances. The high oxidizing power of chlorine dioxide makes it also an excellent bleaching agent for flour, fats and oils, starch, paper, and textiles. Because it is so reactive and, at high concentrations, so unstable, chlorine dioxide is usually prepared for these purposes just before use by means of the reaction of chlorine gas with dry sodium chlorite.

$$Cl_2 + 2NaClO_2 = 2ClO_2 + 2NaCl$$

3. The Hypohalous Acids and the Hypohalites.
As was pointed out in the preceding chapter (p. 389), all the halogens except fluorine undergo slight reaction with water in accordance with the equation

$$X_2 + H_2O = H^+ + X^- + HOX$$

to yield the weak hypohalous and the strong hydrohalic acid. The extent to which this reaction proceeds toward the right is small even in the case of chlorine, and still smaller for bromine and iodine.

In order that appreciable concentrations of the hypohalous acid may be obtained, it is necessary that this equilibrium be shifted, by some means, to the right. This shift may be accomplished by the addition of a substance that will remove the halide ion from solution by forming either a precipitate or a weak electrolyte. These two possibilities are exemplified by the following equations:

$$I_2 + H_2O + Ag^+ = H^+ + AgI_{(s)} + HOI$$

$$2Cl_2 + H_2O + HgO = HgCl_2 + 2HOCl$$
(only slightly ionized)

The hypohalous acids are very unstable, the stability decreasing in the order HOCl > HOBr > HOI. They cannot be prepared in the anhydrous state, and even in solution they readily undergo decomposition. Hypochlorous acid is an extremely weak acid, only about one-tenth as strong as carbonic. This fact may be utilized for the preparation of an aqueous solution of hypochlorous acid from a mixed solution of this substance and hydrochloric acid, such as is obtained when chlorine is passed into water. Thus, when such a solution is treated with calcium carbonate, the hydrochloric acid reacts according to the equation

$$2H^+ + 2Cl^- + CaCO_3 = Ca^{++} + 2Cl^- + H_2O + CO_2$$

Since, however, hypochlorous acid is so weak and the concentration of carbonate ion in the solution is so small, the HOCl molecule does not transfer a proton to the carbonate ion; this acid, therefore, remains unchanged, and a pure solution of it may be obtained by distillation. Hypobromous acid is still weaker than hypochlorous, while hypoiodous acid actually shows a slight basicity, dissociating to a greater extent into I^+ and OH^- than into OI^- and H^+ ions. This gradation in acidity is in accord with the decreasing electron affinity of the halogens in the order Cl > Br > I, as discussed in the last chapter (see also p. 323). There are a number of compounds containing iodine in an oxidation state of $+1$ that may be considered to be derivatives of IOH, e.g., the substance ICl, discussed in the previous chapter.

The equilibrium in the reaction of a halogen with water may be shifted to the right by another means, viz., by the addition of a strong base to reduce the concentration of hydrogen ion in the solution. Under these conditions, the hypohalite, rather than the free acid, is obtained. Thus, when chlorine is passed into a solution of sodium hydroxide, a solution containing sodium chloride and sodium hypochlorite is produced.

$$X_2 + 2OH^- = X^- + OX^- + H_2O$$

Such a solution is readily obtained by the electrolysis of aqueous sodium chloride solution, if the chlorine produced at the anode is permitted to mix with the sodium hydroxide solution from the cathode (compare with Hooker S cell, p. 387).

Since the hypohalous acids are so extremely weak, the hypohalite ion undergoes marked hydrolysis in aqueous solution.

$$OX^- + H_2O = HOX + OH^-$$

The hypohalites, therefore, are stable only in solutions containing a considerable excess of hydroxide ion.

When an acid is added to a solution containing both halide and hypohalite ions, some free halogen is produced in accordance with the equilibria represented by the equations

$$H^+ + OX^- \rightleftharpoons HOX$$

$$H^+ + X^- + HOX \rightleftharpoons X_2 + H_2O$$

The second of these equations is merely the reverse of the equation for the hydrolysis of the halogen, as discussed before. By suitable regulation of the hydrogen ion concentration, almost any desired concentration of free halogen may be obtained—and, furthermore, this concentration may be maintained at an almost constant level as the halogen is consumed. Such a solution of sodium chloride and sodium hypochlorite has been widely used as a surgical antiseptic under the name of Carrel-Dakin solution.

Both the hypohalous acids and the hypohalites readily undergo decomposition in one of two ways. In the presence of sunlight, or of a suitable catalyst such as a cobalt or nickel salt, oxygen is released in accordance with the equation

$$2HOX = 2H^+ + 2X^- + O_2$$

The strong tendency for this reaction to take place probably accounts for the fact that hypofluorites do not exist (p. 389). In the absence of such a catalyst, the heating of solutions of a hypohalite results in the formation of the halate and halide ions. Since this reaction is inhibited by the presence of strong bases, it appears that the reaction involves the free hypohalous acid.

$$3HOX = HXO_3 + 2H^+ + 2X^-$$

Only a small trace of the acid is necessary, however, and, except in very alkaline solutions, a sufficient concentration results from the hydrolysis of the hypohalite ion. The presence of a slight excess of hydrogen ion accelerates the reaction. Hypobromites and hypoiodites undergo this reaction even more readily than do hypochlorites.

The hypohalites are strong oxidizing agents, readily undergoing reduction to the corresponding halides. They are widely used as oxidizing agents in organic chemistry. The oxidizing strength decreases, as would be expected from the discussion of electron affinities in the previous chapter, in the order $OCl^- > OBr^- > OI^-$.

The practical application of the hypohalites depends upon their germicidal and bleaching properties, both of which result from their strong oxidizing action. Solutions of sodium hypochlorite are widely used both as disinfectants and as bleaches. Such a solution for household use is sold under the name of Clorox. The use of hypochlorite solutions in surgical work has already been discussed.

When chlorine gas is passed over dry slaked lime, a reaction takes place which is commonly represented by an equation analogous to that for the corresponding reaction of chlorine with sodium hydroxide.

$$Ca(OH)_2 + Cl_2 = H_2O + CaCl(OCl)$$

The substance thus obtained is known as bleaching powder, and is widely used for that purpose, as well as for disinfecting and deodorizing. The composition of bleaching powder is not correctly represented, however, by the formula $CaCl(OCl)$, for the above reaction is heterogeneous and does not go to completion. Studies of the substance indicate that it is not a pure compound but is of variable composition, consisting of a mixture of calcium hypochlorite, calcium chloride, and unchanged calcium hydroxide, with some water of hydration. On acidification with a strong acid, bleaching powder yields hypochlorous acid, which in turn reacts with hydrogen and chloride ions to yield free chlorine in accordance with equations already given. Because of its deliquescent nature and its tendency to be hydrolyzed, bleaching powder must be protected from moisture until it is used. A product that contains almost twice as great a proportion of hypochlorite as bleaching powder is marketed under the name of H.T.H. (high test hypochlorite).

Hypochlorite solutions, as bleaches for cotton or linen cloth, must be used with caution, because they have a weakening effect on fabrics made from vegetable fibers. Hypochlorites are entirely unsuitable for use on silks and woolens, for such fabrics are rapidly destroyed by these compounds.

4. Chlorous Acid and the Chlorites. The only halogen to form an acid of the formula HOXO is chlorine. The free acid is not highly dissociated, but is considerably stronger than hypochlorous, and somewhat stronger even than carbonic acid. Chlorous acid is similar in oxidizing strength to hypochlorous, but chlorites are somewhat weaker oxidizing agents than are hypochlorites.

We have already seen that chlorites and chlorates are obtained in equivalent quantities when chlorine dioxide is passed into sodium hydroxide solution. Industrial methods have been developed for the manufacture of relatively pure sodium chlorite. This substance is more stable than sodium hypochlorite but less stable than the chlorate. In addition to providing a practical source of chlorine dioxide (p. 404), sodium chlorite has some advantages over the hypochlorite as a bleaching agent. As a weaker oxidizing agent, the chlorite oxidizes the coloring material in paper and textiles without weakening the fibers as does the hypochlorite.

5. The Halic Acids and the Halates. We have already seen (p. 424) that the hypohalites readily undergo decomposition, especially in hot concentrated solution, to form halates. Thus, when chlorine is passed into a hot concentrated hydroxide solution, chlorate ion, rather than hypochlorite, is obtained.

$$3Cl_2 + 6OH^- = ClO_3^- + 5Cl^- + 3H_2O$$

Chlorates are now commonly prepared by the electrolysis of hot solutions of chlorides in cells in which the chlorine evolved at the anode is brought in contact, by means of constant stirring, with the hydroxide ion formed at the cathode. Bromates and iodates may be prepared also by the oxidation of the free halogens with strong oxidizing agents.

The most important of the chlorates is the potassium salt, which is very soluble in hot water, but only slightly soluble in cold. This fact is the basis for a convenient method of preparation of potassium chlorate from a solution containing chlorate ion; potassium chloride is added to the hot solution, and cooling then brings about the crystallization of potassium chlorate.

Sodium iodate, the only oxyhalogen compound which occurs in nature in appreciable quantities, is found in the sodium nitrate beds in northern Chile.

Neither chloric nor bromic acid is stable enough to be prepared in the pure state. A fairly concentrated solution of any of the halic acids may be obtained, however, by treatment of a solution of the barium halate with an equivalent amount of sulfuric acid, followed by filtration from the resulting precipitate of barium sulfate; e.g.,

$$Ba^{++} + 2ClO_3^- + 2H^+ + SO_4^{--} = BaSO_{4(s)} + 2H^+ + 2ClO_3^-$$

Iodic acid, which is considerably more stable than chloric or bromic, may be isolated in the form of a white solid, very soluble in water. All the halic acids, unlike the hypohalous acids and chlorous acid, are strong.

The halates all undergo decomposition to yield, eventually, the halide and oxygen. Thus, potassium chlorate, when heated, decomposes into potassium chloride and oxygen, especially rapidly in the presence of manganese dioxide as a catalyst (p. 200).

$$2KClO_3 = 2KCl + 3O_2$$

The alkali chlorates, however, when carefully heated in the absence of a catalyst, decompose first into perchlorates and chlorides, in accordance with the equation

$$4MClO_3 = 3MClO_4 + MCl$$

The perchlorate, upon further heating, then yields the chloride and oxygen.

$$MClO_4 = MCl + 2O_2$$

In general, the iodates are considerably more stable than either the bromates or the chlorates.

The halates and halic acids, like the other oxyhalogen compounds, are strong oxidizing agents. They are not, however, as strong in this respect as the corresponding hypohalites; nor are the chlorates and chloric acid as strong oxidizing agents as the chlorites and chlorous acid. Mixtures of a chlorate, such as potassium chlorate, with sulfur, phosphorus, charcoal, or an easily oxidizable organic substance such as sugar, react with explosive violence when heated, or sometimes when merely rubbed together. It is regrettable that uninformed persons persist in making unauthorized experiments with these mixtures; every year a number of serious and sometimes fatal accidents result from such reckless experimentation. Potassium chlorate is sometimes used, however, in the manufacture of matches and in pyrotechnics, and, mixed with finely divided magnesium, to make flashlight powder for photographic purposes. The bromates and iodates are considerably weaker in their oxidizing properties than are the chlorates, but are employed as oxidizing agents to some extent.

6. The Perhalic Acids and the Perhalates. Chlorine and iodine are the only halogens which form perhalic acids and perhalates; and because of the marked difference between perchloric acid and periodic acid it will be convenient for us to consider separately these two compounds and their respective salts.

Perchloric acid, $HClO_4$, unlike the other oxyacids of chlorine, is stable in the pure state. It is a volatile liquid at room temperature and decomposes when heated to 92° C. under atmospheric pressure. It may be prepared in the pure state by the action of concentrated sulfuric acid on a perchlorate, followed by distillation under reduced pressure; but it is most often obtained by the action of nitric and hydrochloric acids on ammonium perchlorate. Under the action of a strong dehydrating agent, perchloric acid loses water to form the anhydride, Cl_2O_7. Perchloric acid is both a very strong acid and a strong oxidizing agent. It is a stronger acid, but a weaker oxidizing agent, than hypochlorous, chlorous, or chloric acid. When concentrated perchloric acid is brought in contact with strong reducing agents, violent explosions sometimes result. Since the pure compound decomposes explosively when heated, or sometimes even in storage, perchloric acid is usually supplied in 60 to 70% aqueous solution. It is used in analytical chemistry both as a strong oxidizing agent and as a reagent for the detection of potassium ion (see below).

The perchlorates are considerably more stable than the chlorates, chlorites, or hypochlorites. They do not cause explosions so readily as do the chlorates when heated with reducing agents such as carbon. Although they are strong oxidizing agents, they are weaker in this respect than salts of the other oxy-acids of chlorine. The perchlorates are isomorphous with the corresponding permanganates; in fact, it is only in the resemblance between the perchlorates and the permanganates, and between the heptoxides of chlorine and manganese, that any similarity between families 7a and 7b of the periodic system is apparent. Most of the perchlorates are soluble in water, those of potassium, rubidium, and cesium having the smallest solubility. Potassium perchlorate is precipitated when perchloric acid is added to solutions containing relatively small concentrations of potassium ion; this reaction is sometimes used as an analytical test for potassium ion. Many of the perchlorates are highly deliquescent; magnesium perchlorate, for this reason, is an extremely efficient drying agent. Because of their oxidizing properties, the perchlorates are used in matches, explosives, and pyrotechnics.

Periodates are commonly prepared from iodates by oxidation with chlorine in alkaline solution. Whereas the composition of all of the perchlorates conforms to the simple general formula $MClO_4$, periodates corresponding to each of the formulas MIO_4, M_3IO_5, $M_4I_2O_9$, and M_5IO_6 have been obtained. An aqueous solution of periodic acid may be prepared by treatment of a solution of barium periodate with sulfuric acid, or of silver periodate with hydrochloric acid, followed by filtration of the solution from the precipitated barium sulfate or silver chloride, respectively. The evaporation of such a solution yields mainly H_5IO_6. By the dehydration, under controlled conditions, of this compound, HIO_4 may be obtained. Periodic acid and the periodates are powerful oxidizing agents, especially in acidic solution.

From the existence of the somewhat complex periodates referred to in the preceding paragraph, and the nonexistence of corresponding chlorine compounds, it is apparent that whereas no more than four oxygen atoms may be coordinated about a Cl^- ion, two additional oxide ions may still be coordinated about an I^- ion. This difference may be explained simply in terms of the fact that the radius of I^- is larger than that of Cl^-, and there is therefore more room for oxygen to attach itself to the iodine than to the chlorine. Other examples of this radius effect are well known. Thus, the most stable form of nitrate ion is NO_3^-, while the most stable form of phosphate or arsenate ion is PO_4^{---} or AsO_4^{---}, and that of antimonate ion, $Sb(OH)_6^{---}$. Likewise, whereas sulfuric and selenic acids have the formulas H_2SO_4 and H_2SeO_4, there is a telluric acid of the formula H_6TeO_6, as well as the simpler H_2TeO_4. In general, it may be said that the coordination number of the central ion of such a complex is dependent upon the ratio of the radius of the central cation to the radius of the coordinated anions.

STUDY QUESTIONS AND PROBLEMS

1. Write the equation for the equilibrium which is obtained in solutions of chlorine, bromine, or iodine in water. How may this equilibrium be displaced completely to the right?

2. How would you account for the decrease in the acidity of the hypohalous acids in the order $HOCl > HOBr > HOI$?

3. Write balanced chemical equations for the oxidation of manganous, plumbous, nickelous, cobaltous, and ferrous salts by sodium hypochlorite solution. Write similar equations for the oxidation of phosphites, ammonia (to nitrogen), and hydrogen peroxide by the same reagent.

4. What weight of sodium chlorite would be required to produce the same weight of sulfur by oxidation of hydrogen sulfide as would be produced by the reaction of 100 g. of hydrogen peroxide with hydrogen sulfide?

5. Write the equation for the reaction of chlorine with a cold dilute solution of an alkali. Under what conditions is chlorate rather than hypochlorite formed?

6. How many faradays of electricity would be required to produce electrolytically 106.4 g. of sodium chlorate by the oxidation of sodium chloride? What weight of sodium chloride would be required?

7. What special precautions must be followed in the use of perchloric acid in the laboratory or in industrial processes? In what ways are the perchlorates similar in properties to the permanganates? Is this similarity sufficient reason for placing chlorine and manganese in the same family in the periodic system? Give the basis for your answer.

8. Give the explanation for the fact that perchloric acid has the formula $HClO_4$ whereas the common form of periodic acid has the formula H_5IO_6.

24

Electrochemical Cells—Electron Transfer in Oxidation-Reduction Reactions

1. Importance of Voltaic Cells. As has been pointed out previously (p. 118), any chemical change that takes place spontaneously is accompanied by a decrease in free energy; or, in other words, such a change liberates energy which is capable of being transformed into work. When electrolytes participate in such changes, it is often possible, under suitable conditions to be described in this chapter, to obtain the liberated energy in the form of electrical work. A device by means of which chemical energy is changed into electrical energy is known as a *voltaic cell*. A study of the characteristics and the behavior of voltaic cells is important for at least two reasons. In the first place, an understanding of the reactions that take place at the electrodes of such cells throws much additional light upon the process of oxidation and reduction, discussed previously in Chapter 12. Second, the principle of the voltaic cell finds important practical applications, especially in the dry cell and the storage battery.

2. Essential Characteristics of a Voltaic Cell. Not every reaction that takes place spontaneously may be utilized as a source of electrical energy, for there is an additional requirement that must be met in a voltaic cell. The reaction, in which at least two substances must participate as reactants, must be separable into two partial reactions, in which electrons are lost by one substance and gained by the other. Furthermore, the device must be so arranged that these partial reactions take place at two different points; that is, the substance that gives up electrons and the substance that receives them must not be in direct physical contact with each other.

The concept of a partial reaction that involves either the loss or the gain of electrons, but not both, need not be regarded as a startling innovation at this point, for the occurrence of such changes in electrolysis has already been discussed. It is true that the apparently paradoxical requirement that the reacting substances in a voltaic cell must be kept apart from each other is somewhat perplexing. It will presently be shown, however, that reaction under such conditions is indeed possible, provided that the reacting substances, as in an electrolytic cell, are included in an electrical circuit consisting partly of metallic conductors and partly of an electrolytic solution. The voltaic and the electrolytic cell thus have many properties in common, and may, in fact, be regarded as the two classes of *electrochemical cells* (p. 418).

Despite the restrictions that have just been discussed, there are still many chemical changes which are adaptable to use in voltaic cells. Since the transfer of electrons from one element to another is necessarily accompanied by changes in oxidation state, we may expect to find an abundance of suitable cell reactions among the oxidation-reduction processes which have been discussed in Chapter 12. Several simple specific examples of such oxidation-reduction reactions will be considered in the following section. In addition to this large group of chemical changes, there is also another sort of change which may be used as a source of electrical energy: the transfer of an electrolyte from a more concentrated to a more dilute solution. The source of energy in this case is what may be called the free energy of dilution, which corresponds to the tendency (p. 295) for any dissolved substance to pass spontaneously from a region of higher concentration to one of lower. The special type of cell known as the concentration cell, based upon this tendency, will be considered briefly at the end of the chapter.

3. Reactions Involving Electron Transfer Between Elements. The formation of an electrovalent bond between two atoms consists, as has already been explained (p. 172), in the transfer of one or more electrons from one atom to the other. Accordingly, every instance of the formation of an electrovalent compound from its elements involves the loss of electrons by the metallic element, and the gain of electrons by the nonmetallic element. In the formation of sodium chloride from metallic sodium and free chlorine, for example, an electron is lost by each sodium atom, while one is gained by each atom of chlorine. Since in this exchange the oxidation state of sodium is increased from 0 to $+1$, and that of chlorine decreased from 0 to -1, it is evident, in accordance with the definitions of Chapter 12, that the sodium is oxidized and the chlorine reduced. Now, this oxidation-reduction reaction may, if we choose, be regarded as consisting of two distinct though simultaneous changes, each of which (since one cannot take place without the other) may appropriately be called a half-reaction.

$$2Na = 2Na^+ + 2e^- \text{ (oxidation)}$$

$$Cl_2 + 2e^- = 2Cl^- \text{ (reduction)}$$

In these equations, according to whether the symbols for the elements are thought of as standing for single atoms or for gram-atomic weights of the elements, the symbol e^- correspondingly represents either one electron or one faraday of negative electricity, i.e., 6.024×10^{23} electrons. When these two equations are added together the electrical charge cancels out, and the resulting equation expresses the net result of the two changes.

$$2Na + Cl_2 = 2Na^+ + 2Cl^-$$

It is clear that electron transfer occurs also in the decomposition of an electrovalent compound. When cupric bromide is heated, for example, we may suppose the following two changes, in which the bromine is oxidized and the copper reduced, to take place:

$$2Br^- = Br_2 + 2e^- \text{ (oxidation)}$$
$$2Cu^{++} + 2e^- = 2Cu^+ \text{ (reduction)}$$

The complete change may be represented by the equation

$$2Cu^{++} + 2Br^- = 2Cu^+ + Br_2$$

Any ionic displacement reaction may similarly be regarded as consisting of two half-reactions—oxidation and reduction, respectively. For instance, when a piece of zinc is immersed in a solution of copper sulfate, the half-reactions are represented by

$$Zn = Zn^{++} + 2e^- \text{ (oxidation)}$$
$$Cu^{++} + 2e^- = Cu \text{ (reduction)}$$

and the complete equation is

$$Zn + Cu^{++} = Zn^{++} + Cu$$

(Since the sulfate ion here takes no part whatever in the reaction, it need not be included in the equation.)

Still another type of oxidation-reduction that involves electron transfer may be illustrated by the reaction between solutions of ferric chloride and stannous chloride which gives the ferrous and stannic salts. Here, again, the chloride ion takes no part in the reaction; the cations are the only participants. Hence we have, as half-reactions,

$$Sn^{++} = Sn^{++++} + 2e^- \text{ (oxidation)}$$
$$2Fe^{+++} + 2e^- = 2Fe^{++} \text{ (reduction)}$$

The complete equation is

$$Sn^{++} + 2Fe^{+++} = Sn^{++++} + 2Fe^{++}$$

4. Electron Transfer as a Form of Oxidation-Reduction. As has been illustrated by the equations of the preceding section, the loss of electrons by an element necessarily constitutes oxidation of that element, while the gain of electrons always constitutes a reduction. In fact, in the past, oxidation has often been *defined* as the loss, reduction as the gain, of electrons. The term oxidation-reduction, however, is commonly applied not only to cases like the above, in which there is an outright transfer of electrons from one atom to another, but also to many reactions that involve only covalent bonds and in which no actual electron transfer takes place. It is for this reason that we have chosen not to base our general definition of oxidation and reduction upon electron transfer but to retain the concept of oxidation state as our criterion. However, since the only types of oxidation and reduction that can be utilized for the production of electrical energy in a voltaic cell are those involving electron transfer, it will be convenient, in the present chapter, to confine our attention to such oxidizing agents as undergo reduction by gaining electrons and to such reducing agents as undergo oxidation by losing electrons.

5. A Typical Voltaic Cell. Although any of the reactions discussed in section 3 might, at least theoretically, be used as a source of electrical energy, the choice of a suitable reaction for an actual voltaic cell is somewhat restricted by practical considerations. Thus, the first of the reactions in question would obviously be altogether impracticable, because of both the extremely reactive character of metallic sodium and the difficulties inherent in the handling of chlorine gas. The second reaction is clearly ruled out not only by the fact that cupric bromide undergoes spontaneous decomposition only at temperatures approaching red heat, but also by the impossibility, in any decomposition, of separating the oxidizing and reducing agents from each other. Either of the other two reactions listed, however, might be made the basis for a voltaic cell, and the displacement of copper by zinc has actually been used, in the past, as a source of electrical energy. Because of its simplicity, we shall choose the reaction between zinc and cupric ion for our first illustration of the construction and mode of operation of a voltaic cell.

If a piece of zinc were to be immersed directly in a solution of a cupric salt such as copper sulfate, a deposit of metallic copper would immediately be formed on the surface of the zinc, an equivalent amount of zinc would go into solution as zinc ion, and all of the energy liberated in the reaction would appear in the form of heat. If the energy is to be obtained as electricity, it is essential that the two reactants be kept apart. This separation may be accomplished by means of the device shown in Figure 24.1. The electrode on the left consists of a rod of metallic zinc, while the right-hand compartment contains copper sulfate solution. The porous partition in the center prevents direct mixing of the contents of the two compartments, although it does not obstruct the migration of ions. To complete the cell, it is necessary to provide a conducting solution in contact with the zinc and an electrode in the copper sulfate solution. Since these latter portions of the cell do not take part in the chemical reaction, a wide choice of substances is available for them, the only limitation being that the solution must not react with zinc nor the electrode

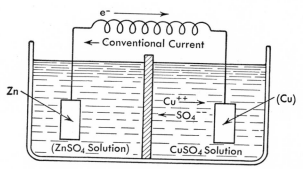

Fig. 24.1.   The copper–zinc displacement cell.

with copper sulfate solution. In order to keep at a minimum the number of elements involved in the cell, we might choose zinc sulfate as the electrolyte of the left-hand compartment and a copper rod as the inert electrode; in this case, we should have the particular combination of materials which characterizes the so-called Daniell cell. In practice, the zinc sulfate solution might be inclosed in a porous cup of unglazed earthenware immersed in a beaker containing the copper sulfate solution; or a dilute solution of zinc sulfate might even be allowed to float above a concentrated copper sulfate solution of much higher density. Such alterations in the details of the device, however, would have no effect on the principles to be discussed.

6. How the Cell Works.

It was stated in an earlier chapter (p. 215) that neither oxidation nor reduction can take place without the simultaneous occurrence of the other. Where the oxidation-reduction consists of electron transfer, this rule is equivalent to the simple statement that one element cannot gain electrons unless they are lost by another. Hence, despite the strong tendency of metallic zinc to lose electrons to cupric ion, thereby reducing it to copper, this change cannot occur as long as the two electrodes remain unconnected. As soon as the zinc and copper rods are connected by means of a wire, however, the oxidation-reduction reaction represented by the equation

$$Zn + Cu^{++} = Zn^{++} + Cu$$

begins to take place. It may readily be shown experimentally that zinc goes into solution from the zinc electrode, while copper is deposited from the solution onto the copper electrode. In the meantime a current flows through the wire from the copper to the zinc, as may be demonstrated by its heating effect on the wire or by its deflection of the needle of a galvanometer included in the circuit. These phenomena continue until the circuit is broken, or until one of the reactants has been used up. The exact magnitude of the electromotive force of this cell would vary, for reasons to be discussed later in this chapter, with the concentrations of zinc and cupric ions in the solutions surrounding the zinc and copper electrodes, respectively. With each of these concentrations at 1 mole per liter, the electromotive force is found to be 1.10 volts.

The question now inevitably arises, "How can the zinc and the cupric ion react with each other when they are not in contact—when neither of them, so to speak, can possibly be aware of the presence of the other in the vicinity?" No entirely satisfactory answer can be given to this question. The following generally accepted explanation, although inadequate, is the best that is at present available.

Let us suppose that when a metal rod is placed in water or in an aqueous solution, some of the metal atoms on the surface of the rod pass into the solution as hydrated cations. The electrons thus released remain behind in the metal, which thereby acquires a negative charge. The extent to which this change takes place depends upon the concentration of hydrated cations already present in the solution, decreasing with increasing concentration; but, in any case, it can occur to a very minute extent only, since the negative charge on the rod acts as a strong deterrent to the departure of any more cations; in other words, an equilibrium is soon reached between the metal and the solution. Since the tendency to form cations varies from one metallic element to another, we may further suppose that the reaction

$$Metal + water = hydrated\ cation + electron(s)$$

will proceed to a different extent for each metal, even when the cations are present at the same concentration. Roughly speaking, the more active the metal, the greater will be the concentration of free electrons in the rod when equilibrium is attained. Thus, if we have two similar rods, one of zinc and the other of copper, each immersed in a solution containing the corresponding cation at the same concentration, it is to be expected that a greater negative charge will be developed on the more active zinc than on the less active copper.

The presence of excess electrons may be supposed to produce a sort of electron pressure within the metal. Because this electron pressure is greater in the zinc than in the copper, there is said to be a difference of potential between the two electrodes, which consists in a tendency for electrons to pass from the zinc to the copper. Even though the two solutions may be in contact, this tendency must remain latent as long as the two electrodes are not connected by a metallic conductor. As soon as such connection is made, however, the difference of potential manifests itself as an electromotive force (abbreviated e.m.f.) that drives electrons through the wire from the zinc to the copper. (The direction of the current, in the conventional sense, is opposite to the direction of electron flow, so that the conventional current is said to flow from the copper to the zinc.) Because of this flow of electrons, the two electrode reactions, or half-reactions, represented by the simplified equations

$$Zn = Zn^{++} + 2e^-$$

and

$$Cu^{++} + 2e^- = Cu$$

are enabled to proceed freely and simultaneously, the electrons liberated by the zinc atoms flowing through the wire into the copper rod and thence to the solution, where cupric ions pick them up and become atoms. Meanwhile, since electrons are being delivered continuously through the wire to the copper electrode, all the positively charged ions (cations) in the solution, both Zn^{++} and Cu^{++}, migrate toward this electrode, while the negatively charged sulfate ions (anions) migrate toward the zinc electrode, from which electrons are being dispatched into the wire. Thus the electrical circuit is complete, and a continuous current passes through the wire and the cell.

7. Conventions of Nomenclature. It is desirable that we stop here for a moment to consider certain conventions of nomenclature which are commonly used in the discussion of electrochemical phenomena. In this connection, we must again emphasize the fact that all electrochemical cells may be divided into two large classes: electrolytic cells (p. 302) and voltaic cells. The former group includes those cells in which, by the application of electrical energy from an outside source, nonspontaneous reactions are caused to take place. On the other hand, voltaic cells, as we have seen, are cells in which reactions resulting in the production of electrical energy take place spontaneously. *In both types of cells, however, the electrode at which elec-*

trons enter the external circuit, and hence the one at which oxidation takes place in the cell, is called the anode. Moreover, in both types of cells, it is toward the anode that the anions of the electrolyte migrate. The electrode at which electrons enter the cell, and hence the one at which reduction takes place in the cell, and toward which the cations of the electrolyte move, is called the cathode. These conventions are illustrated in Figure 24.2.

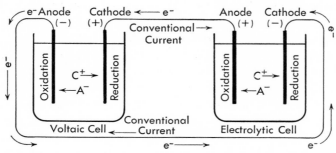

Fig. 24.2.   Conventions of nomenclature for a voltaic and an electrolytic cell.

Electricians uniformly follow the practice of designating the electrodes of a cell as "positive" and "negative," respectively. In a voltaic cell, according to this convention, the anode is called the negative electrode, and the cathode the positive electrode. In an electrolytic cell, however, the anode is called the positive electrode, and the cathode the negative (Figure 24.2). Since this set of conventions is likely to cause confusion, and, in any case, is of little use to the chemist, we shall use, in our discussions, the more logical and consistent designations of anode and cathode.

8. Another Displacement Cell. Let us consider another displacement cell, in which a silver electrode immersed in silver sulfate solution is substituted for the zinc electrode in zinc sulfate. In this case, the flow of electrons in the external circuit is found to be not from the silver to the copper, but from the copper to the silver; while operation of the cell results in the deposition of metallic silver on the silver electrode, and the dissolving of copper from the copper electrode. The half-reactions, then, must be

$$Cu = Cu^{++} + 2e^-$$

and

$$Ag^+ + e^- = Ag$$

Since two silver ions are required to receive the electrons given up by a single cupric ion, the second equation must be multiplied throughout by 2:

$$2Ag^+ + 2e^- = 2Ag$$

When the two half-reactions are added together, we get

$$Cu + 2Ag^+ = Cu^{++} + 2Ag$$

With solutions containing 1 mole of ion per liter, the electromotive force of this cell is 0.46 v.

9. A Different Type of Cell. In each of the cells considered so far, based as they are upon the replacement of one cation by another, one of the electrodes takes an active part in the reaction and the other undergoes an increase in mass as the result of deposition of metal upon it. It is entirely pos-

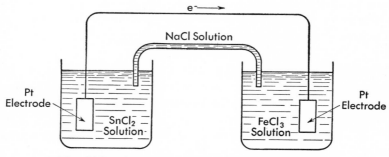

Fig. 24.3.   A stannous chloride–ferric chloride cell.

sible, however, to set up a voltaic cell in which neither electrode is directly involved in the chemical change, which then takes place between two dissolved substances only. In order to illustrate this, we may next consider a cell based upon the reduction of ferric ion to ferrous by stannous ion. In such a case as this, a porous partition will not serve to keep the two reactants apart; the most effective means of separation consists in placing the two solutions (which may be of stannous chloride and ferric chloride, respectively) in two different vessels, as shown in Figure 24.3. Connection between the two is made only by means of an inverted U-tube containing a solution of a third electrolyte which does not react with either of the others. Sodium chloride solution will serve this purpose satisfactorily. This connection, known as a "salt bridge," allows the migration of ions through it, while it prevents any mixing of the ferric and stannous solutions. Since the electrodes are to take no part in the chemical reaction, they must be composed of a substance that is relatively inert. Graphite would serve the purpose; platinum, which is oxidized only with difficulty, may likewise be used.

As in the case of the displacement cells, no reaction takes place until the two electrodes are connected by a wire. As soon as the connection is made, the half-reactions

$$Sn^{++} = Sn^{++++} + 2e^-$$

and

$$2Fe^{+++} + 2e^- = 2Fe^{++}$$

begin to take place simultaneously, and electrons flow through the wire from the electrode immersed in the stannous to that immersed in the ferric solution. The changes may be thought of as occurring in the following way. In the left-hand vessel, stannous ions give up electrons to the electrode (the anode), thereby changing to stannic. Electrons flow through the wire to the other electrode (the cathode), where they enter the solution, reducing ferric ions to ferrous. Chloride ions migrate through the solution toward the anode (from right to left), and ferrous, ferric, stannous, stannic, and sodium ions all migrate toward the cathode (from left to right).

10. A Practical Voltaic Cell—The Dry Cell. From the point of view of practical utility, one of the most important types of voltaic cells is the common dry cell, a convenient device for producing a current at infrequent inter-

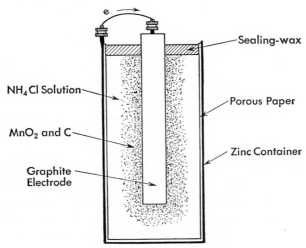

Fig. 24.4. The dry cell.

vals for such purposes as lighting flashlights, ringing doorbells, etc. In normal times, millions of such cells are produced each year. In this cell (Figure 24.4) the container is of zinc, which serves also as one of the electrodes. A lining of thick porous paper separates the metal from the electrolyte, which consists of ammonium chloride solution absorbed in a mixture of solid ammonium chloride and some porous inert substance such as sawdust, paper pulp, or cotton waste. In the center of the cell is a rod of carbon (graphite) around which is packed a layer of a mixture of manganese dioxide and graphite. The cell is sealed with pitch or sealing-wax in order to prevent the evaporation of water; the term "dry cell" is of course a misnomer since the presence of water is essential for the movement of the ions.

When the circuit is closed, zinc from the container goes into solution as zinc ion, thereby acting as anode.

$$Zn = Zn^{++} + 2e^-$$

At the carbon electrode, or cathode, the half-reaction is somewhat more complex; the main reaction, however, appears to be

$$MnO_2 + NH_4^+ + 2H_2O + e^- = Mn(OH)_3 + NH_4OH$$

In order to obtain the complete cell reaction, we must multiply the equation for this half-reaction by 2:

$$2MnO_2 + 2NH_4^+ + 4H_2O + 2e^- = 2Mn(OH)_3 + 2NH_4OH$$

Then, upon the addition of the two half-reactions the electrons cancel out, so that we have

$$Zn + 2MnO_2 + 2NH_4^+ + 4H_2O = Zn^{++} + 2Mn(OH)_3 + 2NH_4OH$$

The electromotive force of the dry cell is about 1.3 v., with the carbon, of course, serving as positive electrode in the conventional sense.

A second type of cell which is of great practical importance is the lead storage cell or accumulator, which will be considered later in the chapter (p. 434).

11. Electrical Energy. The quantity of electrical energy produced in a voltaic cell may be expressed as the product of two factors: the quantity of electrical charge that flows through the cell, and the electromotive force (i.e., the electrical pressure under which it flows). If the electromotive force is expressed in volts and the quantity of electrical charge in coulombs, the product is in volt-coulombs or joules; i.e.,

$$\text{Electrical energy} = \text{e.m.f.} \times \text{quantity of electricity}$$
$$\text{(in joules)} \qquad \text{(in volts)} \qquad \text{(in coulombs)}$$

Now the decrease in free energy that accompanies the chemical change occurring in the cell (often referred to simply as the free energy of the reaction) is, under the most favorable conditions, converted completely into electrical energy. Hence, according to the law of the conservation of energy, it follows that

Free energy of reaction = e.m.f. × quantity of electricity

At a fixed temperature, the electromotive force of a cell depends only upon the nature of the substances participating in the reaction, and to a slight extent upon the concentrations of such of them as are in solution. Hence, the electromotive force of a given cell remains practically constant over the period of time during which the cell is in operation. The free energy of the reaction, however, like the quantity of electricity, depends also upon the amounts of the reacting substances used up. Since, according to Faraday's laws (p. 303), the quantity of electricity that passes through any cell, either voltaic or electrolytic, for every gram-equivalent of chemical change,[1] is 96,500 coulombs, we may write

Free energy of reaction (joules) per gram-equivalent = e.m.f. × 96,500

Since 1 joule is equal to 0.239 calorie, the last equation may alternatively be written

Free energy (calories) per gram-equivalent = e.m.f. × 23,100

12. Half-reaction Potentials. It is customary to regard the electromotive force of a voltaic cell, or the potential difference between its electrodes, as the sum of two separate potential differences, called *half-reaction potentials,* which arise at the points of contact of the two electrodes with the solution. Whether this practice is based upon fact or fancy is a question of little practical importance. From the practical point of view, a table of values of half-reaction potentials would be exceedingly useful; for, with the aid of such a table, the electromotive force of any cell might be computed by combination of its two half-reaction potentials. Furthermore, just as the electromotive force of the cell as a whole is a measure of the free energy of the cell reaction, or of the tendency for this reaction to take place, so each half-reaction potential might be regarded as a measure of the free energy of the corresponding half-reaction. Unfortunately, no satisfactory method for the direct measurement of any half-reaction potential has ever been devised.

There is, nevertheless, a simple expedient by means of which a list of half-reaction potentials useful for comparison purposes may be obtained. This consists in the arbitrary assignment of a value of *zero* to the potential of one

---

[1] It must be remembered that, since oxidation and reduction occur simultaneously, for every gram-equivalent of substance oxidized at the anode there will be one gram-equivalent of another substance reduced at the cathode. The quantity of electricity corresponding to this *combined* change is 96,500 coulombs.

particular electrode, and the referring of all others to this one as a standard. The difference of potential between any other electrode and the standard electrode, which may, of course, be determined experimentally as the electromotive force of a voltaic cell, may thus, by convention, be attributed to the other electrode. The electrode which has been chosen as a standard is the so-called hydrogen electrode, which consists of a piece of platinum foil (coated with platinum black, p. 733, to increase its surface) surrounded by and saturated with hydrogen gas at 1 atm. pressure and immersed in an acid solution containing hydronium ion at a concentration of 1 mole per liter.[2] The half-reaction that takes place at this electrode may be represented either by the equation

$$H_2 = 2H^+ + 2e^-$$

or by the equation

$$2H^+ + 2e^- = H_2$$

according to whether the hydrogen electrode serves as anode or as cathode. Choice of a value of zero for the potential of this electrode is, of course, equivalent to the assignment of a value of zero to the free energy of either of these half-reactions.

In order to illustrate the utility of the idea of half-reaction potentials, let us consider a cell consisting of a zinc rod immersed in a solution of a zinc salt, a connecting tube (salt bridge) filled with potassium chloride solution, and a hydrogen electrode such as has just been described. According to our convention, the entire electromotive force of this cell may be ascribed to the zinc electrode; and the corresponding free energy change may be attributed either to the cell reaction

$$Zn + 2H^+ = Zn^{++} + H_2$$

or to the half-reaction at the zinc anode

$$Zn = Zn^{++} + 2e^-$$

Since, as will be shown later, the tendency for this reaction to proceed toward the right diminishes with increasing concentration of zinc ion in the solution, the corresponding potential varies appreciably according to the concentration of zinc ion. If the zinc electrode is immersed in a solution containing 1 mole of zinc ion per liter, the electromotive force of the hydrogen–zinc cell is found to be 0.76 v. Therefore, we take the value of 0.76 v. as the standard half-reaction potential of the zinc anode and give it a positive sign because

---

[2] Strictly speaking, the standard hydrogen electrode is one in which the effective concentration, or the activity, of hydrogen ion (rather than the concentration of hydronium ion) is 1 mole per liter.

the displacement of hydrogen by zinc proceeds spontaneously. Since this figure may be regarded as a measure of the tendency of zinc to be oxidized to zinc ion, it is commonly designated as the *oxidation potential* of zinc.

The oxidation potential of any other electrode may be determined in a similar way. For example, in the case of the Daniell cell with both electrolytes at unit concentration, we have (using the symbol E to denote the electromotive force corresponding to the reaction)

$$Zn + Cu^{++} = Zn^{++} + Cu; \quad E = 1.10 \text{ v.}$$

$$Zn = Zn^{++} + 2e^-; \quad E = 0.76 \text{ v.}$$

Subtracting the equation for the half-reaction at the zinc electrode from the equation for the entire cell reaction, and correspondingly subtracting the electrode potential of the zinc anode from the electromotive force of the cell, we obtain

$$Cu^{++} + 2e^- = Cu; \quad E = 0.34 \text{ v.}$$

Thus, we obtain the value of 0.34 v. as a measure of the tendency for the cupric ion in molar solution to be reduced; i.e., for the standard copper–cupric ion electrode to act as cathode. In order to obtain the potential of the same electrode acting as anode, we need only bear in mind that the free energy change for the oxidation of copper to cupric ion is equal in magnitude, though opposite in sign, to that for the reduction of cupric ion to copper; since the same relationship must hold for the corresponding half-reaction potentials, we may write

$$Cu = Cu^{++} + 2e^-; \quad E = 0.34 \text{ v.}$$

It is this last value that is known as the standard oxidation potential of copper.

The standard oxidation potentials of the more important metals, together with similar values for a few of the nonmetallic elements, are given in Table 24.1. In each case, the oxidation potential may be regarded as a measure of the tendency of the electrode in question to act as anode; i.e., for a metal to be oxidized to the cation, or, in the case of the nonmetals, for an anion to be oxidized to the free element, as shown by the equation for the corresponding half-reaction. Thus, the oxidation potentials provide a quantitative basis for the two displacement series which have been given previously (p. 210). In Table 24.1, the metals are listed in order of decreasing tendency to form cations, the nonmetals in order of increasing tendency to form anions; in each series, in other words, the order is that of decreasing tendency for the substance on the left side of the equation to release electrons.

Table 24.1

Standard Oxidation Potentials of the Elements (Electromotive Series)

A. Metals

Element	Ion	Half-Reaction	Oxidation Potential (volts)
Lithium	Li$^+$	Li $=$ Li$^+ + e^-$	3.05
Potassium	K$^+$	K $=$ K$^+ + e^-$	2.93
Barium	Ba^{++}	Ba $=$ Ba$^{++} + 2e^-$	2.90
Calcium	Ca^{++}	Ca $=$ Ca$^{++} + 2e^-$	2.87
Sodium	Na$^+$	Na $=$ Na$^+ + e^-$	2.71
Magnesium	Mg^{++}	Mg $=$ Mg$^{++} + 2e^-$	2.37
Aluminum	Al^{+++}	Al $=$ Al$^{+++} + 3e^-$	1.66
Zinc	Zn^{++}	Zn $=$ Zn$^{++} + 2e^-$	0.76
Iron	Fe^{++}	Fe $=$ Fe$^{++} + 2e^-$	0.44
Cadmium	Cd^{++}	Cd $=$ Cd$^{++} + 2e^-$	0.40
Nickel	Ni^{++}	Ni $=$ Ni$^{++} + 2e^-$	0.25
Tin	Sn^{++}	Sn $=$ Sn$^{++} + 2e^-$	0.14
Lead	Pb^{++}	Pb $=$ Pb$^{++} + 2e^-$	0.13
Hydrogen	H$^+$	H$_2 =$ 2H$^+ + 2e^-$	0.00
Copper	Cu^{++}	Cu $=$ Cu$^{++} + 2e^-$	-0.34
Mercury	Hg$_2{}^{++}$	2Hg $=$ Hg$_2{}^{++} + 2e^-$	-0.79
Silver	Ag$^+$	Ag $=$ Ag$^+ + e^-$	-0.80
Platinum	Pt^{++}	Pt $=$ Pt$^{++} + 2e^-$	-1.20
Gold	Au^{+++}	Au $=$ Au$^{+++} + 3e^-$	-1.50

B. Nonmetals

Element	Ion	Half-Reaction	Oxidation Potential (volts)
Sulfur	S^{--}	S$^{--} =$ S $+ 2e^-$	0.48
Iodine	I$^-$	2I$^- =$ I$_2 + 2e^-$	-0.54
Bromine	Br$^-$	2Br$^- =$ Br$_2 + 2e^-$	-1.07
Chlorine	Cl$^-$	2Cl$^- =$ Cl$_2 + 2e^-$	-1.36
Fluorine	F$^-$	2F$^- =$ F$_2 + 2e^-$	-2.65

13. Applications of the Electromotive Series and of Oxidation Potentials of the Elements.

We are now able to explain the statement made in a previous chapter (p. 210) that a metal will spontaneously displace any of those following it in the series from an aqueous solution containing the cation of the latter. The electromotive force of any cell may readily be determined by addition of the potentials of its two electrodes, with due regard to sign. Thus, for example, for a cell with electrodes of iron and silver, immersed in solutions molar in ferrous ion and silver ion, respectively, we have as the half-reactions and the corresponding half-reaction potentials

$$Fe = Fe^{++} + 2e^-; E = 0.44 \text{ v.}$$

$$2Ag^+ + 2e^- = 2Ag \qquad ; E = 0.80 \text{ v.}$$

In the second case, the sign of the half-reaction potential is opposite to that in the table because the half-reaction is the reverse of the one given there. Adding these equations together, we obtain for the entire cell reaction

$$Fe + 2Ag^+ = Fe^{++} + 2Ag; E = 1.24 \text{ v.}$$

Not only are we thus able to determine the electromotive force of a displacement cell with iron and silver electrodes, but also the positive sign of the electromotive force of the cell tells us that the displacement reaction corresponding to the combined equation—read, as usual, from left to right—proceeds spontaneously; in other words, metallic iron displaces silver from solutions of its salts. The same value for the electromotive force of the cell might of course have been obtained by subtraction of the oxidation potential of silver from that of iron: $0.44 - (-0.80) = 1.24$ v., for the cell with iron as anode and silver as cathode. It should be noted further that, since reduction takes place at the silver electrode, electrons will flow in the external circuit from the iron to the silver. In the conventional sense, then, the silver is the positive and the iron the negative electrode of this cell.

In an exactly similar way, we may use the electromotive series to demonstrate that a nonmetallic element will displace any of those *above* it in the series from a solution containing the anion of the latter. Thus, we may imagine a cell consisting of two platinum electrodes, one immersed in a solution molar in bromide ion and saturated with free bromine, the other immersed in a solution molar in chloride ion, and surrounded by chlorine gas; the two solutions are connected by means of a salt bridge. As the half-reactions in such a cell we have

$$2Br^- = Br_2 + 2e^-; E = -1.07 \text{ v.}$$

$$Cl_2 + 2e^- = 2Cl^- \qquad ; E = \quad 1.36 \text{ v.}$$

By addition of these we obtain the equation

$$Cl_2 + 2Br^- = Br_2 + 2Cl^-; E = 0.29 \text{ v.}$$

from which we may conclude that chlorine spontaneously replaces bromine from solutions of bromides.

14. Oxidation Potentials for Other Oxidation-Reduction Reactions.

There are many varieties of chemical change other than those discussed in the previous section that likewise involve the gain or the loss of electrons, and which, therefore, may take place at a cathode or at an anode, respectively. Often the electrode consists of an inert substance which itself takes no part in the chemical change, serving merely as a carrier of electrons to or from the solution. One such type of reaction has been illustrated in the stannous chloride–ferric chloride cell previously described (p. 420), in which each of the cations undergoes a change in charge. In this case, it should be noted that as soon as the circuit has been closed neither electrode is any longer in contact with a single cation; one is in contact with a mixture of stannous and stannic, the other, with a mixture of ferrous and ferric ions. The *standard* oxidation potentials, then, would be, respectively, that of an inert electrode such as platinum immersed in a solution molar with respect to *both* stannous and stannic, and that of a similar electrode in a solution molar with respect to *both* ferrous and ferric ions. The oxidation potentials of such electrodes may be determined by means similar to those already described.

Table 24.2
Standard Oxidation Potentials for Some Important Half-Reactions

Electrode	Half-Reaction	Oxidation Potential (volts)
Fe, Fe(OH)$_2$, OH$^-$	Fe + 2OH$^-$ = Fe(OH)$_2$ + 2e$^-$	0.88
Pt, H$_2$, OH$^-$	H$_2$ + 2OH$^-$ = 2H$_2$O + 2e$^-$	0.83
Cd, Cd(OH)$_2$, OH$^-$	Cd + 2OH$^-$ = Cd(OH)$_2$ + 2e$^-$	0.81
Pb, PbSO$_4$, SO$_4^{--}$	Pb + SO$_4^{--}$ = PbSO$_4$ + 2e$^-$	0.36
Pt, Sn^{++}, Sn^{++++}	Sn^{++} = Sn^{++++} + 2e$^-$	−0.15
Ag, AgCl, Cl$^-$	Ag + Cl$^-$ = AgCl + e$^-$	−0.22
Hg, Hg$_2$Cl$_2$, Cl$^-$	2Hg + 2Cl$^-$ = Hg$_2$Cl$_2$ + 2e$^-$	−0.27
Pt, O$_2$, OH$^-$	4OH$^-$ = O$_2$ + 2H$_2$O + 4e$^-$	−0.40
NiO$_2$, Ni(OH)$_2$, OH$^-$	Ni(OH)$_2$ + 2OH$^-$ = NiO$_2$ + 2H$_2$O + 2e$^-$	−0.49
MnO$_2$, Mn(OH)$_3$, NH$_4$OH, NH$_4^+$	NH$_4$OH + Mn(OH)$_3$ = MnO$_2$ + NH$_4^+$ + 2H$_2$O + e$^-$	−0.50
Pt, Fe^{++}, Fe^{+++}	Fe^{++} = Fe^{+++} + e$^-$	−0.77
Pt, O$_2$, H$^+$	2H$_2$O = O$_2$ + 4H$^+$ + 4e$^-$	−1.23
Pt, Cr^{+++}, Cr$_2$O$_7^{--}$, H$^+$	2Cr^{+++} + 7H$_2$O = Cr$_2$O$_7^{--}$ + 14H$^+$ + 6e$^-$	−1.33
Pt, Mn^{++}, MnO$_4^-$, H$^+$	Mn^{++} + 4H$_2$O = MnO$_4^-$ + 8H$^+$ + 5e$^-$	−1.51
PbO$_2$, PbSO$_4$, H$_2$SO$_4$	PbSO$_4$ + 2H$_2$O = PbO$_2$ + SO$_4^{--}$ + 4H$^+$ + 2e$^-$	−1.69

In Table 24.2 are listed a number of additional electrodes with the corresponding half-reactions (each formulated as an oxidation) and standard oxidation potentials. Inert electrode materials are designated, for brevity, by the symbol Pt. The equation for each half-reaction, it will be noticed, is not only chemically but electrically balanced; that is, just enough electrons have been included on the right side of the equation to make the net electric charge the same on both sides. This aspect of the writing of equations for half-reactions will be considered in greater detail in the next section.

This table, as well as the preceding one, may be utilized to determine whether or not a given oxidation-reduction reaction will proceed spontaneously. For this purpose, it is necessary only to imagine a voltaic cell made up of any two of the electrodes listed in either of the tables; the electromotive force of such a cell may be determined by subtraction of the potential of the electrode serving as cathode from that of the electrode serving as anode. The complete oxidation-reduction reaction will proceed spontaneously in that direction for which a positive value of the electromotive force is obtained. Thus, for example, we find for the stannous–ferric cell

$$Sn^{++} = Sn^{++++} + 2e^- \quad ; E = -0.15 \text{ v. (anode)}$$

$$2Fe^{+++} + 2e^- = 2Fe^{++} \quad\quad\quad ; E = 0.77 \text{ v. (cathode)}$$

$$Sn^{++} + 2Fe^{+++} = Sn^{++++} + 2Fe^{++} ; E = 0.62 \text{ v. (e.m.f. of cell)}$$

Hence, we may conclude: (1) that stannous ion will spontaneously reduce ferric ion to ferrous, being itself oxidized to stannic; (2) that in a voltaic cell made up of the two electrodes Pt, Sn^{++}, Sn^{++++} and Pt, Fe^{++}, Fe^{+++}, electrons will flow in the external circuit from the first electrode to the second; (3) that the electromotive force of such a cell will be 0.62 v.

If, for a given voltaic cell, several alternative cell reactions are imaginable, the one that actually takes place will be that one which is accompanied by the greatest possible decrease in free energy per faraday of electricity; i.e., in general, the one consisting of the two half-reactions which correspond —with due regard to sign—to the highest (most positive or least negative) half-reaction potentials.

15. The Ion-Electron Method of Balancing Oxidation-Reduction Equations.
The equation for any oxidation-reduction equation may be balanced by the use of the oxidation number method described in Chapter 12. When one or more of the participants in the reaction are ions and the reaction can be broken up into half-reactions that may take place at the electrodes of a

voltaic cell (either real or imaginary), a somewhat different procedure, called the ion-electron method, is available. This method consists in the formulation of separate partial equations for the half-reactions of oxidation and reduction. In order that the partial equation may be electrically balanced, one or more electrons will always have to be included on one side or the other. Each partial equation is then multiplied by whatever coefficient is necessary in order that the total number of electrons lost in the oxidation equation may be equal to the total number gained in the reduction equation. Upon addition of these adjusted partial equations, therefore, the electrons cancel out and the complete balanced equation is obtained.

As an illustration of the application of this method, let us consider the reaction between ferrous and permanganate ions, in acid solution, to give ferric ion, manganous ion, and water. Suppose ferrous sulfate solution to be placed in one vessel, and potassium permanganate solution, acidified with dilute sulfuric acid, in another; and suppose the two solutions to be connected electrically, as previously described in connection with the stannous chloride–ferric chloride cell (Figure 24.3). The ferrous ion is then oxidized to ferric, losing an electron in the process.

$$Fe^{++} = Fe^{+++} + e^- \text{ (oxidation)}$$

Meanwhile the permanganate and hydrogen ions are reduced to manganous ion and water.

$$MnO_4^- + 8H^+ = Mn^{++} + 4H_2O$$

Since the total net charge on the left side of the equation is $+7$ and on the right side $+2$, it is evident that five electrons must be added on the left side in order that the equation may be electrically balanced. Therefore, we have as the balanced equation for this half-reaction

$$MnO_4^- + 8H^+ + 5e^- = Mn^{++} + 4H_2O \text{ (reduction)}$$

In order that the two equations may be combined, with no resulting surplus or deficiency of electrons, the equation for the oxidation must be multiplied by 5:

$$5Fe^{++} = 5Fe^{+++} + 5e^-$$

Now, by addition, we obtain

$$5Fe^{++} + MnO_4^- + 8H^+ = 5Fe^{+++} + Mn^{++} + 4H_2O$$

It should be noted that this equation for the complete reaction, like those for the half-reactions, is not only chemically but electrically balanced, with a net charge of $+17$ units on each side of the equation. In this form, the equation includes only those substances which have actually undergone a change in the course of the reaction. If we wished to include also the other ions which are present, although not as participants in the chemical change, we should merely have to add 1 K^+ ion and 9 SO_4^{--} ions to each side of the equation; thus, we should obtain

$$5Fe^{++} + 5SO_4^{--} + K^+ + MnO_4^- + 8H^+ + 4SO_4^{--}$$
$$= 5Fe^{+++} + K^+ + Mn^{++} + 9SO_4^{--} + 4H_2O$$

As a second example of the ion-electron method, let us take the reaction between hydrogen sulfide and dichromate ion, in acid solution, in which the products are free sulfur, chromic ion, and water. The half-reactions are

$$S^{--} = S + 2e^- \qquad (\text{oxidation})$$
$$Cr_2O_7^{--} + 14H^+ + 6e^- = 2Cr^{+++} + 7H_2O \ (\text{reduction})$$

In order that the electrons may cancel out, the first equation must be multiplied by 3:

$$3S^{--} = 3S + 6e^-$$

Then, adding, we get

$$3S^{--} + Cr_2O_7^{--} + 14H^+ = 3S + 2Cr^{+++} + 7H_2O$$

Ionic equations representing oxidation-reduction reactions can also be balanced directly by application of the oxidation number method (p. 216).

16. Electrode Reactions in Electrolysis. Thus far, in this chapter, we have discussed in detail only reactions that take place in voltaic cells; i.e., such as may be used for the production of electrical energy from chemical energy. A reaction that takes place in an electrolytic cell (p. 418) may be regarded as exactly the reverse process; the electrical energy supplied to the electrolytic cell from an external source brings about an oxidation-reduction reaction which would not take place—or rather, which would proceed in the opposite direction—of its own accord. Thus, in this case the reaction is accompanied by an increase rather than a decrease in free energy; or, in other words, electrolysis is a process in which electrical energy is changed into chemical energy.[3] The free energy increase, per faraday of electricity, for any given cell reaction is proportional to the electromotive force of the cell, which

[3] There is one type of electrolysis which does not conform exactly to the definition just given; namely, that in which each of the electrode half-reactions is the exact reverse of the other, and there is neither an increase nor a decrease in free energy during the operation of the cell. Such electrolysis, which occurs in the electrolytic purification of metals and in electroplating, may be regarded as lying on the border line between the processes that take place in a voltaic and in an electrolytic cell, as defined above.

for an electrolytic cell will always be negative; hence, the greater the negative value of the electromotive force, the greater is the amount of energy that must be supplied in order to bring about the corresponding reaction by electrolysis. Furthermore, just as for a voltaic cell, the electromotive force of an electrolytic cell may be obtained by the addition, with due regard to sign, of the half-reaction potentials corresponding to the half-reactions that take place at the electrodes.

If, for a given electrolytic cell, several alternative cell reactions can be formulated, we may be sure that the one which actually occurs will be the one that requires the smallest expenditure of electrical energy. Since each half-reaction potential is regarded as a measure of the relative tendency of the corresponding half-reaction to take place, it follows that, just as in the case of a voltaic cell, the reaction that occurs will, in general, be that consisting of the two half-reactions which, at the respective electrodes, correspond to the highest (least negative or most positive) potentials. With the aid of this simple rule, we are enabled to account for, and even to predict, the products of electrolysis of any electrolyte, as will presently be shown. In the application of this principle, however, it must be remembered that water itself is a possible participant in electrode reactions, since it may be reduced to hydroxide ion and free hydrogen, or oxidized to hydrogen ion and free oxygen. Since the oxidation potentials of the hydrogen and oxygen electrodes in neutral solution are appreciably different from their standard oxidation potentials as given in Tables 24.1 and 24.2, it will be well for us to add the following data to those already tabulated.

Table 24.3

Oxidation Potentials of Hydrogen and Oxygen in Neutral Solutions

Electrode	Half-Reaction	Oxidation Potential (volts)
Pt, H_2, OH^-($10^{-7}M$)	$H_2 + 2OH^- = 2H_2O + 2e^-$	0.41
Pt, O_2, H^+($10^{-7}M$)	$2H_2O = O_2 + 4H^+ + 4e^-$	−0.82

Let us now consider a few typical electrolyses from the point of view just suggested. First, let us suppose an approximately molar solution of nickel iodide, NiI_2, to be electrolyzed between a pair of platinum electrodes. The two reactions that might conceivably take place at the cathode, and the corresponding half-reaction potentials, are

$$Ni^{++} + 2e^- = Ni \qquad ; E = -0.25 \text{ v.}$$

$$2H_2O + 2e^- = H_2 + 2OH^- ; E = -0.41 \text{ v.}$$

Since the first of these has the higher (less negative) potential, the cathode reaction will consist in the deposition of metallic nickel. At the anode, there are three conceivable reactions:

$$2I^- = I_2 + 2e^- \qquad\qquad ; E = -0.54 \text{ v.}$$

$$2H_2O = O_2 + 4H^+ + 4e^- ; E = -0.82 \text{ v.}$$

$$Pt = Pt^{++} + 2e^- \qquad ; E = -1.20 \text{ v.}$$

The first of these has the highest (least negative) potential; hence, iodine will be liberated at the anode.

In the electrolysis of a solution of sulfuric acid between inert electrodes, the only possible cathode reaction is the liberation of hydrogen.

$$2H^+ + 2e^- = H_2; E = 0$$

We might write, as the equation for a conceivable anode reaction,

$$SO_4^{--} = SO_4 + 2e^-; E = \ ?$$

but no such tetroxide of sulfur as is indicated by the formula SO_4 can be obtained in this way. Actually, the anode reaction consists in the liberation of oxygen. We must conclude, therefore, that the half-reaction potential for discharge of sulfate ion to free sulfate radical must have a very high negative value—higher even than that required for the liberation of oxygen from an acid solution:

$$2H_2O = O_2 + 4H^+ + 4e^-; E = -1.23 \text{ v.}$$

Since hydrogen and oxygen are liberated at the electrodes, the net effect of the electrolysis of a dilute solution of sulfuric acid is the decomposition of water into its elements (p. 200). The same result is obtained with solutions of most other oxygen-containing acids.

17. The Storage Cell. A storage cell, or accumulator, is a voltaic cell which, after it has served for a time as a source of electrical energy, can be restored to its original condition by means of electrical energy supplied from an external source. This process of restoration (or *charging* of the cell, as it is called) is brought about by the passage of an electric current through the cell in a direction opposite to that produced by the spontaneous cell reaction; during this electrolytic process, the reactions that take place at the electrodes are the reverse of those that occur spontaneously during the *discharging* of the cell. Most of the voltaic cells that have been described in this chapter might be recharged after the cell reaction has proceeded for a while, but in few, if any, cases, would the electrodes be restored to their original size, shape, and structure. A practical storage cell must contain only inexpensive materials and must be mechanically as well as chemically reversible; there are but very few types that meet all of these requirements.

By far the most widely used accumulator is the lead storage cell. In this cell, the electrodes both consist of grids of lead (usually alloyed with antimony), one packed with lead dioxide, the other with finely divided lead; the electrolyte is sulfuric acid (3.7 molar). During discharge, the half-reaction that occurs at the anode is

$$Pb + SO_4^{--} = PbSO_4 + 2e^-$$

and the half-reaction at the cathode,

$$PbO_2 + 4H^+ + SO_4^{--} + 2e^- = PbSO_4 + 2H_2O$$

Since lead sulfate is but very slightly soluble, it remains on the electrodes. The direction of the electron flow in the external circuit is, of course, from the lead to the lead dioxide electrode; according to convention, then, the lead is called the negative electrode, and the lead dioxide the positive. By adding the half-reactions together, we obtain the entire cell reaction:

$$Pb + PbO_2 + 4H^+ + 2SO_4^{--} = 2PbSO_4 + 2H_2O$$

The electromotive force of a fully charged storage cell is a little over 2 v. As the reaction proceeds, the concentration of sulfuric acid decreases, and the voltage falls off slightly.

If the cell were allowed to discharge completely, the lead dioxide and finely divided lead in the grids would be entirely converted to lead sulfate. In practice, however, the reaction is not allowed to proceed to this extent; before the conversion is complete, the cell is charged by means of a current from some external source, with the grid containing the finely divided lead serving as cathode and the lead dioxide grid as anode. The electrode reactions that take place during this process are exactly the reverse of those given before, so that the lead sulfate which has been formed in the grids is reconverted to lead at the cathode and to lead dioxide at the anode.

The lead storage cell, as it is used for practical purposes, consists not of a single positive and a single negative plate, but of a series of such plates arranged alternately. The positive electrode is made up of a number of connected lead dioxide plates, and the negative electrode of a similar number of lead plates; each lead plate is prevented from coming in contact with the adjacent lead dioxide plates by separators of wood or of perforated rubber. A lead storage battery, such as is used as the familiar source of electrical energy in an automobile, consists of three such lead storage cells arranged in series, and, therefore, gives a total electromotive force of about 6 v. Since the concentration of the sulfuric acid in a storage battery decreases during discharge and increases during charge, the density of the electrolyte, which varies with concentration, is a convenient criterion of the state of charge or discharge.

A second type of storage cell which is of practical importance is the Edison cell. The positive and negative electrodes in this cell are steel plates packed with hydrous nickelic oxide, $NiO_2 \cdot xH_2O$, and finely divided iron, respectively; the electrolyte is potassium hydroxide solution. During discharge, ferrous hydroxide is formed at the anode and nickelous hydroxide at the cathode, by the respective half-reactions

$$Fe + 2OH^- = Fe(OH)_2 + 2e^-$$

$$NiO_2 + 2H_2O + 2e^- = Ni(OH)_2 + 2OH^-$$

The entire cell reaction, therefore, is

$$Fe + NiO_2 + 2H_2O = Fe(OH)_2 + Ni(OH)_2$$

The electromotive force of the cell is about 1.4 v. The Edison storage battery is lighter and more durable than the lead battery, but not so efficient.

Another alkaline storage cell which has recently come into wide use, especially for airplanes, is the nickel–cadmium cell. This is similar to the Edison cell except that the positive plates are packed with finely divided cadmium instead of iron. The half-reaction at the anode, during discharge, is

$$Cd + 2OH^- = Cd(OH)_2 + 2e^-$$

This cell, with about the same electromotive force, is lighter and longer-lived than the Edison cell.

18. The Concentration Cell. Let us consider a cell consisting of two silver electrodes immersed in silver nitrate solutions of different concentrations, in contact through a porous membrane or a salt bridge that retards diffusion (Figure 24.5). Although no oxidation-reduction reaction can take place in this cell, yet electrons flow from the electrode in the more dilute to that in the more concentrated solution. In order to find an explanation for this apparent paradox, we must note that the two half-reactions

$$Ag = Ag^+ \text{ (in dilute solution)} + e^-$$

and

$$Ag^+ \text{ (in concentrated solution)} + e^- = Ag$$

do not exactly cancel each other. The tendency for metallic silver to be oxidized to silver ion in a dilute solution of a silver salt is greater than in a concentrated solution; or, conversely, the tendency for silver ion to be reduced is greater in a concentrated solution than in a dilute. Hence we find that there is a positive electromotive force corresponding to the cell reaction

$$Ag^+ \text{ (in concentrated solution)} = Ag^+ \text{ (in dilute solution)}$$

It follows that the transfer of silver ion from a more concentrated to a more dilute solution is a spontaneous process.[4] This is in accord with previous statements (pp. 295, 413) that a dissolved substance tends to pass of its own accord from a region of higher to one of lower concentration.

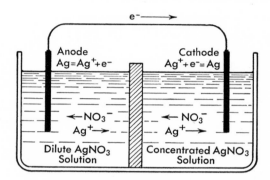

Fig. 24.5.   A concentration cell.

Concentration cells may be constructed with solutions of any salt serving as electrolyte. It may be demonstrated theoretically, and it has been confirmed by experiment, that the oxidation potential of a metal in contact with a solution of its cation decreases by very nearly 0.06 v.—if the cation is univalent—for a tenfold increase in the concentration of the ion. A similar decrease occurs in the reduction potential of a nonmetal, such as iodine, for a tenfold increase in the concentration of the corresponding (univalent) anion in the solution. For a bivalent ion, the decrease in oxidation potential for a similar increase in concentration is only 0.03 v., and for a trivalent ion, 0.02 v. It should be noted that such variation of oxidation potential with ion

---

[4] Actually, it is impossible for a positively charged ionic substance to be transferred from one solution to another without simultaneous transfer of an equivalent quantity of a negatively charged substance, and vice versa. In the cell just described, the migration of nitrate ion through the membrane or salt bridge from the concentrated to the dilute solution is just sufficient to balance the increase in the amount of silver ion in the dilute solution. This increase, in turn, results from the excess of the silver ion formed at the anode, over the silver ion that migrates through the partition from the dilute to the concentrated solution. Silver and nitrate ions, therefore, are transferred from the concentrated to the dilute solution in equivalent amounts; or it might be said that silver nitrate is so transferred.

concentration is quite in accord with the principles of chemical equilibrium (p. 265). Thus, for example, in the half-reaction

$$Zn \rightleftharpoons Zn^{++} + 2e^-$$

it is obvious that an increase in the concentration of zinc ion in the solution must shift the equilibrium to the left, thereby decreasing the tendency for zinc to be oxidized and hence decreasing the oxidation potential; whereas a decrease in the concentration of the zinc ion has the opposite effect.

STUDY QUESTIONS AND PROBLEMS

1. State whether or not each of the following oxidation-reduction reactions could be used as the source of energy in an actual voltaic cell. If the reaction could not be so used, give the reason. If it could be used, state briefly how such a cell could be set up, and write an ionic equation for each electrode half-reaction.

(a) $2K + Cl_2 = 2KCl$
(b) $Zn + Br_2 = ZnBr_2$
(c) $Cd + Pb(NO_3)_2 = Cd(NO_3)_2 + Pb$
(d) $2NO + O_2 = 2NO_2$
(e) $2HgO = 2Hg + O_2$
(f) $Mg + 2HCl = MgCl_2 + H_2$
(g) $Br_2 + 2NaI = I_2 + 2NaBr$
(h) $3SnSO_4 + K_2Cr_2O_7 + 7H_2SO_4 =$
     $3Sn(SO_4)_2 + K_2SO_4 + Cr_2(SO_4)_3 + 7H_2O$

2. Draw a simple diagram of a voltaic cell in which the chemical reaction consists in the displacement of nickel from nickel sulfate, $NiSO_4$, by metallic magnesium. Write equations for the half-reactions (including gain or loss of electrons) that take place at the electrodes during the operation of the cell, and state whether each half-reaction is oxidation or reduction. Add the half-reactions together to give an equation for the entire cell process. Indicate which electrode is anode and which cathode, the direction of flow of electrons in a wire connecting the electrodes, and the direction of migration of magnesium, nickel, and sulfate ions through the solution during the operation of the cell.

3. If the solutions used in the cell described in the preceding question are molar in magnesium and nickel ions, respectively, what is the approximate electromotive force of the cell?

4. What weight of metallic magnesium is used up in the cell of question 2 when it is discharged at the rate of 0.1 amp. for 6 hr. and 26 min.? How many electrons flow past a given point in the external circuit in this time? How many calories of chemical energy are changed to electrical energy in this process?

5. How many coulombs of electricity are supplied when a lead storage cell

is discharged until 20.7 g. of lead have been oxidized? For how long would the cell then have to be recharged, at the rate of 10 amp., in order to restore it to its original condition?

6. State what product would be obtained at each electrode in the electrolysis of each of the following aqueous solutions. (Assume the solutions to be approximately molar, and the electrodes to be of platinum unless otherwise stated.)

(a) Cupric sulfate solution
(b) Cupric sulfate solution, copper electrodes
(c) Sodium chloride solution
(d) Cadmium bromide solution
(e) Cadmium bromide solution, cadmium electrodes

7. Explain why the state of charge or discharge of a lead storage cell can be determined by measurement of the density of the electrolyte.

8. Show how you can predict whether or not mercurous chloride will be reduced to free mercury in a solution approximately molar in stannous, stannic, and chloride ions.

9. Complete, and balance by means of the ion-electron method:

(a) $Fe^{++} + Cr_2O_7^{--} + H^+ =$
(b) $Mn^{++} + PbO_2 + H^+ + SO_4^{--} =$
(c) $Sn^{++} + MnO_4^- + H^+ =$
(d) $Fe^{++} + H^+ + O_2 =$

Sulfur, Selenium, Tellurium, and Polonium

1. Elements of Group 6a. Group 6a of the periodic system includes the elements oxygen, sulfur, selenium, tellurium, and the radioactive element polonium. The first of these elements, oxygen, has already been discussed in Chapter 11.

2. History. Sulfur has been known since ancient times, and there are records of its use for medicinal and fumigation purposes at least as early as 1000 B.C. It was commonly used in the practice of alchemy, and in early times was referred to as "brimstone." Selenium was first isolated by the famous Swedish chemist Berzelius in 1817 and was named from a Greek word *selene*, meaning "moon." Tellurium was discovered by Reichenstein in 1782 and named in 1798 by Klaproth from the Latin word *tellus*, meaning "earth." Polonium was discovered by Marie Curie in 1898 and was named in honor of Poland, her native country.

3. Occurrence and Preparation. Sulfur is one of the more abundant elements, and is estimated to constitute 0.1% of the material in the earth's crust. It occurs most abundantly in the form of the mineral pyrite, which has the formula FeS_2. Many other metal sulfides, including those of lead, zinc, and copper, occur in nature; these substances form an important group of ores of the metals. Sulfates of some of the metals, such as those of calcium and magnesium, occur in nature in large quantities also. In addition to these combined forms, sulfur is found also in the free state, especially in volcanic regions such as Mexico, Sicily, and Japan. Enormous nonvolcanic deposits have been found in Texas and in Louisiana; these deposits furnish the major portion of the sulfur needed for our industries. The sulfur strata in these beds are overlaid by quicksand in such a manner as to preclude ordinary mining operations, so for many years the United States imported from

Sicily most of the sulfur used in its chemical industries. About 1900, an American engineer, Herman Frasch, developed a method whereby the sulfur of the Texas and Louisiana deposits could be brought to the surface. Three concentric pipes are driven down to the sulfur deposit from the surface (Figure 25.1). Water, heated under pressure to about 170° C., is forced down the outer pipe, while hot air is forced down the inner pipe. The sulfur

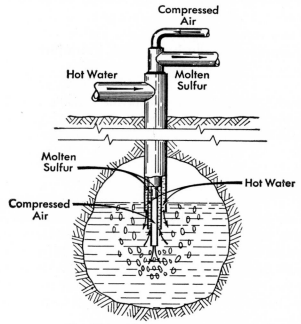

Fig. 25.1.   The Frasch process.

is melted and a froth of water, sulfur, and air rises to the surface through the middle pipe. The process is operated continuously, and up to 500 tons of sulfur are obtained daily from a single installation. The sulfur thus obtained is about 99.5% pure. At present the world's annual production of mined sulfur approaches 6,000,000 tons. The usual commercial forms of sulfur include sticks or rolls, which are known as roll sulfur, and "flowers of sulfur," which is a fine powder obtained by the condensation of sulfur vapor at a temperature below its melting point.

Selenium and tellurium are considerably less common than sulfur; they are estimated to constitute only $10^{-8}\%$ and $10^{-9}\%$, respectively, of the material in igneous rocks. Both of these elements occur as binary compounds with the heavy metals; some free selenium is found in conjunction with sulfur deposits, but little elementary tellurium occurs in nature. Selenium can be obtained in considerable quantities as a by-product of the manufacture of sulfuric acid (from the flue dust in the sulfur burners) and of the electrolytic refining of copper (from the anode mud, p. 763). Tellurium can be obtained in a similar manner.

4. General Characteristics. The electron configurations of the elements of Group 6a are listed in Table 25.1. These elements immediately precede the respective members of Group 7a in the periodic system and differ from the latter in that their atoms have only six valence electrons instead of seven. As

Table 25.1

Element	1 _s_	2 _s p_	3 _s p d_	4 _s p d f_	5 _s p d_	6 _s p_
O	2	2, 4				
S	2	2, 6	2, 4			
Se	2	2, 6	2, 6, 10	2, 4		
Te	2	2, 6	2, 6, 10	2, 6, 10	2, 4	
Po	2	2, 6	2, 6, 10	2, 6, 10, 14	2, 6, 10	2, 4

was pointed out in Chapter 22, the halogens are characterized by a very strong tendency to take up one electron per atom to form singly charged negative ions; the members of Group 6a show a similar tendency to react with metallic elements by taking up two electrons per atom to form doubly charged negative ions, as is indicated by the following general equation:

$$2M \cdot + \cdot \ddot{X} : = 2M^+ + : \ddot{X} :^{--}$$

With elements that release electrons somewhat less readily, complete transfer of electrons does not take place and covalent molecules are obtained. However, in many such cases, the bonds are polar, with the Group 6a element forming the negative end of the bond. It is then still said to have an oxidation number of −2, as in hydrogen sulfide:

$$: \ddot{S} : H$$
$$H$$

As would be expected from their electronic configurations, in accordance with the discussion in Chapter 10 (p. 183), these elements are less nonmetallic than are the halogens; i.e., they have a lesser tendency to take up electrons. However, the properties of the Group 6a elements are still predominantly nonmetallic.

The usual trend within a given family in the periodic system is for the metallic characteristics of the elements to become more prominent with increasing atomic number (p. 185); the members of Group 6a are no exception to this rule. Oxygen and sulfur are distinctly nonmetallic, but selenium and, to a greater extent, tellurium exhibit certain metallic characteristics.

The elements of this family show little or no tendency to form ions with a charge of $+6$ by losing all six of their valence electrons; this fact is in accord with the high ionization potentials of the elements. These data are listed in Table 25.2 (compare Table 22.2, p. 382). In fact, there is no

Table 25.2

Ionization Potentials of the Elements of Group 6a (volts)

	1st	2nd	3rd	4th	5th	6th
Oxygen	13.6	35.1	54.9	77.4	113.0	138.1
Sulfur	10.4	23.4	35.0	47.3	72.5	88.0
Selenium	9.8	21.3	33.9	42.7	72.8	81.4
Tellurium	9.0	. . .	30.5	37.7	60.0	72.0

evidence that any of these elements forms simple positively charged ions of any type, although tellurium does form a few relatively unfamiliar complex cations. It should be noted in this connection that the ionization potentials of the elements of this group follow the usual trend, decreasing with increasing atomic number.

Sulfur, selenium, and tellurium form numerous compounds in which they are in oxidation states other than -2. In these compounds the sulfur, selenium, or tellurium atom shares electrons with a more nonmetallic element such as oxygen or one of the halogens. Particularly important are the compounds in which the Group 6a element is in the $+4$ or $+6$ oxidation state.

5. Physical and Chemical Properties of the Elements. An important and characteristic feature of the elements of this group is the existence of each in a number of allotropic modifications. Thus, sulfur exists in nine crystalline forms in the solid state, as well as in several different molecular species in the liquid and gaseous states; there are also several amorphous and colloidal forms. Elementary selenium exhibits a similar variability in form. We shall consider only the more common of these allotropic modifications.

The familiar form of sulfur, which is stable at room temperature, is rhombic sulfur, so called because of its crystal form. It is odorless, tasteless, and bright yellow in color. It is insoluble in water but readily soluble in carbon disulfide. Its density is 2.07 g. per cc. When rhombic sulfur is heated to 95.5° C. it undergoes slow transformation into a second common variety of the element, known from its crystalline form as monoclinic sulfur. The difference in the crystalline forms of these two modifications is illustrated in Figure 25.2. Like the rhombic variety, monoclinic sulfur is yellow in color

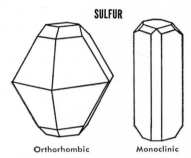

SULFUR

Orthorhombic   Monoclinic

Fig. 25.2.   Crystalline forms of sulfur.

and is insoluble in water but soluble in carbon disulfide. It has a density of 1.96 g. per cc. Monoclinic sulfur may be readily prepared by allowing sulfur to crystallize at temperatures exceeding 95.5° C. On standing, at ordinary temperature, the crystals slowly revert to the more stable rhombic form. Both forms of crystalline sulfur, as well as the liquid forms which are discussed in the next paragraph, are nonconductors of electricity, a property which is in line with their other nonmetallic characteristics. The crystalline forms of sulfur consist of true molecular crystals (p. 189), the points in the crystal lattices being occupied by S_8 molecules with the cyclic structure

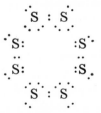

A photograph of a model of this molecule is shown in Figure 25.3.

The determination of the melting point of sulfur is complicated not only by the existence of more than one solid form of the element, but also by the existence of more than one molecular species in the liquid state. If monoclinic sulfur is heated rapidly, it melts at 119° C. to give a liquid composed of S_8 rings. If, however, the melting is carried out slowly so that equilibrium may be attained among the various possible molecular species in liquid sulfur, the melting point observed is 114.5° C. Since the transition from rhombic to monoclinic sulfur is relatively slow, rhombic sulfur may be melted without going through the monoclinic phase. The two melting points corresponding to those just given for the monoclinic form are, respectively, 112.8° C. and 110.4° C.

The proportions of the various molecular species present at equilibrium in liquid sulfur change with temperature. As a result of this variation, liquid sulfur undergoes some remarkable changes in physical properties as the temperature is increased. Just above its melting point, sulfur is a clear yellow liquid, consisting mainly of S_8 molecules. As the temperature is increased, however, the color darkens and the viscosity increases markedly. This change is thought to be due to the breaking of the S_8 rings with the formation of long chains of sulfur atoms. In the range of 165° to 200° C., the viscosity reaches a maximum and the liquid will scarcely flow; on further heating, the viscosity decreases rapidly up to the boiling point, 444.5° C. If liquid sulfur which has been heated almost to its boiling point is cooled suddenly, as by pouring into water, a soft, rubbery mass known as plastic sulfur is obtained. This substance presumably consists chiefly of the long chains of sulfur atoms, and is insoluble in carbon disulfide. On standing, it slowly undergoes crystallization, during which S_8 rings are reformed.

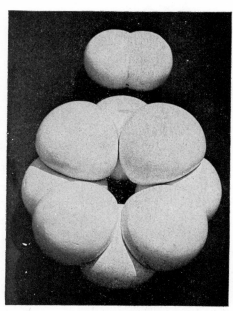

Fig. 25.3. Models of the O_2 molecule and the S_8 molecule. (*Courtesy of Dr. J. A. Campbell, Oberlin College.*)

At temperatures just above the boiling point of sulfur, the vapor consists largely of S_8 molecules, with some S_6 and S_2. At 1000° C. it consists largely of S_2 molecules.

Sulfur can act either as an oxidizing agent or as a reducing agent. It combines with all the elements except the platinum metals, gold, and the inert gases. Its reactions with metals such as iron, copper, or zinc are so vigorous that when the temperature of a mixture of one of these metals with sulfur is raised to the point where reaction begins, enough energy is evolved to heat the mass to incandescence.

Like sulfur, selenium exists in several different solid forms. Commercial selenium is generally either of the finely divided amorphous or of the lump or vitreous variety. These forms are dark red to black in color when in large pieces, but thin sheets appear red by transmitted light. Amorphous and vitreous selenium consist of mixtures of at least two forms. All these varieties of selenium, when heated to about 150° C. or when brought into contact with solvents, undergo transition to hexagonal crystals of what is called gray or metallic selenium, which is the stable form at room temperature. Gray selenium has a metallic luster, and, in contrast to other forms, is insoluble in carbon disulfide and is a conductor of electricity. It is interesting to note that the electrical conductivity of metallic selenium is greatly increased when the substance is exposed to ordinary light, particularly red light with a wave length of 7000 Å. The chemical properties of selenium, also, are similar to those of sulfur. Metallic selenium has a density of 4.79 g. per cc. and melts at 217.4° C. The properties of molten selenium are qualitatively similar to those of liquid sulfur. Selenium boils at 688° C.

In accordance with the increase in the metallic nature of the elements with increasing atomic number, there is no nonmetallic variety of tellurium. The stable form of this element is silvery white in color, brittle, and not very hard; it has a density of about 6.2 g. per cc. Its melting point is 449.8° C., and the liquid boils at 1390° C. Polonium resembles tellurium in its chemical properties, although it is somewhat more metallic in nature.

6. Uses of the Elements. Most of the sulfur used is converted to the very important industrial chemical sulfuric acid, which will be discussed later in the chapter. Smaller quantities are used in manufacturing other sulfur compounds, in the vulcanization of rubber, and as a component in gunpowder and in insecticides. Between two and three million tons of sulfur are produced annually in the United States, at a cost of less than one cent per pound.

Although selenium has no extensive commercial applications, small quantities are used in the manufacture of ruby-red glass for signal lights, and in ordinary glass to neutralize the green tint due to the presence of ferrous silicate. Some selenium is used in the vulcanization of certain kinds of rubber goods. The variation of the electrical conductivity of metallic selenium with the intensity of light falling upon it is applied in the manufacture of selenium photoelectric cells. These cells may be used to measure the intensity of light, as well as for a variety of other purposes. Few uses for elementary tellurium have been developed. Small amounts are sometimes added to the lead used in pipes, in order to increase its tensile strength and resistance to corrosion.

7. Hydrogen Compounds. Though small yields of hydrogen sulfide and hydrogen selenide may be obtained by the action of hydrogen gas on the respective free elements at elevated temperatures, the hydrogen compounds of sulfur, selenium, and tellurium are best prepared by the action of dilute hydrochloric acid on metal sulfides, selenides, or tellurides. Hydrogen sulfide is usually prepared from ferrous sulfide.

$$FeS_{(s)} + 2H^+ = Fe^{++} + H_2S$$

Oxidizing acids such as nitric cannot be used, for they oxidize the hydrogen sulfide, selenide, or telluride to the respective free element. Hydrogen sulfide is also obtained when sulfur is heated with paraffin, which is a mixture of carbon–hydrogen compounds.

$$C_xH_y + \frac{1}{2}yS = xC + \frac{1}{2}yH_2S$$

The compounds H_2S, H_2Se, and H_2Te are colorless gases; all have unpleasant odors and are very poisonous. Together with H_2O, the common oxide of hydrogen, they constitute a series of compounds analogous to the series of hydrogen halides discussed in Chapter 22. Although the properties of the compounds under discussion differ considerably from those of the hydrogen halides, the trends within the two series are, as is indicated in the next paragraph, quite similar. Some of the important physical constants for the Group 6a hydrogen compounds are given in Table 25.3.

Table 25.3

	Melting Point °C.	Boiling Point °C.	Solubility in Water at 25° C. Moles per liter (Pressure = 760 mm.)	Ionization Constants at 25° C. $K_1 = \dfrac{[H^+][HX^-]}{[H_2X]}$	$K_2 = \dfrac{[H^+][X^{--}]}{[HX^-]}$
H_2O	0.00	100.0	......	1.78×10^{-16}	about 10^{-24}
H_2S	−85.60	−60.75	0.102	1.1×10^{-7}	about 10^{-14}
H_2Se	−60.4	−41.5	0.08415	1.88×10^{-4}	1×10^{-14}
H_2Te	−51	− 1.8	......	2.3×10^{-3} (18° C.)	1×10^{-11}

The abnormality of the physical properties of water as compared with the other hydrides of this family has already been discussed in Chapter 14. As is indicated by the data in Table 25.3, the hydrogen compounds of sulfur, selenium, and tellurium are weak diprotic acids. They are much weaker than the hydrohalic acids, but, as in that series, the acidic character of the hydrogen compound increases with increasing atomic number; thus, acidity increases in the series $H_2O < H_2S < H_2Se < H_2Te$, as it does in the series $HF < HCl < HBr < HI$. Also, as in the case of the hydrogen halides, the hydrogen compounds of the Group 6a elements are reducing agents, their reducing power increasing in the same order as the acidity. The stability of these compounds likewise decreases in this same order. Thus, H_2Te and HI are the least stable, and the strongest reducing agents, of their respective groups.

Hydrogen sulfide, when ignited, burns readily in an excess of air.

$$2H_2S + 3O_2 = 2H_2O + 2SO_2$$

In a limited supply of air, sulfur is formed.

$$2H_2S + O_2 = 2H_2O + 2S$$

Hydrogen selenide and telluride undergo reaction with oxygen even more readily, but yield free selenium and tellurium rather than the oxides.

$$2H_2Se + O_2 = 2H_2O + 2Se$$

When hydrogen sulfide gas is passed into nitric acid it is oxidized to free sulfur, or to sulfate ion, depending upon whether the nitric acid is dilute or concentrated.

Since the compounds H_2S, H_2Se, and H_2Te are diprotic acids, they react with bases to yield compounds which are analogous to hydroxides and oxides. Thus, hydrogen sulfide reacts successively with two equivalents of hydroxide in accordance with the equations

$$H_2S + OH^- = HS^- + H_2O$$
$$\text{hydrosulfide ion}$$
$$HS^- + OH^- = S^{--} + H_2O$$
$$\text{sulfide ion}$$

Likewise, H_2Se yields hydroselenide, HSe^-, and selenide, Se^{--}, ions, while H_2Te yields hydrotelluride, HTe^-, and telluride, Te^{--}, ions. Because of the strong tendency of the sulfide and hydrosulfide ions to take up protons, as indicated by the low values of the ionization constants of hydrogen sulfide (Table 25.3), aqueous solutions of soluble sulfides and hydrosulfides are basic, and are appreciably hydrolyzed.

$$HS^- + H_2O = H_2S + OH^-$$
$$S^{--} + H_2O = HS^- + OH^-$$

Selenides, hydroselenides, tellurides, and hydrotellurides are likewise susceptible to hydrolysis, but as would be expected from the more acidic character of H_2Se and H_2Te, they are less so than sulfides and hydrosulfides.

The sulfides of all the metals except those of Groups 1a, 2a, and 3a are only very slightly soluble in water. Because of the weakly acidic nature of hydrogen sulfide, however, the solubilities of these slightly soluble sulfides are markedly increased by the presence of hydrogen ion.

$$MS_{(s)} = M^{++} + \boxed{\begin{array}{c} S^{--} \\ + \\ H^{+} \end{array}} = HS^{-}$$

Because of these facts, the precipitation of metallic sulfides is commonly used in qualitative analytical procedures as a step in the separation of the various cations. As is indicated by the equilibrium

$$H_2S \rightleftharpoons 2H^{+} + S^{--}$$

careful control of the hydrogen concentration of a solution can be used to hold the sulfide concentration in a solution saturated with hydrogen sulfide at such a value that the solubility products of the less soluble sulfides are exceeded, and these substances are precipitated, while the more soluble sulfides remain in solution.

The sulfide ion may be detected by the following method. The solution is acidified with acetic acid and a piece of paper saturated with lead acetate is held above it. On being warmed, the solution releases hydrogen sulfide, which blackens the paper by forming black lead sulfide.

The formation of a black deposit of silver sulfide accounts for the tarnishing of silver metal in the presence of hydrogen sulfide gas.

8. Polysulfides, Selenides, and Tellurides. When elementary sulfur is added to solutions containing sulfide ion, the sulfur unites with the sulfide ion to form polysulfides, according to the equation

$$S^{--} + (x-1)S = S_x^{--}$$

where $x = 2, 3, 4,$ or 5, depending upon the amount of sulfur added. Analogous reactions likewise occur between selenide ion and selenium, and between telluride ion and tellurium. In the case of the alkali metals, these polysalts are readily prepared also by the reaction of sulfur, selenium, or tellurium with solutions of the metals in liquid ammonia. The polysulfides, polyselenides, and polytellurides presumably have structures in which the atoms are connected by electron pair bonds. The S_2^{--} ion has a structure analogous to the peroxide ion, and its formation may be represented thus:

$$: \overset{..}{\underset{..}{S}} : -- + \overset{..}{\underset{..}{S}} : = : \overset{..}{\underset{..}{S}} : \overset{..}{\underset{..}{S}} : --$$

The S_3^{--} ion has the structure

Because of the presence of excess sulfur, the polysulfides can act as oxidizing agents; e.g., stannous sulfide is oxidized to thiostannate ion.

$$\text{SnS} + S_2^{--} = \text{SnS}_3^{--}$$

When solutions of the polysulfides are acidified, hydrogen sulfide and free sulfur in a white, very finely divided form (milk of sulfur), as well as small amounts of H_2S_2, H_2S_3, and perhaps even higher hydrogen polysulfides, are obtained. There is no evidence, however, for the existence of selenium and tellurium compounds analogous to H_2S_2 and H_2S_3.

Calcium polysulfides are constituents of the common insecticide known as lime sulfur spray.

9. Halogen Compounds. Sulfur, selenium, and tellurium form, either directly or indirectly, a large group of halogen compounds. Formulas of the known members of this group are summarized in Table 25.4.

Table 25.4

	F	Cl	Br	I
Sulfur	S_2F_2 SF_4 S_2F_{10} SF_6	S_2Cl_2 SCl_2 SCl_4	S_2Br_2	
Selenium	SeF_4 Se_2F_{10} SeF_6	Se_2Cl_2 $SeCl_2$ $SeCl_4$	Se_2Br_2 $SeBr_2$ $SeBr_4$	
Tellurium	TeF_4 TeF_6 Te_2F_{10}	$TeCl_2$ $TeCl_4$	$TeBr_2$ $TeBr_4$	TeI_2

A few generalizations concerning these compounds may be of interest. All three elements under consideration react directly with fluorine to give fluorides in which the Group 6a element exhibits its highest oxidation state; viz., SF_6, SeF_6, TeF_6. This is an example of the effect of the great oxidizing power of elementary fluorine (p. 383). The stability and variety of these halogen compounds decrease with increasing atomic number of the halogen, i.e., in the order $F > Cl > Br > I$. Most of these halogen compounds, as would be expected of nonmetal halides, are entirely nonsalt-like in nature; at ordinary temperatures they are gases, volatile liquids, or volatile solids. The melting points and boiling points of the chlorides and bromides of tellurium, however, are markedly higher than those of the other chlorides and bromides. Moreover, liquid tellurium dichloride and tellurium tetrachloride are good conductors of electricity. This fact, indicative of the somewhat metallic nature of tellurium, is in accord with the previously discussed increase in metallic character of the elements of Group 6a with increase in atomic number.

THE OXIDES AND OXYGEN ACIDS OF SULFUR, SELENIUM, AND TELLURIUM

10. Oxides of Sulfur, Selenium, and Tellurium. These elements, in several different oxidation states, form a variety of oxides and oxyacids, especially numerous in the case of sulfur. Thus, at least four and perhaps six different oxides and at least twelve and perhaps thirteen oxygen acids of this element are known. A list of the oxides of sulfur, selenium, and tellurium is given in Table 25.5.

Table 25.5

Oxides of Sulfur, Selenium, and Tellurium

S	Se	Te	Name
SO	....	TeO	Monoxide
S_2O_3	....	....	Sesquioxide
SO_2	SeO_2	TeO_2	Dioxide
SO_3	SeO_3	TeO_3	Trioxide
S_2O_7 (?)	....	....	Heptoxide
SO_4	....	....	Tetroxide

We need not consider each of these oxides and each of the many oxygen acids in great detail. By far the most important of these oxygen compounds are the dioxides and trioxides, with their corresponding acids and derivatives.

11. Sulfur Dioxide, Sulfurous Acid, and the Sulfites. Sulfur dioxide, SO_2, is obtained (1) by the burning of sulfur—$S_8 + 8O_2 = 8SO_2$; (2) by the roasting of metal sulfides in the presence of air—$2ZnS + 3O_2 = 2ZnO + 2SO_2$; (3) by the reduction of sulfuric acid, as, for example, with metallic copper—$Cu + 2H_2SO_4 = Cu^{++} + SO_4^{--} + SO_2 + 2H_2O$; (4) by the action of strong acids upon sulfites or bisulfites—$SO_3^{--} + 2H^+ = H_2O + SO_2$.

Sulfur dioxide is a colorless gas with a sharp, irritating odor. It liquefies at a temperature of $-10.02°$ C. under a pressure of 1 atm.; in fact, it is so readily liquefied by moderate cooling or compression that it is widely used in mechanical refrigeration (p. 481). Even at 20° C. sulfur dioxide may be liquefied by a pressure of only 3 atm. The principle upon which its use as a refrigerant is based is described in connection with the discussion of the similar use of ammonia (p. 480). Liquid sulfur dioxide solidifies when cooled to $-75.46°$ C. The liquid is a good solvent for a wide variety of substances, including many salts. Considerable study has been devoted to its use as a medium for chemical reactions, some of which are strikingly analogous to reactions which take place in aqueous solutions. Thus, for example, just as cesium hydroxide dissolved in water reacts with hydrochloric acid to give cesium chloride and water, so cesium sulfite dissolved in liquid sulfur dioxide reacts with thionyl chloride (p. 454) in the same solvent to give cesium chloride and sulfur dioxide, according to the equation

$$Cs_2SO_3 + SOCl_2 = 2CsCl + 2SO_2$$

Sulfur dioxide dissolves readily in water, with which it reacts to yield sulfurous acid, H_2SO_3.

The structure of sulfur dioxide may be represented as a resonance hybrid (p. 196) :

A model of the sulfur dioxide molecule is pictured in Figure 25.4.

Since the oxidation state, $+4$, of sulfur in sulfur dioxide is intermediate between the highest oxidation state that sulfur assumes, $+6$, and the lower oxidation states, sulfur dioxide can act either as an oxidizing or as a reducing agent. Thus, it acts as an oxidizing agent when it reacts with carbon monoxide at 1000° C. to form carbon dioxide and free sulfur.

$$2SO_{2(g)} + 4CO_{(g)} = 4CO_{2(g)} + S_{2(g)}$$

The reducing properties of sulfur dioxide are much more important, however, and many of its industrial applications depend upon its behavior as a reducing agent. Particularly important is the fact that it may be oxidized by atmospheric oxygen to sulfur trioxide, which is in turn converted to sulfuric acid (p. 455).

$$2SO_2 + O_2 = 2SO_3$$

Large quantities of sulfur dioxide are used also to bleach silk, straw, wool, paper-making materials, and many foodstuffs such as dried apples, apricots, and peaches.

One of the outstanding chemical properties of sulfur dioxide is its ability to combine with other substances to form addition compounds. Thus the relatively high solubility of sulfur dioxide in water is attributed to its reaction with water to form the addition compound sulfurous acid, H_2SO_3, which may be represented by the electronic formula

$$\overset{\cdot\cdot}{:}\!\!O\!:$$
$$H:\overset{\cdot\cdot}{O}:\overset{\cdot\cdot}{S}:\overset{\cdot\cdot}{O}:H$$

Sulfurous acid ionizes in steps that may be represented by the following equations (the ionization constants for each step are given also):

$$H_2SO_3 \rightleftharpoons H^+ + HSO_3^-; K_1 = 1.25 \times 10^{-2} \text{ at } 25° \text{ C.}$$

$$HSO_3^- \rightleftharpoons H^+ + SO_3^{--}; K_2 = 5.6 \times 10^{-8} \text{ at } 25° \text{ C.}$$

Because the acid is relatively weak and not very stable (it exists only in aqueous solution), sulfur dioxide gas is liberated whenever solutions of sulfites are strongly acidified.

$$SO_3^{--} + 2H^+ = H_2O + SO_2$$

Since sulfurous acid is diprotic, it forms two series of salts, the normal sulfites, M_2SO_3, and the bisulfites or acid sulfites, $MHSO_3$. Because of the moderately strong proton affinity of sulfite ion, solutions of normal sulfites are slightly basic; however, since the tendency for bisulfite ion to release protons is greater than its tendency to take them up, solutions of bisulfites are slightly acidic.

The sulfites and bisulfites of the alkali metals are soluble in water. They are conveniently prepared by treating solutions of the alkali metal hydroxide with sulfur dioxide. If an excess of sulfur dioxide is added, a solution of the bisulfite is obtained.

$$OH^- + SO_2 = HSO_3^-$$

However, if only one mole of sulfur dioxide for two moles of hydroxide is used, sulfite ion is formed.

$$2OH^- + SO_2 = SO_3^{--} + H_2O$$

The same product is obtained when a bisulfite is treated with an equivalent quantity of hydroxide.

$$HSO_3^- + OH^- = SO_3^{--} + H_2O$$

Under certain conditions, alkali salts of the general formula $M_2S_2O_5$, called pyrosulfites, can be crystallized from alkali bisulfite solutions.

Sulfites of many of the heavy metals are only slightly soluble and may be prepared from solutions of alkali sulfites by precipitation; e.g.,

$$Ba^{++} + SO_3^{--} = BaSO_{3(s)}$$

These sulfites dissolve in strong acids with the evolution of sulfur dioxide, or in excess of sulfurous acid with the formation of bisulfite ion.

$$MSO_{3(s)} + H_2SO_3 = M^{++} + 2HSO_3^-$$

The oxidation state of sulfur in sulfurous acid, as in sulfur dioxide, is $+4$. Both the acid and its salts are excellent and inexpensive reducing agents, their solutions being oxidized by a great variety of substances. In almost every case the sulfurous acid or sulfite ion is converted to sulfate. The sulfur atom in the sulfurous acid molecule or sulfite ion possesses an unshared pair of electrons, and conversion to sulfate consists in the sharing of this pair of electrons with an oxygen atom.

$$: \overset{\cdot\cdot}{O} :^{--} \qquad\qquad : \overset{\cdot\cdot}{O} :$$
$$: \overset{\cdot\cdot}{\underset{\cdot\cdot}{O}} : \overset{\cdot\cdot}{S} : \quad + \overset{\cdot\cdot}{O} : \; = \; : \overset{\cdot\cdot}{\underset{\cdot\cdot}{O}} : \overset{\cdot\cdot}{\underset{\cdot\cdot}{S}} : \overset{\cdot\cdot}{\underset{\cdot\cdot}{O}} :^{--}$$
$$: \overset{\cdot\cdot}{\underset{\cdot\cdot}{O}} : \qquad\qquad : \overset{\cdot\cdot}{\underset{\cdot\cdot}{O}} :$$

Because of their tendency to take up oxygen, solutions of sulfurous acid or its salts, after standing in contact with the air, almost invariably contain sulfate ion. Under certain conditions, sulfurous acid acts, also, as an oxidizing agent; for example, it oxidizes hydrogen sulfide to free sulfur.

$$2H_2S + H_2SO_3 = 3S + 3H_2O$$

Likewise, sulfurous acid is reduced by zinc to a mixture of several substances, among which is hyposulfurous acid, $H_2S_2O_4$.

Sulfites and sulfurous acid, like sulfur dioxide, are applied industrially as bleaching agents and as food preservatives. When wood is treated with a solution of a bisulfite, the cellulose fibers are separated as well as bleached; hence, bisulfites, particularly that of calcium, are widely used in the manufacture of paper pulp. Sulfite solutions are likewise used to remove excess chlorine from textiles after chlorine has been used as a bleaching agent.

$$SO_3^{--} + H_2O + Cl_2 = SO_4^{--} + 2H^+ + 2Cl^-$$

Sulfites are usually detected by the characteristic odor of the sulfur dioxide gas which is evolved when their solutions are acidified, by the low solubility of the alkaline earth metal salts, and by their reducing action on such oxidizing agents as permanganate ion. The purple color of a permanganate solution is completely discharged by an acid solution of a sulfite.

$$2MnO_4^- + 5SO_3^{--} + 6H^+ = 2Mn^{++} + 5SO_4^{--} + 3H_2O$$

12. Dioxides of Selenium and Tellurium, and the Corresponding Acids.

When heated in air, both selenium and tellurium unite directly with oxygen to form the dioxides SeO_2 and TeO_2, respectively. These oxides, unlike sulfur dioxide, are solids at ordinary temperature. Selenium dioxide sublimes without melting under a pressure of 1 atm. and at a temperature of 315° C.; tellurium dioxide melts at dull red heat. Selenium dioxide reacts with water, although less readily than does sulfur dioxide, to form selenious acid. Tellurium dioxide does not react readily with water, but dissolves in alkali hydroxide solutions to form solutions of tellurites, from which the slightly soluble tellurous acid may be precipitated by the addition of strong acids.

$$TeO_2 + 2OH^- = TeO_3^{--} + H_2O$$
$$TeO_3^{--} + 2H^+ = H_2TeO_{3(s)}$$

Selenious acid differs from sulfurous in that it is somewhat less acidic, and particularly in being a much stronger oxidizing agent and a weaker reducing agent than the latter. The oxidizing strength of selenious acid is indicated by the oxidation potential for the following half-reaction:

$$3H_2O + Se = H_2SeO_3 + 4H^+ + 4e^-; E = -0.74 \text{ v.}$$

Both selenites, M_2SeO_3, and biselenites, $MHSeO_3$, are known.

Tellurous acid is the weakest acid of the three, and shows some amphiprotic tendencies.

13. The Thionyl and Selenyl Halides.

An interesting series of derivatives of sulfurous and selenious acids are the oxyhalides of the general formula MOX_2, where M represents S or Se, and X represents one of the halogens. Since these substances may be considered to be formally derived from the corresponding acid by replacement of a hydroxyl group by a halogen, and since they yield acids on hydrolysis, they are called acid halides. Thus, for example,

$$SOCl_2 + 2H_2O = SO(OH)_2 + 2H^+ + 2Cl^-$$

thionyl chloride   sulfurous acid

Thionyl chloride is readily obtained by the action of phosphorus pentachloride on sulfur dioxide, the anhydride of sulfurous acid.

$$SO_2 + PCl_5 = SOCl_2 + POCl_3$$

The compounds SOF_2, $SOCl_2$, $SOBr_2$, $SeOF_2$, $SeOCl_2$, and $SeOBr_2$ have been prepared; they are covalent compounds, being either gases, or volatile liquids, or solids. Thionyl chloride, $SOCl_2$, and selenyl chloride (commonly called selenium oxychloride), $SeOCl_2$, are common laboratory reagents.

14. Sulfur Trioxide. Absolutely pure sulfur trioxide is a liquid at ordinary temperatures. Whenever sulfur trioxide is formed in moist air, however, it appears as silky, asbestos-like fibers. These fibers are actually composed of long, linear molecules formed by the very slight hydration of sulfur trioxide. These molecules may be represented by the following electronic formula, in which n probably has a value of several hundred:

$$
\text{H} : \text{O} : \overset{\displaystyle :\ddot{\text{O}}:}{\underset{\displaystyle :\ddot{\text{O}}:}{\text{S}}} : \left[\overset{\displaystyle :\ddot{\text{O}}:}{\underset{\displaystyle :\ddot{\text{O}}:}{\text{O} : \text{S}}} : \right]_n \overset{\displaystyle :\ddot{\text{O}}:}{\underset{\displaystyle :\ddot{\text{O}}:}{\text{S} : \text{O}}} : \text{H}
$$

Liquid sulfur trioxide boils at about 45° C. The gaseous form consists entirely of SO_3 molecules. Both the liquid and the gas are colorless.

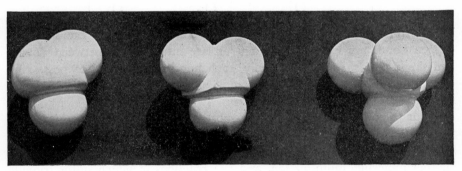

Fig. 25.4. Models of the SO_2 and the SO_3 molecules and the SO_4^{--} ion. (*Courtesy of Dr. J. A. Campbell, Oberlin College.*)

Sulfur trioxide is best obtained by the direct oxidation of sulfur dioxide with atmospheric oxygen, according to the equation

$$2SO_2 + O_2 = 2SO_3 + 46{,}000 \text{ cal.}$$

The equilibrium constant for this reaction at room temperature has a very high value, indicating that a high yield of sulfur trioxide would be obtained at equilibrium. At room temperature, however, equilibrium is attained only immeasurably slowly. The rate at which the system approaches equilibrium may be increased by the use of a catalyst, and by increase in temperature.

However, since the forward reaction which results in the production of the sulfur trioxide is exothermic, the yield of sulfur trioxide at equilibrium is decreased by raising the temperature (p. 267); hence, excessively high temperatures must be avoided. This reaction is of very great practical importance, since it is used in one of the industrial methods for the manufacture of sulfuric acid. In the contact process, as it is called, a mixture of sulfur dioxide and an excess of air is passed over a catalyst, usually consisting either of divanadium pentoxide or of finely divided or spongy platinum, at temperatures of about 400° to 500° C. If platinum is used, the sulfur dioxide must previously be freed from any trace of impurities, and particularly of arsenic compounds, in the presence of which the catalyst soon becomes poisoned; i.e., loses its effectiveness. The sulfur trioxide thus obtained is usually converted directly to sulfuric acid, as is described below.

The sulfur trioxide molecule may be represented electronically as a resonance hybrid, as follows:

$$\left\{ \begin{array}{ccc} \ddot{O} & \ddot{O} & \ddot{O}: \\ O::S & , :\ddot{O}:S & , :\ddot{O}:S \\ \ddot{O} & \ddot{O}: & \ddot{O} \end{array} \right\}$$

This formula is to be interpreted as indicating that all of the sulfur to oxygen bonds are exactly alike and all are intermediate between double and single bonds. More specifically, each bond may be said to possess $1/3$ double and $2/3$ single bond character. A model of this molecule is shown in Figure 25.4.

Sulfur trioxide is a highly reactive substance. Most of its important reactions may be classified in two groups: (1) reactions in which the SO_3 molecule forms an addition compound by accepting a pair of electrons from another molecule, atom, or ion, and (2) reactions in which sulfur trioxide acts as an oxidizing agent.

In the first type of reaction a coordinate bond is formed, the reacting atom or molecule furnishing the necessary pair of electrons. It may be represented by the general equation

$$\begin{array}{cc} :\ddot{O}: & :\ddot{O}: \\ :\ddot{O}:S & +:R = :\ddot{O}:S:R \\ :\ddot{O}: & :\ddot{O}: \end{array}$$

where :R represents the group furnishing the electron pair. For example, sulfur trioxide has an extremely strong affinity for water, with which it reacts vigorously to form sulfuric acid. This reaction may be represented by the equation

$$:\!\overset{\cdot\cdot}{O}\!:$$
$$:\!\overset{\cdot\cdot}{O}\!:\!S \qquad +:\!\overset{\cdot\cdot}{O}\!:\!H = :\!\overset{\cdot\cdot}{O}\!:\!\overset{\overset{\cdot\cdot}{O}}{\underset{\underset{\cdot\cdot}{O}}{S}}\!:\!\overset{\cdot\cdot}{O}\!:\!H$$
$$\overset{\cdot\cdot}{O}\!: \quad H \qquad :\!\overset{\cdot\cdot}{O}\!:$$
$$H$$

sulfuric
acid

There are many similar reactions in which sulfur trioxide is added to a halide, a hydrohalic acid, ammonia, or one of a wide variety of organic bases. Of particular interest are its reactions with metallic oxides to form sulfates. This type of reaction has already been illustrated by the coordination of calcium oxide with sulfur trioxide to form calcium sulfate (p. 325).

As examples of the second type of reaction, in which sulfur trioxide acts as an oxidizing agent, we may cite its many reactions with organic materials, in which, among other products, carbon and sulfur dioxide are formed. Another example is the reaction with iodides to produce free iodine.

$$2SO_3 + 2I^- = SO_2 + I_2 + SO_4^{--}$$

15. Sulfuric Acid and the Sulfates. Sulfuric acid was first prepared on a commercial scale about the middle of the eighteenth century. Since then the industrial production and utilization of the acid have increased until it is the most extensively used manufactured compound in industry. The production of sulfuric acid in this country in 1958 was equivalent to more than sixteen million tons of 100% acid. It fluctuates widely with changing economic conditions and is considered a good index of industrial prosperity.

Sulfuric acid is manufactured by two different methods, both of which involve the catalytic oxidation of sulfur dioxide. The first of these consists in the conversion of sulfur trioxide, produced by the contact process (p. 456), to sulfuric acid. Since sulfur trioxide reacts with water vapor to form a fog of small droplets of sulfuric acid which dissolve only slowly in water, it is not brought directly into contact with water in the industrial process. Instead, the gas from the catalytic chamber is passed into concentrated sulfuric acid, which reacts with the sulfur trioxide to form pyrosulfuric acid.

$$H_2SO_4 + SO_3 = H_2S_2O_7$$

This substance is then treated with the quantity of water required to give sulfuric acid solution of the desired concentration.

$$H_2S_2O_7 + H_2O = 2H_2SO_4$$

In practice, these two steps are ordinarily carried out simultaneously, so that the process is continuous; i.e., water is run into the absorbing acid at a regulated rate, so that the concentration of the acid is maintained at a constant level. This method is used to obtain sulfuric acid of high purity, and of any concentration desired.

The second commercial method is known as the lead-chamber process. Sulfur dioxide, oxygen, water vapor, and oxides of nitrogen are mixed in large, lead-lined chambers, whence the process gets its name. A complicated series of reactions ensue, the net result of which is the combination of sulfur dioxide, oxygen, and water to form sulfuric acid. The oxides of nitrogen are undoubtedly involved in the formation of certain intermediate products but at the end are recovered unchanged; hence, their function is that of a catalyst. The actual mechanism of the process is not entirely understood. It is generally accepted, however, that a compound called nitrosyl sulfuric acid is formed as an intermediate step:

$$2SO_2 + NO + NO_2 + O_2 + H_2O = 2H : \overset{..}{\underset{..}{O}} : \overset{..}{\underset{..}{S}} : \overset{..}{\underset{..}{O}} : \overset{..}{N} : : \overset{..}{O} :$$

nitrosyl sulfuric acid

and that in the presence of an excess of water, this compound is hydrolyzed, giving sulfuric acid.

$$2SO_2(OH)(ONO) + H_2O = 2H_2SO_4 + NO + NO_2$$

For reasons which are not understood, these two successive reactions occur very much more rapidly than the single reaction which represents the overall process:

$$2SO_2 + O_2 + 2H_2O = 2H_2SO_4$$

The liquid product, as run off from the floor of the chambers, is called "chamber acid."

Since the oxides of nitrogen are relatively expensive, it is essential, for economic reasons, to recover them. This is accomplished by their absorption on leaving the chambers, in concentrated sulfuric acid. From this solution, after it has been pumped back to the entrance to the chambers, they are removed by dilution with water or chamber acid (see next paragraph). Inevitably there is a slight loss of oxides of nitrogen in this cycle. This is made good from a pot of nitric acid placed at the entrance to the chambers; some of the entering sulfur dioxide, hot from the sulfur or sulfide burners where it is produced, reduces the nitric acid vapor in accordance with the equation

$$2SO_2 + 2HNO_3 + H_2O = 2H_2SO_4 + NO + NO_2$$

Ordinary "chamber acid" has a concentration of 60 to 70% H_2SO_4 by weight and contains a considerably larger proportion of impurities than acid made by the contact process. Where relatively dilute acid is required, and the presence of small quantities of impurities is of no consequence, the less expensive chamber acid serves the purpose. It may be brought to a concentration as high as 77% by evaporation in lead-lined pans, or to still higher concentrations in silica, glass, porcelain, duriron (an alloy of silicon and iron), or other acid-resistant vessels. Such concentration processes are expensive and tedious, however, so that where acid of high concentration or of high purity is required, "contact" acid is usually employed.

The sulfur dioxide used in these processes is commonly obtained either from the burning of sulfur or from the roasting of pyrite, FeS_2; some sulfur dioxide, however, comes from the roasting of sulfide ores of zinc, copper, or lead, and hence sulfuric acid is sometimes obtained as a by-product of the metallurgy of these metals.

Pure anhydrous sulfuric acid is a colorless liquid, considerably more viscous than water, having a density of 1.85 g. per cc. and freezing at 10.49° C. Because of its "oily" nature, it is sometimes called oil of vitriol. The compound is not very stable, for on being heated it begins to decompose at about 150° C., with the evolution of sulfur trioxide. It starts to boil at about 290° C.; but this temperature is not especially significant, since the solution continues to lose more sulfur trioxide than water and the boiling temperature rises until it reaches 317° C. At this temperature a maximum boiling mixture containing 98.54% of sulfuric acid is obtained. The vapor is largely dissociated into water and sulfur trioxide.

The oxidation state of sulfur in sulfuric acid is +6. Its electronic formula has already been given. The chemical reactions and applications of sulfuric acid may be divided into four main classes: (1) those which depend upon ist low volatility, (2) those which depend upon its strong affinity for water, (3) those in which it acts as an oxidizing agent, and (4) those which depend upon its strongly acidic nature.

As examples of the first we have the use of sulfuric acid in the manufacture of such volatile acids as hydrochloric (p. 392), nitric (p. 496), and hydrofluoric (p. 392), which has already been discussed. The general principle involved in such preparations is that a volatile acid is obtained when one of its salts is heated with a nonvolatile acid. Thus, the volatile acid HX is vaporized when one of its salts, MX, is heated with the nonvolatile acid HY.

$$MX + HY = HX + MY$$

Sulfuric acid exhibits a great affinity for water, and forms three crystalline hydrates, $H_2SO_4 \cdot H_2O$, $H_2SO_4 \cdot 2H_2O$, and $H_2SO_4 \cdot 4H_2O$, the melting points of which are 8.47° C., −39.46° C., and −28.25° C., respectively. A great deal of heat is liberated when concentrated sulfuric acid and water are mixed. When this process of dilution is being carried out, the solution should constantly be well stirred, and the acid should always be poured into the water, not the reverse; by this means, dangerous boiling and splattering may be avoided. The strong affinity of sulfuric acid for water makes it an efficient drying agent; the gas to be dried is bubbled through the concentrated acid. It is commonly used for this purpose with gases such as hydrogen, oxygen, nitrogen, and carbon dioxide, but cannot be used for basic gases such as ammonia. Sulfuric acid brings about the charring of various organic compounds containing carbon, hydrogen, and oxygen, by removing from them the latter two elements in the proportion in which they occur in water. Thus, cellulose materials such as paper, cotton, and wood, and sugars such as sucrose, are charred by the acid.

$$C_{12}H_{22}O_{11} + 11H_2SO_4 = 12C + 11H_2SO_4 \cdot H_2O$$
sucrose

Sulfuric acid participates in two types of oxidation reactions: those which depend upon the oxidizing power of the hydrogen ion, and hence are characteristic of acids in general, and those which involve the sulfate portion of the molecule. The first type includes the reactions of active metals with the dilute acid to yield hydrogen.

$$Zn + 2H^+ + SO_4^{--} = Zn^{++} + SO_4^{--} + H_2$$

This reaction takes place only with metals above hydrogen in the electromotive series. However, most of the metals below hydrogen in the series, as well as many nonmetallic elements, are oxidized by hot concentrated sulfuric acid, which is itself reduced, usually to sulfur dioxide.

$$2Ag + 2H_2SO_4 = 2Ag^+ + SO_4^{--} + SO_2 + 2H_2O$$

$$C + 2H_2SO_4 = CO_2 + 2SO_2 + 2H_2O$$

Sulfuric acid behaves as a diprotic acid in aqueous solution, ionizing in two steps:

$$H_2SO_4 = H^+ + HSO_4^-$$

$$HSO_4^- = H^+ + SO_4^{--}$$

The first step in the ionization is virtually complete in dilute aqueous solution, and the acid thus belongs to the class of strong electrolytes. The second step does not go to completion, however, the ionization constant of bisulfate ion being about 10^{-2}. Sulfuric acid forms two series of salts, the acid sulfates or bisulfates, $MHSO_4$, and the normal sulfates, M_2SO_4, corresponding to the replacement of one and two hydrogen atoms, respectively. Aqueous solutions of the bisulfates, since they contain the acid HSO_4^-, are strongly acidic; solutions of the normal sulfates of strong bases are neutral, for there is practically no tendency for the sulfate ion to be hydrolyzed. Some of the common hydrated sulfates are known as vitriols; thus, copper sulfate is called blue vitriol, ferrous sulfate, green vitriol, and zinc sulfate, white vitriol. Lead, barium, strontium, and radium sulfates are only very slightly soluble in water, and calcium sulfate is slightly soluble; the other common sulfates are readily soluble. Sulfate ion is usually detected by means of the white, acid-insoluble precipitate of barium sulfate which it forms with barium ion.

16. Selenic and Telluric Acids. The trioxides of both selenium and tellurium have been prepared, as well as the corresponding acids. Selenic acid and its salts resemble their sulfur analogs, differing from them chiefly in the greater oxidizing power of the selenium compounds.

Telluric acid is considerably less acidic than sulfuric and selenic acids. The fact that its formula is H_6TeO_6 rather than H_2TeO_4 may be attributed to the large ionic radius of tellurium (p. 411).

17. Pyrosulfuric Acid. Pyrosulfuric acid, $H_2S_2O_7$, is prepared by the union of sulfuric acid wth sulfur trioxide. It is commonly known as oleum, or, because of the white fumes which are released in the presence of moist air, as fuming sulfuric acid. It is a somewhat stronger oxidizing agent and an even more powerful dehydrating agent than sulfuric acid. Its electronic formula may be written

$$\ddot{:}\ddot{O}\ddot{:} \quad \ddot{:}\ddot{O}\ddot{:}$$
$$H:\ddot{O}:\ddot{S}:\ddot{O}:\ddot{S}:\ddot{O}:H$$
$$\ddot{:}\ddot{O}: \quad \ddot{:}\ddot{O}:$$

Pyrosulfates are obtained when acid sulfates are heated; e.g.,

$$2KHSO_4 = K_2S_2O_7 + H_2O$$

18. Sulfuryl Chloride and Chlorosulfonic Acid. These compounds, which have the electronic formulas

$$\begin{array}{ccc} & \overset{\cdot\cdot}{:\text{O}:} & \\ \overset{\cdot\cdot}{:}\ \text{Cl}:\ \text{S}\ :\ \text{Cl}\ : & \text{and} & :\ \text{Cl}:\ \text{S}\ :\ \text{O}\ :\ \text{H} \\ :\ \overset{\cdot\cdot}{\text{O}}: & & :\ \overset{\cdot\cdot}{\text{O}}: \end{array}$$

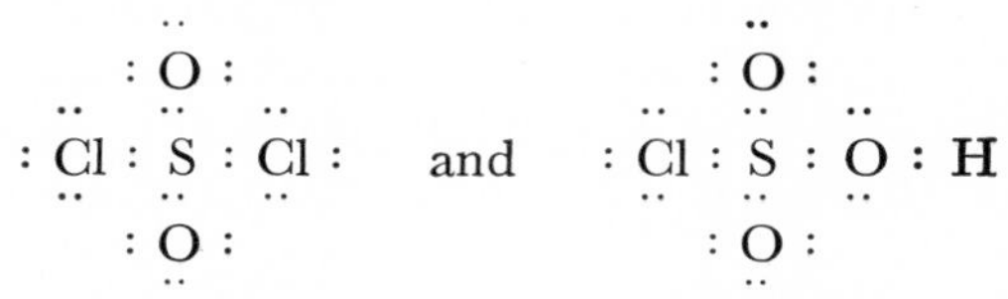

Sulfuryl
chloride

Chlorosulfonic
acid

may be considered as derivatives of sulfuric acid, in which two and one hydroxyl groups, respectively, of the sulfuric acid molecule have been replaced by chlorine atoms. Sulfuryl chloride yields sulfuric acid on reaction with water.

$$\text{SO}_2\text{Cl}_2 + 2\text{H}_2\text{O} = \text{SO}_2(\text{OH})_2 + 2\text{HCl}$$
sulfuric acid

It is best obtained by the combination of sulfur dioxide and chlorine at low temperatures.

$$\text{SO}_2 + \text{Cl}_2 = \text{SO}_2\text{Cl}_2$$

Chlorosulfonic acid, which likewise yields sulfuric acid on reaction with water, is obtained by the direct reaction of sulfur trioxide with hydrogen chloride.

19. Peroxysulfuric Acids. Peroxymonosulfuric acid, H_2SO_5, and peroxydisulfuric acid, $\text{H}_2\text{S}_2\text{O}_8$, the electronic formulas for which are given next, are characterized by the fact that each contains a "peroxy" group (p. 245).

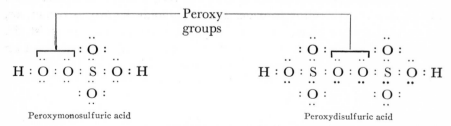

Peroxymonosulfuric acid

Peroxydisulfuric acid

The acids are prepared in the anhydrous state by the reaction of one mole of anhydrous hydrogen peroxide with one and two moles, respectively, of chlorosulfonic acid. Aqueous solutions may be obtained by the electrolytic oxidation, under suitable conditions, of sulfuric acid or of bisulfates, or by the reaction of concentrated sulfuric acid with hydrogen peroxide at low temperatures. By virtue of the peroxy groups which they contain, these acids and

their salts are strong oxidizing agents, as is indicated by the standard oxidation potential for the following half-reaction:

$$2SO_4^{--} = S_2O_8^{--} + 2e^-; E = -2.01 \text{ v.}$$

It should be noted that the oxidation state of sulfur in the peroxysulfates,
just as in sulfates and pyrosulfates, is +6. The oxidizing action of peroxysulfates involves no change in the oxidation state of sulfur, but rather a change
of the "peroxy" oxygen atoms from -1 to -2. The sodium, potassium, and
ammonium peroxydisulfates, $Na_2S_2O_8$, $K_2S_2O_8$, and $(NH_4)_2S_2O_8$, are commonly used in industry and in the laboratory, under the name of persulfates,
as oxiding agents.

20. Thiosulfates. Elementary sulfur reacts with alkaline solutions of sulfites
to form thiosulfates in accordance with the following equation:

thiosulfate ion

This reaction is entirely analogous to the reaction of sulfite ion with oxygen
to produce sulfate (p. 453); in fact, the name "thiosulfate" implies that the
ion is the same as sulfate except that one of the oxygen atoms has been
replaced by a sulfur atom. The oxidation state of sulfur in thiosulfate is +2;
from the electronic formula and by analogy with the sulfate ion, this may be
interpreted as an average between +6 for the central sulfur atom and -2
for the coordinated sulfur atom.

Numerous stable thiosulfates are known, but free thiosulfuric acid, $H_2S_2O_3$,
does not exist even in solution. The thiosulfate ion, in the presence of even
such weak acids as carbonic, is converted to free sulfur and sulfurous acid.

$$S_2O_3^{--} + 2H^+ = S + H_2SO_3$$

Thiosulfates are reducing agents, being oxidized by moderately strong
oxidizing agents such as iodine or ferric ion to tetrathionates (Table 25.6,
p. 464).

$$2S_2O_3^{--} + I_2 = S_4O_6^{--} + 2I^-$$

Such reactions have important applications in analytical chemistry. Stronger
oxidizing agents, such as chlorine, oxidize thiosulfates to sulfate. Because of
this reaction, thiosulfates are useful as "antichlors" to remove excess chlorine
used in bleaching paper and textiles. Thiosulfate ion forms stable complexes
with the ions of several of the less active metals, such as Ag^+ and Au^{+++}.

This accounts for the solubility of silver bromide and chloride in thiosulfate solutions, and the consequent use of these solutions in "fixing" photographic films, plates, and prints (p. 773). The common source of thiosulfate ion in laboratory and industrial practice is the sodium salt, $Na_2S_2O_3 \cdot 5H_2O$, which is commonly but incorrectly called "hypo."

21. Less Important Sulfur Acids. A number of less important oxygen acids of sulfur are summarized in Table 25.6. None of these acids is stable in the free state, and they are known mainly in the form of their salts.

Table 25.6

Less Important Sulfur Acids

Name	Formula
Sulfoxylic	H_2SO_2
Dithionous	$H_2S_2O_4$
(hyposulfurous)	
Dithionic	$H_2S_2O_6$
Trithionic	$H_2S_3O_6$
Tetrathionic	$H_2S_4O_6$
Pentathionic	$H_2S_5O_6$
Hexathionic	$H_2S_6O_6$

STUDY QUESTIONS AND PROBLEMS

1. List the electronic configurations of the elements of the sulfur family. What are the most common oxidation states of sulfur, selenium, and tellurium? Account for these states in terms of the electronic configurations of the elements.

2. Would you expect sulfur to form S^{6+} ions in ordinary chemical reactions? Give the basis for your answer.

3. Arrange the hydrogen compounds of the elements of this family in order of increasing acidity; increasing stability; increasing reducing power.

4. Arrange the elements of the sulfur family in order of increasing metallic character. Explain your answer.

5. Make a table of the physical properties of the crystal modifications of sulfur. Discuss the geometric and electronic structures of the sulfur molecule. Explain the unusual behavior of molten sulfur when it is heated.

6. List the chief industrial applications of elementary sulfur.

7. Give equations for three methods for preparing hydrogen sulfide. Complete and balance the following equations:

$$H_2S + HNO_3 =$$
$$\text{(conc.)}$$

$$H_2S + Fe^{+++} =$$

$$H_2S + O_2 =$$

8. Which is the more basic, a $0.1\,M$ NaSH solution or a $0.1\,M$ solution of NaSeH? Explain your answer.

9. Complete and balance the following equations, indicating changes in oxidation state:

$$Sb_2S_3 + S_2^{--} = SbS_4^{---}$$

$$SnS\ + S_2^{--} =$$

10. Write electronic formulas for SO_2, H_2SO_3, SO_3, H_2SO_4, $H_2S_2O_7$, H_2SO_5, $H_2S_2O_8$, $H_2S_2O_6$, and $H_2S_2O_3$.

11. Give equations for carrying out the following transformations:

$$S \longrightarrow SO_2 \overset{\nearrow SO_2Cl_2}{\longrightarrow} H_2SO_3 \overset{\nearrow SOCl_2}{\underset{\searrow Na_2S_2O_3}{\longrightarrow}} H_2SO_4 \longrightarrow SO_3 \overset{\nearrow SO_2(OH)Cl}{\longrightarrow} H_2S_2O_7$$

12. Complete and balance the following equations:

$$Cu + H_2SO_4 =$$
$$\text{(conc.)}$$

$$C_{12}H_{22}O_{11} + H_2SO_4 =$$

$$Zn + H^+ + SO_4^{--} =$$

$$KF + H_2SO_4 =$$

13. What volume of sulfur dioxide, at standard conditions, could be obtained by the reduction with copper of 100 g. of sulfuric acid of maximum boiling point?

14. What is the normality of ordinary concentrated sulfuric acid, which has a density of 1.84 g. per cc. and contains 96.0% H_2SO_4 by weight? What volume of this acid would you dilute to make 1 l. of 1 N sulfuric acid?

26

Nitrogen and Ammonia

1. Introduction. In order to understand thoroughly the properties of nitrogen, the first member of Group 5a of the periodic system, we must first consider the general characteristics of this group as a whole. The elements of Group 5a are commonly called the nitrogen family.

2. General Characteristics of the Nitrogen Family. The electronic configurations of these elements are listed in Table 26.1. Each of these elements

Table 26.1

Element	1	2	3	4	5	6
	s	s p	s p d	s p d f	s p d	s p
N	2	2, 3				
P	2	2, 6	2, 3			
As	2	2, 6	2, 6, 10	2, 3		
Sb	2	2, 6	2, 6, 10	2, 6, 10	2, 3	
Bi	2	2, 6	2, 6, 10	2, 6, 10, 14	2, 6, 10	2, 3

has five valence electrons per atom, one less than the elements of Group 6a discussed in the preceding chapter. Likewise, they have one less charge on the nucleus than do the elements of that group. The elements of Group 6a and, to an even greater extent, those of Group 7a, exhibit a strong tendency to complete their valence shells by taking up electrons to form doubly charged and singly charged negative ions, respectively. Although there is a tendency in Group 5a to take up electrons from the more metallic elements to form, in this case, triply charged negative ions, it is considerably smaller than the corresponding tendency in Group 6a and much smaller than that of the halogens in Group 7a. The explanation of the lessening of this effect in the order 7a > 6a > 5a lies to a large extent in the decrease in the charges on the nuclei of respective members of the three families in that order. Furthermore, whereas the elements of Group 7a must take up only one electron per atom to complete their valence shells, those of Group 6a must take up two, and those of Group 5a, three. Nitrogen readily forms the nitride ion, N^{---}, on reaction with certain active metals, and phosphorus somewhat less readily forms the phosphide ion, P^{---}; but the other members of the group show little or no inclination in this direction. This is in accord with the general tendency for the elements of a family to become more metallic—or less nonmetallic—as one proceeds from the top of the group toward the bottom (p. 185).

The elements of the nitrogen family form hydrides of the general formula

$$H : \overset{..}{\underset{..}{M}} : H,$$ thus completing their valence shells by the sharing of electrons. They form M_2O_3 oxides which vary from acidic to basic in the order of increasing atomic number, and acidic M_2O_5 oxides that become less acidic in the same order. The changes in properties of the trihalides, MX_3, and of the pentahalides, MX_5, as one passes from nitrogen to bismuth, also reflect the increase in metallic nature of the elements. In addition to the oxidation states -3, $+3$, and $+5$ which are exhibited in the above named compounds, several other oxidation states are shown by some of the elements of this family, especially by nitrogen.

The physical properties of the free elements show a regular gradation from nonmetallic to metallic as one passes from nitrogen to bismuth. Like the first members of other families, nitrogen differs in many respects from the other members of the family, and for this reason, as well as because of its outstanding importance, it is discussed separately in this and the next chapter. The next succeeding chapter will be devoted to phosphorus and its compounds, and will be followed by a chapter on arsenic, antimony, and bismuth.

3. History and Occurrence of Nitrogen. As early as 1772, impure nitrogen had been obtained by the burning of various combustible substances in an enclosed portion of air in order to remove the active component of the atmosphere. It was Scheele who first demonstrated that this inactive gas is a universal and major component of the atmosphere, and Lavoisier who first recognized it as an element. He gave it the name azote (meaning "lazy") because of its relative inertness, and it is still so called by the French, who use the symbol Az. The name nitrogen was suggested in 1823 by Chaptal because the element was found to be a constituent of potassium nitrate, then known as niter; hence, the symbol N.

Though nitrogen makes up four-fifths of the volume of the atmosphere it occurs to such a slight extent in the earth's crust that it constitutes only 0.03% of the material in the earth's crust and the atmosphere together. The only known extensive occurrence of a nitrogen-bearing mineral is in the large deposits of sodium nitrate in northern Chile. This substance, commonly known as Chile saltpeter, is an important source of combined nitrogen which is so necessary for the manufacture of many substances, especially explosives and fertilizers (p. 496).

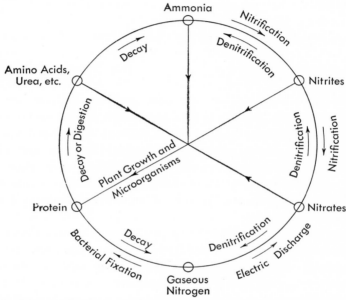

Fig. 26.1.   The nitrogen cycle. (*Courtesy of The Journal of Chemical Education.*)

The presence of nitrogen compounds in the soil is an important factor in its fertility. Growing plants take combined nitrogen from the soil and use it in the formation of complex products known as plant proteins. These plant proteins, when consumed as food by animals, are converted by means of a series of biochemical processes into the animal proteins, which are among the most important structural materials of the animal organism. Since most plants are unable to utilize uncombined nitrogen, the supply of nitrogen compounds in the soil is of the utmost importance. This supply is replenished in several ways: (1) by the decay of organic (plant and animal) matter; (2) by the action of bacteria which live in nodules on the roots of leguminous plants and have the power of converting atmospheric nitrogen into nitrates; (3) by the combination of atmospheric nitrogen and oxygen, during lightning flashes, to form nitrogen compounds which are carried into the soil by rain; and (4) often by the addition of large amounts of combined nitrogen to the soil in the form of commercial fertilizers. The decay of plant and animal proteins results also in the release of elementary nitrogen to the atmosphere. The combination of the opposing processes results in the establishment of the "nitrogen cycle" illustrated in Figure 26.1.

The negative function performed by the inert gas, nitrogen, as a diluent of the much more active oxygen in the atmosphere, has been discussed in a previous chapter (p. 370).

4. Physical and Chemical Properties of Elementary Nitrogen. Free nitrogen is a colorless, odorless, and tasteless gas which, under a pressure of 1 atm., condenses to the liquid state only when the temperature has been lowered to $-195.8°$ C. Liquid nitrogen solidifies at $-210.0°$ C. Determination of the density of nitrogen gas indicates its molecular weight to be approximately 28. Since the atomic weight of nitrogen is 14.008, it is apparent that gaseous nitrogen consists of diatomic molecules, N_2. The weight of a liter of nitrogen under standard conditions is 1.2506 g. Its critical temperature is $-147.1°$ C., and its critical pressure is 33.5 atm. Thus, nitrogen cannot be liquefied at room temperature by any pressure whatsoever, and hence, like oxygen, hydrogen, and some other common gases, it is classed as a so-called "permanent" gas. Nitrogen is only slightly soluble in water, its solubility at $20°$ C. being 0.00189 g. per 100 g. of water. It does not react with water to any detectable extent under ordinary conditions.

The electronic structure of the nitrogen molecule has been the subject of much investigation, and is not as yet completely understood. The fact that molecules of free nitrogen are entirely nonpolar is, however, indicated by its very low boiling point and melting point (p. 189).

The outstanding chemical property of free nitrogen is its low chemical reactivity, which results from the fact that the strong bonding forces between the atoms in the N_2 molecule prevent its ready dissociation into nitrogen atoms. The heat of dissociation of molecular nitrogen into atoms, 169,300 cal. per mole, is, in fact, higher than that of any other known diatomic molecule. At high temperatures nitrogen reacts with a number of metals to form such nitrides as Li_3N, Ca_3N_2, AlN, and CrN. Its reactions with oxygen at high temperatures, and with hydrogen at high temperatures and pressures in the presence of catalysts, will be discussed later (pp. 487 and 478).

5. Preparation and Uses of Elementary Nitrogen. The separation of nitrogen by the fractional distillation of liquid air (p. 374) is the most economical source of the free element and supplies large quantities for industrial use. A number of chemical processes for the production of nitrogen are also available; two of the more important of these are the following.

1. The reaction of ammonium ion and nitrite ion. In practice, a saturated solution of sodium nitrite is added slowly to a hot, saturated solution of ammonium chloride. The reaction proceeds according to the equation

$$NH_4^+ + NO_2^- = N_2 + 2H_2O$$

2. The reaction of ammonia with bromine water. Ammonia gas is bubbled through bromine water and the resulting gaseous mixture is passed through various liquid reagents that absorb water vapor, unreacted bromine, and ammonia, respectively.

$$2NH_3 + 3Br_2 = N_2 + 6HBr_{(aqueous)}$$

Nitrogen, containing small quantities of the inert gases as impurities, may be obtained from air by absorption of the oxygen of the air by means of some such reagent as phosphorus or pyrogallol, $C_6H_3(OH)_3$.

Free nitrogen is used in the manufacture of ammonia (p. 478) and of calcium cyanamide (p. 479), as well as in the production of a few other compounds. It is used also in one method for the case-hardening of steel, in which its effect is similar to that of carbon (p. 754). Bulbs of incandescent lamps are filled with nitrogen or with mixtures of nitrogen and argon. The presence of the gas reduces the tendency of the filament to vaporize and darken the bulb. Nitrogen may be used in place of air whenever a nonoxidizing, nonreducing, inert atmosphere is desired.

Table 26.2

Oxidation State Scale of Nitrogen

Oxidation State	Compounds
+5	Dinitrogen pentoxide (N_2O_5), nitric acid (HNO_3), and nitrates
+4	Nitrogen dioxide (NO_2) and dinitrogen tetroxide (N_2O_4)
+3	Dinitrogen trioxide (N_2O_3), nitrous acid (HNO_2), nitrites, nitrogen trihalides (NX_3)
+2	Nitric oxide (NO)
+1	Nitrous oxide (N_2O), hyponitrous acid ($H_2N_2O_2$), and hyponitrites
0	Elementary nitrogen (N_2)
−1	Hydroxylamine (H_2NOH)
−2	Hydrazine (NH_2NH_2)
−3	Ammonia (NH_3), ammonium salts, and nitrides

6. The Oxidation State Scale of Nitrogen. Nitrogen, in the free state and in its various compounds, exhibits oxidation states all the way from -3 to $+5$. Although, as has been pointed out, there is much that is arbitrary about the assignment of oxidation states, particularly when the structure of the molecule is not known, these numbers do unquestionably provide a convenient basis for organization of the compounds of an element. In Table 26.2 are listed the various oxidation states exhibited by nitrogen, and characteristic compounds corresponding to each state.

AMMONIA AND AMMONIUM SALTS

7. Historical. Pure ammonia gas was first obtained in 1774 by Priestley, who heated sal ammoniac, NH_4Cl, with slaked lime, $Ca(OH)_2$. Ammonia is the most important of the compounds of hydrogen and nitrogen.

8. Physical and Chemical Properties. Like hydrogen fluoride (p. 395) and water (p. 239), ammonia has physical properties that are abnormal with respect to the hydrides of other elements of the same group. In Table 26.3 are listed some of the important physical constants of ammonia (see also

Table 26.3

Physical Constants of Ammonia

Melting point	$-77.74°$ C.
Boiling point	$-33.4°$ C.
Heat of fusion	5,581 cal./mole
Heat of vaporization	3,489 cal./mole
Heat of formation	11,500 cal./mole

Table 29.1, p. 521). The abnormally high melting point, boiling point, heat of fusion, and heat of vaporization of ammonia may, as in the case of water and hydrogen fluoride, be explained as resulting largely from the existence of hydrogen bonds between ammonia molecules. The critical temperature of ammonia is $132.9°$ C., and the critical pressure is 112.3 atm. In the liquid state, ammonia is highly mobile. Its density, which just below its boiling point is 0.677 g. per cc., changes rapidly with temperature. The density of gaseous ammonia corresponds to the formula NH_3. Solid, liquid, and gaseous ammonia are colorless.

Ammonia gas has a sharp, pungent odor, which makes it possible to detect even very small concentrations of the substance in air. Although it is not a highly poisonous gas, ammonia has a strongly irritating action on the mucous membranes of the eyes, nose, throat, and lungs, and the gas in high concentrations may cause severe and permanent injury to the eyes. High concentrations (above 5,000 parts per million) may be fatal.

The electronic formula for ammonia is

$$\text{H} \atop \text{H} : \overset{..}{\underset{..}{\text{N}}} : \text{H}$$

As is indicated by this formula, the ammonia molecule is polar; liquid ammonia is a polar liquid, and, like water, it is highly associated. The structure of the ammonia molecule is illustrated by the model in Figure 26.2.

The many chemical reactions which ammonia undergoes may be grouped into three classes: (1) addition, (2) substitution, and (3) oxidation-reduction.

The first of these classes includes those reactions in which the ammonia molecule, through the unshared pair of electrons on the nitrogen atom, forms coordinate covalent bonds with molecules or ions which can accept an unshared electron pair. The ability of ammonia to form bonds in this way is illustrated by the existence of ammonia complexes with various metal ions, such as the following:

$$
\left[
\begin{array}{c}
\text{H} \\
\text{H} : \overset{..}{\underset{..}{\text{N}}} : \text{H} \\
\text{Ag} \\
\text{H} : \overset{..}{\underset{..}{\text{N}}} : \text{H} \\
\text{H}
\end{array}
\right]^{+}
\qquad
\left[
\begin{array}{ccc}
& \text{H} & \\
& \text{H} : \overset{..}{\underset{..}{\text{N}}} : \text{H} & \\
\text{H} & & \text{H} \\
\text{H} : \overset{..}{\text{N}} : & \text{Cu} & : \overset{..}{\text{N}} : \text{H} \\
\text{H} & & \text{H} \\
& \text{H} : \overset{..}{\text{N}} : \text{H} & \\
& \text{H} &
\end{array}
\right]^{++}
$$

$$
\left[
\begin{array}{ccc}
\text{H} \quad \text{H} & \text{H} \quad \text{H} & \\
\text{N} & \text{N} & \\
\text{H} & \text{H} & \\
\text{H} & & \text{H} \\
\text{H} : \overset{..}{\underset{..}{\text{N}}} : & \text{Cr} & : \overset{..}{\underset{..}{\text{N}}} : \text{H} \\
\text{H} & & \text{H} \\
\text{N} & \text{N} & \\
\text{H} \quad \text{H} & \text{H} \quad \text{H} &
\end{array}
\right]^{+++}
$$

The formation of such complex ions accounts for the fact that a number of slightly soluble compounds of metals dissolve readily in solutions of ammonia. Zinc hydroxide, for example, is readily soluble in a slight excess of aqueous ammonia.

$$\text{Zn(OH)}_{2(s)} + 4\text{NH}_3 = \text{Zn(NH}_3)_4{}^{++} + 2\text{OH}^-$$

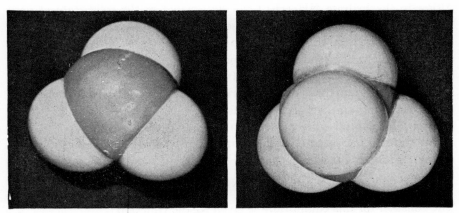

Fig. 26.2. Models of the NH_3 molecule and the $NH_4{}^+$ ion. (*Courtesy of Dr. J. A. Campbell, Oberlin College.*)

Ammonia molecules add readily, also, to neutral molecules in which there is room for an additional pair of electrons in the valence shell of one of the atoms. The reactions with sulfur dioxide (p. 452), sulfur trioxide (p. 456), and boron trifluoride (p. 797) are examples, of which the last may be formulated

$$
\begin{array}{ccc}
:\!\ddot{F}\!: & H & :\!\ddot{F}\!:H \\
:\!\ddot{F}\!:\!\ddot{B} + :\!N\!:H = :\!\ddot{F}\!:B\!:N\!:H \\
:\!\ddot{F}\!: & H & :\!\ddot{F}\!:\ddot{H}
\end{array}
$$

The addition of ammonia to another molecule or ion is commonly called an ammonation reaction; this is analogous to the use of the term hydration for the addition of water (p. 235).

An outstanding property of ammonia is its very high solubility in water (700 volumes of ammonia in one volume of water at $20°$ C. and 1 atm. pressure). This high solubility is undoubtedly due to the tendency of the two substances to react with each other to form addition compounds. These addition compounds result from the formation of hydrogen bonds between molecules of the two substances (p. 236), as represented by the following equation:

$$\text{H} \qquad\qquad\qquad \text{H}$$
$$\text{H} : \overset{\cdot\cdot}{\underset{\cdot\cdot}{\text{N}}} : + \text{H} : \overset{\cdot\cdot}{\underset{\cdot\cdot}{\text{O}}} : = \text{H} : \overset{\cdot\cdot}{\underset{\cdot\cdot}{\text{N}}} : \text{H} : \overset{\cdot\cdot}{\underset{\cdot\cdot}{\text{O}}} :$$
$$\text{H} \qquad\quad \text{H} \qquad\quad \text{H} \qquad \text{H}$$

Although the hydrate $NH_3 \cdot H_2O$ can be isolated in the solid state at very low temperatures, it undoubtedly dissociates to an increasing degree as the temperature is raised, and the extent to which it is present in aqueous solution at room temperature is unknown. Moreover, the possibility of the existence of other hydrates cannot be ignored. It is sometimes assumed, however, that all the dissolved ammonia is in the form of the monohydrate; this substance is called ammonium hydroxide and its formula is written NH_4OH. On the basis of this assumption the presence in such solutions of small concentrations of ammonium and hydroxide ions is said to result from the slight ionization of ammonium hydroxide.

$$NH_4OH \rightleftharpoons NH_4^+ + OH^-$$

The constant for this equilibrium is given by the equation

$$K = \frac{[NH_4^+][OH^-]}{[NH_4OH]}$$

and its value has been found to be 1.8×10^{-5}.

The assumption of the existence of ammonium hydroxide in the solution is not obligatory, however, for the presence of ammonium and hydroxide ions can be accounted for equally well if we assume that ammonia and water react, to a small extent only, according to the equation

$$NH_3 + H_2O = NH_4^+ + OH^-$$

The constant for this equilibrium is given by

$$K = \frac{[NH_4^+][OH^-]}{[NH_3]}$$

Since both $[NH_4OH]$ and $[NH_3]$ refer to the total ammonia in the solution less that in the form of ammonium ion, this constant has the same value as that formulated in the preceding paragraph. The relative validity of these two extreme assumptions is difficult to determine by experiment. Undoubtedly, the truth lies somewhere between them, since the assumption of hydrate formation, to a certain extent at least, is necessary to account for the high solubility of ammonia in water.

Aqueous solutions of ammonia react with acids to produce ammonium salts. This reaction may be interpreted in either of two ways.

1. According to the older Arrhenius concept of acids and bases, the reaction takes place between hydroxide ions from ammonium hydroxide and hydrogen ions from the acid. For example, the reaction of aqueous ammonia with hydrochloric acid would be represented by the following equations:

$$\text{NH}_4\text{OH} = \text{NH}_4{}^+ + \boxed{\begin{array}{c} \text{OH}^- \\[1em] \text{H}^+ \end{array}} + \text{Cl}^-$$

ammonium ion

$$\text{H}_2\text{O}$$

2. The modern Brønsted concept may be applied to reactions of acids with ammonia not only in aqueous solution but also in nonaqueous solutions or even in the gaseous state. According to this concept, ammonia is a base because it can take up, by means of the unshared pair of electrons on its nitrogen atom, a proton from an acid. Thus, the reaction between gaseous ammonia and hydrogen chloride, which results in the formation of a white cloud of ammonium chloride, may be represented by the equation

$$\text{H} \qquad\qquad\qquad \text{H}$$
$$\text{H} : \overset{..}{\underset{..}{\text{N}}} : + \text{H} : \overset{..}{\underset{..}{\text{Cl}}} : = \text{H} : \overset{..}{\underset{}{\text{N}}} : \text{H}^+, : \overset{..}{\underset{..}{\text{Cl}}} : -$$
$$\text{H} \qquad\qquad\qquad \text{H}$$

The reaction of acids with aqueous solutions of ammonia (interpreted by Arrhenius in terms of ammonium hydroxide) may be simply explained as resulting from the transfer of protons from hydronium ions of the aqueous solution of the acid to ammonia molecules to form ammonium ions (see Figure 26.2).

$$\text{H} \qquad\quad \text{H} \qquad\qquad \text{H} \qquad\quad \text{H}$$
$$\text{H} : \overset{..}{\underset{..}{\text{N}}} : + \text{H} : \overset{..}{\underset{..}{\text{O}}} : \text{H}^+ = \text{H} : \overset{..}{\underset{}{\text{N}}} : \text{H}^+ + : \overset{..}{\underset{..}{\text{O}}} : \text{H}$$
$$\text{H} \qquad\qquad\qquad\qquad \text{H}$$

Of course, the precipitation of metal hydroxides from solutions of salts by aqueous ammonia is to be attributed to the presence of hydroxide ion, whether the equation is written

$$\text{Mg}^{++} + 2\text{NH}_4\text{OH} = \text{Mg(OH)}_{2(s)} + 2\text{NH}_4{}^+$$

or

$$\text{Mg}^{++} + 2\text{NH}_3 + 2\text{H}_2\text{O} = \text{Mg(OH)}_{2(s)} + 2\text{NH}_4{}^+$$

In summary, it may be said that aqueous solutions of ammonia behave as if they contained the following substances in equilibrium:

$$NH_3 + H_2O \rightleftharpoons NH_4OH \rightleftharpoons NH_4^+ + OH^-$$

The second type of reaction that ammonia undergoes involves the substitution of an amide group NH_2, an imide group NH, or a nitrogen atom, for an atom or atoms of another molecule. For example, aqueous ammonia reacts with mercuric chloride according to the following equation (p. 788):

$$\overset{\displaystyle H}{: \overset{..}{\underset{..}{Cl}} : Hg : \overset{..}{\underset{..}{Cl}} : + 2NH_3 = : \overset{..}{\underset{..}{Cl}} : Hg : N : H + NH_4^+ + Cl^-}$$

One of the chlorine atoms in the mercuric chloride molecule is thus replaced by an NH_2 group. Other such reactions are those with sulfuryl chloride, SO_2Cl_2, with fluorosulfonic acid, FSO_2OH, and with phosgene, $COCl_2$.

$$SO_2Cl_2 + 4NH_3 = \underset{\text{sulfamide}}{SO_2(NH_2)_2} + 2NH_4^+ + 2Cl^-$$

$$FSO_2OH + 2NH_3 = \underset{\text{sulfamic acid}}{H_2NSO_2OH} + NH_4^+ + F^-$$

$$COCl_2 + 4NH_3 = \underset{\text{urea}}{CO(NH_2)_2} + 2NH_4^+ + 2Cl^-$$

Such reactions as these, in analogy with the corresponding reactions of water which are known as hydrolysis, come under the classification of *ammonolysis*. In general, ammonolytic reactions conform, in their initial step at least, to the general equation

$$AB + NH_3 = ANH_2 + HB$$

which is analogous to the general equation for hydrolysis given on p. 237. Sometimes the product HB undergoes further reaction with ammonia to give ammonium salts, as is the case in all the examples given previously:

$$HB + NH_3 = NH_4^+ + B^-$$

but an analogous process takes place in many hydrolytic reactions; e.g.,

$$SO_2Cl_2 + 2H_2O = \underset{\text{sulfuric acid}}{SO_2(OH)_2} + 2HCl$$

$$HCl + H_2O = H_3O^+ + Cl^-$$

The ammonia molecule undergoes a variety of *oxidation-reduction* reactions in which it acts as a reducing agent, the most important of these reactions being that of ammonia with oxygen. Ammonia burns readily in pure oxygen with the formation of elementary nitrogen and water.

$$4NH_3 + 3O_2 = 2N_2 + 6H_2O$$

It reacts much less readily in air. However, when a mixture of ammonia and air in the ratio of one volume of the former to 7.5 volumes of the latter is passed over hot platinum gauze, which acts as catalyst, the ammonia is oxidized; but in this case nitric oxide, rather than free nitrogen, is the principal product.

$$4NH_3 + 5O_2 = 4NO + 6H_2O$$

If the reactants are supplied in the proper proportions and at a suitable rate, sufficient heat is liberated by the reaction to keep the catalyst hot. Nitric oxide obtained from this reaction, which is known as the Ostwald process, may be converted to nitric acid on an industrial scale, as described in the next chapter (p. 496).

At elevated temperatures, ammonia reduces a number of metal oxides to free metals; thus, when ammonia is passed over hot cupric oxide, copper, water, and nitrogen are obtained.

$$3CuO + 2NH_3 = 3Cu + 3H_2O + N_2$$

Another type of oxidation-reduction reaction which ammonia undergoes—a type in which the oxidation state of the hydrogen, rather than that of the nitrogen, is changed—is the displacement of hydrogen from ammonia by active metals. Thus, metallic sodium reacts slowly with liquid ammonia or rapidly with gaseous ammonia at higher temperatures to produce hydrogen and a compound having the formula $NaNH_2$, and known as sodium amide or sodamide.

$$2Na + 2NH_3 = H_2 + 2NaNH_2$$

Hot magnesium reacts with gaseous ammonia to give magnesium nitride.

$$3Mg + 2NH_3 = Mg_3N_2 + 3H_2$$

The reaction of sodium with ammonia is analogous to the reaction of certain metals with water or with hydrogen halides such as hydrogen chloride, and serves to illustrate that in spite of the predominantly basic nature of ammonia it does, under certain conditions, act as an acid. It is much weaker, however, in its acidic properties than is water, which, in turn, is much less acidic than hydrogen chloride; hence, its conjugate base, i.e., amide ion, NH_2^-, is a much stronger base than is hydroxide ion, OH^-, just as the latter is much more basic than chloride ion, Cl^-. Sodium amide is widely used as a basic catalyst in various organic chemical reactions.

9. Preparation and Uses of Ammonia. The most convenient laboratory method for the preparation of ammonia consists in the reaction of an ammonium salt, either in the dry state or in solution, with a strong base such as sodium, potassium, or calcium hydroxide. As we have already indicated, ammonium and hydroxide ions in aqueous solution are in equilibrium with ammonia and water:

$$NH_4^+ + OH^- \rightleftharpoons NH_3 + H_2O$$

Hence, when large concentrations of hydroxide ion and ammonium ion are brought together much ammonia is formed, and, especially when the solution is heated, ammonia gas is given off. Ammonium hydroxide solution always liberates ammonia gas when heated, but it gives a better yield of ammonia if the hydroxide ion concentration is increased by the addition of a strong base. Since the ammonium salts are themselves produced from ammonia, such methods are, of course, not used for the manufacture of ammonia on an industrial scale.

Ammonia may also be produced in the laboratory by the hydrolysis of such metal nitrides as Mg_3N_2.

$$Mg_3N_2 + 6H_2O = 3Mg(OH)_2 + 2NH_3$$

Ammonia is obtained commercially from three main sources. The most important of these is the direct combination of hydrogen and nitrogen, according to the equation

$$N_2 + 3H_2 = 2NH_3 + 22,100 \text{ cal.}$$

The process for carrying out this reaction was first developed by the German chemist Haber, and involves the reaction of the two gases under high pressures (up to 1000 atm.) at moderately high temperatures (400°–600° C.) in the presence of a catalyst (Figure 26.3). A number of diverse catalytic materials have been used, among which are osmium, uranium, a mixture of iron and molybdenum, and a mixture of iron and potassium aluminate. Although considerable secrecy is maintained as to the exact nature of industrial catalysts for this process, it seems probable that the last-named mixture is the one most commonly employed. This process was discussed in detail in terms of the principles of chemical equilibrium in Chapter 15. It yields an especially pure product.

The next most important source of ammonia is as a by-product in the destructive distillation of coal for the production of coke. Bituminous coal contains, on the average, enough nitrogenous material to give it a nitrogen content of about 1%. When such coal is heated in the absence of air, the nitrogen is given off in the coal gas in the form of ammonia and free nitrogen, along with other substances. The ammonia is absorbed when the gas is bubbled through water; it may be liberated from this solution by treatment with calcium hydroxide and steam. The ammonia thus obtained is usually either redissolved in water and sold as ammonium hydroxide solution or converted to ammonium sulfate by reaction with sulfuric acid. Such ammonium sulfate is used chiefly as a fertilizer.

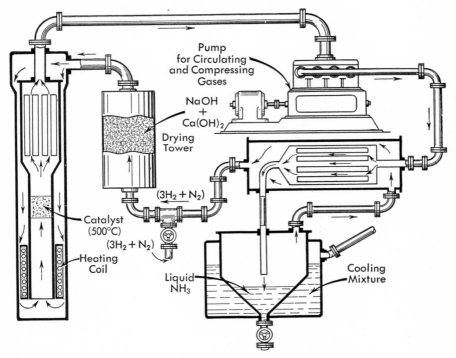

Fig. 26.3.   Diagram of the Haber process.

The third source of ammonia is what is known as the cyanamide process. Calcium carbonate (limestone, p. 669) is heated with an excess of coke in an electric furnace, and calcium carbide, CaC_2, is formed as a product.

$$CaCO_3 + 4C = CaC_2 + 3CO$$

Nitrogen is then passed over the calcium carbide at a temperature of about 1000° C., and calcium cyanamide, $CaNCN$, is obtained:

$$CaC_2 + N_2 = CaNCN + C$$

The calcium cyanamide is then treated with steam under pressure, and ammonia is produced in accordance with the equation

$$CaNCN + 3H_2O = CaCO_3 + 2NH_3$$

The cyanamide process was widely used during World War I, but since that time it has been largely displaced by the more economical Haber process and by production from coal. However, because of its utility as a fertilizer and as an intermediate in the production of other nitrogen compounds, as well as its continued use in the manufacture of a portion of the ammonia of commerce, calcium cyanamide is still an important industrial product.

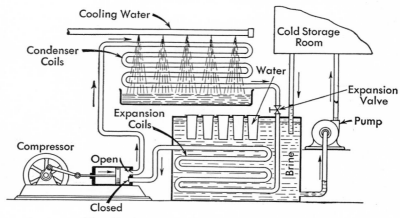

Fig. 26.4.   An ammonia refrigeration system.

Ammonia is one of the most widely used of industrial chemicals and is produced in enormous quantities. Its chief applications are in the manufacture of other nitrogen compounds, particularly nitric acid and ammonium salts; among the latter, the sulfate, nitrate, chloride, and carbonate are especially important. Ammonia is used also in the manufacture of numerous organic chemicals, such as urea, dyes, drugs, and plastics. Aqueous ammonia, because of its mild alkalinity, is a familiar household cleansing agent.

The ease with which gaseous ammonia may be liquefied at ordinary temperatures by the application of pressure, and the high heat of vaporization of the resulting liquid, make ammonia a useful refrigerant, and it is widely used for this purpose. A diagram illustrating an ammonia refrigeration system for the manufacture of ice is given in Figure 26.4. Liquid ammonia is allowed to vaporize in coils in the cooling unit of the system. Because of its high heat of vaporization, the ammonia takes up a great deal of heat and the temperature of the brine (concentrated salt solution) surrounding these coils is lowered. The gaseous ammonia is then compressed to the liquid state in another part of the system. The heat liberated in this change is largely removed as the liquid ammonia passes through coils over which cold water is run. The cool liquid ammonia is then recycled and the process repeated. The same principle is applied in mechanical household refrigerators, although sulfur dioxide, methyl chloride (CH_3Cl), or Freon (dichlorodifluoromethane, CCl_2F_2), rather than ammonia, is commonly employed in units of this type.

10. Ammonium Salts. The fact that aqueous ammonia reacts with acids to produce solutions of ammonium salts has already been noted (p. 475). There is a small tendency for this reaction to be reversed; i.e., solutions of ammonium salts undergo some hydrolysis to yield acidic solutions (p. 321).

$$NH_4^+ + H_2O \rightleftharpoons NH_3 + H_3O^+$$

Ammonium salts of strong acids are stable in the solid state at ordinary temperatures but readily decompose when heated; ammonia is usually, though not always, a product of such decomposition.

$$NH_4Cl = NH_3 + HCl$$
$$(NH_4)_2SO_4 = NH_3 + NH_4HSO_4$$

Ammonium salts of weak acids undergo partial decomposition even at room temperature; thus, a distinct odor of ammonia may be observed over ammonium carbonate. Ammonium salts of extremely weak acids are not formed except at very low temperatures.

Ammonium salts, except for their tendency to be hydrolyzed and to decompose upon heating, closely resemble the corresponding salts of the alkali metals, particularly those of potassium.

Ammonium chloride, NH_4Cl, is used in soldering and in the galvanizing of iron to remove oxides from the metal surface. Large quantities of it are used also in the construction of dry cells (p. 421). Ammonium bromide, NH_4Br, and ammonium iodide, NH_4I, are used in the preparation of photographic materials. Ammonium sulfate, $(NH_4)_2SO_4$, and the phosphates $NH_4H_2PO_4$ and $(NH_4)_2HPO_4$ are used as fertilizers. Ammonium nitrate, NH_4NO_3, though not easily detonated, is a high explosive and is a component in several explosive mixtures (p. 497).

The presence of ammonium ion in a solution may be detected by the addition of a strong base to the solution, which is then warmed gently. The gaseous ammonia thus produced (p. 478) may be detected by its odor, or by the change in color which it brings about in a piece of moist red litmus paper.

11. Liquid Ammonia as a Solvent. No other liquid so nearly approaches water in its solvent properties as does liquid ammonia. Furthermore, the development of the Haber process so reduced the cost of producing ammonia that the pure anhydrous product could, in 1958, be purchased for about 4 cents per pound, thus making the substance readily available for research and industrial application. We have already seen that, like water, pure ammonia has an abnormally high boiling point, melting point, heat of fusion, and heat of vaporization (p. 471). The structure of the ammonia molecule is such that liquid ammonia, like water, is a highly polar solvent (though not as polar as water), and is, therefore, a good solvent for many ionic substances. It is a much better solvent than water for many covalent compounds.

Pure liquid ammonia is an even poorer conductor of electricity than water; ionization does take place to a very slight extent, however, in accordance with the equation (cf. $2H_2O \rightleftharpoons H_3O^+ + OH^-$, p. 339)

$$2NH_3 \rightleftharpoons NH_4^+ + NH_2^-$$

Solutions of acids in liquid ammonia react with the solvent to form ammonium ion, a reaction which is analogous to hydronium ion formation in water. Solutions of ammonium salts in liquid ammonia do indeed behave as acids, affecting indicators, neutralizing bases, and dissolving metals with the evolution of hydrogen. Thus, we have the two analogous reactions

$$Zn + 2NH_4^+ \xrightarrow{\text{liq. } NH_3} Zn^{++} + 2NH_3 + H_2$$

$$Zn + 2H_3O^+ \xrightarrow{\text{water}} Zn^{++} + 2H_2O + H_2$$

Similarly the relationship between amide (NH_2^-) ion and liquid ammonia is analogous to the relationship between hydroxide (OH^-) ion and water. Thus we have the analogous acid-base reactions

$$NH_4^+ + NH_2^- = 2NH_3$$

$$H_3O^+ + OH^- = 2H_2O$$

For example, potassium amide (KNH_2) reacts with solutions of ammonium chloride (NH_4Cl) to give potassium chloride and ammonia, just as potassium hydroxide reacts with an aqueous solution of hydronium chloride (HCl in water) to yield potassium chloride and water.

The ordinary oxygen-containing compounds with which we are most familiar may be considered to be derivatives of water, or may be said to have water as a *parent solvent*, and to constitute the oxygen system of compounds. There is a whole series of nitrogen-containing substances which may similarly be considered as derivatives of ammonia, or to be based upon liquid ammonia as a parent solvent, and to constitute a *nitrogen system of compounds*. Thus,

NaOH belongs to the oxygen system of compounds; and $NaNH_2$ is its analog in the nitrogen system. The concept of the nitrogen system of compounds has been of great assistance in the study and interpretation of the chemistry of nitrogen compounds. Its development is due largely to the work of the American chemist E. C. Franklin (1862–1937).

12. Hydrazine and Hydroxylamine. In the compounds hydrazine, NH_2NH_2, and hydroxylamine, NH_2OH, nitrogen exhibits, respectively, the oxidation states of -2 and -1. Like ammonia, these two substances are basic, each tending to share one of the unshared pairs of electrons on its molecule with a proton.

$$\overset{H}{\underset{\cdot\cdot}{H:N}}\overset{H}{\underset{\cdot\cdot}{:N}}:H + H^+ = \overset{H\quad H}{\underset{\qquad H}{H:N:N:H^+}}$$

$$\overset{H}{\underset{\cdot\cdot}{H:N}}\overset{}{:}\overset{\cdot\cdot}{O}:H + H^+ = \overset{H}{\underset{H}{H:N:}}\overset{\cdot\cdot}{O}:H^+$$

The substances are analogs of hydrogen peroxide, and, like that compound, can act either as oxidizing or reducing agents. The free bases are neither very stable nor easy to handle, so that the substances are commonly used in the form of the salts which they form with hydrochloric or sulfuric acids, $[NH_2NH_3]Cl$, $[NH_2NH_3]_2SO_4$, $[NH_3OH]Cl$, and $[NH_3OH]_2SO_4$. Hydrazine and some of its derivatives are important rocket fuels.

STUDY QUESTIONS AND PROBLEMS

1. List the electronic configurations of the elements of the nitrogen family and show how these configurations may be correlated with the chief oxidation states exhibited by members of this family, viz., -3, $+3$, and $+5$.

2. Which of the nitrogen family elements most readily forms X^{---} ions? Why?

3. List as many trends as you can in properties of nitrogen family elements or their compounds that illustrate decreasing nonmetallic or increasing metallic nature with increasing atomic number within a given family.

4. Explain the very low chemical reactivity of molecular nitrogen.

5. Give equations for two laboratory methods for the preparation of free nitrogen. How is nitrogen obtained industrially?

6. In what respects are the physical properties of ammonia abnormal when compared with the properties of phosphine, arsine, and stibine? How may these abnormalities be explained?

7. List the three types of reactions which ammonia undergoes and give equations for several examples of each type.

8. Criticize the statement: Ammonia reacts with water to give solutions of ammonium hydroxide in which NH_4OH molecules are the chief molecular species present.

9. Give equations and conditions for: (1) a good laboratory method for preparing ammonia, (2) the Haber process, and (3) the cyanamide process.

10. In what ways do ammonium salts resemble corresponding alkali metal compounds? In what ways do they differ?

11. What characteristics does liquid ammonia have which make it interesting as a solvent? What is meant by the "nitrogen system of compounds"?

12. What volume of nitrogen at 25° C. and 750 mm. pressure could be obtained by the reaction of 53.5 g. of ammonium chloride with an excess of sodium nitrite?

27

The Oxides, Oxyacids, and Halides of Nitrogen

1. Positive Oxidation States of Nitrogen. In the preceding chapter, the element nitrogen and those of its compounds in which it has negative oxidation numbers were discussed. In the present chapter, we shall turn our attention to compounds in which nitrogen exhibits positive oxidation numbers. The most important of such compounds are the oxides, the oxyacids and their salts, and to a lesser degree, the halides, and it is with these compounds that this chapter is primarily concerned. Molecular models of N_2, O_2, NO, N_2O, and NO_2 molecules, and of NO_3^- ion are given in Figure 27.1.

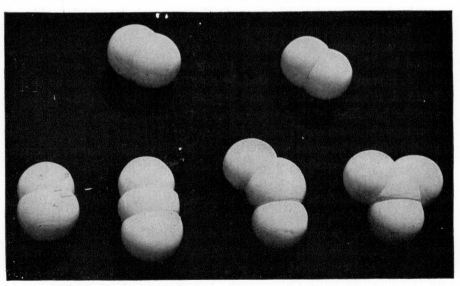

Fig. 27.1. Models of N_2, O_2, NO, N_2O, and NO_2 molecules, and the NO_3^- ion, respectively. (*Courtesy of Dr. J. A. Campbell, Oberlin College.*)

2. Nitrous Oxide. Nitrous oxide, in which nitrogen is in the $+1$ oxidation state, is a colorless gas whose composition and density correspond to the formula N_2O. It condenses to the liquid state at $-88.5°$ C. under a pressure of 1 atm.; the liquid solidifies at the only slightly lower temperature $-90.8°$ C. The formation of nitrous oxide from its elements is accompanied by the absorption of 19,490 cal. of heat per mole of nitrous oxide. When heated above about $550°$ C., the compound undergoes decomposition into its elements at a measurable rate, and readily supports combustion, acting as a source of oxygen. A glowing splint thrust into a container of nitrous oxide bursts into flame much as it would in oxygen.

The nitrous oxide molecule has been shown to be linear (Figure 27.1), with the geometric arrangement $N - N - O$.

Nitrous oxide is most readily and economically prepared by the careful heating of dry ammonium nitrate (or a mixture of sodium or potassium nitrate and ammonium sulfate) to $170°-260°$ C. Decomposition takes place according to the equation

$$NH_4NO_3 = 2H_2O + N_2O$$

Too rapid heating should be avoided, since ammonium nitrate may detonate under such treatment.

Nitrous oxide is moderately soluble in water. Its solubility in ordinary cream has been made the basis of a convenient method of producing whipped cream for restaurants, soda fountains, etc. The gas is forced into a container of cream under pressure. When the valve on a "cartridge" which has been charged in this manner is opened, a stream of "whipped" cream is discharged. Nitrous oxide is also used by dentists and obstetricians as an anesthetic. A mixture of the gas and oxygen is breathed by the patient; in quantities just short of that required to bring about unconsciousness, this mixture produces an exhilarating, intoxicating effect on the patient, often causing hysterical laughter. For this reason it is commonly known as laughing gas. It has no harmful or unpleasant after effects, however.

3. Hyponitrous Acid and Hyponitrites. Hyponitrous acid, $H_2N_2O_2$, has been obtained as a white, crystalline, very unstable solid; on standing, either in the dry state or in solution, it breaks down into nitrous oxide and water. Salts of hyponitrous acid, such as sodium hyponitrite, $Na_2N_2O_2$, which may be obtained by the reduction of nitrites or nitrates with sodium amalgam (an alloy of sodium and mercury), are somewhat more stable.

4. Nitric Oxide. Nitric oxide, in which the nitrogen is in the $+2$ oxidation state, is a colorless, slightly soluble gas, the composition and density of which correspond to the formula NO. It condenses under 1 atm. pressure at a temperature of $-151.7°$ C. to a blue liquid, which at a temperature of $-163.6°$ C. solidifies, forming a clear, blue, ice-like solid. The nitric oxide molecule (Figure 27.1) is one of the few stable ones that contain an odd number of electrons. Because of this feature of its structure, the compound is highly paramagnetic, i.e., is attracted by a magnetic field.

Nitric oxide is an intermediate in the manufacture of the highly important industrial chemical nitric acid, which will be discussed presently. The direct combination of nitrogen and oxygen at high temperatures to form nitric oxide according to the equation

$$N_2 + O_2 = 2NO$$

has already been discussed in Chapter 15. The process now generally employed for the industrial preparation of nitric oxide is the catalytic oxidation of ammonia (p. 477).

Nitric oxide may be prepared for experimental purposes by several methods, among which the reaction of nitrite ion with iodide ion in acid solution is one of the most convenient. The reaction is as follows:

$$2HNO_2 + 2H^+ + 2I^- = 2NO + I_2 + 2H_2O$$

Nitric oxide is obtained also by the reaction of copper with dilute $(6M)$ nitric acid.

$$3Cu + 8H^+ + 2NO_3^- = 3Cu^{++} + 2NO + 4H_2O$$

Since nitric oxide reacts readily with oxygen in the air to yield the dioxide, according to the equation

$$2NO + O_2 = 2NO_2$$

it is necessary that it be prepared and preserved in the absence of oxygen.

Vigorously burning substances such as phosphorus continue to burn if placed in nitric oxide. Less vigorous combustions, however, such as the burning of a candle, cease in an atmosphere of nitric oxide. Nitric oxide resembles carbon monoxide, CO (p. 536), in its ability to react with metal ions to form complexes; the formation of brown $Fe(NO)^{++}$ is used as a test for nitrates (p. 497). Many other similar nitric oxide complexes of such metal ions as Cu^{++}, Co^{++}, and Pt^{++++} are known.

5. Dinitrogen Trioxide. Dinitrogen trioxide, N_2O_3, is the anhydride of nitrous acid, and in it, as in the latter substance, nitrogen exhibits the $+3$ oxidation state. Dinitrogen trioxide is unstable at room temperature or above, decomposing to a large extent into nitric oxide and nitrogen dioxide.

$$N_2O_3 = NO + NO_2$$

When solutions containing nitrite ion are acidified, a gaseous equilibrium mixture of nitric oxide and nitrogen dioxide with small quantities of dinitrogen trioxide is evolved. When this mixture of gases is condensed by being cooled to about $-20°$ C., or when equimolar quantities of nitric oxide and nitrogen dioxide are mixed and so condensed, deep blue liquid dinitrogen trioxide (containing some dissolved NO and N_2O_4) is obtained. This liquid boils under 1 atm. pressure at $3.5°$ C. and solidifies at $-103°$ C. That dinitrogen trioxide is a true anhydride of nitrous acid is indicated by the fact that when it, or the equilibrium mixture formed by its decomposition, is passed into an alkaline solution, a nitrite is formed.

$$N_2O_3 + 2OH^- = 2NO_2^- + H_2O$$

6. Nitrous Acid and the Nitrites. When dinitrogen trioxide is passed into water a solution containing nitrous acid, HNO_2, with variable quantities of other substances such as nitric oxide and nitrogen dioxide, is obtained. At lower temperatures—in ice water, for instance—the amount of nitrous acid obtained is considerably increased. The stability of nitrous acid solutions decreases not only with rising temperature but also with increasing concentration of hydrogen ion. The acid is not known in the pure state, although there is evidence for the existence of HNO_2 vapor in small concentrations in equilibrium with its solutions. It is a weak acid, conductance measurements on its solutions indicating that its ionization constant is approximately 4.6×10^{-4} at $12.5°$ C. The electronic formula of nitrous acid may be written

$$H : \overset{..}{\underset{..}{O}} : N : : \overset{..}{\underset{..}{O}}$$

Nitrous acid and its derivatives, because of their intermediate position on the oxidation state scale of nitrogen, can act both as oxidizing and reducing agents. Nitrous acid is a fairly strong oxidizing agent, as is indicated by the standard potential corresponding to the following half-reaction:

$$NO + H_2O = HNO_2 + H^+ + e^-; \quad E = -1.00 \text{ v.}$$

In the presence of strong oxidizing agents such as chlorine or permanganate ion, nitrous acid is oxidized to nitrate ion.

The alkali and alkaline earth metal nitrites vary in color from nearly colorless to yellow, and are moderately to highly soluble in water; the heavy metal nitrites are usually very much less soluble. The alkali and alkaline earth metal nitrites, in contrast to the free acid, are quite stable, showing very little tendency to decompose even when fused. The sodium and potassium salts are of considerable industrial importance, particularly in the manufacture of organic chemicals and dyes. These salts are usually prepared by one of two methods:

1. The nitrate, or a mixture of the nitrate with the corresponding hydroxide or carbonate, is heated usually in the presence of a reducing agent such as iron or carbon (lead is convenient to use in the laboratory). Reaction in the various cases takes place according to the equations

$$2NaNO_3 = 2NaNO_2 + O_2$$

$$3NaNO_3 + 2Fe = 3NaNO_2 + Fe_2O_3$$

$$NaNO_3 + Pb = NaNO_2 + PbO$$

$$2NaNO_3 + C = 2NaNO_2 + CO_2$$

2. An equimolar mixture of nitric oxide and nitrogen dioxide is passed into a solution of the corresponding hydroxide as previously described (p. 488); or this mixture of gases is absorbed by the solid hydroxide.

$$NO + NO_2 + 2NaOH = 2NaNO_2 + H_2O$$

7. Nitrogen Trihalides and Nitrosyl Halides. When a solution of ammonium chloride is subjected to prolonged action of chlorine, a yellow oily liquid, having the composition expressed by the formula NCl_3, is obtained (p. 389). This substance, which is known as nitrogen trichloride, explodes with great violence when heated or when brought into contact with phosphorus, phosphine, rubber, many carbonaceous materials, potassium hydroxide, or any one of many other substances which react readily with chlorine.

When iodine, either in alcoholic or in aqueous potassium iodide solution, reacts with ammonia, a dark precipitate of a composition corresponding approximately to the formula $NI_3 \cdot NH_3$ is formed. Most of the ammonia in this compound is removed when the precipitate is washed with water. The residue, nitrogen triiodide, like the chloride, is very highly explosive; when it is dry, the slightest touch brings about detonation.

Nitrogen trifluoride, NF_3, is obtained as a colorless gas by the electrolysis of fused ammonium hydrogen fluoride, NH_4HF_2. Though it reacts explosively when mixed with hydrogen, it is, under ordinary conditions, much more stable than either the trichloride or the triiodide. A tribromide has not been prepared; bromine reacts with ammonia to release free nitrogen (p. 470).

Another interesting group of compounds in which nitrogen has an oxidation number of $+3$ are the nitrosyl halides, NOF, NOCl, and NOBr (NOI has not been prepared). These compounds are formed by various methods, among which is the direct combination of nitric oxide with the respective halogen.

$$2NO + X_2 = 2NOX$$

Their properties are summarized in Table 27.1.

Table 27.I

	M.P. (°C.)	B.P. (°C.)	Color
NOF	−132.5	−59.9	Colorless
NOCl	− 64.5	− 6.4	Orange-yellow gas, orange-red liquid
NOBr	− 55.5	≈ 0	Red gas, dark red liquid

The electronic formula for the nitrosyl halides is

$$\ddot{N} :\!: \ddot{O} \cdot$$
$$\ddot{\underset{\cdot\cdot}{X}}$$

These compounds are thus acid halides of nitrous acid. Nitrosyl chloride is used as a reagent in organic chemistry.

8. Nitrogen Dioxide and Dinitrogen Tetroxide. The two compounds nitrogen dioxide, NO_2, and dinitrogen tetroxide, N_2O_4, both of which contain nitrogen in the +4 oxidation state, ordinarily exist in equilibrium with each other:

$$N_2O_4 \rightleftharpoons 2NO_2$$

At room temperature, the gaseous mixture contains only about 20% of the dioxide, but as the temperature is raised the proportion of dioxide increases, until at 135° C. the gas contains 99% of that substance. At still higher temperatures, nitrogen dioxide dissociates into nitric oxide and oxygen.

The nitrogen dioxide molecule (Figure 27.1) like that of nitric oxide, is an "odd" molecule; i.e., it contains an odd number of electrons, and hence at least one unpaired electron. The tendency for two molecules of the dioxide to unite to form one of the tetroxide may be attributed to the tendency of the unpaired electrons on the two molecules to pair off. Likewise, the intense brown color of nitrogen dioxide, as well as its paramagnetic behavior, is attributed to its "odd" character. The tetroxide is colorless and diamagnetic (p. 404). As the temperature of the gas is raised, the color becomes more intense because of the increase in concentration of the dioxide. The gaseous equilibrium mixture of the two oxides condenses to a clear, very pale yellow liquid at a temperature of $21.3°$ C. under a pressure of 1 atm.; the liquid solidifies at $-11.2°$ C. The mixture of oxides has a sharp, irritating odor.

It has already been stated that nitrogen dioxide (i.e., NO_2 and N_2O_4) is obtained by the reaction of nitric oxide with oxygen at ordinary temperatures. For laboratory use, nitrogen dioxide is conveniently obtained by heating dry lead nitrate.

$$2Pb(NO_3)_2 = 2PbO + 4NO_2 + O_2$$

Nitrogen dioxide is an important intermediate in the manufacture of nitric acid (p. 496).

9. Dinitrogen Pentoxide. The highest oxide of nitrogen, dinitrogen pentoxide, N_2O_5, corresponds to the highest oxidation state of nitrogen, $+5$. It is a white, volatile, crystalline solid which has a vapor pressure of 760 mm. at $32.4°$ C. It is not very stable, decomposing slowly, even at room temperature, to yield the dioxide and oxygen.

$$2N_2O_5 = 4NO_2 + O_2$$

As the anhydride of nitric acid, dinitrogen pentoxide yields that substance when added to water, with which it reacts vigorously.

$$N_2O_5 + H_2O = 2HNO_3$$

Dinitrogen pentoxide may be obtained by the dehydration of nitric acid with phosphoric anhydride, or phosphorus (V) oxide, as it has recently come to be called (p. 510):

$$4HNO_3 + P_4O_{10} = 2N_2O_5 + 4HPO_3$$

or, better, by the action of ozone on pure nitrogen dioxide.

$$2NO_2 + O_3 = N_2O_5 + O_2$$

NITRIC ACID AND THE NITRATES

10. Introduction. Nitric acid, HNO_3 is one of the oldest of chemicals, having been used by the alchemists under the name of *aqua fortis* for the separation of silver and gold. In recent times this compound has risen to a position of outstanding importance among industrial chemical products. In fact, an adequate supply of nitric acid and its derivatives is essential to the economy of a nation either in peace or in war, for this substance is indispensable both to the constructive and to the unfortunate destructive activities of mankind.

11. Properties of Nitric Acid. Pure nitric acid is a colorless liquid that boils at a temperature of $83°$ C. under 1 atm. pressure and has an appreciable vapor pressure at room temperature. The liquid has a density of 1.50 g. per cc. at 25° C., and a freezing point of −41.59° C. On being heated, or on standing in sunlight, the pure acid undergoes slow decomposition into nitrogen dioxide, oxygen, and water; hence the pure acid, or its concentrated solutions, become yellow on standing. Nitric acid is miscible in all proportions with water, with which it forms a mixture of maximum boiling point, containing 68% of acid and having a constant boiling point of 120.5° C. and a density of 1.41 g. per cc. at 25° C. This solution is the ordinary concentrated nitric acid which is used industrially and in the laboratory; its concentration is about 15 molar. Because it reacts readily with proteins, concentrated nitric acid, on coming in contact with the skin, rapidly imparts to it a bright yellow color. It is capable of dissolving considerable amounts of nitrogen dioxide to form a reddish brown solution known as fuming nitric acid, which is considerably more reactive than ordinary concentrated nitric acid. At low temperatures nitric acid forms two crystalline hydrates, $HNO_3 \cdot H_2O$, which melts at −37.7° C., and $HNO_3 \cdot 3H_2O$, which melts at −18.5° C.

Various experimental studies indicate that the three oxygen atoms in the nitric acid molecule or in the nitrate ion are grouped about the nitrogen atom at the vertices of an equilateral triangle as shown in the lower right-hand corner of Figure 27.1. The electronic structures of nitric acid and of the nitrate ion, respectively, may be represented as resonance hybrids (p. 195) by the following formulas:

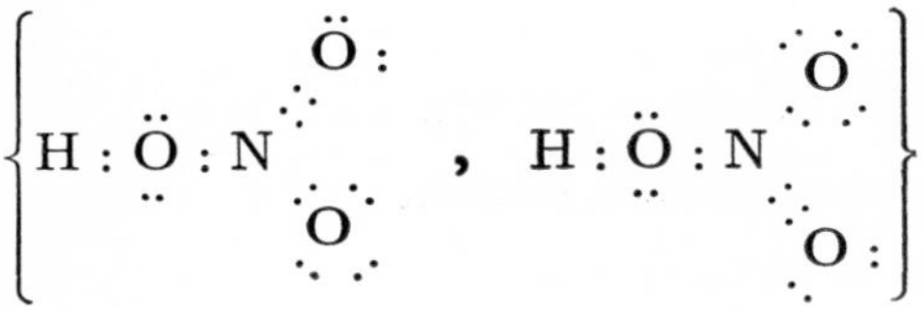

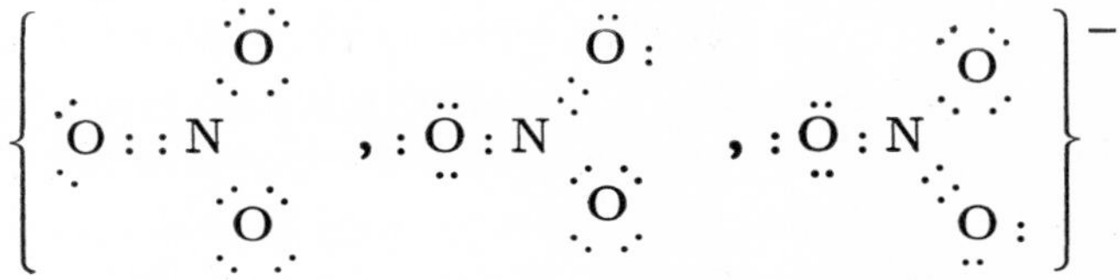

The chemical reactions which nitric acid undergoes may be classified into three groups: (1) acid-base reactions, (2) oxidation-reduction reactions, and (3) nitration reactions.

Since, in dilute solutions at least, nitric acid, like hydrochloric, reacts completely with water to give a solution of the corresponding hydronium compound, it is to be classified as a strong acid. Its aqueous solutions react in such a manner as to support this classification; for example, aqueous nitric acid reacts with basic oxides, hydroxides, or carbonates, to yield solutions of metal nitrates.

$$CuO + 2H^+ + 2NO_3^- = Cu^{++} + 2NO_3^- + H_2O$$

$$Mg(OH)_2 + 2H^+ + 2NO_3^- = Mg^{++} + 2NO_3^- + 2H_2O$$

$$ZnCO_3 + 2H^+ + 2NO_3^- = Zn^{++} + 2NO_3^- + CO_2 + H_2O$$

In its reactions with metals, however, nitric acid shows a distinct difference from such "nonoxidizing" acids as the hydrogen halides. We have already seen that metals above hydrogen in the electromotive series react with hydrochloric and similar acids to yield hydrogen gas. In these reactions the hydrogen ion in the solution is the oxidizing agent.

$$M + 2H^+ = M^{++} + H_2$$

Nitric acid, however, is a much more powerful oxidizing agent than hydrogen ion alone, as is indicated by the standard oxidation potentials for the half-reactions listed in Table 27.2. Since nitric acid is such a strong oxidizing

Table 27.2

	E (volts)
$H_2O + NO_2 = NO_3^- + 2H^+ + e^-$	−0.80
$H_2O + HNO_2 = NO_3^- + 3H^+ + 2e^-$	−0.94
$2H_2O + NO = NO_3^- + 4H^+ + 3e^-$	−0.96
$5H_2O + N_2O = 2NO_3^- + 10H^+ + 8e^-$	−1.12
$6H_2O + N_2 = 2NO_3^- + 6H^+ + 10e^-$	−1.25
$2H_2O + NH_3OH^+ = NO_3^- + 8H^+ + 6e^-$	−0.73
$6H_2O + H_2NNH_3^+ = 2NO_3^- + 17H^+ + 14e^-$	−0.83
$3H_2O + NH_4^+ = NO_3^- + 10H^+ + 8e^-$	−0.88
$H_2 = 2H^+ + 2e^-$	0.00

agent, not only the metals above hydrogen in the electromotive series, but all the remaining metals, with the exception of gold, platinum, and a few others of the rarer metals, react readily with this reagent. The main reduction product obtained in such reactions, even with the more active metals, is never hydrogen, although some hydrogen is liberated by metals as active as magnesium. In the case of zinc and the metals below it, the reduction product is always some compound of nitrogen in a lower oxidation state. As is indicated by the equations for the half-reactions of Table 27.2, a variety of such products are possible. Usually the more dilute the acid, and the more active the reducing agent, the greater is the change in oxidation state which the nitrogen undergoes. This general principle is illustrated by the fact that copper reduces concentrated nitric acid only to nitrogen dioxide.

$$Cu + 4H^+ + 2NO_3^- = Cu^{++} + 2NO_2 + 2H_2O$$

But the same metal reduces the dilute acid to nitric oxide.

$$3Cu + 8H^+ + 2NO_3^- = 3Cu^{++} + 2NO + 4H_2O$$

Nitric acid oxidizes such nonmetals as carbon, sulfur, phosphorus, and iodine to one of their higher oxidation states. Thus, carbon is converted to carbonic acid, sulfur to sulfurous or sulfuric acid, phosphorus to phosphoric acid, and iodine to iodic acid. Dilute nitric acid oxidizes hydrogen sulfide to free sulfur.

$$3H_2S + 2H^+ + 2NO_3^- = 3S + 2NO + 4H_2O$$

The concentrated acid, however, oxidizes the compound to higher oxidation states. Metal sulfides which are insoluble even in concentrated hydrochloric acid are, in most cases, readily acted upon by hot nitric acid; e.g.,

$$3Ag_2S + 8H^+ + 2NO_3^- = 6Ag^+ + 3S + 2NO + 4H_2O$$

Nitric acid reacts with the hydrogen halides to yield the free halogen, which in turn may, in some cases, be further oxidized. The reaction with hydrogen chloride takes place in accordance with the equation

$$6H^+ + 6Cl^- + 2H^+ + 2NO_3^- = 2NO + 3Cl_2 + 4H_2O$$

At ordinary temperatures some nitrosyl chloride, NOCl (p. 490), is formed by the union of nitric oxide and chlorine. A solution containing hydrochloric and nitric acid in the ratio of three moles of the former to one of the latter is known as *aqua regia* (Latin words for "royal water"). It was so named by the alchemists because of its ability to dissolve the noble metals platinum and gold, which are unaffected by nitric acid alone. This property is probably due, not to an increase in the oxidizing strength of the nitric acid because of the presence of hydrochloric acid, but rather to an increase in the reducing strength of the metal because of the availability of chloride ion for the formation of very stable complex ions. This is illustrated by the standard oxidation potentials for the following half-reactions:

$$Au = Au^{+++} + 3e^-; E = -1.50 \text{ v.}$$

$$Au + 4Cl^- = AuCl_4^- + 3e^-; E = -1.00 \text{ v.}$$

The equations for the reaction of gold and platinum with *aqua regia* may be written as follows:

$$Au + 4H^+ + NO_3^- + 4Cl^- = AuCl_4^- + NO + 2H_2O$$

$$3Pt + 16H^+ + 4NO_3^- + 18Cl^- = 3PtCl_6^{--} + 4NO + 8H_2O$$

The class of reactions known as nitration reactions may be subdivided into two types: (1) reactions in which hydrogen atoms of organic molecules are replaced by nitro groups, $-NO_2$, and (2) reactions in which hydroxyl groups on certain types of organic molecules are replaced by nitrate groups, $-ONO_2$. These two types are represented by the following equations, where R represents the remainder of the organic molecule:

1. $$R\,\lfloor H + HO \rfloor\, NO_2 = RNO_2 + H_2O$$

2. $$RO\,\lfloor H + HO \rfloor\, NO_2 = RONO_2 + H_2O$$

The presence of concentrated sulfuric acid or boron trifluoride as a catalyst often aids in carrying out the process.

An important example of type (1) is the reaction of nitric acid with benzene to produce nitrobenzene, a yellow liquid, which is an intermediate in the industrial production of many organic chemicals.

$$C_6H_6 + HONO_2 = C_6H_5NO_2 + H_2O$$

Toluene, $C_6H_5CH_3$, reacts with nitric acid under suitable conditions to form trinitrotoluene, a colorless solid of the formula $CH_3C_6H_2(NO_2)_3$. The reaction may be represented by the following equation:

$$C_6H_5CH_3 + 3HONO_2 = CH_3C_6H_2(NO_2)_3 + 3H_2O$$

The product, commonly known as T.N.T., is widely used as an explosive, since it detonates with great violence when subjected to severe shock. Trinitrophenol, $C_6H_2OH(NO_2)_3$, commonly known as picric acid, which may be formed by the reaction of phenol, C_6H_5OH, with nitric acid, is likewise a high explosive. This compound is a yellow solid; in addition to its use as an explosive, it is used as a yellow dye and in the treatment of burns.

As an important example of (2) we may cite the reaction of nitric acid with glycerol, $C_3H_5(OH)_3$, which takes place according to the equation

$$C_3H_5(OH)_3 + 3HNO_3 = C_3H_5(ONO_2)_3 + 3H_2O$$

The product of the reaction, $C_3H_5(ONO_2)_3$, an oily liquid commonly known as nitroglycerine but more properly called glyceryl trinitrate, is a violent explosive which may be detonated either by shock or by heating. It is dangerous to handle in the pure state, and hence is commonly used industrially in the form of dynamite, which consists of nitroglycerine absorbed in some inactive solid substance such as sawdust; it is considerably less sensitive to heat or shock than the pure substance. A similar reaction occurs when cellulose, the principal constituent of cotton and wood fibers, is treated with nitric acid (p. 600).

12. Manufacture and Uses of Nitric Acid. The application of nitric acid in the manufacture of explosives and of cellulose nitrate products as has just been described, as well as its use in the preparation of many of the metallic nitrates, and in the manufacture of fertilizers and of a variety of dyes, drugs, and other organic chemicals, accounts for its great importance in the chemical industry. For many years the chief source of nitric acid was the reaction, at elevated temperatures, of sodium nitrate with concentrated sulfuric acid. This reaction, analogous to that which takes place in the preparation of hydrochloric acid from salt, may be represented by the equation

$$NaNO_3 + H_2SO_4 = NaHSO_4 + HNO_3$$

A natural supply of sodium nitrate is to be found only in Chile, and the deposits there, though large, are not inexhaustible. Hence, the discovery of methods for the "fixation" of atmospheric nitrogen (i.e., for the preparation of nitrogen compounds directly from nitrogen in the air), which would provide, for the various nations, internal sources of these important compounds, became, in the early years of this century, the most urgent problem of industrial chemistry. Under this stress the arc process (p. 268) for the manufacture of nitric oxide was developed, as well as the Haber process (p. 478) and the cyanamide process (p. 479) for the manufacture of ammonia. Of these, the first is no longer industrially important.

As a result of these developments, the chief source of nitric acid today is from the oxidation of ammonia, although about 8% of the total is still supplied by Chilean sodium nitrate. The Ostwald process for the catalytic oxidation of ammonia to nitric oxide was discussed in the preceding chapter (p. 477). The nitric oxide obtained by means of this reaction, after being cooled, is mixed with oxygen to convert it to the dioxide.

$$2NO + O_2 = 2NO_2$$

The product is then passed into warm water with which it reacts according to the equation

$$3NO_2 + H_2O = 2H^+ + 2NO_3^- + NO$$

The nitric oxide is recovered and recycled. A better yield of nitric acid is obtained when a mixture of nitrogen dioxide and oxygen (the latter to oxidize the nitric oxide formed) is passed into warm water under pressure. About a 60% solution of nitric acid usually results from this process. More concentrated solutions may be prepared by distillation from a mixture of the dilute acid and concentrated sulfuric acid.

13. The Nitrates. Because of the strongly acidic character of nitric acid, nitrates of the metals are, in most cases, readily prepared. Exceptions are the nitrates of metal ions with strong reducing properties such as ferrous and chromous ions; because of the oxidizing power of nitric acid and of the nitrate ion, such nitrates are not readily obtained.

The nitrates are characterized by the fact that they are all quite soluble in water. A few nitrates, such as the bismuth and mercuric salts, undergo hydrolysis in aqueous solution to produce basic salts that are only slightly soluble.

Metal nitrates undergo thermal decomposition in two ways. Nitrates of the heavy metals, when heated, lose nitrogen dioxide and oxygen to form metallic oxide.

$$2Pb(NO_3)_2 = 2PbO + 4NO_2 + O_2$$

The alkali metal nitrates, however, lose oxygen to form the corresponding nitrites.

$$2NaNO_3 = 2NaNO_2 + O_2$$

The unique thermal decomposition of ammonium nitrate has already been discussed (p. 486). Ammonium nitrate detonates when subjected to a shock of sufficient magnitude. It is a component of several powerful explosives; examples are ammonal, a mixture of ammonium nitrate and aluminum powder, and amitol, a mixture of ammonium nitrate and T.N.T. Calcium, potassium, sodium, and ammonium nitrates are important fertilizers.

Nitrate ion may be detected in solution as follows. To the solution, contained in a test tube, freshly prepared ferrous sulfate solution is added. The tube is then tilted, and concentrated sulfuric acid is allowed to flow slowly down the walls of the tube so as to form a separate layer at the bottom. If nitrate ion is present, a brown ring will be formed at the interface between the two liquid layers. This change results from the fact that nitrate ion, in the presence of concentrated sulfuric acid, is reduced by ferrous ion to nitric oxide.

$$3Fe^{++} + NO_3^- + 4H^+ = 3Fe^{+++} + NO + 2H_2O$$

The nitric oxide reacts with excess ferrous ion to form the brown complex ion $Fe(NO)^{++}$. Certain other ions, such as nitrite, iodide, and bromide, also yield colored rings under these conditions, and hence interfere with the test.

HYDRAZOIC ACID AND THE AZIDES

14. Preparation and Properties. When powdered sodium nitrate is added slowly to molten sodium amide ($NaNH_2$), reaction takes place, in accordance with the following equation, to yield sodium azide, NaN_3:

$$3NaNH_2 + NaNO_3 = NaN_3 + 3NaOH + NH_3$$

Azides may also be obtained by means of various other reactions which cannot be discussed here. When an acidified solution of an azide is distilled, free hydrazoic acid, HN_3, is obtained. This is a colorless liquid which boils at 37° C. and freezes to a colorless solid at −80° C. Since the pure liquid is violently and treacherously explosive, it must be handled with extreme care. It is soluble in water, giving a weakly acidic solution ($K = 1.8 \times 10^{-5}$).

Heavy metal azides, such as the lead compound $Pb(N_3)_2$, that explode on being struck, are commonly used as detonators for other explosives. Alkali metal azides are much more stable.

STUDY QUESTIONS AND PROBLEMS

1. Make a chart listing the various oxides of nitrogen, equations for methods of preparation of each, chief physical and chemical properties, and most important industrial applications.

2. Make a similar chart for the oxyacids of nitrogen.

3. What is meant by an "odd" molecule? Using reference works in your library, find out why "odd" molecules are paramagnetic. (See Selwood, *J. Chem. Educ.* **19** (1942), pp. 181–188.)

4. How can you account for the fact that nitrous acid is a much weaker acid than nitric? Write the electronic formula for nitrous acid. Give equations for three methods for preparing sodium nitrite.

5. Complete and balance the following equations:

$HNO_3 + P_4O_{10} =$
$Cu + H^+ + NO_3^- =$
$ZnCO_3 + H^+ + NO_3^- =$
$H_2S + H^+ + NO_3^- =$
$C_6H_6 + HNO_3 =$
$C_3H_5(OH)_3 + HNO_3 =$

6. Write electronic formulas for nitric acid and for nitrate ion.

7. Give the conditions and equations for all reactions for two industrial methods for the manufacture of nitric acid.

8. List and give examples of the most important types of industrial applications of nitric acid and its salts.

9. Complete and balance the equations showing what happens when the following compounds are heated: NH_4NO_3, $NaNO_3$, $Pb(NO_3)_2$.

10. Write equations for six reactions of nitric acid with six different bivalent metals (call them L, M, Q, R, T, and X, if you like, so as not to identify them with any real elements), in each of which a different reduction product of nitric acid is obtained.

11. Suppose air to consist of $\frac{4}{5}$ nitrogen and $\frac{1}{5}$ oxygen by volume, and suppose that by subjecting it to a temperature of 3000° by means of an electric arc, 2% of the oxygen can be made to combine with nitrogen to give nitric oxide. How many liters of nitric oxide, measured under standard conditions, would be formed in this way from 1 cubic meter of air? What would be the weight of this nitric oxide? What additional volume (S.T.P.) of oxygen would be taken up by the cooled nitric oxide, in forming nitrogen dioxide, and what would be the volume (S.T.P.) of the nitrogen dioxide formed, on the assumption that it was entirely in the unassociated state? What weight of nitric acid would be formed upon the first passage of the nitrogen dioxide through water, without recycling the nitric oxide formed at the same time? What volume of 6 N solution could be made from this quantity of nitric acid?

28

Phosphorus and Its Compounds

1. General Characteristics. Phosphorus, the second member of the nitrogen family, is, like nitrogen, a nonmetal, although the expected gradation toward more metallic characteristics with increasing atomic number is shown by the lower acidity of its oxides and hydroxyl compounds compared to the corresponding nitrogen compounds. Furthermore, compounds of phosphorus with other nonmetals, such as oxygen and the halogens, are more stable than the corresponding compounds of nitrogen, while the hydride PH_3 is less stable than ammonia. The role of nitrogen as a key element in plant and animal proteins has been discussed in previous chapters. It is of interest, therefore, to note that phosphorus is likewise an important constituent of certain classes of biologically important substances, and that phosphates, like nitrates, are essential fertilizer materials.

2. History and Occurrence of Phosphorus. The element phosphorus was first isolated in 1669 by the German alchemist Hennig Brand, who obtained it by means of a complex chemical process from human urine. Because this element has the unusual property of glowing in the dark, its discovery was the cause of considerable excitement in alchemical circles. The method by which it was produced, however, was kept a closely guarded secret until 1737, when it became known to the Academy of Sciences in Paris and was at once published. Robert Boyle, the famous English scientist whom we have previously mentioned, discovered the process independently.

Because of its high reactivity toward oxygen, phosphorus does not occur in nature in the free state. The most important sources are the several varieties of so-called phosphate rock, large quantities of which are found in Tennessee, Florida, Wyoming, Idaho, and Montana, as well as in North Africa and many other parts of the world. The principal components of these deposits are calcium phosphate, $Ca_3(PO_4)_2$, and such mixed salts as apatite, $CaF_2 \cdot 3Ca_3(PO_4)_2$. Calcium phosphate is the principal mineral constituent of bones and teeth, and complex organic compounds containing phosphorus are found in the blood, muscles, brains, and nerves of animals. Phosphorus compounds are present in most of the bodily secretions.

3. Physical and Chemical Properties. Like sulfur, its neighbor in the periodic system, phosphorus exists in several different allotropic modifications. The three most important forms of the element are commonly known by names derived from their colors; viz., white phosphorus, red (or violet) phosphorus, and black phosphorus.

White (or yellow, as it is sometimes called) phosphorus is obtained when phosphorus vapor is condensed. It melts at 44.1° C. and boils at 280.5° C. It ordinarily comes on the market in the form of soft, waxlike sticks, which usually have a yellowish color. When deposited from solution it is obtained as colorless, transparent crystals. White phosphorus differs from the other two forms (red and black) in two very important respects: it is highly soluble in carbon disulfide, and moderately soluble in benzene and ether, whereas the other two are almost insoluble; and it is much more reactive toward atmospheric oxygen than the other varieties. White phosphorus, in fact, is so reactive toward air that safety demands that it be stored under water. When it is exposed to air and moisture it undergoes slow oxidation; part of the energy of this reaction is liberated as light, and hence white phosphorus, in the presence of air and moisture, may be observed to glow in the dark. This phenomenon, which is known as phosphorescence (from the Greek word meaning "light-bearing"), gives the element its name. It should be noted, however, that in the case of many other phosphorescent substances, the emission of light is due, not to oxidation, but to an entirely different process.

When white phosphorus is heated in the absence of air to about 245° C., or when it is subjected to the action of x-rays, it changes into the more stable red variety. This same transition takes place slowly under the influence of ordinary light and is catalyzed by a number of substances, among which is iodine. Red phosphorus is composed of very small crystals and differs from the white form in both physical and chemical characteristics. It is more dense than the white form (Table 28.1), melts only when heated under pressure to about 600° C., is insoluble in organic solvents, and is much less reactive than the white modification. It shows no tendency to undergo oxidation at room temperature, though it inflames readily when heated to 240° C. As usually obtained, red phosphorus contains traces of the white form. This impurity can be removed by extraction with carbon

Table 28.1

Physical Properties of Solid Forms of Phosphorus

	Density (g./cc.)	M.P. (°C.)	B.P. (°C.)	Solubility
White	1.8232	44.1	280.5	Sol. in organic solvents
Red	2.34	....	....	Insoluble
Violet	2.34	592.5	....	Insoluble
Black	2.699	587.5	....	Insoluble

disulfide, or by digestion with sodium hydroxide (p. 505), since the red form is unaffected by either reagent. When red phosphorus is dissolved in molten lead, the mass allowed to solidify, and the lead dissolved electrolytically, crystals of violet phosphorus are obtained. The properties of violet phosphorus and of the red form are so similar that it is believed that they are chemically identical, differing only in crystal size.

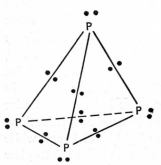

Fig. 28.1. Electronic formula for P₄.

Black phosphorus is obtained by subjecting the white modification to enormous pressures (170,000 lb. per sq. in.). It is similar to graphite (p. 532) in appearance, and, like that substance, is a conductor of electricity. Black phosphorus is somewhat less reactive than the red variety; it changes into the latter form when heated to 550° C.

White phosphorus is extremely poisonous, the fatal dose being less than 0.2 g. The other solid forms, however, are relatively harmless.

Density measurements on phosphorus vapor have indicated that, below 800° C., the vapor consists of tetratomic molecules. The electronic and geometrical structures of these molecules are illustrated in Figures 28.1 and 28.2. As may be seen from these figures, each phosphorus atom completes its valence shell by sharing three pairs of electrons, each pair including one electron from one of the other three atoms in the molecule. Thus, each atom is connected by a single covalent bond to each of the other three, and has in addition an unshared electron pair. At temperatures about 800° C., the P_4 molecules begin to dissociate into P_2 molecules.

Pure liquid phosphorus, which is obtained when pure white phosphorus is melted in the absence of air and light, is clear and colorless; like the gas, is has been found to consist of P_4 molecules.

The nonmetallic nature of phosphorus is indicated by its chemical as well as by its physical properties. The element reacts with the metals, when heated, to produce binary compounds called phosphides. It reacts also with the nonmetals oxygen, sulfur, and the halogens, to produce oxides, sulfides, and halides. The reactivity of phosphorus with respect to these elements varies, as was stated above, with the allotropic form in which the element exists, decreasing in the order white > red > black.

4. Preparation and Uses of Phosphorus. Several methods for the production of phosphorus on an industrial scale have been developed, but the method most generally employed consists in the heating of a mixture of calcium phosphate (rock phosphate or bone ash), silicon dioxide (sand), and carbon (coke) in an electric arc furnace (Figure 28.3). The silicon dioxide, being less volatile than phosphorus (V) oxide (cf. p. 644), displaces the latter from calcium phosphate in accordance with the following equation:

Fig. 28.2.   Models of the N_2 molecule and the P_4 molecule. (*Courtesy of Dr. J. A. Campbell, Oberlin College.*)

$$2Ca_3(PO_4)_2 + 6SiO_2 = 6CaSiO_3 + P_4O_{10}$$

The phosphorus (V) oxide is reduced by the carbon to free phosphorus.

$$P_4O_{10} + 10C = P_4 + 10CO$$

At the temperature at which the reaction is carried out the calcium silicate ($CaSiO_3$) collects as a molten slag at the bottom of the furnace, whence it is easily removed. The phosphorus is liberated in the gaseous state, and passes through an opening in the upper part of the furnace into condensers where it is liquefied.

In addition to its use in the production of phosphorus compounds, elementary phosphorus is used in the manufacture of matches (p. 517) and of certain types of bronzes (p. 765). During World War II, large quantities of phosphorus were used in a very effective type of antipersonnel bomb and in the production of smoke screens for the concealment of ships and troops during military maneuvers. The latter use depends upon the fact that when phosphorus burns in air it produces a dense white cloud of oxide. White phosphorus also finds considerable use as a rat poison.

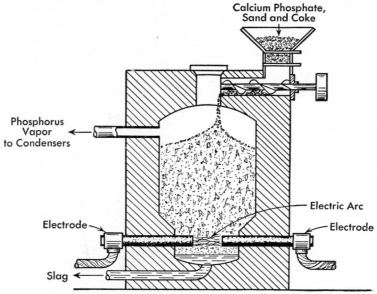

Fig. 28.3.   Diagram of the industrial preparation of phosphorus.

5. The Oxidation State Scale of Phosphorus. As in the case of nitrogen, we shall find it convenient to organize the discussion of the compounds of phosphorus in terms of the various oxidation states exhibited by the element. Table 28.2 is a summary of the oxidation states exhibited by phosphorus and the more important groups of compounds corresponding to each state.

Table 28.2

Oxidation State Scale of Phosphorus

+5	Pentahalides, P_4O_{10}, P_4S_{10}, oxyhalides, the phosphoric acids, and the phosphates
+4	P_2O_4, hypophosphoric acid, and hypophosphates
+3	Trihalides, P_4O_6, phosphorous acid, and phosphites
+1	Hypophosphorous acid and hypophosphites
0	Elementary phosphorus
−3	Phosphine, phosphonium salts, and phosphides

Of these oxidation states, −3, 0, +3, and +5 are the most important and the most frequently encountered.

6. Phosphine and Its Derivatives. Phosphine, the phosphorus analog of ammonia, is a colorless gas at ordinary temperatures; the solid melts at $-132.5°$ C. and the liquid boils at $-86.2°$ C. The substance has a highly offensive odor, and is very poisonous. Its composition corresponds to the formula PH_3, and its properties bear some resemblance to those of ammonia. The structure of the phosphine molecule is analogous to that of ammonia; through the unshared pair of electrons on the phosphorus atom, phosphine can take up a proton to form the phosphonium ion. Thus, when gaseous phosphine and hydrogen iodide are brought together, well formed, white crystals of phosphonium iodide are obtained:

$$\begin{array}{ccc} H & & H \\ \cdot\cdot & & \cdot\cdot \\ H : P : \ + H : \overset{\cdot\cdot}{\underset{\cdot\cdot}{I}} : \ = \ H : P : H^+ \ , \ : \overset{\cdot\cdot}{\underset{\cdot\cdot}{I}} :^- \\ \cdot\cdot & & \cdot\cdot \\ H & & H \end{array}$$

Phosphine is, however, much less basic than ammonia, and phosphonium ion is therefore a stronger acid than ammonium ion (p. 316). It readily releases a proton to water to form hydronium ion. Phosphonium salts break down in water, therefore, according to the following equation:

$$PH_4{}^+ + X^- + H_2O = PH_3 + H_3O^+ + X^-$$

Like ammonia, phosphine forms an unstable monohydrate, $PH_3 \cdot H_2O$, or PH_4OH.

Phosphine is less stable and is a much stronger reducing agent than ammonia. Phosphine can form coordinate covalent bonds with metal ions, though its tendency in this direction is considerably less than that of ammonia.

Phosphine is produced by a variety of chemical reactions. The most important are (1) the reaction of white phosphorus with concentrated solutions of alkalis, and (2) the hydrolysis of metallic phosphides. Examples of these two types are represented by the following equations:

1. $P_4 + 3OH^- + 3H_2O = PH_3 + 3H_2PO_2{}^-$
   hypophosphite ion
2. $Ca_3P_2 + 6H_2O = 3Ca(OH)_2 + 2PH_3$

If the phosphine produced by either of these methods is allowed to come into contact with the air it inflames spontaneously. This is due primarily to the presence of the very inflammable substance P_2H_4, which is formed as an impurity in the phosphine.

7. Hypophosphorous Acid and the Hypophosphites. As was indicated in the preceding paragraph, white phosphorus reacts with strongly alkaline solutions to yield phosphine and a solution of the corresponding hypophosphite. If a solution of barium hypophosphite is treated with dilute sulfuric acid, the resulting precipitate filtered off, and the solution concentrated by evaporation and cooled, colorless crystals of pure hypophosphorous acid, H_3PO_2, melting at 26.5° C., are obtained. The acid is readily soluble in water, and ionizes in accordance with the equation

$$H_3PO_2 = H^+ + H_2PO_2^-$$

The ionization constant for this reaction is 1×10^{-2}, which indicates that hypophosphorous acid is a moderately strong acid. Further ionization does not take place, however, and it is apparent that only one of the hydrogen atoms in the molecule is susceptible to ionization. This fact is in accord with the following electronic formulas:

Hypophosphorous acid   Hypophosphite ion

The configuration indicated by these formulas has been confirmed by x-ray and other types of structural studies. Thus, as might be predicted from the behavior of phosphine, the hydrogen atoms which are attached to the phosphorus atom are not removed by water or hydroxide ion, whereas the hydroxyl hydrogen atom is so removed; hence hypophosphorous acid is a monoprotic acid. A number of hypophosphites, such as NaH_2PO_2 and $Ba(H_2PO_2)_2$, have been prepared. One of the outstanding properties of the hypophosphite ion and of hypophosphorous acid is their strong reducing power.

8. Phosphorus Trihalides and Phosphorus (III) Oxide. It has been stated that white phosphorus reacts vigorously with the halogens, and that red phosphorus also undergoes this reaction, though with less violence. If these reactions are carried out without an excess of the halogen, the product consists, for the most part, of the trihalide, PX_3, but if the ratio of halogen to phosphorus is large, the pentahalide, PX_5, is obtained. In any case, a mixture of halides always results, and the product of the reaction must be fractionally distilled in order to obtain the pure trihalide. Phosphorus trichloride and tribromide are usually prepared by the reaction of the gaseous halogen with white or red phosphorus, and the triiodide by mixing carbon disulfide solutions of white phosphorus and of iodine in the theoretical ratio by weight.

The trifluoride is made from the trichloride by treatment with arsenic trifluoride, antimony trifluoride, or calcium fluoride.

$$PCl_3 + AsF_3 = PF_{3(g)} + AsCl_3$$

When phosphorus and iodine are brought together in carbon disulfide solution in the ratio of one atomic weight of the former to two of the latter, the dihalide, P_2I_4, is obtained. Mixed trihalides such as PF_2Cl, $PFCl_2$, and $PFBr_2$ are known also.

All the trihalides have structures which correspond to the following electronic formula:

$$: \overset{\cdot\cdot}{\underset{\cdot\cdot}{X}} :$$
$$: \overset{\cdot\cdot}{\underset{\cdot\cdot}{X}} : \overset{\cdot\cdot}{\underset{\cdot\cdot}{P}} : \overset{\cdot\cdot}{\underset{\cdot\cdot}{X}} :$$

They are all colorless gases or colorless, volatile liquids (except PI_3, which is a red, low-melting solid, and their properties indicate that the bonds in their molecules are covalent rather than ionic. This, of course, is to be expected, since both phosphorus and the halogens are nonmetals (p. 179). The melting points and boiling points of the phosphorus trihalides are listed in Table 28.3.

Table 28.3

Physical Properties of the Phosphorus Trihalides

	M.P. (°C.)	B.P. (°C.)
PF_3	−151.5	−101.5
PCl_3	−111.8	74.2
PBr_3	− 40.0	175.3
PI_3	61.0	. . . .

All the trihalides are hydrolyzed when brought in contact with water, yielding phosphorous acid and the corresponding hydrohalic acid.

$$PX_3 + 3H_2O = H_3PO_3 + 3H^+ + 3X^-$$

It has already been pointed out that phosphorus, particularly the white variety, reacts vigorously with oxygen to yield a mixture of oxides. In the absence of an excess of oxygen, and when the temperature is held to below 100° C., the major product is the oxide of +3 phosphorus, which was formerly written P_2O_3. However, since the compound is now known to have the structure shown in Figures 28.4 and 28.5, the formula P_4O_6 is to be preferred. Phosphorus (III) oxide is a clear, colorless liquid, which freezes at $23.8°$ C. and boils at $175.4°$ C. Phosphorus (III) oxide is the anhydride of phosphorous acid, which it forms when added to water.

$$P_4O_6 + 6H_2O = 4H_3PO_3$$

With hot water, phosphorus, phosphine, and phosphoric acid, as well as other products, are obtained.

Fig. 28.4. Model of the P_4O_6 molecule. (*Courtesy of Dr. J. A. Campbell, Oberlin College.*)

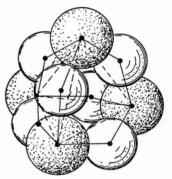

Fig. 28.5 Geometrical arrangement of atoms in the P_4O_6 molecule.

9. Phosphorous Acid and the Phosphites. As was pointed out in the preceding section, phosphorous acid is formed by the hydrolysis of phosphorus trihalides or by the hydration of phosphorus trioxide. When pure, the acid is a colorless solid, melting at about $73°$ C. It is extremely soluble in water, its saturated solution at $25°$ C. containing about 83 g. of acid per 100 g. of solution.

Phosphorous acid is diprotic; salts such as NaH_2PO_3 and Na_2HPO_3 are known, but none of the type M_3PO_3 have been prepared. The failure of the phosphorous acid molecule to release the third hydrogen atom is accounted for by the following electronic formulas (cf. p. 506), in which it is shown that one of the three hydrogen atoms is attached directly to the phosphorus:

$$
\begin{array}{cc}
\ddot{\text{O}}\text{ :} & \ddot{\text{O}}\text{ :} \\
\text{H : \"O : P : \"O : H} & \text{: \"O : P : \"O :} \\
\text{H} & \text{H} \\
\text{Phosphorous acid} & \text{Phosphite ion}
\end{array}
$$

In contrast to the usual situation with "ous" and "ic" acids (p. 324), phosphorous acid, as well as hypophosphorous acid (p. 506), is a stronger acid than phosphoric (p. 513), although only very slightly so.

An aqueous solution of phosphorous acid or of phosphite ion is a strong reducing agent, as is indicated by the standard potentials corresponding to the following half-reactions:

$$H_3PO_3 + H_2O = H_3PO_4 + 2H^+ + 2e^-; \quad E = 0.28 \text{ v.}$$

$$HPO_3^{--} + 3OH^- = PO_4^{---} + 2H_2O + 2e^-; E = 1.12 \text{ v.}$$

Halogens, dichromate ion, mercuric chloride, and silver ion are among the substances which readily oxidize phosphorous acid and phosphites.

A metaphosphorous acid corresponding to the formula HPO_2 is obtained when phosphine is burned in air, but it is of little importance.

In addition to the tetroxide P_2O_4, the acid of the formula $H_4P_2O_6$, called hypophosphoric acid, and its salts, the hypophosphates, also contain phosphorus in the $+4$ oxidation state.

10. Phosphorus Pentahalides and Phosphorus (V) Oxide. In a previous section it was stated that, when an excess of halogen is present, the product of the reaction of phosphorus with a halogen consists chiefly of a pentahalide, of the general formula PX_5. The pentahalides are usually prepared, however, by the reaction of the halogen with the trihalide; e.g.,

$$PCl_3 + Cl_2 = PCl_5$$

The mixed pentahalides PF_3Cl_2, PF_3Br_2, and PCl_3Br_2 may be prepared similarly. The pentaiodide has not been prepared. Some of the physical properties of the pentahalides are given in Table 28.4. In the gaseous and

Table 28.4

Physical Properties of the Phosphorus Pentahalides

	M.P. (°C.)	B.P. (°C.)	Color
PF_5	−83	−75	Colorless
PCl_5	?	160 (sublimes)	Colorless
PBr_5	<100	Decomposes	Two crystalline forms: one yellow, the other red

liquid states the pentahalides are covalent compounds. However, in the solid state or dissolved in liquids of high dielectric constant, PCl_5 and PBr_5 are present as $[PCl_4^+][PCl_6^-]$ and $[PBr_4^+]Br^-$, respectively.

The pentahalides undergo rapid hydrolysis in contact with water. In the presence of a limited quantity of water, the products of such hydrolysis are oxyhalides, which have the general electronic formula

$$
\begin{array}{c}
\ddot{\;}\;\ddot{\;} \\
: \ddot{X} : \\
\ddot{\;}\quad\quad\ddot{\;} \\
: \ddot{O} : P : \ddot{X} : \\
\ddot{\;}\quad\quad\ddot{\;} \\
: \ddot{X} : \\
\ddot{\;}
\end{array}
$$

The reaction may be represented by the equation

$$PX_5 + H_2O = POX_3 + 2H^+ + 2X^-$$

These oxyhalides are either gases, or volatile liquids or solids. With an excess of water, the pentahalides react to yield orthophosphoric acid.

$$PX_5 + 4H_2O = H_3PO_4 + 5H^+ + 5X^-$$
$$\text{orthophosphoric}$$
$$\text{acid}$$

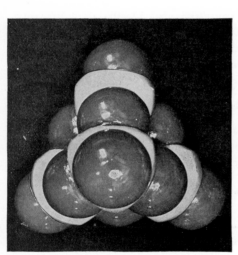

Fig. 28.6. Model of the P_4O_{10} molecule. (*Courtesy of Dr. J. A. Campbell, Oberlin College.*)

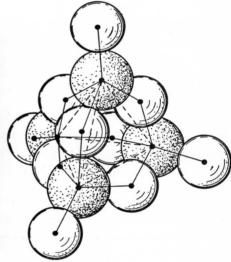

Fig. 28.7. Geometrical arrangement of atoms in the P_4O_{10} molecule.

Phosphorus (V) oxide, a white, difficultly volatile, amorphous powder, is obtained, along with a little (III) oxide, by the oxidation of phosphorus in the presence of an excess of air or oxygen in ordinary combustion. The formula for this oxide was formerly thought to be P_2O_5, and it is commonly called phosphorus pentoxide. The compound is now known to have a molecular weight corresponding to the formula P_4O_{10}; the structure of this molecule is illustrated in Figures 28.6 and 28.7. The outstanding property of phosphorus (V) oxide is its very great tendency to combine with water. Because of this strong affinity, it is one of the most effective dehydrating agents available. Since this reaction results in the formation of phosphoric acids, the oxide is known also as phosphoric anhydride.

11. Hydrates of Phosphorus (V) Oxide. Since the hydrates formed by the extremely vigorous reaction of phosphorus (V) oxide with water (i.e., the phosphoric acids) are, together with their salts, undoubtedly the most important compounds of phosphorus, it is desirable that we discuss them in some detail. In the following table the more important of these acids are listed. These three acids may be converted one into the other by the addition or removal of water, as indicated in the table, and as discussed in detail in succeeding paragraphs.

Table 28.5

Hydrates of P_4O_{10}

H_3PO_4	$\uparrow$	$P_4O_{10} + 6H_2O = 4H_3PO_4$	Orthophosphoric acid
$H_4P_2O_7$	$+H_2O$	$P_4O_{10} + 4H_2O = 2H_4P_2O_7$	$-H_2O$	Pyrophosphoric acid
$(HPO_3)_n$		$nP_4O_{10} + 2nH_2O = 4(HPO_3)_n$	$\downarrow$	Metaphosphoric acid

12. Metaphosphoric Acid and the Metaphosphates. When phosphorus (V) oxide is treated with a small amount of water, or when orthophosphoric acid is strongly heated, substances having the composition represented by the empirical formula HPO_3 are obtained. The molecular constitution of metaphosphoric acid and the metaphosphates has been found to depend upon the method used in their preparation. It has been shown that several metaphosphoric acids and corresponding series of metaphosphates, having different properties but all corresponding to the general formulas $(HPO_3)_n$ and $(MPO_3)_n$, respectively, can be obtained. The difference in properties has been attributed to differences in the value of n in the various cases. The determination of the degree of complexity in any particular case is attended with serious experimental difficulties, so that a great deal of confusion prevails as to the exact structure of many of these substances. It is believed, however, that n may have any integral value up to 6, and even higher values of n have sometimes been reported.

Metaphosphates may be prepared by the neutralization of metaphosphoric acid.

$$HPO_3 + Na^+ + OH^- = Na^+ + PO_3^- + H_2O$$

They are obtained also when primary orthophosphates (p. 515) or second-ary pyrophosphates (p. 513) are heated.

$$NaH_2PO_4 = NaPO_3 + H_2O$$

$$Na_2H_2P_2O_7 = 2NaPO_3 + H_2O$$

Microcosmic salt, a secondary orthophosphate (p. 515) of the formula $NaNH_4HPO_4$, likewise yields a metaphosphate when heated.

$$NaNH_4HPO_4 = NaPO_3 + NH_3 + H_2O$$

Just as metaphosphoric acid may be converted to orthophosphoric acid by reaction with water, so may metaphosphates be converted to orthophos-phates by reaction with metal oxides; e.g.,

$$Ca(PO_3)_2 + 2CaO = Ca_3(PO_4)_2$$

The colored orthophosphates formed when beads of sodium metaphosphate are heated with metal compounds in the flame of a Bunsen burner are of use in identifying certain metals; e.g.,

$$NaPO_3 + CuO = NaCuPO_4$$
$$\text{(blue)}$$

$$NaPO_3 + NiSO_4 = NaNiPO_4 + SO_3$$
$$\text{(green)}$$

Some of the complex metaphosphates are useful as water softeners; sodium "hexametaphosphate," commonly given the formula $(NaPO_3)_6$, but of uncertain composition, is sold under the trade name of Calgon for this purpose (p. 675).

13. Pyrophosphoric Acid and the Pyrophosphates. Pyrophosphoric acid is obtained by the moderate heating of orthophosphoric acid (at about $215°$ C.), and its composition and molecular weight correspond to the formula $H_4P_2O_7$. The electronic formula for the acid is

$$
\begin{array}{ccc}
\text{H} & & \text{H} \\
\vdots\!\ddot{\text{O}}\!: & & :\!\ddot{\text{O}}\!: \\
\text{H}:\ddot{\text{O}}:\text{P}:\ddot{\text{O}}:\text{P}:\ddot{\text{O}}:\text{H} \\
:\ddot{\text{O}}: & & :\ddot{\text{O}}:
\end{array}
$$

As would be expected from this formula, pyrophosphoric acid is a tetraprotic acid. It is interesting to note, however, that only two series of pyrophosphates are readily obtained: namely (1) the secondary pyrophosphates, in which two hydrogen atoms have been replaced, such as $Na_2H_2P_2O_7$, and (2) the quaternary or normal pyrophosphates, in which all four hydrogen atoms have been replaced, such as $K_4P_2O_7$.

The fact that secondary pyrophosphates yield metaphosphates on being strongly heated has already been mentioned. Normal pyrophosphates are obtained when secondary orthophosphates (p. 515) are heated; e.g.,

$$2Na_2HPO_4 = Na_4P_2O_7 + H_2O$$

Most of the pyrophosphates, with the exception of those of the alkali metals, are only slightly soluble in water.

14. Orthophosphoric Acid and the Orthophosphates. Orthophosphoric acid, sometimes called simply phosphoric acid, since it is by far the most important of all the acids of phosphorus, is a white solid which, when pure, melts at 42.3° C. However, since the liquid is very viscous and has a strong tendency to supercool, it is difficult to crystallize. It combines with water to form the solid hydrate $2H_3PO_4 \cdot H_2O$, which melts at 29.35° C. The electronic formula for orthophosphoric acid is

$$
\begin{array}{c}
\text{H} \\
\ddot{\text{O}} : \\
\text{H} : \ddot{\text{O}} : \ddot{\text{P}} : \ddot{\text{O}} : \text{H} \\
: \ddot{\text{O}} :
\end{array}
$$

and, as would be expected from this formula, the acid is triprotic. The ionization constants corresponding to the three steps in the ionization are listed in Table 28.6. In accordance with the values of these constants, the first step of this ionization takes place to a considerable degree, the second step only slightly, and the third step to an extremely small extent only.

Table 28.6

$H_3PO_4 \rightleftharpoons H^+ + H_2PO_4^-$ dihydrogen phosphate ion	$K_1 =$	7.5×10^{-3}
$H_2PO_4^- \rightleftharpoons H^+ + HPO_4^{--}$ monohydrogen phosphate ion	$K_2 =$	6.2×10^{-8}
$HPO_4^{--} \rightleftharpoons H^+ + PO_4^{---}$ phosphate ion	$K_3 =$	1×10^{-12}

There are a variety of chemical reactions which result in the formation of orthophosphoric acid. The best laboratory method for the preparation of a solution of pure orthophosphoric acid consists in oxidation of pure white phosphorus with a solution of nitric acid of specific gravity 1.2 (concentrated nitric acid reacts explosively).

$$3P_4 + 20H^+ + 20NO_3^- + 8H_2O = 12H_3PO_4 + 20NO$$

Two methods for the industrial production of the acid are in use.

1. An 85% solution of phosphoric acid is obtained by the reaction of concentrated sulfuric acid with calcium phosphate (rock phosphate or bone ash).

$$Ca_3(PO_4)_2 + 3H_2SO_4 = 3CaSO_4 + 2H_3PO_4$$

This is the form in which the acid ordinarily is used; because of its viscous nature it is commonly called "syrupy" phosphoric acid.

2. Some orthophosphoric acid is made commercially by the combustion of phosphorus vapor in air; the (V) oxide thus formed, or else obtained from calcium phosphate and sand in the electric furnace, is allowed to dissolve in water.

$$4P + 5O_2 = P_4O_{10}$$

$$2Ca_3(PO_4)_2 + 6SiO_2 = 6CaSiO_3 + P_4O_{10}$$

$$P_4O_{10} + 6H_2O = 4H_3PO_4$$

Because of the stepwise ionization of phosphoric acid, there are three series of orthophosphates known. Examples of each series, with the corresponding names, are listed in Table 28.7; it will be noted that there are several ways of naming these substances.

The alkali metal phosphates and the primary alkaline earth metal phosphates are readily soluble in water, but the other metal phosphates dissolve to only a slight extent. Even the less soluble phosphates dissolve readily in acid solutions because of the tendency for the phosphate and monohydrogen phosphate ions to take up protons.

As would be expected from the small degree of ionization of dihydrogen phosphate and monohydrogen phosphate ions, soluble tertiary phosphates and, to a lesser extent, soluble secondary phosphates undergo a considerable degree of hydrolysis in water, yielding alkaline solutions.

$$PO_4^{---} + H_2O = HPO_4^{--} + OH^-$$

$$HPO_4^{--} + H_2O = H_2PO_4^- + OH^-$$

Because of the strongly alkaline nature of its aqueous solution, tertiary sodium phosphate is an excellent cleansing agent and is used in considerable amounts for this purpose.

Table 28.7

Sodium and Calcium Orthophosphates

	Sodium Salt		*Calcium Salt*
NaH_2PO_4	Monosodium phosphate Sodium dihydrogen phosphate Primary sodium phosphate	$Ca(H_2PO_4)_2$	Primary calcium phosphate
Na_2HPO_4	Disodium phosphate Sodium monohydrogen phosphate Secondary sodium phosphate	$CaHPO_4$	Secondary calcium phosphate
Na_3PO_4	Trisodium phosphate Tertiary sodium phosphate Normal sodium phosphate	$Ca_3(PO_4)_2$	Tertiary calcium phosphate

The most important use of phosphates is in the production of fertilizer. Tertiary calcium phosphate, $Ca_3(PO_4)_2$, which occurs in nature and is marketed as rock phosphate, is too slightly soluble in water to be of much value as a fertilizer. When rock phosphate is treated with sulfuric acid, however, a mixture of the more soluble primary calcium phosphate, $Ca(H_2PO_4)_2$, and calcium sulfate is obtained.

$$Ca_3(PO_4)_2 + 2H_2SO_4 + 4H_2O = Ca(H_2PO_4)_2 + 2(CaSO_4 \cdot 2H_2O)$$

This product, commonly known as "superphosphate of lime," is used in tremendous quantities as a fertilizer. Sodium and ammonium phosphates are likewise important as fertilizers. Primary calcium phosphate is used in certain types of baking powder (p. 653). Phosphates are used also in the weighting of silk, as well as in the fireproofing of certain fabrics.

The phosphate ion is capable of taking part in the formation of a number of complex compounds. For example, the addition of excess phosphoric acid to a solution of a ferric salt results in the formation of soluble complexes such as $H_3[Fe(PO_4)_2]$ and $H_6[Fe(PO_4)_3]$. When a solution containing phosphate ion is treated with a solution of ammonium molybdate in nitric acid solution, a yellow precipitate of ammonium phosphomolybdate is obtained. This substance has an exceedingly complex structure, and its exact nature is still a matter of controversy. Its composition corresponds approximately to the empirical formula $(NH_4)_3PO_4 \cdot 12MoO_3 \cdot 3H_2O$. A number of other phosphomolybdates, as well as a series of phosphotungstates, are known also. The formation of a yellow precipitate of ammonium phosphomolybdate is used as an analytical test for phosphate ion; phosphate cannot be distinguished from arsenate (p. 526) by this means, however, for the latter ion forms a similar yellow precipitate of the arsenomolybdate under the same conditions. Another reaction which is useful as a test for phosphate ion is the formation with silver nitrate solution of a yellow precipitate of tertiary silver phosphate, Ag_3PO_4.

15. Peroxyphosphoric Acids. Two acids of phosphorus are known which are analogous to peroxymonosulfuric and peroxydisulfuric acids (p. 462). They have the formulas H_3PO_5 and $H_4P_2O_8$ and are called, respectively, peroxymonophosphoric acid and peroxydiphosphoric acid. Their electronic formulas follow:

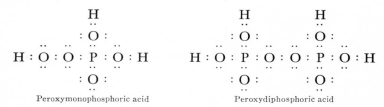

Peroxymonophosphoric acid   Peroxydiphosphoric acid

By virtue of the peroxy group which they contain, these compounds are strong oxidizing agents. They are prepared by methods analogous to those used for the peroxysulfuric acids.

16. The Sulfides of Phosphorus. The sulfides of phosphorus are not analogous to the oxides, and in fact do not, in general, correspond to the usual oxidation states. A considerable number of these sulfides have been reported, among which P_4S_3, P_4S_5, P_4S_7, and P_4S_{10} are the best known.

The first of these, tetraphosphorus trisulfide, P_4S_3, is obtained commercially by heating phosphorus and sulfur together in the correct proportions in an atmosphere of carbon dioxide. It is a yellow solid which, after purification, melts at $171°-172.5°$ C. to a brownish yellow liquid. This compound finds industrial application in the manufacture of matches. The heads of the earliest friction matches to be manufactured contained white phosphorus. This use of white phosphorus was forbidden by law, however, both because of the fire hazard created by such matches and because of the disastrous effect of the phosphorus vapor on the health of the workmen in the match factories. Prolonged exposure to phosphorus vapor brings about a decay or necrosis of the bones, commonly known as "phossy jaw" since it is the jaw-bone that is especially attacked.

The modern nonsafety or "strike anywhere" match is constructed as follows. The end of the stick is coated with paraffin, then with a mixture of an oxidizing agent such as potassium chlorate and combustible materials such as paraffin and sulfur; glue is added as a binding agent, and usually there is, in addition, a filler such as clay or starch, and an abrasive such as ground glass. The tip of the match contains also tetraphosphorus trisulfide, which ignites from the heat developed by friction when the match is struck.

Safety matches, which will not strike readily, contain instead of the phosphorus sulfide a less readily ignited material, usually antimony (III) sulfide, Sb_2S_3. Such matches are ignited by being rubbed against the side of the box, which is coated with a mixture of glue, an abrasive, an oxidizing agent, and red phosphorus. When the match is struck a trace of the red phosphorus is ignited, and this sets fire to the matchhead.

STUDY QUESTIONS AND PROBLEMS

1. If 33.6 liters of phosphorus vapor at 546° C. and 1 atm. pressure weighs 62 g., what is the formula of the phosphorus molecule at this temperature?

2. A solution of 31 g. of white phosphorus in 1000 g. of carbon disulfide has the same freezing point as a solution of 11.5 g. of C_2H_6O in 1000 g. of carbon disulfide. What is the formula for the phosphorus molecule in the solution?

3. Give balanced equations for the commercial preparation of white phosphorus. How is red phosphorus obtained?

4. Contrast the chemical behavior of phosphine and ammonia. Give balanced equations for two methods for preparing phosphine.

5. Which is the weaker acid, PH_4^+ or NH_4^+? Give the experimental evidence for your answer.

6. Write electronic formulas for hypophosphorous, phosphorous, orthophosphoric, and peroxymonophosphoric acids. Contrast the acidic and oxidation-reduction characteristics of these acids. For example, explain why H_3PO_2 is only monobasic, etc.

7. Defend the statement: The phosphorus trihalides are covalent compounds. Cite experimental evidence.

8. Under what definition of acids and bases could the reaction of metal oxides with molten sodium metaphosphate to form colored beads be considered an acid-base reaction? Explain.

29

Arsenic, Antimony, and Bismuth

1. Other Elements of Group 5a. The fact that the elements of Group 5a show a distinct increase in metallic character with increase in atomic number was mentioned at the beginning of Chapter 26. It has been shown in the last three chapters that the properties of nitrogen and phosphorus and their compounds are in accord with this statement. The properties of arsenic, antimony, and bismuth, the last three members of the group, and their compounds, further demonstrate this trend. Like phosphorus, these three elements most commonly exhibit the oxidation states -3, $+3$, and $+5$.

2. History. Though the ancient Greeks and Romans were familiar with a substance known to them as "arsenic," they were unacquainted with the free element. The "arsenic" of their day was a mixture of naturally occurring, poisonous, arsenic sulfides, which was mined by slave labor at the cost of a heavy loss in life. It is not known with certainty who first isolated free arsenic, but credit for this achievement is often given to the German monk Albertus Magnus (1193–1280).

That antimony sulfide was known to the ancients is clear from very early records which indicate that oriental women used the sulfide as a cosmetic for darkening the eyebrows. The metal, also, was almost certainly obtained at that time, but was confused with lead.

Bismuth was likewise obtained in ancient times, although it was not at first distinguished from lead and tin. It was not until about the middle of the eighteenth century that bismuth was recognized as a distinct element and its properties described.

3. Occurrence and Preparation of the Elements. In marked contrast to phosphorus, the elements arsenic, antimony, and bismuth sometimes occur in the free state. The principal ores of arsenic are sulfides: orpiment, As_2S_3, realgar, As_4S_4, and arsenopyrite, FeAsS. Almost invariably arsenic sulfides occur to some extent wherever other metal sulfides are found; hence, arsenic is a common impurity in those metals that are obtained from sulfide ores. Other arsenic minerals include audetite, As_2O_3, and metal arsenides such as $FeAs_2$, $CoAs_2$, and NiAs.

The principal ore of antimony is stibnite, Sb_2S_3, although, as was stated above, the element is sometimes found in the free state. Considerably more than half of the world's supply of antimony is produced in China.

Bismuth, which is by far the least abundant of the three elements, occurs principally as bismuthinite, Bi_2S_3, as bismite, Bi_2O_3, and as bismutite, a carbonate.

These three elements may be obtained from their oxide ores by reduction of these ores with carbon; e.g.,

$$As_4O_6 + 6C = As_4 + 6CO$$

The sulfide ores may be roasted to the oxide and then reduced with carbon.

$$2Sb_2S_3 + 9O_2 = Sb_4O_6 + 6SO_2$$

$$Sb_2O_3 + 3C = 2Sb + 3CO$$

or, in the case of stibnite, the ore may be reduced directly with iron. Two easily separable liquid layers are thus formed, one consisting of antimony metal and the other of ferrous sulfide.

$$Sb_2S_3 + 3Fe = 2Sb + 3FeS$$

Because of its low melting point, bismuth may be obtained from its native ores simply by heating; this melts the bismuth metal, which flows off, leaving rocky impurities behind.

The total amounts of bismuth and antimony produced annually are approximately 2000 and 30,000 tons, respectively.

4. Properties and Industrial Applications. The trend toward metallic properties in this family is markedly illustrated by the physical, as well as the chemical, properties of the elements.

Arsenic exists in two distinct crystalline forms, known respectively as yellow arsenic and metallic arsenic. The yellow form is soft and has the comparatively low density of 3.9 g. per cc. It is obtained when arsenic vapor is passed into cold carbon disulfide and the solution is cooled to $-70°$ C. This form is extremely volatile, subliming even from the heat of the hand. It is metastable and passes rapidly into the metallic form even at low temperature; in sunlight, at room temperature, the change is instantaneous. The molecular weight of yellow arsenic in solution corresponds to the formula As_4 and its structure may be presumed to be analogous to that of P_4 (p. 502). Metallic arsenic consists of silvery gray crystals that have a density of 5.73 g. per cc.; it is very brittle, and, although a good conductor of heat, is a rather poor conductor of electricity. Metallic arsenic sublimes without melting when heated at 610° C. at atmospheric pressure.

Antimony, likewise, exists in a yellow form and also in a metallic form. The yellow form is so unstable that it can be kept only at very low temperatures. Metallic antimony is a silvery white, brittle substance, much less volatile than metallic arsenic, and has a density of 6.7 g. per cc. It melts at 630.5° C. and boils at 1440° C.

Bismuth is the most distinctly metallic element in this group and is known in only one form. This is a light gray metal with a slight pinkish tinge, hard, brittle, and a poor conductor of heat. It melts at 271.3° C. and boils at 1477° C. Its density at 20° C. is 9.80 g./cc.

A number of applications of arsenic compounds are discussed later in the chapter. Metallic arsenic is used in the manufacture of certain types of bronzes (p. 765), as well as other varieties of alloys. Its presence in these alloys increases their fluidity, luster, strength, and hardness. Arsenic is used also in the manufacture of lead shot. In this process, molten lead is poured through a screen, and the liquid is thus broken up into drops, which are allowed to fall through a tower into water. A freely falling liquid body tends to assume a spherical form; the presence of arsenic in the lead increases the fluidity of the metal and thus allows a higher percentage of the drops to attain a spherical form before solidification.

More than half of the antimony consumed in the United States is used in the manufacture of lead storage batteries (p. 434). Lead containing some antimony is harder than ordinary lead, and more resistant to the action of acids; these qualities make it desirable for the construction of storage battery plates. Antimonial lead is used also for bullets and bearings. Because of their low melting points, and the fact that they expand on solidification, lead alloys containing from 15 to 30% of antimony are used as type-metal; the expansion produces a sharp outline in the type.

Bearing-metal alloys usually consist of relatively hard crystals imbedded in a softer matrix. The hard crystals bear the load, while the softer metal wears away slightly, affording shallow valleys through which lubricant films are replenished. An important group of bearing-alloys are the white bearing-metals, of which Babbitt metal is an example. All of these alloys contain antimony, together with one or more of the following: copper, tin, and lead.

The antimony is a minor constituent, usually not exceeding 15% of the alloy, but it provides some of the hard crystals which support the load.

Metallic bismuth also is used in certain types of bearing-metal alloys. More important, however, is its application in the manufacture of low-melting alloys for use in electrical fuses, automatic fire alarms, automatic sprinkler systems (Figure 29.1), safety plugs on boilers, etc. Two examples of these alloys are Wood's metal, which consists of four parts of bismuth, two parts of lead, and one part each of tin and cadmium, and melts at 71° C.; and Rose's metal, which consists of two parts of bismuth and one part each of lead and tin, and melts at 91° C. Because of its very low tendency to absorb neutrons, bismuth alloys are being investigated for use as coolants in atomic piles (p. 149).

5. Hydrogen Compounds. Like nitrogen and phosphorus, the three heavier elements of the nitrogen family form compounds with hydrogen

Fig. 29.1. Safety-valve on an automatic sprinkler system.

which have electronic structures, compositions, and molecular weights corresponding to the general formula

$$H : \overset{\cdot\cdot}{M} : H$$
$$H$$

These are called arsine (AsH_3), stibine (SbH_3), and bismuthine (BiH_3), respectively. Some of the more important physical constants of these compounds are listed in Table 29.1.

Table 29.1
Physical Constants of the Hydrogen Compounds

	NH_3	PH_3	AsH_3	SbH_3	BiH_3
Melting point, °C.	−77.74	−132.5	−119	−88	?
Boiling point, °C.	−33.4	− 86.2	− 55	−18	?
Heat of formation, cal./mole	11,040	2,210	−41,000	−34,000	?
Oxidation potential, volts					
($XH_3 = X + 3H^+ + 3e^-$)	−0.27	0.07	0.60	0.51	>0.8

As the elements become more metallic, we should expect their covalent compounds with hydrogen to become less stable. That this is the case is illustrated by the fact that the heats of formation of the hydrides of the heavier elements of the family are much lower than for ammonia and phosphine, and, in fact, are negative. Bismuthine, the last member of the series, is such an extremely unstable compound that almost nothing is known of its properties. As would be expected, the reducing properties of these compounds increase with their increasing tendency to decompose into the free element and hydrogen (see oxidation potentials in Table 29.1). All these hydrides are colorless, and extremely poisonous, even in small amounts.

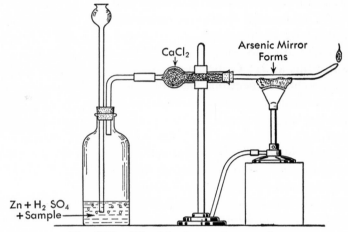

Fig. 29.2. The Marsh test for arsenic.

Two methods are available for the preparation of these compounds, (1) the hydrolysis of metallic arsenides, stibides, or bismuthides:

$$Mg_3Bi_2 + 6H_2O = 3Mg(OH)_2 + 2BiH_3$$

$$Zn_3Sb_2 + 6H_2O = 3Zn(OH)_2 + 2SbH_3$$

$$Na_3As + 3H_2O = 3Na^+ + 3OH^- + AsH_3$$

and (2) the reduction, by active metals in acid solution, of compounds of the elements in the higher oxidation states. As an example of the latter method, we may cite the fact that when a solution of a soluble arsenite (p. 525) in sulfuric acid is treated with metallic zinc, arsine gas is produced and is discharged along with the hydrogen formed by reaction of the zinc with the acid.

$$AsO_3^{---} + 9H^+ + 3Zn = AsH_3 + 3Zn^{++} + 3H_2O$$

Stibine may be obtained in the same manner; the production of bismuthine, however, requires the use of a more active metal, such as magnesium.

The second of these reactions, along with the relatively easy thermal decomposition of arsine and stibine, is used as the basis for an exceptionally sensitive test for these elements, known as the Marsh test. A solution of the substance to be tested is added to a flask containing zinc (or some other active metal) and an acid. If arsenic or antimony is present, the corresponding hydrogen compound is produced and leaves the flask through a calcium chloride drying tube, as shown in Figure 29.2. The delivery tube is heated at some point beyond the drying tube; if one of the hydrides is present, it decomposes at this point to give a mirror-like deposit, shiny black in the case of arsenic, brownish black in the case of antimony. The arsenic mirror is easily soluble in hypochlorite solutions. The antimony mirror is not.

6. Halogen Compounds. Arsenic and antimony form halogen compounds corresponding to the types MX_3 and MX_5, but the complete series corresponding to the latter formula has not been prepared. Antimony forms only the pentafluoride and the pentachloride, and arsenic only the pentafluoride. A series of trihalides of bismuth are known, but no pentahalides. These halogen compounds are volatile liquids or solids, except for the trihalides of bismuth, which have melting points above 200° C., and arsenic pentafluoride, which is a gas at room temperature.

As in the case of the phosphorus halides, these compounds can be prepared by direct union of the elements. Another method which can be used is the reaction of the oxide or sulfide with the halogen; e.g.,

$$2Bi_2O_3 + 6Br_2 = 4BiBr_3 + 3O_2$$

The physical properties of most of these compounds clearly indicate them to be covalent. The halides of arsenic and antimony are soluble in nonpolar solvents such as benzene and carbon disulfide; the bismuth halides, however, being more polar than those of arsenic and antimony, do not dissolve in such solvents.

In this connection it is interesting to consider the hydrolysis of the trichlorides of these elements. We have already seen (p. 507) that phosphorus trichloride is vigorously and completely hydrolyzed in accordance with the equation

$$PCl_3 + 3H_2O = H_3PO_3 + 3H^+ + 3Cl^-$$

Furthermore, this reaction is not reversible with any attainable concentration of hydrochloric acid. The reaction in the case of arsenic trichloride is analogous to the above, but in this case it may be reversed if sufficiently high concentrations of hydrogen chloride are used. In the case of antimony and bismuth trichlorides only two-thirds of the chlorine is involved in the hydrolysis, which yields oxychlorides. The reactions are reversible as is indicated by the following equations:

$$SbCl_3 + 2H_2O \rightleftharpoons [Sb(OH)_2Cl] + 2H^+ + 2Cl^-$$
$$\longrightarrow SbOCl_{(s)} + H_2O$$

$$BiCl_3 + 2H_2O \rightleftharpoons [Bi(OH)_2Cl] + 2H^+ + 2Cl^-$$
$$\longrightarrow BiOCl_{(s)} + H_2O$$

It is apparent from these statements that we have here another manifestation of the increase in metallic characteristics in the series $P < As < Sb < Bi$, for, as the element becomes more metallic, its halogen compounds become more saltlike, and their tendency toward hydrolysis—i.e., the tendency for the ion of the element to form a covalent bond with a hydroxide ion from water (p. 237)—decreases.

7. +3 Oxides and Their Hydrates. Arsenic and antimony each form a $+3$ oxide having the general formula M_4O_6, with a structure presumably analogous to that of P_4O_6 (p. 508); the corresponding bismuth compound, however, being more nearly ionic, is best represented by the empirical formula Bi_2O_3. These compounds are obtained when the elements are burned in air; since these elements, unlike phosphorus, do not form $+5$ oxides by direct union with oxygen, an excess of air is not harmful. They may also be prepared by roasting the sulfides in air, or by heating the corresponding oxide hydrates; e.g.,

$$2Sb_2S_3 + 9O_2 = Sb_4O_6 + 6SO_2$$

$$2BiO(OH) = Bi_2O_3 + H_2O$$

Each of these three oxides occurs in more than one crystalline form; at room temperature, all forms of the arsenic and antimony compounds are white solids, whereas bismuth (III) oxide is yellow.

Arsenic (III) oxide or arsenious oxide, As_4O_6, which is sold under the name of "white arsenic" and is often erroneously referred to simply as "arsenic," is commercially the most important of the arsenic compounds; about 60,000 tons are produced annually. It is a violent poison, and more than half of the annual production in this country is used in the preparation of insecticides, weed killers, certain types of glass, and organic arsenic medicinals.

In contrast to phosphorus (III) oxide, arsenic (III) oxide is only slightly soluble in water, although it does give a slightly acidic solution; antimony and bismuth (III) oxides are even less soluble.

The reactions of these oxides with solutions of acids and alkalis provide an interesting example of the manner in which acidic and basic properties of the oxides of the elements of a given family change from the top to the bottom of the periodic chart. We have seen already that the +3 oxides of nitrogen and phosphorus dissolve in water to form acidic solutions. That arsenic (III) oxide, likewise, has acidic properties is indicated by the fact that it readily dissolves in solutions of alkalis to form salts called arsenites. Arsenic (III) oxide, however, is somewhat amphoteric (p. 204), as shown by the fact that its solubility in water is increased by the presence of hydrogen ion, even in moderate concentrations, though to a much lesser extent than it is by hydroxide ion. Antimony (III) oxide is definitely amphoteric, dissolving readily in either acids or alkalis. Bismuth (III) oxide, on the other hand, is insoluble in alkalis, but readily dissolves in acids; this shows it to be definitely, though weakly, basic. These relationships, and the types of products obtained in the various reactions, are summarized in Table 29.2. Thus it is clear that, as the metallic nature of the element increases with increasing atomic number, there is a concurrent increase in the basicity, or decrease in the acidity, of the corresponding oxides.

Table 29.2

| Oxide | Product obtained from solution | | Nature of oxide |
	in acids	in alkalis	
N_2O_3	....	Nitrites	Acidic
P_4O_6	....	Phosphites	Acidic
As_4O_6	Compounds such as $AsCl_3$, which are hydrolyzed except in very highly acidic solution	Arsenites	Weakly acidic
Sb_4O_6	Basic salts only, such as $(SbO)_2SO_4$	Antimonites	Amphoteric
Bi_2O_3	Both basic salts such as $(BiO)_2SO_4$ and normal salts such as $Bi(NO_3)_3$	....	Weakly basic

The formulas for the numerous arsenites and antimonites are characterized by great variety and complexity; in fact, in many instances they have not been very well established. Arsenites, because of their highly poisonous nature, are extensively used as insecticides and weed killers. Paris green, $Cu_2(C_2H_3O_2)(AsO_2)_3$, and Scheele's green, $CuHAsO_3$, are important both as insecticides and as pigments.

Basic antimony salts containing the group SbO are known as antimonyl compounds. They may be obtained by the action of water on normal antimony compounds.

$$SbCl_3 + H_2O = SbOCl_{(s)} + 2H^+ + 2Cl^-$$

They may also be crystallized from solutions of antimony (III) oxide in the appropriate acid.

$$Sb_4O_6 + 4H^+ + 4NO_3^- = 4SbONO_3 + 2H_2O$$

Potassium antimonyl tartrate, $K(SbO)C_4H_4O_6$, is used in medicine under the name of tartar emetic.

Basic bismuth salts containing the group BiO are sometimes known as bismuthyl compounds. They are formed whenever normal bismuth salts are brought in contact with water.

$$Bi^{+++} + H_2O = BiO^+ + 2H^+$$

The sulfate, $(BiO)_2SO_4$, and the chloride, $BiOCl$, are examples. Large quantities of basic bismuth salts are prepared for pharmaceutical purposes. These substances are mildly astringent and form protective coatings over the gastro-intestinal tract when taken internally. Examples are the basic nitrate and the basic carbonate, known as bismuth subnitrate and subcarbonate, respectively. Bismuth compounds are also used in cosmetics and as antisyphilitic drugs. A precipitate of bismuthyl hydroxide, $BiO(OH)$, is obtained when solutions of bismuth salts are treated with alkalis.

8. +5 Oxides and Their Hydrates. In accord with the increasing difficulty in oxidizing the elements to the +5 oxidation state, the +5 oxides of arsenic, antimony, and bismuth cannot be obtained by direct union of the elements with oxygen. Arsenic (V) oxide, As_4O_{10}, is obtained as a white powder when its hydrate, crystalline orthoarsenic acid, $2H_3AsO_4 \cdot H_2O$, is heated; this latter substance is prepared by evaporation of the solution obtained by the action of nitric acid on arsenic (III) oxide. Numerous salts of arsenic acid, i.e., arsenates, have been prepared; these are similar to the corresponding phosphates in solubility and crystalline form. Like other arsenic compounds, they are highly poisonous; lead and calcium arsenates are widely used as insecticides.

Antimony (V) oxide, Sb_4O_{10}, a pale yellow powder, is obtained in a manner analogous to the preparation of arsenic (V) oxide. Free antimonic acid, however, has not been prepared. A "hydrated" antimony (V) oxide is precipitated when solutions of antimonates are treated with strong acids, but this precipitate is not of constant composition, and appears to be the +5 oxide with more or less absorbed water. Antimonates are known, however, whose formulas indicate that they are derived from an acid of the formula $HSb(OH)_6$; among these are the salts $KSb(OH)_6$ and $NaSb(OH)_6$. This latter salt is one of the least soluble of all sodium salts, and its precipitation is sometimes used as a test for sodium ion.

A solution of antimonic acid is a good oxidizing agent, as is indicated by the oxidation potential for the half-reaction

$$SbO^+ + 5H_2O = HSb(OH)_6 + 3H^+ + 2e^-; E = -0.58 \text{ v.}$$

An oxide, Sb_2O_4, which appears to be an antimonous antimonate, $Sb[SbO_4]$, is obtained as an impurity in the +3 oxide formed when antimony is burned in air. This substance is obtained also when the +3 oxide is heated in air to 300° to 400° C.

Bismuth (V) oxide, Bi_2O_5, is a reddish brown powder obtained by the action of very strong oxidizing agents, such as peroxysulfates and hypochlorites, upon suspensions of bismuth (III) oxide in weakly alkaline solutions. Bismuthic acid is unknown, but the +5 oxide dissolves in concentrated sodium hydroxide solutions to yield sodium metabismuthate, $NaBiO_3$, commonly known simply as sodium bismuthate. This yellow-brown substance is an extremely strong oxidizing agent in acid solution, as is indicated by the highly negative oxidation potential for the following half-reaction:

$$BiO^+ + 2H_2O = HBiO_3 + 3H^+ + 2e^-; E = ca. -1.6 \text{ v.}$$

For example, bismuthate ion in acid solution will oxidize manganous ion to permanganate (p. 714).

9. **Sulfides and Thiosalts.** Arsenic and antimony form both +3 and +5 sulfides, corresponding to the formula M_2S_3 and M_2S_5, respectively. These are usually obtained by precipitation with hydrogen sulfide; e.g.,

$$2H_3AsO_4 + 5H_2S = As_2S_{5(s)} + 8H_2O$$

$$2SbCl_3 + 3H_2S = Sb_2S_{3(s)} + 6H^+ + 6Cl^-$$

The arsenic sulfides are yellow in color, the antimony compounds orange. These sulfides are soluble in concentrated acids; $12M$ hydrochloric acid, however, attacks arsenic sulfide only slowly. The sulfides, like the oxides, are readily soluble in basic solutions; they dissolve readily, for example, in solutions of sodium hydroxide. Of particular interest is their ready solubility in solutions of sulfides or hydrosulfides to yield thiosalts.

$$As_2S_3 + 3S^{--} = 2AsS_3^{---}$$
$$\text{thioarsenite}$$

$$As_2S_5 + 6HS^- = 2AsS_4^{---} + 3H_2S$$
$$\text{thioarsenate}$$

$$Sb_2S_3 + 6HS^- = 2SbS_3^{---} + 3H_2S$$
$$\text{thioantimonite}$$

$$Sb_2S_5 + 3S^{--} = 2SbS_4^{---}$$
$$\text{thioantimonate}$$

This reaction is used, in many qualitative analytical procedures, for the separation of the sulfides of arsenic, antimony, and tin from the sulfides of mercury, lead, copper, bismuth, and cadmium.

When heated, the sulfides of arsenic and antimony combine directly with other metallic sulfides to yield thiosalts; e.g.,

$$As_2S_5 + 3MgS = Mg_3(AsS_4)_2$$

In addition to the $+3$ sulfide and $+5$ sulfide, arsenic forms also a red sulfide of the formula As_4S_4, which occurs in large quantities in nature as the mineral realgar. When orange-colored, precipitated antimony (III) sulfide is heated above $220°$ C., it turns black and acquires the lustrous appearance of natural stibnite (p. 519). When solutions of bismuth salts are treated with hydrogen sulfide, bismuth sulfide, Bi_2S_3, is formed as a black precipitate. This compound also occurs in nature as the mineral bismuthinite. It dissolves in concentrated acids, but not in bases (cf. bismuth (III) oxide, p. 525).

STUDY QUESTIONS AND PROBLEMS

1. Outline the industrial preparations of arsenic, antimony, and bismuth; give the chief industrial applications and the physical or chemical properties upon which these applications are based.

2. How do the properties of the allotropic forms of antimony indicate that it is more metallic than arsenic?

3. Describe and give equations for the Marsh test for arsenic.

4. Complete and balance the following equations:

$$AsO_4^{---} + H^+ + H_2S =$$
$$As_2S_3 + S^{--} =$$
$$Sb_2S_5 + S^{--} =$$
$$BiCl_3 + H_2O =$$

5. How can antimonate ion have the formula $Sb(OH)_6^-$, whereas arsenate ion is AsO_4^{---}?

6. Discuss the trends in properties of the compounds of the Group 5a elements in the $+3$ oxidation state in the series N, P, As, Sb, and Bi.

Carbon and Silicon

1. General Characteristics of Group 4a. The elements of Group 4a of the periodic system are carbon, silicon, germanium, tin, and lead. Their electronic configurations and ionization potentials are listed in Table 30.1. As is shown in the table, atoms of each of the elements of this family have four valence electrons. Thus, this group of elements stands at a sort of halfway point between the halogens, whose atoms lack but a single electron of an inert gas

Table 30.I

	1	2	3	4	5	6	Ionization Potentials			
Element	s	s p	s p d	s p d f	s p d	s p	1st	2nd	3rd	4th
C	2	2, 2					11.3	24.4	47.9	64.5
Si	2	2, 6	2, 2				8.1	16.3	33.4	45.1
Ge	2	2, 6	2, 6, 10	2, 2			8.1	15.9	34.1	45.4
Sn	2	2, 6	2, 6, 10	2, 6, 10	2, 2		7.3	14.5	30.5	39.4
Pb	2	2, 6	2, 6, 10	2, 6, 10, 14	2, 6, 10	2, 2	7.4	15.0	31.9	42.1

configuration with a stable outer shell of eight electrons, and the alkali metals, whose atoms have but one electron in their valence shells and are able to attain inert gas configurations by losing that electron. As would be expected from this fact, and from the relatively large amount of energy required for the removal of the four valence electrons, the elements of Group 4a do not form simple quadruply charged positive ions. In fact, they show little tendency to form simple positive ions of any type; although, as will be pointed out in a later chapter, the heavier members of the group do form positively charged complex ions. Nor is there any appreciable tendency for the members of this family to take up four electrons per atom to form ions of the type M^{4-}. Rather, the overwhelming majority of the bonds that atoms of these elements form are of the covalent type, wherein electrons are shared by the combined atoms. Thus, e.g., the tetrahalides of these elements are all gases, liquids, or easily melted, volatile solids.

With the exception of lead and tin, the elements of Group 4a are, in the vast majority of their compounds, quadricovalent; i.e., they form four covalent bonds per atom. As defined in terms of the admittedly arbitrary conventions set down in Chapter 12, the oxidation state of the Group 4a element in these quadricovalent compounds may vary from -4 to $+4$ (p. 213).

The normal effect of increasing atomic number may be observed again in this group, the ionization potentials decreasing with increasing atomic number—except in the case of lead (see p. 814). There is a corresponding change in the physical and chemical properties of the elements and their compounds: carbon is mainly nonmetallic in its physical properties, and its oxide is weakly acidic; silicon is less nonmetallic and its oxide less acidic; germanium, tin, and lead have the physical properties of metals and their oxides continue to exhibit the trend toward increasing basicity. These relationships may be summarized as follows:

$$\text{C} \qquad \text{Si} \qquad \text{Ge} \qquad \left\{ \begin{array}{l} \text{Sn} \\ \text{Pb} \end{array} \right.$$

$$\xrightarrow{\hspace{4cm}}$$

increasing metallic
characteristics

$$\text{CO}_2 \qquad \text{SiO}_2 \qquad \text{GeO}_2 \qquad \left\{ \begin{array}{l} \text{SnO}_2 \\ \text{PbO}_2 \end{array} \right.$$

$$\xrightarrow{\hspace{4cm}}$$

decreasing acidity
increasing basicity

This trend is manifested further in the fact that, as the atomic number increases, there is an increasing tendency for the elements to react with nonmetals such as chlorine, and a decrease in the stability of the compounds of the elements with hydrogen. Thus, we have the series

$$\text{CH}_4 \quad \text{SiH}_4 \quad \text{GeH}_4 \quad \text{SnH}_4 \quad \text{PbH}_4$$

$$\xrightarrow{\hspace{4cm}}$$

decreasing stability

Because of the shift from nonmetallic to metallic characteristics with increasing atomic number, we shall find it convenient to discuss carbon and silicon in this chapter, and to postpone a consideration of the more metallic elements germanium, tin, and lead to a later point in the text.

CARBON

2. Introduction. More than nine-tenths of all known compounds contain carbon. The chemistry of the hundreds of thousands of carbon compounds constitutes in itself an important branch of chemical science. This branch is usually known as organic chemistry, because the materials of which living organisms, both plant and animal, are constituted consist almost entirely of compounds of carbon. The reasons for the great number and variety of carbon compounds are discussed in the next chapter.

3. Occurrence. Carbon is found in nature in both the elementary and the combined state. Although it is estimated that the earth's crust contains only about 0.03% of carbon, this small amount of the element is nevertheless of very great importance, for, as has been stated, most of the structural materials of which all living organisms are composed are compounds of carbon. Furthermore, the common fuels wood, natural and artificial gas, and petroleum, consist primarily of carbon compounds; coal contains both free carbon and carbon compounds. All our foods of animal or vegetable origin are also composed of compounds of carbon. Vast deposits of metal carbonates, particularly those of calcium and magnesium, are found in the earth's crust in the form of the sedimentary rocks limestone and dolomite (p. 666).

4. Allotropic Modifications of Elementary Carbon. Considerable variety is observed in the properties of the several forms of free carbon obtained from various natural and artificial sources, and there is by no means complete agreement among chemists as to the number of distinct solid forms of this element that exist. All authorities agree that there are two distinct crystalline modifications, *diamond* and *graphite;* and to these two, many chemists add a third form, noncrystalline or at least containing only extremely small or microcrystals. This third form, commonly known as amorphous carbon, is considered by some to consist of very small crystals of graphite, but from a practical point of view it is convenient to consider amorphous carbon as a separate form. Certain varieties of carbon may best be regarded as consisting of mixtures of graphite and amorphous carbon in various proportions.

In the form of diamond, carbon is a colorless, transparent solid, with a density of 3.51 g. per cc., and an extremely high index of refraction. In the diamond crystal, each carbon atom is connected by means of a single covalent bond to each of four other atoms located at the corners of a regular tetrahedron (Figure 30.1); thus the whole crystal must be considered as a single molecule (p. 190). As a result of the strong bonds uniting all the atoms in the crystal into a single unit, diamond is the hardest known substance, and its melting point ($>3500°$ C.) is probably higher than that of any other element. Since all the valence electrons of the carbon atoms are

tied down in covalent bonds, the diamond crystal is a nonconductor of electricity. By virtue of the high refractive index of diamond, white light passing through the crystal is broken up into its component colors and these components are highly dispersed; this gives the crystal a great deal of sparkle or "fire." On this account, and also because of its durability, rarity, and low chemical reactivity, diamond is highly prized as a gem stone. Various modes of cutting diamonds so as to enhance their brilliance and fire are illustrated by the drawings in Figure 30.2.

Fig. 30.1. Crystal structure of diamond.

Diamonds are found in a number of localities, but the two principal diamond producing regions are situated in South Africa and Brazil. Because of the inclusion of various impurities, there are red, yellow, green, blue, and

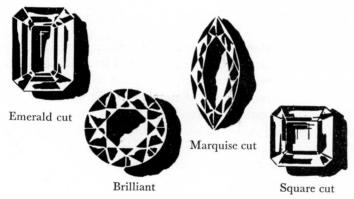

Emerald cut

Marquise cut

Brilliant

Square cut

Fig. 30.2. Illustrating the more common cuts for diamonds. (*Courtesy of H. E. Hawk, Argo & Lehne Jewelers, Columbus, Ohio.*)

even black diamonds, as well as the colorless variety. Diamonds weighing as much as 630 g. (almost $1\frac{1}{2}$ lb.) have been found in nature, but only very small ones have been produced in the laboratory.

It is difficult to imagine two allotropic forms of an element that would differ more drastically than do graphite and diamond. Graphite is a rather soft, gray-black solid (Figure 30.3) which has a density of 2.25 g. per cc., and is a fair conductor of electricity (1/1000 as good as copper). These properties are in accord with the structure illustrated in Figure 30.4. As shown in this figure, each carbon atom in graphite is connected to three other atoms in the same plane by means of strong covalent bonds; thus, layers are formed which are composed of hexagonal rings of carbon atoms. These layers are connected to each other by means of longer, more tenuous bonds, involving the fourth valence electron of some of the carbon atoms. The weakness of these interplanar bonds makes it easy for the planes to slide

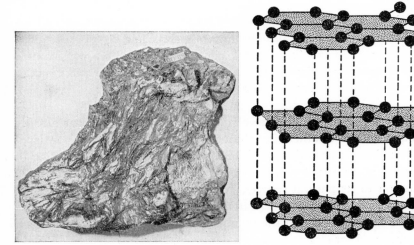

Fig. 30.3.   A piece of mineral graphite.   Fig. 30.4.   Crystal structure of graphite.

over one another, and thus accounts for the softness and the greasy, slippery feel of a graphite crystal. The electrical conductivity may be interpreted as resulting from the fact that the valence electrons in the graphite type of crystal are not completely employed in bond formation, and may move, therefore, when subjected to the influence of an electrical field. Though such data are subject to considerable uncertainty, a melting point of 3500° C. is reported for graphite, and the boiling point of carbon is listed as 4830° C.

Graphite is obtained chiefly from mines in Ceylon and in Madagascar, although it is found in smaller quantities in New York and elsewhere in the United States. Several amorphous carbons are known, among which charcoal is one of the most familiar. Other amorphous forms include lampblack, formed by the incomplete combustion of liquid hydrocarbons (p. 563), carbon black, formed when a flame of burning natural gas is allowed to play upon a cold metal surface, and coke, produced as a residue in the destructive distillation of coal. An outstanding property of the various amorphous forms of carbon, and particularly of charcoal, is their exceptionally high adsorptive capacity. This adsorptive capacity of charcoal may be increased by treatment with steam or with air–steam mixtures for long periods at high temperatures; this increases the porosity, and also brings about the removal of adsorbed hydrocarbons. Charcoal thus treated is known as activated charcoal and has a number of important uses. One cubic centimeter of activated charcoal is estimated to have a surface area of 10,000,000 sq. cm.

The various types of coal are composed largely of amorphous carbon; anthracite or "hard" coal contains the highest percentage of this substance. Bituminous or ordinary "soft" coal contains in addition considerable quantities of complex hydrocarbons, as well as carbon compounds containing oxygen, nitrogen, and some other elements.

5. Preparation and Uses. The use of diamonds as gem stones has already been discussed. Black or otherwise inferior grades of diamonds are powdered and used as abrasive material, particularly for the cutting and grinding of diamonds and other gem stones.

In addition to its natural sources, graphite is made artificially in large quantities by heating anthracite (hard coal) in an electrical furnace. The artificial product is utilized in the manufacture of crucibles for use at high temperatures, and for electrodes for arc lamps and electric furnaces. Graphite, usually mixed with clay in varying proportions, is the black pigment used in lead pencils; the larger the proportion of graphite, the softer is the "lead." Because of the ease with which the planes of carbon atoms in a particle of graphite slide over one another, graphite flakes or suspensions of graphite in oil or water are useful as lubricants in some types of machinery. Granular activated charcoal, because of its adsorptive power, finds an important application in gas masks for the removal of toxic substances from the air that passes through the canister of the mask. Bone charcoal, a mixture of carbon and calcium phosphate obtained by the destructive distillation of bones, is used to remove dark-colored impurities from solutions of unrefined sugar. Carbon black, prepared as described above from natural gas, has a number of uses, the most important of which is in the compounding of rubber for tires. Carbon black also constitutes the pigment used in India inks, printer's ink, stove polish, shoe blacking, and most black paints.

6. Reactions of Elementary Carbon. At ordinary temperatures, carbon is an unreactive substance. However, at elevated temperatures it undergoes numerous reactions. When heated in the presence of oxygen (or air) carbon reacts to form a mixture of carbon monoxide, CO, and carbon dioxide, CO_2, the extent of the oxidation depending upon the concentration of oxygen and also upon the temperature. These reactions are highly exothermic and, once started, are self-sustaining. It is on this account that coal and other highly carbonaceous materials are so valuable as fuels.

When heated to a sufficiently high temperature, carbon combines directly with sulfur to form carbon disulfide, with fluorine to form carbon tetra-fluoride, and with many of the metals to form a variety of metal carbides. All of these compounds will be discussed in the paragraphs that follow.

7. Oxides of Carbon. At temperatures in the neighborhood of 500° C., carbon (even though in excess) reacts with oxygen to yield practically pure carbon dioxide.

$$C + O_2 = CO_2$$

At 1000° C., however, the monoxide is almost the only product of the reaction of carbon (in excess) with oxygen.

$$2C + O_2 = 2CO$$

This last statement is equivalent to saying that at such high temperatures carbon dioxide reacts almost completely with carbon to yield the monoxide.

$$C + CO_2 = 2CO$$

When an excess of oxygen is present, however, except at extremely high temperatures, both carbon and carbon monoxide are oxidized completely to the dioxide, the equation for the latter reaction being

$$2CO + O_2 = 2CO_2$$

Since its reaction with oxygen is highly exothermic (67,630 cal. per mole of carbon monoxide consumed), carbon monoxide has considerable value as a fuel. Artificial fuel gases which contain carbon monoxide as an important component include *water gas* (which was discussed in Chapter 13), *producer gas*, made by the passage of air in limited quantities through red-hot coke or anthracite, and *blast furnace gas*, which consists of the exhaust gases from the smelting of iron ore (p. 741).

Carbon monoxide will remove oxygen from many metal oxides at high temperatures; e.g.,

$$FeO + CO = Fe + CO_2$$

It is, therefore, an effective reducing agent and is widely used for this purpose in metallurgy.

Carbon monoxide is a colorless, odorless gas, which condenses to the liquid state under 1 atm. pressure at $-190°$ C.; this liquid solidifies at $-205°$ C. The carbon monoxide molecule is commonly represented as a resonance hybrid of the following structures:

$$\{: C : : : O :, \quad : C : : O \overset{..}{}, \quad : C : \overset{..}{\underset{..}{O}} :\}$$

Carbon monoxide is only slightly soluble in water at atmospheric pressure and does not, under ordinary conditions, react with water. It does, however, react with sodium or potassium hydroxide, at slightly elevated temperatures, to form the corresponding formate (p. 581).

Carbon monoxide reacts with many metals to produce volatile compounds of the type formula $M_x(CO)_y$, such as $Mo(CO)_6$, $Fe(CO)_5$, $Ni(CO)_4$, $Co_2(CO)_8$, and $K_6(CO)_6$; these compounds are known as metal carbonyls. Nickel carbonyl is of a special importance, since it is made use of in the Mond process for the metallurgy of nickel (p. 723). Carbon monoxide is able also to form coordinate covalent bonds, presumably through the unshared pair of electrons on the carbon atom, with many metal ions; such carbonyl complexes as $[Cu(CO)Cl_2]^-$ and $[Fe(CO)(CN)_5]^{---}$ are thus obtained.

In the presence of sunlight, or of a catalyst such as activated charcoal, carbon monoxide reacts with chlorine to form carbonyl chloride or phosgene, $COCl_2$. This is a colorless, highly poisonous gas of characteristic odor, which, during World War I, was widely used in chemical warfare. Phosgene is the acid chloride of carbonic acid, to be described in the next section.

Carbon monoxide is extremely poisonous; its lethal effect results from the fact that it combines with the hemoglobin of the blood and thus renders the red blood cells incapable of fulfilling their functions as carriers of oxygen. A concentration of 1 part of carbon monoxide in 100 parts of air will cause death if breathed for only a few minutes. Since appreciable quantities of carbon monoxide are present in the exhaust gas from gasoline engines, it is very dangerous to remain in a closed garage in which an automobile engine is left running.

Recent studies of the carbon dioxide molecule indicate that it is best represented as a resonance hybrid of the following structures:

$$\left\{ :\ddot{O}:C:::O:, \quad \dot{O}::C::\dot{O}, \quad :O:::C:\ddot{O}: \right\}$$

This oxide is a colorless and odorless gas at room temperature. The vapor pressure of solid carbon dioxide reaches 760 mm. at a temperature of $-78.5°$ C., which is well below the melting point; hence, at atmospheric pressure the solid passes directly into the gaseous state (sublimes) at a temperature of $-78.5°$ C. The liquid form may exist, however, under increased pressure; the melting point is $-56°$ C. under a pressure of 5.1 atm. The critical temperature of the compound is $31.35°$ C. and its critical pressure, 73 atm.

There are several other reactions, besides the combustion of carbon in an excess of oxygen, that yield carbon dioxide. Among these are (1) the reaction of carbonates with acids

$$MgCO_3 + 2H^+ = Mg^{++} + CO_2 + H_2O$$

(2) the thermal decomposition of carbonates or of bicarbonates

$$CaCO_3 = CaO + CO_2$$

$$2NaHCO_3 = Na_2CO_3 + CO_2 + H_2O$$

(3) the alcoholic fermentation of sugars

$$C_6H_{12}O_6 = 2C_2H_5OH + 2CO_2$$

and (4) the combustion of various compounds of carbon.

$$C_7H_{16} + 11O_2 = 7CO_2 + 8H_2O$$
heptane

Carbon dioxide is handled commercially in the liquid state in steel cylinders. When liquid carbon dioxide is allowed to flow from such a cylinder through a valve into a heavy cloth bag, the absorption of heat by the rapid evaporation of part of the liquid is sufficient to cool a large portion of the remainder to a temperature below $-78.5°$ C., when it solidifies in the form of carbon dioxide "snow." Carbon dioxide is only moderately soluble in water at ordinary pressures. However, as the pressure of carbon dioxide is increased above 5 atm., its solubility increases more rapidly than would be predicted by Henry's law (p. 282) because of its partial reaction with water to form carbonic acid.

$$H_2O + CO_2 = H_2CO_3$$

The occurrence of carbon dioxide in the atmosphere was discussed in Chapter 21, where it was pointed out that a balance between taking up of carbon dioxide by green plants, on the one hand, and its release by animal organisms and oxidation of carbonaceous fuels, on the other hand, maintains a rather constant carbon dioxide content of 0.03 to 0.04% in dry country air.

Fig. 30.5. A liquid carbon dioxide fire extinguisher.

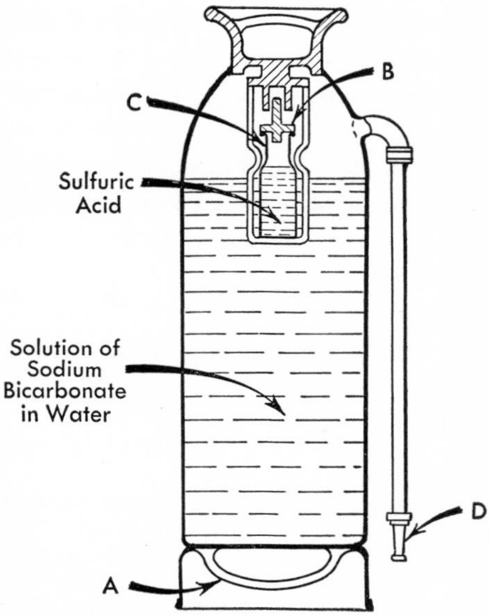

Fig. 30.6. A sodium bicarbonate type fire extinguisher.

Carbon dioxide and water are converted by a very complex and little understood process in green plants to plant carbohydrates such as cellulose, starches, and sugars (p. 596). This process, known as photosynthesis, is endothermic, the energy being furnished by the sun. When plant or animal tissues decompose, carbon dioxide is returned to the air; this continuous absorption and evolution of carbon dioxide in nature is known as the carbon cycle, and may be thought of as one means by which solar energy is made available for animal use.

The principal industrial application of carbon dioxide is in the manufacture of carbonated beverages. Solid carbon dioxide is used as a refrigerant under the name of dry ice. Since it passes directly from the solid to the gaseous state without liquefying, substances packed in dry ice may be shipped in paper cartons, rather than in the heavy, cumbersome containers required when ordinary ice is used for this purpose. Moreover, the use of dry ice makes possible the maintenance of much lower temperatures with smaller weights and volumes of refrigerant than is possible with ordinary ice.

Carbon dioxide does not support combustion, and is widely used as a fire extinguishing agent. Extinguishers employing carbon dioxide are of two types: (1) those containing liquid carbon dioxide (Figure 30.5), and (2) those containing two solutions which, when mixed, produce carbon dioxide. One of the latter type is illustrated in Figure 30.6. When this type of extinguisher is inverted, the sulfuric acid in the inner container mixes with the sodium bicarbonate solution in the outer container, and a stream of foam containing carbon dioxide is produced by the resulting reaction. The carbon dioxide, being heavier than air, blankets the fire and prevents the access of oxygen.

A few very active metals such as magnesium and zinc react with carbon dioxide at high temperatures to produce the metal oxide and free carbon. When carbon dioxide passes through a layer of red-hot coal or coke, carbon monoxide is formed.

$$C + CO_2 = 2CO$$

This reaction occurs in the manufacture of producer gas (p. 535).

8. Carbonic Acid, Carbonates, and Bicarbonates. The fact that carbon dioxide dissolves in water to yield a solution of carbonic acid, H_2CO_3, has already been mentioned. Carbonic acid is, however, a very unstable compound; it is unknown in the free state and, even in solution, is undoubtedly partially decomposed according to the equation

$$H_2CO_3 \rightleftharpoons H_2O + CO_2$$

The solution contains an equilibrium mixture of the solutes H_2CO_3, CO_2, and HCO_3^-, CO_3^{--}, and hydrogen ions. Thus the acid is diprotic, with the following equilibrium constants:

1. $CO_2 + H_2O \rightleftharpoons H^+ + HCO_3^-$ $K_1 = \dfrac{[H^+][HCO_3^-]}{[CO_2]} = 4.2 \times 10^{-7}$

2. $HCO_3^- \rightleftharpoons H^+ + CO_3^{--}$ $K_2 = \dfrac{[H^+][CO_3^{--}]}{[HCO_3^-]} = 4.8 \times 10^{-11}$

On the assumption of complete reaction of carbon dioxide with water to form carbonic acid, the first reaction is commonly written $H_2CO_3 \rightleftharpoons H^+$

+ HCO_3^-. Since, however, a fraction (whose magnitude is not known) of the carbon dioxide remains in the form of free CO_2, the actual ionization constant of carbonic acid must be somewhat larger than the value given for K_1.

Carbonic acid forms two series of salts: (1) carbonates, such as Na_2CO_3 and $CaCO_3$, and (2) bicarbonates, such as $NaHCO_3$ and $Ca(HCO_3)_2$. All the carbonates, except those of the alkali metals, either are only slightly soluble in water or else undergo hydrolysis to give slightly soluble hydroxides or basic carbonates. Bicarbonates in general are more soluble.

The carbonate ion may be represented as a resonance hybrid of the equivalent structures:

$$\left\{ \; \overset{:\ddot{O}:}{\underset{:\ddot{O}:}{\overset{}{C}}} \overset{:\ddot{O}:}{} {}^{--} \; , \; \overset{:\ddot{O}:\;\ddot{O}:}{\underset{:\ddot{O}:}{\overset{}{C}}} {}^{--} \; , \; \overset{:\ddot{O}:\;\;:\ddot{O}:}{\underset{:\ddot{O}:}{\overset{}{C}}} {}^{--} \; \right\}.$$

Because of the tendency for the carbonate ion to take up protons, solutions of carbonates are strongly basic.

$$CO_3^{--} + H_2O = HCO_3^- + OH^-$$

For example, the concentration of hydroxide ion in 0.5 molar sodium carbonate solution is about 0.01 molar; i.e., the solution has a pH of 12. Similarly, bicarbonate ion can also take up protons, and since this tendency predominates over its tendency to give them up, solutions of bicarbonates are likewise basic, although much less so than carbonates at the same concentration.

$$HCO_3^- + H_2O = H_2CO_3 + OH^-$$

A $1M$ solution of sodium bicarbonate is $2 \times 10^{-6}M$ in hydroxide ion.

Since bicarbonate ions can both gain and release protons, two such ions can react with each other according to the equation

$$2HCO_3^- \rightleftharpoons H_2CO_3 + CO_3^{--}$$

The magnitude of the equilibrium constant for this reaction is such that in $1M$ sodium bicarbonate solution the concentrations of carbonate ion and of carbonic acid are each about $0.01M$. This equilibrium explains the fact that carbonates are readily converted to bicarbonates by an increase in the concentration of carbon dioxide (and hence of carbonic acid) in the solution. Likewise, bicarbonates are readily converted to carbonates on being heated.

$$2MHCO_3 = M_2CO_3 + CO_2 + H_2O$$

Carbonates are obtained when solutions of hydroxides are treated with equivalent amounts of carbon dioxide.

$$2OH^- + CO_2 = CO_3^{--} + H_2O$$

When an excess of carbon dioxide is passed into the solution, however, carbonate is converted to bicarbonate as explained in the preceding paragraph.

Many of the slightly soluble carbonates may be prepared by precipitation. However, when a solution of one of the heavy metal ions is treated with an alkali carbonate solution there are three possible courses which the reaction may take: (1) the carbonate of the metal may be precipitated; (2) the hydroxide ion from the hydrolysis of the carbonate ion may cause the precipitation of the metal hydroxide (or hydrous oxide); or (3) a mixture of the hydroxide and the carbonate, or a basic carbonate, may be formed. Which process takes place in any particular case depends upon the relative solubilities of the hydroxide and the carbonate of the metal. In the case of triply or quadruply charged ions such as Fe^{+++}, Cr^{+++}, Al^{+++}, or Ti^{++++}, the hydrous oxide is obtained almost exclusively. Bismuth, cupric, magnesium, zinc, cobalt, and nickel salt solutions yield basic carbonates; calcium, strontium, and barium yield the normal carbonates. Normal carbonates of metals which would otherwise yield basic carbonates may sometimes be obtained by use of an alkali bicarbonate solution (which contains a much lower hydroxide ion concentration than the carbonate solution).

Carbonate ion may be detected by utilization of the fact that solutions containing this ion, on acidification, release odorless carbon dioxide gas, which gives a white precipitate with lime-water (p. 691).

9. Carbon Disulfide. When carbon and sulfur are heated together in an electric furnace, a compound of the formula CS_2, called carbon disulfide, is obtained. This substance is a colorless, highly inflammable liquid, with a not unpleasant odor. On standing in the light it undergoes slow decomposition, acquiring a yellow color and a very disagreeable odor. Carbon disulfide boils at 46.3° C., freezes at −111.6° C., and has a very high refractive index. Its electronic structure, represented as the resonance hybrid

$$\left\{ : \overset{..}{\underset{..}{S}} : C ::: S :, \quad \overset{.}{S} :: C :: \overset{..}{\underset{.}{S}}, \quad : S ::: C : \overset{..}{\underset{..}{S}} : \right\}$$

is analogous to that of carbon dioxide, as are many of its chemical properties. This analogy is illustrated by the following reaction:

$$CO_2 + BaO = BaCO_3 \qquad CS_2 + BaS = BaCS_3$$

barium
thiocarbonate

Carbon disulfide is insoluble in water; it is a good solvent for nonpolar substances, such as sulfur, phosphorus, and the halogens, but does not dissolve salts.

10. Carbides. When heated to a sufficiently high temperature, many metals react with carbon to form binary compounds called carbides. The alkali and alkaline earth metals give carbides corresponding to the general formulas M_2C_2 and MC_2, respectively. Because these compounds yield acetylene,

Fig. 30.7.   Crystals of carborundum.

C_2H_2 (p. 568), on reaction with water, they are more accurately called acetylides. Beryllium and aluminum form the compounds Be_2C and Al_4C_3, which, upon hydrolysis, give methane, CH_4. Many of the other carbides, such as ThC_2, Fe_3C, Ni_3C, Cr_3C_2, W_2C, VC, TaC, B_4C, and Mo_2C, have formulas which are difficult to explain in terms of ordinary electronic structures.

In general, the carbides are characterized by highly crystalline structure and (except as noted) low chemical reactivity. Among those which are especially hard and inert are SiC, TiC, HfC, ThC, TaC and W_2C. Some of these compounds are used as abrasive materials, some for the cutting edges of high-grade machine tools. Perhaps the most important of the carbides are calcium carbide, CaC_2, and silicon carbide or carborundum, SiC. Calcium carbide is made by heating calcium oxide with carbon, usually in the form of coke, to a temperature of about 3000° C. in an electric furnace.

$$CaO + 3C = CaC_2 + CO$$

It is the source of two widely used industrial chemicals, acetylene (p. 568) and calcium cyanamide (p. 479). Carborundum is obtained in a similar manner by heating sand, SiO_2, with carbon in an electrical resistance furnace at about 3500° C.

$$SiO_2 + 3C = SiC + 2CO$$

The product (Figure 30.7) is blue-black, iridescent, and almost as hard as diamond; it is widely used as an abrasive in whetstones and grinding wheels.

11. Cyanogen, Hydrocyanic Acid, and the Cyanides. The simplest binary compound of carbon and nitrogen is a colorless gas whose composition and density correspond to the formula $(CN)_2$, and which is known as cyanogen. Cyanogen, like most other compounds containing the CN radical, is exceedingly poisonous. It is obtained by the thermal decomposition of cyanides of the less active metals.

$$Hg(CN)_2 = Hg + (CN)_2$$

$$2Cu^{++} + 4CN^- = 2CuCN + (CN)_2$$

Cyanogen can act as an oxidizing agent, and otherwise resembles the halogens so closely in its chemical properties that it is sometimes called a pseudo-halogen. The following equations illustrate some of the similarities:

$$Cl_2 + 2OH^- = Cl^- + OCl^- + H_2O$$

$$(CN)_2 + 2OH^- = CN^- + OCN^- + H_2O$$

$$2K + Cl_2 = 2KCl$$

$$2K + (CN)_2 = 2KCN$$

Hydrogen cyanide or hydrocyanic acid, HCN, sometimes called prussic acid, is liberated when metal cyanides are treated with dilute sulfuric acid, since the former acid is both volatile and very weak. (Concentrated sulfuric acid cannot be used for this purpose, since it converts hydrogen cyanide to carbon monoxide.) Hydrogen cyanide is a deadly poison; the pure liquid boils at 26.5° C., yielding a colorless gas with the odor of bitter almonds. It is readily soluble in water, and its ionization constant in aqueous solution at 25° C. is 4×10^{-10}. Solutions of hydrogen cyanide react with basic hydroxides to yield solutions of cyanides.

$$HCN + OH^- = CN^- + H_2O$$

As the conjugate base of a weak acid, cyanide ion is a relatively strong base; solutions of cyanides therefore undergo partial hydrolysis, and are alkaline.

A number of processes have been developed for the production of sodium and potassium cyanides, among which are the following:

(1) fusion of alkali metal ferrocyanides (p. 727) with sodium:

$$K_4Fe(CN)_6 + 2Na = 4KCN + 2NaCN + Fe$$

(2) heating of a mixture of the ferrocyanide with the alkali metal carbonate and carbon:

$$2K_4Fe(CN)_6 + 2K_2CO_3 + C = 12KCN + 2Fe + 3CO_2$$

(3) heating of alkali metal carbonate, powdered coal, and nitrogen in the presence of an iron catalyst:

$$Na_2CO_3 + 4C + N_2 = 2NaCN + 3CO$$

(4) fusion of calcium cyanamide with sodium carbonate and carbon.

$$Na_2CO_3 + CaNCN + C = 2NaCN + CaCO_3$$

Sodium and potassium cyanides are important industrial chemicals; they are used in the metallurgy of silver and gold (p. 765), and in the case-hardening of steel (p. 754). Calcium cyanide is used as a source of hydrogen cyanide for the extermination of vermin.

The cyanide ion has a strong tendency to react with metal ions to form complexes. Complex ions of the types $M(CN)_4^{-4+n}$ and $M(CN)_6^{-6+n}$, where n is equal to the positive charge on the metal ion M, are very common. A number of these complexes are mentioned throughout the text.

12. Cyanates and Thiocyanates. The action of certain mild oxidizing agents on cyanides results in the formation of cyanates. Two such reactions are

$$KCN + PbO = KOCN + Pb$$
$$\text{potassium}$$
$$\text{cyanate}$$

and

$$2Cu(NH_3)_4^{++} + 3CN^- + 2OH^- = 2CuCN_{(s)} + OCN^- + 8NH_3 + H_2O$$

Ammonium cyanate, NH_4OCN, on being heated, rearranges into urea, $CO(NH_2)_2$, which has the same molecular formula as ammonium cyanate but a different structural formula. Compounds that have this relationship are said to be *isomeric* (p. 563).

Thiocyanates are prepared by the fusion of mixtures of cyanides and sulfur.

$$NaCN + S = NaSCN$$

Ammonium thiocyanate, NH_4SCN, on being heated to $140°$ C., rearranges to the isomeric thiourea.

$$NH_4SCN = CS(NH_2)_2$$

This is analogous to the corresponding rearrangement of the cyanate.

SILICON

13. Discovery. Although certain compounds of silicon, which occur abundantly in nature, inevitably attracted attention many centuries ago, the free element was unknown until 1823, when the great Swedish chemist Berzelius obtained it by reduction of potassium fluosilicate, K_2SiF_6, with metallic potassium.

14. Occurrence. Elementary silicon does not occur in nature, but compounds of that element with oxygen and the metals are so abundant that silicon is estimated to constitute about 26% of the earth's crust; thus, silicon is second in abundance only to oxygen among the elements. Silicon dioxide and the silicates, discussed later in the chapter, make up about 87% of the material of the earth's crust. Silicon thus occupies a position in the mineral world comparable in importance to that of carbon in the animal and vegetable kingdoms. Silicon is not entirely absent from the organic world, either, for small quantities of the element are found in many plants, while the skeletons of certain marine animals are composed largely of silicon dioxide.

15. Physical and Chemical Properties, Preparation, and Uses. Two apparently distinct forms of elementary silicon are known. Amorphous (microcrystalline) silicon, a brown powder, is obtained by the reduction of silicon halides with alkali metals at high temperatures, or by the reduction of the dioxide with magnesium.

$$SiCl_4 + 4Na = Si + 4NaCl$$
$$SiO_2 + 2Mg = Si + 2MgO$$

Crystalline silicon, which is semimetallic in properties, having a steel-gray luster and a fairly high electrical conductivity, is obtained by the reduction of sodium fluosilicate with an excess of metallic aluminum.

$$3Na_2SiF_6 + 4Al = 2Na_3AlF_6 + 3Si + 2AlF_3$$

Industrially, crystalline silicon is made by the reduction of the dioxide with carbon in an electric furnace.

$$SiO_2 + 2C = Si + 2CO$$

This process is similar to that employed in the manufacture of silicon carbide, except that smaller quantities of carbon (coke) are used in the production of silicon.

Some of the important physical properties of elementary silicon are summarized in Table 30.2. (The electronic configuration and ionization potentials were given in Table 30.1, p. 529.)

Table 30.2

Physical Properties of Silicon

Melting point	1410° C.
Boiling point	2480° C.
Density (crystalline form)	2.32 g./cc.
Ionic radius (Si^{4+})	0.41 Å

Although silicon is somewhat more metallic than carbon, the fact that its oxide and hydrous oxide are weakly acidic nevertheless demands that the element be classed among the nonmetals. Like carbon, silicon forms binary compounds with both metals and nonmetals, the amorphous variety being somewhat more reactive than the crystalline. When heated with the halogens, oxygen, nitrogen, or sulfur, silicon forms the corresponding binary compound. On the other hand, silicon reacts with many molten metals to form a variety of silicides. It does not react with acids, but it does dissolve in solutions of alkali hydroxides with the evolution of hydrogen (p. 222).

$$Si + 2OH^- + H_2O = SiO_3^{--} + 2H_2$$

Silicon is used industrially chiefly in the form of the iron–silicon alloy known as ferrosilicon, which is prepared by the joint reduction of oxides of iron and silicon with carbon in an electric furnace. It is used in the production of metallic magnesium (p. 664), and is used also in the steel industry, both as a "scavenger" to remove dissolved gases such as oxygen from the steel (p. 751), and as an alloying element. In this latter capacity, silicon up to a content of 5% is added to steel to produce cores for electromagnets and transformers. A silicon content of 14% makes steel highly resistant to corrosion by air or acids; such alloys are of great value in acid manufacturing plants. Silicon is added also to a number of nonferrous alloys in order to bring about desirable modifications in their properties. The principal use of pure silicon is in transistors and rectifiers.

16. Hydrosilicons. In the next chapter we shall see that carbon forms a vast variety of compounds with hydrogen, known as hydrocarbons. Silicon likewise forms compounds with hydrogen, which are known as hydrosilicons. However, because the silicon to silicon bond is much more reactive than the carbon to carbon linkage, as well as for certain other reasons, these compounds are both much less stable and less numerous than the hydrocarbons, though the physical properties of the two groups of compounds are comparable. Hydrosilicons corresponding to the general formula Si_nH_{2n+2}, where n is 1 to 8, have been prepared by such methods as the action of acids on metal silicides. The lowest member of this series, SiH_4, is called silane; like the other hydrosilicons, it ignites spontaneously in air.

17. Halides of Silicon. As pointed out in a previous section, silicon reacts directly with all of the halogens to form halides of the general formula SiX_4. The tendency for this reaction to occur decreases in the order $F > Cl > Br > I$, and the stability of the halides obtained decreases in the same order, SiF_4 being the most stable. Silicon and iodine react only at red heat. The halides of silicon differ from those of carbon (p. 565) in that the former, on contact with water, undergo vigorous hydrolysis to give hydrous silicon dioxide and the corresponding hydrogen halide.

$$SiCl_4 + (x+2)H_2O = SiO_2 \cdot xH_2O_{(s)} + 4H^+ + 4Cl^-$$

Silicon tetrafluoride is not hydrolyzed so readily; in fact, silicon dioxide and the silicates dissolve in aqueous hydrofluoric acid to produce silicon tetrafluoride (p. 396).

Silicon tetrafluoride at room temperature is a colorless gas, which, in the absence of hydrogen fluoride, reacts with water to produce a precipitate of hydrous silicon dioxide and a solution of fluosilicic acid, H_2SiF_6.

$$3SiF_4 + (x+2)H_2O = SiO_2 \cdot xH_2O_{(s)} + 4H^+ + 2SiF_6^{--}$$

Fluosilicic acid is a strong acid. Fluosilicate ion has the structure

$$\left[\begin{array}{ccc} \ddot{}\,F\,\ddot{} & & \ddot{}\,F\,\ddot{} \\ :F: & Si & :F: \\ \ddot{}\,F\,\ddot{} & & \ddot{}\,F\,\ddot{} \end{array} \right]^{--}$$

Silicon tetrachloride, a volatile liquid, is obtained industrially by the reaction of chlorine with a hot mixture of carbon and silicon dioxide.

$$SiO_2 + 2C + 2Cl_2 = SiCl_4 + 2CO$$

Higher silicon chlorides corresponding to the general formula Si_nCl_{2n+2} are also obtained in this reaction. Since it fumes vigorously in moist air, silicon tetrachloride is sometimes used for the production of smoke screens.

18. Silicides. The binary compounds formed by the reaction of silicon with metals at high temperatures are similar to the carbides in physical properties and in the fact that many of them have formulas that are not explainable in terms of the usual types of chemical bonds. Examples of the variety of silicides known are Li_3Si, Mg_2Si, Fe_2Si, Ni_2Si, $MnSi$, $CoSi$, $PbSi$, $CaSi_2$, $SrSi_2$, USi_2, and $CoSi_3$. Silicon carbide, SiC, has already been discussed.

19. Oxides of Silicon. Like carbon, silicon forms both a monoxide and a dioxide. Silicon monoxide is formed by the reaction of carbon with an excess of silicon dioxide at 2000° C., followed by rapid cooling.

$$SiO_2 + C = SiO + CO$$

The substance is a hard solid, yellowish brown in color; it finds some industrial application as a pigment and an abrasive.

Fig. 30.8. A large quartz crystal.

Silicon dioxide, SiO_2, commonly known as silica, occurs in nature in a wide variety of crystal forms and modifications. The three distinct crystal forms of the substance are quartz, cristobalite, and tridymite, each of which has several minor modifications. Quartz is the form which is stable at room temperature; however, the rate of transition from one form to the other is so slow in the absence of catalysts that all three crystal forms occur in nature. Silica may be obtained also in the form of a supercooled liquid or glass (p. 65).

Naturally occurring silicon dioxide in its various forms, among the more familiar of which are sand, flint, and agate, constitutes about one-eighth of the earth's crust. Very large crystals of pure quartz are sometimes found in nature (Figure 30.8). Some of the less pure varieties of silicon dioxide minerals are very beautiful, particularly when polished, and are highly prized for their decorative value. Among such minerals are agate, jasper, and onyx. Quartz is somewhat harder than ordinary window glass; it is further characterized by high transparency to electromagnetic radiation in the wide range from the near infrared region to ultraviolet waves of very high frequency. Since ordinary glass is opaque to ultraviolet light, quartz is used in many optical instruments where transparency to light of such short wave length is necessary. The melting point of quartz is not known exactly, but it is estimated to be in the range from 1600° to 1670° C. Liquid silica is viscous,

Fig. 30.9. Crystal structure of SiO_2. (Redrawn from Wells, *Structural Inorganic Chemistry,* by permission of the Clarendon Press, Oxford, England.)

and when its temperature is lowered it has a strong tendency to supercool, forming quartz glass. This glass, because of its very low coefficient of expansion (i.e., its very small change in volume with changing temperature), is extremely useful for the construction of certain types of chemical apparatus. Even red-hot quartz glass may be plunged into water without cracking.

These physical characteristics of silicon dioxide make it evident that the structure of this compound must differ markedly from that of carbon dioxide. Crystals of the latter substance consist of individual CO_2 molecules held together by weak van der Waals forces; solid carbon dioxide is thus highly volatile. In contrast, however, a crystal of silicon dioxide contains no individual SiO_2 molecules but is composed of a continuous lattice of silicon and oxygen atoms connected by highly polar covalent bonds. The geometry of this lattice, in each of the crystal forms, is such that each silicon atom is attached to four oxygen atoms, and each oxygen atom to two silicon atoms; a diagram of such an arrangement is shown in Figure 30.9. In order that silicon dioxide may be melted, many of these relatively strong bonds must be broken. Thus, solid silicon dioxide is characterized by low volatility and a high degree of hardness. Since the bonds in silicon dioxide are highly polar, crystals of this type may be considered as intermediate between the strictly ionic crystals such as those of sodium chloride, and atomic crystals such as diamond (pp. 186, 190).

Silicon dioxide in any of its various forms is very insoluble in water; it dissolves in solutions of strongly basic hydroxides to form silicates, but is only slightly affected by acids, except hydrofluoric (p. 547).

20. Hydrates of Silicon Dioxide. Silicon dioxide does not combine directly with water as does carbon dioxide. However, if a solution of a soluble silicate is acidified with a strong acid, either a colloidal suspension or a gel (p. 366) of a composition expressed by the formula $(SiO_2)_x(H_2O)_y$ is obtained. When this substance is heated it loses water continuously and gradually until only the dioxide remains. Attempts to prove the existence of definite compounds such as H_4SiO_4 (orthosilicic acid) or H_2SiO_3 (metasilicic acid) have met with only questionable success. Hydrous silicon dioxide, as is indicated by its solubility in alkaline solutions, is indeed acidic, but that it is only weakly so is shown by the high degree of hydrolysis observed in aqueous solutions of the alkali metal silicates.

Hydrous silicon dioxide from which most of the water has been removed has a very high adsorptive power. A product thus prepared is widely used as a dehydrating agent under the name of "silica gel." Other substances adsorbed by silica gel include sulfur dioxide and the vapors of benzene and nitric acid.

21. The Soluble Silicates. The only silicates which are soluble in water are those of the alkali metals. Commercial sodium silicate is prepared by fusion of sodium carbonate with silicon dioxide. The composition of the product varies according to the proportions of the starting materials, so that the reaction may best be represented by the equation

$$Na_2CO_3 + xSiO_2 = Na_2O \cdot xSiO_2 + CO_2$$
(or $Na_2O \cdot CO_2$)

In the commercial product, x usually has a value between 2 and 4, depending upon the use to which the substance is to be put. Sodium silicate is usually sold in the form of its concentrated aqueous solution, a syrupy liquid known as "water glass." Sodium silicates in aqueous solution undergo considerable hydrolysis, and because of their alkalinity are used as cleansing agents. They find application also as adhesives, as waterproofing and fireproofing agents, and in a variety of other ways.

22. The Mineral Silicates. The great abundance of silicate minerals in the earth's crust has already been mentioned, and their quantitative abundance is matched by their great variety and the complexity of their structures. Literally hundreds of mineral silicates are known; among these the feldspars, pyroxenes, micas, zeolites, amphiboles, garnets, talc, and olivine are some of the most common. The empirical formulas for some of these minerals are given in Table 30.3. The elucidation of the structures of such substances as these was a difficult and complex problem; when the clue to its solution was finally discovered, however, it proved to rest upon a relatively simple basis.

Table 30.3

Mineral Silicates

Feldspars:	orthoclase	$KAlSi_3O_8$
	plagioclase	$n(NaAlSi_3O_8) \cdot m(CaAl_2Si_2O_8)$
Pyroxenes:	diopside	$Ca(Mg, Fe)*(SiO_3)_2$
	jadeite	$NaAl(SiO_3)_2$
Micas:	muscovite	$K(OH)_2Al_3Si_3O_{10}$
	biotite	$K(OH)_2(Mg, Fe)_3AlSi_3O_{10}$
Zeolites:	stilbite	$(Na_2, Ca)Al_2Si_6O_{16} \cdot 6H_2O$
	natrolite	$Na_2Al_2Si_3O_{10} \cdot 2H_2O$
Garnets:	almandite	$Fe_3Al_2(SiO_4)_3$
	pyrope	$Mg_3Al_2(SiO_4)_3$
Talc:		$Mg_3(Si_4O_{10})(OH)_2$
Olivine:		$(Mg, Fe)_2SiO_4$

* The symbol (Mg, Fe) indicates one atomic weight of Mg and Fe together, although not in fixed proportions.

According to the present theory of silicate structures—and this theory seems to be pretty well established—the basic structural unit of all silicate minerals is the SiO_4^{----} group, in which each silicon atom is surrounded by four oxygen atoms in such a manner as to form a tetrahedron. The simplest group of silicates are the orthosilicates, such as Zn_2SiO_4, and Be_2SiO_4, which contain discrete SiO_4^{----} anions. An oxygen atom may, however, form a part of more than one such tetrahedron, and as a result other more complex anions may be formed, as is indicated in Figure 30.10. Some of the so-called metasilicates (silicates in which the O to Si atomic ratio is 3:1) actually contain the anion $Si_6O_{18}^{12-}$; e.g., beryl, $Be_3Al_2Si_6O_{18}$. An example of a mineral containing the $Si_3O_9^{6-}$ anion is benitoite. $BaTiSi_3O_9$.

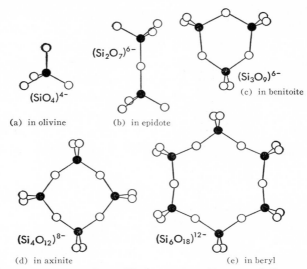

$(Si_2O_7)^{6-}$

$(SiO_4)^{4-}$

$(Si_3O_9)^{6-}$

(c) in benitoite

(a) in olivine   (b) in epidote

$(Si_4O_{12})^{8-}$ $(Si_6O_{18})^{12-}$

(d) in axinite   (e) in beryl

Fig. 30.10. Discrete silicate anions. (Redrawn from Bragg and Bragg, *The Crystalline State,* vol. I, p. 134, by permission of The Macmillan Company.)

Some of the metasilicates contain extended anions of the formula $(SiO_3)_x^{2x-}$ in the form of continuous chains (Figure 30.11). Chains of the type shown in Figure 30.12 are known also. These correspond to the empirical formula $(Si_4O_{11})_x^{6x-}$ and are made up of Si_6O_{18} rings repeated indefinitely. Such extended anion chains are held together by the electro-

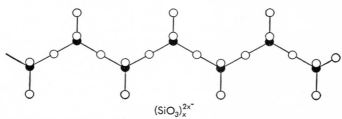

$(SiO_3)_x^{2x-}$

Fig. 30.11. Extended silicate anion (chain) in pyroxene. (Redrawn from Bragg and Bragg, *The Crystalline State,* vol. I, p. 134, by permission of The Macmillan Company.)

static attraction of the metallic (positive) ions in the crystal. Minerals containing these extended anions frequently exhibit a fibrous structure, especially if these chains lie parallel to each other, since the electrostatic attractive forces between the metal ions and the anion chains are less than the forces which unite the atoms in a chain. Asbestos, $CaMg_3(SiO_3)_4$, is an example of such a mineral silicate. Jade also contains extended anions; in this case, however, the mineral fibers are not oriented, but run in all directions.

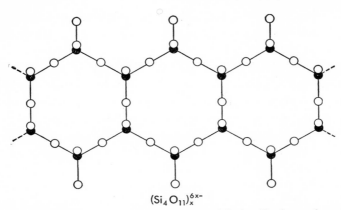

$$(\text{Si}_4\text{O}_{11})_x^{6x-}$$

Fig. 30.12. Extended silicate anion (chain) in amphibole. (Redrawn from Bragg and Bragg, *The Crystalline State*, vol. I, p. 134, by permission of The Macmillan Company.)

Certain other mineral silicates have laminar or sheet-like structures, in which the Si_4O_{11} chains are extended in two dimensions, as shown in Figure 30.13. The empirical formula for such anions is $(\text{Si}_4\text{O}_{10})_x^{4x-}$. The sheets are

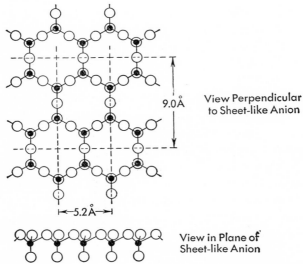

View Perpendicular to Sheet-like Anion

9.0 Å

5.2 Å

View in Plane of Sheet-like Anion

Fig. 30.13. Extended silicate anion (sheet). Muscovite mica has such an anion with ¼ of the Si atoms replaced by Al atoms. (Redrawn from Emeléus and Anderson, *Modern Aspects of Inorganic Chemistry*, by permission of Routledge and Kegan Paul, Ltd.)

held together by the electrostatic attraction of positive ions in the crystal. Such minerals show a pronounced tendency to cleave into thin sheets, since the attractive forces between the extended anion layers and the positive ions are less than the interatomic forces within an anion layer. Examples of this type include talc and the micas; in the latter, however, aluminum is also present.

Aluminum atoms very commonly take the place of some of the silicon atoms in these anions, without appreciable alteration in the structure of the anion. However, since the charge on the aluminum nucleus is one less than on that of silicon, the anion charge is increased by one for every such substitution; this is balanced by the presence of additional metal ions such as Na^+ or Ca^{++}. Reference to Table 30.3 indicates that many of the common minerals are of the aluminosilicate type.

If the process of chaining is extended in three dimensions, an "endless" network having the empirical formula SiO_2 is obtained (cf. Figure 30.9, p. 549). If, however, some of the silicon atoms in this network are replaced by aluminum atoms, the structure becomes electron deficient and requires the presence of Na, K, or Ca to furnish electrons to make up the deficiency. Aluminosilicates belonging to this group include the zeolites and the feldspars. In Table 30.3, it may be seen that the atomic ratio $(Al + Si) : O$ in the formulas for minerals of these two groups is $1 : 2$. The zeolite structure is of an "open" type, containing large cavities and channels which are capable of holding considerable quantities of water. The openings also contain the positive ions which balance the negative charge on the framework; these ions, in zeolites, are readily replaceable by other cations (p. 675).

23. Ceramics. The manufacture of earthenware, bricks, tile, porcelain, terracotta, and pottery from silicate minerals constitutes the large and important ceramics industry. Clay, an impure form of the mineral kaolinite, $H_4Al_2Si_2O_9$, is the most important of minerals used in ceramics. Most types of pottery or bricks are made from naturally occurring clays which contain sand and feldspar. Usually iron oxide is present as an impurity, and hence the product obtained is colored buff or red. The brick, tile, or other ceramic piece is shaped from a plastic mixture consisting of clay and water in the proper proportions, to which quartz, feldspar, or other minerals have been added in the desired amounts. After being dried, the object is placed in a kiln or furnace and heated to a high temperature ("baked" or "fired"). Complex chemical changes take place, in which the mixture changes to a strong, coherent mass. Porcelain and chinaware are made similarly from relatively scarce clays of high purity; since these clays contain no iron or other coloring matter, the products are white. Glazes may be applied to ceramic ware by introducing into the furnace or kiln toward the end of the baking period a substance which will react with the clay at the surface of the piece to give a transparent, nonporous surface layer. Silica brick, containing a very high percentage of SiO_2, is widely used as a refractory material for furnace linings.

24. Glass. Scientifically speaking, the word glass may be applied to any liquid which has been supercooled to a temperature where its viscosity is so great that the substance has the outward physical characteristics of a solid (p. 65). In practice, however, the term glass is usually applied to a noncrystalline, transparent mixture of metal silicates obtained by melting together silicon dioxide, metal carbonates, and other appropriate materials. The common variety of glass, known as "soft" or soda-lime glass, is made by fusing a mixture of calcium carbonate (limestone), sodium carbonate (soda ash), and silicon dioxide (sand). The silicon dioxide displaces the carbon dioxide of both of the carbonates to yield a complex mixture of sodium and calcium silicates. Like other supercooled liquids, glass does not have a definite melting point but gradually softens as it is heated. It is usually formed into the desired shape by use of a blowpipe in the hands of a skilled workman, or by blowing into molds by means of compressed air. In the manufacture of plate glass, however, a mass of hot glass is allowed to flatten out, and is then rolled to the desired thickness. The cooling of glass must be carried out very slowly, i.e., the glass must be annealed, in order to prevent the development of strains due to unequal cooling of various parts of the piece.

Glasses having a wide variety of properties have been prepared. A typical soda glass contains 73% SiO_2, 0.5% Al_2O_3, 8.0% CaO, 3.0% MgO, and 15.5% Na_2O. Pyrex glass, characterized by a low coefficient of thermal expansion and hence a high resistance to cracking on rapid cooling (thermal shock), contains high percentages of acidic oxides and no calcium. A typical Pyrex glass has the composition 80.6% SiO_2, 4.4% Na_2O, 2.0% Al_2O_3, and 13% B_2O_3. Pyrex is also highly resistant to chemical action, and is widely used in laboratory apparatus and in cooking utensils. A glass containing as high as 96% SiO_2 and possessing unusual resistance to thermal shock has been developed. Potash glass (e.g., 80% SiO_2, 0.6% Na_2O, 7% CaO, 12% K_2O, and 0.4% Al_2O_3) is known as hard glass, since it has a higher fusion temperature than soda glass. Flint glass (e.g., 55% SiO_2, 11% K_2O, 33% PbO, and 1% Al_2O_3) has a high density and index of refraction, and is widely used in glass tableware and ornamental "cut" glass, as well as for optical purposes.

In recent years, developments in the production and utilization of glass have come rapidly. To mention only a few of these, we may cite nonshattering safety glass, made by placing sheets of Vinylite plastic (p. 617) between layers of sheet glass, glass bricks for building construction, and glass fibers out of which glass cloth may be spun. Fiber glass and the products made from it have many other important uses, among which heat insulation is one of the most important.

25. Fine-Sized Silica. By a variety of processes involving liquid- or gas-phase precipitation reactions, it has been found to be possible to produce exceedingly finely divided forms of silicon dioxide. These products have very low bulk densities and are useful as fillers for a variety of synthetic materials. Fine-sized silicas are also useful as "flatting agents" for varnishes, to give a dull rather than a shiny gloss to the finished surface.

26. Cracking Catalysts. As is stated in the next chapter (p. 574), one of the processes by which the yield of high octane gasoline from petroleum is increased involves the conversion, at elevated temperatures and in the presence of a catalyst, of high molecular weight hydrocarbons to smaller molecules. This process is known as catalytic cracking. The principal cracking catalysts are either synthetic composites of silica (SiO_2) and alumina (Al_2O_3), or natural aluminosilicates. In addition, cracking catalysts made from silica and magnesia (MgO), silica and zirconia (ZrO_2), or silica, alumina, and zirconia, as well as alumina and boria (B_2O_3), have been employed. One explanation of the catalytic activity of these systems is that the replacement of silicon atoms in the silicon–oxygen network by aluminum or magnesium atoms produces an electron deficient lattice (aluminum has only three and magnesium only two valence electrons, whereas silicon has four), and thus provides, in the Lewis sense (p. 325), an acid center at which the hydrocarbon molecules can react. Zirconium has the same effect because, even though it contains the same number of valence electrons as silicon, zirconium can expand its valence shell and thus act as a Lewis acid.

27. Other Industrial Applications of Silicates. The manufacture and use of Portland cement is discussed in a later chapter (p. 671). Micas find application as insulators, as decorative materials (in paints), and as transparent materials for use at high temperatures. Asbestos is used as a heat insulator and in fireproof fabrics. Talc is an ingredient in talcum powder, and in some soaps, paints, and other products. The use of zeolites as water softeners is discussed later (p. 675). Sand serves as a flux in the manufacture of elementary phosphorus (p. 503), and in many metallurgical processes. These examples illustrate the multitude of practical applications of silicate minerals.

STUDY QUESTIONS AND PROBLEMS

1. Make a table of the electronic configurations of the elements of the carbon family (Group 4a). Discuss the ways in which atoms of these elements enter into chemical combination, the oxidation states which they exhibit, and the general nature of their compounds in terms of these configurations.

2. In what forms does carbon occur in nature? How may free carbon be prepared from natural sources?

3. Make a table contrasting the physical and chemical properties of the two major allotropic modifications of elementary carbon. Explain, in so far as you can, the differences in properties of these two substances in terms of the differences in their structures.

4. Under what conditions is carbon monoxide obtained by the combustion of carbon or its compounds? carbon dioxide? Why is carbon monoxide such a deadly poison?

5. Write the electronic formulas for carbon monoxide and carbon dioxide. Explain why carbon monoxide forms complexes with metals and metal ions whereas carbon dioxide does not.

6. Describe the carbon cycle and explain its fundamental importance to human existence. What are the principal industrial applications of carbon dioxide?

7. Explain briefly why solutions of alkali metal carbonates give aqueous solutions which are alkaline. How may bicarbonates be converted to carbonates? Give two methods.

8. What weight of carbon dioxide can be obtained by the complete combustion of 24 g. of graphite? What volume will this carbon dioxide occupy at 765 mm. pressure and at a temperature of $20°$ C.?

9. Write balanced equations for the industrial preparation of calcium carbide. Write other equations that illustrate the industrial application of this important chemical.

10. Compare the physical properties of silicon dioxide and carbon dioxide. Account for these differences in terms of differences in crystal structure.

11. Make an outline of the various structure types of mineral silicates. Show how our picture of silicate structures accounts for the existence of fibrous silicates such as asbestos, sheet-like silicates such as the micas, and three-dimensional structures such as quartz.

31

The Hydrocarbons and Their Derivatives— Organic Chemistry

1. History and Definition. The early chemists, strongly influenced by the mysticism of alchemy and of the philosophy of their day, thought that the products of plant and animal life differed in some mysterious way from lifeless matter such as rocks and minerals. Chemistry was therefore divided into two broad classifications, the chemistry of minerals, called inorganic chemistry, on the one hand, and the chemistry of substances derived from living matter, called organic chemistry, on the other.

Until slightly over one hundred years ago, it was believed that organic compounds could never be synthesized by the "crude and vulgar inorganic forces" of the laboratory, but were formed only by the action of some "vital force" found in the living plant or animal organism. That this distinction was a false one was first proved in 1824 when the German chemist Friedrich Wöhler (1800–1882) prepared oxalic acid from cyanogen, and again in 1828, when he made urea from ammonium cyanate. Since that time, thousands of organic compounds which occur in living matter or result from life processes have been made in the laboratory and manufactured industrially. Thus, the gulf which separated the two branches of chemistry has been bridged, and it is now recognized that the same fundamental laws and principles apply to both. It soon became apparent, however, that almost all of the typical substances produced by animate nature contained carbon, and the name *organic chemistry* was therefore retained to apply to the study of the compounds of that element. Inorganic chemistry, then, deals with the compounds of all the other elements except carbon.

2. The Multiplicity of Carbon Compounds. Treatment of compounds of carbon as a special class is justified, if for no other reason, by the immense number of carbon compounds known. Up to the present time, over one million organic compounds have been characterized, and new ones are being isolated from natural products and synthesized in the laboratory at an ever increasing rate. The majority of these contain only carbon, hydrogen, oxygen, and nitrogen.

3. Unique Position of Carbon in the Periodic System. One is tempted to wonder by what caprice nature has singled out carbon as the overwhelmingly prolific compound-former of all the elements. The multiplicity of carbon compounds is made possible by the fact that carbon atoms, to an extent unapproached by those of any other element, are capable of sharing electron pairs with one another to form long chain and ring structures, in which the carbon atoms are linked together through covalent bonds. Other elements near carbon in the periodic system, such as silicon, and, to a lesser extent, boron, germanium, tin, lead, and nitrogen, are known to form chains also. But even the silicon chains in compounds thus far reported (see p. 547) reach a maximum of only eight atoms in length, whereas compounds containing hundreds of carbon atoms in a chain are known. Moreover, chains consisting of atoms other than carbon are easily broken by reaction, even at room temperature, with such commonly occurring substances as oxygen or water. Carbon to carbon bonds, on the other hand, are characterized by a remarkable lack of reactivity. Hundreds of thousands of carbon chain and ring compounds occur in nature; and in the vast majority of reactions of organic compounds, the carbon to carbon linkages persist unbroken.

This unique stability of the carbon to carbon bond may be explained in part by the electronic configuration of the carbon atom. Because it has four valence electrons, carbon tends to form compounds in which it shares four pairs of electrons with elements to which it is joined. The carbon atom then has a full octet of electrons, and this octet cannot be expanded because, as has been stated (p. 160), eight is the maximum number of electrons possible in the second shell.[1] This situation is illustrated by the electronic formula of the simple compound ethane:

$$\begin{array}{cc} \text{H} & \text{H} \\ \ddots & \ddots \\ \text{H} : \text{C} : \text{C} : \text{H} \\ \ddots & \ddots \\ \text{H} & \text{H} \end{array}$$

No other element can form chains in which its atoms, in their normal covalent state, possess a full and completely shared electron octet that cannot be expanded; thus, carbon occupies a unique position.

[1] Many compounds of elements of higher atomic number than neon are known, however, in which an atom holds more than eight electrons in its valence shell. See, for instance, the fluosilicate ion (p. 547).

4. Homologous Series. A systematic study of all the thousands of organic compounds might be hopelessly difficult were it not for the fact that these compounds may be grouped into a relatively small number of classes called *homologous series*. All compounds belonging to a given homologous series possess the same characteristic type of structure, are very similar in chemical behavior, and show a regular gradation in most of their physical properties. Thus, a knowledge of the chemistry of one or two representative members of any given series serves to give an excellent picture of the properties and behavior of all the rest. The formula for each compound in a homologous series differs from that of the compound preceding or following it in the series by the increment CH_2.

All the organic compounds that have an open chain structure are classified as *aliphatic*; we shall consider first the various homologous series of the aliphatic type. The simplest of these is the paraffin series of hydrocarbons (compounds composed entirely of carbon and hydrogen).

5. Methane. The first member of the paraffin series of hydrocarbons is methane, CH_4. Methane is formed in nature by bacterial decomposition of cellulose in the absence of oxygen. Gas bubbles containing methane, nitrogen, and carbon dioxide can frequently be observed rising to the surface of the water in stagnant marshes and swamps; hence, methane is often referred to as "marsh gas." It constitutes 50 to 97% of natural gas and exists in solution in petroleum. Methane may occur in the air of coal mines to the extent of 3.5 to 7.5% and is the main component of the combustible gas which the coal miners call "fire damp." Illuminating gas, made by the destructive distillation of either coal or petroleum, sometimes contains as much as 50% methane. Commercially, the compound is produced by the fermentation of cellulosic material, or by the reduction of carbon monoxide at 250–300° C. in the presence of nickel.

$$CO + 3H_2 = CH_4 + H_2O$$

The usual laboratory method for the preparation of small amounts of methane is by heating anhydrous sodium acetate with sodium hydroxide.

$$CH_3\,|\,COONa + NaO\,|\,H \rightarrow CH_4 + Na_2CO_3$$
$$(NaC_2H_3O_2)$$

Methane is a colorless, odorless gas which may be condensed to a liquid with a boiling point of −160° C. It is only slightly soluble in water, 1 volume dissolving in 18 of water at 0° C. As may be deduced from its molecular weight, its gaseous density is only about one-half that of air.

In the methane molecule, each of the four valence electrons of the carbon atom participates in a covalent bond with the electron of one of the four hydrogen atoms. This fact is represented by the following *electronic* formula:

$$H : \underset{\displaystyle H}{\overset{\displaystyle H}{C}} : H$$

Each electron-pair bond is usually indicated by a simple dash, and, thus, the methane molecule may be represented by the following *graphic* formula:

$$H—\underset{\displaystyle H}{\overset{\displaystyle H}{C}}—H$$

Because the carbon atom has four valence electrons available for covalent bond formation with other atoms, the valence of carbon is, except in very few cases, four. Organic chemists employ the existence of four covalent bonds for every carbon atom as the guiding principle in constructing structural

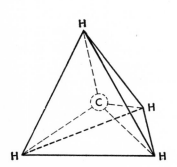

Fig. 31.1. Tetrahedral configuration in methane.

Fig. 31.2. A model of the methane molecule.

formulas. Several different lines of evidence prove that the arrangement of the hydrogen atoms about the carbon atom in methane is a tetrahedral one. The carbon atom may be thought of as being located at the center of a regular tetrahedron with one hydrogen atom at each corner (Figure 31.1). This tetrahedral arrangement is often illustrated by a type of molecular model [2] in which the various atoms are represented to scale and in accurate geometrical relationship to each other (Figure 31.2).

6. The Paraffin Series. The second member of the paraffin series is a color-less, odorless gas, much like methane, called ethane. Quantitative analysis of ethane, together with a determination of its molecular weight, reveals that it has the molecular formula C_2H_6. Similarly, the succeeding members of the series, propane, butane, and pentane, have been shown to possess the molecular formulas C_3H_8, C_4H_{10}, and C_5H_{12}, respectively. The structural relationship between these members of the series is clearly shown by the graphic formulas, which one can readily construct, keeping in mind the tendency of carbon atoms to share electron pairs with each other to form chains, and the fact that hydrogen ordinarily forms a single valence bond whereas the carbon atom is quadrivalent. Frequently the graphic formulas are condensed into the simpler *structural* formulas, also shown for the compounds below.

Graphic Formulas

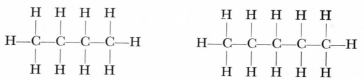

Structural Formulas

CH_3—CH_3 CH_3—CH_2—CH_3
Ethane (C_2H_6)   Propane (C_3H_8)

Graphic Formulas

H H H H   H H H H H
| | | | | | | | |
H—C—C—C—C—H   H—C—C—C—C—C—H
| | | | | | | | |
H H H H   H H H H H

Structural Formulas

CH_3—CH_2—CH_2—CH_3 CH_3—CH_2—CH_2—CH_2—CH_3
Butane (C_4H_{10})   Pentane (C_5H_{12})

It is apparent from these formulas that the members of the paraffin series may be represented by the general type formula C_nH_{2n+2}, in which n is any integer. The graphic formulas shown are projections of three dimensional

---

[2] Fisher-Hirschfelder-Taylor Atom Models.

structures upon a plane and, unless carefully interpreted, are likely to lead to erroneous concepts. For example, the paper formulas suggest that the carbon chains are straight, but actually the tetrahedral structure demands that the carbon atoms have a zigzag arrangement, as shown by a skeleton diagram of the butane molecule (Figure 31.3).

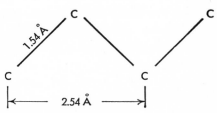

The general gradation in physical properties exhibited by successive members of a homologous series is illustrated in Table 31.1 for several of

Fig. 31.3. Zigzag arrangement in a carbon chain.

the continuous chain members of the paraffin series. With few exceptions, the melting points, boiling points, and densities of the compounds increase with increasing chain length.

Table 31.1
Paraffin Series of Hydrocarbons

Formula	Name	M.P. (°C.)	B.P. (°C.)	Density in g./cc.
CH_4	Methane	−183	−160	
C_2H_6	Ethane	−172	− 88	
C_3H_8	Propane	−187	− 42	
C_4H_{10}	Butane	−135	1	0.601 at 0° C.
C_5H_{12}	Pentane	−130	36	0.631 at 20° C.
C_6H_{14}	Hexane	− 94	69	0.658 at 20° C.
C_7H_{16}	Heptane	− 91	98	0.683 at 20° C.
C_8H_{18}	Octane	− 57	126	0.702 at 20° C.
C_9H_{20}	Nonane	− 54	151	0.719 at 20° C.
$C_{10}H_{22}$	Decane	− 30	174	0.747 at 20° C.
$C_{16}H_{34}$	Hexadecane	18	280	0.775 at M.P.
$C_{20}H_{42}$	Eicosane	37	310	0.778 at M.P.

At room temperature, the first four members of the series are gases, those from C_5H_{12} through $C_{16}H_{34}$ are liquids, and those with more than 16 carbon atoms are solids. All are relatively insoluble in water.

7. Isomerism. All of the compounds listed in the preceding table are constituents of petroleum. An extremely careful study of the gaseous fraction of petroleum has revealed the presence of a second compound, in addition to butane, with the molecular formula C_4H_{10}. This second compound has been named isobutane ("like butane"). The two butanes exhibit similar, but not identical, chemical behavior. Their physical properties are also somewhat different; e.g., butane has a boiling point of $+1°$ C. and isobutane of $-17°$ C. A careful study of the molecular formula C_4H_{10} leads to the prediction that there should, indeed, be two butanes, because the atoms can be arranged to give two different structures:

Butane   Isobutane

These formulas represent molecules of two different compounds because, although the molecules are built up of the same numbers of the same kinds of atoms, the atoms are linked together in different ways. Such substances which have the same molecular formulas but different structural formulas are called *isomers*. From several lines of evidence, including the synthesis of the compounds themselves, it has been proved that butane has the continuous and isobutane the branched carbon chain structure.

Reasoning from the number of different possible structures for the formula C_5H_{12}, we should predict the existence of three isomeric pentanes, as follows:

Pentane   Isopentane

Neopentane

Actually, three different compounds, named pentane, isopentane, and neopentane (the "new pentane"), with the molecular formula C_5H_{12} are known.

The number of possible isomers increases rapidly with increasing molecular complexity. For example, thirty-five different nonanes, with the molecular formula C_9H_{20}, have been described, and calculations based on a rather complex equation show that the theoretical number of possible isomers reaches 69,491,178,805,831 for the formula $C_{40}H_{82}$! It thus becomes apparent that for a majority of organic compounds a simple determination of the numbers of each kind of atom in the molecule does not suffice to identify the substance, any more than a tabulation of the number of times each letter appears on this page would tell what is written. A knowledge of the arrangement of the various atoms within the molecule is of fundamental importance in identifying and distinguishing between organic compounds.

8. Chemical Reactions of the Paraffins. As the name paraffin ("little affinity") implies, the hydrocarbons of this series are rather unreactive. At room temperature, they are inert toward the action of acids, bases, and oxidizing and reducing agents. Chlorine and bromine, however, react with the paraffins even at room temperature, replacing one or more of the hydrogen atoms in stepwise fashion. The halogen atoms are said to substitute for the hydrogen atoms and the reaction is called *substitution*. This general type of reaction is assuming increasing industrial importance as a means for preparing other valuable organic compounds from hydrocarbons found in petroleum.

In methane, all four hydrogen atoms can be successively replaced by chlorine.

$$CH_4 + Cl_2 = HCl + CH_3Cl \quad \text{methyl chloride}$$
$$CH_3Cl + Cl_2 = HCl + CH_2Cl_2 \quad \text{methylene chloride}$$
$$CH_2Cl_2 + Cl_2 = HCl + CHCl_3 \quad \text{chloroform}$$
$$CHCl_3 + Cl_2 = HCl + CCl_4 \quad \text{carbon tetrachloride}$$

Each successive replacement of a hydrogen by a chlorine atom in the methane structure yields a compound that has a higher boiling point and density and is less inflammable than the preceding compound. Methyl chloride is used as a refrigerant in air-conditioning equipment and as a local anesthetic; chloroform is a well known general anesthetic and an excellent solvent for fats and oils; carbon tetrachloride is used as a fire extinguisher (Pyrene) and in dry cleaning.

Carbon tetrachloride is produced commercially not by the reaction of methane with chlorine but rather from carbon disulfide and chlorine in the presence of a suitable catalyst (iodine or iron).

$$CS_2 + 3Cl_2 = CCl_4 + S_2Cl_2$$

Chloroform, in turn, is made commercially by the reduction of carbon tetrachloride with finely divided iron and water in the presence of a catalyst.

All the members of the paraffin series are combustible and burn with the evolution of large amounts of heat. It is this property which makes these hydrocarbons an indispensable source of energy in our machine age. The products of the complete combustion of the paraffin hydrocarbons are carbon dioxide and water.

Vapor phase nitration (p. 495) of the paraffins at elevated temperatures yields *nitroparaffins* of the type of nitromethane, CH_3NO_2. The nitroparaffins are stable, nontoxic, noncorrosive liquids, which have found use as solvents, fuels, and synthetic intermediates.

9. Unsaturated Hydrocarbons—The Olefins. There is a second series of aliphatic hydrocarbons, the *olefins*, whose members have two hydrogen atoms less than the number required to saturate the valences of the carbon atoms, and hence are said to be *unsaturated*. The first member of the olefin series is ethylene, C_2H_4. Each carbon in the ethylene molecule shares a single pair of electrons with each of two hydrogen atoms; the remaining two pairs of valence electrons are shared by the two carbon atoms. In other words, the two carbon atoms are joined by a *double bond*, as indicated by the following electronic and graphic formulas for ethylene:

$$H:C::C:H \qquad H—C=C—H$$

All the members of the olefin series may be considered formally as being derived from the corresponding paraffin compound by the removal of a single hydrogen atom from each of two adjacent carbon atoms. This removal leaves the two adjacent carbon atoms unsaturated, and their valences are satisfied by the existence of a double bond between them. Graphic formulas for several additional simple olefins are

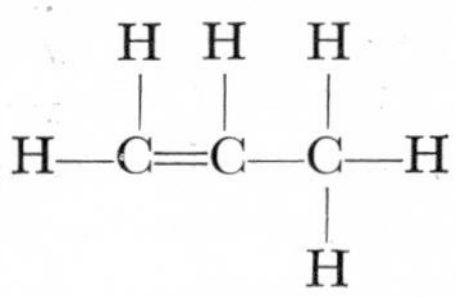

Propylene
or Propene

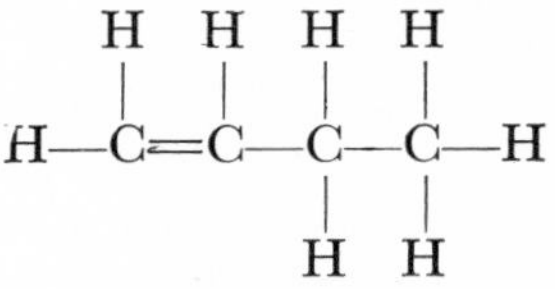

α-Butylene or
1-Butene

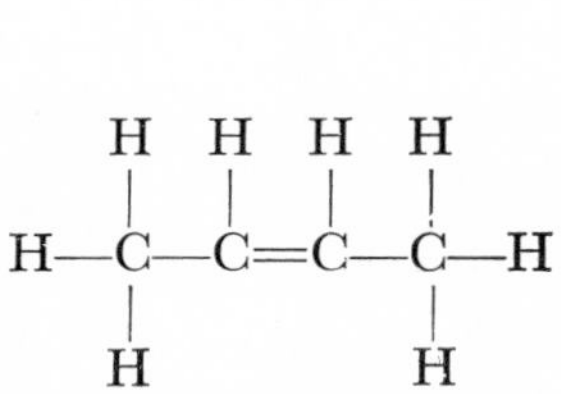

β-Butylene or
2-Butene

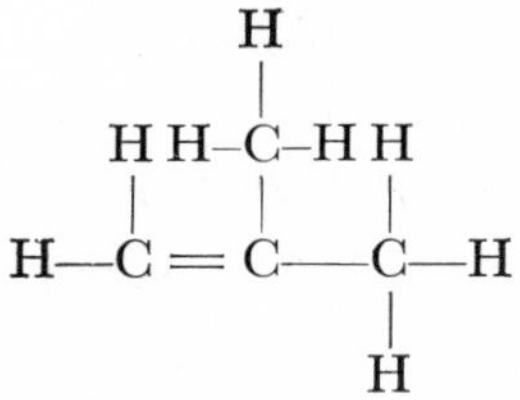

Isobutylene or
Isobutene

From these formulas, it can be deduced that the general type formula for the olefin series is C_nH_{2n}.

The physical properties of the various olefins are quite similar to those of the corresponding paraffin hydrocarbons. In general, those in the C_2–C_4 range are gases under room conditions, those from C_5–C_{18} are liquids, and the higher members are solids. All are only slightly soluble in water.

In contrast to the saturated hydrocarbons, the olefins are highly reactive. The double bond is rather easily converted into a single bond by the addition of other molecules, giving saturated compounds. Thus ethylene, for example, adds a molecule of hydrogen in the presence of a platinum or nickel catalyst to give ethane; it adds bromine readily, forming ethylene dibromide,

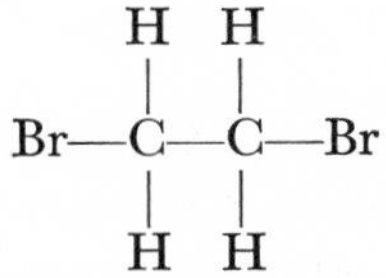

$$
\begin{array}{ccc}
& H & H \\
& | & | \\
Br-&C-&C-Br \\
& | & | \\
& H & H \\
\end{array}
$$

and under the catalytic influence of sulfuric acid can be made to add a molecule of water to form ethyl alcohol,

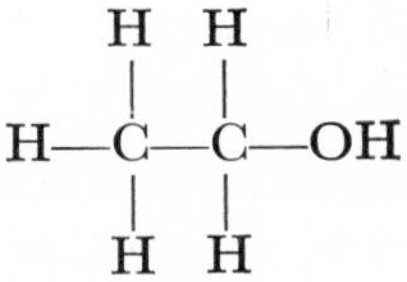

$$
\begin{array}{ccc}
& H & H \\
& | & | \\
H-&C-&C-OH \\
& | & | \\
& H & H \\
\end{array}
$$

Olefin molecules readily add to each other or *polymerize* under the catalytic influence of boron trifluoride. Such polymerization reactions are of great commercial importance in the synthetic rubber (p. 614) and plastics (p. 615) industries. The first step in the polymerization of ethylene, for example, gives as the main product, 1-butene:

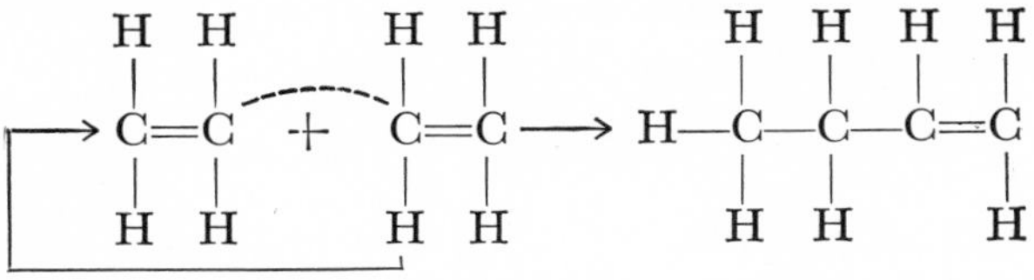

$$
\begin{array}{ccccc}
H\ H & & H\ H & & H\ H\ H\ H \\
|\ \ | & & |\ \ | & & |\ \ |\ \ |\ \ | \\
C{=}C & + & C{=}C & \longrightarrow & H-C-C-C{=}C \\
|\ \ | & & |\ \ | & & |\ \ |\ \ | \\
H\ H & & H\ H & & H\ H\quad H \\
\end{array}
$$

The olefins are produced in quantities in the cracking of petroleum oils (p. 574). Ethylene is obtained commercially on a large scale by the vapor phase cracking of gas oil or of propane from natural gas. It may be synthesized conveniently in the laboratory by the removal of water from ethyl

alcohol under the catalytic influence of sulfuric acid at 170° C. or aluminum oxide at 350° C.

$$
\begin{array}{c}
\text{H}\ \text{H} \\
|\quad| \\
\text{H—C—C—H} \\
|\quad| \\
\boxed{\text{H}\ \ \text{OH}}
\end{array}
\quad\longrightarrow\quad
\begin{array}{c}
\text{H}\ \text{H} \\
|\quad| \\
\text{H—C=C—H}
\end{array}
\quad+\quad \text{H}_2\text{O}
$$

Ethylene is a colorless gas with a rather sweet odor. It is used to some
extent as a nonirritating, quick-acting general anesthetic and rather extensively for the artificial ripening of citrus fruits, for shortening the dormant
period before growth of potatoes and other tubers, and in the production
of ethyl alcohol and of the plastic polyethylene (p. 616). Other olefins are
likewise used industrially for the production of alcohols and plastics.

10. The Diolefins. Hydrocarbons containing two double bonds in the molecule are called diolefins or dienes. Conjugate diolefins, the type in which
double and single bonds alternate, are tremendously important in the synthetic rubber industry. The simplest and most widely used diolefin is butadiene,

$$
\begin{array}{c}
\text{H}\ \ \text{H}\ \ \text{H}\ \ \text{H} \\
|\quad|\quad|\quad| \\
\text{H—C=C—C=C—H}
\end{array}
$$

which is produced commercially by the cracking of petroleum or, in several
steps, from ethyl alcohol.

11. The Acetylene Series. Even more highly unsaturated than the simple
olefins, are the members of the *acetylene* series. The acetylenic hydrocarbons
may be thought of as resulting from the corresponding paraffin hydrocarbons
by the loss of two hydrogen atoms on each of two adjacent carbon atoms,
which are joined by a triple bond, i.e., they share three pairs of electrons.
Acetylene, C_2H_2, the first member of this series that bears its name, is represented electronically and graphically as follows:

$$
\text{H : C : : : C : H} \qquad\qquad \text{H—C}\equiv\text{C—H}
$$

The next member is propyne,

$$
\begin{array}{c}
\qquad\quad \text{H} \\
\qquad\quad | \\
\text{H—C}\equiv\text{C—C—H} \\
\qquad\quad | \\
\qquad\quad \text{H}
\end{array}
$$

Compounds of the acetylene series may be represented by the type formula C_nH_{2n-2}. They are quite similar to the corresponding paraffins and olefins in physical properties. Being highly unsaturated, they readily undergo the type of addition reactions characteristic of the olefins; in most cases they add two molecules of the typical adding reagents. Thus, for example, acetylene adds two molecules of bromine to form acetylene tetrabromide.

$$H-C\equiv C-H + 2Br_2 = \begin{array}{ccc} & Br & Br \\ & | & | \\ H- & C- & C-H \\ & | & | \\ & Br & Br \end{array}$$

Acetylene is the most important compound of the series. It is prepared commercially from calcium carbide (p. 542) and water.

$$CaC_2 + 2H_2O = C_2H_2 + Ca(OH)_2$$

The preparation of acetylene by the dehydrogenation of natural gas at high temperatures is beginning, because of its low cost, to compete successfully with the carbide process.

Acetylene is a colorless gas, almost odorless when pure, the garlic-like odor of the technical product being due to impurities. Acetylene burns in air with a smoky flame. It is especially unstable at high pressures, and is usually marketed as an acetone solution in order to avoid explosions that are otherwise likely to occur when it is compressed. It is used in the oxy-acetylene torch, by means of which temperatures up to 3500° C. can be reached, for the welding and cutting of metals. Acetylene is a cheap key material in the commercial synthesis of other organic compounds; acetaldehyde, acetic acid, acetic anhydride, acetone, neoprene rubber (p. 615), and a number of important plastics and resins are included in the rapidly increasing number of products made from acetylene.

12. Petroleum. The most abundant and important source of aliphatic hydrocarbons is the dark, oily liquid found in underground deposits in various parts of the earth and known as *petroleum* ("rock oil"). Petroleum is not a single compound, but rather an extremely complex mixture of unnumbered gaseous, liquid, and solid hydrocarbons ranging from methane to $C_{40}H_{82}$, with small amounts of sulfur, nitrogen, and oxygen-containing compounds. The hydrocarbons which occur in petroleum are largely of two general types, the paraffins and the cycloparaffins or naphthenes. The latter constitute a homologous series of saturated hydrocarbons quite similar in physical and chemical properties to paraffins, but possessing a cyclic or ring structure.

Cyclopropane, which is an excellent anesthetic, cyclopentane, and cyclohexane are familiar members of the cycloparaffin series.

| Cyclopropane | Cyclopentane | Cyclohexane |

It is evident from these formulas that any cycloparaffin, because of the ring structure, contains two less hydrogen atoms than a paraffin hydrocarbon with the same number of carbon atoms. Since the general type formula of the cycloparaffins is therefore C_nH_{2n}, they are isomeric with the olefins.

Although the crude oils obtained from different parts of the world vary considerably in composition, the low boiling fraction of most petroleums is composed of paraffin hydrocarbons. The main differences appear in the higher boiling fractions. Crude petroleums are classified according to the character of the residue left after the removal of the volatile constituents. In paraffin-base petroleums, this residue consists mainly of a mixture of paraffin hydrocarbons; in asphalt-base petroleums, it is composed principally of cycloparaffins. Pennsylvania oil is of the paraffin-base type; Russian oil, on the other hand, contains almost 80% of cycloparaffins and is therefore of the asphalt-base type. Usually, however, the line of demarcation between the two types is not sharp, and most crude oils are classified as "mixed base." It is now generally believed that petroleum was formed by the decomposition in low temperature reactions (bacterial action, fermentation, etc.) of animal and plant remains imprisoned in rock strata in past geological ages. The petroleum deposits of the earth may, therefore, be considered as vast reservoirs in which the sun's energy, utilized by living organisms through past eras in the reduction of carbon dioxide (photosynthesis), has been stored in the form of chemical energy.

Since 1859, when Colonel E. L. Drake drilled the first oil well at Titusville, Pennsylvania, over 100,000,000,000 barrels (42 gallons per barrel) have been brought to the surface in a total of at least 26 different countries. The United States accounts for almost one-half of the world's current annual production of approximately 6,400,000,000 barrels and is followed by Venezuela (about 14 per cent), Russia, Iran, Romania, Mexico, and Colombia. Texas is the leading oil-producing state in this country, followed by California, Oklahoma, Louisiana, Kansas, and New Mexico. It has been calculated that the energy available from our nation's annual output of petroleum is equivalent to the work of more than 8,000,000,000 men toiling for eight hours a day, six days a week, for one year. Almost two-thirds of the energy consumed in the United States is derived from oil and natural gas.

13. The Refining of Petroleum. Some petroleum is burned directly, with no treatment whatever, as a fuel in industry and under the boilers of steamships. In general, however, crude petroleum is not fit for most uses, and must be piped to refineries for treatment. The total process by which petroleum is converted into a variety of marketable products is called refining. In general, the main operations in the refining of crude oil are *separation, conversion,* and *purification.* The fundamental process in separation is fractional distillation whereby the crude oil is divided into a series of different fractions, each of which boils over a certain temperature range and possesses characteristics that render it a commercially valuable product. Since an increase, for successive fractions, in the average molecular weight of the components parallels the rise in boiling point range, each fraction is actually a complex mixture of hydrocarbons whose molecular weights lie within certain limits. Table 31.2 gives a survey of the boiling and composition ranges, as well as the uses, of the various products obtained by the fractional distillation of crude petroleum.

The gasoline, kerosine, and lubricating oils obtained from petroleum generally require purification to improve their color, odor, and resistance to air oxidation. Olefins, small amounts of which are often present in petroleum products, are objectionable because they may cause gum and tar formation; they are sometimes eliminated by treatment with concentrated sulfuric acid.

Particularly harmful in lubricating oils are compounds which undergo decomposition or slow oxidation at high temperatures with the formation of sludges. Such components are removed by selective adsorption on natural clay, silica gel, or activated charcoal, or by extraction with organic compounds that act as selective solvents. In recent years, lubricants have been greatly improved by the addition of oxidation inhibitors to prevent formation of tars and resins, and of dispersive agents that keep impurities from coagulating. Detergents are added to wash tarry deposits from rings and cylinders, and still other additives have increased enormously the ability of lubricants to maintain proper viscosity under extreme temperature changes.

In straight distillation of petroleum, an average of less than 20% of the crude oil appears in the gasoline fraction. The straight-run gasoline from all the crude oil produced in the world would supply only a small fraction of the total amount required for automobiles and airplanes. Moreover, straight-run gasolines possess poor antiknock properties. As a result, the supplementing of straight-run gasoline by the conversion of other petroleum fractions into what is called high-octane gasoline is an imperative problem of major importance in the petroleum industry. In order to gain some insight into this problem, we shall consider briefly the relationship between the structure of hydrocarbons and their characteristics as fuels in automobile and airplane engines.

Table 31.2

Products Obtained by Fractional Distillation of Petroleum

Product	Approximate Composition	B.P. Range (°C.)	Uses
Gas	C_1–C_4	—164––$+$30	Fuel; making carbon black, polymerized gasoline, and casing-head gasoline
Petroleum ether, ligroin, or naphtha	C_5–C_7	30–90	Solvent, dry-cleaning, refrigerant
Straight-run gasoline	C_5–C_{12}	40–220	Motor fuel
Kerosine *	C_{12}–C_{16}	200–315	Lighting, fuel for oil stoves, Diesel engines, and tractors
Gas oil or fuel oil	C_{15}–C_{18}	up to 375	Furnace oils, fuel for Diesel engines, cracking stock
Lubricating oils	C_{16}–C_{20}	350 up	Lubrication
Greases, vaseline or petrolatum	C_{18} up	Semisolid	Lubrication, sizing paper, ingredient of medicines
Paraffin ("wax")	C_{20} up	Melts 51–55	Candles, impregnating match sticks, waterproofing fabrics, household canning
Pitch and tar (artificial asphalt)		Residue	Roofing, paving, protective paints, manufacture of rubber
Petroleum coke		Residue	Fuel, carbon electrodes

* This spelling has been adopted by the American Society for Testing Materials and other technical societies.

14. Octane Ratings of Gasoline.

For the most efficient operation of internal combustion engines, the compression ratio (volume of the full cylinder with piston drawn to volume in the cylinder with piston at end of in-stroke) should be as high as possible. If the compression is increased beyond certain limits, however, the fuel explodes with extreme rapidity and in a disorderly fashion. This produces a violent jar against the piston and the cylinder wall —the motor is said to knock—with resulting loss in efficiency and damage to the piston and cylinder. The problem of increasing compression ratios while still avoiding knocking has plagued automotive engineers and research chemists for many years. After wide experimentation, an American chemist, Thomas Midgeley, Jr., and co-workers, found in 1922 that tetraethyl lead, $Pb(C_2H_5)_4$, when added to motor fuel in a concentration of 0.01% or less, inhibits knocking. Tetraethyl lead apparently functions as a negative catalyst in the combustion of the fuel. Midgeley's discovery made possible some increase in the compression ratios used in automobile engines, the upper limit being set by the nature of the gasoline used. Tetraethyl lead is now added to about 85% of all the gasoline sold in the United States. In recent years, an organic phosphorus compound, tricresyl phosphate (TCP), and organic boron compounds have come into wide use as gasoline additives.

The attention of research workers has recently turned to the anti-knock properties of the fuel itself. Experimentation with pure hydrocarbons revealed that highly branched paraffins cause less knocking than continuous chain compounds. In fact, because of its excellent antiknock properties, one highly branched chain paraffin, isoöctane (2, 2, 4-trimethylpentane),

$$\begin{array}{ccc} & CH_3 & CH_3 \\ & | & | \\ CH_3\text{---}C\text{---}CH_2\text{---}CH\text{---}CH_3 \\ & | \\ & CH_3 \end{array}$$

was chosen as the reference standard in rating gasolines, and was assigned an octane number of 100. The continuous chain compound, n-heptane, which knocks badly, was given an octane number of 0. The octane rating of any given gasoline is equal to the percentage of isoöctane in a synthetic iso-octane–n-heptane mixture that produces the same degree of knocking as the gasoline being tested. Branched chain paraffins and unsaturated hydrocarbons, in general, have excellent antiknock properties and therefore high octane numbers. Triptane, 2,2,3-trimethylbutane,

$$\begin{array}{cc} CH_3 & CH_3 \\ | & | \\ CH_3\text{---}C\text{----}CH\text{---}CH_3 \\ | \\ CH_3 \end{array}$$

has an octane number of 125, and is said to result in a 25% fuel economy over isoöctane with the production of four times the power.

15. Gasoline by Cracking. The process by which larger and less volatile hydrocarbon molecules are broken down or "cracked" into a variety of

Fig. 31.4. A giant cracking unit as pictured at dusk. This unit produces more than a half-million gallons of high octane gasoline daily. (*Courtesy of Standard Oil Company of Indiana.*)

smaller and more volatile ones is called *cracking*. In commercial practice, excellent yields (up to 90%) of high octane gasoline are obtained by the cracking of the gas oil fraction of petroleum. A wide variety of important catalytic cracking processes are used for the production of gasoline. In general, temperatures between 300° and 600° C. and pressures from 100 to 1000 lb. per sq. in. are employed. Aluminum chloride and aluminum silicate are typical catalysts. The development in this country during World War II of volatile or "fluid" catalysts has made possible the construction of giant cracking stills (Figure 31.4) which operate continuously and almost automatically in producing hundreds of thousands of gallons of high octane gasoline daily.

The chemical reactions involved in cracking are extremely complex and result in the production of many different compounds. It is significant that when a paraffin hydrocarbon is ruptured into two or more simpler molecules, unsaturated hydrocarbons of the olefin and diolefin series are produced. Because the cracked gasolines owe their high octane ratings largely to the presence of unsaturated compounds, current industrial practice is not to remove these compounds, but to add small amounts of organic anti-oxidants by which oxidation of the olefins to gummy, ill-smelling products is prevented.

During the past few years, use of light Diesel fuels has entered into active competition with the cracking plants in its demands for the gas oil fraction of petroleum. The use of Diesel engines is being greatly expanded, especially for trains, ships, busses, heavy trucks, and stationary power units.

16. Polymerization, Alkylation, and Isomerization. Over 300 billion cubic feet of waste gases—mixtures of propane, propene, the butanes, the butenes, and other lower molecular weight hydrocarbons—are produced annually in this country as by-products of the cracking stills. Recently developed processes by which these lower molecular weight hydrocarbons can be recombined to form high octane gasolines have assumed great industrial importance; they are *polymerization* and *alkylation*. Both are essentially the reverse of the main reactions that occur during cracking. In the polymerization process, gaseous unsaturated hydrocarbons are combined or polymerized, in the presence of catalysts such as sulfuric acid or phosphoric anhydride, to form liquid hydrocarbons with highly branched chains. Alkylation consists in the combination of various olefins produced in cracking, such as propylene and the butylenes, with gaseous paraffins, especially isobutane, to produce liquid paraffins having a maximum of chain-branching. Commercially, both thermal alkylation at high pressures, and low temperature catalytic alkylation with sulfuric acid or anhydrous hydrogen fluoride are employed.

The use of still other catalysts (aluminum chloride and aluminum bromide) makes possible the *isomerization* of continuous chain into branched chain paraffins. Isomerization undoubtedly occurs extensively during cracking and is partially responsible for the superior octane rating of the product. In the *reforming* process, platinum-containing catalysts are used to upgrade naphthas through a combination of dehydrogenation, isomerization, and cracking reactions.

Polymerization, alkylation, and isomerization all favor the formation of branched chain hydrocarbons and they therefore give excellent high octane gasolines. A combination of these processes made possible the large-scale production of 100-octane aviation super-fuels that played a vital role in the winning of the war for the Allies, especially in the crucial Battle of Britain (1940). The super-fuels are at present either used directly in aircraft and as super-premium automobile gasolines (octane ratings up to 102) or blended with other stock to produce low-cost premium fuels. In order to take advantage of these new improved fuels, manufacturers probably will increase the compression ratios in automobile engines to an average of about 12 : 1 by 1961 (average in 1913 was 4.0 : 1, in 1940, 6.3 : 1, and in 1957, 9.0 : 1), and it is likely that 25–35 miles per gallon performance will become standard.

17. Petroleum Substitutes. The accelerating rate of consumption of petroleum products, as well as the inadequate sources of supply in some countries, has stimulated an active search for petroleum substitutes. Various substitute motor fuels, such as methyl and ethyl alcohols, benzene (p. 586), compressed fuel gases, producer gas, acetylene, and even hydrogen were used in various European countries during World War II. Sweden has been experimenting on the distillation of oil from shale, and shale oil deposits in the United States may soon be worked profitably.

An important method for the production of motor fuels and lubricating oils widely exploited in Europe is the Bergius process for the hydrogenation of bituminous coal. Pulverized coal mixed with an iron catalyst is suspended in oil and heated to about 400° C., while hydrogen is passed over it at 100–200 atm. pressure. From a metric ton of coal there are obtained, after distillation, about 40 gal. of motor fuel of about 72 octane rating, 50 gal. of Diesel engine oil, 35 gal. of fuel oil, and 10,000 cu. ft. of fuel gas.

Of greater promise for future use in the low-cost manufacture of gasoline in the United States is the Fischer-Tropsch process for the catalytic hydrogenation of carbon monoxide. A 1 : 2 mixture of carbon monoxide and hydrogen, prepared from coke by the water-gas reaction or from natural gas, is heated to 200° C. at 5 to 15 atm. in the presence of a catalyst consisting mainly of cobalt, nickel, and iron. The product is a mixture of saturated and unsaturated hydrocarbons which may be separated by distillation into a rather low-octane gasoline fraction, kerosine, lubricating oil, an excellent Diesel fuel oil, and paraffin.

18. Natural Gas. Abundant underground deposits of natural gas occur in many parts of the United States, the largest being in West Virginia, the midland area, the Gulf coast, and California. Natural gas is made up chiefly of methane, together with some ethane and smaller amounts of the higher members of the methane series up to octane. It contains varying amounts of nitrogen, depending upon its source, and in some deposits, notably those in northern Texas, there is sufficient helium (p. 375) to make its extraction for use in dirigibles practicable. Natural gas is usually closely associated with petroleum and its origins are probably similar. An average of 30 billion cubic feet of natural gas are consumed daily in the United States. It is widely used as a cheap and efficient domestic and industrial fuel.

19. Organic Chemicals from Petroleum and Natural Gas. The magnitude of the gasoline and other industries that employ petroleum products as fuels and lubricants may well tend to dwarf in our minds the tremendous importance of petroleum and natural gas as raw materials for the synthesis of organic compounds. Actually, more than six billion pounds of chemicals,

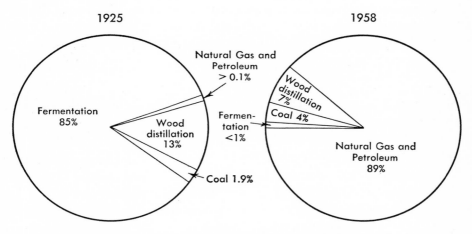

Fig. 31.5. (*Courtesy Union Carbide Chemicals Company.*)

too numerous and varied to be listed here, are derived annually from petroleum and natural gas (see Figure 31.5). These compounds are used in the manufacture of literally hundreds of important products—synthetic rubber, plastics, foods, drugs, textiles, detergents, solvents, explosives, insecticides, fungicides, weed killers, cosmetics, refrigerants, resins, drying oils, surface coatings, and many more.

DERIVATIVES OF THE ALIPHATIC HYDROCARBONS

20. Introduction. All the other aliphatic compounds may be regarded as derived from the aliphatic hydrocarbons, at least formally, by the substitution of some other atom or groups of atoms for one or more hydrogen atoms in the hydrocarbon. For each homologous series, there is a characteristic substituting atom or group of atoms. The nature of the substituting group determines the physical and chemical properties characteristic of the series.

21. Alcohols. The characteristic group for the *alcohols* is the OH (hydroxyl) group. If only one OH group is present, the compound is a monohydric alcohol. The common names of the alcohols are derived from those of the parent hydrocarbons. Some common monohydric alcohols and the hydrocarbon or *alkyl* groups which they contain are as follows:

Formula	Name of alcohol	Alkyl group	Name of alkyl group
CH_3OH	Methyl alcohol	CH_3-	Methyl
CH_3-CH_2OH	Ethyl alcohol	CH_3CH_2-	Ethyl
$CH_3-CH_2-CH_2OH$	Normal (or *n*-) propyl alcohol	$CH_3-CH_2-CH_2-$	*n*-Propyl
$CH_3-CHOH-CH_3$	Isopropyl alcohol	$CH_3-CH-CH_3$	Isopropyl
$CH_3-CH_2-CH_2-CH_2OH$	*n*-Butyl alcohol	$CH_3-CH_2-CH_2-CH_2-$	*n*-Butyl
$CH_3-CHOH-CH_2-CH_3$	Secondary (or *sec*-) butyl alcohol	$CH_3-CH-CH_2-CH_3$	*sec*-Butyl

Alkyl groups are represented by the symbol **R**. Thus, monohydric alcohols have the general type formula **ROH**.

Alcohols are covalent compounds, as indicated by the electronc formulas for methyl and ethyl alcohols:

$$H:\overset{\displaystyle H}{\underset{\displaystyle H}{\overset{..}{\underset{..}{C}}}}:\overset{..}{\underset{..}{O}}:H \qquad H:\overset{\displaystyle H}{\underset{\displaystyle H}{\overset{..}{\underset{..}{C}}}}:\overset{\displaystyle H}{\underset{\displaystyle H}{\overset{..}{\underset{..}{C}}}}:\overset{..}{\underset{..}{O}}:H$$

They are rather extensively associated through the formation of hydrogen bonds (p. 233) between the oxygen atoms, and, as a result, they are considerably less volatile than the corresponding hydrocarbons. The lower alcohols up to lauryl alcohol ($C_{12}H_{25}OH$) are liquids with pleasant odors; the higher alcohols are solids. Alcohols do not react appreciably with water to form either hydronium or hydroxide ions; their water solutions are therefore neutral to litmus and they are classified as nonelectrolytes. Alcohols burn in an excess of air, forming carbon dioxide and water.

Until 1920, methyl or wood alcohol (methanol) was obtained almost entirely by the destructive distillation of wood, but at present about 95% of this country's production is by the almost quantitative catalytic hydrogenation of carbon monoxide.

$$2H_2 + CO = CH_3OH$$

Methyl alcohol is extremely toxic, either when taken internally or when inhaled. It is used as a fuel, a solvent for shellac, a denaturant of ethyl alcohol, and a starting material in the production of formaldehyde.

Ethyl or grain alcohol (ethanol) ranks first among synthetic organic chemicals, both in quantity of production and in total value. One commercial method for its production (in use since antiquity) is the fermentation of glucose, which in turn may be made from starch (p. 598) or molasses. Additional amounts are made by the indirect addition of water to ethylene through the use of sulfuric or phosphoric acid, and by the controlled partial oxidation of natural gas. Ethyl alcohol is a liquid with a characteristic odor; it has a boiling point of 78.4° C. and is miscible with water and many organic solvents in all proportions.

Ethyl alcohol is indispensable to a host of chemical industries, being used in the manufacture of acetaldehyde, acetic acid, dyes, lacquers, medicines, solvents, perfumes, vinegar, collodion, insecticides, varnishes, and cosmetics. It is of vital importance in medicine as the starting material in the synthesis of ether, chloroform, and iodoform, and as a solvent for many medicinals. A 70% aqueous solution of the alcohol is itself an excellent antiseptic. Ethyl alcohol is a good fuel and a widely used solvent in the preparation of varnishes, extracts, essences, and tinctures. Since ancient times, large quantities have been consumed in alcoholic beverages.

Isopropyl and *sec*-butyl alcohols are obtained by the indirect addition of water to propene and the butenes produced in the cracking process. Millions of pounds of *n*-butyl alcohol are prepared by a special bacterial fermentation of corn, rice, rye, and wheat. The acetate esters (p. 583) of these alcohols are widely used as solvents, especially for lacquers. Isopropyl alcohol is also widely sold as rubbing alcohol.

Alcohols containing two OH groups are called dihydroxy alcohols or glycols. The simplest and one of the most important is ethylene glycol, CH_2OH—CH_2OH. It is obtained commercially from ethylene and is widely used, under the trade name of Prestone, as a relatively high boiling, noncorrosive antifreeze for automobile radiators.

Glycerol, CH_2OH—$CHOH$—CH_2OH, is the most important of the trihydroxy alcohols. It is formed as a by-product when fats and oils are hydrolyzed in soap manufacture (p. 602), and since World War II has been obtained also by synthesis from propene. It is used in the manufacture of explosives.

22. Ethers. When two molecules of alcohol combine with the loss of a single molecule of water the resulting product is an *ether*, R—O—R', where R and R' may be the same or different alkyl groups. The ethers are incapable of associating through hydrogen bonds and are more volatile than the isomeric alcohols; for example, dimethyl ether, CH_3—O—CH_3, an isomer of ethyl alcohol, is a gas used to some extent as a refrigerant.

The most important of the ethers, ordinary ether or diethyl ether, is prepared by the dehydration of ethyl alcohol with sulfuric acid at 130–140° C.

$$C_2H_5\overline{OH + H}OC_2H_5 \rightarrow C_2H_5-O-C_2H_5 + H_2O$$

Considered the best general anesthetic, it was first used for that purpose by Dr. Crawford W. Long of Jefferson, Georgia, in 1842, nine years before its structure was known. Diethyl ether is an excellent solvent for organic compounds, including oils and fats. It has a low boiling point (34.6° C.), and is immiscible with water. Its chief disadvantage for practical use is its high inflammability; in other respects, it is, like all ethers, distinctly unreactive.

23. Aldehydes and Ketones. Both aldehydes and ketones may be considered formally as hydrocarbons in which a doubly bonded oxygen atom has replaced two hydrogen atoms. In aldehydes, this replacement is at an end

carbon in the chain; the type formula for *aldehydes* is therefore R—C—H, with the O doubly bonded above C, where R represents H in the simplest aldehyde, formaldehye, but an alkyl group in the higher members of the series. If the substitution is at any carbon other than one at the end of the chain the product is a *ketone*. Hence,

the type formula for ketones is R—C—R′ (O doubly bonded above C). Aldehydes and ketones are oxidation products of alcohols, from which they can be synthesized by the removal of two hydrogen atoms from the corresponding alcohol molecule. Mild oxidation of methyl alcohol, for example, gives formaldehyde. Commercially, this oxidation is accomplished by passing a mixture of methyl alcohol vapor and air over a copper or silver gauze catalyst at 500–600° C.

$$2CH_3OH + O_2 = 2HCHO + 2H_2O$$
formaldehyde

A gas with a boiling point of −21° C., formaldehyde is widely marketed as a 37% solution called formalin, and is used as a preservative for anatomical specimens, in embalming, and as a fumigant. The widely used plastic known as Bakelite is produced by the reaction of formaldehyde with phenol.

Acetaldehyde, CH₃—C—H (O doubly bonded above C), is readily synthesized in the laboratory by the mild oxidation of ethyl alcohol, and commercially by the addition of water to acetylene with sulfuric acid and mercuric oxide as catalysts.

$$H-C\equiv C-H + H_2O = CH_3CHO$$

Acetaldehyde is a cheap starting material in the industrial synthesis of a great variety of important organic compounds including ethyl alcohol, acetone, acetic acid, acetic anhydride, and ethyl acetate.

$$\overset{\text{O}}{\overset{\|}{}}$$

Acetone (dimethyl ketone), CH_3—$\overset{\overset{\text{O}}{\|}}{C}$—$CH_3$, the most important of the ketones, is a pleasant smelling liquid which is widely used as a solvent for varnishes, acetylene, smokeless powder, and other cellulose derivatives, as well as in the manufacture of celluloid and photographic films. It is prepared commercially by the air oxidation of isopropyl alcohol at 450° C. in the presence of a copper catalyst, and (along with n-butyl alcohol) by the bacterial fermentation of starch or molasses.

24. The Aliphatic Acids. The aldehyde group, CHO, is easily oxidized, adding an atom of oxygen to form the *carboxyl* group, COOH. Aliphatic monocarboxylic acids are called fatty acids. These acids may be thought of as hydrocarbons in which all three hydrogen atoms on an end carbon atom in the chain are replaced, two by a doubly bonded oxygen atom and one by an —OH group. They are represented by the type formula

R—$\overset{\overset{\text{O}}{\|}}{C}$—OH, where R is H in the case of formic acid and may be a saturated or unsaturated hydrocarbon radical for the higher acids. Both saturated and unsaturated acids occur in the form of glycerol esters (p. 583) in the common animal fats and animal and vegetable fatty oils, hence the name fatty acids. The names, formulas, occurrence in nature, and boiling and melting points of several of the common fatty acids are listed in Table 31.3.

The members of this series of compounds are only weakly acidic, reacting to a small extent with water to produce hydronium and carboxylate ions.

$$RCOOH + H_2O \rightleftharpoons H_3O^+ + RCOO^-$$

Because of the very stable hydrogen bonds which they form, the molecules of the lower members of this series are associated, even in the vapor state.

Formic acid, H—$\overset{\overset{\text{O}}{\|}}{C}$—OH, is the simplest organic acid. It is manufactured industrially by the reaction between carbon monoxide and sodium hydroxide at 210° C., in which carbon monoxide behaves like a true acid anhydride.

$$CO + NaOH = HCOONa$$
sodium formate

Table 31.3

Common Saturated and Unsaturated Fatty Acids

Name	Formula	Occurrence in Nature	B.P. (°C.)	M.P. (°C).
		Saturated Fatty Acids		
Formic	HCOOH	Ants, caterpillars, pine needles.	100.8	8.6
Acetic	CH_3—COOH	Soured fruit juices.	118.1	16.6
Propionic	CH_3—CH_2—COOH	Distillate from destructive distillation of wood.	114.1	—36.5
Butyric	C_4H_9—COOH	Rancid butter, limburger cheese.	163.5	— 7.9
Palmitic	$C_{15}H_{31}$—COOH	Animals fats (as glycerol esters).	278 (at 100 mm.)	62.4
Stearic	$C_{17}H_{35}$—COOH	Vegetable oils (as glycerol esters).	291 (at 100 mm.)	69.3
		Unsaturated Fatty Acids		
Acrylic	CH_2=CH—COOH		141	12.5
Oleic	$C_{17}H_{33}$—COOH	Fats and oils (as glycerol esters).	286 (at 100 mm.)	14.0

The free acid is liberated from its sodium salt by the action of sulfuric acid. It is used in the dehairing of hides and in the coagulating and reclaiming of rubber.

Acetic acid, CH_3—$\overset{\displaystyle O}{\overset{\displaystyle \|}{C}}$—OH (p. 311), is the most important organic acid of commerce. It is readily prepared in the laboratory by the oxidation of either ethyl alcohol or acetaldehyde. Acetic acid (about 4%) is found in vinegar, which is produced by fermentative oxidation of ethyl alcohol obtained from molasses or cider. The acid is also obtained commercially by the destructive distillation of wood, and by the air oxidation of acetaldehyde (obtained from acetylene) at 60° C. with manganous acetate as catalyst.

$$2CH_3-\overset{O}{\overset{\|}{C}}-H + O_2 = 2CH_3-\overset{O}{\overset{\|}{C}}-OH$$

Acetic acid is employed extensively in the dyeing of textiles; both the acid and its esters are excellent solvents for organic compounds.

Some important acids contain two (dicarboxylic) or three (tricarboxylic) carboxyl groups. Still others, containing both carboxyl and hydroxyl groups, are called hydroxy-acids. Some of these acids are:

$COOH$	CH_3	$COOH$	CH_2—$COOH$	$COOH$
$\mid$	$\mid$	$\mid$	$\mid$	$\mid$
$COOH$	$CHOH$	$CHOH$	HO—C—$COOH$	$(CH_2)_4$
	$\mid$	$\mid$	$\mid$	$\mid$
	$COOH$	$CHOH$	CH_2—$COOH$	$COOH$
		$\mid$		
		$COOH$		
Oxalic	Lactic	Tartaric	Citric	Adipic

Oxalic acid occurs in rhubarb and sorrel; lactic acid is present in sour milk, and plays a vital role in the metabolism of carbohydrates in the body; tartaric acid is the acid of grapes, and citric that of citrus fruit. The monopotassium salt of tartaric acid, potassium hydrogen tartrate ("cream of tartar"), mixed with sodium bicarbonate and starch, is an important ingredient in one common type of baking powder. Adipic acid is produced commercially for use in the manufacture of nylon (p. 619).

25. Esters. Organic acids and alcohols react slowly with the elimination of a molecule of water between the carboxyl group of the acid and the hydroxyl group of the alcohol to form *esters*. Acetic acid and ethyl alcohol, for example, form the ester known as ethyl acetate.

$$\begin{array}{ccc} O & & O \\ \parallel & & \parallel \\ CH_3-C-OH + H O-C_2H_5 = CH_3-C-O-C_2H_5 + H_2O \end{array}$$

The esterification (ester-forming) reaction, which is usually run at somewhat elevated temperatures in the presence of an acid catalyst, may be represented by the following general type equation:

$$\begin{array}{ccc} O & & O \\ \parallel & & \parallel \\ R-C-OH + HO-R' = R-C-O-R' + H_2O \end{array}$$

$$\begin{array}{c} O \\ \parallel \\ \end{array}$$

From the type formula for esters, $R-C-O-R'$, it is seen that an ester differs from an acid only by the substitution of an alkyl group for the hydrogen atom of the carboxyl group.

The lower molecular weight esters are liquids which have pleasant flower-

or fruit-like odors; they are widely used in perfumes and artificial flavorings. For example, isoamyl acetate,

$$CH_3\!-\!\overset{\displaystyle O}{\overset{\displaystyle \|}{C}}\!-\!O\!-\!CH_2\!-\!CH_2\!-\!\underset{\displaystyle \underset{\displaystyle CH_3}{|}}{CH}\!-\!CH_3$$

is the familiar "banana oil." Many esters occur naturally in fruits and flowers and are partially responsible for their characteristic odors.

The esters are excellent solvents; ethyl acetate and *n*-butyl acetate,

$CH_3\!-\!\overset{\displaystyle O}{\overset{\displaystyle \|}{C}}\!-\!O\!-\!CH_2\!-\!CH_2\!-\!CH_2\!-\!CH_3$, particularly, are used as lacquer solvents. The esters of the higher fatty acids with the trihydroxy alcohol glyercol are the naturally occurring fats and oils (p. 601). The true (as distinguished from paraffin) waxes are esters derived from higher molecular weight acids and alcohols; beeswax is myricyl palmitate,

$$C_{15}H_{31}\!-\!\overset{\displaystyle O}{\overset{\displaystyle \|}{C}}\!-\!O\!-\!C_{31}H_{63}$$

26. Amines and Amides. The aliphatic *amines* may be considered as the products formed by the substitution of one or more alkyl groups for the hydrogen atoms of ammonia. Primary amines contain one alkyl group; secondary, two; and tertiary, three—as illustrated here for the methyl amines.

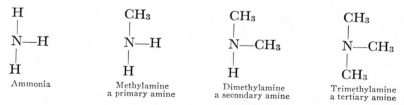

| Ammonia | Methylamine
a primary amine | Dimethylamine
a secondary amine | Trimethylamine
a tertiary amine |

The amines are used extensively in the synthesis of medicinals. Dimethylamine is employed in the preparation of dyes, rubber accelerators, and cleansing compounds. Certain compounds containing two NH_2 or amino groups, the diamines, such as cadaverine, $NH_2\!-\!(CH_2)_5\!-\!NH_2$, are important industrially in the manufacture of plastics and synthetic fibers (p. 617).

Chemically, the amines are similar to ammonia. Like ammonia, they are basic; they form salts with strong acids, and the lower amines, which are water soluble, react with water to a slight extent to form aklylammonium and hydroxide ions, as illustrated for ethylamine.

$$CH_3—CH_2—\underset{\underset{H}{|}}{\overset{\overset{H}{|}}{N}} + HOH \rightleftharpoons CH_3—CH_2—\underset{\underset{H}{|}}{\overset{\overset{H}{|}}{N}}—H^+ + OH^-$$

Base₁   Acid₂   Acid₁   Base₂

Ammonia can be made to react with organic acids at elevated temperatures to produce amides. With acetic acid, for example, ammonia forms acetamide.

$$CH_3—\overset{\overset{O}{||}}{C}—OH + H—NH_2 = CH_3—\overset{\overset{O}{||}}{C}—NH_2 + H_2O$$

acetamide

Amides differ in formula from organic acids only by the substitution of the NH₂ group for the OH group of the acid, and may therefore be repre-

sented by the type formula $R—\overset{\overset{O}{||}}{C}—NH_2$. Primary and secondary amines react with acids in an analogous fashion, forming substituted amides in which one or both of the hydrogen atoms attached to the nitrogen in a simple amide are replaced by alkyl groups. In the reaction, a molecule of water is eliminated between the carboxyl group of the acid and the amino group of the amine. Proteins (p. 603) and nylon (p. 619) are complex substituted polyamides.

27. Amino Acids. Compounds containing both the carboxyl (COOH) and amino (NH₂) groups are called amino acids. The simplest of the

amino acids is glycine or aminoacetic acid, $NH_2—CH_2—\overset{\overset{O}{||}}{C}—OH$. Through the reaction of the carboxyl group of one molecule with the amino group of another, repeated from molecule to molecule, the amino acids are capable of combining with each other indefinitely to form proteins (p. 603), the basic material of living animals and a class of essential foodstuffs. The amino acids are products of the hydrolysis of proteins, both as carried out in the laboratory and in the digestive processes of man.

28. Summary of Types of Derivatives. The various types of homologous series which may be considered as derived from the aliphatic hydrocarbons are listed in Table 31.4.

Table 31.4

Homologous Series Derived from the Aliphatic Hydrocarbons

Characteristic Group	Type Formula	Class of Compound	Formula of an Example	Name
—OH	R—OH	Alcohol	CH_3—CH_2OH	Ethyl alcohol (ethanol)
--OR	R—O—R'	Ether	CH_3—CH_2—O—CH_2—CH_3	Diethyl ether
$-\overset{O}{\overset{\|}{C}}-H$	$R-\overset{O}{\overset{\|}{C}}-H$	Aldehyde	$CH_3-\overset{O}{\overset{\|}{C}}-H$	Acetaldehyde
$-\overset{O}{\overset{\|}{C}}-$	$R-\overset{O}{\overset{\|}{C}}-R'$	Ketone	$CH_3-\overset{O}{\overset{\|}{C}}-CH_3$	Acetone
$-\overset{O}{\overset{\|}{C}}-OH$	$R-\overset{O}{\overset{\|}{C}}-OH$	Acid	$CH_3-\overset{O}{\overset{\|}{C}}-OH$	Acetic acid
$-\overset{O}{\overset{\|}{C}}-OR$	$R-\overset{O}{\overset{\|}{C}}-OR'$	Ester	$CH_3-\overset{O}{\overset{\|}{C}}-OCH_2-CH_3$	Ethyl acetate
--NH_2	R—NH_2	Primary Amine	CH_3—NH_2	Methyl amine
$-\overset{O}{\overset{\|}{C}}-NH_2$	$R-\overset{O}{\overset{\|}{C}}-NH_2$	Amide	$CH_3-\overset{O}{\overset{\|}{C}}-NH_2$	Acetamide

THE AROMATIC HYDROCARBONS AND THEIR DERIVATIVES

29. The Benzene Ring. The aromatic hydrocarbons and their derivatives constitute the second great division of organic compounds. Benzene, C_6H_6, is the parent substance of the *aromatic compounds*, all of which contain as their nucleus a benzene ring, or a double or multiple ring derived from the benzene ring. The carbon atoms in the benzene ring are linked together in a very special manner. The benzene molecule is a symmetrical hexagonal ring consisting of six carbon atoms in a single plane, each bearing one hydrogen atom. If the carbon atoms in the ring are joined by single bonds (i.e., share one pair of electrons), then each carbon atom is left with one unshared electron. The simplest formula which represents all the electrons as shared and gives each carbon a valence of four is one in which single and double bonds alternate around the ring. For a given sextet of carbon atoms, however, two such structures, different, but equally probable, may be formulated as shown:

$$\left\{ \quad \begin{array}{c} \text{H H} \\ \text{C—C} \\ \text{HC} \quad\quad \text{CH} \\ \text{C=C} \\ \text{H H} \\ \text{A} \end{array} \quad , \quad \begin{array}{c} \text{H H} \\ \text{C=C} \\ \text{HC} \quad\quad \text{CH} \\ \text{C—C} \\ \text{H H} \\ \text{B} \end{array} \quad \right\}$$

According to the modern viewpoint, the true structure of benzene is not that represented either by A or B, but rather some structure intermediate between the two, and more stable than either. This is a typical example of resonance, and benzene is said to be a resonance hybrid receiving contributions from structures A and B. The true structure of benzene cannot be represented by a single electronic diagram. The characteristic properties exhibited by benzene and its derivatives by virtue of the resonance in the benzene ring are often referred to as aromatic properties, or aromaticity. Certain of these aromatic properties will become evident as we consider the nature and reactions of a few individual aromatic compounds.

In the writing of formulas, we usually avoid the complexities of resonance by representing the benzene ring as a simple hexagon, ⬡, in which, it is understood, each corner consists of a CH group. For compounds in which a hydrogen atom has been replaced by another atom or group, that atom or group is indicated at the appropriate place in the formula.

30. Sources of Aromatic Compounds. Until very recently, the most important source of aromatic compounds has been coal. Most coal mined in the United States is used directly as a fuel, but some bituminous coal is subjected to heating in retorts in the absence of air (destructive distillation), either for the manufacture of illuminating gas or for the production of coke. In this process a number of by-products are obtained, the most important being ammonia and coal tar (about 6 lb. from 100 lb. of coal). The coal tar, a thick, viscous mass, rich in aromatic compounds, may be separated into fractions by distillation, and refined. Four cuts or fractions are usually taken, light oil, middle (or carbolic) oil, heavy (or creosote) oil, and green (or anthracene) oil. The residue is pitch, which is used in making tarred paper and, mixed with asphalt, in paving.

From the aromatic compounds obtained in the distillation of black, evil-smelling coal tar, the chemist prepares dyes of the most delicate shades, choice perfumes and flavors, life-saving drugs, powerful explosives, valuable plastics, insecticides, lacquers, solvents, and a host of other materials. Im-

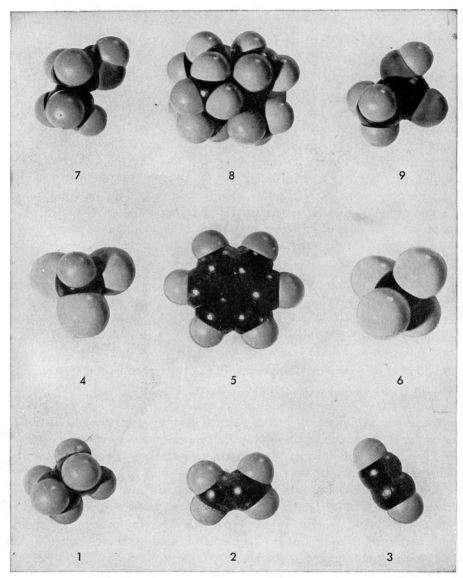

Fig. 31.6. Scale models of some organic molecules: 1. ethane. 2. ethylene. 3. acetylene. 4. chloroform. 5. benzene. 6. carbon tetrachloride. 7. ethyl alcohol. 8. triptane. 9. acetic acid.

portant aromatic compounds derived from coal tar and used industrially, called coal tar crudes, are shown in Table 31.5.

Although these crudes are used chiefly as raw materials in chemical industries, some of them are useful in themselves. Benzene is an important liquid fuel and solvent, especially for rubber. Both benzene and toluene are used as blending agents in high octane gasolines. Phenol ("carbolic acid") is an important disinfectant, and a mixture of the cresols, coal tar creosote, is widely used for the impregnation of wood to protect it against decay and insects. Naphthalene, a solid at ordinary temperatures, is familiar as "moth balls."

Table 31.5

Coal Tar Crudes

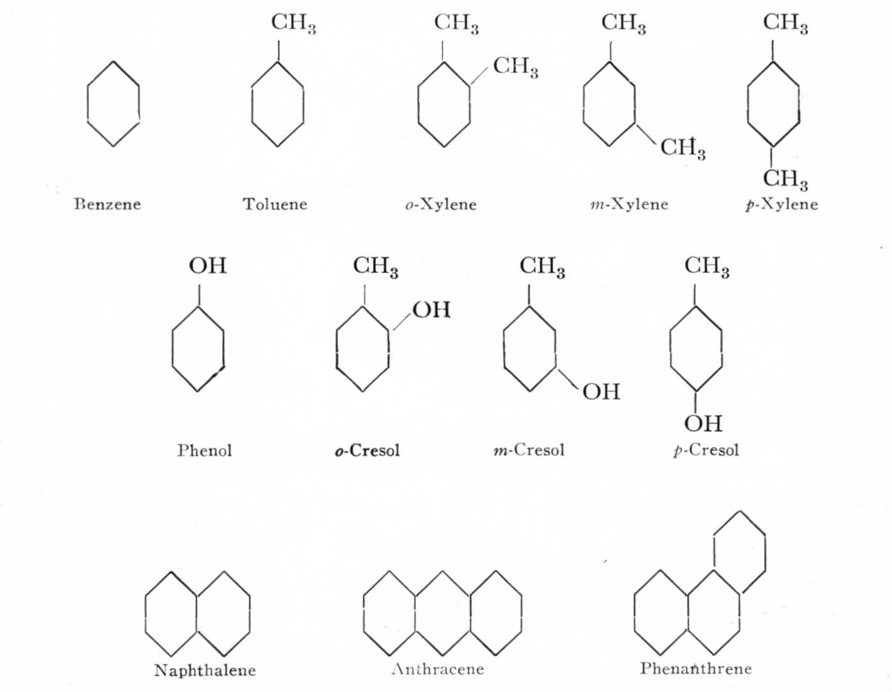

Benzene	Toluene	o-Xylene	m-Xylene	p-Xylene

Phenol	o-Cresol	m-Cresol	p-Cresol

Naphthalene	Anthracene	Phenanthrene

The letter prefixes used in the naming of the isomeric xylenes and the isomeric cresols indicate the relative positions of the substituting groups on the ring. Adjacent positions, or compounds containing substituting groups in such positions, are designated as *ortho* (*o*), those separated by one carbon atom as *meta* (*m*), and opposite positions as *para* (*p*).

The molecule of naphthalene ($C_{10}H_8$) consists of two benzene rings joined together through two carbon atoms which are common to both rings. Similarly, each of the isomers anthracene and phenanthrene, $C_{14}H_{10}$, contains three fused benzene rings. These relationships are more readily seen when the formulas are written as follows (the lines do not represent ordinary single bonds but rather aromatic bonds such as are present in benzene):

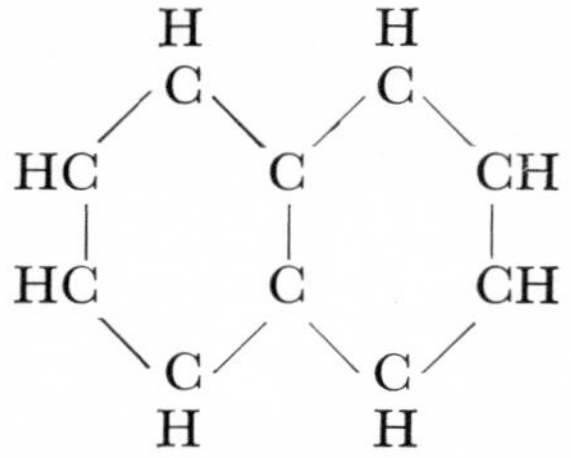

Naphthalene

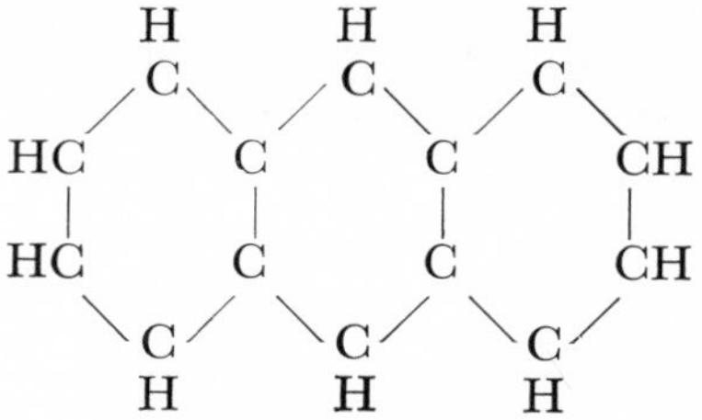

Anthracene

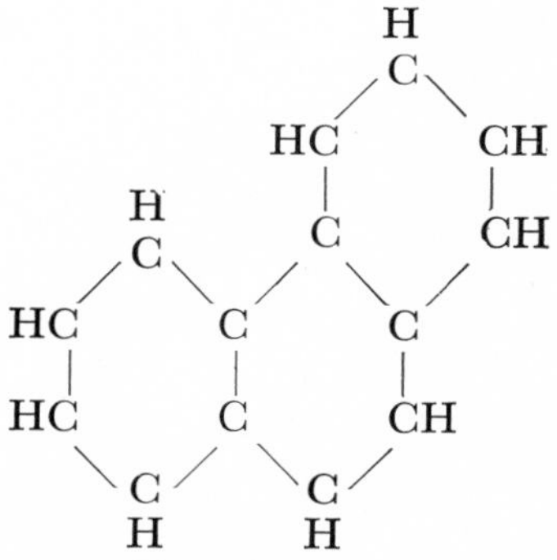

Phenanthrene

Fairly high concentrations of aromatic hydrocarbons occur in mid-continent and especially in California petroleum. In addition, methods were developed during World War II for the large scale production of aromatic hydrocarbons, particularly toluene and styrene, from petroleum products. Consequently, petroleum is now recognized as an important source, not only of aliphatic, but also of aromatic compounds.

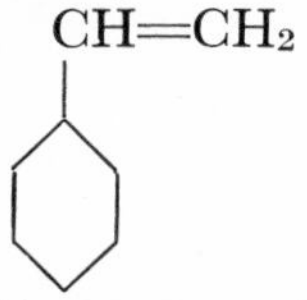

31. Derivatives of the Aromatic Hydrocarbons. The aromatic hydrocarbons form all the various types of derivatives that we have already studied in connection with the aliphatic compounds. Most of these derivatives are prepared from constituents of coal tar, largely through substitution reactions. The outstanding tendency of aromatic compounds to undergo substitution reactions, characteristic of saturated compounds, rather than addition reactions, typical of unsaturated compounds, does not seem surprising when it is recalled that the benzene ring does not contain ordinary olefinic double bonds. In the synthesis of aromatic derivatives from coal tar compounds, three types of attack, all substitution reactions, are widely used. They are chlorination, nitration, and sulfonation. All these reactions may proceed in one or more steps, but in every case the extent of substitution can be controlled. The first step in each type of reaction is illustrated here for benzene.

Chlorination

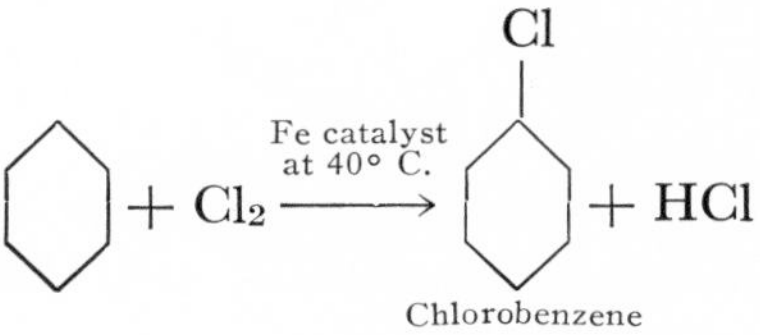

$$\bigcirc + Cl_2 \xrightarrow[\text{at } 40° \text{ C.}]{\text{Fe catalyst}} \overset{Cl}{\bigcirc} + HCl$$

Chlorobenzene

Nitration

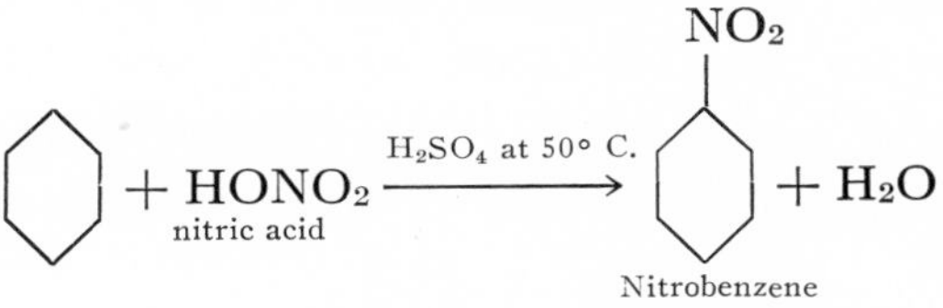

$$\bigcirc + HONO_2 \xrightarrow{H_2SO_4 \text{ at } 50° \text{ C.}} \overset{NO_2}{\bigcirc} + H_2O$$

nitric acid   Nitrobenzene

Sulfonation

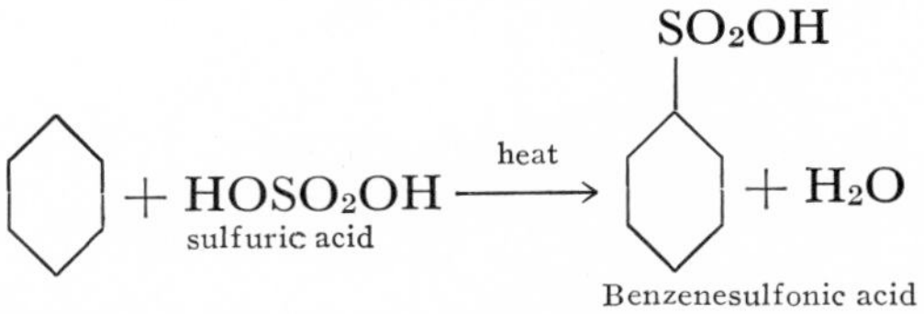

$$\bigcirc + HOSO_2OH \xrightarrow{\text{heat}} \overset{SO_2OH}{\bigcirc} + H_2O$$

sulfuric acid   Benzenesulfonic acid

Chlorobenzene is a colorless liquid used in the manufacture of the insecticide DDT (p. 606). Although a halogen atom attached to an aromatic ring is markedly less reactive than one substituted in a paraffin chain, chlorobenzene is converted to phenol on an industrial scale by being heated with dilute sodium hydroxide, at 300° C. and under very high pressure, in a system of copper pipes.

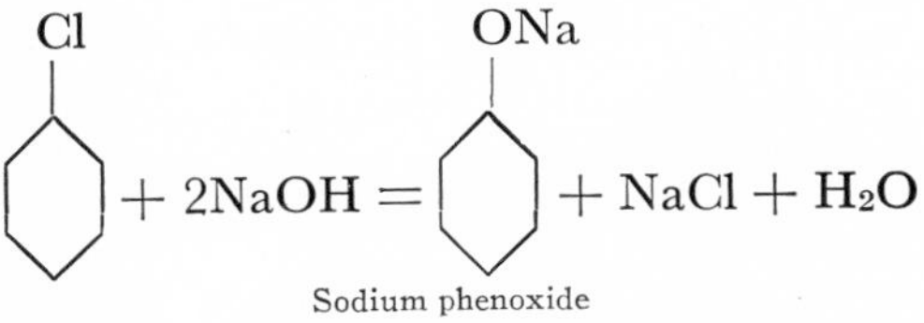

$$\overset{Cl}{\bigcirc} + 2NaOH = \overset{ONa}{\bigcirc} + NaCl + H_2O$$

Sodium phenoxide

Phenol is then liberated from its sodium salt, sodium phenoxide, with carbon dioxide. The intermediate formation of the salt emphasizes the fact that phenolic compounds, in which an OH group is substituted on a benzene ring, are much more acidic than the aliphatic alcohols. The supply of phenol from coal tar is entirely inadequate to meet the demands of the plastics industry (p. 615), and over 90% of the millions of pounds of phenol used annually is now made synthetically.

Aniline, an extremely important primary amine, may be made commercially by heating chlorobenzene and ammonia at 200° C. with a mixture of cuprous oxide and the catalyst cuprous chloride.

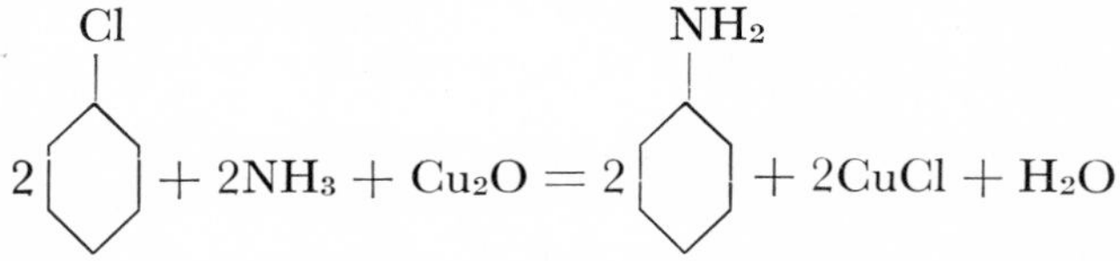

$$2 \left[\underset{}{\overset{Cl}{\bigodot}} \right] + 2NH_3 + Cu_2O = 2 \left[\underset{}{\overset{NH_2}{\bigodot}} \right] + 2CuCl + H_2O$$

Aniline is widely used as a starting material in the manufacture of dyes. The synthetic dyestuffs are complex substances, most of which contain more than one benzene ring in their molecules. One of the simplest is indigo, the oldest of all known dyes, which was formerly isolated from plants, but is now manufactured from aniline. Indigo has the following formula:

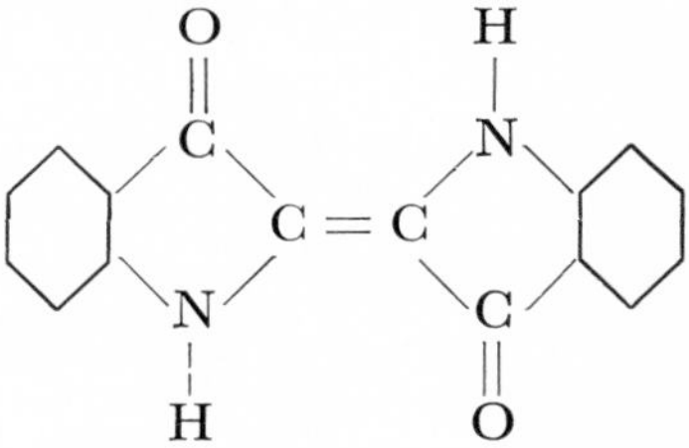

Aniline is used also as a solvent in the preparation of rubber goods, and in making photographic developers, the sulfa-drugs (p. 608), and other medicinals.

The most important commercial source of aniline is nitrobenzene, from which it is obtained by reduction in acid solution. Nitrobenzene is a yellow liquid, also used industrially to some extent as an oxidizing agent.

The three-step nitrations of toluene and phenol give two important high explosives, trinitrotoluene (TNT) and picric acid, respectively.

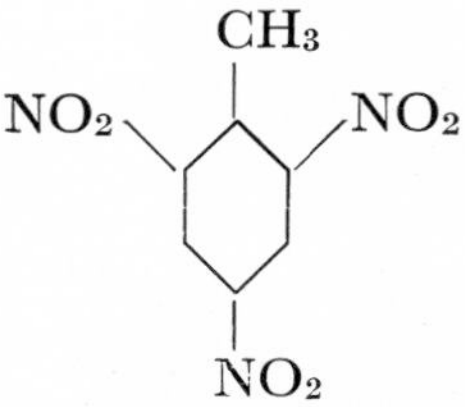

Trinitrotoluene

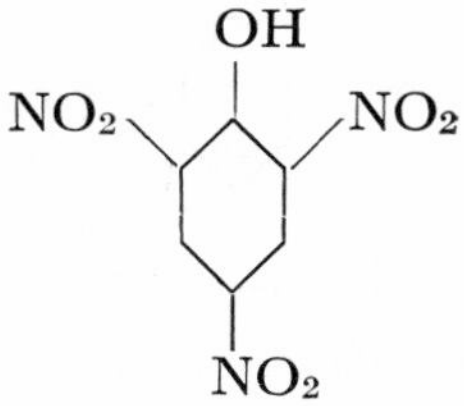

Picric acid

The latter is also used as a yellow dye and in the treatment of burns and ulcers.

Benzenesulfonic acid, a white solid, is converted to phenol commercially by reaction of its sodium salt with sodium hydroxide at 320° C.

$$\underset{\text{SO}_2\text{ONa}}{\bigcirc} + 2\text{NaOH} = \underset{\text{ONa}}{\bigcirc} + \text{Na}_2\text{SO}_3 + \text{H}_2\text{O}$$

The sodium salts of certain sulfonic acids are used as detergents, and derivatives of others are good antiseptics. All of the various sulfa-drugs (p. 609) may be considered as derivatives (amides and substituted amides) of benzenesulfonic acid. Various sulfonated naphthalenes are extensively used as dye intermediates.

STUDY QUESTIONS AND PROBLEMS

1. Write formulas for:
   (a) a pair of homologs
   (b) a pair of isomers
2. Write graphic formulas for the isomeric hexanes (molecular formula C_6H_{14}). Which might be expected to have the best antiknock or octane ratings?
3. Write formulas for the two isomeric compounds that might be obtained by the replacement of a single hydrogen atom in propane by a chlorine atom.
4. Compare the volumes of oxygen required and the volumes of water vapor formed in the complete combustion of 1 l. of ethane, 1 l. of ethylene, and 1 l. of acetylene. (Assume identical conditions of pressure and temperature throughout.) Compare (p. 109) the amounts of heat evolved in the three cases.
5. Represent by an equation, using graphic formulas, the hydrogenation of ethylene; of acetylene.
6. What chemical reaction might be used to distinguish between ethane and ethylene? Would the same test differentiate between ethylene and acetylene?
7. What is noteworthy about the percentage composition of the various hydrocarbons of the ethylene series? What is the empirical formula for all compounds of this series?
8. If you had available both n-heptane and isoöctane, how could you make a synthetic gasoline with an octane number of 90? How do you suppose that octane numbers over 100 are measured?
9. Write a few representative equations showing reactions that might occur during the cracking of n-decane, $C_{10}H_{22}$.
10. By replacing one or more hydrogen atoms in propane by other atoms or groups of atoms, write graphic formulas for: an alcohol, an ether, an aldehyde,

a ketone, a carboxylic acid, an ester, an amine, an amide. Designate the characteristic group in each compound.

11. A student, in preparing diethyl ether by the reaction of sulfuric acid on 100 g. of ethyl alcohol, isolated 50.0 g. of the ether. What percentage of the amount of product that was theoretically possible did he obtain?

12. Why is one hydrogen atom differentiated from the other three in the familiar formula for acetic acid, $HC_2H_3O_2$?

13. See whether you can write three different resonance structures for naphthalene in which the five double bonds are shown in various positions.

14. How does the nature of the reactions of aromatic compounds differ, in general, from that of the reactions of aliphatic unsaturated compounds?

15. What advantage over alcohol does glycerol possess as an antifreeze for use in automobile radiators? If the cost per pound of the two compounds were the same, what advantage would alcohol have?

16. The three hydrides diborane, B_2H_6, disilane, Si_2H_6, and hydrazine, N_2H_4, resemble ethane in that a molecule of each contains two atoms of the same element joined together through a covalent bond. See whether you can draw plausible electronic formulas for these three compounds in which the central atoms possess in their valence shells a full octet of electrons which cannot be expanded and in which all of the electrons are shared. Would you predict that these hydrides are more or less reactive than ethane?

17. A hydrocarbon was found by analysis to contain 85.7% carbon and 14.3% hydrogen. How much can one deduce from these data alone? If the compound has a density of 1.250 g./l. at standard conditions, what is its formula?

18. What is the minimum possible molecular weight for an organic compound which contains 84.2% of bromine? Suggest a reasonable formula for the compound.

19. A compound containing only carbon, hydrogen, and oxygen has an approximate molecular weight of 46. On combustion with excess oxygen, 8.000 mg. of the compound gave 15.28 mg. of carbon dioxide and 9.385 mg. of water. What is the formula of the compound?

20. Write formulas for two members of the alkane series which can form two and only two different dibromo substitution products.

21. How does the reaction of acetic acid with ethyl alcohol to form ethyl acetate (p. 583) differ from the neutralization of acetic acid by sodium hydroxide?

22. If the actual structure for benzene were either that represented by formula A or that represented by formula B on p. 587, how many different o-xylenes should exist? Draw their formulas.

23. The equilibrium constant (K) at 25° for the esterification reaction between acetic acid and ethyl alcohol to form ethyl acetate is 4. If one mole of acetic acid and two moles of ethyl alcohol are mixed at 25°, what will be the composition of the mixture when equilibrium is attained?

32

Organic Chemistry and the World in Which We Live

1. Importance of Organic Chemistry. The remarkable development of organic chemistry during the past century has paved the way for spectacular industrial applications which have enriched our lives in countless ways. Every aspect of society has been influenced by the advance of organic technology —the food we eat, the clothes we wear, the homes we build, the methods by which we have waged war, the means by which we combat disease—all have been fashioned to a considerable extent by organic chemistry. Many valuable natural products are slightly modified chemically in order to make them more useful; others are synthesized much more cheaply and abundantly than they can be wrested from nature. In recent years, synthetic materials closely related in structure to natural products, but with superior qualities, greater versatility, and unique advantages, have been developed. In addition, man has seized upon such abundant raw materials as coal, water, air, petroleum, natural gas, and common farm crops to produce a host of new materials which nature forgot.

Even a brief review of all these ever expanding achievements is impossible here; the purpose of this chapter is to indicate a few ways in which organic chemistry is related to everyday life, and to suggest some of the recent trends in applied organic chemistry.

THE CHEMISTRY OF FOODSTUFFS AND RELATED INDUSTRIES

2. The Chief Classes of Foodstuffs. The essential constituents of the diet of man and animals are usually classified into five major groups, carbohydrates, fats, proteins, vitamins, and minerals. All except the last named are organic in nature. The nutritional completeness of any food is measured by the extent to which it furnishes all five classes of foodstuffs.

3. The Carbohydrates. From the standpoint of plant life, the *carbohydrates* are the most important natural compounds. They are the main product of the life process in plants and may be the biological precursors of some fats, proteins, and vitamins. In addition, they form the supporting structure of plants. The carbohydrates constitute the ultimate source of energy for the whole animal kingdom; not only are they indispensable to man as foods, but such typical carbohydrates as cellulose, starch, glucose, and sucrose, formed currently or in past ages, also provide us with our principal sources of heat, power, clothing, and shelter, as well as many of our other necessities and luxuries. A good diet contains approximately 65% by weight of carbohydrate material; sugar, flour, potatoes, corn syrup, and cereals are the chief sources.

Carbohydrates are composed of carbon, hydrogen, and oxygen; the latter elements are usually present in the same ratio in which they occur in water; hence, most carbohydrates are represented by the general formula $C_x(H_2O)_y$, where x and y may be the same or different numbers. The complex process of *photosynthesis*, by means of which living plants synthesize carbohydrates from carbon dioxide and water in the presence of sunlight and chlorophyll (the green coloring matter in plants), is the most important of all chemical reactions. Since carbohydrates are enormously richer in energy than the water and carbon dioxide from which they are formed, photosynthesis (the basic reaction of which may be represented by the general equation $nCO_2 + nH_2O = [C(H_2O)]_n + nO_2$) constitutes the process through which the radiant energy of the sun is stored as chemical energy. In this form, it is readily utilizable for sustaining animal life and in providing power for man's modern civilization. An estimated 600 tons of carbon and 5 trillion calories of energy are fixed per second, on the average, by all of the plants on the earth.

Carbohydrates are classified systematically into three principal groups: the monosaccharides, the disaccharides, and the polysaccharides. The simplest carbohydrates are the monosaccharides, the most familiar of which have the molecular formula $C_6H_{12}O_6$. Chemical tests reveal that these monosaccharides contain a single aldehyde or ketone group. Each of the remaining five carbon atoms of the molecule bears a single hydroxyl group of the alcohol type, as indicated by the formation of penta-esters in the reaction of the monosaccharides with organic acids. With acetic acid, for example, the products are penta-acetates. In order to indicate the presence of five hydroxyl groups, chemists sometimes write the molecular formula for the common monosaccharides as $C_6H_7O(OH)_5$; the penta-acetates may be represented correspondingly as $C_6H_7O(O\overset{\displaystyle O}{\overset{\displaystyle \|}{C}}—CH_3)_5$.

Both the disaccharides and the polysaccharides are condensation products of the monosaccharides, one molecule of water being lost for each pair of monosaccharide molecules which are linked together. The di- and poly-saccharides may, therefore, be represented by the general formula $(C_6H_{10}O_5)_nH_2O$. Molecules of the disaccharides contain two monosaccharide units, and some of the polysaccharides, as many as several thousand such units.

4. Sugars. All the mono- and disaccharides are colorless, crystalline, water-soluble substances with a sweet taste, and are called *sugars*. Glucose and fructose are the two most important monosaccharides.

Glucose (known also as *d*-glucose, dextrose, grape sugar, or corn sugar) is an aldehyde sugar of the formula $CH_2OH—(CHOH)_4—CHO$. It occurs uncombined in many plants, being found in leaves, sap, flowers, honey, and fruits. Ripe grapes frequently contain as much as 20 to 30% of glucose. Small quantities are normally present in human blood and urine, but the urine of patients with *diabetes mellitus* may contain over 8% of the sugar.

Glucose is obtained commercially by the hydrolysis of starch under pressure in the presence of a small amount of hydrochloric acid. It has important uses in the feeding of infants, and in candy, jams, and table syrups. Glucose serves as a quick source of energy because it is absorbed directly through the intestinal walls without need for previous digestion. In the presence of the enzyme zymase, it can be fermented to ethyl alcohol and carbon dioxide, according to the equation

$$C_6H_{12}O_6 = 2C_2H_5OH + 2CO_2$$

Fructose (*d*-fructose, levulose, or fruit sugar), an isomer of glucose, is a ketone sugar of the formula $CH_2OH—(CHOH)_3—\overset{\overset{\textstyle O}{\|}}{C}—CH_2OH$. The sweetest of all the sugars, it occurs in many fruits and in honey.

The most important of the disaccharides are sucrose (cane or beet sugar), maltose (malt sugar), and lactose (milk sugar). They may be considered as being formed by the combination of two molecules of monosaccharides with the loss of a single molecule of water; hence they have the molecular formula $C_{12}H_{22}O_{11}$. One of the alcoholic hydroxyl groups of each monosaccharide unit is involved in linking the two units; eight such groups remain in the disaccharide molecule, as shown by the formula $C_{12}H_{14}O_3(OH)_8$. In the presence of dilute acids or of certain enzymes, the disaccharides may be hydrolyzed to form two molecules of monosaccharides, according to the general equation $C_{12}H_{22}O_{11} + H_2O = C_6H_{12}O_6 + C_6H_{12}O_6$. Sucrose, for example, gives one molecule of glucose and one of fructose, whereas maltose gives two molecules of glucose. In the digestion of carbohydrates in the body, the disaccharides are hydrolyzed in the alkaline medium of the intestine by the enzymatic action of maltase, invertase, and lactase, present in the pancreatic juice.

The world's annual production of sucrose is in excess of 35,000,000 tons, of which more than half is obtained from sugar cane and the rest largely from sugar beets. Americans consume an average of more than 100 lb. of sucrose per person yearly. In the production of ethyl alcohol from molasses (a by-product in the refining of sugar), the sucrose is first hydrolyzed to glucose and fructose, and these monosaccharides then undergo fermentation. The first reaction is brought about by the action of invertase, the second by the action of zymase; both of these enzymes are present in yeast.

5. Starch. Like the other polysaccharides, *starch* is an amorphous, insoluble substance. It is present as the reserve food material in the tubers and seeds of nearly all plants. It is the cheapest and most abundant of all human food materials; the principal sources are corn, potatoes, wheat, rice, and arrowroot.

The starches obtained from various sources are mixtures rather than pure compounds. Upon complete hydrolysis, starch is converted quantitatively into glucose, and it undoubtedly consists of long branched chain molecules composed of glucose units, each pair of which are linked together with the loss of a molecule of water. The empirical formula for starch is $(C_6H_{10}O_5)_x H_2O$, where x is believed to have varying values up to 3000. The glucose units in the starch molecule retain an average of three alcoholic hydroxyl groups per glucose unit; this fact is often represented by means of the formula $[C_6H_7O_2(OH)_3]_x H_2O$.

When dry starch is heated at 140°–170° C. after having previously been sprayed with dilute hydrochloric acid, it is partially hydrolyzed to form a water-soluble product known as dextrin, which is extensively used as an adhesive for postage stamps and envelopes and as a thickener for dyes and ice cream. By carefully regulated heating with acid, starch may be partially hydrolyzed to yield maltose. In the fermentation of starch to form alcohol, this same change is brought about by the catalytic action of diastase, an enzyme in malt, and in the digestion of starch in the body, by ptyalin, the enzyme of saliva. In each case, the maltose is further hydrolyzed to glucose by the action of maltase, an enzyme present in yeast and in the pancreatic juice. The production of commercial glucose by the complete hydrolysis of cornstarch in acid medium is an important industry in the agricultural Middle West. The equation for the reaction is as follows:

$$(C_6H_{10}O_5)_xH_2O + (x-1)H_2O = xC_6H_{12}O_6$$

Corn syrup is a mixture of glucose, maltose, and dextrin formed by the incomplete hydrolysis of cornstarch.

6. Cellulose. The most abundant of all the carbohydrates is the polysaccharide *cellulose*, which constitutes the skeletal material in all plant life. Cotton is about 90% cellulose, coniferous wood 60%, and cereal straws 35%. Absorbent cotton and filter paper are nearly pure cellulose. Although cellulose cannot be digested by human beings, it plays an important regulatory role in the diet as a roughage or bulk food, aiding digestion and elimination.

Like starch, cellulose has the empirical formula $(C_6H_{10}O_5)_xH_2O$ or $[C_6H_7O_2(OH)_3]_xH_2O$ and is hydrolyzed ultimately to glucose, a reaction which is of importance in the economy of nations at the time of a shortage of sugars. Chemists believe the cellulose molecule to consist of extremely long chains of glucose units, linked in a slightly different fashion than is the case in starch. A great deal of research is at present being directed toward the determination of the exact structure of cellulose.

7. Cellulose Products. Cellulose serves as the raw material for a host of industries. In some, such as the cotton textile, lumber, and paper industries, it is converted into useful products without being altered chemically. In cotton and in the stalk of the flax plant, the cellulose fibers are sufficiently long to be spun directly into cotton or linen threads. Paper consists of a mat of shorter cellulose fibers.

One of the most versatile of all textile fibers is the product known as *rayon*, which is obtained by chemical treatment of cellulose. Originally developed about 1900 as an imitation silk, rayon has long since taken its place as a distinctly different fiber, much less expensive than silk but superior to it in luster and dyeing qualities. About a billion pounds of rayon are produced annually in this country.

Several processes for the manufacture of rayon are in use today, but in each of these, two basic steps are involved: (1) the cellulose or cellulose derivative is brought into solution in a suitable solvent, and (2) the solution is drawn out into very fine streams by being forced under high pressure through a spinneret containing many microscopic holes, under such conditions that the cellulose or cellulose derivative is regenerated in the form of long fine filaments. By extrusion through narrow slits, rather than holes, transparent cellulose films may be obtained. Such films may be further treated to give the tough, pliable, moisture-proof product called cellophane. During the war, a high-strength rayon called "cordura" replaced cotton as the reinforcing fabric in airplane, heavy-duty truck, and bus tires, because it gives a lighter, tougher, more heat-resistant tire, and saves $\frac{2}{3}$ pound of rubber for each pound of rayon used. It is now being used in automobile tires, also.

Upon treatment with a mixture of concentrated nitric and sulfuric acids, cellulose can be nitrated to varying degrees, depending upon the temperature and time of reaction. Completely nitrated cellulose, the trinitrate, $[C_6H_7O_2(ONO_2)_3]_xH_2O$, contains 14.17% of nitrogen.

Cellulose nitrates which contain from 13 to 13.3% of nitrogen are explosive and are known as guncotton. Guncotton is used as such in torpedo heads and submarine mines; mixed with nitroglycerine (p. 495) and other materials, it is used in smokeless powder and in dynamite, which ranks as one of the great labor-saving tools of all time.

Cellulose nitrates containing about 11% of nitrogen are called pyroxylin, which finds extensive use in the manufacture of automobile lacquers, plastics, artificial leather, photographic film, and collodion. Celluloid, the first of the synthetic plastics, consists of a mixture of pyroxylin and camphor. Artificial leather is prepared by coating canvas with a pyroxylin solution containing a suitable pigment. Dissolved in a mixture of alcohol and ether, pyroxylin forms collodion, which is used as a liquid court-plaster.

The esters cellulose diacetate, $[C_6H_7O_2(OH)(O-\overset{\overset{\displaystyle O}{\|}}{C}-CH_3)_2]_xH_2O$,

and cellulose triacetate, $[C_6H_7O_2(O-\overset{\overset{\displaystyle O}{\|}}{C}-CH_3)_3]_xH_2O$, also are important industrial products. The former finds extensive use in the manufacture of acetate rayon (Celanese), the latter in non-inflammable x-ray film and safety film for home motion pictures and in an important group of light-weight plastics.

8. Fats. The second general class of foodstuffs, the fats, are derived largely from meats, dairy products, and vegetables. Suet, lard, cream, butter, oleomargarine, and vegetable shortenings constitute the principal sources of fats in the diet. Fats provide fuel, although to a lesser extent than carbohydrates, and also supply the body with material for storage, repair, and the synthesis of certain essential constituents of the tissues. A well-balanced diet should contain about 10% by weight of fat.

Chemically, the fats are all esters of the trihydroxy alcohol glycerol with fatty acids of high molecular weight. Most of the solid fats are glyceryl esters of the saturated acids palmitic or stearic (p. 582), whereas the liquid fats or fatty oils, such as cottonseed, linseed, olive, coconut, and peanut oil, are glyceryl esters of the unsaturated fatty acids such as oleic acid (p. 582).

Many of the fatty oils have limited use because they are oxidized upon standing to form products of disagreeable odor and taste. The solid fats, on the other hand, are in great demand both for cooking and soap manufacture. Hence, the reduction or hydrogenation of vegetable oils to fats (p. 228) is a process of great commercial importance. The complete hydrogenation, for example, of olein, the glyceryl ester of oleic acid, gives stearin, the glyceryl ester of stearic acid.

$$
\begin{array}{ll}
CH_3(CH_2)_7CH{=}CH(CH_2)_7COOCH_2 & CH_3(CH_2)_{16}COOCH_2 \\
\qquad\qquad\qquad\qquad\qquad\qquad | & \qquad\qquad\qquad | \\
CH_3(CH_2)_7CH{=}CH(CH_2)_7COOCH \ +3H_2 = & CH_3(CH_2)_{16}COOCH \\
\qquad\qquad\qquad\qquad\qquad\qquad | & \qquad\qquad\qquad | \\
CH_3(CH_2)_7CH{=}CH(CH_2)_7COOCH_2 & CH_3(CH_2)_{16}COOCH_2 \\
\qquad\qquad\qquad\qquad \text{olein} & \qquad\qquad \text{stearin}
\end{array}
$$

In commercial practice, finely divided nickel is used as catalyst. The hydrogenation is not carried to completion, but is stopped when a fat of just the desired consistency is obtained. Many liquid fats, such as cottonseed oil, formerly regarded as waste products, are now "hardened" by this hydrogenation process to produce edible fats used in making shortenings (such as Crisco, Dexo, Swift'ning, Fluffo, and Spry) and oleomargarine.

Highly unsaturated oils, such as linseed oil, tung oil, and dehydrated castor oil, in which most of the acid groups contain two or more double bonds, are valuable drying oils, widely used in paints and varnish and in the manufacture of linoleum and oilcloth. The "drying" of such oils consists, not in evaporation, but in complex polymerization reactions which are catalyzed by peroxides formed upon exposure of the oils to air or oxygen.

In recent years, fats have assumed an increasing role as a source of organic chemicals—acids, alcohols, amides, amines, and many others.

All esters, especially under suitable catalysis, react with water to give the alcohol and acid from which the ester is derived. This reaction, which is just the reverse of esterification (p. 503), involves the splitting of a compound by means of water, and is, therefore, called hydrolysis. The equilibrium constant for the esterification reaction of acetic acid with ethyl alcohol at $25°$ is 4; for the reverse reaction, the hydrolysis of ethyl acetate, the constant is of course 0.25. In the hydrolysis of fats and oils, glycerol is always the alcohol produced. Stearin, for example, can be hydrolyzed to form stearic acid and glycerol.

$$C_{17}H_{35}-COOCH_2 \qquad\qquad\qquad CH_2OH$$
$$C_{17}H_{35}-COOCH \; + 3HOH \rightleftharpoons 3C_{17}H_{35}COOH + \; CHOH$$
$$C_{17}H_{35}-COOCH_2 \qquad\qquad\qquad CH_2OH$$

When digested in the body, fats are hydrolyzed to glycerol and fatty acids in the stomach and small intestine by lipases (enzymes for fat) present in the gastric and pancreatic juices. The glycerol and acids diffuse through the intestinal wall and then recombine to form fat in the blood. Part of this fat is stored in the tissues and part is oxidized, furnishing heat and muscular energy.

9. **Soap.** A *soap* is a salt of a high molecular weight fatty acid. Soaps are manufactured commercially on a large scale by the hydrolysis of fats in the presence of sodium or potassium hydroxide. This process is called *saponification* (soap making). The sodium salts of palmitic, stearic, and oleic acids (p. 582) are the most common constituents of ordinary soaps. Saponification of palmitin (glyceryl palmitate), for example, with sodium hydroxide, produces the soap sodium palmitate.

$$C_{15}H_{31}COOCH_2 \qquad\qquad\qquad CH_2OH$$
$$C_{15}H_{31}COOCH \; + 3NaOH = 3\underset{\text{sodium palmitate}}{C_{15}H_{31}COONa} + \; CHOH$$
$$C_{15}H_{31}COOCH_2 \qquad\qquad\qquad CH_2OH$$
$$\underset{\text{palmitin}}{}$$

Glycerol is always a by-product in soap manufacture, and most commercial glycerol is obtained from that source.

The cleansing action of soaps is due to their ability to lower the surface tension of water and thus to form a persistent lather which absorbs dirt and emulsifies fats. These properties of soaps are attributed to the characteristic structure of soap molecules, which contain a water-soluble ionic group at one end, attached to a comparatively long hydrocarbon chain which has a solubilizing effect on organic materials. All but very dilute soap solutions are partly colloidal, which fact accounts for their adsorptive properties (p. 367).

The calcium, magnesium, and iron salts of the high molecular weight fatty acids are insoluble in water and constitute the scum which is formed when ordinary soap is added to hard water (p. 674). In recent years, a large number of nonsoap detergents (cleaning agents) which are equally effective both in hard and in soft water have been placed on the market under familiar trade names such as Dreft, Drene, Vel, Breeze, Fab, and Tide. Most of these detergents are sodium salts of monoalkyl sulfates, having the general type formula $ROSO_2ONa$. The monoalkyl sulfates used are those obtained by the reaction of sulfuric acid with alcohols containing from 7 to 18 carbon atoms; hence the R group in the type formula can vary from C_7H_{15} to $C_{18}H_{37}$. The calcium, magnesium, and iron salts of the monoalkyl sulfates are, of course, soluble in water. Widespread use of such detergents in place of soaps has helped to conserve fats for use as food, and has heightened the interest in synthetic methods for the production of glycerol.

10. Proteins. The proteins (Greek, *proteios*, "primary") derive their name from their great importance in all living matter. They are constituents of all living cells and are essential to vital processes. The proteins serve as the structural materials for animals much as cellulose does for plants. Muscle and nerve tissue, skin, hair, silk, wool, and the horny material of nails, feathers, horns, and hoofs, as well as the solid components of blood, are essentially proteins. In plants, the highest concentration of protein is found in the seeds. Lean meat, fish, eggs, milk, cheese, and cereals are the principal sources of protein in the diet, which should be about 20% by weight protein in nature. The chief function of protein is the building and repair of body tissue.

Chemically, the proteins are extremely complex nitrogen-containing substances. Molecular weight determinations of a large number of different proteins have given values ranging from about 40,000 (for egg albumin, insulin, and others) to 15–20 million (for tobacco mosaic virus).

Upon hydrolysis in acid solution, protein molecules are broken down into hundreds or thousands of molecules of the simple amino acids (p. 585). Thus far, 24 different amino acids have been isolated from the hydrolysis of a variety of proteins. Each known protein gives several different amino acids, but no one protein gives all 24. The simplest of these amino acids is aminoacetic acid or glycine, NH_2CH_2COOH; the others may be regarded as derivatives of glycine in which one of the two hydrogen atoms attached to the carbon is replaced by an organic radical.

The amino acids serve as the building blocks of the proteins by joining to form long chains, the carboxyl group of each molecule combining with the amino group of another. This process may be illustrated for glycine as follows:

Proteins are thus complex substituted polyamides. The grouping $\overset{\text{O}}{\overset{\|}{-\text{C}}}\overset{\text{H}}{\overset{|}{-\text{N}-}}$, formed by the elimination of a molecule of water between a COOH and an NH_2 group, is called a *peptide* linkage. It occurs repeatedly in a protein molecule, serving as a bridge to link the amino-acid units together. The exact shape which the long chain molecules take in various proteins is at present the object of extensive research.

The hydrolysis of proteins to form amino acids is exactly the reverse of the combination process described in the preceding paragraph. In the digestion of proteins in the body, the hydrolysis is brought about through the action of the enzymes *pepsin,* in the gastric juice, and *trypsin,* in the pancreatic juice. The proteins are progressively broken down into simpler substances, first proteoses, then peptides, and finally amino acids. The amino acids, being soluble in water, pass through the intestinal wall into the blood stream to be resynthesized into body protein or oxidized as a fuel.

Recent studies have shown that it may be the amino acids which are important in a balanced diet, and not the proteins. Nine of the 24 amino acids are *essential,* i.e., they cannot be synthesized by animals at a rate necessary for normal growth and health from other materials ordinarily available in foods. Lack of sufficient amounts of any of the essential amino acids in the diet therefore leads to malnutrition. During the past few years, commercially feasible syntheses of several of the essential amino acids have been developed. This is significant in that it provides a method of supplying protein requirements in highly concentrated form, a consideration of particular importance in rushing food to starving populations when transportation is a critical factor.

11. Vitamins. The *vitamins,* or accessory food materials, are complex organic compounds which act as indispensable regulatory agents for various body processes. The profound effects of traces of vitamins in promoting normal growth and health is explained, at least in the case of some of the vitamins, by the fact that vitamins are necessary constituents of certain enzyme systems. Since the turn of the century, when it was first discovered that such diseases as rickets, scurvy, and beriberi are deficiency diseases, spectacular progress has been achieved in the isolation, determination of structure, and synthesis of the vitamins.

No less than nine different vitamins, which have either been proved essential to man or are of undoubted clinical significance, are known as definite chemical substances. The physical, chemical, and nutritional properties of almost all have been established, and their utilization for the pro-

Table 32.1

Sources and Functions of the Vitamins

Vitamin	Some natural sources	Body functions	Deficiency symptoms and diseases
A $C_{20}H_{29}OH$	Fish oils, liver, milk, egg yolk, vegetables	Promotes growth, protects against infections and eye diseases, required for production of visual purple.	Night blindness, inflammation of the eyes
B_1 Thiamin $C_{12}H_{15}N_4SOH$	Yeast, bran of grains, peas, egg yolk, milk, peanuts, oysters	Promotes growth, digestion and appetite; protects against nervous diseases.	Loss of appetite, fatigue, fear, nervousness, beriberi
B_2 Group Niacin or nicotinic acid C_5H_4NCOOH	Yeast, liver, fish, brans	Prevents and cures pellagra.	Diarrhea, skin lesions, beefy tongue, nervous disorders
Riboflavin $C_{17}H_{20}O_6N_4$	Yeast, liver, fish, kidney, milk, eggwhite	Aids growth and maintenance of healthy condition of skin and eyes.	Cracks at corners of mouth, dermatitis, eye defects, retardation of growth
Folic Acid $C_{17}H_{17}O_2N_7(COOH)_2$	Liver, yeast, egg yolk, green vegetables	Relieves symptoms of pernicious and certain other types of anemia, and of sprue.	Anemia and emaciation, dermatitis and malnutrition characteristic of sprue
B_{12} $C_{61-64}H_{86-92}O_{13}N_{14}PCo$	Liver, egg yolk, meat	Combats pernicious anemia.	Pernicious anemia
C Ascorbic Acid $C_6H_8O_6$	Citrus fruits, strawberries, tomatoes, green vegetables	Promotes growth of sound tissue and bones; plays role in keeping teeth and gums healthy, and in healing of wounds.	Spongy gums, hemorrhage, structural weakness in cartilage, bone, and teeth; scurvy
D_2 $C_{28}H_{43}OH$ D_3 $C_{27}H_{43}OH$	Cod, halibut, and tunafish liver, milk, egg yolk, yeast; produced by action of ultraviolet light on skin	Controls calcium and phosphorus balances in body.	Fragile bones, dental caries, rickets
K_1 $C_{31}H_{46}O_2$	Hog liver, leafy vegetables, egg yolk, fish meal, oils of grain and cereals	Essential for clotting of blood.	Slow clotting of blood, hemorrhage

motion of health is in actual practical application. Most of them have been synthesized, and at least four are now being made commercially in quantities of many tons a year.

The nine vitamins of proved value to human beings are listed in Table 32.1. Three of the B group, thiamin, riboflavin, and niacin, have specific enzymatic functions which help to make possible oxidation of foods at the relatively low temperature of the body.

12. More Food on the World's Tables, Thanks to Chemistry. Although chemistry has been applied to agricultural problems, particularly in the production of fertilizers, for many decades, yet chemical research in recent years has introduced a new era in a number of agricultural problems. Just a few years ago insects, weeds, and plant and animal diseases caused a loss of 46% of the world's gross agricultural production. Now methods of insect control have been revolutionized by the use of superior and relatively inexpensive organic insecticides. One of these is DDT, p,p'-dichlorodiphenyltrichloroethane, first and most widely publicized of the group; another is the structurally similar methoxychlor, p,p'-dimethoxydiphenyltrichloroethane.

DDT   Methoxychlor

Others which have come into wide use are the chlorinated hydrocarbons lindane (hexachlorocyclohexane, $C_6H_6Cl_6$), chlordane, dieldrin, and perthane, the phosphorus-containing organic insecticides TEP (tetraethyl pyrophosphate), Parathion, and Malathion, and a synthetic analog of pyrethrin called alethrin. Together these insecticides are effective against the whole range of ravaging insects, and their use results in the saving of billions of dollars in crops in the United States alone.

New synthetic weed killers constitute a formidable weapon for farmers all over the world in their perennial battle against the multibillion dollar weed menace. Two of the most successful are 2,4-D (2,4-dichlorophenoxyacetic acid) and 2,4,5-T (2,4,5-trichlorophenoxyacetic acid).

2,4-D   2,4,5-T

Plant hormones or growth stimulants, such as gibberellin, serve a number of purposes: stimulating root growth in garden crops, increasing the size and decreasing the maturation period of fruits and vegetables, eliminating the need of pollination in the production of certain fruits, producing seedless fruits, preventing blossom drop and preharvest drop on fruit trees, and giving rise to new varieties of fruits and vegetables. In addition, crops are currently kept free from most seed- and soil-borne diseases by the use of synthetic seed disinfectants. Meanwhile, the possibility of soilless gardening and of producing synthetic foods from raw materials such as petroleum is being continually explored.

Recent development of amazingly effective synthetic organic soil conditioners such as Krilium, Aerotil, Agrilon, and Fluffium, polymeric resins formed from acrylonitrile (p. 619), presages eventual control by man over one of agriculture's deepest mysteries—optimum growth conditions. Soil conditioners have already proved their effectiveness, when applied to clayey soils, in promoting plant growth, increasing soil aeration and workability, improving drainage and water capacity, retarding moisture loss through evaporation, and prevention of crusting; they are likely to make an invaluable contribution in the rejuvenation of waste lands and in the control of erosion. Nonagricultural uses of soil conditioners include the improvement of baseball diamonds, football fields, golf greens, tennis courts, and racetracks.

ORGANIC CHEMISTRY IN MEDICINE

13. Hormones. Since 1900, the life expectancy of infants has been almost doubled, many dread diseases have been conquered, and promising advances have been made in the all-out attack on those diseases not yet under satisfactory control. Certain chemical agents have, of course, long been used in the relief of human suffering and in the prevention and cure of disease. Such standbys as quinine, morphine, digitalis, and ether have all been in use for over a century. But most of the dramatic developments in the application of organic chemistry to medicine have come about since the turn of the century.

Only in the last 50 years has research revealed the function and nature of the *hormones*, the secretions of the endocrine or ductless glands of the body which pass directly into the blood stream, where small traces exert profound specific actions in the regulation of body processes. Unlike the vitamins, which they resemble in their catalytic function, the hormones are not normally supplied from without the body in the food, but must be formed continually in the body's complex system of endocrine glands in order to maintain normal body functions. Since 1904, more than a dozen hormones, such as adrenaline, thyroxine, insulin, and the various sex hormones, have been isolated, and several have been synthesized. Most of them are extremely effective therapeutic agents for specific purposes.

One of the most momentous advances in the history of medicine came in 1949 with the discovery that two hormones, cortisone and ACTH (adrenocorticotropic hormone) give dramatic relief in rheumatoid arthritis, as well as in over thirty other afflictions most of which had always before been regarded as completely unrelated—high blood pressure, rheumatic fever, bronchial asthma, kidney troubles, cirrhosis of the liver, previously fatal skin diseases, jaundice, stomach ulcers, and severe burns. Cortisone is one of 28 hormones secreted by the outer covering, or cortex, of two tiny glands, the adrenals, which lie on top of the kidneys. ACTH is produced by the minute (its weight is only a few grams) pituitary gland which lies in a bony pocket right in the middle of the head.

Cortisone has the same general ring structure (called the steroid structure) as the sex hormones, the bile acids, the vegetable heart poisons such as digitalis, vitamin D, and ergosterol (found in yeast). It can be obtained by a long series of difficult chemical reactions, or by microbiological processes, from cattle bile, plant steroids, or ergosterol. ACTH is extracted in small amounts from animal pituitary glands.

Both cortisone and ACTH are being introduced cautiously into medical practice. No other drugs remotely approach their versatility; but although both cortisone and ACTH produce marked relief of disease symptoms, they do not offer permanent cures. The glandular balances of the body are most complex, and alteration of these balances by the use of cortisone and ACTH is often accompanied by serious side effects. Perhaps the greatest significance of these two hormones lies in the clues which they provide to basic knowledge of the body. A complete understanding of the pituitary-adrenal relationships may lead to a discovery of the fundamental causes of diseases; it would certainly mark the opening of a new era in medicine.

14. Chemotherapy. The goal of *chemotherapy* is simply the cure of disease by the use of chemical agents that kill or check the invading organisms without permanently damaging the host. Modern chemotherapy began in 1935 with the epoch-making discovery that a rather simple organic compound, sulfanilamide, NH_2—⟨　⟩—SO_2NH_2, was amazingly effective against the bacteria which cause blood poisoning (streptococci). Within five years, more than a thousand derivatives of sulfanilamide, several of which proved to be even more effective and versatile chemotherapeutic agents than the parent compounds, were synthesized.

Thousands of tons of sulfanilamide, and its derivatives sulfapyridine, sulfathiazole, sulfaguanidine, sulfadiazine, marfanil, and others have since been used with striking success in combating pneumonia, meningitis, gonorrhea, childbed fever, blood poisoning, gas-gangrene, dysentery, cholera, boils, and many other skin infections. These drugs have saved countless lives.

As intriguing as the practical aspects of sulfa-drug therapy is the theory concerning the mode of action of these drugs. They are all quite similar structurally to p-aminobenzoic acid,

$$NH_2-\langle\ \rangle-COOH$$

an enzyme essential for bacterial life. It is thought that the molecules of the sulfa-drugs are accepted by the pathogenic bacteria in place of p-aminobenzoic acid molecules, but then cannot perform the necessary enzymatic function of the acid and thus inhibit the growth and reproduction of the bacteria.

Disease-combating weapons even more powerful than the sulfa-drugs have recently been placed in the hands of the medical profession as a result of the interesting discovery that many types of soil-inhabiting bacteria, fungi, and molds discharge complex metabolic products which are almost unbelievably active against a wide variety of pathogenic bacteria. These so-called antibiotics, such as penicillin, streptomycin, aureomycin, chloromycetin, terramycin, magnamycin, erythromycin, kanamycin, bacitracin, tetracycline, and ristocetin have miraculous curative powers; together they are effective against a host of diseases—scarlet fever, pneumonia, syphilis, gonorrhea, meningitis, tularemia, peritonitis, typhoid fever, dysentery, urinary infections, impetigo, and, to some extent, tuberculosis. No other class of drugs has had a more profound effect on public health than the antibiotics. In dollar sales, they rank as the leading class of prescription drugs, followed by the tranquilizers (p. 610).

Many of these antibiotics are obtained by fermentation processes in which vitamin B_{12} is a by-product. Chloromycetin, which is interesting also because it was the first natural product found to contain an aromatic nitro-group, was for several years the only antibiotic produced commercially by chemical synthesis. In 1957, however, several new synthetic drugs with antibiotic action, including hexetidine, were developed, and the name "synthobiotics" was coined to describe this group. Bacteria do not seem to develop resistance to hexetidine, as they do to the sulfa-drugs and many of the antibiotics.

Quite recently it has been discovered that the fermentation antibiotic products, together with vitamin B_{12}, when added to animal feed even in minute quantities, act as powerful growth stimulants. Their use greatly reduces the amount of feed necessary to raise animals to market size. The antibiotics have also shown promise in plant disease control.

15. The Tranquilizers. A significant break-through in the treatment and study of mental illnesses has occurred with the introduction into medical practice since 1952 of new drugs—the so-called tranquilizers or ataractic drugs—which calm or tranquilize patients without clouding consciousness or removing inhibitions. Reserpine (Serpasil), a complex alkaloid extracted from the Rauwolfia plant of India, and the synthetic drug chloropromazine (Thorazine) have been especially effective in relieving the symptoms of mental distress among severely disturbed, hospitalized patients and rendering them susceptible to psychotherapy. Meprobamate (Miltown or Equanil) has been widely prescribed to relieve tension and anxiety and various emotion-sparked illnesses in persons suffering from mild neuroses.

$$NH_2-\overset{\overset{O}{\|}}{C}-O-CH_2-\overset{\overset{CH_3}{|}}{\underset{\underset{\underset{\underset{CH_3}{|}}{CH_2}}{\underset{|}{CH_2}}}{C}}-CH_2-O-\overset{\overset{O}{\|}}{C}-NH_2$$

Chloropromazine   Meprobamate

Important as these drugs are in bringing relief to the mentally ill and in replacing shock and brain surgery as a form of treatment, they may be of even greater significance in the light they shed upon the deeply hidden factors involved in mental illness and, indeed, upon the precise mechanism of the functioning of the human brain.

16. Unanswered Questions. Less spectacular than the practical discoveries, but equally as important, is the fundamental chemical research being directed at the underlying problems of disease, much of which is now being conducted with the aid of radioactive tracer elements. Exactly what chemical changes do the various diseases bring about in the body? How do chemical agents attack or inhibit pathogenic organisms? What is the relationship between structure and chemotherapeutic action? Complete answers to questions such as these may ultimately make it possible for the chemist to predict in advance the exact structure of a drug that will prove effective against any particular type of disease.

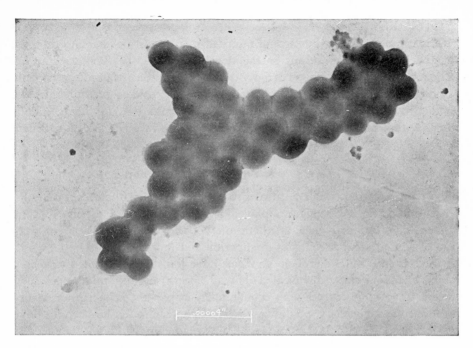

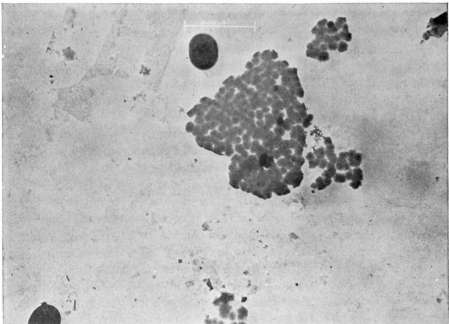

Fig. 32.1. Effect of penicillin on disease-causing bacteria. These micrographs show the bacteria, magnified 38,000 times by means of an electron microscope (top) as a grape-like cluster before penicillin is introduced and (below) after penicillin has affected the microorganisms. (*Courtesy of Radio Corporation of America.*)

The recent brilliant conquest of many of man's most devastating diseases, together with such triumphs as the development of the Salk vaccine for polio and of oral antidiabetic drugs, offers hope, not only that all pathogenic organisms may some day be confined "like other savage creatures, in the zoological gardens of controlled disease," but also that all noninfectious diseases, too, may soon be preventable or curable through use of chemical agents.

THE REALM OF THE GIANT MOLECULE

17. Polymerization. Such natural products as wood, rubber, cotton, silk, wool, and various resins have played a vital role in the shaping of our modern civilization. Hence, synthetic methods for the commercial production of similar, and perhaps even superior and more versatile, materials to be used as substitutes for these products have long been sought. But painstaking chemical research revealed that all natural organic materials which exhibit to varying degrees such economically important properties as structural hardness, elasticity, pliability, resiliency, and high tensile strength have one essential feature in common—all are made up of "giant" molecules whose average weights are tens or hundreds of thousands of atomic weight units. And until 35 years ago almost nothing was known about the architecture of these giant molecules, or about how they were built up in nature or might be reproduced in the laboratory. As a result of large-scale fundamental research on the nature and synthesis of giant molecules which was begun at that time, we now have a detailed knowledge of the structure of natural products of high molecular weight, and the principles underlying the formation of giant molecules have been revealed.

The general line of attack which has subsequently been developed for the synthesis of the whole host of products such as rubber substitutes, plastics, and fibers, is patterned after that which occurs in nature in the formation of these substances. It consists in the combination of simple molecules by some type of reaction which can repeatedly recur, continually leading to the formation of larger and larger molecules. This process by which the simple unit molecules of the starting material, or monomer (Greek, "one part"), undergo combinations that are capable of proceeding indefinitely, is called *polymerization*, and the resulting product is known as a polymer ("many parts").

The development of synthetic polymerization methods has been the key to a whole new world of rubber substitutes, plastics, and synthetic fibers. Actually there is no sharp line of demarcation among these three classes of materials. Their differences lie mainly in the degree of organization among structural units (the giant molecules). The molecular orientation appears to be least in the highly elastic rubber-like materials and greatest in the typical crystalline fibers of high tensile strength.

18. Rubber and Its Substitutes. Rubber is a natural polymer present in colloidal dispersion in the aqueous sap of the rubber tree. It consists of giant molecules in the form of long coiled chains, built up by the polymerization of thousands of molecules of the conjugate diolefin (p. 568) isoprene,

$$CH_3$$
$$|$$
$CH_2{=}C{-}CH{=}CH_2$. Molecule after molecule joins to form the polyisoprene chain of rubber, a section of which is represented as follows:

Three isoprene units as they occur in the rubber molecule.

This process is classed as addition polymerization, because the unit molecules simply add to each other without the formation of any other product; the empirical formula of the resulting polymer is therefore identical with the molecular formula (C_5H_8) of the monomer. Rubber molecules are thought to contain, on the average, over 2000 isoprene units (corresponding to a molecular weight of about 150,000).

Crude rubber is sticky when warm and brittle when cold, has a low tensile strength and resistance to abrasion, and deteriorates through slow atmospheric oxidation. These defects are largely overcome with vulcanization, the process in which rubber is heated with sulfur to about 140° C. in the presence of an accelerator (vulcanization catalyst). Sulfur atoms apparently add to the double bond of some of the isoprene units, thus crosslinking adjacent linear chains into a complex three-dimensional network.

The rigidity of the product depends upon the fraction of the total number of double bonds which react with sulfur in this manner. For most rubber products, 5 to 8% by weight of sulfur is used; addition of 30 to 50% of sulfur gives vulcanite or "hard rubber," a tough plastic. Most rubber substitutes (synthetic rubber)[1] which are rather highly unsaturated are vulcanized in much the same way. Various fillers or pigments such as carbon black, zinc oxide, antimony sulfide, or white lead (p. 823) are added during the vulcanization process in order to increase the wearing quality of the rubber, or to give it a desired color.

[1] Although the synthesis of natural rubber was announced in 1954, no commercial "synthetic rubber" exactly duplicates natural rubber in chemical structure.

Modern mechanized armies roll on rubber; without rubber, our civilian economy would be seriously crippled. Hence, the blow to the United States when 97% of its supply of natural rubber was cut off, following the attack at Pearl Harbor, was almost catastrophic. For although methods for the commercial production of some types of synthetic rubber had been developed before 1941, in that year less than 1.5% of the 820,000 tons of rubber used by this country was synthetic, and part of that was not suited for use in tires. The development, in three short years, by chemists and engineers, of a government-financed industry capable of producing 1,100,000 tons of synthetic rubber annually, was a vital factor in the winning of the war. Petroleum, coal, grain, natural gas, limestone, and salt are the ultimate raw materials of the synthetic rubber industry.

Buna S or GR-S rubber is the all-important tire synthetic which accounted for almost seven-eighths of the government's war-time rubber program. It is a copolymer, built up by the union of molecules of two different unsaturated hydrocarbons, butadiene (p. 568) and styrene (vinylbenzene).

| Butadiene | Styrene | A section of the Buna-S chain |

Actually, there are approximately 6 butadiene units for each styrene unit in the Buna-S chain. Butadiene is obtained from petroleum or from ethyl alcohol, styrene from petroleum and coal. In the copolymerization process, the two reactants are emulsified with the aid of soap, and then heated slightly under pressure in the presence of an organic peroxide as catalyst. This same type of emulsion polymerization is used in the production of most other kinds of synthetic rubber. Buna-S is superior to natural rubber in abrasion resistance, but heats up more rapidly in use at high speeds and with heavy loads.

Butyl rubber is a copolymer of isobutylene, a by-product of petroleum cracking, and small amounts of butadiene.

| Isobutylene | Butadiene | A section of the butyl rubber chain |

It is highly resistant to oxidation, as well as to the action of chemicals, and is much less permeable to gases than natural rubber. Butyl rubber is used widely for inner tubes.

Neoprene, the first American synthetic rubber, was announced in 1931. It is a polymer of chloroprene, which is made from acetylene and hydrogen chloride and differs from isoprene only in the substitution of a chlorine atom for the methyl group. The recurring unit in the neoprene chain is thus $-CH_2-CCl=CH-CH_2-$. Neoprene is more expensive than natural rubber, but because of superior resistance to heat, sunlight, oil and greases, gasoline, and other chemicals, and to abrasion, it finds wide use in oil-resisting tires, tubes, refrigerator door seals, hose, gaskets, gloves, boots, and shoes, and in self-sealing gasoline tanks, conveyor belts, and nonskid flooring.

Thiokol is a copolymer of high sulfur content formed by the combination of ethylene dichloride with an aqueous solution of sodium tetrasulfide.

$$\underset{\text{Ethylene dichloride}}{Cl-\overset{\displaystyle H}{\underset{\displaystyle H}{C}}-\overset{\displaystyle H}{\underset{\displaystyle H}{C}}-Cl} + Na_2S_4 = \underset{\text{A unit of the thiokol chain}}{-\overset{\displaystyle H}{\underset{\displaystyle H}{C}}-\overset{\displaystyle H}{\underset{\displaystyle H}{C}}-\overset{\displaystyle S}{\underset{}{\uparrow}}S-\overset{\displaystyle S}{\underset{}{\uparrow}}S-}{}^2 + 2Na^+ + 2Cl^-$$

This reaction is classed as a condensation type polymerization because a second product in addition to the polymer is formed. Thiokol retains its flexibility at low temperatures and is remarkably resistant to oil, gasoline, and aromatic hydrocarbons, as well as to abrasion. It is used in oil-resistant hose for gasoline, paint sprays, and solvents, in fuel tank seals and linings, for wire insulation, for tire recaps, for converting railroad boxcars into oil carriers, and, more recently, in rocket fuels.

Many rubber-like plastics are used for waterproofing fabrics, in cushions and upholstery, and as protective and packaging film. Koroseal, Pliofilm, and Velon are products of that type.

19. Plastics. Included under the general heading of plastics are a host of polymers which can be molded or cast under pressure into any desired shape, and then rigidified. The first laboratory plastic, celluloid (p. 600), was developed in 1868 by a printer, John Wesley Hyatt, in his attempt to find a substitute for ivory in billiard balls. Celluloid is made by heating cellulose nitrate (pyroxylin) with camphor; the latter serves as a plasticizer, making the product more workable. Both celluloid and the structurally similar cellulose acetate plastics (p. 600), are thermoplastic, i.e., they can be softened

---

[2] A coordinate covalent bond is sometimes represented, as in this formula, by an arrow pointing from the donor to the acceptor atom.

by reheating and then cooled to set again. Neither is a true synthetic plastic, however, as both are simply chemical modifications of a polymer already present in nature.

In recent years, the completely new synthetic plastics manufactured by the polymerization of relatively simple organic compounds have become the basis of a huge new industry. The properties of such plastics may be so widely varied that they are replacing, for thousands of specific purposes, not only many utilitarian materials such as wood, glass, leather, porcelain, metals, and light alloys, but even such luxury items as ivory, jade, tortoise shell, and amber. Formerly used mainly for small articles only, plastics are now finding increased application in building materials, automobiles, aircraft, home furnishings, and machinery. In 1957, more than 4.5 billion pounds of plastics was produced in the United States, and plastic model homes went on display for the first time. It is estimated that in five years the annual per capita consumption of plastics in this country will be 40 pounds.

Bakelite, the first of the synthetic plastics, was developed empirically in 1904, before the riddles of polymer structure were solved. It is made by the condensation of formaldehyde (p. 580) and phenol (p. 589). Water is lost in the reaction and the polymer chain consists of recurring units of the type

Under suitable heat treatment, a mixture of the two reactants sets to a hard, infusible mass which is insoluble in all common solvents and cannot be softened by reheating. These properties are characteristic of the large class of so-called thermosetting plastics. The hardness and resistance to deformation exhibited by Bakelite and other plastics under ordinary conditions are attributed to cross-linking of the linear giant molecules into a rigid three-dimensional network. Bakelite, and the chemically similar products Durez, Textolite, Resinox, and Catalin, are used in innumerable articles—telephones, switchboards, electrical insulating materials, fountain pens, phonograph records, radios, and stereotyping matrixes.

The vinyl plastics are a group of useful thermoplastics formed by the polymerization of ethylene or one of its derivatives such as vinyl chloride

$(CH_2{=}CHCl)$, vinyl acetate $(CH_2{=}CH{-}O{-}\overset{\displaystyle O}{\overset{\|}{C}}{-}CH_3)$, or tetrafluoro-ethylene $(CF_2{=}CF_2)$. Ethylene itself gives polyethylene.

$$\begin{matrix} H & H \\ C & = & C \\ H & H \end{matrix} \quad + \quad \begin{matrix} H & H \\ C & = & C \\ H & H \end{matrix} \quad = \quad \left.\begin{matrix} H & H \\ C & - C \\ H & H \end{matrix}\right. \quad \begin{matrix} H & H \\ C & - C \\ H & H \end{matrix} \quad$$

Two units of the
polyethylene molecule

Polyethylene, currently the number one hit in the plastics parade, is used in bottles, trays, piping, film for packaging, insulation for electrical wiring, toys, and upholstery fabrics, and as a substitute for glass in greenhouses.

Other vinyls such as Vinylite, Butacite, and Teflon, are light, tough, flexible, and resistant to most solvents. They are used in nonbreakable phonograph records, transparent shoes, toys, and novelties, and as electrical insulating and packaging material and binding agents in safety glass.

Polymerization of the unsaturated ester methyl methacrylate gives Plexiglas or Lucite.

$$\begin{matrix} & CH_3 \\ H & | \\ C & = C \\ H & | \\ & COOCH_3 \end{matrix} \quad + \quad \begin{matrix} & CH_3 \\ H & | \\ C & = C \\ H & | \\ & COOCH_3 \end{matrix} \quad = \quad \begin{matrix} & CH_3 \\ H & | \\ C & - C \\ H & | \\ & COOCH_3 \end{matrix} \quad \begin{matrix} & CH_3 \\ H & | \\ C & - C \\ H & | \\ & COOCH_3 \end{matrix}$$

Methyl methacrylate   Two units of the Plexiglas or Lucite molecule

These methacrylate resins are clear, highly transparent materials used in airplane noses, cockpits, reflecting road signs, automobile parts, dentures, lighting fixtures, and furniture, and by dentists and surgeons for "piping" light around sharp angles.

Still other useful plastics are made by the polymerization of styrene (Styron, Polystyrene) and by the condensation of urea and formaldehyde (Unyte, Plaskon, Beetle). The new polyurethane plastics are coming into wide use as plastic foam and plastic sponge.

20. Synthetic Fibers. Rayon (p. 599) may be classed as a semisynthetic fiber, since it is merely a chemical modification of a naturally occurring polymer, cellulose. Recently a number of truly synthetic fibers, e.g., nylon, Orlon, dynel, Acrilan, and Dacron, of completely new structure and made from simple substances derived from such basic raw materials as coal, petroleum, air, water, and limestone, are gaining wide popularity because of their versatility and superior qualities.

The present competition between synthetic and natural fibers amounts to an industrial revolution in the textile world, from which the consumer is certain to benefit.

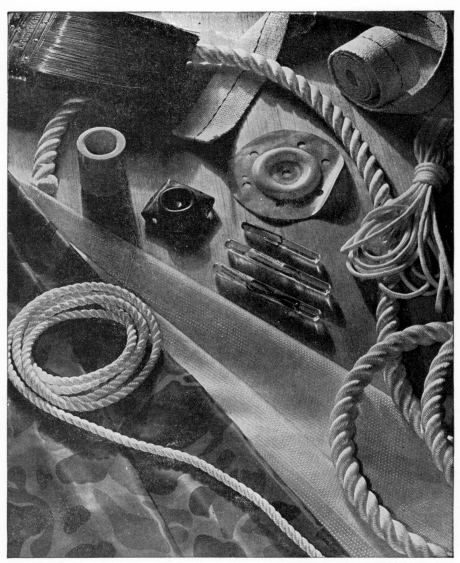

Fig. 32.2. Some articles made from nylon. Arranged clockwise, beginning at the paint brush with tapered nylon bristles, are: parachute harness webbing, parachute shroud lines, heavy nylon rope for military gliders, cargo parachute cloth, camouflaged Army Air Force escape parachute cloth, and light nylon rope. Centered in the photograph are left to right: experimental molded nylon plastic bearing, carburetor diaphragms of nylon fabric, and surgical sutures. (*Courtesy of DuPont Company.*)

Nylon, the first of the man-made fibers, is produced by the condensation of a diamine (p. 584) with a dicarboxylic acid (p. 583). Hexamethylenediamine, NH_2—$(CH_2)_6$—NH_2, and adipic acid, $HOOC$—$(CH_2)_4$—$COOH$, are commonly used. The NH_2 and $COOH$ groups combine with the loss of a molecule of water to form the amide group, —CO—NH—, which links the molecules end to end indefinitely to form a polymer of the structure

$$-\overset{\overset{\displaystyle O}{\|}}{C}-\overset{\displaystyle H}{N}-(CH_2)_6-\overset{\displaystyle H}{N}-\overset{\overset{\displaystyle O}{\|}}{C}-(CH_2)_4-\overset{\overset{\displaystyle O}{\|}}{C}-\overset{\displaystyle H}{N}-, \text{etc.}$$

Desired changes in specific properties of the fiber may be introduced by the use of other diamines and dicarboxylic acids.

Nylon, like the protein silk (p. 603), is a complex polyamide. It also resembles silk in appearance, is equally as tough, and has greater strength and elasticity. It has good resistance to abrasion, heat, and most chemicals, is almost noninflammable, and is not affected by mildew or moths.

Orlon and Acrilan are polymers of acrylonitrile, CH_2=CH—C≡N. They are soft warm fabrics with unusual abrasion and weather resistance. Both are used as substitutes for wool in suits, blankets, sweaters, upholstery, and draperies.

Dynel is a copolymer of acrylonitrile and vinyl chloride (p. 616). It combines warmth, resilience, and rapid drying properties with unusual resistance to chemicals. Dacron is a complex polyester fiber made by reaction of ethylene glycol (p. 579) with a dicarboxylic acid (p. 583). It is remarkably resistant to wrinkling, wetting, and moths. It is nonabsorbent, nonshrinking, nonstretching and quick-drying, and is used in summer suits, shirts, blouses, sweaters, and socks.

21. Silicones. In recent years an entirely new class of polymers, the *silicones*, have made a dramatic appearance upon the industrial scene. Although they contain carbon, the giant molecules of the silicones are built up through repeated silicon to oxygen linkages.

The silicones afford an interesting example of the striking differences in the properties of substances which may arise from slight differences in the chemical properties of similar elements, even those within the same family.

Hydrolysis of compounds of the type $\overset{\displaystyle R}{\underset{\displaystyle R'}{\diagdown\diagup}}SiCl_2$, in which two organic groups replace two of the chlorine atoms of silicon tetrachloride, might be expected to form silicon analogs of the ketones, $\begin{matrix} R \\ \diagdown \\ \diagup \\ R' \end{matrix}$ Si=O. But, apparently because the tendency of silicon to form double bonds with oxygen atoms is much less than that of carbon, the actual products are polymers with an inorganic silicon–oxygen backbone, like that in silica and the silicates, but flanked by hydrocarbon groups.

$$(x + 2) \begin{matrix} R \\ \diagdown \\ \diagup \\ R' \end{matrix} SiCl_2 + (x + 2) H_2O = \begin{matrix} R \\ | \\ -Si-O- \\ | \\ R' \end{matrix} \left[\begin{matrix} R \\ | \\ Si-O- \\ | \\ R' \end{matrix} \right]_x \begin{matrix} R \\ | \\ Si-O- \\ | \\ R' \end{matrix} + (2x + 4) HCl$$

A silicone chain

The silicones combine the stability of glass with the flexibility of organic compounds. They are remarkably stable at high temperatures and are unreactive toward metals and most chemicals. Millions of pounds of these versatile products are sold annually as special lubricants for use over wide temperature ranges and in sealed-in systems, as hydraulic and heat transfer liquids, and as water repellents for fabrics, masonry, ceramics, and paper.

Silicone rubber (in which $x = 2000$ or more) neither hardens nor softens at temperatures from far below zero to over 200° C., and has excellent electrical insulating properties. Silicone resins are used in tough, high-gloss, heat-resistant paints, in high-temperature varnishes for electrical insulation, and as the bonding agent in laminated insulation forms.

STUDY QUESTIONS AND PROBLEMS

1. Oxyhemoglobin, a blood protein, contains 0.335% of iron. What is its lowest possible molecular weight? Under what condition would this be the actual molecular weight? From other evidence, it appears certain that there are four atoms of iron in the oxyhemoglobin molecule. What, then, is the true molecular weight?

2. How do soaps such as sodium stearate react toward litmus? Write an equation for the reaction which accounts for their behavior.

3. Explain how, in the metabolic processes of the body, reactions occur which can be brought about in the laboratory only at considerably higher temperatures.

4. Suggest how radioactive tracers can be used in the study of photosynthesis; of animal metabolism; of diseases; of the action of drugs in the body.

5. What is the essential difference between vitamins and hormones?

6. The osmotic pressure (p. 296) at 27° C. of a solution containing 1.0 g. of a plastic dissolved in 1000 g. of butyl acetate (density 0.88 g./cc.) is 2.0 mm. Calculate the approximate average weight of the molecules of the plastic.

7. Show how glycerol and phthalic acid, $\langle\!\!\!\bigcirc\!\!\!\rangle\!\!\begin{array}{l}\diagup\text{COOH}\\\diagdown\text{COOH}\end{array}$, might be condensed to form a plastic polymer. To what specific class of organic compounds would the product belong? Explain why the reaction between ethyl alcohol and acetic acid cannot lead to polymer formation.

8. Fluoracetic acid, FCH_2—COOH, is a deadly poison. Noting its structural similarity to lactic acid (p. 583), how would you account for its toxicity?

9. The human body has at times been called the most complex chemical factory known. Using this analogy, list the features which distinguish the body, as a chemical plant, from a commercial chemical factory.

10. Write formulas showing probable typical structural units in Neoprene, Dacron, Orlon and Acrilan, and dynel. Which are formed by addition polymerization and which by condensation polymerization?

11. Assume that a molecule of a fat contained one stearic acid, one palmitic acid, and one oleic acid unit. In how many different ways might these units be arranged in the molecule? If you knew only that the saponification of a certain fat produced sodium stearate, sodium palmitate, and sodium oleate, how many different kinds of fat molecules might possibly have been present in the original sample?

12. Oxidation of 1 g. of fat in the body affords 9300 calories. If there are 5 l. of blood in your body, how many ounces of fat would have to be metabolized to provide the heat required to raise the temperature of your blood from room temperature ($70°$ F.) to normal body temperature ($98.6°$ F.)? The specific heat of blood is approximately the same as that of water.

13. Propose the structure of two hypothetical polymers which might be of commercial interest. How would you prepare them?

33

Metals and Their Compounds

1. Physical Characteristics of Metals. It is difficult to frame an exact definition for the word "metal" in terms of physical properties, for, regardless of what definition is adopted, there are always exceptions. Nevertheless, certain physical properties are characteristic of the metallic elements as a group. These characteristics include *high thermal* and *electrical conductivities, hardness,* and *high density.* Most metals have rather *high melting points,* and relatively *low volatilities* and therefore *high boiling points.* The alkali metals, however, are soft, light, and have low melting points. Mercury is the only metal which is a liquid at room temperature. *Malleability,* the capability of being hammered into thin sheets, and *ductility,* the capability of being drawn into wire, are characteristic properties of many of the more important metals. Most metals have relatively *high tensile strengths.* All of the metals are good reflectors of light, i.e., are said to possess *metallic luster.* All metals are *opaque* except in very thin layers.

A few nonmetals exhibit one or more metallic properties. Thus, carbon, in the form of graphite, is a good electrical conductor. Crystals of iodine, another nonmetal, have a metallic luster.

2. Nature of the Metallic State. In Chapter 10 three types of crystalline solids were discussed: ionic, atomic, and molecular. It was pointed out that ionic crystals are composed of positive and negative ions held together by their mutual electrostatic attraction, whereas atomic crystals such as diamond are made up of atoms linked by covalent bonds in a continuous lattice to form one huge molecule; in molecular crystals, such as solid chlorine or carbon dioxide, the molecules are held together by weak intermolecular forces such as those which cause gases to deviate from the gas laws.

To which of these groups, if any, do metallic crystals belong? They do not belong to the ionic class, for metals contain only one kind of atoms and would therefore hardly be expected to furnish both positive and negative ions. Moreover, as is shown subsequently, the common physical characteristics of the metalic state are not those associated with ionic crystal lattices.

That metallic crystals are not of the covalent type is evident from the small number of valence electrons in metallic atoms. Most of the metal atoms have less than four valence electrons—many have only one or two. Yet in the lattices commonly found in metal crystals each atom is surrounded by either eight or twelve "closest neighbors." For example, calcium crystallizes in what crystallographers call a "face-centered cubic" lattice in which each atom is surrounded by twelve "closest neighbor" atoms. With only two valence electrons per atom, it would be impossible for a calcium atom to form twelve covalent bonds. In fact, it is impossible for calcium atoms to be linked by ordinary covalent bonds in any sort of three-dimensional network.

Finally, the weak bonding forces of the typical molecular crystal cannot account for the high strength and hardness or the low volatility of many metals.

Actually metallic solids constitute a fourth type of crystal in which the bonding forces are different from those of the first three types. The hypothesis which has been generally accepted is that a metallic crystal is made up of a lattice of the positive kernels of the metal atoms, held together by the attraction of the valence electrons, which, being mobile, are free to pass from one atom to another. The valence electrons, therefore, belong not to any one particular atom but to the crystal as a whole. Although the manner in which such a structure results in a binding force between the atoms is not obvious, it has been explained on a theoretical basis. The theory makes it possible, moreover, to account for many of the physical properties of the metals.

Since the valence electrons in the metallic crystal are free to move, the application of a difference of potential to a piece of metal produces a flow of electrons through the metal from the negative pole to the positive as shown in Figure 33.1. This picture also explains why the electrical conductivity of most metals decreases with increasing temperature; as the temperature is increased the vibration of the atoms interferes more and more with the flow of electrons. This interference increases the electrical resistance. A few metals when cooled to within a few degrees of absolute zero lose practically all their resistance to electron flow. Displacement of the atoms in a metallic crystal relative to each other does not destroy the

Table 33.1. A Glossary of Metals

ANCIENT METALS: PREHISTORY TO 1900

Name	Main properties	Weight per cu. ft.	Melting pt. in deg. Fahr.	1951 U.S. Consumption short tons	Average 1951 price per lb.	Main uses as pure metal	Main uses as alloy
ANTIMONY	Zinc-like, but hard and brittle	417 lbs.	1167°	40,000	$ .44	None. But used in chemical flame-proofing, paints, ceramics	In lead, tin alloys, printer's-type metal
ARSENIC	Grayish-white, brittle, unworkable, toxic	358	1500° (36 atm.)	28,869 (white)	.065	None. Major use is in chemical insecticides	In copper, lead alloys
BISMUTH	Low thermal conductivity, most diamagnetic metal	608	520°	875	2.25	Few, but new ductile wire and strip open potentialities	With lead for low-melting alloys and solders; additive in stainless steel
COBALT	High strength, oxidation resistance at red heat	555	2696°	4,966	2.40	None	With chromium, nickel, tungsten for high-temperature tools, jet engine parts
COPPER	Second highest in conductivity; workability	558	1981°	1,798,000	.245	Electric wire, cable, equipment, and appliances	With zinc, tin, lead, aluminum for brass or bronze
GOLD	Most ductile and malleable of metals	1,206	1945°	68 (industrial)	35.00 per troy ounce	Too soft for use in pure state	With copper, silver, zinc, nickel for coinage, jewelry
IRON	Greatest, most versatile structural metal	490	2795°	67,320,000	.04 (steel)	Wrought iron	With carbon and other metals for a great range of steels and cast iron
LEAD	Soft, high corrosion resistance, toxic	708	622°	1,184,793	.175	In making chemicals, white lead, antiknock fluid	With tin, antimony, copper for batteries, sheathing, bullets, bearings
MANGANESE	Hard, pinkish metal	449	2300°	723,520	.29	None	Sulfur remover in steel, and as alloy adds hardness, strength, toughness
MERCURY	First known liquid metal at room temperature, toxic	846	−38°	2,158	2.79	In detonators, thermometers, vacuum pumps, cathodes	With tin, silver, gold for dental amalgams
NICKEL	Most versatile alloy metal, corrosion-resistant	555	2646°	86,416	.565	Few, except electroplating	In over 3,000 iron, copper, steel alloys; adds strength at high temperatures
PLATINUM	Highest resistance to corrosion, oxidation	1,333	3190°	7	1,358.00	In electric contacts, glass-fiber dies, chemical equipment, and as catalysts	With palladium, rhodium, gold, iridium for spinnerets, pen nibs, jewelry
SILVER	Highest thermal-electric conductivity	655	1761°	4,839	11.64-13.21	Lining in food and brewing machinery, electrodes	With copper, zinc, nickel for silverware, coinage, plating, jewelry
TIN	Bright, soft, corrosion-resistant	359	449°	98,749	1.28	As thin plating on steel for tin cans	With lead, antimony, copper for solders, bearings
TUNGSTEN	Highest known melting point, lowest vapor pressure	1,204	6100°	secret	6.00	Lamp filaments, plating on special laboratory equipment	In high-temperature steels and carbide cutting tools
ZINC	Bluish-white, high resistance to atmospheric corrosion	446	787°	929,466	.18	In sheet for dry batteries; galvanized coatings on steel	With aluminum, magnesium, for versatile die castings

Reprinted by special permission from January, 1953 *Fortune*. Copyright Time Inc. Some of the data may vary slightly from those given elsewhere in the text, which were obtained from other sources.

MODERN METALS: 1900-1953

Name	Main properties	Weight per cu. ft.	Melting pt. in deg. Fahr.	1951 U.S. Consumption short tons	Average 1951 price per lb.	Main uses as pure metal	Main uses as alloy
ALUMINUM	One-third as dense as steel, conductive, corrosion-resistant	168 lbs.	1220°	1,254,273	$ .19	Cooking utensils, electric wire-cable, foil, chemical equipment	With magnesium, manganese, silicon in aircraft, vehicles, building
BERYLLIUM	Highest-temperature light metal, toxic, scarce	112	2350°	secret	70.00	In new ductile form as atomic-pile moderator, alpha-ray emitter, x-ray tube "window"	In high-strength, corrosion-resistant copper and nickel alloys
BORON	Hard, crystalline, high heat-and-electric resistance	144	4200°	66	250.00	As hard, fusible, oxidation-resistant coatings on high-temperature metals	As ferroboron, reduces use of alloys in low-alloy steels
CADMIUM	Soft, bright, corrosion-resistant	540	610°	3,586	2.55	As rust-preventive plating on bearings, etc.	In fusible alloys, aluminum solders, atomic-power controls
CALCIUM	Soft, white, ductile, light; corrodes rapidly in air and water	97	1490°	under 50	2.05	As reducing agent in securing uranium, other hard metals from ores	As calcium-silicon reducing agent; small amounts harden, strengthen lead
CERIUM	Soft, ductile, spark producing	431	1184°	not available	4.50 (misch metal)	None; pure metal only now being separated	As misch metal in flints; in new steel, cast iron, magnesium alloys
CESIUM	Most reactive of metals, highly photoelectric	117	83°	few grams	1,361.00	In coating light meters; in cesium-vapor rectifiers	None
CHROMIUM	Bright, corrosion-resistant	443	2940°	909,497	1.07	Decorative, non-rusting plating on other metals	Main element in stainless steels, some high-temperature alloys
COLUMBIUM (NIOBIUM)	Gray, highly stable, scarce	524	3542°	763	.88	Only laboratory uses	Indispensable in small amounts in highest-temperature superalloys
GALLIUM	Liquid at body temperature, high boiling point	369	86°	100 lbs. (est.)	2,041.16	In special thermometers, as liquid medium in continuous mass spectrometers	Experimentally in low-melting solders, metals, low-temperature dies
GERMANIUM	Grayish, crystalline semiconductor	334	1756°	secret	340.00	In electronic crystal diodes for TV, other uses	With traces of arsenic for transistors, new, low-power electronic devices
INDIUM	Soft, spreads and adheres closely to metal-ceramic surfaces	454	311°	7,000 lbs. (est.)	32.85	As diffused coating and lubricant on bearings, dies	In new low-melting, corrosion-resistant, glass-adhering solders and alloys
LITHIUM	The lightest metal, but reacts rapidly with air and water	33	367°	few thousand lbs.	9.85-11.00	In organic-chemical synthesis, high-temperature lithium greases	Adds ductility to magnesium; in aluminum welding-brazing fluxes
MAGNESIUM	Two-thirds as dense as aluminum	109	1204°	35,710	.245	Agent in chemical-metallurgical reactions, anodes	With aluminum, zinc, manganese, zirconium, cerium in a range of structural alloys

Table 33.1 A Glossary of Metals *(continued)*

MOLYBDENUM	The most available high-temperature metal	636	4750°	16,846	3.00	In new high-purity form, silicon-coated, forgings stable to 3,200°F.	Adds ductility, heat stability to nickel-chrome, manganese, and tool steels
PALLADIUM	Sister metal to platinum, close in properties	759	2831°	8	350.00	In electric contacts, electrodes, electroplating	In jewelry, dental, chemical-equipment alloys
PLUTONIUM	Radioactive, fissionable	secret	secret	secret	none	Manufactured artificially by uranium fission for use in atomic bomb	None
POLONIUM	Radioactive	587 (theoretical)	1112°	6 curies	5.00 per millicurie	As source of neutrons, ions; in static eliminators, luminous compounds	None
RADIUM	Yardstick of radioactivity	312 (theoretical)	1760°	secret	20.00 (milligram)	In needles, instruments for cancer treatment	With zinc sulfide for luminous watch and instrument dials
RHODIUM	Hard, unworkable platinum-group metal	780	3550°	1,072 lbs.	1,825.00	In furnace-heating resistors, reflectors, electroplating	In platinum alloys
SELENIUM	Brittle, semiconductive, photo-sensitive	299	428°	396	3.00–3.50	In electronic rectifiers, photoelectric-eye tubes	In small amounts adds machinability to stainless steel, copper
SILICON	Most abundant metal, heat-corrosion resistant, but brittle	151	2590°	415,000 (est.)	.20	As coatings on steel, new intermetallic surface on molybdenum for high-temperature use	As ferrosilicon adds elasticity to steel, acts as deoxidizer; in semiconductors
SODIUM	Soft, highly reactive with water and air	61	208°	100,000	.165	As constituent in making tetraethyl lead	In aluminum-silicon alloys; as liquid-metal heat exchanger in atomic-power plants
STRONTIUM	Sister metal to calcium, photoelectric	158	1500°	few lbs.	7.00–35.00	As "getter" in vacuum tubes; in blue-green-sensitive photoelectric cells	None
TANTALUM	Third-highest temperature metal, corrosion-resistant, scarce	1,036	5160°	120	.80	In electronic grids, anodes, surgical pins and plates	In chemical heat-transfer equipment, carbide cutting tools
THORIUM	Radioactive, potentially a source of atomic energy	705	3350°	secret	159–318	Pure metal only recently secured	Adds strength to magnesium, life to resistance-heating alloys
TITANIUM	Light weight, high strength, and corrosion-resistance	281	3300°	495	5.00	As non-structural sheet in jet-engine sheels, ducting, fittings	In high-strength aluminum, magnesium alloys; high-temperature titanium carbides
URANIUM	Radioactive, fissionable	1,166	2071°	secret	none	As source of atomic energy	None
VANADIUM	Soft, corrosion-resistant	372	3110°	secret	3.00–3.20	Pure ductile form only recently achievel, only laboratory uses	Adds extreme toughness to tool-and-die steels, shafts, springs, bearings
ZIRCONIUM	Sister to titanium; high permeability to neutrons	399	3100°	secret	7.00–8.00	As ultrapure ductile metal in atomic reactors	Increasing as alloy in magnesium; deoxidizes steel and iron alloys

FUTURE METALS?

Name	General description	Pounds per cu. ft.	Melting pt. in deg. Fahr.
ACTINIUM	Radioactive, transitional element	Not est.	Not est.
AMERICIUM	Radioactive, artificially made, 1945	Not est.	Not est.
BARIUM	Soft, tarnishes in air, toxic	228	1,300°
BERKELIUM	Radioactive, artificially made, 1950	Not est.	Not est.
CALIFORNIUM	Radioactive, artificially made, 1950	Not est.	Not est.
CURIUM	Radioactive, artificially made, 1944	Not est.	Not est.
DYSPROSIUM	Rare earth	534	Not est.
ERBIUM	Rare earth	572	2,282°?
EUROPIUM	Rare earth, brilliant spark spectrum	319	2,012°
FRANCIUM	Alkali-type metal, discovered 1939	Not est.	73°
GADOLINIUM	Rare earth, highest absorption for slow neutrons	495	Not est.
HAFNIUM	Close to zirconium, twice as heavy; high electron emission	830	3,590°
HOLMIUM	Rare earth	Not est.	Not est.
IRIDIUM	Platinum group, hard, brittle; small use in alloys	1,399	4,450°
LANTHANUM	Among commonest rare earths, ductile	384	1,519°
LUTETIUM	Rarest of rare earths	608	Not est.
NEODYMIUM	Rare earth	434	1,544°
NEPTUNIUM	Radioactive, isolated in 1952	Not est.	Not est.
OSMIUM	Platinum group, hard, unworkable; highest density; small alloy use	1,403	4,892°
POTASSIUM	Alkali metal; soft, reactive	54	144°
PRASEODYMIUM	Rare earth	414	1,724°
PROMETHIUM	Rare earth; artificially made	Not est.	Not est.
PROTACTINIUM	Radioactive	Not est.	5,400°
RHENIUM	Heavy; used as catalyst	1,281	5,740°
RUBIDIUM	Silvery alkali metal; reactive	95	101°
RUTHENIUM	Platinum group, unworkable	761	4,442°
SAMARIUM	Rare earth, oxidizes slowly in air	487	2,462°
SCANDIUM	Rare, only recently isolated	188	2,192°
TECHNETIUM	First artificially made element, 1937	Not est.	4,900°
TELLURIUM	Semi-metallic; a semiconductor	389	846°
TERBIUM	Among scarcest rare earths	520	621°
THALLIUM	Soft; between lead and alkali metal	739	578°
THULIUM	Rare earth	583	Not est.
YTTERBIUM	Rare earth, close to lutetium	447	3,272°
YTTRIUM	Among more available rare earths	344	2,714°

general attractive force which holds the crystal together; hence metals are malleable and ductile. In ionic crystals such displacements bring into such close contact ions of like charge that their repulsion "breaks" the crystal. Ionic crystals, therefore, are not malleable or ductile. This contrasting behavior of metallic and ionic crystals is illustrated in Figure 33.2.

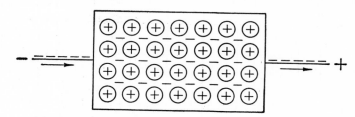

Fig. 33.1. Conduction of an electric current by a metal.

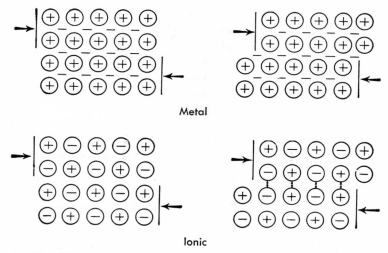

Metal

Ionic

Fig. 33.2. Effect of deformation on metallic and ionic crystals.

3. Chemical Characteristics of Metals. As has been pointed out (p. 179), atoms of metallic elements react with atoms of nonmetals by transferring electrons to the nonmetal atoms to form positive and negative ions. Atoms of certain metals, however, particularly those of low ionic radius and large ionic charge, may share electrons with certain nonmetal atoms to form covalent molecules, such as, for example, anhydrous aluminum chloride (p. 806) and stannic chloride (p. 821). Since atoms of most metallic elements have a relatively small attraction for their valence electrons, the hydroxides of the metals tend to yield hydroxide rather than hydronium ions in solution, and are thus to be classed as bases rather than acids (p. 323). This same low attraction for valence electrons (low ionization potential) causes the more reactive metals to be strong reducing agents.

4. Natural Sources of the Metals. The naturally occurring minerals from which the metals are extracted (called *ores*) are in most instances compounds, though a few of the less active metals sometimes occur in the uncombined state. The ores are generally associated with extraneous rocky material called *gangue*. The percentage of ore which a given material must contain to be used profitably as a source of a metal depends upon the value of the metal and the nature of the impurities.

The important types of ores, with examples, are listed in Table 33.2.

Table 33.2

Type of ore	Examples	Remarks
Native metals	Ag, Au, Hg, Cu, Bi, As, Sb, Pt	
Halides	Halides of Na, K, Mg	Found in salt beds—soluble in water
	AgCl	Insoluble in water
Sulfates	$CaSO_4 \cdot 2H_2O$, $SrSO_4$, $BaSO_4$, $PbSO_4$	
Oxides	Oxides of Fe, Mn, Cr, Al, Cu, Sn, and others	
Sulfides	Sulfides of Hg, Cu, Zn, Pb, Ni, Co, Sb, Bi, Ag	Very important
Silicates	Silicates of Ni and Zn	Most silicates unsuitable as ores because of difficult metallurgy
Carbonates	$CaCO_3$, $MgCO_3$, $FeCO_3$	

5. Metallurgy. The science dealing with the extraction of metals from their ores is called *metallurgy*. The process actually used in the extraction of a given metal depends upon a number of factors, among which are (1) the nature of the ore, (2) the amount and type of impurities present, (3) the chemical properties of the metal, and (4) the uses to which the metal is to be put. For example, copper which is to be used in electrical apparatus must be more highly purified than that used in the making of brass or bronze. There are, therefore, a large number of different metallurgical procedures, some of which will be taken up as the individual metals are discussed in the chapters that follow.

Most metallurgical processes can be separated into three main parts: (1) preliminary treatment, (2) reduction, and (3) refining.

1. *Preliminary Treatment.* Many ores contain such a high percentage of extraneous rocky material that it is necessary that the ore be concentrated, i.e., that much of the gangue be removed, before the reduction of the metallic compound itself is carried out. The first step in the *concentration* is the mechanical grinding of the ore. This is followed by separation of the rocky material from the ore particles. Sometimes this separation is carried out by means of simple washing; the rocky materials, being lighter than most ore particles, are more easily washed away. Slightly inclined shaking tables are sometimes employed to separate the heavier ore particles from the lighter impurities. Certain ores are affected by a magnetic field, and in such cases magnetic separation may be used. Other minerals readily become charged in an electrostatic field, so that electrostatic separation becomes possible. The recently developed flotation process (p. 761) is widely applied in the concentration of low-grade sulfide ores. The process which is used in the concentration of a given ore depends, of course, on the nature of the ore. Certain high-grade ores require no concentration.

Following concentration, many ores are *roasted* in the presence of a plentiful supply of air. The object of this treatment is to drive off any volatile material, and, in the case of sulfide, carbonate, and hydrous oxide or hydroxide ores, to change at least part of the ore to oxide, which is generally more convenient to handle in the reduction stage of the process.

2. *Reduction.* Most reduction processes are carried out at high temperatures, and result in the liberation of the free metal in the fused state. Such a reduction process is called *smelting.* In this process two agents are usually added to the ore: (a) a *reducing agent,* and (b) a *flux.* Most ores, even after concentration, still contain considerable amounts of gangue. It is the function of the flux to react with the gangue to form a substance that will melt at the smelting temperature. The product of this reaction is called *slag.* The gangue materials most commonly found in ores are silica and silicates. Limestone reacts with these substances to form easily fusible calcium silicates, and hence is commonly employed as a flux.

The most common reducing agent employed in the reduction of oxide ores, or of ores which are readily converted by the roasting process into oxides, is carbon. At higher temperatures, carbon reacts with many metallic oxides to give the free metal and carbon monoxide or carbon dioxide; e.g.,

$$SnO_2 + 2C = Sn + 2CO; \quad ZnO + C = Zn + CO$$

Sometimes, carbon is first converted to carbon monoxide, which then acts as the reducing agent, as in the reduction of iron ore.

$$Fe_2O_3 + 3CO = 2Fe + 3CO_2$$

Aluminum, calcium, and hydrogen also are used as reducing agents, but since they are more expensive than carbon they are resorted to only where, for some reason, carbon is unsatisfactory.

The reduction of ores of the more active metals such as sodium, potassium, and calcium, cannot readily be achieved by purely chemical means. Reduction to the free metal is generally accomplished by the electrolysis of a fused compound.

The native ores of such metals as copper, silver, or gold require no reducing agent but may be smelted by melting the metal and allowing it to drain away from the rocky material.

3. *Refining.* Most metals as obtained in the primary reduction of their ores contain considerable amounts of impurities. If these impurities are objectionable, the metal must be purified or refined. The methods used for refining vary widely. Low melting metals, such as tin, are sometimes refined by liquation, i.e., by melting the impure metal on an inclined table and allowing the metal to flow away from the solid impurities. Low boiling metals, such as zinc and mercury, are sometimes purified by distillation. Electrolytic methods of purification, in which the impure metal is made the anode and the pure metal the cathode in an electrolytic cell, are becoming more and more common in metallurgical practice, particularly in the production of high-grade copper, gold, lead, zinc, chromium, and aluminum. In the refining of many metals, a more active metal (known as a scavenger) is added to remove dissolved gases such as nitrogen or oxygen and to reduce any unreduced oxide or sulfide.

6. Alloys. One of the most important properties of metals is their ability to form *alloys*. An alloy may be defined as a metallic product consisting of two or more metals. Alloys are commonly, though not always, prepared by melting together the component metals and allowing the molten mass to solidify. By far the greater portion of the metallic materials in everyday use are alloys rather than pure metals. Coins, jewelry, steel rails, battery plates, solder, brass valves, electrical heating elements, the cores of electromagnets —these are only a few examples of the endless array of metallic products composed of alloys.

By variation in composition and method of preparation, series of alloys with a wide range of properties may be obtained. The cause of the difference between the tough, but relatively soft, wrought irons and the hard, but brittle, cast irons is mainly the 2 to 3% carbon content of the latter. Because of the different types of internal structures which may exist in the various alloys, the relationship between the properties of a given alloy and those of the component metals is not a simple one. Alloys may be made up of separate crystals of the components, solid solutions, intermetallic compounds, or various combinations of these types.

In general, the properties of alloys are not the average of those of the component metals. Many alloys have lower melting points than any of their components. The electrical conductivity of an alloy of a metal is generally considerably lower than that of the pure metal. Thus, brass is a much poorer conductor than copper. Nichrome and chromel, alloys of chromium and nickel, are notable for their high resistance. Alloys, in most cases, are harder and more resistant to corrosion than the pure metals. Alloys that contain intermetallic compounds, such as Cu_3Al, Fe_5Zn_{21}, Cu_5Sn, and Cu_2Mg, are quite different from their component metals.

7. Classification of Salts. Salts may be classified as *acid, basic,* or *normal* depending upon whether they contain, respectively, ionizable hydrogen, unneutralized oxide or hydroxide, or neither.

Acid salts	Basic salts	Normal salts
$NaHCO_3$	$Pb(OH)_2 \cdot 2PbCO_3$	$CaCO_3$
KHF_2	$Mg(OH)Cl$	$Bi(NO_3)_3$
NaH_2PO_4	$SbOCl$	K_2SO_4

Since all the above salts contain no other component than a single kind of cation and a single kind of anion, plus, in some instances, hydrogen, hydroxide, or oxide ion, they are all classified as *simple* salts. Many salts, such as $Zn(CN)_2 \cdot 2KCN$, $NiCl_2 \cdot 6NH_3$, $Na_2SO_4 \cdot Al_2(SO_4)_3 \cdot 24H_2O$, and $KCl \cdot MgCl_2 \cdot 6H_2O$, are formed by the union of two simple salts or of a simple salt with neutral molecules. These substances are of two types:

(a) *Double salts.* If the substance gives solutions containing only the simple ions found in solutions of its component salts, it is called a double salt. The last two examples are of this type. Thus $KCl \cdot MgCl_2 \cdot 6H_2O$ dissolves in water to give potassium, magnesium, and chloride ions.

(b) *Complex salts.* If the salt gives solutions containing complex ions it is called a complex salt. For example, solutions of $Zn(CN)_2 \cdot 2KCN$ contain potassium ion and $Zn(CN)_4^{--}$ complex ion. Likewise, solutions of $NiCl_2 \cdot 6NH_3$ contain $Ni(NH_3)_6^{++}$ ion and Cl^- ion.

Bonding forces in these complex ions are of two principal types: (a) coordinate covalent bonds, already discussed in Chapter 9; and (b) ion-dipole forces, which consist in the attraction of the positive metal ions for the negative ends of polar molecules (or in certain instances for coordinated negative ions), as indicated by the following structural formula:

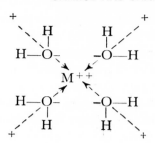

The number of bonds formed by the central atom in a complex ion is called its *coordination number*. In the above example zinc and copper have coordination numbers of four.

8. Charge and Shape of Complex Ions. The charge on a complex ion is determined by adding the charges on its component parts. Thus the charge of -2 for the complex $Zn(CN)_4^{--}$ is obtained by adding $+2$ (from Zn^{++})

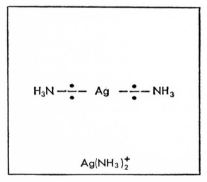

Fig. 33.3.

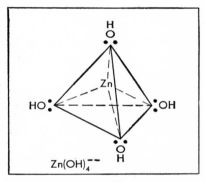

Fig. 33.4.

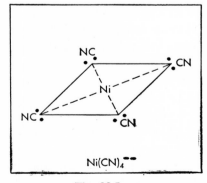

Fig. 33.5.

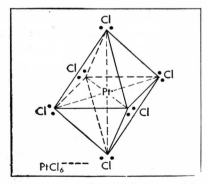

Fig. 33.6.

and $4 \times (-1)$ (from $4CN^-$ ions). Likewise the charge of -2 for $PtCl_6^{--}$ is obtained by adding $+4$ (from Pt^{4+}) and $6 \times (-1)$ (from $6Cl^-$ ions).

Complex ions are of a variety of shapes. Examples of several common types are shown in Figs. 33.3, 33.4, 33.5, and 33.6.

9. Solubilities of Metallic Compounds. A series of general rules applying to the solubility in water of some of the more important compounds may be stated as follows:

1. Nitrates and acetates are soluble.

2. Salts of sodium, potassium, rubidium, cesium, and ammonium, with very few exceptions, are soluble.

3. Sulfates, except those of calcium, strontium, barium, and lead, are soluble.

4. Chlorides, except those of lead, silver, copper (-ous), mercury (-ous), and thallium (-ous), are soluble.

5. Hydroxides of lithium, sodium, potassium, rubidium, and cesium are very soluble; those of calcium, strontium, and barium are moderately soluble; other hydroxides are only very slightly soluble.

6. Carbonates, phosphates, borates, arsenates, and arsenites, except those of sodium, potassium, rubidium, cesium, and ammonium, are only very slightly soluble.

STUDY QUESTIONS AND PROBLEMS

1. Make a chart listing the outstanding physical characteristics of metals; the outstanding chemical characteristics.

2. What are the chief points of the present theory of the metallic state? How does this theory explain malleability, ductility, and high electrical conductivity of metals?

3. What is the relationship of oxidation state to the basicity of the oxides of a multivalent metal? Explain.

4. How do metals and nonmetals compare as to ionization potential? Explain.

5. Define the term "ore." Are all minerals ores? List the most important ores of ten familiar metals.

6. What are the names and functions of the principal steps of the typical metallurgical process?

7. Assuming 100% efficiency, calculate how many faradays of electricity would be required to produce 50 lb. of sodium from sodium chloride.

8. Suggest methods of preparing $Co(NO_3)_2$, $PbSO_4$, $La_2(CO_3)_3$, and $LiClO_4$.

9. What three simple types of structure are possible in a binary alloy?

10. Define and give four examples of each of the following: (a) acid salt, (b) basic salt, (c) normal salt, (d) double salt, (e) complex salt.

11. What is the percentage of aluminum in common clay, the composition of which is represented approximately by formula $H_2Al_2(SiO_4)_2 \cdot H_2O$? Why is clay not commonly regarded as an ore of aluminum?

12. Which is richer in uranium, the mineral carnotite, the formula of which may be written $K_2U_2V_2O_{12} \cdot 3H_2O$, or a rock containing 65% of pitchblende, U_3O_8?

13. What is the maximum percentage of sand, SiO_2, with which the mineral magnetite, Fe_3O_4, may be contaminated if the mixture is still to contain as large a percentage of iron as pure hematite, Fe_2O_3?

14. Although the mineral willemite, $ZnSiO_4$, contains a higher percentage of zinc than does franklinite, a mixed oxide of zinc, manganese, and iron, the latter is more highly regarded as a zinc ore. Why?

15. Metals that are highly prized for use in jewelry occur in nature in the native state. Explain why this would be expected.

16. What property largely determined for any given metal how early in history it was discovered and used by man?

17. Recall from earlier chapters metals which are used as catalysts in industrial chemical processes. Circle these metals in a periodic table. Can you make any generalizations as a result of your study?

18. Name as many metals as you can which play a vital role in the human body.

34

The Alkali Metals

1. General Characteristics. The members of the family of elements which follows immediately after that of the inert gases in the periodic system are known as the *alkali metals*. It has already been shown that the atoms of the elements belonging to the inert gas family have stable electron configurations and show no tendency to react either by losing, sharing, or gaining electrons. An atom of each member of the alkali metal family has one more electron than an atom of the corresponding inert gas (see Table 34.1).

Table 34.I

Element	1 s	2 s p	3 s p d	4 s p d f	5 s p d	6 s p	7 s
Li	2	1					
Na	2	2, 6	1				
K	2	2, 6	2, 6	1			
Rb	2	2, 6	2, 6, 10	2, 6	1		
Cs	2	2, 6	2, 6, 10	2, 6, 10	2, 6	1	
Fr	2	2, 6	2, 6, 10	2, 6, 10, 14	2, 6, 10	2, 6	1

The elements of the alkali metal family are, therefore, characterized by the relative ease with which they release the single valence electron in each atom and thus attain stable inert gas configurations. On the other hand, the alkali metals do not release more than one electron per atom in any chemical reaction. The ease with which one electron is lost and the difficulty of removing more than one electron from the atoms of the alkali metals is indicated by the values of their ionization potentials. These are lower for the alkali metals than for those of any other family. It is not surprising, therefore, that these are the most active of all the metals. Since they lose electrons so easily, the atoms of this family are readily oxidized to the corresponding singly charged positive ions, and are among the strongest reducing agents known. They are always univalent and, with very few exceptions, form electrovalent bonds.

Table 34.2

Ionization Potentials (volts)

	Li	Na	K	Rb	Cs
1st electron	5.4	5.1	4.3	4.2	3.9
2nd electron	75.6	47.3	31.8	27.4	23.4

Table 34.2 indicates also that the ionization potentials of these elements decrease in the order of increasing atomic weights. This results, as was indicated in Chapter 10, from the fact that the valence electron in an atom of one of the heavier members of the family is farther from the nucleus than in a lighter member, is shielded from the nucleus by a greater number of electron shells, and is thus held less tightly. Since the ionization potentials decrease in the order Li, Na, K, Rb, Cs, the reactivities of the elements increase in the same order. Cesium is, thus, the most active of all the metals.[1] The strong reducing power of these elements is illustrated by the vigor with which they react with water to release hydrogen.

$$2M + 2H_2O = H_2 + 2M^+ + 2OH^-$$

The metals are so reactive that they must be stored in the absence of air and moisture, generally under some inert liquid such as xylene, toluene, or kerosine.

The alkali metals dissolve readily in liquid ammonia, giving dark blue solutions which apparently contain metal ions and free electrons, and which are very strong reducing agents. On standing, they slowly decompose with the production of hydrogen and the alkali metal amide—this reaction being catalyzed by finely divided iron or platinum.

$$2M + 2NH_3 = H_2 + 2M^+ + 2NH_2^-$$

The ions formed by the alkali metals are large compared with those of the other metals (see Figure 10.9, p. 193). The ionic radii for the alkali metal ions are given in Table 34.3.

Because of the small charge and the large size of these ions, the electrostatic attractive forces that operate in crystals of alkali metal salts are relatively small. Hence, crystals of these compounds are easily broken down in water. This accounts for the high solubility in water which is characteristic of alkali metal compounds. The same factors account for the high solubility in

[1] For reasons to be discussed in a later chapter (p. 759) we should expect francium to be less reactive than cesium.

water and high degree of ionization of the hydroxides of the alkali metals, and for the strongly basic nature of their aqueous solutions. It is this characteristic basicity of alkali metal hydroxides which gives the family its name. The hydroxide, carbonate, and phosphate of lithium are much less soluble in water than the corresponding compounds of the other members of the family. In this regard, it is interesting to note that the lithium ion is the smallest of the alkali metal ions and is thus surrounded by a stronger electrical field than the others. Lithium compounds are quite similar to those of magnesium, the second element in the next family. This diagonal relationship also exists between beryllium, the first element of Group 2a, and aluminum, the second element in Group 3a. Likewise, boron and silicon resemble each other.

Table 34.3

Ionic Radii (Å)	
Li^+	0.60
Na^+	0.95
K^+	1.33
Rb^+	1.48
Cs^+	1.69

The large size and small charge of the alkali metal ions do not favor the formation of coordination bonds with donor molecules and ions. Alkali metal ions, therefore, form very few complexes. In fact, the formation even of salt hydrates in this family is almost entirely restricted to salts of the first two ions, sodium and lithium, which, because of their smaller size, are surrounded by more intense electrical fields than the other ions of the family.

The standard oxidation potentials for the alkali metals are, as would be expected, very high. They are listed in Table 34.4.

Table 34.4

Standard Oxidation Potentials (volts)

Li	=	Li^+	+	e^-		3.05
Na	=	Na^+	+	e^-		2.71
K	=	K^+	+	e^-		2.93
Rb	=	Rb^+	+	e^-		2.93
Cs	=	Cs^+	+	e^-		2.92

The extraordinarily high oxidation potential of lithium is due to the high heat of hydration of the lithium ion. The standard oxidation potentials are measures of the tendency for metals to go into aqueous solution with the formation of hydrated ions. This process may be considered as equivalent to the sum of the following three steps:

1. $M_{(s)} = M_{(g)}$ ... sublimation of the metal
2. $M_{(g)} = M_{(g)}^+ + e^-$ ... ionization
3. $M_{(g)}^+ + water = M^+$ (hydrated) ... hydration of the ion

With respect to the first step, it may be shown that the ease of sublimation of the metals increases from lithium to cesium. With respect to the second step, it has been shown that lithium has a smaller tendency to lose electrons than any of the other alkali metals. However, in the third step, the smaller size of the lithium ion causes it to have a much greater tendency to form bonds with water molecules (p. 235), i.e., to become hydrated, than the other alkali metal ions, and this is sufficient to raise its oxidation potential to the same level as that of cesium.

The physical properties of the alkali metals are unusual for metallic elements. Some of these properties are listed in Table 34.5.

Table 34.5
Physical Properties of the Alkali Metals

	Li	Na	K	Rb	Cs
Melting point (°C.)	186	97.9	62.7	39.0	28.4
Boiling point (°C.)	1336	880	776	679	680
Density (g./cc.)	0.53	0.97	0.86	1.53	1.90
Flame color	red	yellow	violet	violet	violet

As is shown in the table, these metals have very low melting points—cesium melting only a little above room temperature. They are outstanding also for their low density. The elements have a bright metallic luster when freshly cut, but very quickly corrode in the presence of air. They are very soft, so that with the exception of lithium they can be flattened between the fingers. They are excellent conductors of electricity and readily emit electrons under the influence of light, thus exhibiting the photoelectric effect.

Another consequence of the fact that the outer electrons in the atoms of the alkali metals are held so loosely is that these electrons are easily raised to higher energy levels even by the relatively low energies available at the temperature of the Bunsen flame. When such excited atoms revert to their normal states they give off the absorbed energy in the form of light. The result is that these elements impart characteristic colors to the Bunsen flame. Solutions of chlorides are commonly used in making these flame tests because the chlorides are more volatile than the oxides, nitrates, or sulfates. Since there is only one valence electron per atom, the spectra of these elements contain relatively few lines.

The alkali metal ions are colorless and hence their compounds are either colorless or, if the anion is colored, have the color of the anion. Thus, potassium permanganate, which contains the purple permanganate ion, is dark purple in color.

2. Occurrence of the Alkali Metals. Since they are so reactive, the alkali metals never occur in the uncombined state. Sodium and potassium compounds, however, are widely distributed in nature.

Sodium is a constituent of a large number of silicate minerals. The mineral albite, $NaAlSi_3O_8$, is one of the most common. The weathering processes that break down these silicate rocks liberate simple water-soluble sodium compounds, which are carried to the sea. In past geologic ages, changes in the earth's crust have at various times caused large sections of the sea to be cut off and gradually dried up. This process has resulted in the deposition of large beds of salts which are found in arid or semi-arid regions. For a long time immense deposits of sodium nitrate, $NaNO_3$, in northern Chile were the main source of combined nitrogen (p. 468). Large deposits of borax, $Na_2B_4O_7 \cdot 10H_2O$, and related substances are found in the Death Valley region in California. Considerable deposits of a mineral containing sodium carbonate, called "trona," are also found in California. By far the most important sodium mineral, however, is sodium chloride. This compound is the ultimate source of nearly all sodium compounds, as well as of free sodium and chlorine and many chlorine compounds. Sodium chloride is found in brine wells, in sea water (of which it constitutes about 2.5% by weight), and in large underground deposits of rock salt or halite. An extremely large bed of rock salt underlies about 100,000 square miles of Texas, Oklahoma, and Kansas, and runs from about 300 to 600 ft. in thickness. This one deposit would supply this country for about a million years at the present rate of consumption.

Potassium salts occur in sea water only in very small concentrations, but the element is found abundantly in many silicate minerals, of which orthoclase, $KAlSi_3O_8$, is a good example. These silicates are too stable to be used as practical sources of potassium compounds. Fortunately, through processes analogous to those described before, geologic weathering has broken down a portion of these minerals, and deposits of soluble potassium salts such as sylvite, KCl, carnallite, $KCl \cdot MgCl_2 \cdot 6H_2O$, kainite, $KCl \cdot MgSO_4 \cdot 3H_2O$, schönite, $K_2SO_4 \cdot MgSO_4 \cdot 6H_2O$, and polyhalite, $K_2SO_4 \cdot 2CaSO_4 \cdot MgSO_4 \cdot 2H_2O$, are found at various localities on the earth's surface. The Stassfurt and Alsace deposits in Germany furnish large amounts of potassium minerals. The stimulus of World War I, during which an acute shortage of potassium compounds was experienced in this country, resulted in the development of a domestic potassium industry. The main domestic sources of potassium salts are the Carlsbad region in New Mexico and the brines from the Searles Lake region in southern California.

Lithium is not particularly abundant. It is found in lepidolite,[2] $Li_2(F,OH)_2$ $Al_2(SiO_3)_3$, and spodumene, $LiAl(SiO_3)_2$. Geographical sources in this country are Maine, South Dakota, California, and North Carolina.

Rubidium and cesium are rare elements. Rubidium occurs as an impurity in many minerals, e.g., lepidolite, and cesium as the uncommon aluminate, pollucite. Francium is obtained only as artificially produced isotopes (p. 146).

Fig. 34.1.   Location of sources of alkali metals in the U.S.

3. Preparation and Uses of the Metals. Atoms of the alkali metals lose electrons extremely readily, and the reverse process of converting the ions to atoms is a difficult one. In fact, free sodium and potassium were not known until 1807, when Sir Humphry Davy obtained them by electrolysis of the molten hydroxides. Lithium was discovered in 1817 by Arfvedson and isolated in 1855 by Bunsen, who, with Kirchhoff, discovered rubidium and cesium in 1860 through the use of the spectroscope.

Metallic sodium, which is the most important of these metals, for a long time was prepared mainly by the electrolysis of fused sodium hydroxide, as in the Castner process (Figure 34.2). This process has the advantage that sodium hydroxide is readily fusible (m.p. 318° C.). Most metallic sodium today, however, is made by the Downs process (Figure 34.3), which

---

[2] $(F,OH)_2$ indicates a total of two equivalents of F^- and OH^- together; proportions of these two are variable.

consists in the electrolysis of molten sodium chloride, thus eliminating the necessity for the intermediate conversion to sodium hydroxide. Sodium chloride melts at 800° C., but in practice other salts such as sodium carbonate or calcium chloride are added to lower the melting point of the electrolyte. The equation for this electrolysis is

$$2NaCl = 2Na + Cl_2$$

Metallic sodium may also be prepared by heating a mixture of sodium monoxide and carbon to 2500° C. under vacuum.

$$Na_2O + C = 2Na + CO$$

The sodium metal distills off as a vapor.

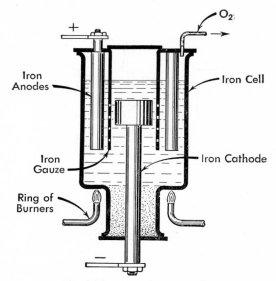

Fig. 34.2. The Castner cell.

Metallic sodium is used in large quantities where a powerful reducing agent is required. It is used, for example, in the manufacture of certain organic dyes and drugs, and in the reduction of compounds of the rarer metals to the free metals. Its use as a dehydrating agent in the preparation of certain anhydrous organic solvents depends upon the marked reactivity of sodium with water. The largest users are the manufacturers of sodium cyanide (p. 544), sodium peroxide (p. 647), and tetraethyl lead (p. 573). The activity of metallic sodium makes it useful as a deoxidizing agent in the manufacture of certain metallic alloys, and in the removal of halogens and sulfur from organic compounds. It forms a number of alloys, the most useful of which are sodium amalgam (an alloy of sodium and mercury) and a sodium lead alloy. Since the great activity of sodium is somewhat reduced by its dilution with inactive elements, these alloys are convenient and easily handled reducing agents. The high electrical conductivity of metallic sodium has been applied in certain installations where large electric currents must

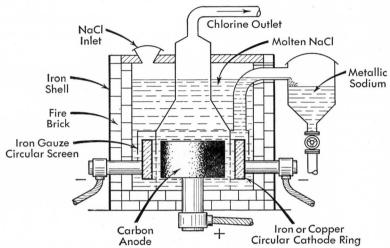

NaCl Inlet

Chlorine Outlet

Molten NaCl

Iron Shell

Metallic Sodium

Fire Brick

Iron Gauze Circular Screen

Carbon Anode

＋

Iron or Copper Circular Cathode Ring

Fig. 34.3. The Downs cell for producing metallic sodium.

be conducted for short distances with low voltage drops; iron pipes filled with metallic sodium are used as conductors. The high rate of heat transfer of sodium metal is applied in the manufacture of aircraft engine exhaust valves. These hollow steel valves are filled with sodium metal; the high thermal conductivity of the molten sodium inside the valve helps to prevent overheating. Sodium vapor lamps, which give an intense yellow light, are sometimes used for the illumination of highways.

Metallic potassium is best obtained by the reduction of potassium carbonate with metallic sodium at high temperatures in the absence of air.

$$K_2CO_3 + 2Na = Na_2CO_3 + 2K$$

The difficulty of reduction of potassium compounds, as well as the relative scarcity of simple potassium salts, causes the production of potassium to be considerably more expensive than that of sodium. Hence, since there are few major uses for metallic potassium to which sodium metal may not equally well be applied, the production of the former metal is limited.

Metallic lithium is obtained by the electrolysis of its molten chloride or bromide. Lithium is an efficient drying agent, and is also used as a scavenger in the purification of certain metals. Its ability to take up hydrogen to form the hydride, and to combine with oxygen, nitrogen, and sulfur, is bringing about its increased use in metal melting, refining, and casting operations. Lithium is also useful in a variety of organic chemical processes, as well as in nuclear chemical applications (p. 143). Spectroscopic evidence for lithium in the high atmosphere was first reported in December of 1958, and touched off speculation that the United States may have developed a lithium bomb, in which lithium is converted into tritium by means of a conventional A-bomb trigger.

Cesium and rubidium may be prepared by methods analogous to those described above. Cesium, because of its high photosensitivity, finds some application in the manufacture of photoelectric cells.

It is interesting to note that, under certain conditions, active metals can be obtained by the reduction of their compounds by less active metals. For example, potassium may be obtained by heating potassium hydroxide with a mixture of iron and iron carbide, sodium by the reduction of sodium carbonate with iron, and cesium by the reduction of cesium chloride with calcium. This apparent paradox may be explained on the basis of the high volatility of the alkali metals. Thus, in the case of the reduction of cesium chloride by calcium, we may write the equation

$$2CsCl + Ca = CaCl_2 + 2Cs_{(g)}$$

Even though cesium is much more active than calcium, the equilibrium is shifted to the right because cesium (b.p. 680° C.) boils away at the temperature of the reduction. A similar explanation applies to the production of sodium by the reduction of sodium monoxide with carbon, and to the reduction of potassium carbonate with sodium metal, as discussed earlier.

The marked similarity between ammonium compounds and those of the alkali metals, which has been previously mentioned (p. 481), strongly suggests that if it were possible to reduce ammonium salts by the addition of a single electron per NH_4^+ ion, the product would be a metal resembling sodium or potassium. Many attempts have been made thus to produce free ammonium, none of which has been entirely successful. If, however, an aqueous solution of ammonium chloride is electrolyzed with a mercury cathode or is treated with sodium or potassium amalgam, a product is obtained which is undoubtedly ammonium amalgam. At sufficiently low temperature (−85°) this is a hard, stable substance, metallic in appearance, but at room temperature it is a pasty mass which, on standing, readily decomposes into mercury, ammonia, and hydrogen. Nevertheless, the existence of this alloy confirms the essentially metallic nature of free ammonium.

COMPOUNDS OF THE ALKALI METALS

4. Importance of Sodium Compounds. The compounds of sodium are especially important commercially because of their low cost and high solubility in water. The paragraphs that follow deal with such compounds as halides, hydroxides, hydrides, carbonates and bicarbonates, and nitrates.

5. Halides. Each of the halogens reacts vigorously with each of the alkali metals to form a very stable binary compound, according to the equation

$$2M + X_2 = 2MX$$

Since these alkali metal halides are electrovalent compounds, they have high melting points, are good conductors of electricity in the molten state, and have other properties which are characteristic of this class of compounds. With the exception of lithium fluoride, they are quite soluble in water.

Sodium chloride crystallizes in cubic crystals which melt at $800°$ C. As has been pointed out, it occurs in nature in tremendous quantities. Not only is it the immediate source of the many millions of pounds of sodium compounds used annually, but it is also the source of practically all the chlorine and hydrogen chloride which are manufactured.

The layman is more familiar with sodium chloride than with any other salt. It is used in practically all foods, and hence is known as "table salt." Not only does salt improve the taste of many of our foods, but also it is essential in the bodily processes. Pure sodium chloride is nonhygroscopic under ordinary conditions and hence does not "cake" on standing in moist air unless the humidity is very high. The caking of table salt usually results from the presence of impurities, chiefly calcium or magnesium chloride. A little baking soda (p. 653) converts the hygroscopic calcium and magnesium chlorides to the nonhygroscopic carbonates and thus prevents caking. Sodium chloride is purified by dissolving the crude salt in water and evaporating the solution under reduced pressure to bring about crystallization; most of the impurities stay in the solution. "Free-running" salt is obtained by the precipitation of the calcium and magnesium ions from the solution by the addition of trisodium phosphate and sodium carbonate, before crystallization of the sodium chloride. Very pure sodium chloride may be obtained by precipitation from concentrated sodium chloride solution with concentrated hydrochloric acid.

Sodium chloride solution (brine) is used in the refrigeration industry because of its low freezing point. The salt is used as a preservative, in ceramics, in the metallurgy of silver, lead, and copper, and for many other purposes.

Potassium chloride is the starting point in the preparation of metallic potassium and its compounds. One of the most important uses of crude potassium chloride is in the manufacture of fertilizer, while the purer compound is used in the production of other potassium compounds, such as potassium hydroxide and potassium nitrate.

Bromides and iodides of sodium and potassium are prepared by the reaction of the corresponding halogen with the respective hydroxide. The preparation of potassium bromide is typical. Bromine is passed into hot potassium hydroxide solution, yielding bromide and bromate according to the equation

$$3Br_2 + 6OH^- = 5Br^- + BrO_3^- + 3H_2O$$

The solution is then evaporated to dryness and the residue is heated; this decomposes the bromate and leaves the bromide as a white powder.

Sodium and potassium bromides are used in the practice of medicine as sedatives, and in the preparation of silver bromide emulsion on photographic plates or films. The iodides find some use in photography, and are used medicinally to insure proper functioning of the thyroid gland. A lack of sufficient iodine in the diet brings about the abnormal enlargement of the thyroid gland known as goiter. "Iodized" salt contains a small fraction of a per cent of sodium or potassium iodide and is used in regions where the normal food supply is deficient in iodine.

6. Oxides. It might be supposed that all the alkali metals would react with oxygen to yield oxides of the general formula M_2O, according to the equation

$$4M + O_2 = 2M_2O$$

However, lithium is the only one of these metals which yields the monoxide by direct reaction with an excess of oxygen. Sodium reacts with an excess of oxygen or air to yield the peroxide, Na_2O_2, while potassium, rubidium, and cesium form the oxides KO_2, RbO_2, and CsO_2, respectively; these last three compounds are sometimes called "superoxides." It should be pointed out that in all these compounds the alkali metal is univalent and exists as a singly charged positive ion. The electronic structure of Na_2O_2 is indicated by the formula

$$2Na^+. \; : \overset{..}{\underset{..}{O}} : \overset{..}{\underset{..}{O}} : \; ^{--}$$

which shows that the two oxygen atoms have taken one electron each from the sodium atoms and then have completed their valence shells by sharing a pair of electrons between them. The structure of the superoxide ion, O_2^-, is more complex.

The monoxides of the alkali metals (with the exception of Li_2O) cannot be prepared in the expected manner by heating the hydroxides or carbonates, for the latter compounds are unusually stable. They may be obtained by heating the nitrate or the hydroxide with the free metal. For example:

$$2KNO_3 + 10K = 6K_2O + N_2$$

$$2NaOH + 2Na = 2Na_2O + H_2$$

Sodium peroxide is the only commercially important alkali metal oxide. In the preparation of this compound, trays of sodium metal are passed through a long furnace at a temperature of $400°$ C. from one end, while a stream of air is passed through the furnace from the other direction. This is conducive to smooth and complete reaction, for the fresh sodium comes in contact with air from which much of the oxygen has been removed and as it passes through the furnace the oxygen content of the air with which it reacts becomes progressively larger. The principle applied here is known as the "principle of counter-currents." Pure sodium peroxide is a white solid, sometimes called "oxone," and is used commercially as a strong oxidizing agent, and as a source of oxygen and hydrogen peroxide. In acids or in an excess of water, if kept cool, it liberates hydrogen peroxide according to the equations

$$O_2^{--} + 2H^+ = H_2O_2$$

$$O_2^{--} + 2H_2O = H_2O_2 + 2OH^-$$

If only a small quantity of water is added, or if the temperature is allowed to rise, oxygen is obtained.

$$2O_2^{--} + 2H_2O = 4OH^- + O_2$$

If sodium peroxide is barely moistened in contact with combustible materials, combustion is almost certain to result; hence this substance must be handled with care in the laboratory.

Sodium monoxide, Na_2O, is an extremely efficient drying agent because of its great tendency to form the hydroxide.

$$Na_2O + H_2O = 2NaOH$$

7. Hydroxides. When the monoxides of the alkali metals are allowed to react with water, they form hydroxides, with the liberation of heat.

$$M_2O + H_2O = 2MOH$$

This cannot be used as a practical method for the manufacture of the hydroxides, however, for the monoxides (except Li_2O) are, as was shown in the preceding paragraph, difficult to obtain.

There are, in general, two types of methods commonly used for the preparation of alkali hydroxides: (1) the reaction of carbonates or sulfates of the alkali metals with the hydroxide of calcium or barium, respectively, and (2) electrolytic methods. The first type may be illustrated by the following equations:

$$Ca(OH)_{2(s)} + 2Na^+ + CO_3^{--} = CaCO_{3(s)} + 2Na^+ + 2OH^-$$

$$Ba^{++} + 2OH^- + 2K^+ + SO_4^{--} = BaSO_{4(s)} + 2K^+ + 2OH^-$$

The first equation represents the oldest method of manufacturing sodium hydroxide; it is known as "causticization" and is still widely used. A suspension of calcium hydroxide is mixed with an equivalent amount of sodium carbonate solution, and the calcium carbonate which is precipitated is filtered off. The remaining solution is evaporated to dryness and the residue fused to insure removal of all the water.

The second type of method has already been illustrated in the description of the production of chlorine in the Hooker S cell (p. 386). In this process, a solution of sodium chloride is electrolyzed, and hydrogen, chlorine, and sodium hydroxide are obtained according to the equation

$$2Na^+ + 2Cl^- + 2H_2O = 2Na^+ + 2OH^- + H_2 + Cl_2$$

The sodium hydroxide thus prepared commonly contains some sodium chloride as an impurity, since it is difficult to separate the two compounds completely. If very pure sodium hydroxide is desired, it may be prepared by treating the product from the electrolytic process with alcohol, in which the sodium chloride is not appreciably soluble. The alcoholic solution may then be evaporated to give pure sodium hydroxide. Very pure sodium hydroxide may also be prepared in small quantities by reaction of the pure metal with water. Special types of cells which the avoid the difficulty of separating the chloride from the hydroxide have been designed. A typical example of this type is the Castner-Kellner cell illustrated in Figure 34.4.

Potassium hydroxide is prepared commercially by methods analogous to those given for sodium hydroxide.

The alkali hydroxides are white solids which, with the exception of lithium hydroxide, show little tendency to decompose on being heated. All except lithium hydroxide melt without loss of water and, in fact, may even be volatilized without decomposition. They are very unusual in this respect,

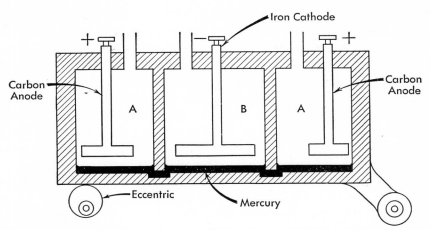

Fig. 34.4. The Castner-Kellner cell. Sections A contain sodium chloride solution. Section B contains water. Electrolysis forms sodium amalgam in sections A. The amalgam reacts with water in B to produce sodium hydroxide. The mercury is shifted between sections by a rocking motion produced by the eccentric. (From McCutcheon, Seltz, and Warner, *General Chemistry*, D. Van Nostrand Co., Inc.)

for other hydroxides readily lose water, when heated, to form oxides. The alkali hydroxides are extremely hygroscopic and are very soluble in alcohol and in water, dissolving in the latter with marked evolution of heat. They are very strongly basic, since they are completely ionized in dilute aqueous solution. Because of their strongly basic nature, their solutions readily absorb carbon dioxide from the atmosphere to form carbonates.

$$2OH^- + CO_2 = CO_3^{--} + H_2O$$

Hence, if solutions of the hydroxides are to be kept pure, they must be protected from the air. These hydroxides disintegrate most animal and vegetable material with which they come in contact. Because of this property, the hydroxides of sodium and potassium are commonly called caustic soda and caustic potash, respectively. Commercial grade sodium hydroxide is also known as lye. Solutions of these hydroxides have a soapy feeling when rubbed between the fingers because they dissolve a thin layer of the skin. These solutions also attack glass, so that glass vessels in which they are stored for any length of time become etched.

Large quantities of sodium hydroxide are used annually. Sodium and potassium hydroxides react with fats to give soaps and glycerol. The latter is of great importance to the explosives industry (p. 495). Sodium hydroxide is used in "mercerizing" cotton thread. The alkaline solution dissolves "fuzzy" fibers from the thread, giving a smooth surface and a higher luster.

Other important uses are in the rayon industry, in the purification of petroleum and of vegetable oils, in the manufacture of paper, in the reclamation of rubber, and in other chemical manufactures. Potassium hydroxide is used to a smaller extent, its great similarity to sodium hydroxide and its higher cost tending to limit its industrial application. There are, however, a few specific uses for potassium hydroxide. The fact that it is more soluble in alcohol than sodium hydroxide makes it useful in organic reactions where an alcoholic solution of a strong alkali is required. It is used also in the manufacture of soft soap. Where carbon dioxide is to be continuously removed from the atmosphere, as in submarines, etc., the use of potassium hydroxide is much more effective than that of sodium hydroxide; for, since potassium carbonate is deliquescent, the surface of the absorbent remains moist and active, even after a considerable amount of potassium carbonate has been formed.

8. Hydrides. When the alkali metals are heated with hydrogen they are converted to white, crystalline compounds of the general formula MH (p. 227). These hydrides are saltlike in character, having the same crystal structure as sodium chloride. In the fused state these compounds conduct electricity, and, upon electrolysis, hydrogen is obtained at the *anode*. These facts indicate that the compound is made up of positive alkali metal ions and negative hydride ions, H^-. The fact that the alkali metal atoms can reduce hydrogen to an oxidation state of -1 is another indication of the ease with which they give up electrons. These salt-like hydrides are finding increasing application as reducing agents in industrial chemical processes.

9. Carbonates and Bicarbonates. All the alkali metals form carbonates of the general formula M_2CO_3. These alkali metal compounds differ from the carbonates of other metals in two respects: (1) even when heated to very high temperatures, they do not decompose to give the metal oxide and carbon dioxide, and (2) with the exception of lithium carbonate, they are all quite soluble in water.

It is interesting to consider some of the implications of the first point. In the decomposition of a carbonate, the metal ion takes the oxide ion from the carbonate ion to form carbon dioxide and the metal oxide. As might be expected (cf. p. 195), the affinity of positive ions for oxide ions varies inversely with the size of the metal ion and directly with the charge on the ion. Since the alkali metal ions are relatively large and bear only a single charge, they have a relatively small attraction for oxygen atoms in the carbonate group. Thus the alkali metal carbonates show little tendency to decompose when heated. It is interesting to note that the only exception to this statement is lithium carbonate, which may be decomposed at atmospheric pressure by heating the substance to $1270°$ C. This bears out the present discussion, for the lithium ion, being the smallest of the alkali metal ions, should have the strongest affinity for oxide ions.

Since carbonic acid is a weak acid, the soluble alkali metal carbonates and bicarbonates are hydrolyzed in water to give basic solutions (p. 540).

All the alkali metal bicarbonates decompose on heating to give the normal carbonate, carbon dioxide, and water.

$$2MHCO_3 = M_2CO_3 + CO_2 + H_2O$$

The temperature required for this reaction increases with the increasing size of the M^+ ion, or, in other words, in the order $Li < Na < K < Rb < Cs$.

Sodium carbonate and sodium bicarbonate are by far the most important of these compounds from the industrial point of view. Sodium carbonate rivals sulfuric acid and chlorine in importance in chemical industry. An adequate supply of sodium carbonate is essential for the operation of many industrial processes. Most of the sodium carbonate produced at present is manufactured by one of two methods: (1) the Solvay process, or (2) the electrolytic process.

The first of these processes was developed by Ernest Solvay, a Belgian chemical engineer. The apparatus is illustrated in Figure 34.5. In this process, ammonia and carbon dioxide are passed successively into a saturated solution of sodium chloride and reactions take place which may be expressed by the equations

$$CO_2 + H_2O \rightleftharpoons HCO_3^- + H^+$$
$$+ \qquad\qquad +$$
$$Na^+ \qquad\qquad NH_3$$
$$\updownarrow \qquad\qquad \updownarrow$$
$$NaHCO_{3(s)} \quad NH_4^+$$

The presence of ammonia shifts the equilibrium to the right, increasing the concentration of the bicarbonate ion in the solution. In the presence of the high concentration of sodium ion from the sodium chloride, sodium bicarbonate crystallizes out and may be filtered off. After it has been washed, sodium bicarbonate may be converted to the carbonate by heating, the carbon dioxide given off being used over again.

$$2NaHCO_3 = Na_2CO_3 + CO_2 + H_2O$$

The economic success of this process depends upon the recovery of the ammonia, which is the only expensive raw material used. This recovery is effected by heating the mother liquor from the sodium bicarbonate precipitation with lime, CaO. The reaction that takes place is represented by the equation

$$2NH_4^+ + 2Cl^- + CaO = 2NH_3 + H_2O + Ca^{++} + 2Cl^-$$

Both the lime and the carbon dioxide used in the main reaction are obtained by the heating of limestone, $CaCO_3$.

$$CaCO_3 = CaO + CO_2$$

Thus the only by-product is the calcium chloride obtained in the recovery of the ammonia. This substance is not very valuable and is often allowed to accumulate in waste heaps, although it has some uses that will be discussed in the next chapter.

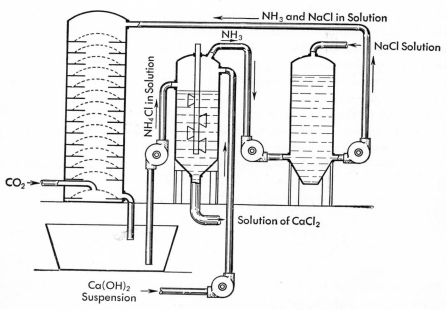

Fig. 34.5.   Solvay process for sodium carbonate manufacture.

In the electrolytic process, a solution of sodium chloride is electrolyzed and saturated with carbon dioxide. As has already been shown, such electrolysis yields hydrogen, chlorine, and sodium hydroxide. In the presence of an excess of carbon dioxide, the sodium hydroxide is converted to bicarbonate.

$$OH^- + CO_2 = HCO_3^-$$

Use of a smaller quantity of carbon dioxide results in the formation of carbonate.

$$2OH^- + CO_2 = CO_3^{--} + H_2O$$

The carbon dioxide is obtained, as in the Solvay process, by heating calcium carbonate. Valuable by-products of the electrolytic process are hydrogen, chlorine, lime, and bleaching powder, the last of which can be prepared by the reaction of the chlorine with the lime (p. 407).

Sodium carbonate forms a number of hydrates. When it is crystallized from water at room temperature, it forms crystals of the composition corresponding to the formula $Na_2CO_3 \cdot 10H_2O$. In warm dry air or on being heated to 32° C., this compound changes to $Na_2CO_3 \cdot 7H_2O$, which, on further heating to 35.4° C., is converted to $Na_2CO_3 \cdot H_2O$. At still higher temperatures, anhydrous sodium carbonate, known commercially as soda ash, is obtained. The alkalinity of sodium carbonate solutions accounts for their cleansing action. The decahydrate, $Na_2CO_3 \cdot 10H_2O$, is frequently used as a cleansing agent because of its rapid rate of solution in water and is known as washing soda or sal soda. Soda ash is a constituent of many of the cheaper soaps and soap powders, as well as of scouring powders.

The largest use of sodium carbonate is in the manufacture of glass (p. 555). Other important applications occur in paper manufacture, water softening (p. 674), textile manufacture, chemical manufacture, and petroleum technology.

The most important use of sodium bicarbonate is as a leavening agent in baking; it is, therefore, commonly called baking soda. In the presence of acids, bicarbonate ion is converted to carbonic acid, which immediately decomposes to give carbon dioxide gas.

$$H^+ + HCO_3^- = H_2O + CO_2$$

The formation of carbon dioxide gas causes the dough to rise and gives the desired lightness and porosity of texture to the culinary product. An acidic substance such as sour milk (containing lactic acid) is therefore added to react with the sodium bicarbonate. Baking powders commonly used in the modern kitchen consist of mixtures of bicarbonate of soda and a solid substance that has acidic properties. There are three common types: (1) alum baking powders, which contain sodium alum, i.e., sodium aluminum sulfate, $Na_2SO_4 \cdot Al_2(SO_4)_3 \cdot 24H_2O$, (2) tartrate baking powders, which contain potassium acid tartrate, $KHC_4H_4O_6$, and (3) phosphate baking powders, which contain calcium dihydrogen phosphate, $Ca(H_2PO_4)_2$. The reactions which take place when each type is moistened are represented respectively by the following equations:

1. $Al(H_2O)_6^{+++} + HCO_3^- = Al(H_2O)_5(OH)^{++} + H_2O + CO_2$

2. $HC_4H_4O_6^-\qquad + HCO_3^- = C_4H_4O_6^{--} + H_2O + CO_2$

3. $H_2PO_4^-\qquad\quad + HCO_3^- = HPO_4^{--} + H_2O + CO_2$

Even in the absence of an acidic substance, baking soda would, of course, give off carbon dioxide on being heated, but the presence of the residual sodium carbonate would impart an undesirable flavor to the product.

Potassium carbonate is commonly known as potash, for it was first obtained by leaching the ashes of wood and other materials derived from land plants. It is used in the manufacture of other potassium compounds and of certain types of glass. Potassium carbonate may be prepared by a method analogous to the electrolytic method for sodium carbonate.

10. Nitrates. Sodium nitrate, found in large beds thickly scattered throughout the desert areas of northern Chile, and commonly called Chile saltpeter, is an important source of nitric acid and other nitrogen compounds (p. 496).

Potassium nitrate, commonly known as saltpeter or niter, has had an important effect on the course of world events since the fourteenth century. It is a constituent of black powder, for a long time the most important military explosive. Black gunpowder consists of a mixture of potassium nitrate, sulfur, and carbon, all in a finely divided state and thoroughly mixed. When the mixture is ignited, the potassium nitrate, which is a good oxidizing agent, reacts vigorously with the sulfur and carbon; in this reaction large volumes of gas and a great deal of heat are liberated. The gases are chiefly free nitrogen, sulfur dixode, carbon monoxide, and carbon dioxide. A number of solids, including carbon and sulfur, make up the smoke resulting from the explosion. Since sodium nitrate is deliquescent, it is not satisfactory for the manufacture of gunpowder. Smokeless powder (p. 600) has largely replaced black powder as a military explosive, but the black powder is still used in certain blasting operations and in pyrotechnics. Potassium nitrate is also useful as a fertilizer and in certain types of food processing.

Potassium nitrate is found in the soil in small amounts, especially where heaps of animal or vegetable refuse are allowed to decay in the presence of wood ashes; this formerly constituted the only source of the compound. At present, however, it is generally prepared from potassium chloride. Among the methods used are the reactions of potassium chloride with nitric acid and with nitrogen dioxide.

$$3KCl + 4HNO_3 = 3KNO_3 + Cl_2 + NOCl + 2H_2O$$

$$KCl + 2NO_2 = KNO_3 + NOCl$$

The nitrates of sodium, potassium, rubidium, and cesium all yield nitrites and oxygen when heated to moderately high temperatures.

$$2MNO_3 = 2MNO_2 + O_2$$

This is interesting in light of the fact that other metal nitrates, including lithium nitrate, decompose under these conditions to give metal oxides, oxides of nitrogen, and oxygen. Perhaps we may attribute this difference in behavior to the large size and small charge of the Na^+, K^+, Rb^+, and Cs^+ ions, which reduce their affinities for oxide ions and hence their tendencies to form oxides under the conditions of the reaction (cf. p. 650).

11. Other Compounds. There are a large number of other important sodium and potassium salts, which include sodium sulfate, $Na_2SO_4 \cdot 10H_2O$ (Glauber's salt) and Na_2SO_4; sodium sulfite, Na_2SO_3; sodium bisulfite, $NaHSO_3$; sodium cyanide, $NaCN$; borax, $Na_2B_4O_7 \cdot 10H_2O$; disodium phosphate, Na_2HPO_4; sodium sulfide, Na_2S; sodium thiosulfate, $Na_2S_2O_3 \cdot 5H_2O$; the various sodium silicates; potassium chlorate, $KClO_3$, and potassium perchlorate, $KClO_4$; and many others. These are discussed in other sections of the text.

12. Detection of the Alkali Metal Ions. Since the alkali metal ions form so few insoluble salts, their detection rests in great measure upon flame or spectroscopic tests. The colors of the flame tests for the various alkali metal ions are listed in Table 34.5. The slight solubilities of potassium acid tartrate, $KHC_4H_4O_6$ (white), potassium perchlorate, $KClO_4$ (white), potassium hexanitritocobaltiate, $K_3Co(NO_2)_6$ (yellow), and potassium hexachloroplatinate, K_2PtCl_6 (yellow), are sometimes made use of in testing for potassium. Similarly the formation of a white precipitate of sodium antimonate, $Na[Sb(OH)_6]$—sometimes, for no apparent reason, written $Na_2H_2Sb_2O_7 \cdot 5H_2O$, and called sodium pyroantimonate—is sometimes used as a test for sodium. None of these precipitation tests for the alkali metals is very sensitive.

STUDY QUESTIONS AND PROBLEMS

1. Make a table of the electronic configurations, ionization potentials, and ionic radii of the alkali metals. Discuss the changes in ionization potential and

ionic radius in the series Li, Na, K, Rb, and Cs, and explain these changes in terms of the structures of the atoms.

2. Why are the second ionization potentials of the alkali metals so much higher than the first?

3. Explain in detail why the standard electrode potentials of the alkali metals do not change in the same order as the ionization potentials.

4. Explain why salts of alkali metals are, in the main, quite soluble in water.

5. Why do alkali metal ions show no more than a slight tendency toward complex ion formation?

6. Make a brief outline of the distinctive physical and chemical characteristics of the alkali metals. In so far as you can, account for these characteristics in terms of the atomic structures of these elements.

7. Make a list of the principal sources of the alkali metals. Why are these metals not found in the free state in nature?

8. Discuss the methods by which metallic sodium is prepared industrially. Why is sodium not obtained in the electrolysis of brine solution? What are the principal industrial applications of sodium metal?

9. Make a chart showing the principal chemicals which are manufactured from sodium chloride and write balanced equations for the reactions involved.

10. Make a table showing the formulas, chemical names, methods of preparation, and principal industrial applications of caustic soda, soda ash, bicarbonate of soda, oxone, caustic potash, and potassium nitrate.

The Alkaline Earth Metals

1. Introduction. Early in the history of the science, chemists were familiar with a group of substances which, because of their basic nature and their resistance to thermal decomposition, were called *alkaline earths*. This group includes the substances then known as magnesia, lime, strontia, and baryta, all of which, until the time of Lavoisier, were thought to be elements. Following a suggestion of Lavoisier's that these earths might in reality be oxides, Sir Humphry Davy, in 1808, was able to decompose them electrolytically and to obtain the free metals, magnesium, calcium, strontium, and barium. These elements, together with beryllium, which was first isolated by Wöhler in 1828, and radium, discovered by the Curies many years later (Chapter 8), constitute Group 2a in the periodic system and are known as the *alkaline earth metal* family.

2. General Characteristics. The members of this family follow immediately after the alkali metals in the periodic system. Each of the alkaline earth metals, therefore, has an atomic number one greater than that of the corresponding alkali metal. The electronic configurations of the atoms of the corresponding members of the two families are the same except that the alkaline earth metals have two valence electrons per atom (Table 35.1), while the alkali metals have only one.

Just as an atom of an alkali metal readily loses its one valence electron to form a singly charged ion (p. 636), so does an atom of an alkaline earth metal lose both of its valence electrons to form a doubly charged ion. Each atom of an alkaline earth metal, as has been mentioned, bears a nuclear charge one greater than that of an atom of the corresponding alkali metal. Consider, for example, the nuclear charges and electron configurations of sodium and magnesium as shown in Table 35.1 and in Table 34.1 (p. 636). In each case, the valence shell is shielded from the nucleus by the same num-

Table 35.1

Element	1	2	3	4	5	6	7
	s	s p	s p d	s p d f	s p d	s p	s
Be	2	2					
Mg	2	2, 6	2				
Ca	2	2, 6	2, 6	2			
Sr	2	2, 6	2, 6, 10	2, 6	2		
Ba	2	2, 6	2, 6, 10	2, 6, 10	2, 6	2	
Ra	2	2, 6	2, 6, 10	2, 6, 10, 14	2, 6, 10	2, 6	2

ber and type of inner electron shells. Since the nuclear charge is one greater in the magnesium atom, the two valence electrons in the magnesium atom are held more firmly than is the single valence electron in the sodium atom. The same sort of reasoning may be applied to the other corresponding pairs of members of the two families, so that the general conclusion that the alkaline earth metal atoms release electrons less readily than atoms of the corresponding alkali metal is inescapable. The conclusion is further substantiated by a comparison of the measured values of the ionization potentials of the two families (Tables 34.2 and 35.2).

Table 35.2

Ionization Potentials (volts)

	Be	Mg	Ca	Sr	Ba
1st electron	9.3	7.6	6.1	5.7	5.2
2nd electron	18.2	15.0	11.9	11.0	10.0
3rd electron	153.9	80.1	51.2	. . . .	. . . .

This smaller tendency of the alkaline earth metals to lose electrons accounts for the fact that, while these metals are still highly reactive, they are, nevertheless, considerably less so than the corresponding alkali metals. The comparative ease of removal of *two* valence electrons from an alkaline earth metal atom, as compared with the difficulty of removal of more than two, is also indicated by the values in the table. It should be noted further that ionization potentials of the elements of this group decrease with increasing atomic weight (p. 184).[1] This fact is in accord with the experimental observation that reactivity in this series increases in the order $Be < Mg < Ca < Sr < Ba$.

[1] As a result of the "rare earth interlude" discussed on page 760 the ionization potential of radium is slightly higher than that of barium.

The elements of the alkaline earth metal family (with the exception of beryllium) are, therefore, strong reducing agents. Their compounds are, for the most part, electrovalent, although there are exceptions, particularly in the case of the compounds of beryllium. The reducing power of the elements is illustrated by the vigor of their reactions with various nonmetals. The following equations represent some of these reactions:

$$2M + O_2 = 2MO \qquad\qquad M + 2C = MC_2 \text{ (high}$$
$$M + X_2 = MX_2 \text{ (X = any} \qquad 3M + 2P = M_3P_2 \quad \text{temperature)}$$
$$M + S \ = MS \qquad \text{halogen)} \qquad 3M + N_2 = M_3N_2$$

Calcium, strontium, and barium are sufficiently active to form saltlike hydrides of the type discussed in the preceding chapter (p. 650).

$$M: + H:H = M^{++}, 2H:^-$$

These three elements, also, will burn in carbon dioxide. The reactions take place according to the general equation

$$M + CO_2 = MO + CO$$

The increasing reactivity in the series beryllium to barium is illustrated by the behavior of the metals toward water. Beryllium does not react with water even at very high temperatures. Magnesium, however, reacts readily with boiling water, while calcium, strontium, and barium react vigorously even with cold water, according to the equation

$$M + 2H_2O = M^{++} + 2OH^- + H_2$$

Though the atoms of the alkaline earth metals differ by one electron from the alkali metal atoms which precede them in the periodic system, the electron configurations of the *ions* formed by corresponding members of the two families are identical, both families forming ions having an inert gas configuration. The alkaline earth metal ions bear a greater nuclear charge, however, and hence draw the electrons closer in toward the nucleus, so that their ions are smaller than those of the corresponding alkali metals. The ionic radii of the ions of the two families are given in Table 35.3.

Table 35.3

	Ionic Radii (Angstrom Units)				
	Li^+	Na^+	K^+	Rb^+	Cs^+
Alkali metals	0.60	0.95	1.33	1.48	1.69
	Be^{++}	Mg^{++}	Ca^{++}	Sr^{++}	Ba^{++}
Alkaline earth metals	0.31	0.65	0.99	1.13	1.35

Since the charges on the alkaline earth metal ions are double those on the alkali metal ions, and the radii of the former are also much smaller than those of the latter, the ratios of ionic charge to radius for the alkaline earth metal family are considerably greater than the corresponding ratios for the alkali metals. The consequent increased strength of the electrical field surrounding an alkaline earth metal ion manifests itself in the tendency for the member with the smallest ionic radius, beryllium, to form covalent compounds. Anhydrous beryllium halides are poor conductors of electricity in the fused state, a fact which indicates that these compounds are largely covalent in character. Beryllium hydroxide, furthermore, is amphoteric; and the smaller alkaline earth metal ions show a much greater tendency to form complex ions than do those of the alkali metals.

The compounds of the alkaline earth metals are, in general, less soluble in water than the corresponding alkali metal compounds, though there are a number of exceptions to this rule, particularly among the halides and nitrates.

The standard oxidation potentials for the alkaline earth metals are listed in Table 35.4.

Table 35.4
Standard Oxidation Potentials (volts)

Ba	$=$	Ba^{++}	$+$	$2e^-$	2.90
Sr	$=$	Sr^{++}	$+$	$2e^-$	2.89
Ca	$=$	Ca^{++}	$+$	$2e^-$	2.87
Mg	$=$	Mg^{++}	$+$	$2e^-$	2.37
Be	$=$	Be^{++}	$+$	$2e^-$	1.85

These high potentials are in line with the reactivity of the elements with water. It may be noted that the standard oxidation potentials for calcium, strontium, and barium are higher than that for sodium. This is due, in part, to the fact that ions of this group have much higher heats of hydration than

Table 35.5
Heats of Hydration of the Gaseous Ions of the Alkali and Alkaline Earth Metals
(Cal./mole)

Li	123	Be	...
Na	97	Mg	460
K	77	Ca	395
Rb	70	Sr	355
Cs	63	Ba	305

do the alkali metal ions (p. 638). The fact that the heats of hydration of the alkaline earth metal ions are four to five times those of the corresponding alkali metal ions is, in itself, an indication of the much greater tendency for the former to form complex ions than the latter.

Some of the important physical properties of the alkaline earth metals are listed in Table 35.6.

Table 35.6

	Be	Mg	Ca	Sr	Ba
Melting point (°C.)	1284–1300	651	850	770	710
Boiling point (°C.)	2970(?)	1103	1440	1380	1500
Density (g./cc.)	1.84–1.85	1.74	1.55	2.6	3.5
Flame color	none	none	orange-red	crimson	light green

These metals have a white luster when freshly cut, but, with the exception of beryllium, they tarnish readily. They are considerably harder than the alkali metals, beryllium being hard enough to scratch glass. They are good conductors of electricity. Compounds of calcium, strontium, and barium readily impart to the flame of a Bunsen burner the colors listed in the table. These flame colors are commonly used in the detection of calcium, strontium, and barium. The ions derived from atoms of these metals are colorless, and their compounds are white unless the anion is colored, in which case the compound has the color which is characteristic of the anion.

BERYLLIUM

3. Uses, Occurrences, Preparation. Only a relatively few years ago, beryllium was a laboratory curiosity, the difficulty and expense of its extraction having been a strong deterrent to its industrial application. The extraordinary properties of some of its alloys, however, have stimulated the development of methods of extraction which are beginning to make its application commercially feasible. Of particular importance are the alloys with copper and with nickel. The beryllium–copper alloy which contains about 2% by weight of beryllium may be heat treated so as to attain a tensile strength greater than that of some types of steel. Because of its high resilience, high tensile strength, relatively high electrical conductivity, resistance to elastic fatigue, and resistance to wear and corrosion, beryllium–copper is particularly useful in the manufacture of various types of high-grade springs. Alloys of beryllium are used in fire-control apparatus on large guns, in delicate parts for aircraft engines and instruments, and in many other sensitive devices. In powder factories and other plants where electric sparks constitute a dangerous fire hazard, nonsparking tools made from beryllium–copper are used. The application of beryllium alloys is steadily widening.

Pure beryllium metal is hard and brittle. Because of its low atomic weight, it is transparent to x-rays and is used as windows in x-ray tubes.

Beryllium is always found in combination, usually in the form of complex silicates and aluminates. Beryl, $Be_3Al_2(SiO_3)_6$, the most important of these minerals, occurs in large hexagonal crystals, widely distributed but in rather small deposits. It is estimated that beryllium makes up about $1 \times 10^{-5}\%$ of the earth's crust. Most beryllium ore comes from the Union of South Africa, Southern Rhodesia, Brazil, and India, although there are workable supplies of domestic ores in Colorado, South Dakota, and New England.

Most pure beryllium metal is obtained by the reduction of its fluoride with magnesium. The ease with which beryllium is oxidized at high temperatures makes it difficult to alloy. Hence, beryllium–copper alloys are made directly by the reduction of beryllium oxide with carbon in the presence of copper. Continued exposure to beryllium or its compounds may lead to a serious and occasionally fatal disease called berylliosis.

MAGNESIUM

4. Importance. Under the stimulation given the aircraft industry by the advent of World War II, the production of magnesium has increased from 7,000,000 pounds in 1939 to over 800,000,000 pounds in recent years.

5. Occurrence. Magnesium is too active to occur free in nature, but its compounds are abundant. It ranks sixth among the metals in the earth's crust, as it is estimated to compose 2.09% of all igneous rocks. Magnesium occurs in many varieties of siliceous minerals such as talc, $H_2Mg_3(SiO_3)_4$, and asbestos, $CaMg_3(SiO_3)_4$. Dolomitic limestone, $CaCO_3 \cdot MgCO_3$, occurs in enormous quantities. Magnesite, $MgCO_3$, is less common, but is a valuable magnesium ore. Magnesium salts are found in some of the large salt beds discussed in the preceding chapter. The Stassfurt beds, for example, contain large deposits of the magnesium-containing minerals, carnallite, kainite, schönite, and polyhalite (p. 640). Magnesium salts are obtained in large quantities from sea water and brine walls.

6. Metallurgy. The high chemical activity of magnesium makes the reduction of its compounds difficult. In the most commonly used process, fused magnesium chloride monohydrate, $MgCl_2 \cdot H_2O$, obtained from sea water or from brine wells, is electrolyzed. The recovery from sea water, which contains magnesium salts to the extent of 0.13% of magnesium, is particularly interesting. The sea water is treated with a slurry of calcium hydroxide, causing the less soluble magnesium hydroxide to precipitate.

$$Mg^{++} + Ca(OH)_{2(s)} = Mg(OH)_{2(s)} + Ca^{++}$$

The magnesium hydroxide is filtered off and dissolved in hydrochloric acid.

$$Mg(OH)_{2(s)} + 2H^+ + 2Cl^- = Mg^{++} + 2Cl^- + 2H_2O$$

The solution of magnesium chloride is concentrated and purified, the mono-hydrate, $MgCl_2 \cdot H_2O$, is crystallized out, and this salt is then used in the electrolytic cells. The lime used is obtained by the roasting of sea shells ($CaCO_3$), followed by the hydration of the oxide thus produced (p. 668).

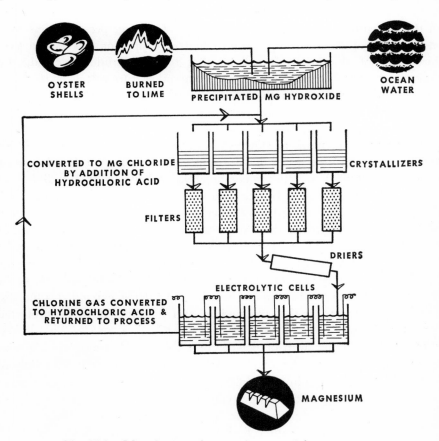

Fig. 35.1. Manufacture of magnesium metal from sea water.

Other processes include (1) the electrolysis of fused anhydrous magnesium chloride produced by the reaction at high temperature of carbon monoxide and chlorine on magnesium oxide from magnesite,

$$MgO + CO + Cl_2 = MgCl_2 + CO_2$$

(2) the reduction of pure magnesium oxide with carbon at 2000° C., and (3) the heating of briquets formed from roasted dolomite ($CaO + MgO$) and ferrosilicon to 1150° C. under high vacuum. In the last process the ferrosilicon reduces the magnesium oxide, and the magnesium metal distills off.

7. Properties and Uses of Magnesium Metal. Magnesium is the lightest of all the structurally useful metals. Its density of 1.74 g. per cc. is less than one-fourth that of iron, only one-fifth that of copper or nickel, and two-thirds that of aluminum. It can be cast, rolled, extruded, welded, and easily machined. Pure magnesium, like many other pure metals, is relatively soft, and does not possess the necessary strength and related properties which would fit it for structural purposes. It forms alloys with certain other metals, however, which are strong although still very light. A series of alloys known by the trade name of Dowmetal are among the most important. The various alloys in this series have compositions falling in the following range: aluminum, 1 to 10%; manganese, 0.1 to 1.5%; zinc, 0 to 3%; and the remainder magnesium. In one such alloy, 3 to 4% of cadmium is used. Further, magnesium is used in smaller percentages in various aluminum alloys (p. 804). Alloys of the Dowmetal type are at present employed in the aircraft industry for aircraft engine castings, landing wheels, pilot seats, shelves, brackets, crankcases, and other nonstructural parts of the plane. As the knowledge of magnesium technology increases, it is to be expected that the use of the metal will be still further expanded. One disadvantage, however, is that magnesium and its alloys must be protected against corrosion.

Magnesium in the form of powder or ribbon combines vigorously with oxygen when ignited; the reaction is accompanied by the radiation of intense white light rich in ultraviolet rays, and by the evolution of a great deal of heat. Because of this property, magnesium is used in the preparation of incendiary bombs, signals, flares, and other military pyrotechnic products, as well as in photographic flash powders and flash bulbs.

The great affinity of magnesium for oxygen and nitrogen is applied in its use as a deoxidizer (or scavenger) in the metallurgical industry, and as a degasser (or "getter") in the manufacture of radio tubes.

8. Compounds of Magnesium. When magnesium carbonate (magnesite) is heated at temperatures from 600° to 800° C., it undergoes decomposition according to the equation

$$MgCO_3 = MgO + CO_2$$

The product obtained is a light fluffy powder consisting of magnesium oxide with a few per cent of undecomposed carbonate and known as "light-burnt magnesia." In this form, the oxide is slowly hydrated when added to water.

$$MgO + H_2O = Mg(OH)_2$$

This light-burnt magnesia is soluble also in carbonic acid solutions.

$$MgO + 2H_2CO_3 = Mg^{++} + 2HCO_3^- + H_2O$$

Light-burnt magnesia is a constituent of many medicinal and toilet preparations. When this form of magnesia is mixed with a solution of magnesium chloride, the mass sets to a very strong cement known as Sorel's cement or zyolith. If magnesium carbonate is heated at temperatures above 1400° C., however, the magnesium oxide obtained is inert to water and is much denser than that described above. This "dead-burnt magnesia" melts only at extremely high temperature and is therefore a very useful refractory for furnace linings and other structures which have to withstand high temperatures without undergoing either physical collapse or chemical decomposition.

Dead-burnt magnesium oxide is a very poor conductor of heat and is widely used as an insulating material.

When aqueous solutions containing magnesium ion are treated with solutions containing hydroxide ion, a white gelatinous precipitate of magnesium hydroxide is formed.

$$Mg^{++} + 2OH^- = Mg(OH)_{2(s)}$$

It dissolves readily in acids—even in such weak acids as solutions of ammonium salts. A suspension of magnesium hydroxide is used medicinally as an alkalizing agent under the name of milk of magnesia. The low solubility of the hydroxide accounts for the mild basicity of this product.

When solutions of magnesium salts are treated with an alkali carbonate solution, a precipitate consisting of a mixture of magnesium carbonate and magnesium hydroxide is obtained. This basic magnesium carbonate is light and bulky. Mixed with about 15% of asbestos fiber, it is widely used as an insulating material for boilers and steampipes. This substance is soluble in solutions of acids or of ammonium salts.

Magnesium sulfate occurs in nature as the mineral epsomite, $MgSO_4 \cdot 7H_2O$. This salt is soluble in water and, under the name of Epsom salts, is used in veterinary medical practice as a purgative. It is used also for the weighting of cotton goods and for the fireproofing of textile fabrics.

Magnesium chloride, $MgCl_2 \cdot 6H_2O$, not only is a common laboratory reagent, but also has several commercial applications. Anhydrous magnesium perchlorate, "anhydrone," $Mg(ClO_4)_2$, is a very efficient drying agent. Care must be exercised in its use, however, for if it is acidified in the presence of organic matter a violent explosion is likely to result.

When a solution containing ammonium ion, monohydrogen phosphate ion, and ammonia is added to a solution containing magnesium ion, a white, crystalline precipitate of magnesium ammonium phosphate, $MgNH_4PO_4$, is formed.

$$Mg^{++} + HPO_4^{--} + NH_3 = MgNH_4PO_4$$

This is the form in which magnesium is usually precipitated for analytical purposes. When magnesium salts are treated with sodium hydroxide solution in the presence of the organic dye p-nitrobenzeneazoresorcinol (commonly known as S and O reagent), a bright blue gelatinous precipitate is formed. This precipitate consists of magnesium hydroxide on which the dye has been adsorbed, forming what is known as a "lake"; this constitutes a sensitive test for magnesium ion.

CALCIUM, STRONTIUM, AND BARIUM

9. Occurrence. Calcium, strontium, and barium are much too reactive to be found in the free state. Calcium compounds, however, occur in enormous quantities in many different localities. Calcium, in fact, is the third most abundant of all the metals, since it constitutes over 3.4% of the earth's crust. Calcium carbonate is the commonest of all minerals that do not contain silicon. It occurs as limestone, marble (metamorphosed limestone having a harder, more compact structure), and in other less important forms such as chalk, the shells of mollusks, egg-shells, coral, and pearls. Other important calcium minerals include dolomite, $CaCO_3 \cdot MgCO_3$, anhydrite, $CaSO_4$, gypsum, $CaSO_4 \cdot 2H_2O$, fluorspar, CaF_2, and apatite, $Ca(F,Cl)_2 \cdot 3Ca_3(PO_4)_2$. Calcium phosphate is the chief constituent of the bones and teeth of animals.

Strontium minerals are much rarer than those of calcium; strontium constitutes only 0.019% (1.9×10^{-4}) of the earth's crust. The most important strontium minerals are strontianite, $SrCO_3$, and celestite, $SrSO_4$.

Barium occurs less abundantly than calcium, but much more abundantly than strontium; it constitutes 0.05% of the earth's crust. The commonest and most important barium mineral is barite, $BaSO_4$; witherite, $BaCO_3$, is found in smaller quantities.

10. The Metals. Metallic calcium, strontium, and barium are all active metals, their activity increasing in the order named. The most important methods for producing these metals, therefore, are those in which their molten salts (generally the chlorides) are electrolyzed. The metals are obtained also by reduction of their oxides by aluminum metal at high temperatures in a vacuum, the alkaline earth metal then distilling off.

$$3BaO + 2Al = 3Ba + Al_2O_3$$

Calcium is also separated as an impurity from metallic sodium produced by the Downs process (p. 641).

Metallic calcium has enjoyed increasing use during recent years and is beginning to assume an important place in industry. It is particularly useful as a purifying agent in the metallurgy of a number of important industrial metals such as copper, cast iron, steel, nickel, lead, and aluminum. Some of the alloys of calcium, especially those with lead, are of practical importance. An alloy of lead with 1 to 2% of calcium is a useful bearing-metal. There are a number of special uses of calcium which depend upon its reactivity.

Strontium metal has few industrial uses since it is similar in properties to metallic calcium but more expensive to produce.

Metallic barium is considerably softer than calcium, magnesium, or beryllium, and is used to a much smaller extent than calcium metal. An alloy known as Frary's metal, consisting of 98% of lead and 2% of calcium and barium, is used as a bearing-metal. Barium is used also in the manufacture of radio tubes for the removal of the last traces of gases.

11. Oxides. When the carbonates of the alkaline earth metal family are heated to sufficiently high temperatures, they undergo a decomposition which yields the oxides and carbon dioxide.

$$MCO_3 = MO + CO_2$$

The temperature required for the carrying out of this decomposition increases with increasing size of the metal ion. Specifically, the temperatures at which the partial pressures of carbon dioxide in equilibrium with the carbonates become equal to 1 atm. are, respectively, about 900° C. for $CaCO_3$, 1250° C. for $SrCO_3$, and 1420° C. for $BaCO_3$. The increase in the stability of carbonates with increasing radius of the metal ion is discussed in the preceding chapter (p. 650). Calcium oxide (quicklime) is manufactured from limestone by this reaction. The decomposition is made to proceed at temperatures lower than 900° C. by passing a stream of air through the reaction chamber (lime kiln). This reduces the partial pressure of carbon dioxide and shifts the equilibrium to the right in the reaction

$$CaCO_3 \rightleftharpoons CaO + CO_2$$

Quicklime (or unslaked lime as it is sometimes called) is one of the most important of industrial chemicals. It is widely used as a cheap base, particularly for softening water. Other important applications occur in the manufacture of slaked lime, calcium carbide, bleaching powder, sodium carbonate, cement, glass, leather, and many other products. Further, large quantities of quicklime are used as a flux in the metallurgy of iron and steel.

Barium oxide is difficult to obtain by the heating of barium carbonate because of the excessively high temperature required for the reaction. The process can be carried out at more convenient temperatures in the presence of carbon, which reacts with carbon dioxide, lowering its partial pressure and shifting the equilibrium so as to cause the decomposition to take place at a lower temperature.

The alkaline earth metals also form peroxides of the general formula MO_2. Barium peroxide may be obtained by heating the monoxide with oxygen at temperatures slightly below 700° C.

$$2BaO + O_2 \rightleftharpoons 2BaO_2$$

This is an equilibrium process, and may be reversed by reduction of the partial pressure of oxygen.

12. Hydroxides. When the monoxides of calcium, strontium, or barium are added to water, they combine with it with the formation of the corresponding hydroxides and the evolution of a large amount of heat.

$$MO + H_2O = M(OH)_2$$

The tendency for the oxides of the alkaline earth metals to be hydrated increases with increasing atomic weight of the metal. Beryllium oxide shows little tendency to react with water; magnesium oxide reacts but slowly, the other oxides vigorously. The increasing reactivity of the oxides toward water is indicated by the following heats of hydration of the oxides: MgO, 5400; CaO, 15,100; SrO, 17,700; and BaO, 22,300 cal. per mole. The solubility of the hydroxides in water increases in the same direction; the solubilities of the hydroxides at 20° C. are: $Be(OH)_2$, 2×10^{-6}; $Mg(OH)_2$, 2×10^{-4}; $Ca(OH)_2$, 0.021; $Sr(OH)_2 \cdot 8H_2O$, 0.066; and $Ba(OH)_2 \cdot 8H_2O$, 0.23 mole per liter.

Calcium hydroxide is known commercially as slaked lime or hydrated lime. It is dangerous to store unslaked lime in combustible containers, for, if it comes in contact with water, the resulting heat of hydration is so great as to create a fire hazard. Slaked lime does not have this disadvantage and may be stored even in paper bags without danger. It is important as a cheap alkaline substance. Its usefulness in this respect is diminished by its low solubility, although in many cases this disadvantage may be overcome in some degree by the use of a suspension of the hydroxide in water. Such a suspension is known as "milk of lime." Among the more important uses of calcium hydroxide is the making of lime mortar or plaster, which consists of a mixture of slaked lime, sand, and water. Preliminary setting is due largely to drying, but hardening takes place slowly over a number of years as a result of the reaction with carbon dioxide in the air to form calcium carbonate.

$$Ca(OH)_2 + CO_2 = CaCO_3 + H_2O$$

A saturated solution of calcium hydroxide in water, known as lime-water, is a common laboratory reagent. It is used especially in a test for carbon dioxide, based upon a reaction similar to the one just described but taking place in solution.

Strontium hydroxide is similar to calcium hydroxide in properties and in method of preparation, except for its higher solubility. Barium hydroxide, the most soluble of the alkaline earth hydroxides, crystallizes from solutions at ordinary temperature in the form of the hydrate $Ba(OH)_2 \cdot 8H_2O$. It is widely used in analytical chemistry, since it has the advantage over sodium hydroxide or potassium hydroxide that any carbonate which is formed on contact with the air precipitates out, leaving the solution relatively pure. This is important in certain acid-base titrations in which the presence of carbonate ion interferes with certain indicator changes.

13. Carbonates. Calcium carbonate occurs in nature in two distinct crystalline forms, known as calcite (Figure 35.2) and aragonite, respectively. The latter is comparatively rare. A mineral consisting of large, clear crystals of pure calcite, which occurs fairly commonly in nature, is known as Iceland spar. By far the most abundant source of this compound, however, lies in the immense limestone deposits previously referred to, which form an appreciable part of the earth's crust. These beds of impure calcium carbonate are largely of marine origin, having been formed from the exoskeletons of myriads of minute marine organisms. The fossilized remains of many of these organisms are still to be found in many of the deposits, and limestone strata have yielded and are yielding a wealth of information concerning the history of organic evolution. Coral reefs are composed largely of calcium carbonate deposited by a certain type of marine animal. A pearl, which is built up of concentric layers deposited by the oyster upon a foreign particle which has entered its shell, consists mainly of calcium carbonate and is therefore readily soluble in acids.

Whereas calcium carbonate is only very slightly soluble in pure water, it is readily attacked by water containing carbon dioxide. The reaction takes place according to the following equation:

$$CaCO_{3(s)} + CO_2 + H_2O \rightleftharpoons Ca^{++} + 2HCO_3^-$$

Limestone strata are thus especially subject to the action of ground water, which always contains some carbon dioxide dissolved from the atmosphere. Where the limestone stratum is near the surface, large numbers of lakes are likely to be found; an example of this phenomenon occurs in the lake region of central Florida. On the other hand, where the limestone underlies other less soluble strata, the formation of limestone caverns results. Examples of this are the Luray Caverns in Virginia, Mammoth Cave in Kentucky, and the Carlsbad Caverns in New Mexico. Ground water that has seeped through seams in a limestone stratum, particularly if it is under pressure, contains considerable calcium bicarbonate. When this water enters a cavern the pressure is released somewhat, some of the calcium bicarbonate is converted to calcium carbonate according to the equilibrium equation, and this is deposited on the roof of the cavern. There is a corresponding formation of calcium carbonate on the floor of the cavern where the water strikes as it drips off the roof. These two types of formation are known respectively as stalactites and stalagmites, and, in many cases, are structures of great beauty (Figure 35.3).

Fig. 35.2.   A calcite ($CaCO_3$) crystal.

Fig. 35.3. Stalactites and stalagmites, Luray Caverns, Virginia. (*Courtesy of Luray Caverns Corporation.*)

Limestone is widely used as a structural material in the form either of gravel or of large blocks. Also, calcium carbonate is the ultimate source of all calcium compounds, as well as of calcium metal.

14. Cement. Large quantities of limestone are employed in the manufacture of various types of cements, the most important of which is known as Portland cement because of its resemblance to a famous variety of building stone quarried near Portland, England. In general, the raw materials are some calcareous (lime-containing) substance such as limestone, chalk, oyster shells, or slag, and some argillaceous (clay-containing) substance such as clay or shale. The raw materials used in making the cement are very thoroughly mixed, finely ground, and roasted in a rotary kiln heated by gas or powdered coal to a temperature between 1450° and 1500° C. This process yields lumps of "clinker," which are then mixed with a little gypsum and again very finely ground. The average composition of a number of American cements is given in Table 35.7.

Table 35.7

SiO_2	21.91%
CaO	62.92%
Al_2O_3	5.91%
Fe_2O_3	2.91%
MgO	2.54%
Miscellaneous (SO_3, Na_2O, K_2O, TiO_2, etc.)	3.81%

Individual cements, however, may vary widely in composition from that given in this table. These oxides, of course, are not present in the cement as such, but combine during the roasting process, so that the main components of the finished Portland cement, obtained by averaging a large number of American cements, are those listed in Table 35.8.

Table 35.8
Components of Portland Cement

Ca_3SiO_5	Tricalcium silicate	40.7%
Ca_2SiO_4	Dicalcium silicate	32.1%
$Ca_3Al_2O_6$	Tricalcium aluminate	10.7%
$Ca_4Al_2Fe_2O_{10}$		8.9%
$CaSO_4$		2.9%

When the ground clinker is mixed with water, the material sets to a rocklike mass. Concrete, which is formed by the hardening of a mixture of cement, sand and gravel, and water, is one of the most important of modern structural materials.

The chemistry involved in the use of Portland cement is complex and incompletely understood. It may be stated, however, that there are two steps in the process: (1) the initial set, which solidifies the mass, and (2) hardening, in which strength is developed. Both of these steps involve reaction with water—hydration and hydrolysis—and it is therefore necessary that the mass be kept wet during the hardening process.

15. Sulfates. As has been pointed out, the sulfates of calcium, strontium, and barium all occur in nature, and those of calcium and barium, at least, are industrially important. The solubility in water of the sulfates of the alkaline earth metals decreases with increasing atomic weight of the metal—the solubilities in moles per liter at 20° C. being: $BeSO_4 \cdot 4H_2O$, 3.6; $MgSO_4 \cdot 7H_2O$, 2.7; $CaSO_4 \cdot 2H_2O$, 0.015; $SrSO_4$, 7×10^{-4}; and $BaSO_4$, 1×10^{-5}.

The mineral gypsum, $CaSO_4 \cdot 2H_2O$, is widely used in the production of plaster of Paris. When the dihydrate is heated at 125° C., partial dehydration to the hemihydrate takes place according to the following equation:

$$2(CaSO_4 \cdot 2H_2O) = (CaSO_4)_2 \cdot H_2O + 3H_2O$$

When the hemihydrate, or plaster of Paris, as it is called, is mixed with water at ordinary temperatures, it takes up water to form a hard mass that has the same composition as the original gypsum, but which differs from the mineral in that it is harder and less readily dehydrated. The hydration is accompanied by slight expansion and by the evolution of heat. Since this setting takes place rather rapidly, plaster of Paris finds application in the production of replicas of statuary, as well as in surgical casts and molds. Large quantities of plaster of Paris are used for wall plaster, which usually consists of a mixture of plaster of Paris, wood fiber, hair, and sand. Plaster of Paris is used also in the manufacture of wallboard.

Barium sulfate, $BaSO_4$, as the mineral barite, is the most important source of barium compounds. Its low solubility, however, prevents its ready conversion to other salts. It is usually first changed to the carbonate by fusion with sodium carbonate,

$$Na_2CO_3 + BaSO_4 = BaCO_3 + Na_2SO_4$$

or to the sulfide by reduction with carbon at a high temperature.

$$BaSO_4 + 4C = BaS + 4CO$$

The carbonate and sulfide are both soluble in the common acids, and thus may be readily converted to other salts; e.g.,

$$BaS + 2HCl = BaCl_2 + H_2S$$

Barium sulfate is used as an extender in the manufacture of paints and as a filler in rubber, paper, linoleum, etc.

16. Other Common Salts. Other useful calcium compounds include calcium chloride, $CaCl_2 \cdot 6H_2O$, which because of its very deliquescent nature is used to keep down dust on highways and in coal mines. Calcium chloride, usually in the form of the dihydrate, is used also as a drying agent. Bleaching powder, $CaCl(OCl)$, and calcium hypochlorite, $Ca(OCl)_2$ (p. 407), calcium cyanamide, $CaNCN$ (p. 479), and the calcium phosphates (p. 515), have been discussed in previous chapters. Calcium sulfite, $CaSO_3$, and calcium bisulfite, $Ca(HSO_3)_2$, have considerable use in the paper industry for removing the brown lignin from wood pulp, leaving nearly pure white cellulose.

The most important use of strontium compounds is in the production of red fire in various pyrotechnical applications, such as fireworks, military flares, and railway fuses. Strontium nitrate, $Sr(NO_3)_2$, is the salt generally used for these purposes. Barium nitrate, $Ba(NO_3)_2$, and barium chlorate, $Ba(ClO_3)_2$, are likewise used in pyrotechnics to produce green fire.

Barium chloride, $BaCl_2 \cdot 2H_2O$, which may be obtained by treatment of the carbonate (witherite) or the sulfide with hydrochloric acid, is a very common laboratory reagent.

17. Hard Water. Ground water commonly contains calcium, magnesium, ferrous, and other multiply charged cations along with bicarbonate, sulfate, and other such anions. Water containing considerable concentrations of these cations is called *hard water* because of its action on soap. Soap consists of the sodium or potassium salts of certain high molecular weight organic acids (p. 602). These salts are soluble in water and are capable of bringing oils and greases into colloidal suspension in water. This accounts for their cleansing action. The calcium, magnesium, and iron salts of these acids, however, are insoluble in water, and when soap is added to hard water, much of it is wasted in forming precipitates of these salts.

When hard water is used industrially in boilers of steam engines, the bicarbonates decompose with the formation of precipitates of calcium, magnesium, and iron carbonates. Furthermore, as the water is evaporated, deposits of other slightly soluble salts, such as $CaSO_4$, are obtained. These deposits prevent good contact between the water and the boiler tubes and may cause the tubes to become overheated and to fail under pressure. The removal of the hardness of the water, i.e., water-softening, is, therefore, an important industrial problem.

18. Treatment of Hard Water. For convenience in the consideration of the softening of water, hardness may be classified into two types: (1) bicarbonate hardness, and (2) noncarbonate hardness. Bicarbonate hardness, which results from the presence of bicarbonate ion, may be removed by boiling the water, which brings about the evolution of carbon dioxide and the precipitation of the carbonate.

$$Ca^{++} + 2HCO_3^- = CaCO_{3(s)} + H_2O + CO_2$$

This method of softening, however, is too expensive in terms of fuel to be applied on a large scale. Hence, chemical methods such as treatment with calculated quantities of ammonia or slaked lime are commonly employed.

$$Ca^{++} + 2HCO_3^- + 2NH_3 = CaCO_{3(s)} + 2NH_4^+ + CO_3^{--}$$

$$Ca^{++} + 2HCO_3^- + Ca^{++} + 2OH^- = 2CaCO_{3(s)} + 2H_2O$$

For the removal of noncarbonate hardness from water, sodium carbonate is often used.

$$Ca^{++} + SO_4^{--} + 2Na^+ + CO_3^{--} = CaCO_{3(s)} + 2Na^+ + SO_4^{--}$$

The use of lime and sodium carbonate for water softening is commonly called the "lime-soda" treatment. Certain other substances such as borax, $Na_2B_4O_7 \cdot 10H_2O$, trisodium phosphate, Na_3PO_4, and sodium metasilicate, $Na_2SiO_3 \cdot 5H_2O$, are sometimes used in water softening. These substances give alkaline solutions and thus change bicarbonate to carbonate, while their anions, along with the carbonate ion thus formed, react with calcium ion to form insoluble precipitates.

A complex sodium phosphate commonly called sodium hexametaphosphate is used to soften water in smaller quantities. This substance has the peculiar property of binding the calcium ion in the form of a complex ion of unknown composition, and thereby prevents it from forming a precipitate with soap.

A series of complex sodium aluminosilicates known as zeolites have been found to possess the property of exchanging their sodium ion for calcium or magnesium ion in solution (p. 554). Thus if water which contains calcium or magnesium ion is allowed to come in contact with one of these zeolites, the calcium and magnesium ions are removed according to the equation

$$Na_2 \text{ zeolite} + (Ca^{++} \text{ or } Mg^{++}) \rightleftharpoons (Ca \text{ or } Mg) \text{ zeolite} + 2Na^+$$

Since this method does not require careful and frequent chemical control, it is particularly applicable to homes, hospitals, and small manufacturing units. When the zeolitic material has become "saturated" with calcium and magnesium ions, it is regenerated by treatment with concentrated sodium chloride solution, which reverses the reaction. Recently ion-exchanging materials which are far more effective than the zeolites have been made by the sulfonation of synthetic resins, and by other methods.

RADIUM

19. Occurrence, Uses, Preparation. The chemical properties of radium and its compounds, in so far as they are known, indicate that the element might appropriately be discussed along with calcium, strontium, and barium. In fact, the chemical properties of radium and radium compounds are exactly what would be expected of the last member of the group of alkaline earth metals; the resemblance to barium is especially close. The fact, however, that interest in the radioactivity of radium (p. 123) has so long diverted attention from its purely chemical properties makes it desirable that this element be considered apart from its chemical relatives, the other alkaline earth metals.

Radium occurs in all uranium minerals, but only in extremely small proportions. It is estimated that the ratio of radium to uranium in uranium minerals is about $1:3,000,000$. Because of this fact, the extraction of radium from such minerals is an extremely tedious and costly process. This difficulty in extraction, together with the great practical and scientific usefulness of radium, accounts for the very high price of radium compounds.

The earliest source of radium was pitchblende ore, containing the oxide U_3O_8, obtained from Bohemia. This, however, was soon supplanted by carnotite, $2K(UO_2)VO_4 \cdot 3H_2O$, from Colorado and Utah. In 1922, a rich deposit of pitchblende, which is still being worked, was discovered in the Belgian Congo. Still more recently, however, extensive deposits have been found near Great Bear Lake in Mackenzie, one of the Northwest Territories of Canada. Despite great transportation difficulties, these Canadian ores are supplying a considerable and ever increasing fraction of the total world production, which is now in the neighborhood of 100 g. of radium per year. The price of radium compounds, once as high as $150,000 per gram of radium content, has now dropped to less than $25,000 per gram of radium.

Considerable quantities of radium compounds are used in the manufacture of luminous paint, which is applied to watch and clock dials, door numbers, airplane instrument dials, and similar objects, to make them visible in total darkness. For this purpose, a very minute amount of a radium salt or other radioactive substance is incorporated into a pigment consisting of some fluorescent material such as impure zinc sulfide. A few cents' worth of the radium compound suffices to render the paint continuously luminous over a long period of years.

The largest use of radium compounds, however, is for therapeutic purposes, especially in the treatment of cancer. Since the radiations are only slightly less destructive to healthy than to diseased tissue, this method of treatment is largely restricted to the surface of the body. In many hospitals, the main supply of radium is kept in a vault, and the radon which it gives off is collected in thin-walled glass tubes and used in the treatment of malignant growths. Recent developments in nuclear chemistry lead to the expectation that artificially produced radioactive isotopes, such as Co^{60}, will replace radium in this type of therapy (p. 147).

From the position of radium in the periodic table, it is to be expected that its compounds will be difficult to reduce to the free metal. It was not until 1910 that Madame Curie succeeded in obtaining metallic radium. This was accomplished by the electrolysis of a solution of radium chloride, with a mercury cathode. From the radium amalgam thus obtained, the mercury was removed by distillation. Radium was found to be a white metal which, as would be expected, is highly reactive, vigorously displacing hydrogen from water and rapidly tarnishing in air. Its standard oxidation potential is 2.92 volts, and its ionization potential is 5.3 volts.

STUDY QUESTIONS AND PROBLEMS

1. Contrast the members of Group 2a with the corresponding alkali metals as to volatility, hardness, reactivity, ionization potential, basicity of oxides and hydroxides, tendency to form complex ions, solubility of compounds in water, and ionic radii. Explain the differences in these two families in terms of their atomic structures.

2. Discuss briefly the chief magnesium ores and the methods by which the free metal is obtained from these ores.

3. Indicate by means of equations why magnesium carbonate dissolves in aqueous solutions of ammonium salts.

4. List the chief minerals of calcium, strontium, and barium. What equilibria are involved in the formation of limestone caverns, stalactites, and stalagmites? Why are limestone strata of great interest to the historical geologist?

5. A limestone sample contains 80% $CaCO_3$. Calculate the weights of quicklime, slaked lime, calcium bicarbonate, and calcium chloride which could be obtained from 1250 lb. of this material, assuming 100% yield in all processes. Write balanced equations for the reactions involved in these processes.

6. Discuss briefly the relative ease with which the carbonates of calcium, strontium, and barium are decomposed to the oxides. Explain, in so far as you can, the differences in the stability of these three salts.

7. What are the chief components of Portland cement? What sort of reactions are involved in its hardening?

8. What is meant by hard water? Why is it undesirable? How is it treated?

9. From what you know of the periodic system what would you predict as to the relative ionization potentials of barium and radium? After you have made your answer read pp. 759 and 760 in Chapter 41. Would you change your answer?

CHAPTER

36

Some Transition Elements

1. Definition. In the discussion of the electronic configurations of the elements in relation to the position of elements in the periodic system (Chapter 9), it was pointed out that beginning with scandium there occurs a series of nine elements in which the d subshell underlying the valence shell of the atoms is being filled up, raising the number of electrons in the next to the outer shell of the atom from 8 to 18 (Table 9.4). From the tables of electron configurations in Chapter 9, we see that a similar series of elements begins with yttrium and ends with silver, and another such series begins with lanthanum and ends with gold. A fourth such series starts with actinium. The elements in these series are called *transition elements,* and the families which comprise them, viz., 3b, 4b, 5b, 6b, 7b, 8b, and 1b, are known as transition families. In the third transition series, which occurs in the sixth period of the periodic system, there is the additional complication that, in addition to the completion of the $5d$ subshell, the $4f$ subshell also fills up, thus giving the fourth shell its maximum number of 32 electrons. Lanthanum and the series of succeeding elements, cerium to lutetium, in which electrons are being added to the $4f$ subshell are known as the rare earth elements or the *lanthanides.* Similarly, with the element thorium, the $5f$ shell begins to fill, so that the elements actinium, thorium, protactinium, and uranium constitute the beginning of a second "rare earth" series, which is known as the *actinide* series.

The elements of family 2b, zinc, cadmium, and mercury, are not commonly classed as transition elements because both the s and d subshells are now complete (see tables of electron configurations, Chapter 9), and further, because the properties of zinc, cadmium, and mercury do not correspond to the properties of the transitional elements.

2. General Characteristics of the Transition Elements. The elements of the transition families have many characteristics in common. In the first place, they are all metallic in the free state, and their physical properties are very similar. Since they all have only one or two valence electrons in the outer shell, it might be expected that these elements would show oxidation states of $+1$ or $+2$ only. However, the electrons in the incomplete subshell just inside the outer shell may also take part in compound formation. The transition elements are characterized, therefore, by great variability of oxidation state. It is significant, however, that in most cases the maximum oxidation number of a transition element has the same value as the total number of its electrons that are available for bond formation. Careful scrutiny of Tables 9.4, 9.5, and 9.6 will reveal that this total number of valence electrons available from the outer electron shell and the incomplete inner subshells is usually the same as the number of the group to which the element has been assigned. This fact has, indeed, already been mentioned (p. 214). Moreover, it is only in compounds in which the maximum number of electrons is called into play that the resemblance between the elements of the a and b subgroups of a given group becomes apparent. Some of the properties of the members of the first transition series are listed in Table 36.1.

Table 36.1

Properties of Transition Elements of the First Series

	Electron Configurations	Melting Point (°C.)	Density (g./cc.)	Oxidation States	Ionization Potentials (v.) Electrons				
					1st	2nd	3rd	4th	5th
Sc	2 2,6, 2,6,1 2	1200	2.5	3	6.6	12.9	24.8	73.9	92
Ti	2 2,6, 2,6,2 2	1690	4.5	2,3,4	6.8	13.6	28.1	43.2	99.8
V	2 2,6, 2,6,3 2	1900	6.1	3,4,5	6.7	14.2	29.7	48	65.2
Cr	2 2,6, 2,6,5 1	1550	7.1	2,3,6	6.8	16.6	31	50.4	72.8
Mn	2 2,6, 2,6,5 2	1245	7.4	2,3,4,6,7	7.4	15.7	32	52	75.7
Fe	2 2,6, 2,6,6 2	1540	7.9	2,3,6	7.9	16.2	...	...	...
Co	2 2,6, 2,6,7 2	1493	8.9	2,3	7.9	17.3	...	...	...
Ni	2 2,6, 2,6,8 2	1455	8.9	2,4	7.6	18.2	...	...	...
Cu	2 2,6 2,6,10 1	1084	8.9	1,2	7.7	20.3	29.5	...	...

Likewise, the transition elements are characterized by the ability to form a great variety of complex compounds, many of which are unusually stable. Further, the transition elements are notable for the formation of compounds of many different colors. Substances of almost all shades and hues are to be found among the simple and complex compounds of these elements. One transition element, chromium, derives its name from the Greek word *chroma*, meaning "color." The catalysts commonly used for many important reactions consist of transition elements or their compounds.

THE SCANDIUM FAMILY (GROUP 3b)

3. General Characteristics. The first of the transition families is family 3b, which, in addition to scandium and yttrium, includes the fifteen rare earth elements, sometimes called lanthanides, and the members of the incomplete second "rare earth series" commonly called actinides. The elements scandium and yttrium are of little commercial significance. As was shown in Chapter 9, each of these elements has two electrons in its outermost electron shell and one electron in the incomplete inner d subshell. It might be expected, therefore, that they would all form bivalent ions. Such is not the case, however, for the one electron in the incomplete inner subshell is so easily removed that it acts as a valence electron, causing these elements characteristically to exhibit the $+3$ oxidation state. This is indicated for scandium, for example, by the very large increase in ionization potential which occurs between the third and fourth electrons to be removed rather than between the second and third (Table 36.1). The triply charged ions of this family resemble aluminum ion in many respects, although their oxides and hydroxides are more basic than the corresponding aluminum compounds.

4. The Rare Earth Elements (The Lanthanide Series). The rare earth elements include all those of atomic number 57 to 71, inclusive: namely, lanthanum, cerium, praseodymium, neodymium, promethium, samarium, europium, gadolinium, terbium, dysprosium, holmium, erbium, thulium, ytterbium, and lutetium. For a long time these elements baffled the makers of charts of the periodic system, for their properties are so very similar that they all apparently occupy the same place on the chart. The reason for this unusual similarity is now clear, however; for, as can be seen from Table 36.2, the electron configurations of these fifteen elements differ principally in the number of electrons in the $4f$ and $5d$ subshells, rather than in the outer electron shell.

The rare earth elements are found in nature mainly in the mineral monazite, which occurs in alluvial deposits in various mountainous regions (p. 685). It consists chiefly of a complex mixture of the phosphates of these elements and of thorium. The close similarity in the physical and chemical properties of these elements and their compounds has made their separation an exceedingly laborious task. Until recently, the only effective method was that of fractional crystallization, involving hundreds or even thousands of crystallizations. Recent research, however, has resulted in the development of certain ion-exchange techniques which have greatly improved the separation of the rare earth elements. Although some of these elements occur fairly abundantly, others are very rare. In fact, promethium probably does not occur in nature at all.

While the chief oxidation state exhibited by the rare earth elements is +3, in some cases other oxidation states are exhibited. For example, europium and ytterbium may be reduced to the +2 oxidation state, and cerium and praseodymium may be oxidized to the +4 oxidation state. Because of the difference in the properties of compounds which accompanies a difference in the oxidation states of the metal, the chemical separation of two rare earth elements is greatly facilitated if one of them can exist in an oxidation state other than +3.

Table 36.2

Electron Configurations of the Rare Earth Elements

Element	1	2		3			4				5			6
	s	s	p	s	p	d	s	p	d	f	s	p	d	s
La	2	2,	6	2,	6,	10	2,	6,	10		2,	6,	1	2
Ce	2	2,	6	2,	6,	10	2,	6,	10,	2	2,	6		2
Pr	2	2,	6	2,	6,	10	2,	6,	10,	3	2,	6		2
Nd	2	2,	6	2,	6,	10	2,	6,	10,	4	2,	6		2
Pm	(2)	(2),	(6)	(2),	(6),	(10)	(2),	(6),	(10),	(5)	(2),	(6)		(2)
Sm	2	2,	6	2,	6,	10	2,	6,	10,	6	2,	6		2
Eu	2	2,	6	2,	6,	10	2,	6,	10,	7	2,	6		2
Gd	2	2,	6	2,	6,	10	2,	6,	10,	7	2,	6,	1	2
Tb	2	2,	6	2,	6,	10	2,	6,	10,	9	2,	6		2
Dy	2	2,	6	2,	6,	10	2,	6,	10,	10	2,	6		2
Ho	2	2,	6	2,	6,	10	2,	6,	10,	11	2,	6		2
Er	2	2,	6	2,	6,	10	2,	6,	10,	12	2,	6		2
Tm	2	2,	6	2,	6,	10	2,	6,	10,	13	2,	6		2
Yb	2	2,	6	2,	6,	10	2,	6,	10,	14	2,	6		2
Lu	2	2,	6	2,	6,	10	2,	6,	10,	14	2,	6,	1	2

5. The Actinide Series. The production by nuclear processes of the elements neptunium, plutonium, americium, curium, berkelium, californium, einsteinium, fermium, mendelevium, and nobelium, and an examination of their properties, has led to the conclusion that they constitute a series of elements whose electronic configurations and periodic system relationships are analogous to those of rare earth elements (or lanthanides). Whereas in the series of lanthanides the 4f subshell is being filled, in the series of heavier elements electrons are being added to the 5f subshell. It is for this reason that the name actinides has been applied to actinium and succeeding elements in the periodic system. The electronic configurations of the actinides in so far as they are known are listed in Table 36.3.

Table 36.3

Electronic Configurations of the Actinides

	1	2	3	4	5	6	7
Element	*s*	*s p*	*s p d*	*s p d f*	*s p d f**	*s p d**	*s*
Ac	2	2, 6	2, 6, 10	2, 6, 10, 14	2, 6, 10,	2, 6, 1	2
Th	2	2, 6	2, 6, 10	2, 6, 10, 14	2, 6, 10	2, 6, 2	2
Pa	2	2, 6	2, 6, 10	2, 6, 10, 14	2, 6, 10, 2	2, 6, 1	2
U	2	2, 6	2, 6, 10	2, 6, 10, 14	2, 6, 10, 3	2, 6, 1	2
Np	2	2, 6	2, 6, 10	2, 6, 10, 14	2, 6, 10, 4	2, 6, 1	2
Pu	2	2, 6	2, 6, 10	2, 6, 10, 14	2, 6, 10, 5	2, 6, 1	2
Am	2	2, 6	2, 6, 10	2, 6, 10, 14	2, 6, 10, 6	2, 6, 1	2
Cm	2	2, 6	2, 6, 10	2, 6, 10, 14	2, 6, 10, 7	2, 6, 1	2
Bk	2	2, 6	2, 6, 10	2, 6, 10, 14	2, 6, 10, 8	2, 6, 1	2
Cf	2	2, 6	2, 6, 10	2, 6, 10, 14	2, 6, 10, 9	2, 6, 1	2
Es	2	2, 6	2, 6, 10	2, 6, 10, 14	2, 6, 10, 10	2, 6, 1	2
Fm	2	2, 6	2, 6, 10	2, 6, 10, 14	2, 6, 10, 11	2, 6, 1	2
Md	2	2, 6	2, 6, 10	2, 6, 10, 14	2, 6, 10, 12	2, 6, 1	2
No	2	2, 6	2, 6, 10	2, 6, 10, 14	2, 6, 10, 13	2, 6, 1	2

* Whereas the total numbers of electrons in the $5f$ and $6d$ subshells are presumably correct, the distribution between these subshells is still not known with certainty. There may well be, as in the lanthanides, some shifting back and forth between the two subshells.

Actinium, like scandium, yttrium, and lanthanum, readily loses three electrons to form a triply charged positive ion. There is no evidence for any other oxidation states. Thorium exhibits an oxidation state of $+4$ only, from which it may be concluded that the $7s$ and the $6d$ electrons may be involved in valence bond formation. Hence thorium is similar to the elements of the titanium family (4b) and its chemistry is discussed along with the members of that family in the next section of this chapter. Protactinium is a radioactive element which, on radioactive disintegration, loses alpha particles to yield actinium—hence its name. It is a very rare element, estimated to occur in uranium ore to the extent of about 0.25 g. per ton.

Uranium, the first radioactive element to be discovered, is estimated to make up about $8 \times 10^{-5}\%$ of the igneous rocks in the earth's crust. Its ores include uraninite, UO_2; pitchblende, U_3O_8; and carnotite, $2K(UO_2)VO_4 \cdot 3H_2O$. The main sources of uranium minerals are the Belgian Congo, the Great Bear Lake region in Canada, Colorado, and Utah.

Although uranium metal has been tried in certain experimental alloy steels, there was little industrial use for this method until the development of atomic energy. The use of uranium in the release of nuclear energy has already been discussed (p. 149). Pure metallic uranium may be prepared (1) by the reduction of uranium tetrachloride by calcium or other alkali or alkaline earth metal at high temperature under vacuum.

$$UCl_4 + 2Ca = 2CaCl_2 + U$$

or (2) by the electrolysis of a solution of a potassium uranium fluoride of the formula KUF_5 in a fused mixture of calcium and sodium chlorides.

Elementary uranium is a white, lustrous metal, which, on standing in air, slowly turns brown because of the formation of a film of oxide. The metal melts at $1133°$ C. and boils at about $3927°$ C.; its density is 19.05 g. per cc. Uranium is a moderately active metal, which, in a finely divided condition, spontaneously ignites in air.

Uranium forms compounds in which it exhibits oxidation states of $+2$, $+3$, $+4$, $+5$, and $+6$, but it is only those in which it is in the $+4$ or $+6$ state that are of any importance. The $+4$ oxidation state is represented by the dioxide, UO_2, and the hydrous oxide, $UO_2 \cdot 2H_2O$ [or $U(OH)_4$]. These compounds are basic; they dissolve in solutions of strong acids to yield solutions of uranous salts, such as $U(SO_4)_2$ and UCl_4.

The oxide of sexavalent uranium, uranium trioxide, UO_3, which is obtained when ammonium uranate or uranyl nitrate is heated, is orange-red in color and amphoteric in nature. It dissolves in strongly acidic solutions to yield uranyl salts containing the ion UO_2^{++}, according to the equation

$$UO_3 + 2H^+ = UO_2^{++} + H_2O$$

These uranyl salts are the so-called "uranium" salts of commerce. Among the more common uranyl salts are the nitrate, $UO_2(NO_3)_2 \cdot 6H_2O$, and the acetate, $UO_2(C_2H_3O_2)_2 \cdot 2H_2O$. Uranium trioxide reacts with strong bases to form uranates. The alkali metal uranates are only slightly soluble in water and, when an excess of an alkali metal hydroxide is added to a solution of uranyl salt, a precipitate of the alkali metal uranate is obtained. There are several series of uranates, the most important of which are the diuranates which have the general formula $M_2U_2O_7$. Sodium diuranate, $Na_2U_2O_7 \cdot 6H_2O$, often called uranium yellow, is used for color glazes on ceramic ware and in the manufacture of a yellow fluorescent glass for ornamental purposes.

Elements 93 through 102, as was pointed out in Chapter 8 (p. 146), are not found in appreciable amounts in nature but are prepared by nuclear reactions. Large amounts of plutonium have been obtained, and sufficient quantities of neptunium, americium, and curium to allow their chemistry to be investigated. Neptunium exhibits the oxidation states $+3$, $+4$, $+5$, and $+6$ in its compounds, but is relatively more difficult to oxidize to the higher states than uranium. Plutonium shows these same oxidation states but is still more difficult to oxidize than neptunium. In the case of americium the $+3$ oxidation state, which is stable in aqueous solution, is the most important, and no compounds of curium in any but the $+3$ state have been obtained. The increasing difficulty of oxidizing these elements to higher oxidation states is analogous to that observed in the first half of the lanthanide series.

Plutonium as a source of atomic energy has already been discussed.

THE TITANIUM FAMILY (GROUP 4b)

6. General Characteristics. This family includes titanium, zirconium, and hafnium. In addition, the element thorium, one of the actinide series, because of its close similarity to these elements, is commonly considered to be a member of this family. Titanium is one of the more abundant elements. It ranks ninth among the elements in abundance in the earth's crust (0.63% of total), and seventh among the metals. Zirconium is estimated to make up 0.028% of the earth's crust and is thus far more abundant than such familiar metals as lead, copper, nickel, zinc, mercury, and tin. Hafnium and thorium are less abundant, constituting only $3 \times 10^{-5}\%$ and $2 \times 10^{-5}\%$ of the earth's crust, respectively.

The electronic configurations for these elements are given in Table 36.4.

Table 36.4

Element	1	2	3	4	5	6	7
	s	$s\ p$	$s\ p\ d$	$s\ p\ d\ f$	$s\ p\ d\ f$	$s\ p\ d$	s
Ti	2	2, 6	2, 6, 2	2			
Zr	2	2, 6	2, 6, 10	2, 6, 2	2		
Hf	2	2, 6	2, 6, 10	2, 6, 10, 14	2, 6, 2	2	
Th	2	2, 6	2, 6, 10	2, 6, 10, 14	2, 6, 10	2, 6, 2	2

The outermost electron shell of each of these atoms contains only two electrons. Two electrons from the incomplete adjacent inner subshell may also, however, readily act as valence electrons, and as a result, the elements are most commonly quadrivalent. Titanium, however, exhibits the oxidation states of $+2$ and $+3$, as well as of $+4$.

7. Sources of the Elements. Titanium deposits of various types are fairly widely distributed over the earth. From the commercial standpoint, the most important ores are rutile, TiO_2, and ilmenite, $FeTiO_3$. The most important deposits of these ores are found in Virginia, Quebec, Brazil, Norway, and South Australia.

The chief ores of zirconium are zircon, $ZrSiO_4$, and baddeleyite, ZrO_2. Workable sources are found in Florida, California, Oregon, Idaho, Australia, India, and Brazil. Hafnium is almost always found in conjunction with zirconium; the average Hf:Zr ratio in zirconium minerals is about 1:60.

The most important source of thorium is monazite sand, which may contain as high as 30% of ThO_2. This mineral is obtained from North Carolina, Brazil, the Union of South Africa, India, and Ceylon. Other thorium minerals include thorianite, ThO_2, and thorite, $ThSiO_4$.

8. Preparation and Properties of the Metals.

The metals of this family are difficult to obtain in the free state because of their high melting points, the readiness with which they combine with the common nonmetallic elements, and the ease with which they form alloys with the common metals. The free metals have been most successfully prepared by processes involving the reduction of halogen compounds of the metals with active metals. Some properties of the metals are listed in Table 36.5.

Table 36.5

	Ti	Zr	Hf	Th
Melting point (°C.)	1690	1830	1975	1840
Boiling point (°C.)	3535	5000	5400	5200
Density (g./cc.)	4.51	6.50 (20°)	13.09 (20°)	11.75

Pure titanium, zirconium, and hafnium have been prepared by the thermal decomposition of their tetraiodides on a hot tungsten filament. On an industrial scale, the principal method for producing these metals is by the reduction of the corresponding tetrachlorides with magnesium.

The elements of this family are not very active at low temperatures, but on being heated they show remarkable affinity for the common nonmetallic elements, such as oxygen, nitrogen, sulfur, and the halogens. They react also with water and with hydrogen chloride at elevated temperatures to release hydrogen. All these elements precede hydrogen in the electromotive series, and react with strong acids to release hydrogen.

Because of its high strength, low density, and resistance to corrosion (at low temperatures), titanium is finding widespread application, particularly in aircraft, jet engines, and missiles. Production for the year 1957 will approximate 22,000,000 pounds and the price has been reduced to $2.25

per pound. As the price is reduced, it is expected that titanium will find use in ships' hulls and equipment subject to salt-water corrosion.

Because of the small tendency for zirconium nuclei to take up neutrons, zirconium has undergone an extraordinarily rapid development as a structural material for nuclear reactors. From 1945 to 1956, the price dropped from $300 to less than $15 per pound. Zirconium is now being produced at a rate of close to 6,000,000 pounds per year.

In contrast to zirconium, hafnium is a good absorber for neutrons. It therefore offers great promise in the construction of neutron-absorbing elements in nuclear power plants. Hafnium also has a high rate of heat transfer and has been proposed for possible use in jet engines.

9. Compounds of Bivalent and Trivalent Titanium. Titanium forms a series of compounds in which it is bivalent. Among these compounds are TiO, $Ti(OH)_2$, $TiCl_2$, TiS, and $TiSO_4$. Since these compounds are readily oxidized, even by the air, they are not very important. They are generally prepared by the reduction of compounds of titanium in higher oxidation states. It should be noted that $Ti(OH)_2$ is a basic hydroxide.

Titanium forms also a series of compounds—the titanous compounds—in which it is trivalent. Titanous salts such as $TiCl_3$ and $Ti_2(SO_4)_3$ are obtained by reduction of the titanic compound with zinc or tin, or by electrolysis. Solutions of titanous salts are violet, and are strong reducing agents.

10. Compounds of Quadrivalent Titanium, Zirconium, Hafnium, and Thorium. As was pointed out earlier in this chapter (p. 684), all these elements form compounds in which they are quadrivalent. Since the ratio of charge to ionic radius for the quadruply charged ions of this family is unusually high, these ions have a strong attraction for electrons (p. 195); or, stated in another way, a very large amount of energy would be required to remove four electrons from an atom of one of these elements to form quadruply charged positive ions. Among their compounds, therefore, there are few, if any, that are truly ionic.

All these elements form dioxides of the general formula, MO_2, as well as hydrous oxides, $MO_2 \cdot xH_2O$, all of which, except $ThO_2 \cdot xH_2O$, are amphoteric. Thus in the series, TiO, Ti_2O_3, TiO_2, the oxides steadily decrease in basicity with increasing oxidation number of the metal. All four elements form anhydrous covalent halides having the formula MX_4. Titanium tetrachloride is a colorless liquid which boils at 136° C. and melts at —23° C. It is readily hydrolyzed, even in cold water, according to the equation

$$TiCl_4 + 4H_2O = Ti(OH)_4 + 4H^+ + 4Cl^-$$

This hydrolysis may be reversed by hydrochloric acid, and in the presence of an excess of this reagent the acid H_2TiCl_6 is formed. A number of salts of the general formula M_2TiCl_6 are known. Tetrachlorides of zirconium, hafnium, and thorium undergo only partial hydrolysis on contact with water to give "oxy" compounds, e.g.,

$$ZrCl_4 + H_2O = ZrOCl_2 + 2HCl$$

All the elements of this family also form complex ions of the type MF_6^{--} which presumably have the electronic formula

$$
\begin{array}{ccc}
& :\!\ddot{F}\!: \quad :\!\ddot{F}\!: & ^{--} \\
:\!\ddot{F}\!: & M & :\!\ddot{F}\!: \\
& :\!\ddot{F}\!: \quad :\!\ddot{F}\!: &
\end{array}
$$

Such ions are formed by the coordination of two F^- ions to the MF_4 molecule.

The most important industrial application of titanium compounds is the use of titanium dioxide as a white paint pigment. In recent years such pigments have had an extremely rapid development. The advantages claimed for them are high opacity, inertness toward hydrogen sulfide, light weight, nonpoisonous nature, ease of wetting and dispersion in oil, and resistance to high temperature.

The hydrolysis of titanium tetrachloride, which occurs when the liquid comes in contact with moist air, makes it useful for the production of smoke screens in military operations. The cloud of hydrated titanium tetrachloride and hydrous oxide which is formed under these conditions produces a screen of high opacity. This smoke is used also for study of the air stream around airplane models in wind tunnels.

The most important commercial zirconium compound is the oxide, ZrO_2, which has had some application as a refractory, though difficulties encountered in the preparation of the pure oxide make it expensive and thus limit its use. Naturally occurring zirconium silicate, zircon ($ZrSiO_4$), is used as a gem stone. It occurs in various colors and is known by various names such as hyacinth (red), jacinth (yellow, brown), and jargon (white). The form known as "starlite," which is in greatest demand as a gem, is blue in color and is not only found in nature but also may be obtained by a process of coloring the brown or reddish zircons obtained from Siam.

Thorium oxide is used in the manufacture of the once widely used Welsbach gas mantle. Small percentages of metallic thorium greatly improve the quality of tungsten incandescent light filaments, since they decrease the tendency for the filament to crystallize, become brittle, and break.

THE VANADIUM FAMILY (GROUP 5b)

11. General Characteristics. The vanadium family, which follows immediately after the titanium family in the periodic system, consists of the three elements of Group 5b. These elements differ from those of the previous family in that their atomic numbers are one greater than those of the respective elements in the titanium family, and their atoms have therefore one more electron available for valence bond formation. The electron configurations are given in Table 36.6.

Table 36.6

Element	1	2		3			4				5			6			7
	s	s	p	s	p	d	s	p	d	f	s	p	d	s	p	d	s
V	2	2,	6	2,	6,	3	2										
Nb *	2	2,	6	2,	6,	10	2,	6,	4		1						
Ta	2	2,	6	2,	6,	10	2,	6,	10,	14	2,	6,	3	2			

* Until 1950, this element was known as columbium, with the symbol Cb.

As their electron configurations indicate, these are typical transition elements. The electrons in the incomplete inner subshell, as well as those in the outer shell, may act as valence electrons; since there is a total of five such electrons per atom, the maximum oxidation state is $+5$. The minor variation in the pattern of the electron configuration in the case of niobium is without consequence, since the total number of potential valence electrons is the same as for the other elements. It is only in the oxidation state of $+5$ that these elements show any resemblance to the members of the nitrogen family (5a).

12. Occurrence of the Metals. Vanadium is estimated to make up 0.017% of the earth's crust, and is thus more abundant than lead, zinc, copper, tin, mercury, or bismuth. Although the element is widely distributed, ores containing commercially important quantities of vanadium are not common. The most important of these ores are: vanadinite, $3Pb_3(VO_4)_2 \cdot PbCl_2$; descloizite, $4(Pb,Zn)O \cdot V_2O_5 \cdot H_2O$; carnotite, which is actually a hydrated potassium uranyl vanadate, the formula of which may be written $2K(UO_2)VO_4 \cdot 3H_2O$, and which is valuable for its uranium and radium content; roscoelite, a complex silicate containing V_2O_3; and patronite, a complex sulfide ore. Until 1930 the patronite ores of Peru furnished most of the world's vanadium; in recent years, however, the Peruvian production has been exceeded by the output of the United States, Southwest Africa, Northern Rhodesia, and Mexico. The most important domestic supplies are the roscoelite ores in southwest Colorado, and the cast-off carnotite ore which accumulated in dumps when western Colorado and southeastern Utah produced much of the world's radium (p. 676).

Niobium and tantalum are closely associated in nature and for many years were supposed to be the same element. They are found, usually as mixtures of niobates and tantalates, in many rare minerals, but seldom in quantities of commercial significance. Pure columbite ore consists of $(Fe,Mn)(NbO_3)_2$, and pure tantalite ore of $(Fe,Mn)(TaO_3)_2$, but minerals of various compositions intermediate between the niobate and the tantalate are more common. The most important sources of ores high in tantalum are Western Australia, Brazil, and Belgian Congo, whereas the main source of ores high in niobium is in Nigeria. The Black Hills region in South Dakota is the most important domestic source of tantalum-bearing ores.

13. Metallurgy, Properties, and Uses of the Metals. Pure metallic vanadium is difficult to prepare because of the high reactivity of the element with carbon, oxygen, and nitrogen at elevated temperatures. Vanadium of better than 99% purity has been prepared by heating the +5 oxide with calcium and calcium chloride in a steel bomb at 900–950° C. The absence of traces of air and moisture is assured by the inclusion of small quantities of sodium in the reaction mixture. Most industrial vanadium is used in the form of the alloy ferrovanadium, which is obtained by the reduction of a mixture of divanadium pentoxide and ferric oxide with carbon in an electric furnace.

Pure vanadium has been found to be soft, ductile, and capable of being cold-drawn or cold-rolled. Small amounts of impurities such as carbon, oxygen, or hydrogen, however, greatly change the properties of the metal, causing it to be hard, brittle, and difficult to work. It melts at 1900° C. and has a density of 6.1 g. per cc. At high temperatures it combines readily with chlorine, oxygen, carbon, and nitrogen. Vanadium does not dissolve in hydrochloric or in dilute sulfuric acid, but is readily attacked by nitric, concentrated sulfuric, or hydrofluoric acid.

There are no important industrial applications of pure vanadium metal, but considerable quantities of ferrovanadium are used in the steel industry, where it serves both as a scavenger (p. 631) and as a component of alloy steels. The presence of a small percentage (generally less than 0.3%) of vanadium in steel alloys tends to give the metal a uniform, fine-grained structure, a higher tensile strength, an increased resistance to shock, strain, vibration, and abrasion, and improved machining qualities. Vanadium is able to compete with cheaper alloying elements because it also acts as a scavenger and because of the very small quantity required to yield superior results. Although the average motor car contains only about a quarter of a pound of vanadium, the benefits from this small amount are enormous.

Tantalum metal is prepared either by the reduction of potassium fluotantalate, K_2TaF_7, with sodium, or by the electrolysis of a solution of ditantalum pentoxide in the fused fluotantalate. The cast iron cell serves also as cathode; graphite rods are used as anodes. The tantalum powder obtained by the first method, or the mass of small crystals obtained by the second, is converted into bars by means of heat treatment, in the absence of air, under pressures as high as 50 tons per sq. in. The coherent mass thus obtained is hammered and reheated under vacuum, after which it may be cold-rolled or drawn. Niobium is obtained by heating a mixture of equivalent amounts of diniobium pentoxide and carbon to above 1600° C. in a vacuum. Niobium melts at 2415° C., boils at about 3000° C., and has a density of 8.57 g. per cc. Tantalum melts at 2996° C., boils at about 5300° C., and has a density of 16.6 g. per cc.

Both niobium and tantalum are silvery white, malleable, ductile metals, have high tensile strengths and are good thermal conductors. Tantalum has the highest melting point of any metal except tungsten and rhenium. Both metals react readily, at elevated temperatures, with oxygen, carbon, halogens, nitrogen, sulfur, and other nonmetals. Tantalum, however, is resistant to the action of all common acids except hydrofluoric and hot concentrated sulfuric, although it dissolves readily in concentrated alkali solutions. Its position in the electromotive series is close to that of gold.

Until 1933, niobium metal was little more than a laboratory curiosity. Since that time, however, new applications have greatly stimulated its production. Stainless steel, an alloy containing high percentages of chromium and nickel, formerly could not be welded or subjected to other high-temperature treatment because it lost its resistance to corrosion under these conditions. In 1933, it was found that the addition of about 1% of niobium, in the form of an iron–niobium alloy, "stabilizes" stainless steel so that it may be subjected to high temperatures without deterioration. Pure niobium is used in atomic reactors, and alloys of high niobium content offer promise of usefulness in aircraft jet engine parts.

Tantalum has had a longer industrial career, and is more widely used than niobium. The most important uses of tantalum depend upon its corrosion resistance, high thermal conductivity, and high melting point. It has found many applications in chemical industry in the form of heat exchangers, agitators, distilling equipment, aerating devices, thermometer wells, and corrosion resistant valves (Figure 36.1). The usefulness of tantalum for heat exchangers is due not only to its high heat conductivity but also to the fact that its corrosion resistance permits the use of very thin walls. The high melting point of the metal, as well as its tendency to react with most gases at high temperatures, makes it useful for internal parts of vacuum tubes. Tantalum is used also in surgery to suture wounds and to mend bone fractures.

Tantalum readily acts as a cathode in an electrolytic cell; when it is used as an anode, however, it quickly becomes coated with a thin layer of the +5 oxide, which stops the flow of current. This property has been applied in a rectifying device for alternating current.

14. Compounds of Vanadium. Vanadium forms compounds in which it exhibits +2, +3, +4, and +5 oxidation states. As would be expected, the basicity of the oxides corresponding to these states decreases with increasing oxidation number. Vanadium monoxide, VO, and divanadium trioxide, V_2O_3, are basic, whereas the dioxide, VO_2, and divanadium pentoxide, V_2O_5, are amphoteric. Compounds in the lower oxidation states are usually obtained by the reduction of compounds corresponding to the +5 oxidation state.

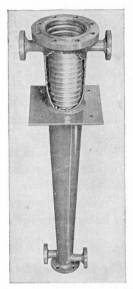

Fig. 36.1. Tantalum tapered condenser for corrosive vapors. The high rate of heat transfer through tantalum causes such equipment to have a high efficiency in a small space. (*Courtesy of Fansteel Metallurgical Corporation.*)

Divanadium pentoxide, V_2O_5, is one of the most important of vanadium compounds. It is obtained in the form of yellowish red crystals when ammonium metavanadate is heated.

$$2NH_4VO_3 = V_2O_5 + H_2O + 2NH_3$$

Divanadium pentoxide has found application as a catalyst in a variety of industrial processes, including the contact process for the oxidation of sulfur dioxide to sulfur trioxide, and many organic oxidations.

Divanadium pentoxide is unaffected by slightly acidic solutions but dissolves in strongly acidic solutions to yield the vanadyl ions, VO_2^+ [or $V(OH)_4^+$] and VO^{+++}. Divanadium pentoxide dissolves also in solutions of alkali hydroxides to form vanadates. Salts of meta-, ortho-, and pyro-vanadic acids are known; for example, sodium metavanadate, $NaVO_3$, sodium orthovanadate, Na_3VO_4, and sodium pyrovanadate, $Na_4V_2O_7$. In addition a number of more complex vanadates such as $Na_4H_2V_4O_{13}$ and $Na_2H_2V_6O_{17}$ are formed as the acidity of the solution is increased. The formation of such "condensed" ions in acidic solutions is characteristic of several of the transition metals (p. 702) in their higher oxidation states.

15. Compounds of Niobium and Tantalum. Whereas niobium and tantalum both form compounds in oxidation states lower than $+5$, such compounds are, in general, unimportant and not very stable. Both these elements form pentoxides of the general formula M_2O_5, which are only very slightly soluble in dilute acids except hydrofluoric. The pentoxides are also inert in alkali solutions, but react with fused alkali hydroxides to form water-soluble complex niobates and tantalates.

When a mixture of one of the pentoxides and carbon is heated in a stream of halogen gas the corresponding pentahalide is obtained.

$$Nb_2O_5 + 5C + 5Cl_2 = 2NbCl_5 + 5CO$$

The facts that these compounds are readily volatile and are completely hydrolyzed in water indicate that they are not ionic compounds. When added to water, the pentachlorides yield the meta-acids, $HTaO_3$ and $HNbO_3$. These hydrated pentoxides, or acids, are soluble in hydrofluoric acid; when such solutions are treated with alkali fluorides complex salts such as K_2NbF_7, K_2NbOF_5, and K_2TaF_7 are obtained.

When tantalum powder is heated with carbon at very high temperatures, or when the oxide is reduced with carbon at high temperatures, tantalum carbide, TaC, is obtained. This compound is extremely hard and has a melting point near $4000°$ C. Under the name of Ramet, this material, usually bound with cobalt, nickel, or iron, is used in the preparation of excellent cutting tools. Carbides of tungsten, niobium, and titanium are also useful for this purpose.

STUDY QUESTIONS AND PROBLEMS

1. Explain briefly, in terms of atomic structure, what is meant by the term "transition element."

2. What are the chief characteristics of transition elements in general? Explain, in so far as you can, these properties in terms of atomic structure.

3. Why should ferrous and manganous compounds show a closer similarity to each other than do manganous compounds and permanganates?

4. What are the chief chemical and physical properties of the rare earth elements?

5. What are the chief ores of uranium? How may free uranium metal be prepared?

6. What are the chief uses of TiO_2, $ZrSiO_4$, ZrO_2, and $TiCl_4$?

7. List the chief ores of tantalum. How is the metal prepared? What are some of its important industrial applications?

8. What weight of uranium could be obtained from 1128 lb. of a rock containing 80% of carnotite?

CHAPTER

37

The Chromium Family

1. General Characteristics. The chromium family, consisting of the elements of Group 6b in the periodic system, is one of the most important of the transition families. All the elements in this family, chromium, molybdenum, and tungsten, are not only well known both in the free state and in the form of their compounds, but also have important industrial applications. The three elements are tough, heavy metals with very high melting points. The electron configurations of these elements are listed in Table 37.1.

Table 37.I

Element	1 s	2 s p	3 s p d	4 s p d f	5 s p d	6 s
Cr	2	2, 6	2, 6, 5	1		
Mo	2	2, 6	2, 6, 10	2, 6, 5	1	
W	2	2, 6	2, 6, 10	2, 6, 10, 14	2, 6, 4	2

Since there is a total of six electrons in the outer shell and the incomplete inner subshell of each atom, the maximum oxidation number of each of these elements is $+6$. When the elements are in this oxidation state, their corresponding compounds bear a close resemblance to each other and, to a somewhat lesser extent, to those of the elements of Group 6a, particularly sulfur. The oxides in which these elements exhibit the $+6$ oxidation state are acidic, CrO_3 being the most acidic. The acids corresponding to these oxides show a marked tendency toward condensation to "poly" acids (p. 702).

Chromium, molybdenum, and tungsten also exhibit a number of lower oxidation states. In a given oxidation state, the resemblance between two elements of the family is less pronounced than the resemblance of either to the corresponding members of the succeeding and preceding families. Thus,

694

for example, compounds of chromium in the $+3$ oxidation state are more similar to corresponding compounds of $+3$ vanadium, $+3$ iron, and $+3$ manganese than to the corresponding derivatives of $+3$ molybdenum. Such relationships are characteristic of the transition elements.

2. Occurrence of the Elements. None of these elements occurs naturally in the freee state. Chromium is the most abundant, constituting about 0.037% of the igneous rocks in the earth's crust. While chromium is found in a variety of minerals, the most important source of this metal is chromite ore, the composition of which, in the pure state, corresponds to the formula $Fe(CrO_2)_2$. Domestic production of chromite ore is very small because of the low grade of the available deposits. Most of the world's production is now obtained from Southern Rhodesia, Turkey, Russia, Union of South Africa, Cuba, India, Greece, New Caledonia, Yugoslavia, and Japan.

Molybdenite, the composition of which, in the pure state, corresponds to the formula MoS_2, is the most important ore of molybdenum. Molybdenite strongly resembles graphite, which was formerly known as black lead. It was from the Greek word *molybdos,* meaning "lead," that the name of the mineral and the element are derived. Wulfenite, $PbMoO_4$, and molybdic ocher, $Fe_4(MoO_4)_6 \cdot 15H_2O$, are other important sources of this element. Though molybdenum is fairly widely distributed over the earth, practically all the commercial working of its ores takes place in the United States, Australia, Canada, and Norway. Domestic production, which is larger than that of any other country, is centered mainly in Colorado and, in lesser amounts, in Arizona, New Mexico, and Utah. Molybdenum is estimated to make up $10^{-6}\%$ of the igneous rocks in the earth's crust.

Though the estimated occurrence of tungsten ($5 \times 10^{-5}\%$ of igneous rocks) is slightly higher than that of molybdenum, the former metal is less widely distributed. The forms in which tungsten most commonly occurs are scheelite, $CaWO_4$, and wolframite, $(Fe,Mn)WO_4$. Fairly large deposits of these ores are found in Burma, China, Bolivia, Portugal, and the United States; the bulk of the tungsten produced comes from these five countries. Domestic production depends mainly upon the high grade scheelite deposits in California and Nevada, and the wolframite deposits in Colorado. Tungsten ores are notable for their high density and the name tungsten is derived from the Swedish words meaning "heavy stone."

3. Metallurgy, Properties, and Uses of the Metals. Pure chromium metal may be prepared by the redutcion of chromic oxide with aluminum (p. 803).

$$Cr_2O_3 + 2Al = 2Cr + Al_2O_3$$

It melts at 1550° C., boils at 2482° C., has a density of 7.14 g. per cc., and is a hard, crystalline, silvery white metal which takes a high polish. Though it reacts with oxygen and with water at high temperatures, chromium metal resists atmospheric corrosion and retains its brilliant luster almost indefinitely under ordinary conditions. Chromium ordinarily dissolves readily in dilute acids such as hydrochloric or sulfuric. If, however, the metal is first treated with concentrated nitric acid, chromic acid, hydrogen peroxide, or other oxidizing agents, or if it is exposed to the air for a considerable period of time, or is made the anode in an electrolytic cell which contains nitrate ion, sulfate ion, or hydroxide ion, it is unaffected by dilute acids. The metal under such conditions is said to have been rendered *passive*.

A number of metals, among which are cobalt, bismuth, molybdenum, tungsten, iron, and nickel, show similar behavior under certain conditions. The passive condition is not a permanent one, however, and disappears when the metal is heated, subjected to mechanical strain, brought into contact with active metals, or allowed to stand in dilute acid solutions. A number of theories have been advanced to account for the phenomenon of passivity, but none of them has been generally accepted.

The brilliant luster, hardness, and resistance to corrosion exhibited by chromium have greatly stimulated its use as a plating metal, especially over iron and steel. "Chrome plate" is now so common that it might, with some justice, be said that we are living in the chrome-plated era. The electrolyte used in the industrial chromium-plating process is an acidic solution of chromic chromate, $Cr_2(CrO_4)_3$, containing, in addition, sulfate, phosphate, or borate ion.

The most important industrial application of chromium, however, is its use in the manufacture of alloy steels. The chromium is added in the form of ferrochrome, an alloy obtained by the direct reduction of chromite ore with carbon in an electric furnace. The reaction proceeds according to the equation

$$Fe(CrO_2)_2 + 4C = Fe + 2Cr + 4CO$$

Ferrochrome usually contains several per cent of carbon, though its carbon content is considerably reduced when the alloy is heated with an excess of chromite ore.

In small quantities (up to 1 or 2%) chromium increases the strength and toughness of steel. Medium chromium steels (4 to 10% chromium) retain their strength at moderately high temperatures and have increased resistance to corrosion; these steels are used extensively in petroleum refineries where high-temperature, high-pressure processes are carried out. High chromium steels, usually called "stainless" steels, contain more than 10% of chromium and are frequently alloyed with nickel, a popular variety containing 18% chromium and 8% nickel. The high resistance of stainless steels to atmospheric corrosion and to the action of many chemicals accounts for their use in the chemical, food, and oil industries. These steels have, in addition, excellent structural properties and are widely used in the transportation industries, as, for example, in the manufacture of light-weight streamlined trains.

A considerable portion of the chromite ore produced is used in the manufacture of chromite brick, a refractory prepared from a mixture of pulverized chromite ore, clay, and magnesium oxide. Chromite brick is widely used in lining high-temperature furnaces.

A number of processes have been employed for producing metallic molybdenum from its ores; the following is one of the most important. Molybdenum sulfide ore (MoS_2) is roasted in the presence of air until completely converted to molybdenum trioxide, MoO_3, which is then extracted from the gangue with dilute aqueous ammonia. The ammoniacal solution is then evaporated until ammonium molybdate, $(NH_4)_6Mo_7O_{24}\cdot4H_2O$, crystallizes; the crystals are then roasted to the oxide, which is reduced to the free metal by means of carbon or hydrogen in an electric furnace. The metal is thus obtained in the form of a gray powder which is converted into bars of molybdenum metal by the application of high pressure, followed by hammering at high temperatures in an atmosphere of hydrogen. Metallic molybdenum is a hard, silvery white metal which, in a sufficiently high state of purity, is ductile and malleable, but in the presence of such impurities as carbon is much harder and more brittle. Molybdenum melts at the very high temperature of 2622° C., and has a density of about 10.2 g. per cc. While it is relatively unreactive at ordinary temperatures, molybdenum combines readily with oxygen, sulfur, the halogens, phosphorus, boron, carbon, and silicon when it is heated. The metal is unattacked by nonoxidizing acids but dissolves in nitric and in hot concentrated sulfuric acids.

Metallic molybdenum is used as a support for tungsten filaments in incandescent lamps, for windings in electrical resistance furnaces, and in other high-temperature electrical appliances. The major portion of the molybdenum produced, however, is used in the manufacture of molybdenum alloy steels. For this purpose the molybdenum is added in the form of the oxide, the molybdate, or as ferromolybdenum, an alloy of iron and molybdenum which is prepared by the joint reduction of molybdenum and iron ores in an electric furnace. Molybdenum increases the hardness and strength of steel at high temperatures, increases the corrosion resistance of chromium–nickel

steels, and decreases the brittleness of chromium steels. Of particular importance are the molybdenum–chromium–nickel steels, which maintain their
hardness even at red heat. Such alloys are known as high-speed steels because
of their usefulness in high-speed machine tools. The high temperatures
developed at the speeds at which such tools operate would cause ordinary
steels to lose their hardness. As is noted below, tungsten also is used in the
production of high-speed steels, but a higher percentage of tungsten than
of molybdenum is required.

The method usually followed in the extraction of tungsten from its ores
consists of fusion of the ore with sodium carbonate, and removal of the
sodium tungstate thus formed from the fusion mixture by extraction with
water.

$$4FeWO_4 + O_2 + 4Na_2CO_3 = 4Na_2WO_4 + 2Fe_2O_3 + 4CO_2$$

Treatment of the sodium tungstate solution with calcium chloride brings
about the precipitation of calcium tungstate, which is converted to insoluble
tungstic acid by treatment with hydrochloric acid. Purification of the tungstic acid is accomplished by repeated solution in aqueous ammonia, evaporation to crystallization of ammonium tungstate, and reconversion to tungstic
acid with nitric acid. After purification the tungstic acid is ignited to the
oxide, WO_3, from which tungsten metal is produced in the form of a
powder by reduction with hydrogen at an elevated temperature (1200° C.) ;
this powder is formed into porous, brittle bars by subjecting portions of it to
high pressure at high temperatures. Ductile tungsten is obtained from these
bars by heat treatment at an extremely high temperature (3200° C.) obtained by means of an electric current through them, followed by a high-
speed hammering or "swaging" treatment as the temperature is gradually reduced. This process yields thin tungsten rods, which may be drawn
through dies of gradually decreasing diameter until filaments as fine as one-
fifteenth the diameter of a human hair are obtained. Tungsten filaments are
now almost universally used in incandescent lamps and are much more efficient for this purpose than any other type of filament known.

Much larger quantities of tungsten, however, are used in conjunction with
chromium, nickel, cobalt, vanadium, and molybdenum in the production of
high-speed steels (p. 755). The tungsten is added to these steels in the form
of ferrotungsten, which is prepared by the reduction of ferrous tungstate in
an electric furnace.

The properties of metallic tungsten vary greatly with the treatment to
which the metal has been subjected. The ductile variety prepared as described above has an extremely high tensile strength and is one of the hardest

of the metals. Tungsten, with a density of 19.26 g. per cc., is also one of the heaviest of the metals; its melting point (3400° C.) is higher than that of any other metal, and its boiling point is over 5900° C. At ordinary temperatures tungsten is relatively unreactive, but at elevated temperatures it reacts readily with water, oxygen, sulfur, phosphorus, the halogens, and carbon. It is unaffected by cold dilute nonoxidizing acids, but is attacked slowly by hot concentrated hydrochloric or sulfuric acid, and vigorously by a mixture of nitric and hydrofluoric acids.

4. Compounds of Chromium. Chromium forms series of compounds corresponding to the oxidation states +2, +3, and +6, respectively. The general relationships among these three series of compounds are outlined in Table 37.2.

Table 37.2

Oxidation State	Hydroxide, etc.		Typical Salt	Designation	Color
+2	$Cr(OH)_2$	Basic	$CrCl_2$	Chromous	Blue
+3	$Cr_2O_3 \cdot xH_2O$	Amphoteric	$CrCl_3$	Chromic	Green or violet
			$NaCr(OH)_4$ ($NaCrO_2$)	Chromite	Green
+6	(H_2CrO_4)	Acidic	K_2CrO_4	Chromate	Yellow
	$H_2Cr_2O_7$	Acidic	$K_2Cr_2O_7$	Dichromate	Orange

(↑ Increasing basicity / Decreasing acidity)

The general principle of increasing acidity of the oxides with increasing oxidation number is valid for chromium, as for the other multivalent elements, for CrO is basic, Cr_2O_3 is amphoteric, and CrO_3 is strongly acidic.

5. Chromous Compounds. Chromous compounds, in which chromium exhibits the +2 oxidation state, are so readily oxidized on standing in air or in aqueous solution that they are of little importance, and they are seldom encountered in laboratory work except when special provisions are made for their preparation. Chromous hydroxide is a moderately strong base, and chromous salts show little tendency to be hydrolyzed in aqueous solution.

6. Chromic Compounds. If solutions of chromic salts are treated with equivalent quantities of sodium hydroxide, or with an excess of ammonia, a gray-green precipitate of the hydrous oxide $Cr_2O_3 \cdot xH_2O$ is obtained. This compound is amphoteric and dissolves in an excess of a strong base. Thus, in sodium hydroxide solution hydrous chromic oxide dissolves to form the chromite ion, $Cr(OH)_4^-$ (sometimes written in the anhydrous form, CrO_2^-). Anhydrous chromites are readily formed by the direct combination of chromic oxide with metallic oxides at elevated temperatures.

$$ZnO + Cr_2O_3 = Zn(CrO_2)_2$$

Chromite ore, $Fe(CrO_2)_2$, is a compound of this type.

Chromic oxide is a green powder usually obtained by the reduction of chromates at elevated temperatures in the dry state; e.g., by the reduction of sodium dichromate with sulfur,

$$Na_2Cr_2O_7 + S = Cr_2O_3 + Na_2SO_4$$

or with an ammonium salt.

$$Na_2Cr_2O_7 + 2NH_4Cl = Cr_2O_3 + N_2 + 4H_2O + 2NaCl$$

Because of its low solubility in water and its bright green color, chromic oxide is used as a pigment under the name of chrome green.

The hydrated chromic ion, $Cr(H_2O)_6^{+++}$, which is present in solutions of many soluble chromic salts, is violet in color. Solutions of chromic salts are acidic, being subject to very considerable hydrolysis. This phenomenon is best interpreted as resulting from the tendency of water molecules which are coordinated to small, highly charged metallic ions such as the chromic ion, to lose protons (p. 322).

$$Cr(H_2O)_6^{+++} + H_2O \rightleftharpoons Cr(H_2O)_5(OH)^{++} + H_3O^+$$

The precipitation of hydrous oxides of the heavy metals by the addition of equivalent quantities of hydroxide ion and the dissolving of these precipitates, when they are amphoteric, in a solution containing excess of hydroxide ion, are best accounted for by the same sort of mechanism. In the case of chromium, for example, hydrated chromic ions in aqueous solution lose protons to a small extent only. However, upon the addition of three equivalents of hydroxide ion, not only is the above equilibrium displaced completely to the right, but protons are relinquished also by two more water molecules, as is shown by the following equation:

$$Cr(H_2O)_6^{+++} + 3OH^- \rightleftharpoons Cr(H_2O)_3(OH)_{3(s)} + 3H_2O$$

and the electrically neutral hydrous oxide thus formed is precipitated. The composition of the precipitate does not, of course, correspond exactly to the formula $Cr(OH)_3(H_2O)_3$, for it carries excess water down with it; and when the precipitate is dried it is very difficult to tell at what point the loss of physically absorbed water ends and loss of chemically bound water begins. The limit of the ability of the aggregate to lose protons has not been reached, however, for in the presence of an excess of hydroxide ion the precipitate redissolves to form a negatively charged complex ion, by processes of the type shown by the following equation:

$$Cr(H_2O)_3(OH)_3 + OH^- = Cr(H_2O)_2(OH)_4^- + H_2O$$

$$\left. \begin{array}{c} \downarrow \\ Cr(OH)_4^- \\ \downarrow \\ CrO_2^- \end{array} \right\} \text{dehydration}$$

Fig. 37.1. Scale models of the $Cr(NH_3)_6^{+++}$ ion and the $Cr(H_2O)_6^{+++}$ ion.

Anhydrous chromic halides may be prepared by passage of the appropriate halogen over the metal or over a mixture of chromic oxide and carbon at elevated temperatures. Anhydrous chromic chloride is obtained as reddish violet, lustrous flakes by this method.

$$2Cr + 3Cl_2 = 2CrCl_3$$

This compound may be prepared also by passing carbon tetrachloride vapor over hot chromic oxide. It dissolves extremely slowly in water.

Chromium in the +3 oxidation state is outstanding for the large number of complex compounds which it forms. As was pointed out in Chapter 33 (p. 633), complexes of this type result from the coordination of ions or molecules to a central iron. Chromic ion has a coordination number of six in virtually all of its complexes. Examples of such complexes include $[Cr(NH_3)_6]^{+++}$, $[Cr(NH_3)_5Cl]^{++}$, $[Cr(CN)_6]^{---}$, and $[Cr(NH_3)_4$-$(NO_2)_2]^+$. Complexes such as these exhibit a great variety of colors.

Chromic salts are generally obtained by the reduction of chromates or dichromates. When a solution of potassium dichromate is acidified with sulfuric acid and treated with a reducing agent such as sulfur dioxide or ethyl alcohol, and the resulting solution is evaporated at moderate temperatures (less than $60°$ C.), violet octahedral crystals of potassium chromic alum, $K_2SO_4 \cdot Cr_2(SO_4)_3 \cdot 24H_2O$, are obtained (p. 806).

$$2K^+ + Cr_2O_7^{--} + 3SO_2 + 2H^+ + SO_4^{--} + 23H_2O$$
$$= K_2SO_4 \cdot Cr_2(SO_4)_3 \cdot 24H_2O$$

Ammonium chromic alum, $(NH_4)_2SO_4 \cdot Cr_2(SO_4)_3 \cdot 24H_2O$, is obtained by the evaporation of a solution of equal numbers of moles of ammonium sulfate and chromic sulfate. Chromic salts have a number of applications as mordants (p. 806) in the textile industry, and in the chrome-tanning process of the leather industry.

7. Chromium Trioxide and Its Derivatives. Chromium trioxide, CrO_3, or chromic anhydride, as it is sometimes called, is a deep red crystalline compound, in which chromium is in the $+6$ oxidation state. It is obtained by the addition of concentrated sulfuric acid to solutions of chromates or dichromates. As the anhydride of the chromic acids, it is itself sometimes erroneously called "chromic acid." Chromic acid, H_2CrO_4, which might be expected to be formed when chromium trioxide is added to water, is not stable, since it undergoes immediate reaction to form dichromic acid, $H_2Cr_2O_7$. More highly condensed chromic acids such as trichromic, $H_2Cr_3O_{10}$, and tetrachromic, $H_2Cr_4O_{13}$, are found in strongly acidic solutions. As we have seen above, in concentrated sulfuric acid solutions, the free oxide, CrO_3 (which, in a polymeric form, is the end-product of the condensation process), is obtained. This tendency to form poly or condensed acids is characteristic of the elements of Groups 5b (p. 692) and 6b (p. 694) and is even more pronounced in the case of the molybdic and tungstic acids than in the chromic. In all of these compounds, one or more pairs of metal atoms are each linked through an oxygen atom. The electronic structure of dichromic acid, for example, is exactly analogous to that of pyrosulfuric acid (p. 461).

It is evident that several series of chromate salts are possible. The most important and most common of these are the chromates, containing CrO_4^{--}

ion, and the dichromates, which contain $Cr_2O_7^{--}$ ion. As indicated in the equilibrium below, chromate ion is stable only in alkaline solution, whereas dichromate is stable in acid solutions. Since chromate ion is yellow and dichromate ion orange, the shift in the equilibrium between dichromate and chromate on the addition of acid or base to the solution may be followed by the change in the color of the solution.

$$2CrO_4^{--} + 2H^+ \rightleftharpoons Cr_2O_7^{--} + H_2O$$

Yellow   Orange

The alkali metal chromates are obtained when chromite ore is roasted in the presence of air and some alkaline substance such as potassium carbonate. The following equation represents an example of such a process:

$$4Fe(CrO_2)_2 + 7O_2 + 8K_2CO_3 = 8K_2CrO_4 + 2Fe_2O_3 + 8CO_2$$

Potassium chromate is extracted with water from the insoluble residue of ferric oxide and the solution evaporated until crystallization takes place. Dichromates may be obtained by the recrystallization of chromates from acidic solutions. One of the most important dichromates is the orange-colored salt potassium dichromate, $K_2Cr_2O_7$.

The chromates of many of the heavy metals are only very slightly soluble in water, and are readily prepared by precipitation from solutions of the alkali metal chromates. These insoluble chromates are generally yellow in color, although, in the case of a few elements, such as silver, for example, orange or red chromates are obtained. The heavy metal chromates dissolve in solutions of acids because of the change of chromate to dichromate ion and the resulting shift in the solubility equilibrium.

Some of the heavy metal chromates are used as paint pigments; e.g., chrome yellow, $PbCrO_4$, zinc chromate, $ZnCrO_4$, and chrome red, $PbO \cdot PbCrO_4$.

Chromates and dichromates have a number of other laboratory and industrial applications, many of which depend upon their oxidizing properties. The standard oxidation potential for the half-reaction

$$2Cr^{+++} + 7H_2O = Cr_2O_7^{--} + 14H^+ + 6e^-$$

is -1.33 volts. This indicates that dichromate ion is a fairly strong oxidizing agent, especially in strongly acidic solutions. Dichromate solutions are widely used in analytical chemistry for the titration of reducing agents, such as ferrous salts.

$$Cr_2O_7^{--} + 6Fe^{++} + 14H^+ = 2Cr^{+++} + 6Fe^{+++} + 7H_2O$$

In the chrome-tanning of leather, the hide is treated with dichromate solution, which is then subjected to reduction. This results in the precipitation of hydrous chromic oxide in the pores of the hide, which brings about changes in the proteins which render them resistant to decay.

Chromate or dichromate may be detected in solution by the formation of a yellow precipitate of lead chromate with lead acetate solution in the presence of acetic acid. Another sensitive test consists in the formation of an unstable blue compound with hydrogen peroxide in acidic solutions; this blue substance may be extracted with ether, in which it is both more soluble and more stable than in the aqueous solution. The exact nature of the blue compound is a subject on which there is no general agreement. It is generally accepted, however, that the compound contains a peroxide group, O_2^{--}, coordinated to the chromium.

When a mixture of a chloride and a dichromate is heated with concentrated sulfuric acid, or when chromium trioxide in the presence of concentrated sulfuric acid is treated with hydrochloric acid, a volatile, dark red liquid called chromyl chloride, CrO_2Cl_2, is obtained.

$$4NaCl + Na_2Cr_2O_7 + 3H_2SO_4 = 3Na_2SO_4 + 2CrO_2Cl_2 + 3H_2O$$

$$CrO_3 + 2HCl = CrO_2Cl_2 + H_2O$$

In each of these cases the excess sulfuric acid acts as a dehydrating agent, taking up the water formed in the reaction. Chromyl chloride may be considered as being derived from chromic acid, the formula of which may be written $CrO_2(OH)_2$, by the replacement of its hydroxyl groups by chlorine atoms; it is therefore an acid chloride analogous to sulfuryl chloride, SO_2Cl_2 (p. 462). The acid which would be obtained by replacing one hydroxyl group by a chlorine atom, viz., $CrO_2(OH)Cl$ or $HCrO_3Cl$, is unstable, but salts of this acid, such as $KCrO_3Cl$, have been prepared, and are known as chlorochromates.

8. Compounds of Molybdenum and Tungsten. The chemistry of these elements is complicated by the multiplicity of oxidation states which they show and by their great tendency to form complex compounds.

Molybdenum forms series of compounds in which it exhibits the oxidation states $+2$, $+3$, $+4$, $+5$, and $+6$. Some typical compounds of molybdenum in these oxidation states are shown in Table 37.3.

Tungsten, like molybdenum, exhibits oxidation states of $+2$, $+3$, $+4$, $+5$, and $+6$. Compounds of tungsten in all except the last of these states are unimportant, however.

The most important compounds of tungsten are tungsten trioxide, WO_3, and its derivatives, the tungstates. The oxide is a yellow solid which is obtained when solutions of alkali metal tungstates, acidified with hydrochloric acid, are heated. If the treatment is carried out in the cold, tungstic acid, $H_2WO_4 \cdot H_2O$, is precipitated. Tungsten trioxide, like its molybdenum analog, is amphoteric, with acidic properties predominating. Although normal tungstates such as $Na_2WO_4 \cdot 2H_2O$ are easily obtained, tungsten trioxide, like molybdenum trioxide, forms many poly acids and salts. Examples of the more complex polytungstates are $K_6(H_2W_{12}O_{40}) \cdot 18H_2O$ and $(NH_4)_6W_7O_{24} \cdot 6H_2O$. With the exception of the alkali metal and ammonium compounds, the tungstates are not appreciably soluble in water. Sodium tungstates are applied commercially to the fireproofing of fabrics and the weighting of silk, and as mordants in the dye industry (p. 806).

Table 37.3

Oxidation State	Oxide	Chemical Nature of Oxide	Other Typical Compounds	General Characteristics
+2	MoO	Basic	$Mo_6Cl_{12} \cdot 8H_2O$	Unstable in water; strong reducing agent.
+3	Mo_2O_3	Basic	$MoCl_3$, $MoBr_3$, K_3MoCl_6	Reducing agents; some compounds soluble and stable in water.
+4	MoO_2	Basic	MoS_2, $MoCl_4$, $K_4Mo(CN)_8$	Mo^{4+} ion not stable in water; a number of stable, water-soluble complexes known, however.
+5	Mo_2O_5	Weakly basic	$MoCl_5$, $MoOCl_3$, K_2MoOCl_5	Mainly basic salts.
+6	MoO_3	Amphoteric	MoF_6, MoO_2Cl_2, K_2MoS_4	Hexafluoride is a volatile liquid.
			Na_2MoO_4, $(NH_4)_6Mo_7O_{24} \cdot 4H_2O$, $H_4SiMo_{12}O_{40} \cdot 24H_2O$	Most important and stable of the molybdenum compounds.

Complex tungstates containing other acid-forming elements such as silicon, phosphorus, and boron can also be prepared. Phosphotungstic acid, $H_3PW_{12}O_{40} \cdot 29H_2O$, is used in organic chemistry to precipitate alkaloids and proteins; silicotungstic acid, $H_4SiW_{12}O_{40} \cdot 24H_2O$, has similar properties.

Other compounds of +6 tungsten include the hexahalides, WX_6, and the oxyhalides, WOX_4 and WO_2X_2.

STUDY QUESTIONS AND PROBLEMS

1. Explain, in so far as you can, why compounds of $+3$ chromium should resemble those of $+3$ manganese and $+3$ vanadium more than those of $+3$ molybdenum.

2. Discuss briefly the ores and metallurgy of chromium, molybdenum, and tungsten.

3. What is meant by the passive state of metals? How may it be induced? How may it be removed?

4. What are the properties of chromium which account for the widespread use of chromium plating? What is meant by a stainless steel?

5. What are high-speed steels? For what are they used?

6. What properties of tungsten make it a desirable substance for the production of filaments for incandescent lamps?

7. Show the oxidation states of chromium, the oxides and hydroxides corresponding to each, the character of the hydroxides (acidic or basic), typical salts corresponding to each oxidation state, names, colors, and chemical behavior of each series.

8. From reference works in your library, find the names, colors, formulas, and methods of preparation of ten complex compounds of chromium.

9. Write balanced equations for the following transformations:

$$Na_2Cr_2O_7 \longrightarrow Cr_2O_3$$

$$K_2Cr_2O_7 \longrightarrow K_2SO_4 \cdot Cr_2(SO_4)_3 \cdot 24H_2O$$

$$Cr^{+++} \longrightarrow CrO_2^-$$

$$CrO_3 \longrightarrow Na_2CrO_4$$

$$CrO_4^{--} \longrightarrow Cr_2O_7^{--}$$

$$Fe(CrO_2)_2 \longrightarrow Na_2CrO_4$$

10. Show by means of electronic formulas the differences in structure of chromate and dichromate ions, and their interconversion by change in the pH of the solution.

The Manganese Family

1. Introduction. The manganese family (Group 7b) contains three elements: manganese, technetium, and rhenium. The first of these elements is of great industrial importance, but technetium is known only in the form of radioactive isotopes, artificially produced (p. 146), and has not been found in nature. Rhenium is fairly well known in the laboratory, but is found only in small quantities in nature, and is of little commercial significance. The electronic configurations of these elements are listed in Table 38.1.

Table 38.1

Element	1	2	3	4	5	6
	s	s p	s p d	s p d f	s p d	s
Mn	2	2, 6	2, 6, 5	2		
Tc	(2)	(2, 6)	(2, 6, 10)	(2, 6, 6)	(1)	
Re	2	2, 6	2, 6, 10	2, 6, 10, 14	2, 6, 5	2

These electron configurations indicate, of course, that the elements are transitional in nature. They are quite similar to the elements of the chromium and other transition families, having the properties which have been shown to accompany the transitional type of atomic structure (Chapter 36). Like members of other transition families, these elements are metallic in the free state, and have physical properties which correspond closely to those of the elements immediately preceding and following (p. 170). The most characteristic chemical property of the elements of this family is their maximum oxidation number of +7. This arises from the fact that there is a total of seven electrons in the outer shell and the incomplete inner subshell of each of their atoms. It is only in their highest oxidation state that the elements of this family show any resemblance to the halogens, the other family in Group VII. The perhalates and the permanganates have many properties in common.

2. Occurrence of the Elements. None of these elements occurs naturally in the free state, and only manganese compounds are found in sufficient quantities to attract industrial interest. Manganese is a common element, ranking eighth among the metals in order of abundance and constituting an estimated 0.10% of the igneous rocks in the earth's crust. The most important manganese ore is the dioxide, MnO_2, which occurs as the soft, black mineral known as pyrolusite. This name is derived from two Greek words meaning "fire" and "to wash," because since ancient times the mineral has been used in glass-making to decolorize the product. Other manganese ores include braunite, Mn_2O_3, hausmannite, Mn_3O_4, manganite, $Mn_2O_3 \cdot H_2O$, and rhodochrosite, $MnCO_3$. Manganese ores, like those of chromium, are commonly associated with oxides of iron.

Many nations produce manganese ores, but the major portion of the world's supply comes from Russia, India, Union of South Africa, Ghana, Brazil, Egypt, and Cuba. In addition, a small amount of manganese ore is mined in this country, but domestic ores are of low grade and supply only a small percentage of our annual consumption. An adequate supply of manganese is essential for any large industrialized nation, and, prior to World War II, all the major nations of the earth built up large strategic reserves of this important material.

Rhenium is quite rare but has been found to occur in certain German copper ores up to the extent of five parts per million.

3. Metallurgy, Properties, and Uses of the Metals. The only industrial method for the production of pure manganese metal consists in the electrolysis of solutions of manganous sulfate or chloride, in a cell in which the anode and cathode compartments contain different solutions separated by a porous diaphragm. The necessity for a divided cell arises from the following facts. Manganese is so active a metal that it cannot be deposited from neutral or acidic solutions.

$$Mn = Mn^{++} + 2e^-; \ E = 1.18 \text{ v.}$$

In alkaline solution, however, oxides or hydroxides of manganese are likely to be precipitated. Hence the anode compartment contains a solution of manganous sulfate, ammonium sulfate, and sulfuric acid of pH 1, while the cathode solution is slightly alkaline, of pH 7.2 to 7.6.

Manganese is a reddish gray metal which melts at 1245° C. and boils at 2097° C. It exists in three different crystalline modifications, α, β, and γ. The α- and β-forms are hard enough to scratch glass, but the γ-form (unstable at room temperature) is flexible and soft. The density of the α-form is 7.44 g./cc. at 20° C.

As indicated by its high oxidation potential, manganese readily displaces hydrogen from solutions of strong acids. It tarnishes rapidly in moist air, and reacts readily with halogens to form halides. At higher temperatures the metal reacts with sulfur, carbon, nitrogen, and, phosphorus to form compounds of the formulas MnS, Mn_3C, Mn_3N_2, and Mn_3P_2, respectively.

Electrolytic manganese is used as a source of pure manganese compounds, as an alloying element in various ferrous and non-ferrous alloys, and as a purifying agent or scavenger (p. 750) in the production of various common metals, including especially iron and steel alloys. For this last purpose, however, manganese is commonly applied not in the pure state but in the form of one or the other of the iron–manganese alloys known as ferromanganese (75 to 81% Mn) and spiegeleisen (15 to 20% Mn). These alloys may be prepared by the reduction of mixtures of iron and manganese oxides with carbon in a blast furnace, in which case they contain up to 6% of carbon. The carbon content of ferromanganese, however, may be reduced to less than 1% by treatment with manganese dioxide in the electric furnace. As a scavenger, manganese improves the quality of the steel by removing traces of oxygen and sulfur in the form of manganous oxide and sulfide, which are carried away in the slag. Almost the entire output of steel is subjected to this treatment. A second function of manganese is in the preparation of alloy steels containing 8 to 10% of manganese, which are very hard and show great resistance to wear and abrasion; they are largely used for rails in crossings and switches, and for rock crushers, conveyor chains, teeth for the dippers of steam shovels, and various other types of machinery which must stand rough treatment.

Important nonferrous alloys of manganese include the manganese bronzes and manganin. The manganese bronzes contain about 16 to 17% of manganese, along with minor quantities of other metals, in copper. Manganin consists of 84% of copper, 12% of manganese, and 4% of nickel, and is notable for the fact that its electrical resistance changes only very slightly with changing temperature; it is useful, therefore, in the manufacture of standard resistances for electrical instruments. Most commercial aluminum and magnesium alloys contain small amounts of manganese.

Rhenium metal is obtained as a powder when any rhenium compound is reduced with hydrogen at elevated temperatures (1000° C.). Potassium perrhenate is commonly used as a source of the metal.

$$2KReO_4 + 7H_2 = 2KOH + 6H_2O + 2Re$$

Coherent deposits of rhenium are obtained by the electrolytic reduction of perrhenate ion in sulfuric or perchloric acid solution. Massive rhenium is a bright metal which melts at 3170° C., and has a density greater than 20 g.

per cc. In general, rhenium is less electropositive than manganese; while it dissolves in concentrated nitric, or in hot concentrated sulfuric acid, it is unaffected by nonoxidizing acids such as hydrochloric acid. No industrial use for rhenium has as yet been developed.

4. Compounds of Manganese. The chemistry of manganese is even more complex than that of chromium, for manganese forms series of compounds in which it is in the oxidation states $+2$, $+3$, $+4$, $+6$, and $+7$, and at least one compound, $K_5Mn(CN)_6$, is known in which it has an oxidation number of $+1$. This variability in oxidation state, as in the other transition families, results from the fact that one or more electrons from the incomplete inner subshell can enter into compound formation.

A summary of these series of manganese compounds is given in Table 38.2. It may be seen from this table that, as in the case of compounds of chromium and other multivalent elements, the basicity of the oxides and hydroxides decreases with increasing oxidation number.

Table 38.2

Oxidation State	Hydroxide, etc.	Character	Typical Salts	Name	Color
$+2$	$Mn(OH)_2$	Basic	$MnCl_2$ $MnSO_4$	Manganous	Pink
$+3$	$Mn_2O_3 \cdot xH_2O$	Weakly basic	$MnCl_3$ MnF_3	Manganic	Violet
$+4$	$MnO_2 \cdot xH_2O$	Amphoteric	$MnCl_4$	. . . .	Green
			$CaMnO_3$	Manganites	Brown
$+6$	(H_2MnO_4)	Weakly acidic	K_2MnO_4	Manganates	Green
$+7$	$HMnO_4$	Strongly acidic	$KMnO_4$	Permanganates	Purple

5. Manganous Compounds. When manganese dioxide, or any of the other higher oxides of manganese, is heated in a stream of hydrogen gas, the pale green manganous oxide, MnO, is obtained.

$$MnO_2 + H_2 = MnO + H_2O$$

The basic character of this oxide is indicated by the fact that it dissolves readily in acids. Manganous hydroxide, $Mn(OH)_2$, is obtained as a pinkish-white gelatinous precipitate when solutions of manganous salts are treated with alkali hydroxide or ammonia solutions. Like magnesium and ferrous hydroxides, however, manganous hydroxide is soluble even in such weak acids as ammonium ion, and, therefore, is not precipitated by ammonia in the presence of large concentrations of ammonium salts. On standing in air, the precipitated manganous hydroxide slowly darkens because of oxidation to hydrous manganic oxide ($Mn_2O_3 \cdot xH_2O$). This behavior, which distinguishes manganous from magnesium hydroxide, is quite similar to that of the corresponding ferrous and chromous compounds.

Most manganous salts are pale pink in color in the solid state or in concentrated aqueous solution. In dilute solutions, however, the color of manganous ion is so faint as to be imperceptible. The more familiar soluble manganous salts are the sulfate, $MnSO_4 \cdot 5H_2O$, the nitrate, $Mn(NO_3)_2 \cdot 6H_2O$, and the chloride, $MnCl_2 \cdot 4H_2O$. All these salts are moderately stable in solution, undergoing only slight hydrolysis.

The more common slightly soluble manganous compounds include the pink sulfide, MnS, which is soluble in dilute acids, the light buff-colored carbonate, $MnCO_3$, which turns brown or black on standing in air because of oxidation, and the pink phosphate, $Mn_3(PO_4)_2$, and oxalate, $MnC_2O_4 \cdot 2H_2O$, also soluble in acids. In the presence of ammonium ion, ammonia, and hydrogen phosphate ion, manganous ion forms a pale pink precipitate of manganous ammonium phosphate, $MnNH_4PO_4$, which when heated yields the pyrophosphate, $Mn_2P_2O_7$. In general, the solubility relationships of manganous compounds are very similar to those of magnesium and ferrous compounds. This is not surprising in view of the equal charge and similar size of manganous, ferrous, and magnesium ions.

In neutral or acidic solution manganous compounds are oxidized only by relatively strong oxidizing agents; they are, therefore, only weak reducing agents.

6. Manganic Compounds. Manganic ion is unstable in aqueous solution, since it tends to react with water in accordance with the equation

$$2Mn^{+++} + 2H_2O = Mn^{++} + MnO_2 + 4H^+$$

Hence, the only manganic compounds which are stable in aqueous solution, or in contact with water, are those which are either only slightly dissociated or only slightly soluble.

7. Manganese Dioxide and Its Derivatives. Since the quadruply charged ion, Mn^{+4}, is unstable in aqueous solution, the chemistry of manganese in the +4 oxidation state is largely that of the dioxide, MnO_2, or the hydrous dioxide, $MnO_2 \cdot xH_2O$. When a solution of manganous salt is made alkaline and treated with sodium peroxide, black or dark brown hydrous manganese dioxide is obtained.

$$Mn^{++} + O_2^{--} + xH_2O = MnO_2 \cdot xH_2O$$

The same substance is obtained by the oxidation of manganous ion with potassium chlorate in nitric acid solution.

$$3Mn^{++} + ClO_3^- + (3 + 3x)H_2O = 3(MnO_2 \cdot xH_2O) + 6H^+ + Cl^-$$

Manganese dioxide is a fairly strong oxidizing agent, as is shown by the standard oxidation potential for the following half-reaction:

$$Mn^{++} + 2H_2O = MnO_2 + 4H^+ + 2e^-; \quad E = -1.23 \text{ v.}$$

One of the earlier commercial processes for the manufacture of chlorine involved the oxidation of hydrochloric acid by manganese dioxide; although this method has been supplanted by the electrolysis of sodium chloride solution, it is still used in the laboratory (see next two equations).

Although manganese dioxide is not very reactive toward either acids or bases, it is, nevertheless, an amphoteric oxide. When treated with cold concentrated hydrochloric acid it dissolves, giving a dark green solution of the tetrachloride.

$$MnO_2 + 4HCl = MnCl_4 + 2H_2O$$

When the solution is warmed the tetrachloride decomposes into manganous chloride and free chlorine.

$$MnCl_4 = MnCl_2 + Cl_2$$

A solution of the sulfate $Mn(SO_4)_2$ may be prepared also, but it slowly decomposes with the evolution of oxygen.

Although manganese dioxide does not readily react with alkaline solutions, manganites such as $CaMnO_3$ can be prepared by the fusion of manganese dioxide with suitable basic oxides. The intermediate oxide, Mn_3O_4, which is obtained when manganous oxide is heated in air, may be considered to be a manganous manganite of the formula $Mn_2^{II}(Mn^{IV}O_4)$.

The time-honored use of pyrolusite in glass-making depends upon the fact that manganese dioxide oxidizes the ferrous compounds present as impurities, and thus destroys the green tint which such impurities impart to the glass. Manganese dioxide is used in large amounts in the manufacture of dry cells (p. 421). It is used also in the paint and varnish industry as a catalyst for the familiar "drying" process which results in the hardening of the oils used in paint or varnish.

8. Manganese Trioxide and the Manganates. Manganese trioxide, MnO_3, is a red, deliquescent solid which is obtained when a solution of potassium permanganate in concentrated sulfuric acid is added dropwise to anhydrous sodium carbonate, and the fumes thus obtained condensed in a chilled U-tube. It decomposes when warmed, and dissolves in alkali solutions to give manganates. Manganic acid, H_2MnO_4, is known only in the form of its salts, as it is unstable both in the pure state and in aqueous solution. The behavior of its salts, however, is such as to indicate that it would be weakly acidic.

Manganates of the general formula M_2MnO_4 are obtained when manganese dioxide is fused with sodium or potassium hydroxide in the presence of air.

$$2MnO_2 + O_2 + 4KOH = 2K_2MnO_4 + 2H_2O$$

The manganates are isomorphous with the chromates, sulfates, and selenates of the same metals. Sodium and potassium manganates are soluble in water, giving dark green solutions. When a solution containing manganate ion is diluted with a large volume of water, or is acidified, the manganate ion reacts with water in accordance with the following equation:

$$3MnO_4^{--} + 2H_2O = MnO_2 + 2MnO_4^- + 4OH^-$$

Aqueous solutions of manganates, therefore, are stable only in the presence of excess hydroxide ion, which tends to reverse this reaction.

9. Permanganates. If the mass obtained from the fusion of manganese dioxide with an alkali metal hydroxide is dissolved in water, and chlorine is passed into the solution, a solution of the corresponding alkali metal permanganate is obtained.

$$2MnO_4^{--} + OCl^- + H_2O = 2MnO_4^- + Cl^- + 2OH^-$$

It should be noted that the formulas for manganate and permanganate ions are the same, except that the latter bears one less negative charge than the former. This means that the manganate ion, in being oxidized to permanganate ion, loses one electron, presumably from the incomplete $3d$ subshell of the manganese atom. The electronic formula for either of the ions, neglecting the charges, may be written as follows:

$$
\begin{array}{c}
: \overset{..}{\underset{..}{O}} : \\
: \overset{..}{\underset{..}{O}} : Mn : \overset{..}{\underset{..}{O}} : \\
: \overset{..}{\underset{..}{O}} :
\end{array}
$$

The color of permanganate ion, and hence of most permanganates, is a very deep purple. Even very dilute solutions of soluble permanganates possess a definite pink color. The permanganates resemble the perchlorates in their oxidizing properties and in their solubility relationships; e.g., both the perchlorates and the permanganates of the heavy metals and of the alkaline earth metals are very soluble. Corresponding perchlorates and permanganates also are isomorphous, giving mixed crystals.

The most familiar permanganate is the anhydrous potassium salt, $KMnO_4$. The hydrated sodium salt (4, 6, or 10 moles of water of hydration) is more difficult to obtain in the pure state and is less commonly used in the laboratory. The most important use of potassium permanganate is as a strong oxidizing agent. The outstanding oxidizing properties of permanganate ion are indicated by the high negative potentials for the following half-reactions:

$$Mn^{++} + 4H_2O = MnO_4^- + 8H^+ + 5e^-; \quad E = -1.51 \text{ v.}$$

$$MnO_2 + 4OH^- = MnO_4^- + 2H_2O + 3e^-; \quad E = -0.59 \text{ v.}$$

$$MnO_2 + 2H_2O = MnO_4^- + 4H^+ + 3e^-; \quad E = -1.70 \text{ v.}$$

Only the weakest of reducing agents can escape oxidation in the presence of permanganate ion. Correspondingly, only the strongest of chemical oxidizing agents can oxidize manganese in one of its lower valence states to permanganate ion. The customary qualitative test for manganous ion depends upon the oxidation of manganous ion in nitric acid solution to permanganate ion by lead dioxide or sodium bismuthate, both of which are very strong oxidizing agents.

$$2Mn^{++} + 5NaBiO_3 + 14H^+ = 2MnO_4^- + 5Bi^{+++} + 7H_2O + 5Na^+$$

Since there are inevitably a great many oxidation-reduction reactions involved in the chemistry of manganese compounds, the student may find the following rules helpful:

1. In the presence of excess reducing agent *in acidic solution*, permanganate ion is generally reduced to manganous ion; e.g.,

$$5Fe^{++} + MnO_4^- + 8H^+ = 5Fe^{+++} + Mn^{++} + 4H_2O$$

2. An excess of reducing agent *in alkaline solution* reduces permanganate ion only to manganese dioxide; e.g.,

$$3NO_2 + MnO_4^- + 2OH^- = 3NO_3^- + MnO_2 + H_2O$$

3. In acidic solutions, manganous ion is oxidized to manganese dioxide by permanganate.

$$2MnO_4^- + 3Mn^{++} + 2H_2O = 5MnO_2 + 4H^+$$

4. In strongly basic solutions, permanganate oxidizes manganese dioxide to manganate ion.

$$MnO_2 + 2MnO_4^- + 4OH^- = 3MnO_4^{--} + 2H_2O$$

Unlike manganic acid, permanganic acid, which is a fairly strong acid, is stable in dilute aqueous solution. Such a solution may be prepared by the reaction of solutions of equivalent quantities of barium permanganate and sulfuric acids, followed by the removal of the precipitated barium sulfate.

$$Ba^{++} + 2MnO_4^- + 2H^+ + SO_4^{--} = 2H^+ + 2MnO_4^- + BaSO_{4(s)}$$

The anhydride of permanganic acid, dimanganese heptoxide, Mn_2O_7, is prepared by the treatment of potassium permanganate with concentrated sulfuric acid, which acts as a dehydrating agent.

$$2MnO_4^- + 2H^+ = Mn_2O_7 + H_2O$$

Dimanganese heptoxide is a brown, oily liquid which is very explosive; the reaction given, therefore, should be carried out only with extreme precautions to prevent rise in temperature.

10. Compounds of Rhenium. Rhenium is similar to manganese in that it forms a weakly basic oxide, Re_2O_3, an amphoteric oxide, ReO_2, and acidic oxides, ReO_3 and Re_2O_7. The $+7$ oxide dissolves readily in water, giving solutions of perrhenic acid, $HReO_4$. The perrhenates are relatively poor oxidizing agents as compared with the permanganates. A number of halogen compounds of rhenium in various oxidation states have been described.

STUDY QUESTIONS AND PROBLEMS

1. What properties of the elements of the manganese family justify the classification of this family as a transition family? Explain these properties in terms of the electronic configurations of the elements.

2. Arrange the oxides Mn_2O_7, MnO, MnO_2, MnO_3, and Mn_2O_3 in order of increasing acidic character. What general rule covers this situation? Explain this rule in terms of atomic and ionic properties.

3. Discuss briefly the oxidizing properties of permanganate ion. What are the products formed from permanganate ion when it acts as oxidizing agent in acidic solution? in basic solution?

4. Complete and balance the following equations:

$$MnO_4^- + H^+ + Fe^{++} =$$
$$MnO_2 + H^+ + Cl^- =$$
$$MnO_2 + MnO_4^- + OH^- =$$
$$Mn^{++} + PbO_2 + H^+ =$$
$$MnO_4^- + NO_2^- + H_2O =$$

5. What weight of potassium permanganate would be required to oxidize to sulfuric acid the sulfur dioxide formed by the combustion of 64 g. of sulfur?

6. Show by means of the standard oxidation potentials for the half-reactions involved that the following reactions will not take place to an appreciable extent:

(a) $3Mn^{++} + 5NO_3^- + 2H_2O = 3MnO_4^- + 5NO + 4H^+$

(b) $3MnO_2 + 2Cr^{+++} + H_2O = 3Mn^{++} + Cr_2O_7^{--} + 2H^+$

7. In what type of compounds can a similarity be observed between elements of the manganese family and the halogens? Choosing one specific pair of corresponding compounds from the two families, list as many common properties as you can find.

8. Evidence has recently been obtained for the existence of potassium rhenide, KRe, as a salt-like compound. Would you expect the properties of rhenide ion to be closely similar to those of the halide ions? Give a reason for your answer.

9. Manganese is estimated to be a thousand times as abundant as copper in the earth's crust. The United States, however, exports metallic copper and imports manganese ore. How can this fact be explained?

10. What weight of spiegeleisen containing 18% of manganese would have to be added to 100 lb. of manganese-free iron to give an alloy containing 10% of manganese?

11. Predict as many as you can of the physical and chemical properties of technetium.

12. Describe the procedures and write equations for the reactions that might be used to prepare each of the following compounds from manganese dioxide: $MnCl_2$, $MnSO_4$, $Mn_3(PO_4)_2$, $Mn_2O_3 \cdot xH_2O$, Na_2MnO_4, $NaMnO_4$.

39

Iron, Cobalt, Nickel, and the Platinum Metals

1. Relationships Among Elements of Group 8. The marked similarity among transition elements in the same horizontal sequence has already been emphasized in the preceding chapters. Among the transition metals previously considered, however, the vertical or group relationships have held our attention because each of the elements in a given vertical column has had the same maximum oxidation number. Thus, all the elements in the vanadium family have a maximum oxidation number of $+5$, those in the chromium family, of $+6$, and those in the manganese family, of $+7$.

Following the manganese family in the periodic system, however, three columns of transition elements occur which lack this unifying factor, and in which vertical relationships are less prominent than in the families previously studied—in which, in fact, they are subordinate to the horizontal similarities mentioned above. The elements in these three columns, iron, cobalt, nickel, ruthenium, rhodium, palladium, osmium, iridium, and platinum, have traditionally been considered together as Group 8 of the periodic system. The resemblance of the elements iron, cobalt, and nickel to each other is so marked that we shall find it convenient to consider these elements together in one section. The other six elements known as the platinum metals, which are also very similar to each other, will be discussed in a later portion of the chapter.

IRON, COBALT, AND NICKEL

2. General Characteristics. The similarity of iron, cobalt, and nickel to each other and to other members of the first transition series is especially notable in the appearance, melting points, densities, ionization potentials, and other physical properties of the elements (Table 36.1, p. 679). The close resemblance in physical, as well as chemical, properties of these three elements is explained by the similarity in the electron configurations of their respective atoms (Table 39.1).

Table 39.1

Element	1 s	2 s p	3 s p d	4 s
Fe	2	2, 6	2, 6, 6	2
Co	2	2, 6	2, 6, 7	2
Ni	2	2, 6	2, 6, 8	2

From these electron configurations it would appear that, since iron has a total of eight $4s$ and $3d$ electrons, this element should exhibit a maximum oxidation number of $+8$, just as the maximum oxidation number of manganese is $+7$, and that of chromium $+6$. Likewise, one might predict a maximum oxidation number of $+9$ for cobalt, and of $+10$ for nickel. The elements do not exhibit these oxidation states, however. The metals are all readily oxidized to doubly charged ions, and, in the case of iron, an additional electron is fairly easily removed from the $3d$ subshell to yield a triply charged ion. Co^{+++} is much more difficult to obtain, however, and the existence of Ni^{+++} has not been established. Less important compounds involving higher oxidation states are obtained by the use of very powerful oxidizing agents in alkaline solution. Under such conditions iron in the $+6$ oxidation state and cobalt and nickel in the $+4$ oxidation state may be obtained.

Each of these three elements, as would be expected from its transitional character, forms a great many complex ions, most of which are intensely colored. The free metals are strongly attracted by a magnetic field; the name *ferromagnetism* has been given to this phenomenon.

3. Occurrence. Iron is the second most abundant metallic element in the earth's crust, being surpassed only by aluminum. It constitutes about 5% of all igneous rocks. However, the percentage of iron is believed by many to increase to a considerably higher value than this in the lower-lying basaltic rocks; indeed, there is considerable evidence for the supposition that the core of the earth, variously estimated at from 4000 to 5000 miles in diameter, is composed largely of metallic iron. This belief is supported by the fact that meteoric material which is gathered in from outer space by the gravitational field of the earth contains high percentages of metallic iron, as well as by the fact that the average density of the earth is much greater than that of the crust alone.

With the exception of relatively recent meteorites which have not yet rusted away, iron is never found on the earth's surface in the free state. In igneous rocks, it occurs mainly in the form of sulfides, such as pyrite, FeS_2, and pyrrhotite, $FeSS_x$; ferrous silicates, such as $(Mg, Fe)_2SiO_4$; and ferric aluminosilicates, such as $K(Al, Fe)Si_3O_8$. These minerals are not at all suitable for the extraction of metallic iron, and the outstanding importance of iron as an industrial metal is due in no small degree to the fact that the weathering of these igneous rocks has resulted in the formation of immense deposits of simpler iron compounds from which the free metal can readily be obtained. These minerals include ferric oxide, Fe_2O_3, known as hematite, a number of hydrous ferric oxides, $Fe_2O_3 \cdot xH_2O$, known as brown hematites or limonites; ferrous carbonate, $FeCO_3$, known as siderite, and ferrosoferric oxide, Fe_3O_4, commonly known, because of its magnetic properties, as magnetite or lodestone. The largest known deposits of iron ores are found in the Lake Superior region and in Alabama in the United States, and in Germany, Russia, England, and Sweden; but smaller quantities are found in many other countries. In addition to these large deposits, iron compounds occur in nearly all rocks and soils, much of the red and brown color of many rock formations being due to the presence of oxides of this element. Iron is assimilated by plants and animals; indeed, it plays a vital role in life processes, for the hemoglobin in red blood cells is a complex compound containing iron.

Cobalt and nickel are much less abundant than iron. The estimated occurrence of these two elements in the earth's crust is $1 \times 10^{-5}\%$ and 0.02%, respectively. Cobalt commonly occurs in the form of arsenides or sulfides, generally associated with the corresponding compounds of iron, silver, nickel, and copper. The most important ores of cobalt are cobaltite, $CoAsS$, smaltite, $CoAs_2$, erythrite, $Co_3(AsO_4)_2 \cdot 8H_2O$, and linnaeite, Co_3S_4. The richest deposits of cobalt ores are found in Ontario, Belgian Congo, Northern Rhodesia, Morocco, Burma, and Australia.

Although nickel is widely distributed, deposits of ores rich enough to be profitably mined are relatively rare. The most important nickel ores are pentlandite, $NiS \cdot 2FeS$, and garnierite, $(Ni, Mg)SiO_3 \cdot xH_2O$; these commonly occur in association with sulfides of iron and copper. By far the most valuable source of nickel is the Sudbury district of Ontario, from which 90% of the world's annual production of nickel is obtained. A second important source of the metal is the island of New Caledonia in the Southwest Pacific. Nickel is also found in meteorites, ranking second to iron in abundance in such bodies. For this reason, metallic nickel also is believed to be present in the core of the earth.

4. Metallurgy, Properties, and Uses of the Metals. Iron is by far the most important of all the industrial metals. Although it was not the first metal used by man, it has been known and utilized for more than 5000 years. It is undoubtedly true that developments in the technology of the production of iron and iron alloys have made possible the great industrial progress of the past two centuries. The fact that iron is used to a greater extent than all the other metals together may be attributed (1) to the existence of large, rich deposits of iron ores in many different parts of the earth, (2) to the development of large scale, low cost methods for the reduction of these ores, and (3) to the wide variety of different properties which can be obtained by variation of the method of treating the iron and by the addition of various other elements to form iron alloys.

Because of the outstanding importance of the iron industry, the metallurgy and uses of iron and steel will be discussed in considerable detail in the next chapter. Briefly, we may state at this point that the reduction of the oxide ores of iron is accomplished by the process of mixing the ore with carbon and limestone and subjecting the mixture to a blast of hot air in a blast furnace (Figure 40.1, p. 739). The oxygen reacts with the carbon to form carbon monoxide, which then reduces the iron oxide to metallic iron. The limestone acts as a flux, forming a slag with the sandy impurities in the ore. The iron obtained from this process, commonly known as pig iron, is impure and its properties are not very desirable for most purposes; it is, therefore, usually subjected to further treatment before use. The student is referred to the following chapter for a more complete discussion of the manufacture of pig iron and its conversion to wrought irons, cast irons, or steels.

Pure iron is of very little commercial importance and is not prepared on a large scale. It may be obtained by the electrolysis of ferrous sulfate solution between iron electrodes, or by the passage of hydrogen over hot ferric oxide. In each case the iron obtained must be heated to remove gaseous hydrogen which has dissolved in the metal. Pure iron has a silvery white luster and is malleable, ductile, and relatively soft at room temperature. It exists in three allotropic forms: α-iron, the soft, malleable form which is stable at room temperature and is very highly ferromagnetic; γ-iron, which is stable above $910°$ C. and is harder and much less magnetic than α-iron; and δ-iron, which is stable above $1403°$ C. These allotropic forms differ in the geometrical arrangement of the atoms in the crystal lattice, α-iron and δ-iron having body-centered cubic lattices and γ-iron a face-centered cubic lattice. Pure iron melts at $1540°$ C. and boils at about $2735°$ C.; the density of solid α-iron is about 7.86 g. per cc. The physical properties of iron are so greatly altered by the presence of small amounts of impurities that these data are valid only for very pure iron.

The reactions of metallic iron with solutions containing hydrogen ion to produce hydrogen, with sulfur and the halogens to produce sulfides and halides, and with steam to produce hydrogen, indicate that iron is a relatively active metal. The values of the standard oxidation potentials of iron in acidic and basic solutions support this observation.

$$Fe = Fe^{++} + 2e^-; \qquad E = 0.44 \text{ v.}$$

$$Fe + 2OH^- = Fe(OH)_2 + 2e^-; E = 0.88 \text{ v.}$$

Finely divided iron burns vigorously when heated in oxygen, or even in air. When heated with carbon, phosphorus, or silicon, iron forms the compounds Fe_3C, Fe_3P, and $FeSi$, respectively. Like chromium and certain other metals (p. 696), iron may be rendered passive by treatment with powerful oxidizing agents; in this condition its activity is greatly decreased, and it will neither displace hydrogen from solutions of acids nor copper from solutions containing cupric ion. Finely divided metallic iron, when heated to 120° C., reacts slowly with carbon monoxide to form iron pentacarbonyl, a liquid having the formula $Fe(CO)_5$.

In the presence of air and moisture, metallic iron slowly corrodes, or rusts, forming hydrous ferric oxide, $Fe_2O_3 \cdot xH_2O$. Pure iron corrodes much less rapidly than do many impure forms. The prevention of corrosion is one of the most important problems associated with the industrial utilization of iron, and a great deal of time and money has been spent on the study of the reactions involved in the corrosion process and of means by which corrosion may be prevented or retarded. The corrosion of iron under ordinary circumstances depends upon the combined action of water, oxygen, and carbon dioxide. The carbon dioxide makes the water acidic. The iron dissolves in the acid, displacing hydrogen, which collects on the metal as an adherent film.

$$Fe + 2H_2CO_3 = H_2 + Fe^{++} + 2HCO_3^-$$

The oxygen reacts in accordance with the following equation to produce hydrous ferric oxide and, at the same time, to release most of the carbonic acid:

$$4Fe^{++} + 8HCO_3^- + O_2 + 10H_2O = 2(Fe_2O_3 \cdot 3H_2O) + 8H_2CO_3$$

The film of hydrogen on the iron, which would tend to stop the reaction, is removed by the action of oxygen.

The metallurgy of cobalt is complicated by the necessity of separating it from the other metals, such as nickel, iron, and copper, with which it commonly occurs. The process employed varies considerably with the nature of the ore, but the final step generally involves either the reduction of cobalt oxide with carbon or the electrolytic reduction of cobalt sulfate solution.

Cobalt is a silvery white metal which differs from nickel in that it has a slight bluish cast. Cobalt is harder than nickel and is very resistant to atmospheric corrosion; it is affected only slowly by most common acids, except nitric, in which it dissolves rapidly. The metal melts at $1493°$ C., boils at $3550°$ C., and has a density of 8.92 g. per cc. The reactions of metallic cobalt are similar, in general, to those of iron, although cobalt is less active than iron, as may be seen by comparison of their oxidation potentials.

$$Co = Co^{++} + \qquad 2e^-; E = 0.28 \text{ v.}$$

$$Co + 2OH^- = Co(OH)_2 + 2e^-; E = 0.73 \text{ v.}$$

Cobalt is not of major industrial importance, since the total annual production for the world is less than 10,000 tons. Its chief use is in a series of very hard corrosion resistant alloys known as stellites, composed of cobalt and one or more of the metals tungsten, iron, nickel, chromium, molybdenum. Retaining their hardness even at red heat, they are excellent for high-speed cutting tools. Surgical instruments made from these alloys may be sterilized in a flame without injury. Cobalt steels and other cobalt alloys such as Alnico (aluminum, nickel, and cobalt) are used in permanent magnets.

The radioisotope Co^{60} has recently become an important radio-therapeutic agent. As an easily controlled source of gamma radiation similar to that from a well-shielded radium source, it is widely used in the treatment of cancer and in various other applications.

The addition of cobalt oxide imparts a deep blue color to glass. This oxide is used also in ceramics for the production of blue glazes and enamels.

The metallurgy of nickel, also, varies considerably with the nature of the ore. The ores from the Sudbury district in Ontario, which contain iron and copper sulfides in addition to nickel sulfide, are smelted in a blast furnace, yielding a "matte" composed of these sulfides. This matte is then mixed with silica and treated in a Bessemer converter (p. 749) until the iron sulfide has been changed to the oxide, which is then converted to ferrous silicate slag. The resulting matte of copper and nickel sulfides is generally treated in one of two ways. In the Orford process, this matte is heated with sodium sulfide (or a mixture of sodium sulfate and carbon, which yields sodium sulfide at high temperatures), and allowed to solidify. Two separate layers are obtained, the top layer containing most of the sodium sulfide and copper sulfide, and the bottom layer most of the nickel sulfide. The layer containing the nickel sulfide is roasted to form the oxide, which is then reduced with carbon. In the Mond process, the copper sulfide–nickel sulfide matte is roasted to copper and nickel oxides, which are reduced to the metals by means of water gas $(H_2 + CO)$ at 300° C. The mixture of metals is then treated with carbon monoxide at 50 to 100° C.; this results in the formation of nickel carbonyl, $Ni(CO)_4$, which distills off. On being heated to 180° C., nickel carbonyl decomposes, yielding a deposit of metallic nickel 99.8% pure.

If the matte contains copper, nickel, and iron sulfides in the correct proportions, it is sometimes roasted to the oxides and these reduced directly with carbon; by this means an alloy known as Monel metal (67% nickel, 28% copper, and a small amount of iron) is obtained. This alloy, because of its resistance to corrosion, has important industrial applications in the manufacture of coverings for soda fountains and of valves, steam fittings, and blades of propellers and turbines.

Nickel is a silvery white metal which may be polished to a high luster. Although moderately hard, it is both malleable and fairly ductile. The pure metal melts at 1455° C., boils at 2732° C., and has a density of 8.85 g. per cc. It is resistant to the action of the common acids, except nitric, in which, like cobalt, it dissolves readily. Its standard oxidation potentials are similar to those of cobalt.

$$Ni = Ni^{++} + \quad 2e^-; E = 0.25 \text{ v.}$$

$$Ni + 2OH^- = Ni(OH)_2 + 2e^-; E = 0.72 \text{ v.}$$

The reactions of metallic nickel, like those of cobalt, are similar to those of iron, although, as is indicated by the values of the respective electrode potentials, both nickel and cobalt are less reactive than iron.

Although metallic nickel is of course not used on the same scale as iron, it is nevertheless an important industrial metal. The annual world production of nickel metal is well over 100,000 tons. Its most important use is in the manufacture of special alloy steels (p. 754) and cast irons. Monel metal and other nickel–copper alloys are produced in large quantities, and a number of ternary alloys containing nickel and copper are also of importance. Among these the German silvers, containing copper with 5 to 45% of zinc and 5 to 30% of nickel, are of especial interest. They are used as a base metal on which silver is plated for tableware, and also in the manufacture of various other types of hardware. Because of its hardness, resistance to corrosion, and ability to take a high polish, nickel is widely used for the electroplating of more active metals, particularly iron and steel. Other applications of nickel include: (1) heat-resistant alloys such as nichrome and chromel, which contain nickel, chromium, and sometimes iron, and are used in the manufacture of electrical heating devices; (2) low thermal expansion alloys of the type of Invar, which are iron–nickel alloys containing 30 to 40% of nickel; (3) alloys of special magnetic properties such as the Alnico mentioned in the discussion of cobalt. Finely divided nickel is used as a catalyst in many industrial processes, particularly in the hydrogenation of oils (p. 601).

5. Ferrous Compounds. When iron is dissolved in nonoxidizing acids such as hydrochloric or dilute sulfuric, solutions containing the doubly charged ferrous ion are obtained.

$$Fe + 2H^+ = Fe^{++} + H_2$$

Such solutions are likewise formed by the action of metallic iron on solutions containing the triply charged ferric ion.

$$2Fe^{+++} + Fe = 3Fe^{++}$$

When a solution of a pure ferrous salt is treated with an alkali hydroxide, a white, gelatinous precipitate of ferrous hydroxide, $Fe(OH)_2$, is obtained.

$$Fe^{++} + 2OH^- = Fe(OH)_{2(s)}$$

Ferrous hydroxide resembles magnesium and manganese hydroxides in that it dissolves in solutions of such weak acids as ammonium ion.

$$Fe(OH)_2 + 2NH_4^+ = Fe^{++} + 2H_2O + 2NH_3$$

Ferrous hydroxide is a fairly strong base, as is indicated by the fact that ferrous salts are not greatly hydrolyzed. In the presence of air, ferrous hydroxide quickly turns green, and then slowly becomes reddish brown as it is oxidized to hydrous ferric oxide.

$$4Fe(OH)_2 + O_2 = 2Fe_2O_3 + 4H_2O$$

Because of this fact, it is difficult to obtain pure white ferrous hydroxide, and ferrous oxide, FeO, is prepared by the thermal decomposition of ferrous oxalate, FeC_2O_4, rather than by the dehydration of ferrous hydroxide.

$$FeC_2O_4 = FeO + CO + CO_2$$

Solutions containing ferrous ion have a pale green color. In the presence of air, ferrous ion is slowly oxidized to ferric. This oxidation takes place much more readily in alkaline than in acidic solution, as is indicated by the standard potentials for the following half-reactions:

$$Fe^{++} = Fe^{+++} + e^-; E = -0.77 \text{ v.}$$

$$Fe(OH)_2 + OH^- = Fe(OH)_3 + e^-; E = 0.56 \text{ v.}$$
$$(Fe_2O_3 \cdot xH_2O)$$

The most important ferrous compound is the sulfate, which is prepared on an industrial scale by the atmospheric oxidation of moist pyrite, FeS_2.

$$2FeS_2 + 7O_2 + 2H_2O = 2FeSO_4 + 2H_2SO_4$$

Ferrous sulfate crystallizes from aqueous solution as the heptahydrate, $FeSO_4 \cdot 7H_2O$, commonly known as copperas, or, because of its pale green color, as green vitriol. It may be recalled that a commercial name for sulfuric acid is oil of vitriol (p. 459); hence, the hydrated sulfates of a number of bivalent metals are known as vitriols. Ferrous sulfate is used as a disinfectant, a weed killer, a substitute for aluminum sulfate in water purification, and in the preparation of the "blue-black" inks. Such inks contain a blue dye and the colorless ferrous salt of an organic compound called gallotannic acid. On standing a few minutes in air, this salt is oxidized to the black ferric compound; thus the ink "writes blue and dries black." Because of the ease with which ferrous compounds are oxidized, particularly in alkaline solution, ferrous sulfate is widely used in chemical industry and in the laboratory as a reducing agent.

When equimolar proportions of ferrous sulfate and ammonium sulfate are brought together in aqueous solution, and the solution is evaporated until crystallization takes place, a double salt of the formula $(NH_4)_2SO_4 \cdot FeSO_4 \cdot 6H_2O$, known as Mohr's salt, is obtained. Many of the sulfates of bivalent metals form double salts of this type, not only with ammonium sulfate but also with potassium, rubidium, or cesium sulfate. The composition of these double sulfates may be represented by the general formula $M_2^{I}SO_4 \cdot M^{II}SO_4 \cdot 6H_2O$; all the members of this series are isomorphous. In the solid state, Mohr's salt is not oxidized by the air, and it is useful, therefore, as a dependable source of ferrous ion free from ferric. It is commonly used in analytical chemistry, for example, for the preparation of standard ferrous ion solutions for oxidation-reduction titrations.

The ferrous halides are most readily prepared by the action of solutions of the corresponding hydrogen halides upon metallic iron. The chloride crystallizes as the green hydrate $FeCl_2 \cdot 4H_2O$ when its solution is evaporated out of contact with the air. Anhydrous ferrous chloride may be obtained as white scales by the passage of hydrogen chloride gas over hot iron; the scales are formed in the cold portions of the tube.

$$Fe + 2HCl = FeCl_2 + H_2$$

Ferrous sulfide, FeS, is obtained either by direct union of iron and sulfur or by the action of hydrogen sulfide on neutral or basic solutions of ferrous ion.

$$Fe^{++} + S^{--} = FeS_{(s)}$$

The black precipitate of FeS obtained in this reaction is readily soluble in even weakly acidic solutions.

A disulfide, FeS_2, is formed by the combination of ferrous sulfide with free sulfur. This compound occurs in nature as the brass-colored mineral known as pyrite. This mineral is the "fool's gold" which has duped many prospectors, including the fortune hunters among the early colonists of Virginia.

6. Ferric Compounds. The iron atom has only two electrons in its outer ($4s$) shell. It may, however, lose or share in addition an electron from the incomplete $3d$ subshell, thereby attaining an oxidation state of $+3$. Solutions of ferric salts contain the hydrated ferric ion, which may be represented by the formula $Fe(H_2O)_6^{+++}$. Because of the small size and high charge on the ferric ion, there is a tendency for the hydrated ion to release protons (p. 322).

$$Fe(H_2O)_6^{+++} + H_2O \rightleftharpoons Fe(H_2O)_5(OH)^{++} + H_3O^+$$

A similar phenomenon in solutions of chromic ion has already been discussed (p. 700). This tendency causes aqueous solutions of ferric salts to be acidic. When solutions of ferric salts are boiled, basic ferric salts or even hydrous ferric oxide may be precipitated. The yellow color of solutions of ferric salts is largely due to complex hydrated ions or to colloidal hydrous ferric oxide.

When a solution of a ferric salt is treated with ammonia, or with a soluble hydroxide, a red-brown gelatinous precipitate of hydrous ferric oxide is obtained, which, like the corresponding compounds of aluminum and chromium, readily goes into the colloidal condition. Since its composition varies with the method of preparation, no definite formula may be assigned to it; it is best represented as $Fe_2O_3 \cdot xH_2O$. In accordance with the general principle previously stated (p. 324), hydrous ferric oxide is a weaker base than ferrous hydroxide. It is also much less soluble. It does not dissolve, as does ferrous hydroxide, in solutions of ammonium salts, nor is it amphoteric like the hydrous oxides of trivalent chromium and aluminum. Ordinary rust is a form of hydrous ferric oxide containing some carbonate.

When hydrous ferric oxide is strongly heated, it loses all of its water and yields the anhydrous oxide, Fe_2O_3. This oxide exists in a number of crystalline modifications, the particular form depending upon the method by which it is obtained. As the mineral hematite, ferric oxide occurs in large quantities in the earth's crust. Finely divided ferric oxide obtained by the burning of pyrite is used as a red pigment or as a mild abrasive under the names of Venetian red or rouge. When this oxide is heated above 1000° C., or when iron burns in oxygen or is heated in steam, ferrosoferric oxide, Fe_3O_4, is obtained. This compound occurs naturally as the ore called magnetite, some samples of which are highly paramagnetic and are known as lodestones. This oxide may also be regarded as ferrous ferrite, and its formula accordingly may be written $Fe(FeO_2)_2$; or, as a compound of ferrous and ferric oxides, its formula may be written $FeO \cdot Fe_2O_3$.

The most important salt of ferric iron is ferric chloride. This compound, however, is a true salt only when hydrated, for the physical properties of the anhydrous form indicate that it is covalent. Anhydrous ferric halides are obtained by the passage of a current of the corresponding halogen gas over heated iron. Under these conditions, ferric chloride, for example, crystallizes in black crystals in the cold parts of the tube. The density of the vapor formed when these crystals are volatilized ($280°$ C.) indicates that the formula of the compound is Fe_2Cl_6. Anhydrous ferric chloride dissolves readily in water to yield a yellow solution of the hydrated compound. Several solid hydrates are obtainable, the most familiar being $FeCl_3 \cdot 6H_2O$. Ferric chloride solution finds numerous practical applications; for example, as a coagulant to stop bleeding, as a mordant (p. 806) in the dye industry, and, in the form of a tincture (dilute solution in alcohol), in the treatment of anemia.

Ferric sulfate, $Fe_2(SO_4)_3 \cdot 9H_2O$, is obtained by the oxidation of ferrous sulfate. On evaporation of solutions containing equimolar proportions of ferric sulfate and an alkali or ammonium sulfate, a series of violet-colored ferric alums (p. 806) are obtained, e.g., $(NH_4)_2SO_4 \cdot Fe_2(SO_4)_3 \cdot 24H_2O$. Ferric nitrate, also, may be obtained in violet-colored crystals, having the formula $Fe(NO_3)_3 \cdot 9H_2O$. It appears, therefore, that the true color of hydrated ferric ion is pale violet.

7. Complex Compounds of Iron. As would be expected of such a typically transitional element, iron in both the $+2$ and $+3$ oxidation states forms many complex compounds. Of these, the complex cyanides, because of their high stability, are particularly important.

When solutions containing ferrous ion are treated with an excess of cyanide ion, the pale yellow complex ferrocyanide ion is obtained. This ion is so stable that solutions of ferrocyanides have none of the properties either of ferrous or of cyanide ion.

$$Fe^{++} + 6CN^- = Fe(CN)_6^{----}$$

The most familiar ferrocyanides are the readily soluble sodium and potassium salts, $Na_4Fe(CN)_6 \cdot 10H_2O$ and $K_4Fe(CN)_6 \cdot 3H_2O$, the latter being known as "yellow prussiate of potash." These compounds are commonly manufactured from the hydrogen cyanide obtained as a by-product in the destructive distillation of coal. Likewise, when solutions containing ferric ion are treated with an excess of cyanide ion, the very stable red ferricyanide complex is obtained.

$$Fe^{+++} + 6CN^- = Fe(CN)_6^{---}$$

The most important ferricyanide is the potassium salt, $K_3Fe(CN)_6$, known as "red prussiate of potash." It is obtained industrially by the oxidation of the ferrocyanide with chlorine.

$$2K_4Fe(CN)_6 + Cl_2 = 2K_3Fe(CN)_6 + 2KCl$$

These complex cyanide ions form precipitates with a number of metal ions and are therefore useful in analytical chemistry. Of particular interest are the substances obtained when solutions containing ferrocyanide or ferricyanide ion are allowed to react with ferric ion or ferrous ion, respectively. When an aqueous solution of potassium, sodium, or other soluble ferrocyanide reacts with an equimolar portion of a soluble ferric salt, a dark blue precipitate is obtained which has incorrectly been said to be soluble because of the ease with which it goes into colloidal suspension. When an excess of ferric ion is added to the ferrocyanide solution, a dark blue precipitate which does not readily go into colloidal suspension is obtained. Both of these precipitates have complex structures and are called Prussian blue; the first precipitate mentioned, however, is designated as "soluble" Prussian blue. Likewise, when a solution of a soluble ferricyanide, such as that of potassium, is treated with a soluble ferrous salt, a dark blue precipitate known as Turnbull's blue is obtained. The composition of this precipitate varies considerably with the conditions under which the reaction is carried out. The important fact, however, is that ferrous ion reacts with ferricyanide ion to give a dark blue precipitate, whereas ferric ion reacts with ferrocyanide to give a precipitate of practically identical color. On the other hand, pure ferrous ion forms a white precipitate with ferrocyanide ion, and ferric ion reacts with ferricyanide ion to yield a brown solution containing a complex of unknown composition. These reactions provide a convenient method for testing for ferrous and ferric ions, and for distinguishing between them.

Potassium ferricyanide is used in the making of blueprints. A sheet of paper is coated with a solution of ferric ammonium citrate and potassium ferricyanide, and is allowed to dry in the absence of light. The paper is covered with tracing cloth on which the drawing to be reproduced has been made, and is exposed either to sunlight or to light from an electric arc. This

brings about the reduction of the ferric ammonium citrate to the corresponding ferrous compound, and the consequent precipitation of Turnbull's blue,
except where the lines of the drawing have protected the paper from the
light. The drawing, therefore, after the excess of reagents has been washed
away, appears in white on a blue background.

The addition of a solution containing thiocyanate ion, SCN^-, to a solution containing ferric ion produces a deep red color. More than one colored
complex ion is formed, but in each of these complexes, thiocyanate ions are
coordinated to the ferric ion. This reaction constitutes a very sensitive test
for ferric ion.

8. Compounds of Cobalt. Cobalt, like iron, forms two important series of
compounds: (1) the cobaltous compounds, in which cobalt exists in the
$+2$ oxidation state, and (2) the cobaltic compounds, in which cobalt is in
the $+3$ oxidation state. Unlike the case of iron, however, it is very difficult
to oxidize cobaltous ion to cobaltic in neutral or acidic solution. This is indicated by the standard potential for the following half-reaction:

$$Co^{++} = Co^{+++} + e^-; E = -1.82 \text{ v.}$$

Hence, only a few simple cobaltic salts are known; these include the fluoride,
CoF_3, which is obtained by heating cobalt in a current of fluorine, and the
blue sulfate, $Co_2(SO_4)_3 \cdot 18H_2O$, which is obtained by the electrolytic oxidation of cobaltous sulfate solutions, and which forms a series of blue alums
(p. 806).

The great majority of the simple cobalt salts, therefore, belong to the
-ous series. Among the most familiar of the soluble cobaltous salts are the
halides, such as $CoCl_2 \cdot 6H_2O$, the sulfate, and the nitrate; each of the last
two forms a series of hydrates. These hydrated cobaltous salts are red, and
dissolve in water to give pink solutions; the anhydrous form of many of these
salts, however, is blue. The behavior of the hydrated chloride is particularly
interesting. When a concentrated solution (red) of cobaltous chloride is
heated, the color of the solution changes to a dark purple; on cooling, the
red color is regained. Likewise, if the chloride ion concentration of the solution is increased, as by the addition of concentrated hydrochloric acid, the
color of the solution changes to a deep blue. In fact, the color of any solution
of cobaltous ion may be changed to blue by greatly increasing the chloride
ion concentration. While these color changes have not been completely
explained, it is believed that they are due to equilibria of the following type:

$$\underset{\text{pink}}{Co(H_2O)_6^{++}} + 4Cl^- \rightleftharpoons \underset{\text{blue}}{CoCl_4^{--}} + 6H_2O$$

This equilibrium is shifted toward the right either by increased temperature or by increased concentration of chloride ion.

Black cobaltous sulfide is precipitated by sulfide ion in alkaline solution. Although this compound does not come down in acid solution, yet, once it has been precipitated, it dissolves only extremely slowly in dilute hydro-chloric acid.

Treatment of solutions containing cobaltous ion with alkalis yields a gelatinous precipitate of cobaltous hydroxide, $Co(OH)_2$. This precipitate exists in both pink and blue forms, depending upon the conditions of the reaction. Ammonia solutions also cause the precipitation of cobaltous hydroxide, but the precipitate dissolves in an excess of either ammonia or ammonium salts.

On standing in air, cobaltous hydroxide darkens because of oxidation to the hydrous cobaltic oxide, $Co_2O_3 \cdot xH_2O$. As in the case of bivalent iron, oxidation of $+2$ cobalt to the $+3$ oxidation state takes place much more readily in alkaline than in neutral or acidic solutions. This difference is indicated by a comparison of the standard potential for the following half-reaction with that given above for neutral or acidic solutions.

$$Co(OH)_2 + OH^- = \underset{(Co_2O_3 \cdot xH_2O)}{Co(OH)_3} + e^-; E = -0.17 \text{ v.}$$

When cobaltous hydroxide is heated in the absence of air, green cobaltous oxide, CoO, is obtained. When this oxide is heated in air, cobalto-cobaltic oxide, Co_3O_4, is formed. Cobaltic oxide, Co_2O_3, is obtained when cobaltous nitrate is heated, and a still higher oxide, CoO_2, is produced by the treatment of cobaltous hydroxide with powerful oxidizing agents such as hypochlorite ion in alkaline solution.

In addition to the simple salts, oxides, and hydroxides discussed in the preceding paragraphs, cobalt forms a large number of complex compounds. In contrast to the simple salts, complex cobaltic compounds are much more stable than cobaltous complexes. This is illustrated by the standard potentials for the two half-reactions

$$Co^{++} = Co^{+++} + e^-; E = -1.82 \text{ v.}$$

$$Co(CN)_6{}^{----} = Co(CN)_6{}^{---} + e^-; E = 0.8 \text{ v.}$$

Therefore, the great majority of the more stable cobalt complexes contain cobalt in the $+3$ oxidation state. Some of the more familiar cobaltic complexes are $[Co(NH_3)_6]^{+++}$, $[Co(NH_3)_5Cl]^{++}$, $[Co(NH_3)_4Br_2]^+$, $Co(NH_3)_3(NO_2)_3$, and $[Co(CN)_6]^{---}$. The formation of a yellow precipitate of potassium hexanitritocobaltiate, $K_3[Co(NO_2)_6]$, when a solution containing cobaltous ion is made weakly acidic with acetic acid and treated with potassium nitrite, is an important analytical test for cobaltous ion, and is useful in the separation of cobalt from nickel.

$$Co^{++} + 3K^+ + 7NO_2^- + 2H^+ = K_3[Co(NO_2)_6]_{(s)} + NO + H_2O$$

9. Compounds of Nickel. With the exception of one oxide of doubtful composition, all the familiar compounds of nickel contain that element in the +2 oxidation state. The hydrated nickel ion is bright green in color, and the hydrates of most of the simple nickel salts are also green. The familiar soluble nickel salts include the sulfate, $NiSO_4 \cdot 7H_2O$, the nitrate, $Ni(NO_3)_2 \cdot 6H_2O$, and the chloride, $NiCl_2 \cdot 6H_2O$. Nickel sulfate forms a double salt, $(NH_4)_2SO_4 \cdot NiSO_4 \cdot 6H_2O$, analogous to Mohr's salt; nickel chloride likewise forms a double salt with ammonium chloride, $NH_4Cl \cdot NiCl_2 \cdot 6H_2O$.

When solutions containing nickel ion are treated with alkali hydroxides, a light green precipitate of nickel hydroxide, $Ni(OH)_2$, is obtained. This hydroxide is soluble in an excess of ammonia solution, giving the violet colored complex, $Ni(NH_3)_6^{++}$.

$$Ni(OH)_2 + 6NH_3 = Ni(NH_3)_6^{++} + 2OH^-$$

When the hydroxide is heated, dark green nickelous oxide, NiO, is obtained.

Nickel sulfide, NiS, is obtained as a black precipitate when sulfide ion is added to nickel ion in neutral or alkaline solution. Like cobalt sulfide, nickel sulfide, though not precipitated in the presence of dilute acids, dissolves only very slowly in such solutions.

Like cobalt and iron, nickel forms many complex ions. In most of these complexes, however, nickel has a coordination number of 4 rather than 6; thus the formula of the nickel cyanide complex is $Ni(CN)_4^{--}$. When ammoniacal or weakly acidic solutions of nickel ion are treated with dimethylglyoxime, CH_3—C=NOH, a rose-red crystalline precipitate of the

$$CH_3-\overset{|}{C}=NOH$$

composition $Ni(C_4H_7N_2O_2)_2$ is obtained. The formation of this easily recognized precipitate constitutes a convenient test for nickel ion, and provides an excellent means for distinguishing and separating nickel ion from cobalt ion, which gives only a red-brown, soluble complex with dimethylglyoxime.

THE PLATINUM METALS

10. History and General Characteristics. The six remaining members of Group 8 have many properties in common and are known collectively as the platinum family. While platinum, in the form of its alloys with gold and silver, was probably known as early as 700 B.C., it was introduced into

Modern Europe centuries later by the Spaniards, who found it in Peru and Mexico. It was not held in very high regard at first; in fact the Spanish government tried to prevent its exportation to Europe to avoid its being used as an adulterant for gold. A fairly complete description of the properties of platinum was published in 1750. The other platinum metals were unknown until the discovery of osmium, iridium, rhodium, and palladium in the years 1802 to 1804. Ruthenium was not definitely established as a new element until 1845. Platinum was named from the Spanish word *platina*, meaning "little silver," and osmium from the Greek word *osme*, meaning "odor," because of the sharp odor of osmium tetroxide. Iridium was so named because of the variety of colors observed during its chemical transformations; rhodium gets its name from *rhodon*, the Greek word for "rose," referring to the rose-red color of rhodium salts. Palladium was named for Pallas, a new planetoid discovered in the same year as the element, and ruthenium for Ruthenia, an old name for Russia.

The relationship of the two triads of elements in the platinum family to the second and third transition series, respectively, is analogous to that of iron, cobalt, and nickel to the first transition series. The electron configurations and some of the important physical properties of these elements are listed in Table 39.2.

Table 39.2

Element	1	2	3	4	5	6	Density	M.P.	B.P.
	s	s p	s p d	s p d f	s p d	s	(g./cc.)	(°C.)	(°C.)
Ru	2	2, 6	2, 6, 10	2, 6, 7	1		12.2	2400	4900
Rh	2	2, 6	2, 6, 10	2, 6, 8	1		12.44	1966	4500
Pd	2	2, 6	2, 6, 10	2, 6, 10			12.02	1554	3980
Os	2	2, 6	2, 6, 10	2, 6, 10, 14	2, 6, 6	2	22.5	2700	5500
Ir	2	2, 6	2, 6, 10	2, 6, 10, 14	2, 6, 9		22.5	2454	5300
Pt	2	2, 6	2, 6, 10	2, 6, 10, 14	2, 6, 9	1	21.45	1773	4530

As would be expected from the transitional nature of these electron configurations, the platinum metals form series of compounds in several different oxidation states, including a large number of complex compounds, many of which are brightly colored. All of the free elements are notable for their low chemical activity.

11. Occurrence. Because of their low reactivity, the platinum metals occur chiefly in the free state, almost always associated with each other and mixed with ores of other metals such as gold, silver, copper, nickel, and iron. The metals are usually found in the form of small grains (rarely in nuggets) in alluvial deposits of heavy sands. Platinum is the most abundant, usually making up 60 to 80% of the crude native metal ores. Various naturally occurring alloys such as osmiridium (Os–Ir) and platiniridium (Pt–Ir), as well as natural alloys of gold with palladium and rhodium, are known. Sperrylite, an arsenide of the formula $PtAs_2$, is one of the few well-defined mineral compounds of the platinum metals. Although deposits of the platinum metals are fairly widely distributed, platinum is estimated to constitute only $10^{-9}\%$ of the igneous rocks in the earth's crust. Estimated percentages of other platinum metals are Ir, 10^{-10}; Os, 10^{-10}; Rh, 10^{-10}; and Ru, 10^{-11}. The most important deposits of the platinum metals occur in the Ural Mountain region in Russia, the Sudbury district in Ontario, Transvaal, Colombia, California, Oregon, and Alaska. Because of the recovery of platinum from the copper and nickel ores of the Sudbury district, Canada has been the chief producer in recent years. The methods of separation of the metals of the platinum family from each other and from other metals are too complex to fall within the scope of this text.

12. Properties and Uses of Platinum. Platinum is a soft white metal which is very malleable and ductile. It has a relatively low electrical conductivity and the lowest coefficient of expansion of all the metals. Like the other members of the family, platinum is very unreactive and retains its silvery color even when heated in air. Pure platinum is unaffected by any single acid, but dissolves readily in aqua regia. It also reacts readily with chlorine, and, at high temperatures, with fused caustic alkalies, nitrates, and peroxides. Since platinum readily forms alloys with many of the less active metals, easily reducible metallic oxides should not be heated in platinum ware.

Because of its pleasing appearance and high degree of chemical inertness, platinum is highly prized for use in the manufacture of jewelry. More than half of the annual production of about half a million ounces is used for this purpose. The next most important application is in chemical and dental industries. Considerable quantities of the metal are made into crucibles and evaporating dishes for use in the chemical laboratory (Figure 39.1) and it is almost indispensable for the manufacture of many other types of scientific instruments. Either in the form of wire gauze or in a finely divided state, platinum acts as a catalyst for many chemical reactions (see, for example, p. 477). Spongy platinum, a gray, porous mass obtained by the heating of ammonium chloroplatinate, absorbs hydrogen readily and catalyzes the reaction of hydrogen with oxygen. Likewise, platinum black, a fine powder obtained by the reduction of platinic chloride with zinc, alcohol, or sodium formate, is so active a catalyst for the reaction of hydrogen and oxygen that

Fig. 39.1.   Platinum crucible, evaporating dish, and electrodes.

it will cause an explosion if introduced into a mixture of these two gases. For catalytic use platinum is commonly deposited on some fibrous or porous substance such as asbestos or silica gel. A coil of fine platinum wire, when heated to red heat and placed in contact with a mixture of ammonia and air, will continue to glow because of the heat of the reaction between ammonia and oxygen which takes place at the surface of the platinum (p. 477).

13. Compounds of Platinum. Compounds are known in which platinum exhibits the oxidation states $+1$, $+2$, $+3$, $+4$, and $+6$; only the $+2$ and $+4$ states (platinous and platinic, respectively) are of any importance, however. Both these series of compounds are characterized by ease of thermal decomposition and low degree of dissociation or low solubility; both include many complexes.

When platinum is dissolved in aqua regia the solution contains chloroplatinate ion.

$$3Pt + 16H^+ + 18Cl^- + 4NO_3^- = 3PtCl_6^{--} + 4NO + 8H_2O$$

On evaporation, brownish yellow crystals of chloroplatinic acid, having the formula $H_2PtCl_6 \cdot 6H_2O$, are obtained. This is a strong acid and reacts readily with hydroxides and carbonates to form chloroplatinates, among which the ammonium and potassium salts, $(NH_4)_2PtCl_6$ and K_2PtCl_6, are well known; in fact, the chloroplatinates are the most important platinum compounds. The low solubilities of the chloroplatinates of cesium, rubidium, ammonium, and potassium are sometimes made use of in the analytical precipitation of these cations. A multitude of complex ions of $+4$ platinum are known; $[Pt(NH_3)_6]^{4+}$, $[Pt(NH_3)_5Cl]^{+++}$, $[Pt(NO_2)_4Cl_2]^{--}$, $[Pt(OH)_6]^{--}$ and $[Pt(SCN)_6]^{--}$ are typical examples. The chloride $PtCl_4$ and the oxide PtO_2 are also well known.

Platinous chloride, $PtCl_2$, dissolves readily in aqueous hydrochloric acid to give solutions of chloroplatinous acid, H_2PtCl_4; this acid is more readily obtained, however, by reduction of chloroplatinic acid with sulfur dioxide. A series of chloroplatinites, such as the potassium salt, K_2PtCl_4, have been prepared.

Platinous complex ions include such ions as $[PtBr_4]^{--}$, $[Pt(NO_2)_4]^{--}$, $[Pt(NH_3)Cl_3]^-$, and $[Pt(CN)_4]^{--}$, in which the coordination number of platinum is 4 (p. 633).

14. Ruthenium. Ruthenium is a grayish white metal, harder and more brittle than platinum. No commercial applications for the metal have been developed. Ruthenium forms compounds in which it exhibits the oxidation states $+2$, $+3$, $+4$, $+6$, $+7$, and $+8$, the last being represented by the volatile tetroxide, RuO_4. It also forms many complex compounds.

15. Rhodium. Rhodium is a ductile, malleable metal. Like the other members of the family, the element can assume a number of different oxidation states, $+1$, $+2$, $+3$, $+4$, and $+6$; the most important of these, however, are $+3$ and $+4$. Rhodium also forms a number of complex ions. Whereas rhodium metal, when heated, is readily attacked by chlorine, it is highly resistant to the action of acids and of aqua regia. Its great resistance to corrosion and its high brilliance account for its use in the electroplating of jewelry, tableware, and reflectors for flood lights. A considerable amount of rhodium is used in the manufacture of platinum alloy crucibles, dishes, and other laboratory ware, since the addition of a small percentage of rhodium greatly reduces the volatility and increases the hardness of platinum. Platinum–rhodium alloys are used also in electric furnace windings and in high-temperature thermocouples.

16. Palladium. Palladium is very similar to platinum in appearance, and like platinum forms two important series of compounds, palladous, in which the metal is in the $+2$ oxidation state, and palladic, in which it assumes the $+4$ oxidation state. These palladium salts are very similar in properties to the corresponding platinum compounds. Palladium also forms a large number of complex compounds. Unlike platinum, however, palladium dissolves in concentrated acids, particularly nitric. The greater reactivity of palladium is shown also by the readiness with which it reacts with the halogens, sulfur, oxygen, and arsenic at moderately high temperatures.

Palladium has the lowest melting point and the highest volatility of any of the platinum metals.

An outstanding characteristic of palladium metal is its ability to take up hydrogen gas. Massive palladium can absorb 800–900 times its own volume of hydrogen, and in the colloidal condition it adsorbs 3000 times its own volume. The hydrogen thus taken up is in an active state; e.g., palladium charged with hydrogen brings about the precipitation of metallic copper from a solution of cupric ion. Because of its ability to adsorb and activate hydrogen and certain other gases, such as carbon monoxide and acetylene, palladium is used as a catalyst in a number of industrial catalytic processes, particularly those involving hydrogenation.

Palladium is used, in the form of its alloys with platinum and gold, in jewelry, dentistry, and laboratory ware. The palladium–gold alloys are particularly useful as substitutes for platinum for these purposes.

17. Osmium. Osmium is a brittle metal which is hard enough to scratch glass; it has the greatest density (22.5 g. per cc.) of any known substance. While there is some uncertainty as to its melting and boiling points, they appear to be considerably higher than those of the other platinum metals. Osmium is the only one of the platinum metals which unites readily with oxygen, combination in the case of the finely divided metal taking place at room temperature. The product formed in this reaction, as well as in the reaction of the metal with steam, is the tetroxide, OsO_4. Although it has no acid properties, this compound has been called osmic acid because of its corrosive properties, which are due, actually, to its oxidizing power. Osmic acid is reduced by organic tissue with the deposition of metallic osmium, and is therefore used as a stain in the preparation of microscopic sections for biological work. This compound melts only a little above room temperature, and is readily volatilized to a poisonous, vile-smelling vapor, which gives the element its name (p. 732). When hot osmium metal reacts with fluorine, the octafluoride, a compound of the formula OsF_8, is obtained. In addition to these compounds in which it is in the $+8$ oxidation state, osmium also forms compounds in which it exhibits the oxidation states $+2$, $+3$, $+4$, and $+6$. In general, these are similar to the corresponding compounds of ruthenium.

Osmium is not used commercially in the pure state, but finds some application, in the form of its alloys, in fountain-pen points and bearings in fine instruments.

18. Iridium. Iridium is a hard, brittle metal which resists the action of aqua regia but is attacked by chlorine at high temperature. The most important oxidation states of iridium, as of rhodium, are $+3$ and $+4$. Iridium forms a number of complex compounds. The metal is not used commercially in the pure state but has fairly wide application in the form of its platinum alloys. Commercial specimens of platinum almost invariably contain iridium, usually to the extent of about 2%. Special alloys containing higher percentages of iridium find such applications as fountain-pen points, surgical instruments, bearings in fine instruments, electrical equipment, chemical utensils, and hypodermic needles. The international standard kilogram and standard meter are made of a platinum–iridium alloy containing 10.1% of iridium; this alloy has a very low coefficient of thermal expansion and, of course, has absolutely no tendency to corrode under the conditions in which the standards are kept. Because of its scarcity and usefulness, iridium is the most expensive of the platinum metals.

STUDY QUESTIONS AND PROBLEMS

1. Discuss the general characteristics of the Group 8 elements in terms of their atomic structures. Can you justify the inclusion of three columns in the periodic system in this single group?

2. Make a brief list of the principal ores of iron, cobalt, and nickel. Are the most abundant iron minerals used as ores? Why, or why not?

3. What factors account for the outstanding industrial importance of iron?

4. Discuss briefly the allotropic forms of iron, and their properties. Are these properties the ones which are familiarly associated with the word "iron"?

5. Outline briefly the metallurgy and principal industrial applications of cobalt and nickel.

6. Give balanced chemical equations for the preparation of ferrous chloride (anhydrous), ferrous oxide, ferric hydroxide, ferrous sulfate (hydrated), ferrosoferric oxide, ammonium ferric alum, and potassium ferricyanide.

7. State the changes which are observed when:

(a) KSCN solution is added to a solution containing Fe^{+++} ion.

(b) A very concentrated cobalt chloride solution is heated.

(c) Cobalt chloride solution is treated with concentrated HCl solution.

(d) A solution of ferrous sulfate is added to $K_3Fe(CN)_6$ solution.

(e) An excess of ammonia is added to a solution of nickel nitrate.

(f) The solution obtained in (e) is treated with dimethylglyoxime.

8. From reference works in your library find the formulas, methods of preparation, and geometrical configurations of five cobalt complexes and five nickel complexes.

9. What are the chief modes of occurrence of the platinum metals?

10. Make a table of the principal commercial applications of ruthenium, rhodium, palladium, osmium, iridium, and platinum. Why should the last three of these be less reactive than the first three (see p. 760)?

CHAPTER

40

The Iron and Steel Industry

1. Importance of Iron and Steel. Although our attention has been drawn in recent years to the phenomenal developments in the production and utilization of such light metals as magnesium and aluminum, and although the plastics are popularly considered to be a magic panacea for industrial problems, it is nevertheless true that iron and steel still are, and are likely to remain for many years, our most important engineering materials. The annual production of light metals, it is true, may now be counted in millions of pounds, but the world's production of iron and steel annually runs to well over a hundred million tons.

2. Production of Pig Iron in the Blast Furnace. The raw materials employed in the production of crude iron are iron ore (in this country generally hematite, Fe_2O_3), carbon in the form of coke, calcium carbonate in the form of limestone, air, and water. (The water is used only for cooling the hotter parts of the furnace.) It must be remembered, however, that the ore is not pure ferric oxide, the limestone is not pure calcium carbonate, nor is the coke pure carbon. The nature and amount of the impurities present have much to do with determining the method of operation of the furnace and the quality of the iron obtained.

The reduction of the ore is carried out in the blast furnace. A cross-sectional diagram of a typical blast furnace is given in Figure 40.1. Figure 40.2a shows a photograph of several such furnaces with their accompanying stoves; the furnaces are constructed of steel lined with firebrick, and frequently exceed 100 ft. in height and 30 ft. in diameter (see Figure 40.2b).

Once a blast furnace has been put into operation it is run continuously. At regular intervals, alternate charges of ore, limestone, and coke are introduced at the top of the furnace through the charging bell. Near the bottom of the furnace, a blast of preheated air is introduced through ten or more water-cooled nozzles called "tuyères"; this air has been preheated to 500°–600° C. by contact with brick checker-work in one of the hot blast stoves, of which there are usually four to a furnace. While one is employed in heating the blast, and is thus being cooled, the other three are being heated by combustion of the exhaust gases from the furnace; there is a systematic alternation of the stoves so as to maintain the temperature of the blast at a constant level.

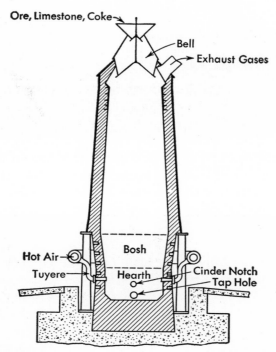

Fig. 40.1. Cross-sectional diagram of a typical blast furnace.

When the oxygen in the air comes in contact with the coke in the furnace, it reacts rapidly with the formation of carbon dioxide.

$$C + O_2 = CO_2$$

The heat liberated in this reaction keeps the temperature at the tuyère level at about 1500° C. At this high temperature the carbon dioxide is rapidly changed to carbon monoxide on contact with excess coke.

$$CO_2 + C = 2CO$$

As the charge of limestone, ore, and coke descends through the column of the furnace, the rising carbon monoxide reduces the iron oxide to iron; this

Fig. 40.2a. Photograph of several blast furnaces with stoves. (*Courtesy of Youngstown Sheet and Tube Company.*)

Fig. 40.2b. Photograph of the lower section of a blast furnace. (*Courtesy of Youngstown Sheet and Tube Company.*)

change apparently proceeds in steps, the most important reactions being those represented by the following equations:

$$3Fe_2O_3 + CO = 2Fe_3O_4 + CO_2$$

$$Fe_3O_4 + CO = 3FeO + CO_2$$

$$FeO + CO = Fe + CO_2$$

The carbon dioxide so formed is continuously reconverted to carbon monoxide by reaction with the hot coke. As the gases rise through the furnace they are cooled by transfer of heat to the descending charge. The gas discharged from the furnace is at a temperature of only 180 to 280° C. and consists mainly of carbon monoxide, carbon dioxide, and nitrogen, with small amounts of water vapor, hydrogen, and methane. Having considerable fuel value, it is used to heat the hot blast stoves and to run the blowing engines.

When the charge has descended as far as the top of the lower half of the furnace, the temperature and carbon dioxide pressure are such that the calcium carbonate in the limestone begins to dissociate according to the equation

$$CaCO_3 = CaO + CO_2$$

In the lower third of the furnace the calcium oxide, acting as a flux, reacts with the impurities in the ore, primarily silica (SiO_2) with some alumina (Al_2O_3), to form a molten slag composed of calcium silicates and aluminates. The following equation is typical:

$$CaO + SiO_2 = CaSiO_3$$

After the iron oxide has been reduced to iron, the metal takes up a considerable amount of carbon, by reaction either with carbon or with carbon monoxide according to the equations

$$3Fe + 2CO = Fe_3C + CO_2$$

$$3Fe + C = Fe_3C$$

This process, which is known as carbonization, lowers the melting point of the iron, and this lowering, together with the high temperature in the lower part of the furnace (the "bosh"), enables the iron to melt. Molten layers of iron and slag collect, therefore, on the hearth of the furnace. The temperature of the bosh is so high that the furnace walls at this level must be water-cooled to prevent melting of the lining. It should be noted that the diameter of the furnace increases from the top almost down to the bosh; this facilitates the settling of the charge. In the bosh, however, the diameter diminishes from top to bottom, for the volume of the charge decreases as the slag and iron begin to liquefy. It is also of interest to note that the hot blast does not penetrate to the center of the furnace, so that a column of unburned coke extends up from the hearth, thus helping to support the charge.

Every four or five hours the iron is tapped from the bottom of the furnace and either is taken directly in the molten state to the steel mill, or is poured into molds on a conveyor, which, after passage through a tank or spray of water, dumps the cold "pigs" into a car for shipment. The product of the blast furnace is known as pig iron. The slag also is drawn off every few hours. It is sometimes used for road building, or in the manufacture of Portland cement (p. 671).

A modern blast furnace will produce as much as 1000 tons of pig iron each day. In producing this amount of crude metal, the furnace consumes about 1000 tons of coke, 2000 tons of ore, and 500 tons of limestone. In addition there are required between 5 and 7 million gallons of water for cooling the furnace walls, and more than 100 million cubic feet of air for the hot blast.

More than half of the world's pig iron is produced in the United States. The Lake Superior region of northern Michigan and Minnesota furnishes 80% of the iron ore mined in this country. This ore is shipped by lake steamer at very low cost to cities in northern Ohio, Indiana, Illinois, and southern Michigan—which are relatively close to the coal fields and limestone beds of the East—and is there reduced. These states provide half of the crude iron produced in the United States, and Pennsylvania another 25%. Northern Alabama has important supplies of coal and limestone, as well as ore, and is, therefore, an important iron-producing area, with its center at Birmingham.

3. Composition and Properties of Pig Iron. The crude iron obtained from the blast furnace contains a number of impurities, the major one being the carbon which dissolves in the iron while it is in contact with unburned coke; the carbon content of pig iron usually runs between 3.5 and 4.5%. Phosphates are commonly present in the ore, limestone, and coke, and since these compounds are almost as readily reduced as the iron oxide, practically all of the phosphorus in the charge appears in the resulting pig iron. The raw materials usually contain sulfates also, which are easily reduced to sulfides under the conditions of blast furnace operation. Both sulfur and phosphorus are undesirable in iron and steel products; phosphorus causes "cold-shortness," or brittleness at room temperature, and sulfur causes "red-shortness," or brittleness at high temperatures. Pig iron also contains silicon and manganese, resulting from the reduction of their respective oxides. The blast furnace thus produces alloys containing only 92 to 96% of iron; these alloys are relatively weak and brittle, corrode rapidly in the presence of air and moisture, and, in general, are unsuitable for most industrial purposes until subjected to further treatment. The products obtained from pig iron may be divided into three major classifications: cast irons, wrought irons, and steels.

4. Iron—Carbon Alloys. One of the most important single characteristics of an iron product is its carbon content. Steels, cast irons, and wrought irons are alloys of iron and carbon, along with various other elements, and they differ in composition from each other chiefly in the percentage of carbon they contain. The properties of an iron—carbon alloy change greatly with relatively small changes in carbon content. In order for this effect to be understood it must be realized that, in most of these alloys, the carbon is present in the form of the hard, brittle compound cementite, Fe_3C. Since the atomic weight of carbon (12.01) is so very low compared to three atomic weights of iron (3×55.85), a small change in the carbon content of the alloy brings about a relatively large change in the percentage of cementite; in fact, pure cementite itself contains only 6.7% of carbon.

Figures 40.3 to 40.6 show microphotographs of a number of alloys of iron and carbon. These pictures clearly demonstrate that these alloys are not homogeneous, but contain more than one kind of crystals. The composition, size, distribution, and relative amounts of the various types of crystals determine the physical properties of the alloy. The crystalline structure is determined, in turn, by the composition of the alloy and the treatment to which it has been subjected.

Cementite is soluble in molten iron, and, if the percentage of carbon does not exceed 1.7, it remains dissolved in the iron upon solidification, thus yielding crystals of a single type, viz., a solid solution (called austenite) of cementite in γ-iron. If the solid alloy is allowed to cool very slowly after solidification, the γ-iron changes to α-iron in the range of about 700 to 1100° C., the transition point depending on the percentage of carbon present. Though cementite is soluble in solid γ-iron, it is practically insoluble in α-iron; hence, as the change to α-iron proceeds, cementite separates out of the solid solution, giving an alloy composed of a mixture of the two types of crystals, α-iron and cementite. Such a transition in the solid state, however, can take place only at relatively high temperatures, for at low temperatures the mobility of the atoms in the crystals is so slight as to make the change immeasurably slow. Hence, if this alloy is quenched, i.e., cooled very rapidly, the temperature soon drops to such a low level that the transition from austenite to α-iron and cementite cannot take place. Most of the γ-iron does, indeed, change to

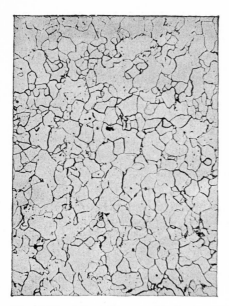

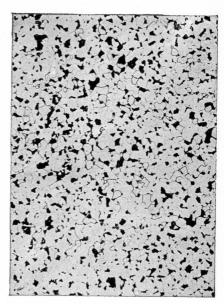

Fig. 40.3. Microphotograph of almost pure iron ($\times$ 66). (*Courtesy of Battelle Memorial Institute.*)

Fig. 40.4. Microphotograph of a low-carbon steel ($\times$ 66). (*Courtesy of Battelle Memorial Institute.*)

Fig. 40.5. Microphotograph of a medium-carbon (0.83%) steel ($\times$ 800). (*Courtesy of Battelle Memorial Institute.*)

Fig. 40.6. Microphotograph of a high-carbon steel ($\times$ 66). (*Courtesy of Battelle Memorial Institute.*)

α-iron, but the cementite does not have time to crystallize. The product, therefore, is a solid solution of cementite in α-iron; since the solubility of cementite in this form of iron is very low, the solution is supersaturated. Crystals of this supersaturated solid solution are extremely hard; hence the quenching treatment yields a very hard alloy. A lesser degree of hardness may be obtained by means of a slower rate of cooling, which permits a greater portion of the cementite to crystallize as such from the solid solution. An iron–carbon alloy that contains less than 1.7% of carbon and which may be hardened by quenching is known as a *steel*.

If an iron–carbon alloy contains more than 1.7% carbon, the proportion of cementite formed is in excess of its solubility even in γ-iron; when such an alloy solidifies completely, two types of crystals, austenite and cementite, are first obtained. On further cooling, the austenite breaks down as in the case of steels. Iron–carbon alloys containing more than 1.7% of carbon are known as *cast irons*; commercial types of cast iron have carbon contents ranging from 2 to 4%.

Wrought irons contain only a very small proportion of carbon (normally 0.02 to 0.04%), but include 1.0 to 2.0% of ferrous silicate slag which has been incorporated during their production. Because of their low carbon content, wrought irons cannot be hardened by quenching.

5. Manufacture, Properties, and Uses of Cast Iron. Of the three common types of iron–carbon alloys, the cast irons differ least from pig iron in composition; in fact, some pig irons are of suitable composition to be cast without further treatment. In general, however, cast iron is made by the process of melting together pig iron and cast iron scrap or steel scrap; the presence of these latter substances reduces the percentage of carbon and other impurities in the melt. Ordinary cast irons contain 2.0 to 4.0% of carbon, 0.5 to 3.0% of silicon, 0.5 to 1.0% of manganese, 0.05 to 0.20% of sulfur, and 0.10 to 1.0% of phosphorus. The high percentage of impurities accounts for the low melting points of cast irons and their consequent usefulness in casting operations.

The silicon content is an important factor in determining the properties of cast irons, for silicon catalyzes the decomposition of cementite into iron and graphite. When cast iron containing only a small percentage of silicon is rapidly cooled, all the carbon remains in the combined form (cementite). Because of the large proportion of cementite crystals, such a cast iron gives a silvery white fracture; a product of this type is known, therefore, as a white cast iron (Figure 40.7). White cast irons are so hard that they cannot be machined with ordinary tools, but must be formed by casting and finished

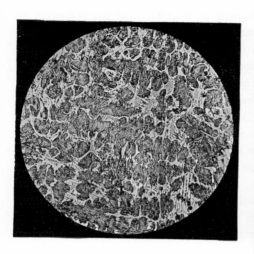

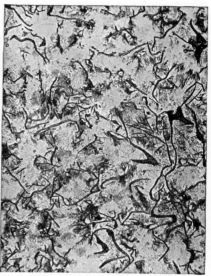

Fig. 40.7. Microphotograph of a white cast iron ($\times$ 66). The light areas are cementite. (*Courtesy of Battelle Memorial Institute.*)

Fig. 40.8. Microphotograph of a gray cast iron ($\times$ 66). The dark areas are graphite. (*Courtesy of Battelle Memorial Institute.*)

by grinding. They are used for plowshares, brake shoes, and other articles for which high resistance to abrasion is required.

When, on the other hand, a cast iron containing a relatively high percentage of silicon is slowly cooled, much of the cementite decomposes into α-iron and graphite. Such a cast iron gives a gray fracture and is known as a gray cast iron (Figure 40.8). An alloy of this type consists of a matrix of α-iron and undecomposed cementite in which graphite is dispersed, and its properties are largely dependent upon the size, shape, and distribution of the graphite particles. Because of the low proportion of silicon in most steels, practically no graphite is obtained when these steels are cooled. Gray cast irons are much inferior to steels in tensile strength, toughness, and ductility, but have the advantages of low cost, ease of machining (the graphite flakes cause the chips to break off and clear the point of the tool), and high compressive strength. Cast irons cannot be forged, rolled, hammered, or pressed at any temperature and must be formed by casting and machining.

Cast irons are sometimes alloyed with nonferrous metals such as nickel, chromium, copper, and molybdenum; the object of such additions is usually to control the distribution and size of the graphite particles, or to improve corrosion resistance.

6. Wrought Iron. Until a relatively few years ago, wrought iron was manufactured by an expensive, small-scale process involving much hand labor. In this procedure the charge of pig iron is melted on the hearth of a small reverberatory furnace, i.e., a furnace in which the flames from the combustion chamber are deflected from the roof onto the charge (Figure 40.9). The

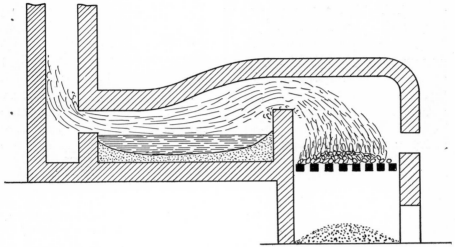

Fig. 40.9. A reverberatory furnace. (Adapted from Babor, *Basic College Chemistry*, The Thomas Y. Crowell Company, by permission of the publishers.)

hearth of the furnace is lined with ferric oxide and, from time to time, hematite, Fe_2O_3, or mill scale, Fe_3O_4, is added to the charge. The carbon in the molten metal reacts with the iron oxide to form carbon monoxide, which passes off.

$$Fe_2O_3 + 3C = 2Fe + 3CO$$

Manganese and silicon impurities are completely oxidized to the oxides MnO and SiO_2, which unite with iron oxide to form a molten iron manganese silicate slag. Phosphorus and part of the sulfur are likewise oxidized, and the products are taken up by the slag. In order that these reactions may take place more rapidly, the charge is stirred, or "puddled," as it is called, by means of long iron rods. As the impurities are removed from the iron, its melting point rises and it begins to solidify, so that, at the end of the refining period, a pasty mass of iron and slag is obtained. This product is worked into balls of about 150 to 200 lb., which are removed from the furnace on the ends of the puddling rods and passed through rollers to squeeze out excess slag.

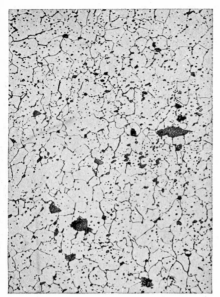

Fig. 40.10. Microscopic structure of wrought iron, transverse section (× 66). (*Courtesy of A. M. Byers Company.*)

Fig. 40.11. Microscopic structure of wrought iron, longitudinal section (×66). (*Courtesy of A. M. Byers Company.*)

In 1925, James Aston developed a large-scale process for the manufacture of wrought iron. In this process, molten iron that has been purified in a Bessemer converter (p. 749) is poured into molten slag, the composition of which approximates that of the slag from the old puddling process, and the temperature of which is below the melting point of iron. The iron solidifies as it strikes the cooler slag, forming a spongy mass which may be treated in the same manner as the "puddle ball" obtained in the older process.

The microscopic structure of wrought iron (Figures 40.10 and 40.11) consists of threads of practically pure iron separated by films of glassy slag. While the slag does not contribute to the strength of the product, it does increase resistance to fracture by alternate bending stresses, since it permits the iron fibers to slip with reference to each other. The film of slag also prevents corrosion, serving in a manner analogous to that of the silicate enamel on certain types of cooking utensils. Wrought iron gives a rough, fibrous fracture, somewhat as if it consisted of strands like those of a wire rope. Because of its fibrous structure, the strength of a bar of wrought iron in a longitudinal direction, i.e., parallel to the fibers, is greater than that in a transverse direction.

Since wrought irons contain so very little cementite, they are soft and cannot be hardened by quenching. Because of their high purity they have high melting points and are, therefore, not suitable for casting operations; they may readily be welded, however.

Although the tonnage of wrought iron produced annually is very small compared with that of low-carbon steels, the ductility, toughness, and weldability of wrought iron account for its continued use in the manufacture of locomotive stay bolts, heavy chains and hooks, rivets, certain types of pipes and boiler tubes, and ornamental iron ware.

7. Manufacture of Steel. Since steels are iron–carbon alloys which contain lower percentages of carbon and other impurities than do the pig irons, the process of converting pig iron to steel is essentially one of purification. The only practicable method of accomplishing such purification is by atmospheric oxidation, in which advantage is taken of the fortunate circumstance that most of the impurities may be oxidized before much oxidation of iron has taken place. Before the middle of the nineteenth century the only purified iron available was wrought iron, and steel was produced by the addition of the required amount of carbon to this substance. This process, however, was both expensive and poorly adapted to large-scale operation.

The first large-scale process for the manufacture of steel was devised by Sir Henry Bessemer in 1856. This process, which bears his name, is still in use, and, for a period of about fifty years (until about 1910), held a dominant position in the steel industry. The Bessemer process consists essentially of the blowing of air under pressure through molten pig iron until the impurities are oxidized. Diagrams of a Bessemer converter are shown in Figure 40.12. These converters are made of steel and are lined with refractory materials, which in this country are usually composed largely of silica, SiO_2. They are set on trunnions so that they can readily be tilted, and accommodate charges of from 10 to 25 tons. Air is introduced through one of the trunnions, whence it is conducted to tuyères in the bottom of the converter. After the charge of molten pig iron has been introduced, the converter is turned to the vertical position, and air at from 10 to 25 lb. pressure is automatically turned on. As the silicon and manganese are oxidized, a shower of sparks and a great deal of brown smoke are discharged.

$$Si + O_2 = SiO_2$$

$$2Mn + O_2 = 2MnO$$

After about 5 minutes this gives way to a clear, brilliant flame, about 30 ft. in height, as the carbon burns out of the charge.

$$2C + O_2 = 2CO$$

When this flame drops, the converter is turned down, and the consequent automatic shutting off of the air prevents excessive oxidation of the iron. At best, however, some ferrous oxide is formed; a part of this dissolves in the iron and another part reacts with the silicon dioxide to form part of the slag.

$$FeO + SiO_2 = FeSiO_3$$

The manganous oxide is also incorporated in the slag.

$$MnO + SiO_2 = MnSiO_3$$

The "blow" usually requires only about 10 to 15 minutes; at the end of this time, the product is practically free of carbon, manganese, and silicon, but does contain a considerable amount of dissolved ferrous oxide. The metal must, therefore, be "deoxidized" and the amount of carbon required to

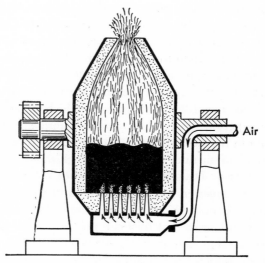

Fig. 40.12. A Bessemer converter. (Adapted from Babor, *Basic College Chemistry,* The Thomas Y. Crowell Company, by permission of the publishers.)

give an iron–carbon alloy of the desired composition must be added. The deoxidizer most frequently used in modern practice is spiegeleisen (p. 709), which, along with the required amount of carbon (charcoal), is added to the molten metal after it has been poured from the converter into a large ladle. The manganese in the spiegeleisen reacts with ferrous oxide according to the equation

$$FeO + Mn = Fe + MnO$$

The manganous oxide passes into the slag. Other deoxidizers such as aluminum or ferrosilicon may be used, and other alloying elements also may be added.

The Bessemer process, as described here, removes none of the phosphorus and little of the sulfur in the pig iron. The sulfur can be removed, for the most part, by proper operation of the blast furnace, but the phosphorus cannot. This process therefore requires raw materials which contain very little phosphorus. The increasing scarcity of ores of Bessemer grade, and the fact that the process is not readily adaptable to the reworking of large quantities of scrap steel, account for the great decrease in the scope of its application during the last few decades. For certain purposes, however, Bessemer steel is still unexcelled, and in recent years the proportion of Bessemer steel to the total produced in this country has remained approximately constant at 8 to 10%.

About 85% of the steel produced in this country is made by what is known as the basic open-hearth process. An open hearth is any shallow hearth over which the gases of combustion sweep; the relatively small puddling furnace used in the manufacture of wrought iron, for instance, is a simple type of open-hearth furnace. The modern open-hearth furnace was developed from the puddling furnace by the application of the regenerative system of firing, and by the use of gaseous fuels. The regenerative system involves the use of exhaust gases from the furnace to preheat incoming fuel gas and air (see next paragraph). The introduction of this device made possible the economical operation of the furnace at a much higher temperature than is used in the manufacture of wrought iron. In the puddling furnace, the mass becomes pasty so that slag can be removed only by mechanical treatment; in the modern open-hearth furnace, the mass remains fluid throughout the treatment, easily separated liquid layers of steel and slag being obtained. The regenerative principle was first applied to the making of steel by Siemens, and the process, after modification by the Martin brothers, came to be known as the Siemens-Martin process.

A diagram of a typical open-hearth furnace is given in Figure 40.13. Two sets of brick checkers on each side of the furnace are necessary for the operation of the furnace according to the regenerative principle. While the fuel gas and air are taken into the furnace through one set of checkers, the exhaust gases pass out through the other set. On the next half-cycle the flow is reversed, and the incoming fuel gas and air are preheated by the hot checkers. The lining of the hearth is composed of dead-burnt magnesia, MgO (p. 665). Since magnesium oxide is itself basic, a basic flux that permits the removal of the phosphorus from the pig iron may be used without injury to the furnace lining. The fuels used in the operation of open-hearth furnaces include principally natural gas, coal gas, coal tar, fuel oil, and producer gas. The furnace is so constructed that the flame is directed down upon the charge; this sort of construction permits more efficient use of the heat and protects the roof of the furnace, even though the temperature of the furnace is readily maintained at above 1600° C. Open-hearth furnaces with capacities as high as 350 tons are in operation, but 100 tons is the usual size.

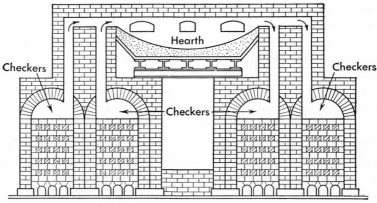

Fig. 40.13.   An open-hearth furnace. (Adapted from Babor, *Basic College Chemistry,* The Thomas Y. Crowell Company, by permission of the publishers.)

The raw materials employed in the open-hearth process are primarily pig iron; iron ore or mill scale to oxidize the carbon, silicon, and other impurities from the pig iron; scrap steel; and limestone to provide a basic slag. Usually the scrap steel, iron ore, and limestone are introduced first and are heated for about 2 hours, after which molten pig iron from the blast furnace is added. The silicon, manganese, and phosphorus are immediately oxidized by the iron ore to the corresponding oxides, which pass into the basic slag. The carbon also begins to be oxidized, and the evolution of carbon monoxide keeps the charge well stirred. Since the operation takes place relatively slowly, its progress can be checked from time to time by means of rapid analysis of samples of the furnace charge. Further quantities of iron ore are added from time to time until the carbon content has been lowered to the desired value. The molten metal and slag are then tapped from the bottom of the hearth into a large ladle. Since the heavier steel forms the lower layer and comes off first, it is readily separated from the slag. The necessary amount of spiegeleisen or other deoxidizer is then added to the metal in the ladle. Since the amount of metal is much larger than that from a single Bessemer heat, it holds its heat longer and hence a longer time is available for the deoxidizing action.

About 8 to 10 hours are required for a single run in an open-hearth furnace; hence, despite the larger size of the charge, the open-hearth process is considerably slower than the Bessemer. Further, the construction of the furnace and the continuous use of fuel add to the cost of open-hearth steel. The advantages of the basic open-hearth process, however, more than offset the disadvantages. The open-hearth method permits great latitude in the selection of raw materials; the ratio of pig iron to scrap steel may be varied over wide limits and may be adjusted in terms of the relative prices of pig iron and scrap. This process also makes possible very close control of the temperature, as well as of the chemical reactions taking place in the furnace, and also permits more thorough deoxidation of the steel than is possible in the Bessemer process.

In some cases a "duplex" process is employed for high-phosphorus pig irons. Most of the silicon, manganese, and carbon are removed in a Bessemer converter, and the charge is then transferred to a basic open-hearth furnace for the removal of the phosphorus. The time during which the open-hearth furnace must be operated is greatly shortened by this procedure, with a consequent saving of fuel.

An acid open-hearth process, i.e., a process using an open hearth lined with an acidic (high-silica) refractory, is used for the manufacture of certain special types of steel from steel scrap. It is little used for the conversion of pig iron to steel, however, for, as in the acid Bessemer process, a basic flux may not be used and the phosphorus therefore cannot be removed.

The use of an electric furnace permits even closer control over the steel-making process, since not only the temperature but also the atmosphere of the furnace can be very closely controlled. Higher temperatures can be obtained by this means than in the gas-fired furnace. The cost of electric power, however, restricts the use of electric furnaces to the production of steels of the best quality, particularly alloy steels.

8. Influence of Chemical Composition and Heat Treatment on the Properties of Steels. It has already been explained that steels are hardened and embrittled by sudden cooling or quenching. On the other hand, maximum softness and ductility are obtained by means of very slow cooling. In most cases intermediate properties are desirable, and, in order that the brittleness and hardness of a quenched steel may be somewhat reduced, the metal is subjected to a process known as *tempering*. Tempering consists in the reheating of the quenched steel, for various periods of time, to temperatures up to 650° C.; this yields products having various combinations of hardness, ductility, strength, and toughness. The change in properties due to tempering is explained by the fact that the reheating of the steel allows conversion of the hard crystals of the solid solution of cementite in α-iron to the relatively soft mixture of crystals of the two substances, to proceed to a greater extent than is possible when the steel is quenched. The extent to which this transition takes place during the tempering process determines the degree of hardness and brittleness of the steel, and is regulated by the temperature and duration of the treatment. The tempering process also relieves the internal stresses developed by the rapid and uneven cooling of the steel during quenching.

In general, it may be said that strength and "hardenability" of steel are increased, while toughness and ductility are decreased, by an increase in the carbon content of the steel. Thus, high strength and hardness are obtained in high-carbon steels at the price of lowered ductility and toughness. By means of a process known as case-hardening, steel objects with a tough, ductile, low-carbon core and a hard, wear-resisting, high-carbon surface are obtainable. In this process, the steel article is either packed in a solid carbonaceous material, submerged in a molten bath of fused salts containing a cyanide, or exposed to an atmosphere of some carbon-containing gas such as carbon monoxide, methane, or ethane, and heated to about 900° C. After the absorption of carbon in the surface has proceeded to the desired extent, the steel is removed and quenched. A similar effect is produced by "nitriding" the steel surface. In this process a steel usually containing about 1% of aluminum is heated in an atmosphere of ammonia. The ammonia decomposes, producing a hard surface of iron and aluminum nitrides.

9. Alloy Steels. If an element other than carbon is added to a steel, for a purpose other than deoxidation and in sufficient quantity to modify its properties, the product is known as an alloy steel. Several hundred varieties of alloy steels, containing from one to a half-dozen alloying elements, contribute greatly to our industrial civilization. Among the more important elements used in the manufacture of alloy steels are manganese, nickel, chromium, tungsten, vanadium, molybdenum, copper, and silicon. A discussion of the effects of even the more important of these alloying elements on such properties as hardness, ductility, tensile strength, and corrosion resistance, would be beyond the scope of this text. It is sufficient to point out that by the proper choice of alloying elements, as well as by the application of various types of thermal and mechanical treatment, a wide variety of alloy steels, exhibiting an extensive range of properties, are obtainable. A few of the more important types, however, have been discussed under the main alloying element which they contain and are summarized in Table 40.1.

Table 40.1

Some Typical Alloy Steels

Alloying Element or Elements	Typical Composition	Special Properties and Uses
Silicon	13.5 to 14.5% Si; 0.8 to 1.0% C	Hard, acid-resistant. An example is Duriron.
Copper	>0.2% Cu; 0.15 to 0.30% C	"Copper-bearing" steels. Increased corrosion resistance.
Manganese	>10% Mn; 1.0 to 1.4% C	Very hard, ductile. Railway crossings and switches. Rock crushers, teeth for steam shovel dippers, conveyer chains, etc.
Nickel	3% Ni; 0.3% C	Increased strength and ductility. Propeller shafts, gear steel, high grade steel castings.
Chromium	0.6 to 1.1% Cr; 0.2 to 0.5% C	Increased strength and toughness. Recommended for heat-treated forgings.
Chromium	4 to 10% Cr; <0.2% C	Increased hardness and resistance to corrosion. Used for high-temperature, high-pressure equipment in oil refineries.
Chromium–Nickel	17 to19% Cr; 7 to 9% Ni; 0.08 to 0.2% C	Stainless steels. High corrosion resistance, strength, hardenability, and ductility.
Chromium–Vanadium	0.8 to 1.1% Cr; 0.15 to 0.18% V; 0.10 to 1.05% C	Used for balls, ball bearings, and tool steels.
Tungsten–Chromium	18% W; 4% Cr; 1% C	High-speed steel. Keeps hardness at high temperatures. Used in high-speed tools. Molybdenum has an effect similar to that of tungsten.

STUDY QUESTIONS AND PROBLEMS

1. Discuss the production of pig iron from iron ore, giving starting materials, describing the operation of the furnace in which the process is carried out,

giving the equations for all the reactions involved, and stating the function of each substance used in the process. What is the nature of the iron obtained in this process?

2. Explain briefly what is meant by a steel, and why steels may be hardened by quenching.

3. How does wrought iron differ in composition and properties from a typical cast iron? from a steel?

4. What are the principal industrial applications of cast irons? What are the differences in composition, properties, and methods of preparation of white and gray cast irons?

5. How is wrought iron prepared? For what is it used? Explain, in so far as you can, the physical properties of wrought iron in terms of its composition and structure.

6. Contrast briefly the Bessemer and the open-hearth processes for making steel as to time required, expense, and quality of product. Describe both processes, giving equations for the reactions involved.

7. How may a steel be tempered? Explain why this treatment yields the desired results.

8. Define the following terms: α-iron, cementite, austenite, γ-iron, converter, reverberatory furnace, flux, and slag.

9. Why may a high-carbon steel be hardened to a greater extent than a low-carbon steel?

The Copper Family

1. History. The elements copper, silver, and gold, constituting Group 1b of the periodic system, are commonly known as the copper family. This family is unique in that all its elements are well known and have been used since before the dawn of recorded history. Copper, silver, and gold are among the six metals mentioned in the Old Testament. Copper instruments and other articles known to be more than 6000 years old are to be seen in many of the world's museums, and man has counted his wealth in terms of gold and silver for many centuries (Figure 41.1).

2. General Characteristics. Each of the three elements of this family is the last member of one of the three series of transition elements. As is shown by the electron configurations listed in Table 41.1, the d subshell which immediately underlies the valence shell, and which has been in the process of filling up throughout the transition series, has reached completion in the elements of the copper family. Listed in the same table are the configurations of the corresponding members of Group 1a, the alkali metal family.

Table 41.1

Element	1 s	2 s p	3 s p d	4 s p d f	5 s p d	6 s
Group 1a						
K	2	2, 6	2, 6	1		
Rb	2	2, 6	2, 6, 10	2, 6	1	
Cs	2	2, 6	2, 6, 10	2, 6, 10	2, 6	1
Group 1b						
Cu	2	2, 6	2, 6, 10	1		
Ag	2	2, 6	2, 6, 10	2, 6, 10	1	
Au	2	2, 6	2, 6, 10	2, 6, 10, 14	2, 6, 10	1

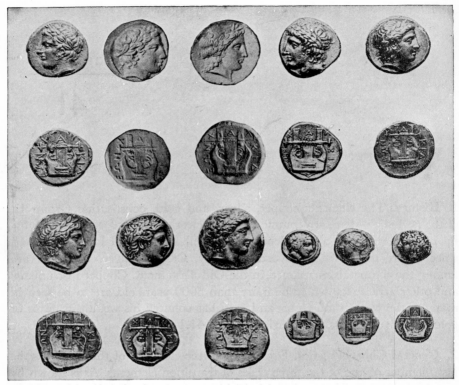

Fig. 41.1.   Ancient Greek silver coins struck at Olynthus in the first half of the fourth century B.C. (Part of Plate XXXV in *Excavations at Olynthus,* Part IX by David M. Robinson and Paul Augustus Clement. *Courtesy of Johns Hopkins University Press.*)

It might be surmised that, since an atom of each of the elements of either family has but a single valence electron, the properties of the elements of the two families should be similar. That this is far from the truth, however, may be seen from Table 41.2, where some of the important properties of corresponding members of the two groups are listed.

The smaller ionic radii and larger ionization potentials of the elements of the copper family help to explain the fact that the oxides and hydroxides of these elements are much less basic than the corresponding compounds of the alkali metals (p. 638). Likewise, as might be expected from their smaller ionic radii, the elements of the copper family form covalent as well as electrovalent compounds and show a pronounced tendency toward the formation of complex ions. Also in line with their transitional character is the variable oxidation state of these elements. Whereas the alkali metals show only one oxidation state, $+1$, the members of the copper family exhibit the oxidation states $+1$, $+2$, and $+3$. In fact, compounds of $+2$ copper and of $+3$ gold are more important than those in which these elements have an oxidation number of $+1$. This variability in oxidation state is attributable to the possibility of removal of electrons from the newly completed d subshell just under the valence shell of the atom.

Table 41.2

Properties of Corresponding Members of Groups 1a and 1b

	Atomic Number	Ionization potential (v.)	Ionic radius (Å)	Density (g./cc.)	Melting point (°C.)	Boiling point (°C.)	Oxidation potential $M=M^++e^-$ (v.)	Tensile strength (lb./sq. in. for cold-drawn wire)
K	19	4.3	1.33	0.86	62.7	776	2.93	very small
Cu	29	7.7	0.96	8.92	1083	2595	−0.52	60,000
Rb	37	4.2	1.48	1.53	39.0	679	2.93	very small
Ag	47	7.6	1.26	10.5	960.5	2212	−0.80	51,000
Cs	55	3.9	1.69	1.90	28.4	680	2.92	very small
Au	79	9.2	1.37	19.3	1063	2966	ca.−1.68	37,000

The striking contrast between these two groups of elements with similar electronic structures is due to the fact that whereas corresponding members of the two families have the same number of electron shells, the nuclear charge of each member of the copper family is greater than that of the corresponding alkali metal. The larger nuclear charges provide a partial explanation of the higher ionization potentials, the lower ionic radii, and the consequent lower reactivity of the elements of the copper family.

It has been briefly noted that the ionization potential of the heaviest member of each of several of the families is larger than would be expected from the trend within the family. This is particularly noticeable in the copper family, for, whereas there is first a decrease in potential from copper to silver, there is a sharp rise from silver to gold, so that gold has the highest ionization potential and is the least active of the three elements. In this connection it may be observed that the elements before and after gold in the third transition series, viz., hafnium through mercury, are the least active elements in their respective families. Whenever ionization potential data are available, they support this conclusion. Even thallium, lead, and radium have slightly higher ioniza-tion potentials than do indium, tin, and barium, respectively. The explana-tion of this apparent paradox is to be found in the fact that these elements of the third transition series follow immediately after the rare earth elements. In Chapter 36 it was pointed out that in the series of rare earth elements electrons are being added to the $4f$ subshell, thus building up the 4th shell from 18 to 32 electrons. Thus, in this series the nuclear charge increases from 57 to 71 without increase in the number of electron shells. Hence, in the atoms of the elements following the rare earth elements, the electrons are held more tightly by the increased nuclear charge than they would be if the rare earth "interlude" had not intervened. For example, in the interval from cop-per to silver, where the charge on the nucleus increases from 29 to 47, the effect of the increased nuclear charge is more than counterbalanced by the fact that the valence electron in the silver atom is one shell farther away from the nucleus. Hence the ionization potential of silver is less than that of copper. This is the usual sequence. However, in the interval from silver to gold, the charge on the nucleus is increased by a much larger amount, from 47 to 79, because of the rare earth interlude. Although in this case, also, there is an increase by one in the number of electron shells, the effect of the very large increase in nuclear charge predominates, and thus the ionization potential of gold is not only higher than that of silver but even higher than that of copper. A similar explanation may be applied to other elements that follow the rare earths in the table, among which are many of the most "noble" of the metals. This effect is known as the "lanthanide contraction."

3. Occurrence of the Elements. All the members of this family are among the less common elements. Copper is estimated to constitute about $10^{-4}\%$ of the igneous rocks in the earth's crust, silver $10^{-8}\%$, and gold even less. All these elements occur in both the free and the combined states in nature.

The ores of copper may be divided into three classes: (1) native or free copper, large quantities of which have been mined in northern Michigan; (2) sulfide ores, including such minerals as chalcocite, Cu_2S, chalcopyrite, $CuFeS_2$, and bornite, Cu_3FeS_3; and (3) oxidized ores, of which malachite, $Cu(OH)_2 \cdot CuCO_3$, azurite, $Cu(OH)_2 \cdot 2CuCO_3$, cuprite, Cu_2O, and melac-onite, CuO, are examples. Many countries mine some copper ores, but the leading producer is the United States, followed by Chile, Northern Rhodesia, Canada, Russia, Belgian Congo, and Japan. The major copper-mining states in this country are Arizona, Utah, and Montana.

The most important ores of silver include (1) free silver, which commonly occurs in the form of alloys with other noble metals; (2) sulfide ores, such as argentite, Ag_2S, proustite, Ag_3AsS_3, and pyrargyrite, Ag_3SbS_3; and (3) horn silver, $AgCl$. Silver ores are often found in conjunction with ores of other metals such as copper, lead, and gold. The major silver-producing countries are Mexico, the United States, Canada (Ontario), and Peru. The leading silver-mining states in this country are Idaho, Montana, Utah, Colorado, and Arizona.

While there are a few minerals such as the telluride, $AuTe_2$, and the double telluride $AuAgTe_4$, in which gold occurs in the combined state, the most important sources of gold are natural deposits of the free metal. Sometimes nuggets of gold are found, but generally the metal occurs as fine grains or flakes in quartz veins, or in sand and gravel beds that have been formed from the weathering and washing of gold-containing rocks. Native gold almost always contains some platinum metals, as well as silver. The Union of South Africa produces more gold than any other country; other large producers are Canada, Russia, the United States, Australia, the Philippines, Japan, and Mexico.

4. Metallurgy, Properties, and Uses of the Metals. The metallurgy of ores containing native copper is relatively simple, since it involves only the concentration of the ore by grinding and washing, followed by the heating of the concentrate in a furnace in the presence of limestone. The limestone serves as a flux, reacting with the gangue to form a slag, while the copper melts and forms a layer beneath the molten slag. Copper obtained from these ores is about 99.9% pure; it is known as "Lake" copper, and for a time constituted our main domestic supply. However, Lake copper represents only about 5% of our present production.

The sulfide ores, found mainly in Montana and Utah, yield about 70% of the copper produced in this country. The metallurgy of sulfide ores of copper is complicated by two factors: (1) the copper content of these ores is not high, seldom exceeding 15% and not unusually running as low as 2%; (2) other metals are commonly associated with the copper. Because of the low percentage of copper-bearing material, concentration of these ores is an essential step in their treatment. The recently developed flotation process has proved a great boon to the copper and other metal industries, for it has made possible the economical treatment of many ores of such low grade that treatment by older procedures would be unprofitable. In this process, the finely ground ore is worked into a slime with water containing about 1% of an oily reagent such as coal tar or creosote. This slime is then introduced into a large volume of water, and the mixture is beaten or blown so as to produce a heavy froth. (Sometimes pine oil is added as a "frother.") The sulfide ore particles are "wetted" by the oily reagent and therefore adhere to the oily air bubbles in the froth, while the gangue is more readily "wetted" by water and sinks to the bottom. The froth is skimmed off and dehydrated, and the oil is then distilled off, leaving the dry concentrate. It is possible by this process to remove 95% of the copper from an ore having a copper content as low as 2%, while as much as two-thirds of the useless gangue is left behind.

The second step in the process is the roasting of the concentrated ore. This is carried out at red heat in a plentiful supply of air, and results both in the volatilization of the major part of the oxides of arsenic and antimony which are generally present, and in the oxidation of part of the metal sulfides to the corresponding oxides and sulfur dioxide.

The roasted ore is then smelted in a large reverberatory furnace similar to that used in the open-hearth process for the manufacture of steel. Silica (sand) is introduced to combine with iron oxide to form a slag, and sometimes lime, also, is added to make the slag more fusible through the formation of calcium silicate. Much of the iron is thus removed in the form of ferrous silicate slag. A heavy molten layer of a mixture of cuprous sulfide and the remaining iron sulfide, which is known as matte, collects under the slag.

The next step in the process takes place in a converter similar to that used in the Bessemer process for making steel. Air is blown under pressure through a charge consisting of molten matte and a little sand. The following reactions take place, yielding free copper:

$$2FeS + 3O_2 = 2FeO + 2SO_2$$

$$FeO + SiO_2 = FeSiO_3$$

$$2Cu_2S + 3O_2 = 2Cu_2O + 2SO_2$$

$$2Cu_2O + Cu_2S = 6Cu + SO_2$$

The metallic copper obtained from this process is about 99% pure. It is usually called blister copper because sulfur dioxide which was dissolved in the molten metal is discharged during the solidification, with the formation of bubbles or blisters.

In a preliminary refining process, a stream of air is directed on the surface of the molten copper in order to oxidize active metal impurities, and the metal is then stirred with poles of green wood to reduce any cuprous oxide which has been formed. Finally the copper is refined by electrolysis. The partially purified blister copper is cast into plates which serve as anodes; thin sheets of pure copper form the cathodes, and the electrolyte consists of a solution of sulfuric acid and copper sulfate containing a little chloride. When a current is passed through the cell, copper dissolves from the impure anode

$$Cu = Cu^{++} + 2e^-$$

and plates out on the cathode.

$$Cu^{++} + 2e^- = Cu$$

By proper regulation of the potential drop across the cell, metallic impurities which are less active than copper, such as gold, silver, and platinum, may be prevented from dissolving. (A little silver may dissolve but this is precipitated as silver chloride.) As the copper disintegrates, these substances drop from the anode and form the "anode sludge." The recovery of gold, silver, and platinum from this sludge constitutes a considerable source of profit. On the other hand, metallic impurities which are more active than copper dissolve from the anode, but, if the potential drop across the cell is maintained at a sufficiently low value, they may be prevented from plating out on the cathode. Copper purified in this way is about 99.955% pure.

Oxidized ores of copper are usually treated with sulfuric acid, which dissolves the copper oxide or carbonate, and the cupric ion in the solution thus obtained is reduced either electrolytically or by means of metallic iron.

Some of the physical constants of metallic copper have been listed in Table 41.2. Copper is the only markedly reddish-colored metal. It has the highest electrical conductivity per unit cross section of any of the metals except silver, and is also a very good conductor of heat. The electrical conductivity of copper is greatly reduced, however, by even small quantities of impurities; e.g., 0.03% of arsenic lowers the conductivity 14%. When cooled rapidly, copper becomes soft, malleable, and ductile, but slow cooling yields a brittle product.

On standing in moist air copper becomes coated with a green film of basic copper carbonate, which, however, protects the metal from further corrosion.

$$2Cu + O_2 + CO_2 + H_2O = Cu(OH)_2 \cdot CuCO_3$$

In dry air, copper gradually loses its bright color because of the formation of an oxide film. This film also is protective, and corrosion is only superficial. Copper is not affected by hydrogen ion and hence does not dissolve in nonoxidizing acids. The standard oxidation potentials, as listed below, are in line with this fact.

$$Cu = Cu^+ + \quad e^-; E = -0.52 \text{ v.}$$
$$Cu = Cu^{++} + 2e^-; E = -0.34 \text{ v.}$$

Metallic copper dissolves readily in nitric acid or in hot concentrated sulfuric acid.

$$3Cu + 8H^+ + 2NO_3^- = 3Cu^{++} + 2NO + 4H_2O$$
$$\text{dil. } HNO_3$$

$$Cu + 4H^+ + 2NO_3^- = Cu^{++} + 2NO_2 + 2H_2O$$
$$\text{conc. } HNO_3$$

$$Cu + 2H_2SO_4 = Cu^{++} + SO_4^{--} + SO_2 + 2H_2O$$

In the presence of oxygen and moisture, copper is attacked by ammonia.

$$2Cu + 8NH_3 + O_2 + 2H_2O = 2Cu(NH_3)_4^{++} + 4OH^-$$

When copper is heated to temperatures above 300° C. in the presence of oxygen, it is converted to black cupric oxide.

$$2Cu + O_2 = 2CuO$$

On further heating to above 1000° C., however, red cuprous oxide is formed.

$$4CuO = 2Cu_2O + O_2$$

Metallic copper reacts readily with sulfur vapor and with the halogens, according to the equations

$$Cu + X_2 = CuX_2 \qquad (X = F, Cl, Br)$$

$$2Cu + I_2 = 2CuI$$

$$2Cu + S = Cu_2S$$

Copper ranks next to steel in its world-wide importance as an engineering material; the annual world production of copper exceeds two million tons. Its importance results from its high thermal and electrical conductivities, and from its ductility, malleability, and resistance to corrosion. More than half of the copper used in this country goes into the manufacture of electrical machinery, wire, transmission lines, instruments, etc. Copper of high purity is indispensable to the electrical industries.

Because of its flexibility and resistance to corrosion, copper is used in high-quality plumbing, roofing, screens, and gutters. Boilers, stills, and condensers, as well as various utensils used in the kitchen, are often constructed of copper. Wooden ship bottoms are commonly sheathed with copper.

About one-fourth of the copper produced is used to make copper alloys, of which a very large number are manufactured. The most important types of these alloys are the brasses and the bronzes. The brasses are composed mainly of copper and zinc, but small quantities of various other metals may also be present; generally the zinc content does not exceed 40%. The various brass alloys are generally stronger, more ductile, cheaper, and more easily machined than copper; on the other hand they are much poorer conductors of electricity and are less resistant to corrosion. Among the articles for which brasses are used are cartridge cases, tubing, valves, and automobile radiators.

The bronzes are composed mainly of copper and tin, but, as in the case of the brasses, other elements are sometimes incorporated; generally the tin content is less than 19%. Bronzes are stronger and more resistant to corrosion than pure copper.

A number of different processes are used for the extraction of silver from its ores, the process employed depending upon the nature of the ore. Much silver is obtained as a by-product of the metallurgy of lead and copper. Silver is recovered from lead by the Parkes process, in which the silver is extracted from the molten lead by means of metallic zinc. Molten zinc and lead are only very slightly soluble in each other, and metallic silver is 3000 times as soluble in molten zinc as in molten lead at the melting point of the latter. Therefore, when small amounts of molten zinc are stirred in a large batch of silver-bearing lead, the silver dissolves in the zinc, which rises to the surface and is skimmed off. The zinc is removed from the silver by distillation of the zinc. Traces of lead are removed by cupellation, as described subsequently. For reasons of economy, silver ore is rarely smelted alone, but is usually mixed with lead ore before smelting and the resulting silver-lead alloy is separated by the Parkes process. Silver, along with gold and other noble metals, is recovered from the "anode mud" obtained in the refining of copper.

In the amalgamation process, the finely crushed silver ore, together with a little roasted copper ore (containing copper sulfate) and salt, is treated with metallic mercury. Silver sulfide is converted to silver chloride by reaction with cupric chloride (from the copper sulfate and sodium chloride).

$$Ag_2S + CuCl_2 = 2AgCl + CuS$$

This silver chloride, along with any silver chloride present in the original ore, is reduced to metallic silver by reaction with the mercury.

$$2AgCl + 2Hg = 2Ag + Hg_2Cl_2$$

The silver thus formed, along with any free silver present in the original ore, dissolves in the excess of mercury to form an amalgam, from which it is removed by distilling off the mercury.

The amalgamation process is gradually being replaced by a process involving the action of solutions of sodium or potassium cyanide on the finely ground silver ore. The usefulness of this cyanide process depends upon the fact that silver metal and all of its compounds dissolve readily in solutions of cyanides, in the presence of air, to yield the complex ion $Ag(CN)_2^-$.

$$4Ag + 8CN^- + O_2 + 2H_2O = 4Ag(CN)_2^- + 4OH^-$$

$$2Ag_2S + 8CN^- + O_2 + 2H_2O = 4Ag(CN)_2^- + 2S + 4OH^-$$

$$AgCl + 2CN^- = Ag(CN)_2^- + Cl^-$$

The silver is precipitated from the solution of the cyanide complex by the addition of aluminum or zinc.

$$2Ag(CN)_2^- + Zn = 2Ag + Zn(CN)_4^{--}$$

Silver obtained by any of the above processes must usually be refined. The electrolytic process for the refining of silver is similar to the corresponding process for copper. The anode is composed of impure silver, the cathode of pure silver, and the electrolytic solution contains silver nitrate and nitric acid.

The more active metal impurities may be removed from silver by passage of a current of air over the impure molten silver on a hearth composed of some porous material such as bone ash. These impurities either are converted to oxides which are volatilized and pass out in the stream of air, or are absorbed by the porous lining of the hearth. This process is known as cupellation.

Gold is separated from silver either electrolytically or by solution of the silver in hot concentrated sulfuric acid, which leaves the gold unaffected.

Some of the important physical constants for metallic silver are listed in Table 41.2. Silver is a white, lustrous, malleable, ductile metal, slightly harder than copper. It has the highest electrical conductivity per unit cross section of any of the metals and is also a good conductor of heat.

Silver retains its lustrous appearance in the presence of air and moisture unless hydrogen sulfide is present, in which case superficial tarnishing occurs because of the formation of black silver sulfide. The standard oxidation potential for the half-reaction, $Ag = Ag^+ + e^-$, is -0.80 v.; silver is, therefore, unaffected by hydronium ion. It dissolves readily, however, in nitric or in hot concentrated sulfuric acid.

$$3Ag + 4H^+ + NO_3^- = 3Ag^+ + NO + 2H_2O$$

$$2Ag + 2H_2SO_4 = 2Ag^+ + SO_4^{--} + SO_2 + 2H_2O$$

Silver is widely used in coins, usually in the form of an alloy with copper. Sterling silver contains 7.5% of copper, while the silver used for coinage in the United States contains 10% of copper. The function of the copper is to increase the hardness of the alloy, and thus to improve its wearing qualities. The beautiful appearance and relative scarcity of silver favors its use in various kinds of jewelry; for this purpose, also, it is alloyed with copper.

Considerable quantities of silver are consumed in the manufacture of silver-plated cutlery and other tableware. The object to be plated is made the cathode of an electrolytic cell, a piece of pure silver is the anode, and the electrolyte is a solution of sodium silver cyanide, $Na[Ag(CN)_2]$. The cyanide complex is in equilibrium with silver ion and cyanide ion,

$$Ag(CN)_2^- \rightleftharpoons Ag^+ + 2CN^-$$

and maintains a low but relatively constant concentration of silver ion in the electrolyte. This fact favors the formation of a smooth adherent plate, rather than the loose crystalline deposit which would be obtained from a solution of silver nitrate.

Mirrors are made by the deposition of a coating of metallic silver on one surface of a piece of glass. This process is usually carried out by reduction of a solution containing the ammonia complex, $Ag(NH_3)_2^+$, by means of an organic reducing agent such as formaldehyde.

In past centuries gold was obtained from the richer deposits by placer mining, which consists of the washing of the gold-bearing gravel with water to remove the lighter sandy materials from the heavier gold particles; this, however, is a wasteful procedure, in that only the larger particles of the metal are recovered. The amalgamation process for the recovery of gold has also been in use for many centuries. The modern metallurgy of gold is very similar to that of silver. Gold is recovered together with silver from copper and lead ores, and the silver is separated from the gold, by methods already described. The application of a cyanide process analogous to the one used in silver metallurgy has made possible the commercial treatment of low-grade gold ores and of "tailings" from less efficient processes.

Some of the more important physical constants for metallic gold are listed in Table 41.2. Gold is the most malleable and ductile of all the metals; it can be hammered into sheets only 0.00001 mm. thick, and drawn into a wire of which a piece a mile and a quarter long would weigh only one gram. Gold is the least active of the elements of the copper family, as is indicated by the low standard oxidation potential for the reaction, $Au = Au^+ + e^-$; $E =$ about -1.68 v. The metal is not affected by any single common acid, even by concentrated nitric. It is acted upon, however, by selenic acid, H_2SeO_4, and it dissolves readily in aqua regia.

$$Au + 4H^+ + NO_3^- + 4Cl^- = AuCl_4^- + NO + 2H_2O$$

Because of its bright yellow color and its low chemical reactivity, gold has long been a favorite metal both for the manufacture of jewelry and for coinage. It is never used for these purposes in the pure state, however, but is always alloyed with other metals, commonly with copper, to increase its hardness. White gold usually contains silver, palladium, or nickel. The gold content of the gold alloys is usually expressed in "karats," a designation that indicates the number of parts by weight of gold in 24 parts of alloy. Thus 10-karat gold contains $41\frac{2}{3}\%$ $(10/24)$ of gold. Cheap jewelry is made of less expensive metals plated with gold. As in silver plating, the electrolyte used is a complex cyanide, in this case $Na[Au(CN)_2]$.

COMPOUNDS OF COPPER, SILVER, AND GOLD

5. General Characteristics. In contrast to the elements of the alkali metal family, which are characterized by the rarity of covalent bonds or complex ions among their compounds and by the high solubility of their compounds in water, the elements of the copper family form many complex ions, a number of covalent compounds, and many compounds having only limited solubility in water.

6. Cuprous Compounds. Although the electronic configuration for the copper atom shows only one electron in the outer shell, the cuprous compounds, i.e., those in which copper exhibits the $+1$ oxidation state, are relatively unimportant as compared with the cupric compounds, or those containing copper in the $+2$ oxidation state. Cuprous ion is unstable in aqueous solution and decomposes into free copper and cupric ion.

$$2Cu^+ = Cu^{++} + Cu$$

However, when the cuprous ion enters into the formation of a very stable complex ion or of a very slightly soluble compound, this order of stability is reversed. Thus the best known cuprous compounds are complexes or slightly soluble solids. This principle is illustrated by the formation of cuprous iodide or cyanide when solutions of cupric ion are treated with a soluble iodide or cyanide.

$$2Cu^{++} + 4I^- = 2CuI + I_2$$

$$2Cu^{++} + 4CN^- = 2CuCN + C_2N_2$$

Cuprous chloride and bromide are only slightly soluble in water, but dissolve readily in solutions containing excess halide ion.

$$CuX + X^- = CuX_2^-$$

Many cupric compounds are decomposed to cuprous compounds at elevated temperatures. Among the cuprous compounds which may be prepared in this manner are the oxide, sulfide, fluoride, chloride, and bromide. Cuprous salts of oxygen-containing acids, except possibly the sulfite, Cu_2SO_3, are unknown.

7. Cupric Compounds. An outstanding characteristic of cupric salts is the light greenish-blue color of their dilute aqueous solutions, which is due to the presence of the hydrated cupric ion, $Cu(H_2O)_4^{++}$. Most hydrated cupric salts are blue in the solid state, for the same reason. When solutions of cupric salts are treated with solutions of alkalis, a pale blue, flocculent precipitate of cupric hydroxide, $Cu(OH)_2$, results. If the suspension is heated, or if the precipitation is carried out in a hot solution, a black precipitate of cupric oxide, CuO, is obtained. Cupric hydroxide is a weak base and is somewhat amphoteric, dissolving in concentrated solutions of alkali hydroxides to give deep blue solutions of cuprate ion, probably $Cu(OH)_4^{--}$.

When solutions containing the hydrated cupric ion are treated with solutions of ammonia, a precipitate of cupric hydroxide is at first formed, but with the addition of excess ammonia this precipitate immediately dissolves to give a deep violet-blue solution. The change of color of a solution of cupric ion from light greenish-blue to deep violet-blue with excess of ammonia results from the formation of the tetrammino cupric ion, $Cu(NH_3)_4^{++}$, and constitutes a very characteristic test for copper.

$$\begin{bmatrix} & & H & \\ & & \overset{..}{\underset{}{O}}:H & \\ H & & & \\ H:\overset{..}{\underset{..}{O}}: & Cu & :\overset{..}{\underset{..}{O}}:H \\ & & H & \\ & H:\overset{..}{\underset{..}{O}}: & & \\ & H & & \end{bmatrix}^{++} + 4NH_3 = \begin{bmatrix} & & H & \\ & & H:\overset{..}{\underset{}{N}}:H & \\ H & & & H \\ H:\overset{}{\underset{\overset{..}{H}}{N}}: & Cu & :\overset{}{\underset{\overset{..}{H}}{N}}:H \\ & H:\overset{}{\underset{\overset{..}{H}}{N}}:H & & \end{bmatrix}^{++} + 4H_2O$$

light greenish-blue   deep violet-blue

Cupric hydroxide dissolves in aqueous solutions of a number of organic compounds with the formation of cupric complexes. For example, it dissolves in alkaline solutions containing tartrate ion, $C_4H_4O_6^{--}$, to yield a deep blue solution containing the cupric tartrate complex $Cu(OH)_2(C_4H_4O_6)_2^{----}$. This solution, known as Fehling's solution, is reduced by aldehydes (p. 580) to yield a bright red precipitate of cuprous oxide, Cu_2O. Since many sugars are complex aldehydes, Fehling's solution is an important re-agent in the study of sugars.

The cupric halides, except the iodide, which is unstable, are all soluble in water. A concentrated aqueous solution of cupric chloride is yellow-green, but the color changes to the characteristic light blue as the solution is diluted. This color change is due to the fact that in concentrated solutions of cupric chloride, part of the copper is present as the yellow complex ion $CuCl_4^{--}$. As the solution is diluted, this complex is progressively converted to the blue hydrated ion according to the equation

$$\underbrace{\underset{\text{blue}}{Cu(H_2O)_4^{++}} + \underset{\text{yellow}}{CuCl_4^{--}}}_{\text{green}} + 4H_2O \rightleftharpoons 2\underset{\text{blue}}{Cu(H_2O)_4^{++}} + 4Cl^-$$

Solutions of cupric bromide show similar behavior, changing from a deep red-brown color in concentrated solution to the typical blue color in dilute.

The most important copper salt is cupric sulfate. The anhydrous salt, $CuSO_4$, is white, but the hydrated form, $CuSO_4 \cdot 5H_2O$, is bright blue, and is commonly known as blue vitriol. It is obtained by roasting copper sulfide to the oxide, which is then converted to the sulfate by treatment with sulfuric acid. Copper sulfate is used as the electrolyte in copper-plating processes, in electrotyping, and in the manufacture of fungicides. Added in very minute quantities to water reservoirs and swimming pools, it prevents the growth of algae. Because of the readiness with which it takes up water to form the blue hydrate, the white anhydrous salt is used as a drying agent for certain organic liquids and also as a sensitive reagent for the detection of water.

Other common soluble cupric salts include the blue nitrate, $Cu(NO_3)_2 \cdot 6H_2O$, and the blue-green acetate, $Cu(C_2H_3O_2)_2 \cdot H_2O$. Common slightly soluble copper compounds include the basic carbonates, azurite, $Cu(OH)_2 \cdot 2CuCO_3$ (bright blue), and malachite, $Cu(OH)_2 \cdot CuCO_3$ (green); the light blue phosphate, $Cu_3(PO_4)_2$; and the black sulfide, CuS. Cupric sulfide has a very low solubility in water and may be precipitated even in the presence of high concentrations of hydrogen ion. A mixed acetate and arsenite of the formula $Cu(C_2H_3O_2)_2 \cdot 3Cu(AsO_2)_2$, known as Paris green, is used as an insecticide.

Compounds in which copper has an oxidation number of $+3$ are not well known, but a few have been reported.

8. Argentous Compounds.

Whereas silver may, with some difficulty, be oxidized to an oxidation state of $+2$, or even of $+3$, all of the familiar compounds of silver contain that element in the $+1$ oxidation state. Like the other elements of this family, silver forms large numbers of complex ions and slightly soluble compounds. The singly charged ion, Ag^+, called argentous, or often simply silver, ion, is colorless.

When a solution containing argentous ion is treated with a solution of an alkali hydroxide a brown precipitate of argentous oxide, Ag_2O, is formed. The hydroxide is unstable and exists only momentarily.

$$2Ag^+ + 2OH^- = \underset{\text{unstable}}{(2AgOH)} = Ag_2O_{(s)} + H_2O$$

This oxide is distinctly basic in most of its reactions, although it dissolves slightly in highly alkaline solutions. When heated to about 200° C., it decomposes to give the free metal and oxygen. It dissolves readily in aqueous ammonia to form the complex ion $Ag(NH_3)_2{}^+$.

$$Ag_2O + H_2O + 4NH_3 = 2Ag(NH_3)_2{}^+ + 2OH^-$$

All the argentous halides, with the exception of the fluoride, are very slightly soluble in water, the solubility decreasing in the order $AgF >$ $AgCl > AgBr > AgI$. The fluoride and the chloride are white, but the bromide is pale yellow and the iodide a slightly deeper yellow; this change in color may be associated with the increasingly covalent character of the bonds in the crystals of the halides. The chloride dissolves readily in dilute aqueous ammonia,

$$AgCl + 2NH_3 = Ag(NH_3)_2{}^+ + Cl^-$$

the bromide only in concentrated ammonia. The iodide is quite insoluble in this reagent. The chloride and the bromide are both readily soluble, however, in sodium thiosulfate solution,

$$AgBr_{(s)} + 2S_2O_3{}^{--} = Ag(S_2O_3)_2{}^{---} + Br^-$$

and all the halides dissolve in solutions of alkali cyanides to form the argentocyanide complex.

$$AgI_{(s)} + 2CN^- = Ag(CN)_2{}^- + I^-$$

The least soluble of all the argentous compounds is the sulfide; it is precipitated when any one of the aforementioned precipitates or complexes is treated with hydrogen sulfide. The solubility of the sulfide is so low that even metallic silver is slowly acted upon by solutions of hydrogen sulfide, with the liberation of hydrogen.

$$2Ag + H_2S = Ag_2S_{(s)} + H_2$$

Stated in another way, the electrode potential of silver in contact with a molar solution of sulfide ion is $+0.71$ v., as compared with -0.80 v. for the standard electrode potential of silver.

Other common slightly soluble argentous compounds include the dark red arsenate, Ag_3AsO_4; the yellow arsenite, Ag_3AsO_3; the pale yellow phosphate, Ag_3PO_4; the red chromate, Ag_2CrO_4; and the orange ferricyanide, $Ag_3Fe(CN)_6$. Silver nitrite, $AgNO_2$, and silver sulfate, Ag_2SO_4, are only moderately soluble in water.

Silver nitrate, $AgNO_3$, is the most widely used of the silver compounds. It is characterized by its low melting point ($212°$ C.) and its very high solubility in water. It is prepared on an industrial scale by the action of nitric acid on silver metal. It is used medicinally under the name of "lunar caustic," in dilute solutions as an antiseptic, and in concentrated solutions as a caustic. It is reduced to free silver when in contact with organic material, and therefore produces a black stain on the skin or on fabrics. Silver nitrate is the starting material from which other silver compounds are made and is used in large quantities in the silver-plating and photographic industries.

9. The Photographic Process. The argentous halides are sensitive to light; that is, on standing in the light they slowly decompose into silver and the free halogen. Ordinary black-and-white photography is based upon this property. In the preparation of a photographic plate or film, glass or celluloid is coated with a layer of a colloidal suspension of argentous bromide in gelatin. This emulsion is prepared from concentrated solutions of potassium bromide and gelatin, and argentous nitrate; the mixture is heated until it forms a jelly. The argentous bromide precipitate remains in the colloidal state because of the protective action of the gelatin (p. 367). The film must, of course, be prepared either in the dark or in very faint red light.

When the film is exposed in the camera, a real inverted image is produced on the film by light reflected from the object and focused by the lens. Such exposure, which is usually of very short duration, "sensitizes" the silver bromide at the point where the light strikes. The nature of the sensitization process is not very well understood, but it is believed that a few silver and bromide ions are converted to the free atoms without disturbing the crystal lattice; no visible effect is observable at this stage, however, and the film is said to bear a "latent image."

After exposure, the film is developed by immersion in a solution of an organic reducing agent such as hydroquinone or pyrogallol. At the points where the film has been sensitized by the action of light, the reduction of the argentous bromide to free silver is catalyzed, the speed of reduction being

 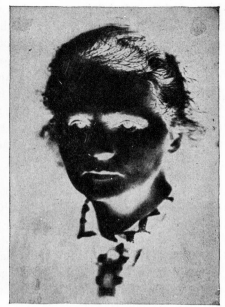

Fig. 41.2. A photographic print of Madame Curie, and the negative from which it was made. (*Courtesy of Journal of Chemical Education.*)

proportional to the intensity of illumination during the exposure. Thus a visible image is obtained in which the darker regions (those having heavy silver deposits) correspond to the lighter portions of the object, and the lighter regions to the darker portions of the object. When the development has proceeded to the proper degree, the film is removed from the solution, washed, fixed by treatment with sodium thiosulfate solution (sometimes called "hypo") to dissolve the unchanged silver bromide, and again thoroughly washed. The film thus prepared is called a negative.

A print is made by exposure of photographic paper, coated with silver bromide or chloride emulsion, to light which has passed through the negative. This results in reversal of the image, so that the location of the light and dark portions corresponds to that in the original object. The exposed paper is then developed and fixed in the same manner as the negative. A photographic print and the negative from which it was made are shown in Figure 41.2.

10. Compounds of Silver in Higher Oxidation States. Because of the fact that silver in all its familiar compounds is in the $+1$ oxidation state, the existence of well-defined stable compounds in which it has oxidation numbers of $+2$ and $+3$ is commonly overlooked. Argentic oxide, AgO, may be obtained as a black powder by the reaction of argentous nitrate with a mixture of sodium carbonate and potassium persulfate. This oxide dissolves in concentrated sulfuric, perchloric, or nitric acid to give solutions of strong oxidizing power. Argentic fluoride, AgF_2, contaminated with some argentous fluoride, is obtained by the action of fluorine on silver or silver salts. A number of stable complexes are known, also, in which silver has an oxidation number of $+2$. Compounds of $+2$ silver are very strong oxidizing agents, as is indicated by the oxidation potential for the following half-reaction:

$$Ag^+ = Ag^{++} + e^-; E = -1.98 \text{ v.}$$

Compounds of $+3$ silver are even less familiar than argentic compounds but the mixed oxide $Ag_2^{III}O_3 \cdot 2Ag^{II}O$ has been prepared, as have several complexes of the triply charged silver ion.

11. Compounds of Gold. The relationship between the compounds of $+1$ gold (aurous) and those of $+3$ gold (auric) is somewhat similar to the corresponding relationship between cuprous and cupric compounds. Aurous ion, like cuprous, is unstable in aqueous solution, reacting with water according to the equation

$$6Au^+ + 3H_2O = Au_2O_3 + 4Au + 6H^+$$

Hence the only aurous compounds and complexes which are stable in aqueous solution are those that are less soluble or less dissociated than the corresponding auric compounds or complexes. The most stable aurous ion is aurocyanide, $Au(CN)_2^-$.

When metallic gold is treated with fluorine, chlorine, or bromine at slightly elevated temperatures, the corresponding auric halide is obtained.

$$2Au + 3X_2 = 2AuX_3$$

These halides are hydrolyzed in water to give brown hydrous auric oxide, $Au_2O_3 \cdot xH_2O$. The addition of hydroxides to auric solutions likewise precipitates the hydrous oxide. Black auric oxide is amphoteric, dissolving in highly alkaline solutions to give aurate ion, AuO_2^- or more probably $Au(OH)_4^-$, and in acids to give auric solutions. The sulfides of gold, Au_2S and Au_2S_3, may likewise be designated as amphoteric, since they dissolve in solutions of sulfides to form thioaurites and thioaurates.

When auric chloride is dissolved in excess of hydrochloric acid, or when gold is dissolved in aqua regia (p. 494), a solution of chlorauric acid, $HAuCl_4$, is obtained.

$$AuCl_3 + HCl = H^+ + AuCl_4^-$$

A sensitive test for gold consists in the treatment of a dilute solution of the gold compound with a solution of a mixture of stannous and stannic chlorides. Upon being heated, the solution yields a deep purple precipitate known as purple of Cassius, which consists of colloidal gold adsorbed on colloidal stannic acid (p. 818).

STUDY QUESTIONS AND PROBLEMS

1. Outline the most important physical properties of copper metal and show how these properties are exploited in industrial applications of copper.

2. Write electronic formulas for the following: (a) $Cu(NH_3)_4^{++}$, (b) $AuCl_4^-$, and (c) $Ag(CN)_2^-$.

3. Account for the color changes which occur when a saturated cupric chloride solution is diluted; when ammonia is slowly added to a solution containing cupric ion until an excess is present.

4. Silver metal is unaffected by dilute hydrochloric acid. Explain the fact that it dissolves in solutions of the very weak acid H_2S, with the evolution of hydrogen.

5. Outline the steps in making a black-and-white photograph. Give, in so far as you are able, the chemistry of the various processes involved.

6. Would AgF_2 be a good oxidizing agent? Why, or why not?

7. How many grams of 14 karat gold could be made from 32.4 g. of sodium auricyanide, $Na[Au(CN)_4]$?

42

The Zinc Family

1. History. The elements zinc, cadmium, and mercury, commonly known as the zinc family, constitute Group 2b of the periodic system. Although the zinc alloy known as brass had been made for many centuries by the reduction, in the presence of copper, of minerals which we now know to be zinc ores, it was not until 1746 that free zinc metal was prepared and its identity as a distinct element well established. Cadmium was not discovered until 1817, when it was recognized as an impurity in many zinc preparations. Mercury, however, was well known to the ancient world, since the easy reducibility of its ores had led to its early discovery. Large quantities of mercury were used in the practice of alchemy.

Table 42.1

Element	1	2	3	4	5	6
	s	s p	s p d	s p d f	s p d	s
Group 2a						
Ca	2	2, 6	2, 6	2		
Sr	2	2, 6	2, 6, 10	2, 6	2	
Ba	2	2, 6	2, 6, 10	2, 6, 10	2, 6	2
Group 2b						
Zn	2	2, 6	2, 6, 10	2		
Cd	2	2, 6	2, 6, 10	2, 6, 10	2	
Hg	2	2, 6	2, 6, 10	2, 6, 10, 14	2, 6, 10	2

2. General Characteristics. As may be seen from the electronic configurations in Table 42.1, the relationships between the electronic configurations of the elements of Groups 2a and 2b are analogous to those between the configurations of Groups 1a and 1b. It is not surprising, therefore, to find a contrast between the zinc family and the alkaline earth metals similar to that between the copper family and the alkali metals. The elements of the zinc family are much less reactive than the corresponding alkaline earth metals. Whereas the oxides and hydroxides of the alkaline earth metals are strongly basic, the corresponding compounds of the zinc family are much less so, zinc oxide and hydroxide being amphoteric. The elements of the zinc family show a strong tendency to form complex ions, whereas the corresponding alkaline earth metals show a relatively slight tendency in this direction. The halides of the zinc family, both in the molten condition and in aqueous solution, are poor conductors of electricity, a property which indicates a definite tendency for the elements of the zinc family to form covalent bonds. These differences in properties are explained by the fact that the elements of the zinc family have higher ionization potentials and smaller ionic radii than do the corresponding alkaline earth metals. The reasons for these differences in ionic radius and ionization potential are similar to those given in the discussion of the copper family (p. 759).

The elements of the zinc family, however, are more reactive than those of the copper family. This is particularly true of zinc and cadmium, which are above hydrogen in the electromotive series and hence dissolve readily in nonoxidizing acids, and whose oxides are relatively difficult to reduce. Mercury, however, is much less active than zinc and cadmium, and is well below hydrogen in the oxidation potential series. The explanation of this fact was given in the preceding chapter, in the discussion of the analogous relationship of gold to copper and silver (p. 759).

While many of the properties of zinc, cadmium, and mercury are similar to those of the transition metals, the zinc family cannot be considered as a true transition family, for there is no evidence that electrons from any shell other than the outermost one enter into chemical bond formation. The highest oxidation state of all these elements is $+2$, corresponding to the loss of two electrons in the valence shell. Mercury, it is true, forms also a series of compounds in which it has an oxidation number of $+1$, but it has been shown that these compounds contain the ion Hg_2^{++}, which has the electronic formula

$$^+Hg : Hg^+$$

and thus results from the loss of one electron by each mercury atom and the formation of a covalent bond between the two by means of the remaining valence electron of each.

Some of the important properties of the elements of the zinc family are summarized in Table 42.2.

Table 42.4

	Zn	Cd	Hg
Atomic number	30	48	80
Ionization potential (v.)			
1st electron	9.4	9.0	10.4
2nd electron	17.9	16.8	18.7
Ionic radius (Å)	0.74	0.97	1.10
Density (g./cc. at 25° C.)	7.14	8.65	13.55
Melting point (°C.)	419.4	320.9	−38.87
Boiling point (°C.)	907	767	356.9
Oxidation potential (v.)			
$M = M^{++} + 2e^-$	0.76	0.40	−0.85

3. Occurrence of the Elements. Because of its relatively high activity, zinc is never found in the free state in nature. In the form of its compounds, however, zinc is widely distributed and is estimated to constitute $4 \times 10^{-5}\%$ of the igneous rocks in the earth's crust. By far the most important zinc ore is the sulfide, ZnS, known as sphalerite or zinc blende. This ore usually contains varying amounts of iron, lead, silver, and cadmium sulfides, as well as other mineral impurities. Other zinc ores include calamine, $Zn_2SiO_4 \cdot H_2O$, franklinite, $(Zn, Mn, Fe)O \cdot (Fe, Mn)_2O_3$, smithsonite, $ZnCO_3$, and zincite, ZnO. The United States leads the world in the amount of zinc ores mined. The major sources of domestic production are the sphalerite deposits of the Joplin district including sections of Kansas, Oklahoma, and Missouri, and the franklinite and calamine deposits of New Jersey. Major foreign sources of zinc ore include Canada, Italy, Australia, Russia, Poland, and Mexico.

Like zinc, cadmium occurs only in the combined form in nature. No important ores of cadmium are known. It almost invariably occurs as an impurity in zinc ores, generally in the ratio of about 1 part of cadmium to 200 parts of zinc.

Mercury is estimated to make up $10^{-7}\%$ of the igneous rocks in the earth's crust. Metallic mercury, as well as alloys of mercury with gold and silver, is occasionally found in nature. The most important source of mercury, however, is the dark red sulfide mineral, HgS, known as cinnabar. Italy and Spain produce the major portion of the world's mercury. The United States ranks third, followed by Russia and Mexico.

4. Metallurgy, Properties, and Uses. Most ores of zinc must be concentrated before reduction. In the case of the sulfide this is done by flotation (p. 761), whereas either simple washing or magnetic separation is used for

Fig. 42.1. Horizontal retort zinc furnace. The carbon monoxide burns to carbon dioxide at the mouth of each retort.

the oxidized ores. The ore is then converted to the oxide. In the case of the sulfide ore, the sulfur dioxide obtained as a by-product of the roasting process is used as a source of sulfuric acid (p. 459), and therefore plays an important role in the economy of the operation.

$$2ZnS + 3O_2 = 2ZnO + 2SO_2$$

Three methods for the reduction of the roasted zinc ore to the metal are in use. The oldest and most commonly used of these is known as the retort process. It consists in the reduction of zinc oxide with carbon at high temperatures. A finely divided mixture of roasted zinc ore and hard coal is placed in cylindrical earthenware retorts about 8 in. in inside diameter and 5 ft. in length. Each retort is connected to an aircooled condenser. A number of these retorts are arranged in tiers in a large furnace, as is shown in Figure 42.1. These retorts are heated to a temperature of about 1100° C. At this temperature the zinc oxide is reduced to metallic zinc according to the following equilibria:

$$ZnO + CO \rightleftharpoons Zn + CO_2$$
$$CO_2 + C \rightleftharpoons 2CO$$

Since the first of these equilibria is readily shifted to the left at high temperatures, it is necessary that an excess of coal be used so as to prevent the building up of an appreciable concentration of carbon dioxide. Likewise, since zinc reacts readily with oxygen at high temperatures, air must be excluded from the retort. As the temperature at which the process is carried out is well above the boiling point of zinc, the metal is liberated in the form of vapor, which condenses to the liquid state in clay condensers. At intervals the liquid metal is removed from the condensers and cast into ingots; in this form it is known as spelter. Although it contains a number of impurities, among which cadmium and lead are the most important, spelter is used for many purposes without refining. If desired, however, refining may be carried out by liquation or redistillation.

The second method is known as the electrothermic process and consists in reduction of zinc oxide by coke in an electric resistance furnace in which the zinc oxide–coke mixture acts as the resistor. The furnace consists of a refractory-lined cylinder about 40 ft. in height and 6 ft. in diameter, with electrodes located near the top and bottom. The furnace is operated at a temperature of $1200°$ C.; the charge is automatically introduced at the top and the spent material withdrawn at the bottom. Zinc vapor and carbon monoxide are withdrawn near the top of the furnace, and the zinc vapor is condensed in an earthenware condenser.

In the third, or electrolytic, method, the roasted ore is treated with sulfuric acid, which yields a solution of zinc sulfate. The solution contains various impurities, the nature of which depends upon the composition of the original ore. The purification process to which the solution is subjected depends, of course, on the nature of these impurities. Very pure zinc metal is obtained from the purified solution by electrolysis. The sulfuric acid used in the treatment of the roasted product is made from the sulfur dioxide obtained during the roasting of the original sulfide ore.

Zinc is a white, highly crystalline, but not particularly strong metal. Because of its low melting point, its high fluidity in the molten state, and the fact that it shrinks but little on solidification, zinc is a good casting metal. It is hard and brittle at room temperature, especially if impure, but when heated to between 100 and $150°$ C. its malleability and ductility increase so that it may be rolled into sheets or drawn into wire. At higher temperatures the metal again becomes very brittle.

As indicated by its relatively high electrode potential (+0.76 v.), zinc dissolves in acids with the release of hydrogen. Zinc metal reacts with superheated steam to produce hydrogen and zinc hydroxide.

$$Zn + 2H_2O = Zn(OH)_2 + H_2$$

Because of the amphoteric nature of zinc hydroxide, zinc dissolves also in alkali hydroxide solutions, to yield hydrogen and solutions of the corresponding alkali zincate.

$$Zn + 2OH^- + 2H_2O = Zn(OH)_4^{--} + H_2$$

On standing in air, zinc becomes coated with a thin film of basic zinc carbonate which serves as a protection against further corrosion. At temperatures above 500° C. zinc burns in air with the formation of white clouds of zinc oxide. Zinc metal reacts with the halogens to form halides, and with sulfur, selenium, tellurium, phosphorus, arsenic, and other nonmetals to form the sulfide, ZnS, selenide, $ZnSe$, phosphide, Zn_3P_2, arsenide, Zn_3As_2, etc., respectively.

The most important use of metallic zinc is as a protective coating for iron. It may seem strange that a relatively active metal such as zinc should be used to protect iron, a less active metal, from corrosion. There are two reasons why zinc is serviceable for this purpose. The first is that although zinc readily forms a film of basic carbonate on contact with air, this film protects the metal against further action. The second reason is that zinc, being more active than iron, releases electrons to the corroding agent, such as atmospheric oxygen or moisture, more readily than does iron, and hence protects the iron against oxidation by itself becoming oxidized. Thus, even though small holes are made in the zinc coating, the iron, unlike iron coated with tin, still does not corrode. Zinc is applied to iron objects by several different methods. Ordinary galvanized iron is prepared by immersion of the iron object in dilute sulfuric acid to remove oxide film, and then in molten zinc. Electrogalvanized iron is prepared by electrolytic deposition of zinc on the iron surface. Sherardized iron is prepared by treatment of iron objects with zinc dust in a rotating drum at a temperature sufficiently high to vaporize the zinc, which alloys with the iron at the surface of the object. Sometimes, as in Schoop's process, molten zinc is sprayed on the iron surface.

The second most important use of zinc, accounting for between one-fourth and one-third of the zinc used in this country, is in the manufacture of brass (p. 764).

Rolled sheet zinc is used for roofing, gutters, vat linings, containers for dry cells (p. 421), and other minor applications. The excellent casting properties of zinc have brought about its increasing use in the die-casting of light fixtures, automobile parts, ornamental hardware, and other such objects which do not require high strength.

Metallic cadmium is obtained as a by-product of the zinc industry; since it is more volatile than zinc, the metals may be separated by distillation. Cadmium has a lower electrode potential than zinc, and therefore, by careful regulation of the potential applied to the cell in the electrolytic process, pure cadmium may be obtained before any zinc is deposited. Cadmium may also be precipitated from the sulfate solution, along with other less active metals, by the addition of metallic zinc.

$$Cd^{++} + Zn = Cd + Zn^{++}$$

Cadmium is a bluish-white metal, somewhat softer than zinc, as well as more malleable and ductile. The chemical reactions of cadmium are similar to those of zinc, with such modifications as would be expected from the lower reactivity of cadmium. Since cadmium hydroxide is not appreciably amphoteric, cadmium is unaffected by solutions of alkali hydroxides.

The major use of cadmium is as a protective coating, usually applied electrolytically, on iron and steel. Cadmium alloys (99% Cd, 1% Ni; 98.7% Cd, 0.7% Ag, 0.6% Cu) are used as bearing-metals (p. 520) in aircraft engines. Cadmium is used also in low-melting alloys (p. 521), and as a replacement for tin in some solders (p. 816). Sponge cadmium is used as anode in the nickel–cadmium storage battery (p. 435).

Mercury is obtained by the roasting of cinnabar in the presence of air. The sulfur in the mercuric sulfide is oxidized to sulfur dioxide according to the equation

$$HgS + O_2 = Hg + SO_2$$

The mercury is not changed to the oxide, however, but is reduced; for, at the temperature of the furnace, the oxides of mercury are unstable. Mercury vapor, therefore, is distilled from the furnace, and is collected in a condensing system. The liquid product is purified by filtration through chamois skin or linen, followed by washing with dilute nitric acid or mercurous nitrate solution to oxidize the metallic impurities. Mercury may also be purified by redistillation in the presence of air; in this case, nonvolatile metallic impurities are left behind, while volatile impurities such as cadmium and zinc are oxidized to the nonvolatile oxides.

Mercury is the only metallic element which is a liquid at room temperatures. The symbol Hg is derived from the Latin word *hydrargyrum*, meaning "liquid silver." Mercury is a good conductor of electricity, both in the liquid and in the solid state. Compared with other common liquids, mercury has a very low vapor pressure at room temperature. The thermal coefficient of expansion of liquid mercury is almost constant over the temperature range of 0 to about 300° C. All the common metals, except iron and platinum, dissolve in mercury to form alloys which are known as amalgams.

As is indicated by its high ionization potential and its low electrode potential, mercury is a relatively inactive metal. It shows little tendency to corrode in air, except in the presence of hydrogen sulfide, and is unaffected by hydrogen ion. It does dissolve in nitric acid, however, yielding mercuric nitrate with an excess of the hot concentrated acid, and mercurous nitrate if the acid is dilute and the metal in excess.

$$Hg + 4H^+ + 2NO_3{}^- = Hg^{++} + 2NO_2 + 2H_2O$$

$$6Hg + 8H^+ + 2NO_3{}^- = 3Hg_2{}^{++} + 2NO + 4H_2O$$

It likewise dissolves in an excess of hot concentrated sulfuric acid to form mercuric sulfate; the presence of an excess of mercury, however, results in the formation of the mercurous compound.

$$Hg + 2H_2SO_4 = Hg^{++} + SO_4{}^{--} + SO_2 + 2H_2O$$

$$2Hg + 2H_2SO_4 = Hg_2{}^{++} + SO_4{}^{--} + SO_2 + 2H_2O$$

When heated in air to about 300° C., mercury is oxidized to mercuric oxide.

Most of the mercury consumed industrially is used in the manufacture of various mercury compounds, the most important of which will be discussed subsequently. A relatively small quantity of metallic mercury is used in the manufacture of scientific instruments; this, however, is an extremely important application. The almost uniform thermal coefficient of expansion of mercury and the fact that it does not wet glass account for its use in thermometers, while its high density and low vapor pressure make it ideal for use in barometers. Among other scientific applications are its use in mercury vapor vacuum pumps, gas analysis apparatus, and mercury arc rectifiers.

Cold mercury vapor is a nonconductor of electricity, yet, once an electric arc has been struck through it, the mercury vapor conducts electricity readily, with the emission of a spectrum rich in green and ultraviolet light. Mercury vapor lamps are used in the treatment of certain diseases and, in general, as a source of ultraviolet radiation. The increasingly familiar fluorescent lamp consists of a tube coated internally with a layer of phosphorescent materials, which, under the stimulation of ultraviolet light from a mercury vapor arc inside the tube, emit a light that is the nearest approach to daylight which has as yet been obtained artificially.

The use of mercury in the amalgamation process for the extraction of gold and silver from their ores has already been discussed (Chapter 41).

Not only mercury vapor, but all soluble mercury salts, are exceedingly poisonous to human beings; liquid mercury, however, except in an extremely finely divided state, is nonpoisonous.

5. Compounds of Zinc and Cadmium. The rather close resemblance be-tween zinc and cadmium makes it convenient to consider the compounds of these two elements together. Mercury, however, stands apart because of its relatively low activity and the consequent low stability of many of its compounds.

The doubly charged ions of zinc and cadmium are hydrated in aqueous sclution; by analogy with other complexes which these ions form, we may represent the hydrates by the formulas $Zn(H_2O)_4^{++}$ and $Cd(H_2O)_4^{++}$. These ions, which are colorless, are poisonous to most organisms. Because of the small size and relatively high charge of the zinc ion, the water molecules which are part of the zinc complex release protons readily. This fact accounts for the strongly acidic nature of solutions of zinc salts.

$$Zn(H_2O)_4^{++} + H_2O \rightleftharpoons Zn(H_2O)_3(OH)^+ + H_3O^+$$

In accord with the larger ionic radius of the cadmium ion, solutions of cadmium salts are but slightly acidic.

In the presence of equivalent quantities of hydroxide ion, however, both cadmium and zinc ions release two protons each, to form uncharged gelatinous precipitates of the hydroxides.

$$M(H_2O)_4^{++} + 2OH^- = M(H_2O)_2(OH)_2 + 2H_2O$$

Since the proportion of water in these precipitates is indefinite, water is usually omitted from the equation.

$$M^{++} + 2OH^- = M(OH)_2$$

The zinc hydroxide precipitate may lose more protons to an excess of hydroxide ion, in accordance with its amphoteric nature.

$$Zn(H_2O)_2(OH)_2 + OH^- = Zn(H_2O)(OH)_3^- + H_2O$$

$$Zn(H_2O)(OH)_3^- + OH^- = Zn(OH)_4^{--} + H_2O$$

The $Zn(OH)_4^{--}$ complex is known as the zincate ion. Thus, when zinc hydroxide is dissolved in an excess of sodium hydroxide solution, a solution of sodium zincate is obtained. The above equilibria are shifted sharply to the left in the absence of excess hydroxide ion; zincates are therefore extensively hydrolyzed, to give alkaline solutions.

Cadmium hydroxide is not appreciably soluble in an excess of hydroxide ion. Both zinc and cadmium hydroxides, however, dissolve in aqueous solutions of ammonia, or of alkali cyanides, with the formation of the complex, ions $Zn(NH_3)_4^{++}$, $Zn(CN)_4^{--}$, $Cd(NH_3)_4^{++}$, or $Cd(CN)_4^{--}$. The electronic formulas for these zinc and cadmium complexes are as follows:

```
          H                  ++            H              ++
          ..                          H : N : H
        : O : H                           H            H
   H              ..                 ..          ..
   ..        ..              H : N :    M    : N : H
H : O :   M   : O : H             H            H
   ..              ..                 ..
          H                       H : N : H
        ..                            H
      H : O :
          ..
          H
```

```
          N                  --            H              --
          ::                              ..
          ::                            : O :
          C                        ..          ..
          ::                  H : O : Zn : O : H
    :N:::C: M :C:::N:               ..    ..
          C                            : O :
          ::                            ..
          ::                             H
          N
          ..
```

Zinc oxide, the most important of all the compounds of zinc, is prepared industrially either by the direct reaction of zinc vapor with oxygen in the air, or by the roasting of a mixture of an oxidized zinc ore (particularly franklinite or calamine) and carbon in a blast of air. Although the oxide is reduced by the carbon, the zinc vapor thus formed is immediately oxidized again to a finely powdered oxide, which is carried along with the air blast and is collected in filter bags. Zinc oxide is extensively employed as a filler in rubber goods, as a component of various glazes and enamels, and as a white pigment. Although its covering power is inferior to that of white lead (p. 823), zinc oxide in paints has the advantage of not turning black in the presence of hydrogen sulfide. Because of its antiseptic and mildly basic nature, zinc oxide is used in ointments and antiseptic dusting powders. Over 300,000,000 lb. of ZnO is produced annually in the United States.

White zinc sulfide, ZnS, and yellow cadmium sulfide, CdS, are only very slightly soluble in water. Zinc sulfide dissolves in dilute solutions of strong acids but may be precipitated in acetic acid solutions if a sufficient concentration of acetate ion is present. Cadmium sulfide is much less soluble and may be precipitated even from solutions containing moderately high concentrations of hydrogen ion. Because of the formation of ammonia complexes, both sulfides dissolve slightly in aqueous ammonia. Both zinc sulfide and cadmium sulfide (cadmium yellow) are used as pigments.

786 THE ZINC FAMILY

Both cadmium and zinc form stable halides with all four halogens. The chlorides, bromides, and iodides of these metals are readily soluble in water, the fluorides moderately so. Concentrated solutions of these halides have exceptionally low electrical conductances; this fact has been attributed to the formation of complex ions of the type MX_4^{--} (cf. copper halides, p. 770). Such complex ion formation occurs to a small extent with the zinc halides, but to a much greater degree in the case of the cadmium compounds. Thus, even in a $0.05M$ solution of cadmium iodide, the conductance is only one-fifth of that to be expected if the salt were completely ionized into simple ions.

The highly acidic character of solutions of zinc halides is manifested in their ability to dissolve oxides of other metals. Zinc oxide dissolves in concentrated solutions of zinc chloride to produce a basic zinc chloride which sets to a hard mass, and thus may be used as a cement. Because of its ability to dissolve metallic oxides, zinc chloride solution is used as a flux in soldering. Zinc chloride gelatinizes cellulose and is therefore used in the manufacture of wallboard and for the preservation of wood.

Both zinc and cadmium sulfates are readily soluble in water. At ordinary temperatures, these salts crystallize as the hydrates $ZnSO_4 \cdot 7H_2O$, known as white vitriol, and $3CdSO_4 \cdot 8H_2O$, respectively. The most important use of zinc sulfate is in the manufacture of the white paint pigment known as lithopone. This substance, which consists of a mixture of the insoluble salts zinc sulfide and barium sulfate, is manufactured by a process represented by the equation

$$Zn^{++} + SO_4^{--} + Ba^{++} + S^{--} = ZnS + BaSO_4$$

Cadmium sulfate is used in the manufacture of standard voltaic cells for use in precise electrical measurements.

6. Compounds of Mercury. It was pointed out earlier in this chapter that mercury forms two series of compounds, mercuric, in which it occurs in the form of the doubly charged positive ion Hg^{++}, and mercurous, which contain the Hg_2^{++} ion. That mercurous compounds actually contain this ion, rather than the singly charged ion Hg^+, is indicated by a number of experimental observations, among which are vapor density measurements on volatile mercurous compounds, and magnetic data.

From the following oxidation potentials:

$$Hg = Hg^{++} + 2e^-; E = -0.85 \text{ v.}$$
$$2Hg = Hg_2^{++} + 2e^-; E = -0.79 \text{ v.}$$

it may be shown (p. 429) that mercuric ion is reduced to mercurous ion by free mercury;

$$Hg^{++} + Hg = Hg_2^{++}$$

or, to put it another way, mercurous ion, under ordinary conditions, does not decompose into mercuric ion and mercury. However, in the presence of an anion that forms a much less soluble compound with the mercuric than with the mercurous ion, this order of stability is reversed; thus, mercurous oxide, which is obtained as a black precipitate when solutions of mercurous salts are treated with solutions containing hydroxide ion, slowly decomposes into mercuric oxide and free mercury. Mercurous sulfide undergoes a similar decomposition almost immediately after precipitation.

The mercurous halides are similar to those of silver in their slight solubility in water. The most important of these is the chloride Hg_2Cl_2, which is obtained by the addition of a solution of a soluble chloride to a solution of mercurous nitrate, or by the heating of a mixture of mercuric chloride and free mercury. In the latter case mercurous chloride sublimes from the mixture. Mercurous chloride is used as an internal medicine under the name of calomel. This is possible, in spite of the highly poisonous nature of mercury compounds, because of the low solubility of this substance. Mercurous chloride, white in color, turns black upon the addition of ammonia solution; white insoluble mercuric amidochloride and free mercury are formed.

$$Hg_2Cl_2 + 2NH_3 = HgNH_2Cl + Hg + NH_4^+ + Cl^-$$

The black color is due to the presence of free mercury in a finely divided condition. This reaction serves as a good qualitative test for mercurous ion. Soluble mercurous salts, except in the presence of moderately high concentrations of hydrogen ion, undergo hydrolysis to form precipitates of basic salts.

Mercuric oxide is obtained when mercury is heated in air at about 300° C., or, more commonly, by the heating of a mixture of mercury and mercuric nitrate.

$$Hg(NO_3)_2 + Hg = 2HgO + 2NO_2$$

The oxide is precipitated from solutions of mercuric salts by the addition of solutions of alkali hydroxides, mercuric hydroxide being unstable. The oxide exists in a yellow form and a red form, which apparently differ only in their state of subdivision, rather than in their crystal structure. On being heated to temperatures much above 300° C. mercuric oxide decomposes to give free mercury and oxygen.

Mercuric sulfide is obtained as a black precipitate when solutions of mercuric salts are treated with hydrogen sulfide, even in the presence of a very high concentration of hydrogen ion. The insolubility of mercuric sulfide in boiling dilute nitric acid is utilized in the separation of mercuric ion from other heavy metal cations. Naturally occurring mercuric sulfide (cinnabar) is red in color. The red form may also be obtained artificially from mercury and sulfur at elevated temperatures; this product is used as a paint pigment under the name of vermilion.

Mercuric chloride, $HgCl_2$, commonly known as corrosive sublimate or bichloride of mercury, is obtained when mercury is heated in an atmosphere of chlorine. Since mercuric chloride is readily volatile, however, it is most commonly prepared by volatilization from a dry mixture of sodium chloride and mercuric sulfate.

$$HgSO_4 + 2NaCl = HgCl_2 + Na_2SO_4$$

Because of its reaction with proteins in the cells of an organism, it is a violent poison. A very dilute solution (1 : 1000), however, is used as an antiseptic. Mercuric chloride reacts with solutions of ammonia to form insoluble white mercuric amidochloride.

$$HgCl_2 + 2NH_3 = HgNH_2Cl + NH_4^+ + Cl^-$$

Solutions of the mercuric halides, like those of the corresponding cadmium compounds, are poor conductors of electricity, because of the formation of complexes of the type HgX_4^{--}. The solubilities of the mercuric halides in water decrease in the order $HgF_2 > HgCl_2 > HgBr_2 > HgI_2$, the iodide having a very low solubility. These solubilities, however, are increased by the presence of excess halide ion, mercuric iodide being readily soluble in solutions of potassium iodide.

$$HgI_2 + 2I^- = HgI_4^{--}$$

Mercuric oxide likewise dissolves in solutions of iodides to yield the same complex.

$$HgO + H_2O + 4I^- = HgI_4^{--} + 2OH^-$$

A solution of potassium hydroxide and the soluble complex salt K_2HgI_4, known as Nessler's reagent, gives a yellow precipitate with ammonium ion, and is used as a sensitive test for the latter substance. Soluble mercuric salts are readily hydrolyzed to form precipitates of basic salts, except in the presence of rather high concentrations of hydrogen ion.

A considerable fraction of the world's supply of mercury is used in the production of mercuric fulminate, $Hg(OCN)_2$, by the addition of alcohol to the solution obtained by the reaction of hot nitric acid on mercury. Mercuric fulminate explodes violently when struck and is used in the manufacture of percussion caps for the detonation of other explosives.

One of the most characteristic tests for mercuric ion is the formation of a white to gray precipitate when solutions containing this ion are treated with stannous chloride. The reaction proceeds in two steps.

$$2Hg^{++} + Sn^{++} + 2Cl^- = Sn^{++++} + Hg_2Cl_2$$
white

$$Hg_2Cl_2 + Sn^{++} = Sn^{++++} + 2Hg + 2Cl^-$$
black

STUDY QUESTIONS AND PROBLEMS

1. Summarize the general characteristics of the elements of the zinc family and relate these characteristics to the electronic configurations of their atoms.

2. Outline briefly the methods by which metallic zinc is prepared from its ores. Upon what principle does the use of zinc to protect iron from corrosion depend?

3. Suggest methods whereby it could be shown experimentally that the formula of mercurous chloride is Hg_2Cl_2 rather than $HgCl$.

4. The formula for zincate ion is sometimes written ZnO_2^{--} rather than $Zn(OH)_4^{--}$. Can you think of any means by which it could be shown which is the correct formula?

5. Amalgams are commonly considered to be solutions of one or more metals in mercury. How would you go about proving that a given amalgam is not a chemical compound?

43

The Aluminum Family

1. History. The aluminum family consists of the elements of Group 3a of the periodic system: boron, aluminum, gallium, indium, and thallium. None of these elements was known in the free state prior to the beginning of the nineteenth century. Boron was isolated by Sir Humphry Davy and by Gay-Lussac and Thenard in 1808, and aluminum by Oersted in 1825 and by Wöhler in 1827. Gallium was first prepared by the French chemist de Boisbaudran in 1875, indium by the German chemist Reich in 1863, and thallium by Sir William Crookes in 1861. Aluminum derives its name from alum (p. 806), an aluminum compound known to the ancients, while the word boron comes from borax, of Arabic origin. De Boisbaudran named gallium from the Latin name for France (*Gallia*), indium was named from the bright indigo lines in its spectrum, and Crookes chose the name thallium (Greek *thallos*, meaning "green twig") because of the bright green line in the spectrum of that element.

2. General Characteristics. The electron configurations of the atoms of the aluminum family are listed in Table 43.1.

Table 43.1

Element	1 s	2 s p	3 s p d	4 s p d f	5 s p d	6 s p
B	2	2, 1				
Al	2	2, 6	2, 1			
Ga	2	2, 6	2, 6, 10	2, 1		
In	2	2, 6	2, 6, 10	2, 6, 10	2, 1	
Tl	2	2, 6	2, 6, 10	2, 6, 10, 14	2, 6, 10	2, 1

On the basis of their electron configurations, the elements of this family fall into two classes. Boron and aluminum follow immediately after the corresponding alkaline earth metals in the periodic system, and thus differ from them by a single additional unit of positive charge on the nucleus of the atom and a single additional electron in the valence shell. The atoms of these two elements, like those of the alkali and the alkaline earth metals, are left with inert gas configurations when their valance electrons are removed. Gallium, indium, and thallium, however, are separated from the corresponding members of the alkaline earth family by a group of transition metals; atoms of these three elements have completed shells of 18 electrons underlying their valence electrons, and do not, therefore, attain inert gas configurations when their valence electrons are lost.

Another interesting point in connection with the aluminum family is that the three valence electrons, in each case, are not all alike. Both the valence electrons of an atom of an alkaline earth metal belong to the s subshell of the valence shell, and hence have the same energy. The valence electrons in the atoms of elements of the aluminum family are of two types, however; for two of the three are s electrons and the other is a p electron. In general, p electrons are slightly more easily removed than s electrons in the same shell (p. 184). This accounts for the fact that, in spite of the larger charge on the boron and aluminum nuclei, the first ionization potentials of boron and aluminum are lower than those of beryllium and magnesium. Gallium, which has a nuclear charge 11 units higher than that of calcium, nevertheless has a lower first ionization potential; and the first ionization potential of indium is only slightly higher than that of strontium. Even thallium, with a nuclear charge 25 units larger than that of barium, has a first ionization potential only about one volt higher than that of the latter element. However, the second ionization potentials of the elements of the aluminum family are distinctly higher than the second ionization potentials of the alkaline earth metals, for here s electrons are involved in both cases, and the normal effect of increased nuclear charge comes into play.

The low values of the first ionization potentials account for the fact that compounds of gallium, indium, and thallium readily give characteristic colors in a Bunsen flame (see p. 639).

The data in Table 43.2 show that the ionization potentials do not decrease steadily with increasing atomic number in Group 3a as they do in Groups 1a and 2a. Instead there is a slight increase in ionization potential from aluminum to gallium, due probably to the change from a type of configuration in which the valence shell is underlain by a shell of eight electrons to one in which it is underlaid by a shell of eighteen; the increase in nuclear charge from aluminum to gallium is 10 units greater than from boron to aluminum. There is also a marked increase in ionization potential from indium to thallium; the explanation for this is entirely analogous to that for the corresponding increases from silver to gold and from cadmium to mercury (p. 777).

Table 43.2

Ionization Potentials of the Elements of Groups 2a and 3a

Electron	B	Al	Ga	In	Tl
1st	8.3	6.0	6.0	5.8	6.1
2nd	25.1	18.8	20.4	18.8	20.3
3rd	37.9	28.4	30.6	27.9	29.7
4th	259.3	120.0	63.8	57.8	50.5
	Be	Mg	Ca	Sr	Ba
1st	9.3	7.6	6.1	5.7	5.2
2nd	18.2	15.0	11.9	11.0	10.0
3rd	153.9	80.1	51.2	. . .	. . .

The great differences between the third and fourth ionization potentials of the elements of the aluminum family indicate that, as indeed would be expected from their electron configurations, each of these elements attains a maximum oxidation number of $+3$. Furthermore, in the light of the previous discussion concerning the marked difference in the first and second ionization potentials of these elements, it is not surprising that the elements gallium, indium, and thallium also form compounds in which they lose only one electron and hence exhibit an oxidation state of $+1$. Such compounds of thallium are especially important.

Table 43.3

Ionic Radii of the Elements of Groups 1a, 2a, and 3a (Angstrom Units)

Li^+	0.60	Na^+	0.95	K^+	1.33	Rb^+	1.48	Cs^+	1.69
Be^{++}	0.31	Mg^{++}	0.65	Ca^{++}	0.99	Sr^{++}	1.13	Ba^{++}	1.35
B^{+++}	0.20	Al^{+++}	0.50	Ga^{+++}	0.62	In^{+++}	0.81	Tl^{+++}	0.95

In the discussion of the alkaline earth metals (p. 659), it was pointed out that, because of the larger nuclear charge of their atoms, the doubly charged ions of these elements have smaller ionic radii than do the corresponding singly charged alkali metal ions, even though corresponding ions of the two families have the same electron configurations. Similarly, the triply charged ions of the aluminum family elements have smaller radii than do the doubly charged alkaline earth metal ions. The radii of the ions of these three families are compared in Table 43.3.

The low ionic radii and triple charges of the ions of the aluminum family account for the fact that the hydroxyl compounds (or hydrous oxides) of these elements are much less basic than the hydroxides of the alkaline earth and alkali metals. In fact, the boron compound is a weak acid, whose formula is commonly written H_3BO_3. The hydrous oxide of aluminum is amphoteric, as are the corresponding compounds of gallium and indium. However, as would be expected, the acidic characteristics become less pronounced with increasing ionic radius; hydrous thallic oxide does not possess acidic properties. These facts are brought out by the acid ionization constants given in Table 43.4.

Table 43.4

Ionization Constants of the Hydroxides of Group 3a

	Equilibrium			K
H_3BO_3	$=$	H^+	$+$ $H_2BO_3^-$	6×10^{-10}
H_3AlO_3	$=$	H^+	$+$ $H_2AlO_3^-$	4×10^{-13}
H_3GaO_3	$=$	H^+	$+$ $H_2GaO_3^-$	1×10^{-15}
H_3InO_3	$=$	H^+	$+$ $H_2InO_3^-$	$<K$ for H_3GaO_3

Again, because of the small radii and the triple charge on the ions of this family, there is relatively little tendency for atoms of these elements to lose three electrons to form simple ions of the form M^{+++}. Most of their compounds are either covalent or else contain the elements of this group in the form of complex ions such as $Al(H_2O)_6^{+++}$ or BF_4^-. As a rough indication of the increased tendency for the Group 3a elements to form covalent rather than electrovalent bonds, we may observe, from the data in Table 43.5, the

Table 43.5

Melting Points (°C.) of the Anhydrous Chlorides of the Elements of Groups 1a, 2a, and 3a

1a		2a		3a		
LiCl	613	$BeCl_2$	440	BCl_3	-107	
NaCl	800	$MgCl_2$	708	$AlCl_3$	190	(2.5 atm.; sublimes at 177.8° C.
KCl	776	$CaCl_2$	772	$GaCl_3$	78	at 1 atm.)
RbCl	715	$SrCl_2$	873	$InCl_3$	...	(Sublimes at 400° C.)
CsCl	646	$BaCl_2$	962	$TlCl_3$	25	

fact that the chlorides of this group melt at much lower temperatures than do the chlorides of the elements of Groups 1a and 2a. In connection with this table it should be recalled that beryllium chloride, which has a relatively low melting point, is also covalent (p. 660).

Table 43.6

Standard Oxidation Potentials

$Al = Al^{+++} + 3e^-$	$E =$	1.66 v.
$Ga = Ga^{+++} + 3e^-$	$E =$	0.53 v.
$In = In^{+++} + 3e^-$	$E =$	0.34 v.
$Tl = Tl^{+++} + 3e^-$	$E =$	-0.72 v.
$Tl = Tl^{+} + e^-$	$E =$	0.34 v.

The elements of the aluminum family are, as would be expected, less reactive than the alkaline earth metals. The standard oxidation potentials (except for boron, which does not form positive ions in aqueous solution) are listed in Table 43.6. These potentials, although lower than those of the alkaline earth metals, are nevertheless considerably higher than would be expected from the high gaseous ionization potentials of the Group 3a elements. This fact may be explained on the basis of the high heats of hydration of the positive ions (p. 660), as is shown in Table 43.7. These high heats of hydration result from the high charges and small radii of the ions.

Table 43.7

Heats of Hydration of Group 3a Ions

Al^{+++}	1409 Cal./mole
Ga^{+++}	1397 Cal./mole
In^{+++}	1293 Cal./mole
Tl^{+++}	1310 Cal./mole

Of the five elements in this family, only boron and aluminum are of much industrial significance. Boron, largely nonmetallic in its properties, is important mainly for its compounds, while aluminum is one of the most widely used of the metals. It will be convenient, therefore, to consider these two elements and their compounds in separate sections, and to devote a single section to the consideration of gallium, indium, and thallium, and their compounds.

BORON

3. Occurrence. Boron occurs in nature chiefly in the form of boric acid and its salts, and as a constituent of certain complex alumino-silicate minerals which are widely distributed in the rocks in the earth's crust. Free boron is never found in nature. Large beds of such minerals as kernite, $Na_2B_4O_7 \cdot 4H_2O$, colemanite, $Ca_2B_6O_{11} \cdot 5H_2O$, and ulexite, $CaNaB_5O_9 \cdot 8H_2O$, are found in arid regions of western United States, where they were laid down during the evaporation of ancient inland seas. Boric acid, H_3BO_3, occurs in solution in the water from certain hot springs in northern Italy. It is estimated that boron constitutes 0.001% of the earth's crust.

4. Preparation and Properties. Boron is usually prepared by the reaction of boric oxide with magnesium at a high temperature, followed by the removal of the excess magnesium and the magnesium oxide from the product with dilute acid.

$$B_2O_3 + 3Mg = 2B + 3MgO$$

Prepared in this way, boron, contaminated with magnesium boride, is a dark brown, apparently amorphous powder. Pure boron ($>99\%$) has been made by the thermal decomposition or hydrogen reduction of boron trichloride or tribromide, and by the electrolytic reduction of solutions of potassium fluoborate in fused potassium chloride.

Boron has few properties in common with the metals, and is best classified as a nonmetal. It has a density of about 2.34 g. per cc. It melts at a temperature between 2100 and 2200° C., and when cooled from the molten state yields an extremely hard, brittle product. Boron is a very poor conductor of electricity at room temperature, but its conductivity increases enormously with rise in temperature; this is in direct antithesis to the typical behavior of metals (p. 623). Liquid boron boils at about 2550° C.

The chemical properties of the element support its classification as a nonmetal. When heated in the presence of air it burns with a green flame, to yield the acidic oxide B_2O_3. It combines vigorously with fluorine at ordinary temperatures, and with the other halogens when heated, to yield nonsaltlike halides of the general formula BX_3. It reacts also with a wide variety of metals to form extremely hard and nonvolatile borides. Boron does not dissolve in acids, but reacts with fused alkalis to yield borates and hydrogen.

$$2B + 6KOH = 2K_3BO_3 + 3H_2$$

5. Compounds. As was pointed out at the beginning of the chapter, the hydroxyl compound $B(OH)_3$, or orthoboric acid, has no basic properties but acts as a very weak acid. Boric acid is only slight soluble in cold water but dissolves readily in hot: 5.15 g. per 100 ml. at 21° C., and 39.1 g. per 100 ml. at 100° C. It is precipitated in the form of soft, pearly white crystals having a "greasy" feel, when a cold, aqueous solution of a borate, such as borax, is acidified.

When heated to about 100° C., orthoboric acid loses water to form metaboric acid, HBO_2. On further heating, dehydration to pyroboric or tetraboric acid, $H_2B_4O_7$, is reported to occur, and finally, at red heat, complete dehydration to the oxide B_2O_3 takes place. The oxide is obtained by this method as a hard, brittle glass. Because of its tendency to take up water to form boric acid, this substance, when finely divided, is useful as a dehydrating agent. Most metal oxides dissolve in and react with molten boric oxide to give solutions which on solidification yield characteristically colored borate glasses.

Boric acid, sometimes also called boracic acid, is a mild antiseptic and is used medicinally as an eyewash.

Few orthoborates, M_3BO_3, are known. When boric acid is dissolved in sodium hydroxide, a solution of sodium tetraborate, $Na_2B_4O_7$, results.

$$4H_3BO_3 + 2OH^- = B_4O_7^{--} + 7H_2O$$

When this solution is allowed to crystallize at a temperature below 60° C., the hydrate $Na_2B_4O_7 \cdot 10H_2O$ is obtained. This is the most important of the compounds of boron and is commonly known as borax.

As the conjugate base of the weak acid tetraboric acid, tetraborate ion undergoes hydrolysis and borax gives a mildly alkaline aqueous solution. This fact, together with the low solubility of calcium and magnesium borates, explains the use of borax as a water-softener. It is used also as a component of certain soaps, as a preservative, and as an antiseptic, as well as in the manufacture of certain types of glass (p. 555), enamels, and glazes, and as a mordant in the dye industry.

Since sodium tetraborate contains an excess of boric oxide as compared with the metaborate, it is capable, in the molten state, of dissolving metal oxides. On being cooled, these solutions yield clear glasses of characteristic colors. The following equation represents a typical reaction of this type:

$$Na_2B_4O_7 + CoO = 2NaBO_2 + Co(BO_2)_2$$

Such reactions form the basis for the "borax bead tests" by means of which certain metals may be detected from the color which their compounds yield on being heated in a Bunsen flame with a borax bead in a loop of platinum wire. The excess of acidic oxide in borax accounts also for its use to remove coatings of oxides from metal surfaces before soldering or welding.

In addition to the tetraborates, a number of metaborates are known, many of which, such as $AgBO_2$, $Ba(BO_2)_2$, $Pb(BO_2)_2$, and $Mg(BO_2)_2$, are only slightly soluble in water. A large number of complex polyborates of the general empirical formula $(M_2O)_m(B_2O_3)_n$ have also been prepared; n may be as large as six, while m is usually not greater than three. The structures of many of these borates are more complex than is indicated by the empirical formulas.

When solutions of boric acid are heated with methyl or ethyl alcohol, a volatile compound having the formula $B(OCH_3)_3$ or $B(OC_2H_5)_3$, respectively, is obtained. These compounds impart a green color to a flame, and this property may be used as a means of detecting borate ion.

$$B_4O_7^{--} + 2H^+ + 5H_2O = 4B(OH)_3$$

$$B(OH)_3 + 3HOCH_3 = B(OCH_3)_3 + 3H_2O$$

When borate solutions are treated with hydrogen peroxide, or subjected to electrolytic oxidation, compounds commonly known as perborates, but more correctly called peroxyborates, are obtained; the most important of these is the sodium salt $NaBO_3 \cdot 4H_2O$. This compound is a strong oxidizing agent; it is used as a bleaching agent and as an antiseptic component of certain tooth powders.

As was indicated previously, the halides of boron are covalent, wholly non-saltlike compounds. The fluoride and chloride are gases at room temperature, the bromide and iodide a volatile liquid and a solid respectively. It is apparent from the electronic formula for these halides,

$$
\begin{array}{c}
: \ddot{X} : \\
B : \ddot{X} : \\
: \ddot{X} :
\end{array}
$$

that the valence shell of the boron atom is still incomplete; it is not surprising, therefore, to find that the halides tend to complete this shell by accepting pairs of electrons from various donor molecules or ions. This tendency to form complex molecules or ions is particularly strong in the case of boron trifluoride and boron trichloride. The following equations represent typical reactions of this type, which are conveniently classified as acid-base coordinations in the Lewis sense (p. 325):

$$
\begin{array}{ccc}
: \ddot{F} : & H & : \ddot{F} : H \\
: \ddot{F} : B & + : N : H = : \ddot{F} : B : N : H \\
: \ddot{F} : & H & : \ddot{F} : H
\end{array}
$$

$$:\overset{\cdot\cdot}{\underset{\cdot\cdot}{F}}: \qquad\qquad :\overset{\cdot\cdot}{\underset{\cdot\cdot}{F}}:$$

$$:\overset{\cdot\cdot}{\underset{\cdot\cdot}{F}}:B \quad + \quad :\overset{\cdot\cdot}{\underset{\cdot\cdot}{F}}:^{-} \quad = \quad :\overset{\cdot\cdot}{\underset{\cdot\cdot}{F}}:B:\overset{\cdot\cdot}{\underset{\cdot\cdot}{F}}:^{-}$$

$$:\overset{\cdot\cdot}{\underset{\cdot\cdot}{F}}: \qquad\qquad :\overset{\cdot\cdot}{\underset{\cdot\cdot}{F}}:$$

The BF_4^- complex is known as the fluoborate ion. Solutions of the corresponding acid, HBF_4, have been prepared, as well as numerous fluoborates such as $NaBF_4$. Boron trifluoride is an excellent catalyst for many organic chemical reactions which are catalyzed by electron-pair acceptors (Lewis acids).

ALUMINUM

6. Occurrence. Aluminum occurs in greater abundance in the earth's crust than any other metal, and indeed is exceeded in abundance by only two nonmetals, silicon and oxygen. It is estimated that aluminum constitutes 8.13% of the igneous rocks. The strong affinity of the element for oxygen precludes the natural occurrence of the free metal, but a wide variety of aluminum compounds occur in nature. Of these, the most abundant aluminum minerals are the aluminosilicates, among the common types of which are the feldspars, such as orthoclase, $KAlSi_3O_8$; the micas, such as muscovite, $KH_2Al_3(SiO_4)_3$; and the clays, such as kaolin, $H_2Al_2(SiO_4)_2 \cdot H_2O$.

The anhydrous oxide of aluminum, Al_2O_3, occurs naturally as the extremely hard and chemically inert mineral corundum. Because of its hardness, the common form of this mineral is used as an abrasive. A number of varieties of gem stones consist of transparent crystalline corundum, colored by the presence of small amounts of other metal oxides such as Cr_2O_3, TiO_2, Mn_2O_3, and Fe_2O_3. Among such gems are the ruby, the sapphire, the oriental emerald, the oriental topaz, and the oriental amethyst. Artificial (so-called synthetic) rubies and blue sapphires, which differ from the natural gems only in price and in the shape of the microscopic imperfections which they contain, are made from corundum and chromic oxide, and corundum and cobalt oxide, repectively. Other naturally occurring gem stones which contain aluminum include the garnets, complex aluminosilicates with various other metals such as calcium, iron, and magnesium; the turquoise, a basic copper aluminum phosphate; and the topaz, $Al_2(F,OH)_2SiO_4$.

A hard, naturally occurring mixture of anhydrous aluminum oxide and iron oxides (Fe_3O_4 or Fe_2O_3), known as emery, is commonly used as an abrasive. Certain types of garnet are likewise used as abrasive material.

Because of the difficulty and expense involved in their treatment, however, none of the above minerals has been of much value as a source of the metal. For this purpose, we are dependent upon two minerals: bauxite, $Al_2O_3 \cdot xH_2O$, generally associated with considerable quantities of silicon dioxide and ferric oxide, and cryolite, Na_3AlF_6. Bauxite is obtained in quantity from southeastern France (the ore is named for the French village of Baux), Jamaica, Italy, Dutch and British Guiana, Yugoslavia, Russia, Greece, and Indonesia; also in the United States, principally from Arkansas, Georgia, Alabama, and Tennessee. Cryolite is obtained commercially from the island of Greenland only.

In recent years experiments on the extraction of aluminum from clay have met with some success, but as yet such processes have not been widely applied on a commercial basis.

7. Metallurgy. In view of the great abundance of aluminum compounds in nature, and of the many desirable properties of the metal (see p. 804), it is somewhat surprising that it is only within the last half-century that alumi-

num has attained the rank of an important industrial product. The explanation of this paradox lies in the great stability of naturally occurring aluminum compounds, and in the resulting difficulty and expense of extracting the free metal from them.

Although free aluminum was obtained by Oersted as early as 1825 and by Wöhler in 1827, the French chemist Sainte-Claire Deville, in 1854, prepared the first aluminum in commercial amounts by the reduction of aluminum chloride with sodium. Since the cost of aluminum was thus tied to that of sodium, a relatively expensive metal, this method offered no prospect of reasonably cheap aluminum. Improvements in the method for pro-

Fig. 43.1.   Aluminum statue of Charles M. Hall in the Chemistry Building at Oberlin College. (*Courtesy of Oberlin College.*)

ducing sodium brought the price of aluminum down from about $545 per pound in 1852 to $8 per pound in 1886, but it is estimated that less than 20 tons of the metal had been produced by that time. Attempts to obtain aluminum by the electrolysis of aqueous solutions of aluminum salts, or by the electrolysis of molten sodium aluminum chloride and cryolite, had been equally unsuccessful. It was at about this time that Charles M. Hall, a student at Oberlin College, was inspired by Professor F. F. Jewett, a former student of Wöhler's, to undertake the series of experiments which resulted in the ultimate solution of the problem (Figure 43.1). Though hampered by the limitations of his woodshed laboratory and improvised electrical equipment, the twenty-two year old Hall nevertheless persisted, and was even-

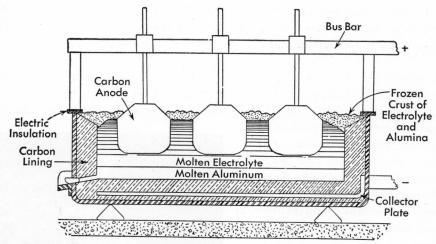

Fig. 43.2. Diagram of an electrolytic cell for the production of aluminum. (*Courtesy of The Aluminum Company of America.*)

tually able to announce, in February, 1886, that he had obtained pure aluminum by the electrolysis of a solution of aluminum oxide in molten cryolite. Only three months later, the French chemist Paul Heroult, also twenty-two years of age and unaware of Hall's work, made the same discovery. The industrial development of the process discovered by these two men progressively lowered the price of aluminum until in 1941 it sold for 15 cents per pound.

Since the refining of metallic aluminum is very difficult, it is desirable, in order that relatively pure metal may be obtained, to purify the aluminum oxide used in the electrolysis. Bauxite is purified by digestion of the finely ground ore in sodium hydroxide solution under pressure in steam-jacketed autoclaves. Since aluminum oxide is amphoteric, it dissolves, yielding a solution of sodium aluminate (p. 805). Ferric oxide, clay, and most of the other impurities do not dissolve. Silicon dioxide does dissolve to some extent, but is precipitated as sodium aluminum silicate during the digestion. After

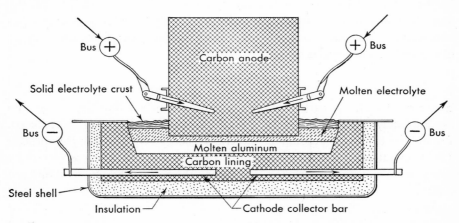

Fig. 43.3. A recently developed aluminum reduction cell, developed by Reynolds Metals, consumes 4000 lbs. of aluminum oxide and about 1000 lbs. of carbon anode material and produces 2000 tons of high grade aluminum daily. The carbon anode is lowered continuously as it is consumed.

these impurities have been removed by filtration, the sodium aluminate solution is diluted and cooled. This causes the precipitation of hydrous aluminum oxide. The precipitate is filtered off and heated to drive off the water, and pure anhydrous aluminum oxide remains.

The cell used in the modern adaptation of the Hall process is illustrated in Figures 43.2 and 43.3. The cells consist of large rectangular steel boxes lined with a layer of refractory material and having an inner lining of carbon which acts as the cathode. Anodes, also composed of carbon, are suspended in the cell. To prepare the bath, cryolite (or an equivalent artificially prepared mixture of fluorides) is melted, and a sufficient quantity of purified aluminum oxide is dissolved in it to yield a 5% solution. In this solution, aluminum oxide dissociates into Al^{+++} and O^{--} ions. As the current is passed through the cell, the Al^{+++} ions migrate toward the cathode (the cell lining), where they are reduced to metallic aluminum.

$$2Al^{+++} + 6e^- = 2Al$$

Since the temperature of the operation is maintained above the melting point of aluminum by the heat developed by the electric current, the liberated metal is obtained in the liquid state. The composition of the bath having been adjusted so that its density is lower than that of aluminum, the molten metal collects at the bottom of the cell, whence it is tapped at regular intervals. The O^{--} ions migrate toward the anode, where they release electrons to form oxygen atoms.

$$3O^{--} = 3O + 6e^-$$

These react with the carbon anodes to produce carbon dioxide; the anodes are gradually consumed, therefore, and from time to time must be replaced. Because of the large amount of electrical energy required for this process (10 kilowatt-hr. per lb. of aluminum produced), and because electricity from steam power is much too expensive, aluminum reduction plants are located near hydroelectric power plants.

Although aluminum having a purity between 99.0 and 99.3% is marketed as "commercially pure" aluminum, it is possible to obtain aluminum of a purity of 99.9% by the process given above. Metallic aluminum is not easy to refine, but the recently developed Hoopes process yields aluminum with a purity as high as 99.99%. A molten alloy of impure aluminum, copper, and silicon at the bottom of the cell employed in this process is the anode. Above this is a layer consisting of a molten bath of sodium, barium, and aluminum fluorides, which serves as electrolyte. At the top of the cell a layer of pure molten aluminum acts as cathode. The molten layers maintain their relative positions because of differences in density. As the current is passed through the cell, aluminum dissolves from the alloy at the bottom and is plated out at the top layer as pure aluminum.

8. Properties and Uses. Although, as is indicated by its high electrode potential (Table 43.6), aluminum is a relatively active metal, it is not appreciably affected by air or moisture. This resistance to atmospheric corrosion is attributed to the formation at the surface of the metal of a thin film of oxide that prevents further corrosion. When amalgamated with mercury (the presence of which prevents the formation of an adherent film), aluminum is rapidly corroded in moist air and dissolves readily in water with the evolution of hydrogen. At high temperatures, aluminum is oxidized to a considerable extent in the presence of air and, when finely divided, burns with a brilliant light. This reaction is highly exothermic.

$$4Al + 3O_2 = 2Al_2O_3$$

Powdered aluminum reacts also with many metallic oxides at high temperatures to produce aluminum oxide and the free metal. Such reactions, usually known as Goldschmidt reductions, proceed with the evolution of so much heat that the reduced metal is obtained in the molten state. A high temperature at some one point is necessary to start the reaction, however, and hence an ignition powder, such as a mixture of barium peroxide and powdered aluminum or magnesium, is commonly used.

A common example of a Goldschmidt reaction is the "thermite" process. Thermite, which consists of a mixture of aluminum powder and either ferric or ferrosoferric oxide, is used to weld breaks in large pieces of equipment that are difficult to move. The joint to be welded is surrounded by a suitable mold and hot iron from the thermite reaction crucible is allowed to flow in and fill up the joint. On cooling, the mass solidifies as a unit. Many metallic sulfides also react with aluminum powder, and such compounds may therefore be reduced by means of the Goldschmidt reaction.

Aluminum is used as a deoxidizer or scavenger in the metallurgy of other less active metals, particularly in the metallurgy of iron and steel (p. 751).

Aluminum metal dissolves in solutions of most strong acids, but it is rendered passive (p. 696) by nitric acid (and other strong oxidizing agents) so that this acid may even be shipped in aluminum containers. The reactivity of aluminum with acids, however, is affected in great measure by the presence of impurities in the metal. Aluminum of high purity is dissolved by dilute hydrochloric acid only exceedingly slowly. Aluminum alloys are considerably less resistant to corrosion than pure aluminum. "Alclad" sheet consists of a layer of high-strength aluminum alloy between two thin layers of aluminum, which protect it against corrosion.

As would be expected from the amphoteric nature of aluminum oxide and hydrous oxide, metallic aluminum dissolves readily in solutions of caustic alkalis, with the evolution of hydrogen and the formation of aluminate ion.

$$2Al + 2OH^- + 6H_2O = 2Al(OH)_4{}^- + 3H_2$$

Aluminum reacts with the halogens to yield anhydrous halides, with sulfur and nitrogen at high temperatures to yield the sulfide, Al_2S_3, and the nitride, AlN, respectively, and with carbon monoxide at high temperature according to the equation

$$6Al + 3CO = Al_4C_3 + Al_2O_3$$

The aluminum electrode is highly "irreversible"; i.e., as cathode, it readily allows a current to pass through it but as anode it exerts an enormous resistance. Hence, a cell with an aluminum electrode and any one of a number of oxygen-containing salts (usually phosphates) as electrolyte acts as a rectifier, allowing only one phase of an alternating current to pass through it.

Except for magnesium and beryllium, aluminum is the lightest of all the metals which are permanent in air; its density of 2.7 g. per cc. is only about one-third that of steel. It has a silvery white luster, which, along with its permanence in air, makes it useful as a decorative metal in various types of construction. It melts at 660° C. and boils at 2056° C. Aluminum is an excellent conductor of both heat and electricity. The high thermal conductivity of the metal, together with its light weight and its corrosion resistance, accounts for its general use in the manufacture of cooking utensils and vessels for many types of reactions in chemical industry. It is interesting to note that, whereas an aluminum wire is a poorer conductor of electricity than a copper wire of the same length and cross section, yet the conductance of the aluminum wire is twice as great as that of a copper wire of equal length and weight. Aluminum wire (sometimes reinforced with a steel core) is therefore widely used for electric power transmission lines.

By far the most important uses to which aluminum metal is applied, however, lie in the aircraft and other transportation industries. Here the lightness of the metal and its fairly high strength and toughness are particularly important. Aluminum is ductile and malleable, and may be rolled into sheets only 0.0005 in. thick. When the metal is rolled or drawn in the cold, its hardness is increased and its tensile strength may be raised to about 24,000 lb. per sq. in. Various aluminum alloys show even more useful mechanical properties. The most important of these alloys are the duralumins (Cu 3.5–4.5%, Mg 0.3–1.0%, Mn 0.4–1.0%, Si 0.3–1.0%, and Al 92.5–95.5%). These, with proper heat treatment and working, attain tensile strengths as high as 63,000 lb. per sq. in. Aluminum and its alloys are the major construction materials of the aircraft industries, and between 1940 and 1956 the U.S. production of aluminum increased from 163,000 to approximately 1,500,000 tons.

Less important uses of aluminum metal or its alloys, not yet mentioned, include the manufacture of furniture, aluminum shingles, corrugated roofing and siding, fruit jar caps, collapsible tubes for pastes, etc. In the form of finely divided flakes, aluminum is used as a paint pigment; aluminum paints have outstanding characteristics both as decorative and as protective coatings. Aluminum foil is used in the food industry as a wrapping material.

9. Compounds. The great tendency for the small, triply charged aluminum ion to become hydrated has already been discussed (p. 310). The hydrated ion is usually represented by the formula $Al(H_2O)_6^{+++}$, in accordance with the formula for hydrated aluminum chloride, $AlCl_3 \cdot 6H_2O$. As has already been pointed out (p. 322), water molecules coordinated to small highly charged positive ions tend to lose protons, and thus aluminum salts tend to give acidic solutions, in accordance with equilibrium equations of the following type:

$$Al(H_2O)_6^{+++} + H_2O \rightleftharpoons Al(H_2O)_5(OH)^{++} + H_3O^+$$

Aqueous solutions of aluminum salts of all of the strong acids are acidic (note the use of aluminum salts in baking powder, p. 653).

The behavior of aluminum ion is similar in many ways to that of chromic ion. The precipitation of hydrous aluminum oxide, $Al_2O_3 \cdot xH_2O$, in the presence of equivalent amounts of OH^- ion, and the dissolving of this precipitate in the presence of an excess of OH^- to form aluminate ion, $Al(OH)_4^-$ (or AlO_2^-), are analogous to the corresponding chromium reactions (p. 700). Sodium and potassium aluminates, obtained when hydrous aluminum oxide is dissolved in solutions of the respective alkali hydroxides, are readily soluble in water, although they are highly hydrolyzed except in strongly alkaline solutions.

The solubility of hydrous aluminum oxide in solutions of ammonia is small in any case and is almost negligible in the presence of an excess of ammonium ion. Aluminum may thus be readily separated both from cations such as Co^{++}, Ni^{++}, and Zn^{++}, which form ammonia complexes, and also from cations such as Mn^{++}, Fe^{++}, and Mg^{++}, whose hydroxides are soluble in solutions containing ammonium ion. The solubility of hydrous aluminum oxide in an excess of sodium hydroxide solution provides a means for the separation of aluminum ion from ions such as Ag^+, Hg^{++}, and Fe^{+++}, whose hydroxides (or hydrous oxides) are not amphoteric.

The precipitate of hydrous aluminum oxide is characterized by a highly gelatinous structure and a strong adsorptive tendency. If this substance is precipitated in the presence of the complex organic dye ammonium aurintricarboxylate, commonly known as aluminon, the dye is adsorbed on the oxide, giving it a bright red color. The formation of this red "lake," as it is called, is used as a means of identification of aluminum ion. The adsorptive power of gelatinous hydroxides and hydrous oxides also finds practical application in the dye industry. There are numerous dyes whose molecules, although they adhere readily to fibers of animal origin such as silk and wool, do not attach themselves firmly to the vegetable fibers of such fabrics as cotton and linen. If, however, the cloth is soaked in a solution of an aluminum salt and then treated so as to bring about the precipitation of the hydrous oxide in the fibers, many of these dyes are adsorbed on the hydrous oxide and hence are held firmly in the cloth. Such coloring materials are known as mordant dyes, and the substance used to produce the precipitate is known as a mordant. Common mordants include salts of aluminum, iron, and tin (stannic), as well as potassium dichromate, which on reduction in basic solution yields hydrous chromic oxide. The adsorptive capacity of hydrous aluminum oxide likewise is the basis for the use of aluminum salts in water purification (p. 239).

When hydrous aluminum oxide is heated to dull redness, it undergoes dehydration to the anhydrous oxide, Al_2O_3, which is formed as a soft white powder, readily soluble in acids and strong alkalis. If this is heated strongly, i.e., at temperatures above 1000° C., it changes into a much denser form of the oxide, insoluble in acids and bases. When bauxite is heated to 3000° C., artificial corundum, usually sold under the trade name of alundum, is obtained. Like corundum, this substance is used as a refractory and an abrasive. The manufacture of artificial gems from aluminum oxide has already been discussed (p. 798).

The most important salt of aluminum is the sulfate, which is obtained by the reaction of sulfuric acid with bauxite or clay.

$$Al_2O_3 \cdot xH_2O + 3H_2SO_4 = 2Al^{+++} + 3SO_4^{--} + (3+x)H_2O$$

$$H_2Al_2(SiO_4)_2 \cdot H_2O + 3H_2SO_4 = 2Al^{+++} + 3SO_4^{--} + 2H_2SiO_3 + 3H_2O$$

In the latter case, the insoluble silicic acid is filtered off and the filtrate evaporated. By this means, crystals of a hydrate having the formula $Al_2(SO_4)_3 \cdot 18H_2O$ are obtained. When solutions containing equimolar amounts of aluminum sulfate and potassium sulfate are evaporated, octahedral crystals of a double salt long known as alum, and having the formula $K_2SO_4 \cdot Al_2(SO_4)_3 \cdot 24H_2O$, are formed. Similar double salts are obtained with other alkali metal sulfates; further, the aluminum may be replaced by other triply charged ions. Hence, there exists a whole series of double sulfates of the general formula $M_2^{I}SO_4 \cdot M_2^{III}(SO_4)_3 \cdot 24H_2O$, where M^I is Li^+, Na^+, K^+, Rb^+, Cs^+, NH_4^+, Ag^+, or Tl^+, and M^{III} is Al^{+++}, Fe^{+++}, Cr^{+++}, Mn^{+++}, Ti^{+++}, or some other triply charged cation. All of these compounds form octahedral crystals, isomorphous with each other, and all are known as alums (pp. 653, 702).

The anhydrous halides of aluminum may be prepared by the direct action of the halogen on the metal. With the exception of the fluoride, the anhydrous halides of aluminum are not ionic compounds. The low melting points ($AlCl_3$, 190° C. at 2.5 atm.; $AlBr_3$, 97.5° C.; AlI_3, 191° C.) and boiling points of the chloride, bromide, and iodide, together with their solubility in such weakly polar or nonpolar solvents as ether, pyridine, carbon disulfide, benzene, and liquid bromine, confirm the covalent nature of these compounds. Measurements of the vapor densities of these halides, and of their molecular weights in nonpolar solvents, indicate that their molecules may be represented by the formula Al_2X_6 (Figure 43.4). The electronic structure of these molecules appears to be

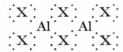

With molecules having a strong tendency to share a pair of electrons (donor molecules or Lewis bases, p. 325), these complex aluminum halide molecules react to form coordination compounds. It is because of this tendency to act as Lewis acids that anhydrous aluminum halides have the ability to "activate" certain organic molecules, and hence to catalyze many organic chemical reactions.

Fig. 43.4. Model of the Al_2Cl_6 molecule. (*Courtesy of Dr. J. A. Campbell, Oberlin College.*)

For a similar reason the aluminum halides react vigorously with water. Whereas the anhydrous molten chloride, bromide, and iodide are poor conductors of electricity, aqueous solutions of these compounds are good conductors. The following equation explains this change in behavior:

$$Al_2Cl_6 + 12H_2O = 2Al(H_2O)_6^{+++} + 6Cl^-$$

Thus, water molecules displace the halide ions to give hydrated aluminum ions, $Al(H_2O)_6^{+++}$, and free halide ions, which yield a conducting solution. When such solutions are evaporated, crystals of highly hydrated compounds such as that represented by the formula $AlCl_3 \cdot 6H_2O$ are obtained.

GALLIUM, INDIUM, AND THALLIUM

10. Occurrence. These three elements, while widely distributed, occur in much smaller quantities than the first two elements of the family. It is estimated that the average percentages of these elements in igneous rocks are as follows: gallium, 10^{-11}; indium, 10^{-11}; and thallium, 10^{-10}. These elements occur chiefly as minor impurities in many ores and minerals of some of the more familiar elements. The processes by which they are extracted vary with the nature of the source and, in general, are rather complex.

11. Properties and Uses. The electronic configurations, ionization potentials, ionic radii, electrode potentials, and other properties of gallium, indium, and thallium are listed in Tables 43.1 to 43.7. Gallium is a silvery white metal with a slight bluish tint. It melts at 29.75° C. and boils at 1983° C.; hence, the range of temperature over which this element remains in the liquid state is extraordinarily wide. Furthermore, the liquid may be supercooled to a temperature as low as 0° C. Since the liquid metal, when pure, does not wet glass or quartz, it has been suggested as a useful material for the construction of high-temperature thermometers. Solid gallium is malleable, ductile, and soft enough to be cut with a knife; its density at 20° C. is 5.91 g. per cc. Gallium is unaffected by air at room temperature, but undergoes superficial oxidation when heated. It reacts vigorously with boiling water and dissolves readily in cold hydrochloric acid or in sodium hydroxide solution, from each of which it liberates hydrogen. With other metals it forms a number of alloys, some of which are liquid at room temperature.

Indium is a malleable, silver-white, highly crystalline metal, softer than lead. Like gallium, indium remains liquid over a wide range of temperature; it melts at 156.4° C. and boils at 2000° C. It is unaffected by boiling water, but burns with a blue flame when heated in air. Indium is readily dissolved by acids, but, unlike aluminum and gallium, it is not attacked by solutions of alkali hydroxides. It forms alloys with many other metals, the general effect of the presence of indium being to harden and strengthen the element with which it is alloyed, as well as to increase its resistance to tarnish. Alloys of indium with precious metals show some promise for jewelry and dental work. Indium is used principally in aircraft sleeve bearings, in low-melting alloys, and in alloys for making glass-to-metal seals.

Thallium is a white metal with a slight bluish tint; it is so soft that it may be marked with the thumbnail or made to leave a black streak on paper. It melts at 303° C. and boils at 1457° C.; its density is 11.85 g. per cc. Thallium is oxidized slowly in air at room temperature, but as the temperature is raised above 100° C. the rate of oxidation rapidly increases. Thallous oxide, Tl_2O, is formed at lower temperatures, and thallic oxide, Tl_2O_3 at red heat. The metal is not affected by oxygen-free water at room temperature, although at red heat it liberates hydrogen from steam. Thallium dissolves slowly in sulfuric acid to yield a solution of thallous sulfate, Tl_2SO_4. With nitric acid, however, the reaction is much more rapid. The reason that thallic salts are not obtained when the metal reacts with nonoxidizing acids is evident from the fact that although the standard potential for the half-reaction, $Tl = Tl^+ + e^-$, is above that of hydrogen, the standard potential for the corresponding half-reaction for thallic ion is well below that of the hydrogen electrode (Table 43.6).

12. Compounds. The compounds of gallium are similar to those of aluminum, except for the differences which arise from the less acidic and more basic nature of hydrous gallic oxide, as compared with the corresponding aluminum compound.

Compounds of $+3$ indium are similar to those of gallium and aluminum, except for the still more basic character of the oxide and the hydrous oxide, In_2O_3 and $In_2O_3 \cdot xH_2O$. The soluble indic halides, nitrate, sulfate, and alums are not hydrolyzed to so great an extent as are the corresponding gallic compounds. A few indous compounds such as the halides, InX, have been prepared.

Thallium forms two well-defined series of compounds: the thallous, in which thallium is in the $+1$ oxidation state, and the thallic, in which its oxidation number is $+3$. As would be expected from the small tendency for a thallium atom to release three electrons, thallic compounds are fairly strong oxidizing agents, being readily reduced to thallous compounds by such reducing agents as stannous ion, sulfurous acid, ferrous ion, arsenite ion, and metallic thallium.

$$Tl^{+++} + 2Tl = 3Tl^+$$

As was indicated in the opening discussion of this chapter, formation of these thallous, as well as of the corresponding gallous and indous compounds, results from the fact that the single p electron in the valence shell of these atoms is much more easily removed than are the two s electrons. The thallous ion still has the pair of s electrons in its valence shell.

Thallous compounds in general resemble the corresponding silver or plumbous (Pb^{++}) compounds in their solubilities, whereas thallic compounds resemble those of aluminum. In its ionic radius and in its lack of any tendency to form complex ions, however, thallous ion resembles potassium ion; furthermore, thallous oxide, Tl_2O, and the hydroxide, $TlOH$, are strongly basic in character.

Thallic ion resembles aluminum, gallic, and indic ions. Its hydrous oxide is very insoluble and is only weakly basic, hence soluble thallic salts undergo considerable hydrolysis. Unlike the corresponding aluminum compound, however, hydrous thallic oxide has no acidic properties (Table 43.4). Thallic chloride, which is readily soluble in water, is obtained as the hydrate $TlCl_3 \cdot 3H_2O$ when its solutions are evaporated. In general, thallic compounds decompose to thallous on being heated.

$$TlCl_3 = TlCl + Cl_2$$

$$Tl_2S_3 = Tl_2S + 2S$$

Compounds containing both thallous and thallic ion are known also. Tl_2Cl_4 is known as thallous chlorothallate, and is properly represented by the formula $Tl^I[Tl^{III}Cl_4]$; other compounds of this type include $Tl_3^I[Tl^{III}Cl_6]$, $Tl^I[Tl^{III}Br_3Cl]$, $Tl^I[Tl^{III}Br_4]$, and $Tl_3^I[Tl^{III}Br_6]$.

Like compounds of lead, both thallous and thallic compounds are cumulative poisons; thallous sulfate, in particular, is used as a rat and ant poison. At one time, a number of accidental deaths resulted from the exploitation and sale of thallous acetate for use as a depilatory.

STUDY QUESTIONS AND PROBLEMS

1. Suppose that a chemist, studying the reaction of indium metal with fluorine, reports the formation of a compound to which he assigns the molecular formula InF_2. Would you be inclined to credit this report? Give the reasons for your answer. Does the compound of empirical formula $TlCl_2$ contain divalent thallium? Explain.

2. The differences in radii between Be^{++} and B^{+++} and between Mg^{++} and Al^{+++} are, in each case, about 0.1 Å; yet the differences in the radii of Ca^{++} and Ga^{+++} and of Sr^{++} and In^{+++} are more than 0.3 Å. Explain this in terms of atomic structure.

3. According to what definition of acids and bases would BCl_3 be considered an acid? Write three electronic equations which demonstrate this acidic property.

4. Outline the method by which metallic aluminum is obtained from its ores. What are the chief industrial applications of aluminum metal?

5. Make a table of chemical properties common to both Cr^{+++} and Al^{+++} ions. Explain why these two ions resemble each other so closely. What are the chief differences in the properties of Cr^{+++} and Al^{+++} ions? Explain these differences in terms of the structures of the ions.

6. What is the electronic formula for anhydrous aluminum chloride? Show how it is possible for this substance to act as a Lewis acid (p. 325).

Germanium, Tin, and Lead

1. Metals of Group 4a. The general characteristics of the elements of Group 4a, as related to their electron configurations and to their positions in the periodic system, were discussed in the first section of Chapter 30. In that discussion it was noted that the first two elements of this family, carbon and silicon, are chiefly nonmetallic in their properties, whereas the last three, germanium, tin, and lead, may be classified as metals. The chemistry of carbon and silicon and their compounds having already been discussed (Chapter 30), we shall now turn our attention to germanium, tin, and lead.

2. History and Occurrence. Tin and lead are among the few metals which have been known since ancient times. Germanium, however, has been known for only slightly more than half a century. One of the elements whose discovery was predicted by Mendeleeff after he had set up his form of the periodic table he named eka-silicon. Less than two decades later (1886) the missing element was discovered by Clemens Winkler, professor of chemistry at Freiburg, Germany, who named it germanium in honor of that country.

These three elements are not very abundant in the earth's crust, estimated percentages being $1 \times 10^{-11}\%$ for germanium, $1 \times 10^{-6}\%$ for tin, and $2 \times 10^{-5}\%$ for lead. Germanium minerals are decidedly rare. The commonest mode of occurrence of the element is in the form of sulfide ores associated with other metal sulfides, especially those of lead, antimony, zinc, silver, and tin. Some of these ores appear to be thiogermanates, e.g., Ag_4GeS_4 and Pb_2GeS_4.

There are numerous naturally occurring compounds of tin, but the only tin mineral of any considerable importance as an ore is cassiterite, SnO_2. Very little tin ore is mined within the boundaries of the United States, the chief sources being the Malay States, Bolivia, and Indonesia.

The chief ore of lead is galena, PbS, which is found in nature associated with other metal sulfides such as those of silver, copper, bismuth, arsenic, antimony, and tin. Cerussite, $PbCO_3$, and anglesite, $PbSO_4$, presumably secondary minerals formed by the weathering of the sulfide, are also important. The chief lead-producing countries of the world are the United States, Australia, Mexico, Germany, and Canada. Most of the lead produced in this country comes from Missouri, Idaho, and Utah.

3. Metallurgy. Germanium has not been of sufficient industrial interest for its metallurgy to have been well developed. The metal may be obtained, however, by the reduction of the dioxide, GeO_2, with carbon, or by the reduction of the oxide or sulfide with an alkali cyanide. Germanium is obtained as a by-product of the metallurgy of zinc and lead.

In the metallurgy of tin, the cassiterite ore is usually concentrated by various washing and roasting processes; cassiterite is comparatively dense, and the lighter impurities such as sand and clay are easily removed when the finely ground ore is washed. After concentration, the oxide is reduced by means of charcoal, coal, or coke in a blast or reverberatory furnace.

Among the processes used in the refining of crude tin is liquation, in which the impure tin is heated on a sloping hearth to a temperature only a little above the melting point of pure tin. The greater part of the tin melts and drains off, leaving impure metal behind in solid form. Further purification is sometimes carried out by a process called "poling," in which the molten tin is stirred with poles of green wood. The evolution of gases from the wood stirs the liquid thoroughly. Nonmetallic substances rise to the surface, and metallic impurities are oxidized; the dross of impurities thus formed is then skimmed from the surface. Tin may also be refined electrolytically, a fluosilicic acid solution serving as electrolyte.

More than one-third of the tin used in this country is reclaimed tin, i.e., tin recovered from waste material. Most of the reclaimed metal comes either from drosses formed in the production of tin plate, or from clippings obtained in the manufacture of tin cans. Three methods are used in the recovery of the tin from tin plate scrap: (1) the tin is removed by treatment of the scrap with aqueous sodium hydroxide solution and is then reduced electrolytically; (2) the scrap is heated with chlorine gas at a high temperature, and the tin is obtained as the volatile chloride, $SnCl_4$, most of which is used for the weighting of silk, or as a mordant in the dyeing of this fabric; (3) the plate is treated with hot aqueous sodium hydroxide solution and an oxidizing agent; this yields stannic oxide, which is either reduced to metallic tin, or used in the manufacture of metal enamels.

The metallurgy of lead is complex, not because the reduction of galena or cerussite is difficult, but rather because of the many compounds of other metals which are commonly associated with the lead sulfide or carbonate. Some of these associated metals are valuable, and it is desirable for economic reasons to separate them from the lead. Others must be removed because they would have adverse effects on the properties of lead metal. A considerable part of the associated metal compounds, as well as of the gangue materials, is removed from the lead ore by a series of selective flotation processes. The concentrate thus obtained is roasted in the presence of air, much of the sulfide ore being thus converted to oxide. The roasted product is mixed with coke, scrap iron, and fluxes, and is melted in a blast furnace. The reduction of the lead oxide and lead sulfide proceeds in accordance with the following equations:

$$PbO + C = Pb + CO$$

$$PbO + CO = Pb + CO_2$$

$$PbS + Fe = Pb + FeS$$

Copper and iron sulfides collect in a matte above the layer of molten lead, and above this is a layer of slag consisting of the silicates of calcium and iron. These layers are tapped at intervals, and the copper is recovered from the matte.

A second method for the extraction of metallic lead involves the leaching of galena, which may or may not have been roasted to lead sulfate, with a concentrated solution of sulfuric acid saturated with sodium chloride. The solution obtained is electrolyzed, yielding a spongy lead which is pressed into cakes for melting. This method has become increasingly important in recent years.

The removal of silver from crude lead by the Parkes process has already been discussed (p. 765). Usually the amount of silver obtained from crude lead in this way is sufficient to pay the cost of its extraction. More active metals are removed from lead by an oxidation process in which the oxides of these impurities collect as a dross on the surface of the molten lead and are skimmed off. An electrolytic method for refining lead is also in use; it is known as the Betts process and is similar to that used in the refining of copper. The electrolyte is a solution of lead fluosilicate, $PbSiF_6$; the anode consists of impure lead, and the cathode of pure lead. Gold, silver, and bismuth collect in the anode slime, from which the gold and silver are recovered.

4. Properties and Uses. The electronic configurations of germanium, tin, and lead were listed in Table 30.1, p. 529. The important physical properties of these elements are summarized in Table 44.1.

Table 44.1

Physical Properties of Germanium, Tin, and Lead

	Ge	Sn	Pb
Melting point, °C.	$937.2 \pm 0.5°$ C.	231.8	327.5
Boiling point, °C.	2700 (approx.)	2270	1717
Density, g./cc.	5.32	7.30 (white) 5.75 (gray)	11.35
Tensile strength, lb./sq. in.	....	2000	1600 (very pure) 2000 (ordinary)
Ionic radius (M^{++++}), Å	0.53	0.71	0.84
Ionization potential, v.			
1st electron	8.1	7.3	7.4
2nd electron	15.9	14.5	15.0
3rd electron	34.1	30.5	31.9
4th electron	45.5	39.4	42.1

Germanium is a hard, brittle, grayish white metal which is resistant to tarnish; it is not a good conductor of electricity. Its crystal structure is similar to that of diamond and silicon. In its physical and chemical properties germanium is intermediate between the nonmetal silicon and the more metallic element tin.

Tin occurs in two allotropic forms, known as alpha and beta tin, or, more commonly, as "gray tin" and "white tin," respectively. The common form is the beta or white variety, which is stable at temperatures from 18° C. up to the melting point. It is malleable and has a bright luster, but is a poor conductor of heat and electricity. When a bar of beta tin is bent, it emits a low squeaking sound known as "tin cry." Although alpha or gray tin is the stable variety at temperatures below 18° C., the change from the beta to the alpha form is extremely slow and likely to be suspended altogether unless the temperature is reduced far below this point. If articles composed of tin are kept at low temperatures for a long time, they may fall to a gray powder. The transition is accelerated by the presence of some of the stable alpha form; hence, once started, it spreads rapidly. This change is often referred to as "tin disease." Alpha tin has a diamond type of crystal structure similar to germanium and silicon, but the beta form crystallizes in a more characteristically metallic type of lattice.

Both tin and lead are notable for their low melting points, and, as we shall see, many of their industrial applications depend upon this property. Both metals are characterized also by their low tensile strength. Lead is the softest and the most dense of the common metals; it has a bluish gray color, and, when freshly cut, shows a typical metallic luster. Lead is readily malleable and can be extruded, under pressure, into tubes, rods, and wire. The hardness and brittleness of both tin and lead are increased markedly by the presence of relatively small amounts of impurities.

The chemical reactions of the free metals indicate, as would be expected, a considerable degree of resemblance among the three elements. The differences observable in their reactions illustrate the increasing tendency, with increasing atomic number, for the element to go into the $+2$ rather than the $+4$ oxidation state, as well as the trend toward increasing metallic character in the same direction (p. 185).

Tin is very resistant to atmospheric corrosion, which accounts for its use (as discussed subsequently) as a protective coating on less resistant metals. A bright lead surface rapidly darkens in the air, but under ordinary conditions the corrosion is only superficial.

Metallic lead is resistant to the action of dilute to moderately concentrated solutions of sulfuric acid, presumably because of the formation of a coating of insoluble lead sulfate. In the presence of oxygen, lead readily dissolves even in weak acids. It is also attacked by pure water in the presence of oxygen; hard water, however, does not affect lead, because of the formation of a surface layer of insoluble compounds of lead with the sulfate, bicarbonate, and other such anions which are usually present in hard water.

The major use of metallic germanium is in the production of electronic equipment, particularly transistors which fulfill a function similar to that of electronic vacuum tubes. Several thousand pounds of germanium are produced each year. The current price is between $300 and $400 per pound.

The world's annual production of tin is over a quarter of a million tons. The chief use of this metal is in the coating of steel for the manufacture of tin plate. Tin-plated cans serve a great many familiar purposes, chief among which, of course, is their use for the preservation of food. One method of application of the coating consists in dipping the steel plate into molten tin; this method is wasteful, however, since it usually results in a somewhat heavier layer of the metal than is necessary. Electrolytic methods, which give a thinner but more uniform coating, have recently been developed; also, the tin is sometimes applied by spraying. The manufacture of terneplate, sheet steel coated with a lead–tin alloy, likewise consumes a large amount of tin. This product is widely used for roofing, and for the production of such articles as gasoline tanks. Other major uses of tin include the manufacture of solders, Babbitt metal (tin, antimony, and copper alloys used as bearing-metals), brasses, and bronzes (p. 765). Solders are readily fusible alloys suitable for joining two metal surfaces. The most widely used solders are lead–tin alloys, the commonest having the composition 50% tin and 50% lead. As has already been pointed out (p. 764), brasses are alloys having copper and zinc as their major components; other elements are commonly added, however, and tin in brasses in amounts up to 2% increases hardness, tensile strength, and resistance to salt-water corrosion.

The annual world production of metallic lead exceeds 2 million tons, which is greater than that of any other metal except copper and iron. Over one-fourth of this is used in the manufacture of lead storage batteries (p. 434), and more than one-fifth in the production of white lead (p. 823) and other lead pigments. Other important uses include the manufacture of cable coverings, ammunition, and a variety of alloys. These alloys include solder and bearing-alloys (p. 520), low-melting alloys (p. 521), and type-metals (p. 520). Large amounts of lead are used also in the sulfuric acid industry for the lining of the lead chambers and of the vats in which the chamber acid is concentrated (p. 458).

COMPOUNDS OF GERMANIUM, TIN, AND LEAD

5. General Characteristics. Each of these elements forms two series of compounds: (1) the -ous compounds, in which the oxidation number of the element is +2, and (2) the -ic compounds, in which the element exhibits an oxidation state of +4. The explanation of this duality of oxidation state is entirely analogous to that given for the existence of +1 and +3 series of compounds of gallium, indium, and thallium in the preceding chapter (p. 792). The atoms of germanium, tin, and lead each contain four valence electrons, two p and two s electrons. For reasons which have already been discussed, the p electrons are considerably more readily lost (or shared) than are the s electrons. Hence, it is possible for either two or four electrons to be used in bond formation, giving rise to the -ous and the -ic series, respectively. In the order Ge, Sn, Pb, the +2 oxidation state becomes relatively more important than the +4 oxidation state. Thus, germanic compounds are much more numerous and more stable than germanous compounds. On the other hand, plumbous compounds, are much more numerous, and in general more stable, than plumbic. The increasing stability of the compounds in which the metal is in the +2 state (as compared to those in which it is in the +4 state) with increasing atomic number is in line with the standard potentials for the following half-reactions:

$$Ge^{++} + 2H_2O = GeO_2 + 4H^+ + 2e^-; E = 0.2 \text{ v.}$$

$$Sn^{++} = Sn^{++++} + \quad 2e^-; E = -0.13 \quad \text{v.}$$

$$Pb^{++} + 2H_2O = PbO_2 + 4H^+ + 2e^-; E = -1.46 \quad \text{v.}$$

These indicate the greatly decreasing tendency, as the atomic number in-creases, for the doubly charged ion to lose electrons.

6. Oxides and Hydrous Oxides. All three of the elements under discussion form oxides of the general formulas MO and MO₂. The monoxides, corre-sponding to the +2 oxidation state, are all amphoteric, dissolving readily either in acids or in strong bases. Black stannous oxide, SnO, is obtained when hydrous stannous oxide or stannous oxalate, SnC_2O_4, is heated; while plumbous oxide, PbO, commonly known as litharge, is obtained when lead metal is heated in air. Litharge is an orange-yellow substance which is used in the glazing of some kinds of ceramic ware and in the manufacture of cer-tain types of glass.

Hydrates of all the -ous oxides have been prepared, but their exact com-position is somewhat in doubt. They are white in color. The stannous and plumbous compounds apparently have the compositions expressed by the formulas $(SnO)_2 \cdot H_2O$ and $(PbO)_2 \cdot H_2O$. It is customary to consider these compounds as hydroxides; and the formulas $Sn(OH)_2$ and $Pb(OH)_2$, with the corresponding names, stannous and plumbous hydroxide, are ordinarily assigned to them.

All the hydrous monoxides are amphoteric, their basic characteristics in-creasing somewhat, as would be expected, from the germanium compound to that of lead. The salts formed when the hydrous monoxides dissolve in basic solutions are known respectively as germanites, stannites, and plumbites. Thus, we have the following equations for typical reactions:

$$Sn(OH)_2 + OH^- = HSnO_2^- + H_2O$$
stannite ion

$$Pb(OH)_2 + OH^- = HPbO_2^- + H_2O$$
plumbite ion

Stannite solutions are strong reducing agents, as is indicated by the standard potential corresponding to the following half-reaction:

$$HSnO_2^- + 3OH^- + H_2O = Sn(OH)_6^{--} + 2e^-; E = 0.90 \text{ v.}$$

Stannous and plumbous oxides, both hydrous and anhydrous, dissolve readily in dilute acids to yield stannous and plumbous salts, which will be discussed presently.

The dioxides, corresponding to the $+4$ oxidation state, are all nonvolatile solids. Germanium dioxide is usually prepared by roasting germanium disulfide in air; it is unaffected by nitric or sulfuric acids, but dissolves in hot concentrated hydrochloric acid.

$$GeO_2 + 4HCl = GeCl_4 + 2H_2O$$

The dioxide dissolves more readily, however, in alkali hydroxide solutions yielding solutions of germanates, such as K_2GeO_3.

Tin dioxide, SnO_2, or, as it is commonly called, stannic oxide, occurs in nature as the important tin ore cassiterite; when pure, it is white in color. It is formed when stannous oxide is heated in air,

$$2SnO + O_2 = 2SnO_2$$

or when hydrous stannic oxide, $SnO_2 \cdot xH_2O$, is heated.

$$SnO_2 \cdot xH_2O = SnO_2 + xH_2O$$

The exact chemical composition of hydrous stannic oxide, sometimes called stannic acid, is not known; but it is apparent from its chemical behavior that it exists in at least two forms. The first of these varieties, called the α-form, is obtained by the acidification of aqueous solutions of alkali metal stannates. It is readily soluble in acids to yield stannic compounds, and in solutions of alkali hydroxides to yield stannates.

$$SnO_2 \cdot xH_2O + 4H^+ + 6Cl^- = SnCl_6^{--} + (x+2)H_2O$$

$$SnO_2 \cdot xH_2O + 2OH^- = Sn(OH)_6^{--} + (x-2)H_2O$$

It is, however, more acidic and less basic than hydrous stannous oxide. The β-form of hydrous stannic oxide is obtained by the action of concentrated nitric acid on metallic tin,

$$Sn + 4H^+ + 4NO_3^- + (x-2)H_2O = SnO_2 \cdot xH_2O + 4NO_2$$

or by the hydrolysis of stannic compounds in hot solution

$$SnCl_4 + (x+2)H_2O = SnO_2 \cdot xH_2O + 4H^+ + 4Cl^-$$

This variety of the hydrous oxide dissolves in alkali hydroxides, but not in acids. Prolonged treatment with hot concentrated hydrochloric acid converts it to a colloidal suspension which dissolves in dilute acids. Sodium stannate is widely used for the weighting of silk fabrics.

It is interesting to note that although both stannous and stannic oxides and hydrous oxides are amphoteric, the stannous compounds, in accordance with the general rule stated on p. 324, are considerably more basic than the stannic. It is not surprising to learn, therefore, that whereas all tin salts are hydrolyzed to an appreciable extent, stannic salts have a much greater tendency in this direction than do stannous; hence, pure stannic salts are much more difficult to prepare than stannous. On the other hand, since stannic oxide and hydrous oxide are more acidic than the stannous compounds, stannates are less subject to hydrolysis than are stannites.

Lead dioxide, a dark brown, insoluble solid, is most easily obtained by the oxidation of plumbous oxide or a plumbite in alkaline solutions; e.g.,

$$PbO + OCl^- = PbO_2 + Cl^-$$

Lead dioxide is sometimes formed at the anode when solutions containing plumbous ion are electrolyzed. This oxide is unaffected by dilute alkali, but reacts with concentrated solutions of alkali hydroxides to yield plumbates, such as $CaPbO_3$ and Ca_2PbO_4. Plumbates are formed also by the fusion of lead dioxide with alkali hydroxides, or with such basic oxides as those of the alkaline earth metals. The reaction of lead dioxide with concentrated hydrochloric acid ordinarily takes place according to the equation

$$PbO_2 + 4HCl = PbCl_2 + Cl_2 + 2H_2O$$

At low temperatures, however, the liquid tetrachloride, $PbCl_4$, is obtained.

Compounds containing lead in the +4 oxidation state, e.g., lead dioxide, in the presence of a dilute acid such as nitric acid, are very strong oxidizing agents, as is indicated by the standard potential for the following half-reaction:

$$Pb^{++} + 2H_2O = PbO_2 + 4H^+ + 2e^-; E = -1.46 \text{ v.}$$

A mixture of lead dioxide and nitric acid will, for example, oxidize manganous ion to permanganate (p. 714). The dioxide slowly dissolves in dilute nitric acid, the Pb^{4+} ion formed oxidizing the water, in the absence of other reducing agents, with the evolution of oxygen. The use of lead dioxide in the lead storage cell has already been discussed (p. 434).

Two other oxides of lead are known, the orange-yellow trioxide, Pb_2O_3, and an orange-red compound, called red lead or minium, having the composition expressed by the formula Pb_3O_4. These oxides contain lead in both the +2 and +4 oxidation states; they may be considered as plumbous plumbates, and their formulas may be written $Pb^{II}(Pb^{IV}O_3)$ and $Pb_2^{II}(Pb^{IV}O_4)$ respectively. Red lead is obtained when plumbous oxide is heated in the air at 430° C. It reacts with nitric acid to yield the dioxide and a solution of plumbous nitrate.

$$Pb_2(PbO_4) + 4H^+ = 2Pb^{++} + PbO_2 + 2H_2O$$

Red lead is widely used as a paint pigment, although usually not because of its color; it is especially useful for the first coat of paint applied to structural iron, since it effectively protects the iron from corrosion. This oxide is used also in the manufacture of certain types of glass.

7. Sulfides. Germanium and tin each form a monosulfide, MS, and a disulfide, MS_2; lead, however, forms only a monosulfide. Germanium may be precipitated as the disulfide from concentrated sulfuric acid solutions by means of hydrogen sulfide; in dilute acid, only a colloidal suspension of the disulfide is obtained. Germanium monosulfide, or germanous sulfide, is obtained when the disulfide is heated.

Both the mono- and the disulfide of tin, usually known as stannous and stannic sulfide, respectively, may be prepared by direct union of the elements at elevated temperatures. As the temperature increases the stannic sulfide becomes less stable with respect to the stannous compound, and decomposes in accordance with the equation

$$SnS_2 = SnS + S$$

The sulfides of tin are readily precipitated from slightly acidic solutions of stannous and stannic compounds by hydrogen sulfide. Stannous sulfide obtained in this manner is brown in color, and stannic sulfide so obtained is yellow.

Plumbous sulfide, usually referred to simply as lead sulfide, occurs in nature as the important lead ore galena; in this form it is a heavy, cubically crystalline, silvery-gray to black substance, with a metallic luster. The same compound may be prepared by precipitation with hydrogen sulfide from an acidic solution of a plumbous compound; when prepared in this manner, lead sulfide is black. It may also be prepared by the direct combination of lead and sulfur at elevated temperatures.

The disulfides of germanium and tin are similar to the dioxides in that they have acidic properties, which are manifested by the fact that they dissolve in solutions of the alkali hydroxides. They are soluble also in solutions of the alkali metal and ammonium sulfides, yielding solutions of thiosalts; this may be accounted for in terms of the fact that sulfide ion, according to the Lewis definition (p. 325), is a fairly strong base.

$$GeS_2 + S^{--} = GeS_3^{--}$$
thiogermanate ion

$$SnS_2 + S^{--} = SnS_3^{--}$$
thiostannate ion

Stannic sulfide dissolves also in concentrated hydrochloric acid, and is thus, like the dioxide, an amphoteric substance. None of the monosulfides is soluble in sulfide solutions; germanous and stannous sulfides readily dissolve, however, in alkali metal or ammonium polysulfide solutions, since the polysulfide ion oxidizes the tin or germanium to the +4 oxidation state (p. 449).

$$GeS + S_2^{--} = GeS_3^{--}$$

$$SnS + S_2^{--} = SnS_3^{--}$$

When a mixture of tin, sulfur, ammonium chloride, and mercury is heated, stannic sulfide is obtained in the form of brilliant golden yellow crystals. This product is used as a gilding pigment under the name of "mosaic gold."

8. Tetrahalides, Hydrides, and Related Compounds. Germanium, tin, and lead, like carbon and silicon, combine with the halogens to form volatile tetrahalides of the general formula MX_4. These halides are, in the main, liquids or low-melting solids, and hence are definitely non-saltlike.

These halides have electronic structures corresponding to the general formula

$$: \overset{..}{X} :$$
$$: \overset{..}{X} : \overset{..}{M} : \overset{..}{X} :$$
$$: \overset{..}{X} :$$

Since it is possible for germanium, tin, and lead to have more than eight electrons in their valence shells, the tetrahalides are able to form coordination complexes with certain electron donors. Examples include $SnCl_6^{--}$, GeF_6^{--}, and $SnCl_4 \cdot 2(C_2H_5)_2O$. These anhydrous tetrahalides, however, on contact with water, are very readily hydrolyzed, yielding basic halides or the hydrous dioxides.

$$MX_4 + (x + 2)H_2O = MO_2 \cdot xH_2O + 4H^+ + 4X^-$$

This tendency towards hydrolysis is repressed by considerable concentrations of hydrohalic acid, so that the tetrahalides dissolve in such solutions without the precipitation of basic salts. The tetrahalides of these elements are pseudosalts (p. 309), for, whereas the anhydrous liquids are nonconductors of electricity, their aqueous solutions are conductors.

Germanium, tin, and lead resemble carbon and silicon in that they all form hydrides of the general formula MH_4. The stability of these hydrides decreases in the order $CH_4 > SiH_4 > GeH_4 > SnH_4 > PbH_4$ (p. 530); the lead compound is extremely unstable.

Germanium, tin, and lead show their family resemblance to carbon and silicon also in the fact that they form compounds of the type MR_4, where R represents a hydrocarbon radical such as ethyl, C_2H_5, or methyl, CH_3 (p. 578). Examples of such compounds include $Ge(CH_3)_4$, $Sn(C_3H_7)_4$, and $Pb(C_2H_5)_4$. The variety and the stability of the organic derivatives of these elements, like the stability of the hydroxides, decreases (as would be expected) in the order C > Si > Ge > Sn > Pb; i.e., in the order of increasing metallic character of the elements. Lead tetraethyl, $Pb(C_2H_5)_4$, is of considerable practical importance because of its use as an antiknock material in gasoline. Gasoline containing this compound is known as ethyl gasoline (cf. p. 573).

9. Other Compounds of Tin. The most important compounds of tin in which it has an oxidation number of $+2$ are the stannous halides. These are prepared by dissolving tin metal in the appropriate hydrohalic acid, or by reduction of the corresponding stannic compound with metallic tin.

$$Sn + 2H^+ + 2X^- = Sn^{++} + 2X^- + H_2$$

$$SnX_4 + Sn = 2SnX_2$$

Stannous chloride is a mild reducing agent. On standing in solution, it is slowly oxidized by the air unless a little metallic tin is present to keep it in the reduced state. Solutions of stannous halides are readily hydrolyzed to form precipitates of basic salts, unless such hydrolysis is prevented by the presence of an excess of hydrogen ion.

$$Sn^{++} + Cl^- + H_2O = Sn(OH)Cl + H^+$$

Stannous and stannic nitrates and sulfates may be prepared in solution by treatment of the hydrous oxides with the appropriate acid. They are difficult to crystallize, however, because of their tendency to undergo hydrolysis to basic salts. This is particularly true of the stannic compounds (p. 821). Tin salts of weak acids, such as acetates and carbonates, are completely hydrolyzed.

10. Plumbous Compounds. With the exception of the tetrahalides, the tetracetate, the dioxide, and a very few other such compounds, the only important compounds of lead are the plumbous compounds. Many of these compounds are only slightly soluble in water, and a number of the soluble salts are but slightly dissociated.

The most important soluble lead salt is the nitrate, $Pb(NO_3)_2$, which may be obtained by dissolving metallic lead in nitric acid. A slight excess of hydrogen ion must be present in order to prevent the precipitation of a basic lead nitrate. Another of the soluble lead salts is the acetate, which crystallizes as $Pb(C_2H_3O_2)_2 \cdot 3H_2O$. This substance is only very slightly dissociated in aqueous solution; as a result of this fact, many slightly soluble lead salts dissolve readily in solutions containing acetate ion, with the formation either of undissociated lead acetate, or, in the presence of an excess of acetate ion, of such complex ions as $Pb(C_2H_3O_2)_3^-$ or $Pb(C_2H_3O_2)_4^{--}$. All the soluble lead salts are extremely poisonous. Since lead is not easily thrown off by the animal organism, it is a cumulative poison; the gradual addition of small increments of lead over a period of time may eventually result in severe lead poisoning.

Among the more familiar lead salts of low solubility are the halides, the sulfate, the chromate, the sulfide, and the carbonate. The sulfide has already been discussed. The halides may be precipitated by means of the corresponding hydrogen halide from solutions containing lead ion. The solubility of the lead halides decreases in the order $PbCl_2 > PbBr_2 > PbI_2 > PbF_2$, the fluoride and the iodide having nearly the same solubility. The solubilities of all of the halides increase rapidly with increasing temperature; the chloride and the bromide are moderately soluble in boiling water.

Lead sulfate is only very slightly soluble in water, but dissolves readily in solutions containing acetate or hydroxide ion.

$$PbSO_{4(s)} + C_2H_3O_2^- = Pb(C_2H_3O_2)^+ + SO_4^{--}$$

$$PbSO_{4(s)} + 3OH^- = HPbO_2^- + SO_4^{--} + H_2O$$

When lead sulfide is roasted in an air blast, a substance of the composition represented by the formula $PbO \cdot PbSO_4$ sublimes out of the mixture. This basic lead sulfate is used as a white paint pigment under the name of "sublimed white lead."

A much more important white paint pigment, however, is the basic carbonate $Pb(OH)_2 \cdot 2PbCO_3$, known as white lead. It is prepared by a number of different processes, all of which involve the action of air, carbon dioxide, and acetic acid on lead metal. In the presence of air and acetic acid the lead is oxidized to a basic lead acetate, which reacts with carbon dioxide and water to give the basic carbonate. White lead, because of its great covering power, is an excellent pigment; it has the disadvantage of darkening in the presence of hydrogen sulfide because of the formation of black lead sulfide. Another important lead pigment is lead chromate, $PbCrO_4$, which is sold under the name of chrome yellow. Lead chromate is only very slightly soluble in water, but dissolves readily in solutions of strong acids (p. 703), or in solutions of alkalis.

STUDY QUESTIONS AND PROBLEMS

1. Correlate the following characteristics of germanium, tin, and lead with the atomic structures of the elements or with the structures of the compounds or ions.

(a) The elements exhibit oxidation states of $+2$ and $+4$.

(b) The tetrahalides of the elements are covalent compounds.

(c) The tetrahalide molecules are nonpolar, even though they contain polar covalent bonds.

(d) The sulfide of $+4$ tin is amphoteric.

(e) The oxide and hydrous oxide of $+2$ tin are more basic and less acidic than the corresponding compounds of $+4$ tin.

(f) Pure $+4$ tin salts such as $Sn(SO_4)_2$ are difficult to prepare.

2. Is the reaction $Pb_3O_4 + 4H^+ = 2Pb^{++} + PbO_2 + 2H_2O$ an oxidation-reduction reaction? Why, or why not?

3. Outline briefly the ores of tin and lead, the metallurgical methods used for these metals, and their industrial applications.

Appendix

Vapor Pressure of Water

(Both the Fahrenheit (F.) and the Centigrade (C.) Temperatures Are Given)

Temperature °F.	°C.	Pressure, in mm. of Mercury	Temperature °F.	°C.	Pressure, in mm. of Mercury
32	0	4.6	77.0	25	23.6
41	5	6.5	78.8	26	25.1
46.4	8	8.0	80.6	27	26.5
48.2	9	8.6	82.4	28	28.1
50.0	10	9.2	84.2	29	29.8
51.8	11	9.8	86.0	30	31.5
53.6	12	10.5	87.8	31	33.4
55.4	13	11.2	89.6	32	35.4
57.2	14	11.9	91.4	33	37.4
59.0	15	12.7	93.2	34	39.6
60.8	16	13.5	95.0	35	41.8
62.6	17	14.4	104.0	40	54.9
64.4	18	15.4	122.0	50	92.5
66.2	19	16.3	140.0	60	148.9
68.0	20	17.5	158.0	70	233.3
69.8	21	18.5	176.0	80	354.9
71.6	22	19.7	194.0	90	525.5
73.4	23	20.9	212.0	100	760.0
75.2	24	22.2			

The Metric System

Length. 1 meter (1 m.) = 10 decimeters = 100 centimeters (100 cm.) = 1000 millimeters (1000 mm.)

1 kilometer = 1000 meters (1000 m.) = 0.6214 mile.

1 meter = 1.094 yd. = 3.281 ft. = 39.37 in.

Volume. 1 liter = 1000 milliliters (100 ml.) = 1000.028 cubic centimeters (cc.).

1 liter (1 l.) = 0.03532 cu. ft. = 61.03 cu. in. = 1.057 quarts = 33.8 fl. oz.

1 fluid ounce = 29.57 ml.

1 cu. ft. = 28.32 l.

Weight. 1 gram (1 g.) = wt. of 1 ml. of water at 4° C.

1 kilogram = 1000 g.

1 gram = 10 decigrams = 100 centigrams (100 cg.) = 1000 milligrams (1000 mg.).

1 kilogram (1 kg.) = 2.205 lb. avoir.

1000 kilograms = 2205 lb. = 1 metric ton.

1 lb. avoir. = 453.6 g.

1 oz. avoir. = 28.35 g.

Index

Periodic Classification

1a	2a			Transition Elements				
		3b	4b	5b	6b	7b		8b
1 **H** 1.0080								
3 **Li** 6.940	4 **Be** 9.013							
11 **Na** 22.991	12 **Mg** 24.32							
19 **K** 39.100	20 **Ca** 40.08	21 **Sc** 44.96	22 **Ti** 47.90	23 **V** 50.95	24 **Cr** 52.01	25 **Mn** 54.94	26 **Fe** 55.85	27 **Co** 58.94
37 **Rb** 85.48	38 **Sr** 87.63	39 **Y** 88.92	40 **Zr** 91.22	41 **Nb** 92.91	42 **Mo** 95.95	43 **Tc**	44 **Ru** 101.1	45 **Rh** 102.91
55 **Cs** 132.91	56 **Ba** 137.36	57-71 see La Series	72 **Hf** 178.50	73 **Ta** 180.95	74 **W** 183.86	75 **Re** 186.22	76 **Os** 190.2	77 **Ir** 192.2
87 **Fr**	88 **Ra** 226.05	89-102 see Ac Series						

Lanthanide Series

57 **La** 138.92	58 **Ce** 140.13	59 **Pr** 140.92	60 **Nd** 144.27	61 **Pm**	62 **Sm** 150.35	63 **Eu** 152.0

Actinide Series

89 **Ac** 227	90 **Th** 232.05	91 **Pa** 231	92 **U** 238.07	93 **Np**	94 **Pu**	95 **Am**